Developmental Mathematics

3 RD EDITION

Mervin L. Keedy

Purdue University

Marvin L. Bittinger

Indiana University—Purdue University at Indianapolis

Judith A. Beecher

Indiana University—Purdue University at Indianapolis

Addison-Wesley Publishing Company

Reading, Massachusetts • Menlo Park, California • New York
Don Mills, Ontario • Wokingham, England • Amsterdam • Bonn
Sydney • Singapore • Tokyo • Madrid • San Juan • Milan • Paris

Sponsoring Editor	Melissa Acuña
Managing Editor	Karen Guardino
Production Supervisor	Jack Casteel
Design, Editorial, and Production Services	Quadrata, Inc.
Illustrators	ST Associates, Inc., and Scientific Illustrators
Manufacturing Supervisor	Roy Logan
Cover Design	Peter Blaiwas

PHOTO CREDITS

1, Elliott Erwitt/Magnum Photos, Inc.   **75,** Bjorn Bolstad/Photo Researchers, Inc.   **123,** Jean-Claude Lejeune/Stock, Boston   **165,** Teri Leigh Stratford/Photo Researchers, Inc.   **223,** AP/Wide World Photos   **265,** The Image Bank   **341,** Bohdan Hrynewych/Stock, Boston   **409,** Bill Bachman/Photo Researchers, Inc.   **471,** Peter Menzel/Stock, Boston   **543,** Coco McCoy/Rainbow Pictures   **603,** Peter Menzel/Stock, Boston   **669,** Mark Antman/Stock, Boston   **723, 747,**   Denny's Restaurants   **769,** David Frazier/Photo Researchers, Inc.   **813,** Bohdan Hrynewych/Stock, Boston

"TASP" is a trademark of the Texas Higher Education Coordinating Board, the Texas Education Agency, and National Evaluation Systems, Inc.

7 8 9 10-KE-9594

ISBN 53770
ISBN 52591

Contents

8 Solving Equations and Inequalities   409

9 Polynomials: Operations   471

10 Polynomials: Factoring   543

15 **Quadratic Equations** 813

FINAL EXAMINATION   857

APPENDIXES

TABLES

ANSWERS   A-1

INDEX   I-1

Preface

Intended for use by students needing a review of arithmetic skills before covering introductory algebra topics, this text begins with a review of arithmetic concepts, and then develops statistics, geometry, and introductory algebra. It is part of a series of texts that includes the following:

Bittinger/Ellenbogen: *Prealgebra,*
Keedy/Bittinger: *Basic Mathematics,* Sixth Edition,
Keedy/Bittinger: *Introductory Algebra,* Sixth Edition,
Keedy/Bittinger: *Intermediate Algebra,* Sixth Edition,
Keedy/Bittinger/Rudolph: *Essential Mathematics,* Sixth Edition.

Developmental Mathematics, Third Edition, is a significant revision of the Second Edition, with respect to content, pedagogy, and an expanded supplements package. Its unique approach, which has been developed over many years, is designed to help today's students both learn *and* retain mathematical concepts. All of the topics on the recently developed Texas Academic Skills Program test (TASP), and the majority of the topics on the state-level mathematics tests, including the CSU Entry Level Mathematics Test (ELM) and the CUNY Mathematics Skills Assessment Test, are incorporated in this edition. Guidelines from many states and educational institutions were considered while planning the revision, including those for the Florida CLAST test, the Alabama Junior College Curriculum, the Tennessee State Board of Regents, and the mathematics requirements of the New York Commissioner's Regulations. Many of the skills required by these guidelines are covered in *Developmental Mathematics,* Third Edition. The Third Edition is accompanied by a comprehensive supplements package that has been integrated with the text to provide maximum support for both instructor and student.

Following are some distinctive features of the approach and pedagogy that we feel will help meet some of the challenges all instructors face teaching developmental mathematics.

APPROACH

CAREFUL DEVELOPMENT OF CONCEPTS   We have divided each section into discrete and manageable learning objectives. Within the presentation of each objective, there is a careful buildup of difficulty through a series of developmental and followup examples. These enable students to thoroughly understand the mathematical concepts involved at each step. Each objective is constructed in a similar way, which gives students a high level of comfort with both the text and their learning process.

FOCUS ON "WHY"   Throughout the text, we present the appropriate mathematical rationale for a topic, rather than mathematical "shortcuts." For example, when manipulating rational expressions, we remove factors of 1 rather than cancel, although cancellation is mentioned with appropriate cautions. This helps prevent student errors in cancellation and other incorrectly remembered shortcuts in later courses.

PROBLEM SOLVING   We include real-life applications and problem-solving techniques throughout the text to motivate students and encourage them to think about how mathematics can be used. We also introduce a five-step problem-solving process early in the text and use the basic steps of this process (Familiarize, Translate, Solve, Check, and State the Answer) whenever a problem is solved.

PEDAGOGY

INTERACTIVE WORKTEXT APPROACH   The pedagogy of this text is designed to provide students with a clear set of learning objectives, and involve them with the development of the material, providing immediate and continual reinforcement.

Section objectives are keyed to appropriate sections of the text, exercises, and answers, so that students can easily find appropriate review material if they are unable to do an exercise.

Numerous *margin exercises* throughout the text provide immediate reinforcement of concepts covered in each section.

STUDY AID REFERENCES   Many valuable study aids accompany this text. Each section is referenced to appropriate videotape numbers to make it easy for students to find and use the correct support materials.

VERBALIZATION SKILLS AND "THINKING IT THROUGH"   Students' perception that mathematics is a foreign language is a significant barrier to their ability to think mathematically and is a major cause of math anxiety. In the Third Edition, we have encouraged students to think through mathematical situations, synthesize concepts, and verbalize mathematics whenever possible.

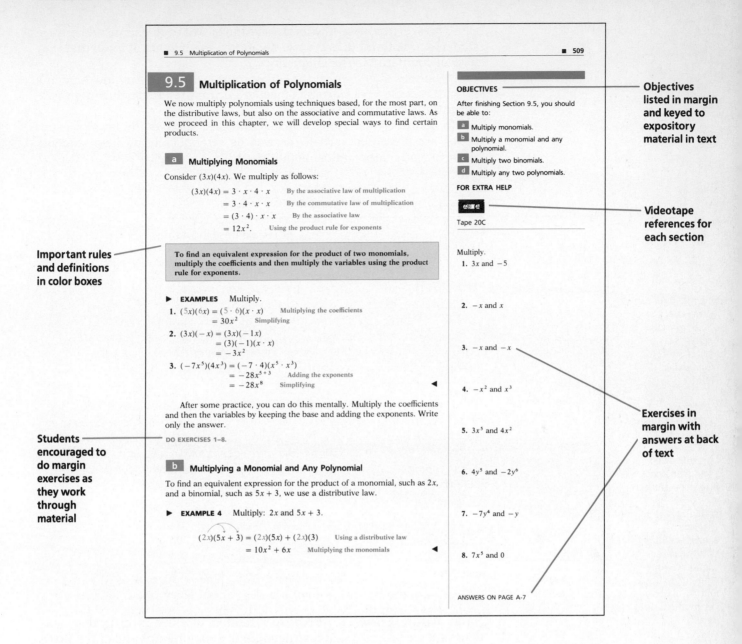

Important rules and definitions in color boxes

Students encouraged to do margin exercises as they work through material

Exercises on tearout sheets for each section

Exercises keyed to objectives and material in text

Objectives listed in margin and keyed to expository material in text

Videotape references for each section

Exercises in margin with answers at back of text

Answer space provided for quick and easy grading

9.5 Multiplication of Polynomials

We now multiply polynomials using techniques based, for the most part, on the distributive laws, but also on the associative and commutative laws. As we proceed in this chapter, we will develop special ways to find certain products.

a Multiplying Monomials

Consider $(3x)(4x)$. We multiply as follows:

$$(3x)(4x) = 3 \cdot x \cdot 4 \cdot x \quad \text{By the associative law of multiplication}$$
$$= 3 \cdot 4 \cdot x \cdot x \quad \text{By the commutative law of multiplication}$$
$$= (3 \cdot 4) \cdot x \cdot x \quad \text{By the associative law}$$
$$= 12x^2. \quad \text{Using the product rule for exponents}$$

> To find an equivalent expression for the product of two monomials, multiply the coefficients and then multiply the variables using the product rule for exponents.

▶ **EXAMPLES** Multiply.

1. $(5x)(6x) = (5 \cdot 6)(x \cdot x) \quad \text{Multiplying the coefficients}$
$= 30x^2 \quad \text{Simplifying}$

2. $(3x)(-x) = (3x)(-1x)$
$= (3)(-1)(x \cdot x)$
$= -3x^2$

3. $(-7x^5)(4x^3) = (-7 \cdot 4)(x^5 \cdot x^3)$
$= -28x^{5+3} \quad \text{Adding the exponents}$
$= -28x^8 \quad \text{Simplifying}$ ◀

After some practice, you can do this mentally. Multiply the coefficients and then the variables by keeping the base and adding the exponents. Write only the answer.

DO EXERCISES 1–8.

b Multiplying a Monomial and Any Polynomial

To find an equivalent expression for the product of a monomial, such as $2x$, and a binomial, such as $5x + 3$, we use a distributive law.

▶ **EXAMPLE 4** Multiply: $2x$ and $5x + 3$.

$(2x)(5x + 3) = (2x)(5x) + (2x)(3) \quad \text{Using a distributive law}$
$= 10x^2 + 6x \quad \text{Multiplying the monomials}$ ◀

OBJECTIVES
After finishing Section 9.5, you should be able to:

a Multiply monomials.

b Multiply a monomial and any polynomial.

c Multiply two binomials.

d Multiply any two polynomials.

FOR EXTRA HELP

Tape 20C

Multiply.
1. $3x$ and -5
2. $-x$ and x
3. $-x$ and $-x$
4. $-x^2$ and x^3
5. $3x^5$ and $4x^2$
6. $4y^5$ and $-2y^6$
7. $-7y^4$ and $-y$
8. $7x^5$ and 0

ANSWERS ON PAGE A-7

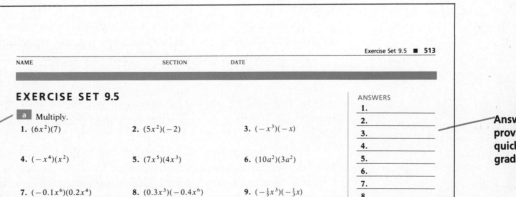

Exercise Set 9.5 ■ 513

NAME   SECTION   DATE

EXERCISE SET 9.5

a Multiply.

1. $(6x^2)(7)$ **2.** $(5x^2)(-2)$ **3.** $(-x^3)(-x)$

4. $(-x^4)(x^2)$ **5.** $(7x^5)(4x^3)$ **6.** $(10a^2)(3a^2)$

7. $(-0.1x^6)(0.2x^4)$ **8.** $(0.3x^3)(-0.4x^6)$ **9.** $(-\frac{1}{8}x^3)(-\frac{1}{3}x)$

ANSWERS
1. ___
2. ___
3. ___
4. ___
5. ___
6. ___
7. ___
8. ___
9. ___

"Thinking It Through" exercises at the end of each chapter encourage students to both think and write about key mathematical ideas that they have encountered in the chapter.

"Synthesis Exercises" at the end of most exercise sets require students to synthesize several learning objectives or to think through and provide insight into the present material.

In addition, many important definitions, such as the laws of exponents, are presented verbally as well as symbolically, to help students learn to read mathematical notation.

Skill Maintenance exercises at the end of most exercise sets review concepts from earlier chapters.

Synthesis exercises require students to synthesize objectives and provide insight into the material.

Thinking It Through exercises at the end of each chapter require students to think and write about key mathematical ideas.

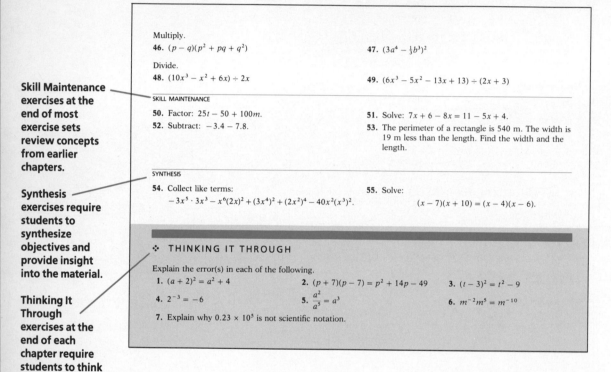

Multiply.

46. $(p - q)(p^2 + pq + q^2)$

47. $(3a^4 - \frac{1}{3}b^3)^2$

Divide.

48. $(10x^3 - x^2 + 6x) \div 2x$

49. $(6x^3 - 5x^2 - 13x + 13) \div (2x + 3)$

SKILL MAINTENANCE

50. Factor: $25t - 50 + 100m$.

51. Solve: $7x + 6 - 8x = 11 - 5x + 4$.

52. Subtract: $-3.4 - 7.8$.

53. The perimeter of a rectangle is 540 m. The width is 19 m less than the length. Find the width and the length.

SYNTHESIS

54. Collect like terms:
$-3x^5 \cdot 3x^3 - x^6(2x)^2 + (3x^4)^2 + (2x^2)^4 - 40x^2(x^3)^2$.

55. Solve:
$(x - 7)(x + 10) = (x - 4)(x - 6)$.

❖ THINKING IT THROUGH

Explain the error(s) in each of the following.

1. $(a + 2)^2 = a^2 + 4$

2. $(p + 7)(p - 7) = p^2 + 14p - 49$

3. $(t - 3)^2 = t^2 - 9$

4. $2^{-3} = -6$

5. $\frac{a^2}{a^5} = a^3$

6. $m^{-2}m^5 = m^{-10}$

7. Explain why 0.23×10^5 is not scientific notation.

SKILL MAINTENANCE Because retention of skills is critical to students' future success, skill maintenance is a major emphasis of the Sixth Edition.

Each chapter begins with a *"Points to Remember"* box, which highlights key formulas and definitions from previous chapters.

In addition, we include *Skill Maintenance Exercises* at the end of most exercise sets. These review skills and concepts from earlier sections of the text.

At the end of each chapter, our *Summary and Review* summarizes important properties and formulas and includes extensive review exercises.

Each *Chapter Test* tests four review objectives from preceding chapters as well as the chapter objectives.

We also include a *Final Examination* at the end of the text. This reviews material from all preceding chapters in the text.

At the back of the text are answers to all review exercises, together with section and objective references, so that students know exactly what material to restudy if they miss a review exercise.

TESTING AND SKILL ASSESSMENT   Accurate assessment of student comprehension is an important factor in a student's long-term success. In the Third Edition, we have provided many assessment opportunities.

Chapter Pretests diagnose student skills and place the students appropriately within each chapter, allowing them to concentrate on topics with which they have particular difficulty.

Chapter Tests at the end of each chapter allow students to review and test comprehension of chapter skills.

Answers to each question on all tests are included at the back of the text.

For additional testing options, we have developed an Instructor's Manual and Printed Test Bank with many alternative forms of each chapter test in both open-ended and multiple-choice formats. For a greater degree of flexibility in creating chapter tests, the text is also accompanied by an extensive computerized testing program for the IBM computer.

Key properties and skills from preceding material summarized at beginning of chapter

Chapter Pretest evaluates student's strengths and weaknesses in upcoming material

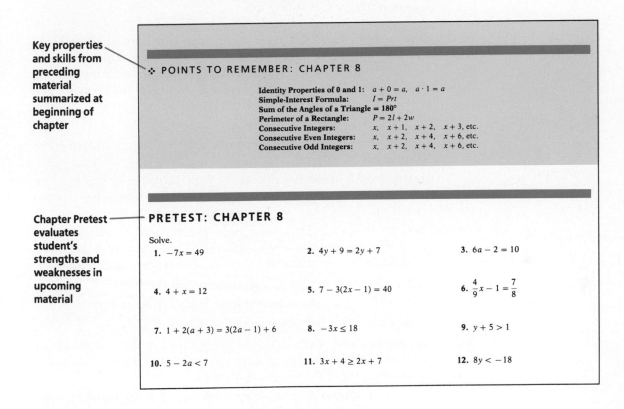

❖ POINTS TO REMEMBER: CHAPTER 8

Identity Properties of 0 and 1:	$a + 0 = a,\ \ a \cdot 1 = a$
Simple-Interest Formula:	$I = Prt$
Sum of the Angles of a Triangle = 180°	
Perimeter of a Rectangle:	$P = 2l + 2w$
Consecutive Integers:	$x,\ \ x + 1,\ \ x + 2,\ \ x + 3$, etc.
Consecutive Even Integers:	$x,\ \ x + 2,\ \ x + 4,\ \ x + 6$, etc.
Consecutive Odd Integers:	$x,\ \ x + 2,\ \ x + 4,\ \ x + 6$, etc.

PRETEST: CHAPTER 8

Solve.

1. $-7x = 49$

2. $4y + 9 = 2y + 7$

3. $6a - 2 = 10$

4. $4 + x = 12$

5. $7 - 3(2x - 1) = 40$

6. $\dfrac{4}{9}x - 1 = \dfrac{7}{8}$

7. $1 + 2(a + 3) = 3(2a - 1) + 6$

8. $-3x \leq 18$

9. $y + 5 > 1$

10. $5 - 2a < 7$

11. $3x + 4 \geq 2x + 7$

12. $8y < -18$

FLEXIBILITY OF TEACHING MODES

The flexible worktext format of *Developmental Mathematics* allows the book to be used in many ways.

- **In a standard lecture.** To use the book in a lecture format, the instructor lectures in a conventional manner and encourages students to do the margin exercises while studying on their own. This greatly enhances the readability of the text.

- **For a modified lecture.** To bring student-centered activity into the class, the instructor stops lecturing and has the students do margin exercises.

- **For a no-lecture class.** The instructor makes assignments that students do on their own, including working the margin exercises. During the class period following the assignment, the instructor answers questions, and students have an extra day or two to polish their work before handing it in. In the meantime, they are working on the next assignment. This method provides individualization while keeping a class together. It also minimizes the number of instructor hours required and has been found to work well with large classes.

- **In a learning laboratory.** Because this text is highly readable and easy to understand, it can be used in a learning laboratory or any other self-study situation.

KEY CONTENT CHANGES

In response to both extensive user comments and reviewer feedback, there have been many organizational revisions to the Third Edition. Detailed information about the changes made in this material is available in the form of a Conversion Guide. Please ask your local Addison-Wesley sales representative for more information. Following is a list of the major organizational changes for this revision:

- More exercises have been added throughout the text, increasing the overall number by 10%.

- A five-step problem-solving process is now introduced early in the text, and these steps are used throughout the text whenever a problem is solved.

- The two geometry chapters have been revised and condensed into one chapter. This material now appears in Chapter 6. Measurement topics, both American and metric, are now in Appendixes A and B.

- Geometry problems are integrated throughout the text.

- Inductive and deductive reasoning have been added as Appendix F.

- Descriptive statistics have been added as Chapter 5.

- The presentation of operations and properties for the real numbers has been streamlined by integrating the real numbers into each section of the chapter that introduces algebra.

- The chapter on inequalities has been integrated into material on solving equations where appropriate. Solving inequalities is now covered in the chapter on solving equations, and graphing inequalities is now covered in the chapter on graphing equations.

- Division of polynomials has been moved from the chapter on rational expressions to the chapter on polynomial operations.

SUPPLEMENTS

This text is accompanied by a comprehensive supplements package. Below is a brief list of these supplements, followed by a detailed description of each one.

For the Instructor

Instructor's Solutions Manual

Instructor's Manual and Printed
  Test Bank

Lab Resource Manual

Computerized Testing

For the Student

Student's Solutions Manual

Videotapes

Comprehensive Tutorial Software

Drill and Practice Software

SUPPLEMENTS FOR THE INSTRUCTOR

All supplements for the instructor are free upon adoption of this text.

Instructor's Solutions Manual

This manual by Judith A. Penna contains worked-out solutions to all even-numbered exercises and discussions of the "Thinking It Through" sections.

Instructor's Manual and Printed Test Bank

This guide contains the following:

- Extra practice problems for some of the most challenging topics in the text.
- Indexes to the videotapes and software that accompany the text.
- 5 alternative test forms for each chapter with questions in the same topic order as the objectives presented in the chapter.
- 5 alternative forms for each chapter with the questions in a different order.
- 3 multiple-choice test forms for each chapter.
- 2 cumulative review tests for each chapter.
- 9 alternative forms of the final examination, 3 with questions organized by chapter, 3 with questions scrambled, and 3 with multiple-choice questions.
- Answers to all the exercises in the text, which you can make available to your students.

Lab Resource Manual

This manual contains a selection of essays on setting up learning labs, including information on running large testing centers and setting up mastery learning programs. It also includes a directory of learning lab coordinators who are available to answer questions.

Computerized Testing

OmniTest II (IBM PC)

This algorithm-driven testing system for the IBM allows you to create up to 99 variations of a customized test with just a few keystrokes, choosing from over 300 open-ended and multiple-choice test items. You can also select and print tests by chapter, level of difficulty, type of problem, or your own coding.

The IBM testing program, OmniTest II, also allows users to enter their own test items and edit existing items in an easy-to-use WYSIWYG format with variable spacing.

SUPPLEMENTS FOR THE STUDENT

Student's Solutions Manual

This manual by Judith A. Penna contains completely worked-out solutions with step-by-step annotations for all the odd-numbered exercises in the text. It is free to adopting instructors and may be purchased by your students from Addison-Wesley Publishing Company.

Videotapes

Using the chalkboard and manipulative aids, Donna DeSpain lectures in detail, works out exercises, and solves problems from most sections in the text on approximately 30 70-minute videotapes. These tapes are ideal for students who have missed a lecture or who need extra help. Each section in the text is referenced to the appropriate tape number and section, underneath the icon ▪▪▪▪. A complete set of videotapes is free to qualifying adopters.

Tutorial Software

A variety of tutorial software packages is available to accompany this text. Please contact your Addison-Wesley representative for a software sampler that contains demonstration disks for these packages and a summary of our distribution policy.

Comprehensive Tutorials

Instructional Software for Algebra (Apple II series).

This software covers selected algebra topics. It also gives students brief explanations and examples, followed by practice exercises with interactive feedback for student error.

Drill and Practice Packages

The Math Lab by Chris Avery and Chris Barker, DeAnza College (Apple II series, IBM PC, or Macintosh).

Students choose the topic, level of difficulty, and number of exercises. If they get a wrong answer, *The Math Lab* will prompt them with the first step of the solution. This software also keeps detailed records of student scores.

Professor Weissman's Software by Martin Weissman, Essex County College (IBM PC or compatible).

Professor Weissman's Software generates exercises based on the student's selection of topic and level of difficulty. If they get a wrong answer, the software gives them a step-by-step solution. The level of difficulty increases if students are successful.

In the back of this text is a coupon for *Professor Weissman's Software* that allows students to buy the software directly from Martin Weissman.

The Algebra Problem Solver by Michael Hoban and Kathirgama Nathan, La Guardia Community College (IBM PC).

After selecting the topic and exercise type, students can enter their own exercises or request an exercise from the computer. In each case, *The Algebra Problem Solver* will give the student detailed, annotated, step-by-step solutions.

ACKNOWLEDGMENTS

Many of you who teach developmental mathematics have helped to shape the Third Edition of this text by reviewing and spending time with us on your campuses. Our heartfelt thanks to all of you, and many apologies to anyone we have missed on the following list.

Max Cisneros, *Albuquerque Technical-Vocational Institute*
Jean Ann Irwin, *Walters State College*
Gerald LePage, *Bristol Community College*
Wendell Neal, *Houston Community College*
Margaret Ramsey, *Chattanooga State Technical Community College*
Holly Roe, *University of Texas at San Antonio*
Joan Smith, *New Mexico Highlands University*
John Vangor, *Housatonic Community College*

We also wish to thank the many people without whose committed efforts our work could not have been completed. In particular, we would like to thank Barbara Johnson and Judy Penna for their work on proofreading the manuscript. We would also like to thank Pat Pasternak, who did a marvelous job typing the text manuscript and answer section, and John Baumgart, Larry Bittinger, John Irons, and Jennifer Alsop, who did a thorough and conscientious job of checking the manuscript.

M.L.K.
M.L.B.
J.A.B.

To The Student

This text has many features that can help you succeed in introductory algebra. To familiarize yourself with these, you might read the preface that starts on page xi, and study the annotated pages that are included. Following are a few suggestions on how to use these features to enhance your learning process.

BEFORE YOU START A CHAPTER

The chapter opening page gives you an idea of the material that you are about to study and how it can be used. The chapter opening introduction also tells you what sections you will need to review in order to do the skill maintenance exercises on the chapter test. It's a good idea to restudy these sections to keep the material fresh in your mind for the midterm or final examination.

The first page of each chapter lists "Points to Remember" that will be needed to work certain examples and exercises in the chapter. You should try to review any skills listed here before beginning the chapter and learn any formulas or definitions.

This same page also includes a chapter pretest. You can work through this and check your answers at the back of the text to identify sections that you might skip or sections that give you particular difficulty and need extra concentration.

WORKING THROUGH A SECTION

First you should read the learning objectives for the section. The symbol next to an objective (a , b , c) appears next to the text and exercises that correspond to that objective, so you can always refer back to the appropriate material when you need to review a topic.

As you work through a section, you will see an instruction to "Do Exercises x–xx." This refers to the exercises in the margin of the page. You should always stop and do these to practice what you have just studied because they greatly enhance the readability of the text. Answers to the margin exercises are at the back of the text.

After you have completed a section, you should do the assigned exercises in the exercise set. The exercises are keyed to the section objectives, so that if you get an incorrect answer, you know that you should restudy the text section that follows the corresponding symbol.

Answers to all the odd-numbered exercises are at the back of the text. A solutions manual with complete worked-out solutions to all the odd-numbered exercises is available from Addison-Wesley Publishing Company.

PREPARING FOR A CHAPTER TEST

To prepare for a chapter test, you can review your homework and restudy sections that were particularly difficult. You should also learn the "Important Properties and Formulas" that begin the chapter's summary and review and study the review sections that are listed at the beginning of the review exercises.

After studying, you might set aside a block of time to work through the summary and review as if it were a test. You can check your answers at the back of the text after you are done. The answers are coded to sections and objectives, so you can restudy any areas in which you are having trouble. You can also take the chapter test as practice, again checking your answers at the back of the text.

If you are still having difficulties with a topic, you might try either going to see your instructor or working with the videotapes that are referenced at the beginning of the text sections. Be sure to start studying in time to get extra help before you must take the test.

PREPARING FOR A MIDTERM OR FINAL EXAMINATION

To keep material fresh in your mind for a midterm or a final examination, you can work through the chapter tests at the end of each chapter. You can also use these as practice midterms or finals. In addition, there is a final examination at the end of the text that has answers to all of its exercises at the back of the text.

OTHER STUDY TIPS

There is a saying in the real-estate business: "The three most important things to consider when buying a house are *location, location, location.*" When trying to learn mathematics, the three most important things are *time, time, time.* Try to carefully analyze your situation. Be sure to allow yourself *time* to do the lesson. Are you taking too many courses? Are you working so much that you do not have *time* to study? Are you taking *time* to maintain daily preparation? Other study tips are provided on pages marked "Sidelights" in the text.

Developmental Mathematics

3RD EDITION

INTRODUCTION This chapter considers addition, subtraction, multiplication, and division of whole numbers. Then we study the solving of simple equations and apply our skills to the solving of problems. Factorizations, divisibility, and least common multiples are also studied. ❖

Operations on the Whole Numbers

1

AN APPLICATION

The John Hancock Building in Chicago is 1107 ft tall. It has two 342-ft antennas on top. How far are the tops of the antennas from the ground?

THE MATHEMATICS

Let $h =$ the height in question. Since we are combining lengths, addition can be used. We translate the problem to this equation:

$$h = 1107 + 342.$$

Here is how addition can occur in problem solving.

Area of a Rectangle: $A = l \cdot w$
Area of a Square: $A = s \cdot s$, or s^2

PRETEST: CHAPTER 1

1. Write a word name: 3,078,059.

2. Write expanded notation: 6987.

3. Write standard notation: Two billion, forty-seven million, three hundred ninety-eight thousand, five hundred eighty-nine.

4. What does the digit 6 mean in 2,967,342?

Use either $<$ or $>$ for ▓ to write a true sentence.

5. 346 ▓ 364

6. 54 ▓ 45

7. Add.

$$\begin{array}{r} 7\,3\,1\,2 \\ +\,2\,9\,0\,4 \\ \hline \end{array}$$

8. Subtract.

$$\begin{array}{r} 7\,0\,1\,2 \\ -\,2\,9\,0\,4 \\ \hline \end{array}$$

9. Multiply: $359 \cdot 64$.

10. Divide: $23{,}149 \div 46$.

Solve.

11. $326 \cdot 17 = m$

12. $y = 924 \div 42$

13. $19 + x = 53$

14. $34 \cdot n = 850$

Solve.

15. Betsy weighs 121 lb and Jennifer weighs 109 lb. How much more does Betsy weigh?

16. How many 12-jar cases can be filled with 1512 jars of spaghetti sauce?

17. The population of Illinois is 11,418,500. The population of Ohio is 10,797,600. What is the total population of Illinois and Ohio?

18. A lot measures 48 ft by 54 ft. A pool that is 15 ft by 20 ft is put on the lot. How much area is left over?

19. Evaluate: 4^3.

20. Find the LCM of 15 and 24.

Simplify.

21. $8^2 \div 8 \cdot 2 - (2 + 2 \cdot 7)$

22. $108 \div 9 - \{4 \cdot [18 - (5 \cdot 3)]\}$

23. Determine whether 59 is prime, composite, or neither.

24. Find the prime factorization of 140.

25. Determine whether 788 is divisible by 8.

26. Determine whether 1503 is divisible by 9.

1.1 Standard Notation; Order

We study mathematics in order to be able to solve problems. In this chapter, we learn how to use operations on the whole numbers to solve various kinds of problems. We begin by studying how numbers are named.

a From Standard Notation to Expanded Notation

To answer questions such as "How many?", "How much?" and "How tall?" we use whole numbers.* The set of whole numbers is

$$0, 1, 2, 3, 4, 5, 6, 7, 8, 9, 10, 11, 12, \ldots .$$

The set goes on indefinitely. There is no largest whole number, and the smallest whole number is 0. Each number can be named using various notations. For example, the height of the John Hancock Building (excluding antennas) is 1107 ft. **Standard notation** for this is 1107. We find **expanded notation** for 1107 as follows:

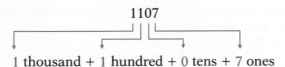

1 thousand + 1 hundred + 0 tens + 7 ones

▶ **EXAMPLE 1** Write expanded notation for 3742.

3742 = 3 thousands + 7 hundreds + 4 tens + 2 ones ◀

▶ **EXAMPLE 2** Write expanded notation for 54,567.

54,567 = 5 ten thousands + 4 thousands
                + 5 hundreds + 6 tens + 7 ones ◀

DO EXERCISES 1 AND 2 (IN THE MARGIN AT THE RIGHT).

▶ **EXAMPLE 3** Write expanded notation for 7091.

7091 = 7 thousands + 0 hundreds + 9 tens + 1 one, or
           7 thousands + 9 tens + 1 one ◀

▶ **EXAMPLE 4** Write expanded notation for 3400.

3400 = 3 thousands + 4 hundreds + 0 tens + 0 ones, or
           3 thousands + 4 hundreds ◀

DO EXERCISES 3–5.

---

*The set 1, 2, 3, 4, 5, . . . , without 0, is called the set of **natural numbers**.

Write expanded notation.
1. 3728

2. 36,223

Write expanded notation.
3. 3021

4. 2009

5. 5700

Write standard notation.

6. 5 thousands + 6 hundreds +
8 tens + 9 ones

7. 8 ten thousands + 7 thousands +
1 hundred + 2 tens + 8 ones

8. 9 thousands + 0 hundreds +
0 tens + 3 ones

Write a word name.
9. 57

10. 29

11. 88

b   From Expanded Notation to Standard Notation

▶ **EXAMPLE 5**   Write standard notation for 2 thousands + 5 hundreds + 7 tens + 5 ones.

Standard notation is 2575.   ◀

▶ **EXAMPLE 6**   Write standard notation for 9 ten thousands + 6 thousands + 7 hundreds + 1 ten + 8 ones.

Standard notation is 96,718.   ◀

▶ **EXAMPLE 7**   Write standard notation for 2 thousands + 3 tens.

Standard notation is 2030.   ◀

DO EXERCISES 6–8.

c   Word Names

"Three," "two hundred one," and "forty-two" are **word names** for numbers. When we write word names for two-digit numbers like 42, 76, and 91, we use hyphens.

▶ **EXAMPLES**   Write word names.

8. 42   Forty-two

9. 76   Seventy-six

10. 91   Ninety-one   ◀

DO EXERCISES 9–11.

For large numbers, digits are separated into groups of three, called **periods.** Each period has a name like *ones, thousands, millions, billions,* and so on. When we write or read a large number, we start at the left with the largest period. The number named in the period is followed by the name of the period, then a comma is written and the next period is named. Recently, the U.S. national debt was $2,830,127,000,000. We can use a **place-value** chart to illustrate how to use periods to read the number 2,830,127,000,000.

PLACE –VALUE CHART

Periods →	Trillions			Billions			Millions			Thousands			Ones		
			2	8	3	0	1	2	7	0	0	0	0	0	0
	Hundreds	Tens	Ones	Hundreds	Tens	Ones	Hundreds	Tens	Ones	Hundreds	Tens	Ones	Hundreds	Tens	Ones

2 trillion,   830 billion,   127 million,   0 thousands,   0 ones

▶ **EXAMPLE 11**   Write a word name for 46,625,314,732.

Forty-six **billion**

six-hundred twenty-five **million,**

three hundred fourteen **thousand,**

seven-hundred thirty-two ◀

> The word "and" *does not* appear in word names for whole numbers. Although we commonly hear such expressions as "two hundred *and* one," the use of "and" is not, strictly speaking, correct in word names for whole numbers. For decimal notation like 317.4, it is appropriate to use "and" for the decimal point and read this as "three hundred seventeen *and* four tenths."

DO EXERCISES 12–15.

d Standard Notation

▶ **EXAMPLE 12**   Write standard notation.

Five hundred six **million,**

three hundred forty-five **thousand,**

two hundred twelve

Standard notation is 506,345,212. ◀

DO EXERCISE 16.

e Digits

A **digit** is a number 0, 1, 2, 3, 4, 5, 6, 7, 8, or 9 that names a place-value location.

▶ **EXAMPLES**   What does the digit 8 mean in each case?
13. 278,342   8 thousands
14. 872,342   8 hundred thousands
15. 28,343,399,223   8 billions ◀

DO EXERCISES 17–20.

▶ **EXAMPLE 16**   In 278,346, what digit tells the number of:
a) Hundred thousands?   2
b) Thousands?   8 ◀

DO EXERCISES 21–24.

Write a word name.

12. 204

13. 19,204

14. 1,719,204

15. 22,301,719,204

16. Write standard notation.

Two hundred thirteen million, one hundred five thousand, three hundred twenty-nine

What does the digit 2 mean in each case?

17. 526,555

18. 265,789

19. 42,789,654

20. 24,789,654

In 7,890,432, what digit tells the number of:

21. Hundreds?

22. Millions?

23. Ten thousands?

24. Thousands?

ANSWERS ON PAGE A-1

ANSWERS

29. _____

30. _____

31. _____

32. _____

33. _____

34. _____

35. _____

36. _____

37. _____

38. _____

39. _____

40. _____

41. _____

42. _____

43. _____

44. _____

45. _____

46. _____

47. _____

48. _____

49. _____

50. _____

51. _____

52. _____

53. _____

54. _____

d Write standard notation.

29. Two million, two hundred thirty-three thousand, eight hundred twelve

30. Three hundred fifty-four thousand, seven hundred two

31. Eight billion

32. Seven hundred million

33. Two hundred seventeen thousand, five hundred three

34. Two hundred thirty billion, forty-three million, nine hundred fifty-one thousand, six hundred seventeen

Write standard notation for the number in the sentence.

35. In a recent year, two million, one hundred seventy-three thousand, six hundred thirty-eight people visited the Grand Canyon.

36. The population of Russia is two hundred sixty-two million, four hundred thirty-six thousand.

37. In one year, Americans use two hundred six million, six hundred fifty-eight thousand pounds of toothpaste.

38. The people of the United States burn seven hundred forty-nine million, five hundred seventy-eight thousand, six hundred fifty-three gallons of fuel annually driving to see motion pictures.

e What does the digit 5 mean in each case?

39. 235,888   **40.** 253,888   **41.** 488,526   **42.** 500,346

In 89,302 what digit tells the number of:

43. Hundreds?   **44.** Thousands?

45. Tens   **46.** Ones?

f Use < or > for ■ to write a true sentence. Draw a number line if necessary.

47. 0 ■ 17   **48.** 32 ■ 0   **49.** 34 ■ 12   **50.** 28 ■ 18

51. 1000 ■ 1001   **52.** 345 ■ 456   **53.** 133 ■ 132   **54.** 999 ■ 997

1.2 Addition and Subtraction

a Addition and the Real World

Addition of whole numbers corresponds to combining or putting things together. Let us look at various situations in which addition applies.

Combining Sets of Objects

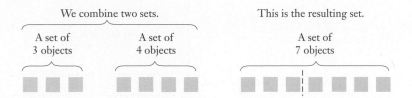

The addition that corresponds is

$$3 + 4 = 7.$$

We can find the number of objects in a set by counting. We count and find that the two sets have 3 members and 4 members, respectively. We count after combining and find that there are 7 objects. We say that the **sum** of 3 and 4 is 7. The numbers added are called **addends.**

| 3 | + | 4 | = | 7 |
| Addend | | Addend | | Sum |

▶ **EXAMPLE 1** Write an addition that corresponds to this situation.

A student has $3 and earns $10 more. How much money does the student have?

The addition that corresponds is

$$\$3 + \$10 = \$13.$$ ◄

DO EXERCISE 1.

Addition also corresponds to combining distances or lengths.

▶ **EXAMPLE 2** Write an addition that corresponds to this situation.

A car is driven 3 mi (miles) from Dustville to Rainville. It is then driven 5 mi from Rainville to Mudville. How far is it from Dustville to Mudville along the same route?

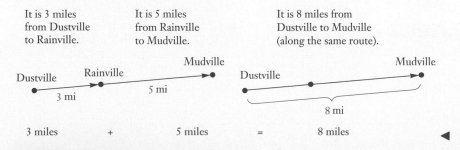

It is 3 miles from Dustville to Rainville. It is 5 miles from Rainville to Mudville. It is 8 miles from Dustville to Mudville (along the same route).

3 miles + 5 miles = 8 miles ◄

DO EXERCISES 2 AND 3.

Write an addition that corresponds to the situation.

1. John has 4 marbles. Then he wins 6 more. How many does he have in all?

Write an addition that corresponds to the situation.

2. A car is driven 40 mi from Lafayette to Kokomo. Then it is driven 50 mi from Kokomo to Indianapolis. How far is it from Lafayette to Indianapolis along the same route?

3. A rope 5 ft long is tied to a rope 7 ft long. How long is the resulting rope (ignoring the amount of rope it takes to tie the two ropes together)?

ANSWERS ON PAGE A-1

4. Add.

```
   6 2 0 3
 + 3 5 4 2
```

5. Add.

```
   7 9 6 8
 + 5 4 9 7
```

b | Addition of Whole Numbers

To add numbers, we can add the ones first, then the tens, then the hundreds, and so on.

▶ **EXAMPLE 3**   Add: 7312 + 2504.

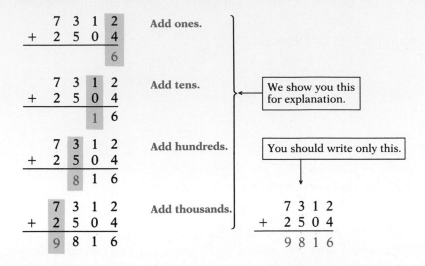

Add ones.

Add tens.

We show you this for explanation.

Add hundreds.

You should write only this.

Add thousands.

```
   7 3 1 2
 + 2 5 0 4
   9 8 1 6
```

◀

DO EXERCISE 4.

▶ **EXAMPLE 4**   Add: 6878 + 4995.

```
      1
   6 8 7 8
 + 4 9 9 5
         3
```

Add ones. We get 13 ones, or 1 ten + 3 ones. Write 3 in the ones column and 1 above the tens. This is called *carrying*.

```
    1 1
   6 8 7 8
 + 4 9 9 5
       7 3
```

Add tens. We get 17 tens, or 1 hundred + 7 tens. Write 7 in the tens column and 1 above the hundreds.

```
  1 1 1
   6 8 7 8
 + 4 9 9 5
     8 7 3
```

Add hundreds. We get 18 hundreds, or 1 thousand + 8 hundreds. Write 8 in the hundreds column and 1 above the thousands.

```
  1 1 1
   6 8 7 8
 + 4 9 9 5
 1 1 8 7 3
```

Add thousands. We get 11 thousands.

◀

DO EXERCISE 5.

▶ **EXAMPLE 5**   Add: 2391 + 3276 + 8789 + 1498.

```
        2
  2  3  9 │1│
  3  2  7 │6│
  8  7  8 │9│
+ 1  4  9 │8│
          │4│
```

Add ones: We get 24, so we have 2 tens + 4 ones. Write 4 in the ones column and 2 above the tens.

```
     3 │2│
  2  3 │9│ 1
  3  2 │7│ 6
  8  7 │8│ 9
+ 1  4 │9│ 8
       │5│ 4
```

Add tens: We get 35 tens, so we have 30 tens + 5 tens. This is also 3 hundreds + 5 tens. Write 5 in the tens column and 3 above the hundreds.

```
  1 │3│ 2
  2 │3│ 9  1
  3 │2│ 7  6
  8 │7│ 8  9
+ 1 │4│ 9  8
    │9│ 5  4
```

Add hundreds: We get 19 hundreds, or 1 thousand + 9 hundreds. Write 9 in the hundreds column and 1 above the thousands.

```
 │1│ 3  2
 │2│ 3  9  1
 │3│ 2  7  6
 │8│ 7  8  9
+│1│ 4  9  8
│1  5│ 9  5  4
```

Add thousands: We get 15 thousands.

◀

DO EXERCISES 6 AND 7.

c **Subtraction and the Real World: Take Away**

Subtraction of whole numbers corresponds to two kinds of situations. The first one is called "take away."

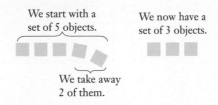

We start with a set of 5 objects.

We now have a set of 3 objects.

We take away 2 of them.

The subtraction that corresponds is as follows.

$$5 - 2 = 3$$

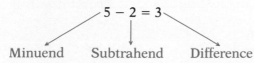

Minuend   Subtrahend   Difference

6. Add.

```
  1 9 3 2
  6 7 2 3
  9 8 7 8
+ 8 9 4 1
```

7. Add.

```
  2 0 4 3
  1 8 0 6
  5 6 9 0
+ 3 4 4 4
```

Write a subtraction that corresponds to the situation. You need not carry out the subtraction.

8. A cook pours 5 oz (ounces) of cooking oil out of a pitcher containing 16 oz. How many ounces are left?

9. A farm contains 400 acres. The owner sells 100 acres of it. How many acres are left?

Write a related addition sentence.

10. $7 - 5 = 2$

11. $17 - 8 = 9$

Write two related subtraction sentences.

12. $5 + 8 = 13$

13. $11 + 3 = 14$

▶ **EXAMPLE 6**   Write a subtraction that corresponds to the following situation.

A bowler starts with 10 pins and knocks down 8 of them. How many pins are left?

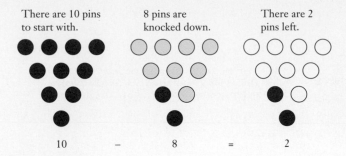

| There are 10 pins to start with. | 8 pins are knocked down. | There are 2 pins left. |

$$10 \quad - \quad 8 \quad = \quad 2 \qquad ◀$$

DO EXERCISES 8 AND 9.

d   Related Sentences

Subtraction is defined in terms of addition. For example, $5 - 2$ is that number which when added to 2 gives 5. Thus for the subtraction sentence

$$5 - 2 = 3, \qquad \text{**Taking away 2 from 5 gives 3.**}$$

there is a related addition sentence

$$5 = 3 + 2. \qquad \text{**Putting back the 2 gives 5 again.**}$$

In fact, we know answers to subtractions are correct only because of the related addition, which provides a handy way to check a subtraction.

▶ **EXAMPLE 7**   Write a related addition sentence: $8 - 5 = 3$.

$$8 - 5 = 3$$

↑

This number gets added (after 3).

> By the commutative law of addition, there is also another addition sentence:
> $$8 = 5 + 3.$$

$$8 = 3 + 5$$

The related sentence is $8 = 3 + 5$.   ◀

DO EXERCISES 10 AND 11.

▶ **EXAMPLE 8**   Write two related subtraction sentences: $4 + 3 = 7$.

$$4 + 3 = 7 \qquad\qquad 4 + 3 = 7$$

↑   ↑

This number gets subtracted (moved).   **This number gets subtracted (moved).**

$$4 = 7 - 3 \qquad\qquad 3 = 7 - 4$$

(7 take away 3 is 4.)   (7 take away 4 is 3.)

The related sentences are $4 = 7 - 3$ and $3 = 7 - 4$.   ◀

DO EXERCISES 12 AND 13.

e How Much More?

The second kind of situation for which subtraction corresponds is called "how much more"? From the related sentences, we see that finding a *missing addend* is the same as finding a *difference*.

Missing addend   Difference

$$12 = 3 + \blacksquare \qquad 12 - 3 = \blacksquare$$

▶ **EXAMPLE 9** Write a subtraction that corresponds to the following situation. You need not carry out the subtraction.

It is 134 mi from Los Angeles to San Diego. A driver has gone 90 mi of the trip. How much farther does the driver have to go?

Distance already driven	plus	Distance to drive	is	Distance from L.A. to San Diego
90 mi	+	■	=	134 mi

Now we write a related subtraction:

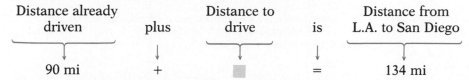

$$90 + \blacksquare = 134$$
$$\blacksquare = 134 - 90. \qquad \textbf{90 gets subtracted (moved).} \qquad ◀$$

DO EXERCISES 14 AND 15.

f Subtraction of Whole Numbers

To subtract numbers, we can subtract ones first, then tens, and so on.

▶ **EXAMPLE 10** Subtract: $9768 - 4320$.

$$
\begin{array}{cccc}
9 & 7 & 6 & 8 \\
-\,4 & 3 & 2 & 0 \\
\hline
 & & & 8
\end{array}
$$ Subtract ones.

$$
\begin{array}{cccc}
9 & 7 & 6 & 8 \\
-\,4 & 3 & 2 & 0 \\
\hline
 & & 4 & 8
\end{array}
$$ Subtract tens.

$$
\begin{array}{cccc}
9 & 7 & 6 & 8 \\
-\,4 & 3 & 2 & 0 \\
\hline
 & 4 & 4 & 8
\end{array}
$$ Subtract hundreds.

$$
\begin{array}{cccc}
9 & 7 & 6 & 8 \\
-\,4 & 3 & 2 & 0 \\
\hline
5 & 4 & 4 & 8
\end{array}
$$ Subtract thousands.

This is for explanation.

$$
\begin{array}{cccc}
9 & 7 & 6 & 8 \\
-\,4 & 3 & 2 & 0 \\
\hline
5 & 4 & 4 & 8
\end{array}
$$ You should write only this.   ◀

DO EXERCISE 16.

Write an addition sentence and a related subtraction sentence corresponding to the situation. You need not carry out the subtraction.

14. There are 32 million kangaroos and 15 million people in Australia. How many more kangaroos are there than people?

15. A set of drapes requires 23 yd of material. The drapemaker has 10 yd of material. How much more is needed?

16. Subtract.
$$
\begin{array}{cccc}
7 & 8 & 9 & 3 \\
-\,4 & 0 & 9 & 2 \\
\end{array}
$$

Subtract. Check by adding.

17. 8 6 8 6
        − 2 3 5 8

18. 7 1 4 5
        − 2 3 9 8

Subtract.

19. 7 0
        − 1 4

20. 5 0 3
        − 2 9 8

Subtract.

21. 7 0 0 7
        − 6 3 4 9

22. 6 0 0 0
        − 3 1 4 9

23. 9 0 3 5
        − 7 4 8 9

Sometimes we need to borrow.

▶ **EXAMPLE 11** Subtract: 6246 − 1879.

         3 16
   6 2 4 6   We cannot subtract 9 ones from 6 ones, but we can subtract 9
 − 1 8 7 9   ones from 16 ones. We borrow 1 ten to get 16 ones.
         7

        13
      1 3 16
   6 2 4 6   We cannot subtract 7 tens from 3 tens, but we can subtract 7
 − 1 8 7 9   tens from 13 tens. We borrow 1 hundred to get 13 tens.
       6 7

     11 13
   5 1 3 16
   6 2 4 6   We cannot subtract 8 hundreds from 1 hundred, but we can
 − 1 8 7 9   subtract 8 hundreds from 11 hundreds. We borrow 1 thousand
   4 3 6 7   to get 11 hundreds.

We can always check the answer by adding it to the number being
subtracted.

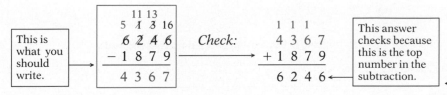

This is what you should write.

     11 13
   5 1 3 16
   6 2 4 6   *Check:*   1 1 1
 − 1 8 7 9   4 3 6 7
   4 3 6 7   + 1 8 7 9
                              6 2 4 6

This answer checks because this is the top number in the subtraction. ◀

DO EXERCISES 17 AND 18.

▶ **EXAMPLE 12** Subtract: 902 − 477.

    8 9 12
    9̶ 0̶ 2̶   We cannot subtract 7 ones from 2 ones. We have 9 hundreds, or
  − 4 7 7   90 tens. We borrow 1 ten to get 12 ones. We then have 89 tens.
    4 2 5   ◀

DO EXERCISES 19 AND 20.

▶ **EXAMPLE 13** Subtract: 8003 − 3667.

   7 9 9 13
   8̶ 0̶ 0̶ 3̶   We have 8 thousands, or 800 tens.
 − 3 6 6 7   We borrow 1 ten to get 13 ones. We then have 799 tens.
   4 3 3 6   ◀

▶ **EXAMPLES**

14. Subtract: 6000 − 3762.

   5 9 9 10
   6̶ 0̶ 0̶ 0̶
 − 3 7 6 2
   2 2 3 8

15. Subtract: 6024 − 2968.

           11
   5 9 1 14
   6̶ 0̶ 2̶ 4̶
 − 2 9 6 8
   3 0 5 6   ◀

DO EXERCISES 21–23.

EXERCISE SET 1.2

a Write an addition that corresponds to the situation.

1. A seamstress buys 3 yd of fabric on one day and 6 yd on the next day. How many yards of fabric did the seamstress buy in all?

2. A jogger runs 4 mi one day and 5 mi the next. What total distance was run in the two days?

3. A student earns $23 one day and $31 the next. How much did the student earn in all?

4. You own a 40-acre farm. Then you buy an adjoining 80-acre farm. You now own a farm of how many acres?

b Add.

5. 3 6 4 + 2 3	**6.** 1 7 2 1 + 3 4 8	**7.** 1 7 1 6 +3 2 8 2	**8.** 7 5 0 3 +2 6 8 3

9. 999 + 111

10. 839 + 386

11. 909 + 101

12. 707 + 909

13. 811 + 390

14. 271 + 333

15. 356 + 491

16. 280 + 347

17. 8 7 1 9 +1 4 2 0	**18.** 3 6 5 4 +2 7 0 0	**19.** 4 8 2 5 +1 7 8 3	**20.** 6 7 7 5 +1 4 3 2

21. 9 9 9 9 +6 7 8 5	**22.** 4 5,8 7 9 +2 1,7 8 6	**23.** 7 7,5 4 3 +2 3,7 6 7	**24.** 4 4,6 5 4 + 4,7 6 5

25.   2 6
  8 2
+6 1
	26. 3 2 4
	  1 2 6
	+4 8 2
		27. 3 4 2 0
		  8 7 1 9
		  4 3 1 2
		+6 2 0 3
			28. 2 0 0 3
			  1 4 9
			    5 8
			+3 4 2 6

c Write a subtraction that corresponds to each situation. You need not carry out the subtraction.

29. A gasoline station has 2400 gal of lead-free gasoline. One day it sells 800 gal. How many gallons are left in the tank?

30. A consumer has $650 in a checking account and writes a check for $100. How much is left in the account?

ANSWERS

1. _____
2. _____
3. _____
4. _____
5. _____
6. _____
7. _____
8. _____
9. _____
10. _____
11. _____
12. _____
13. _____
14. _____
15. _____
16. _____
17. _____
18. _____
19. _____
20. _____
21. _____
22. _____
23. _____
24. _____
25. _____
26. _____
27. _____
28. _____
29. _____
30. _____

ANSWERS

31. _____

32. _____

33. _____

34. _____

35. _____

36. _____

37. _____

38. _____

39. _____

40. _____

41. _____

42. _____

43. _____

44. _____

45. _____

46. _____

47. _____

48. _____

49. _____

50. _____

51. _____

52. _____

53. _____

54. _____

55. _____

56. _____

57. _____

58. _____

59. _____

d Write a related addition sentence.

31. $10 - 7 = 3$ **32.** $12 - 5 = 7$ **33.** $13 - 8 = 5$ **34.** $9 - 9 = 0$

Write two related subtraction sentences.

35. $6 + 9 = 15$ **36.** $7 + 9 = 16$ **37.** $8 + 7 = 15$ **38.** $8 + 0 = 8$

e Write an addition sentence and a related subtraction sentence corresponding to each situation. You need not carry out the subtraction.

39. One week a car dealer sets a goal of selling 220 cars. By Thursday it sells 190 cars. How many more does it have to sell in order to meet its goal?

40. Tuition will cost a student $3000. The student has $1250. How much more money is needed?

f Subtract.

41. $86 - 47$ **42.** $73 - 28$ **43.** $625 - 327$ **44.** $726 - 509$

45.
$$\begin{array}{r} 866 \\ -333 \\ \hline \end{array}$$
46.
$$\begin{array}{r} 526 \\ -323 \\ \hline \end{array}$$
47.
$$\begin{array}{r} 3982 \\ -2489 \\ \hline \end{array}$$
48.
$$\begin{array}{r} 5046 \\ -2859 \\ \hline \end{array}$$

49.
$$\begin{array}{r} 12{,}647 \\ -4{,}899 \\ \hline \end{array}$$
50.
$$\begin{array}{r} 46{,}771 \\ -12{,}977 \\ \hline \end{array}$$
51.
$$\begin{array}{r} 140 \\ -56 \\ \hline \end{array}$$
52.
$$\begin{array}{r} 2300 \\ -109 \\ \hline \end{array}$$

53.
$$\begin{array}{r} 7000 \\ -2794 \\ \hline \end{array}$$
54.
$$\begin{array}{r} 8001 \\ -6543 \\ \hline \end{array}$$
55.
$$\begin{array}{r} 48{,}000 \\ -37{,}695 \\ \hline \end{array}$$
56.
$$\begin{array}{r} 17{,}043 \\ -11{,}598 \\ \hline \end{array}$$

SKILL MAINTENANCE

The exercises that follow are *skill maintenance exercises,* which review any skill previously studied in the text. You can expect such exercises in most exercise sets.

57. What does the digit 7 mean in 6,375,602?

58. Write a word name for 6,375,602.

SYNTHESIS

Synthesis exercises are extra and optional, and usually more challenging, requiring you to put together objectives of this section or preceding sections of the text.

59. Try to discover a faster way of adding all the numbers from 1 to 100 inclusive.

1.3 Multiplication and Division

a Multiplication and the Real World

Multiplication of whole numbers corresponds to two kinds of situations.

Repeated Addition

The multiplication 3×5 corresponds to this repeated addition:

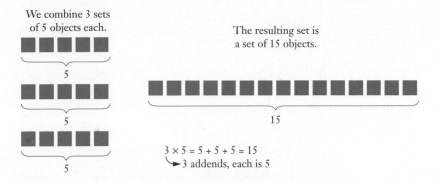

We combine 3 sets of 5 objects each.

The resulting set is a set of 15 objects.

$3 \times 5 = 5 + 5 + 5 = 15$
↳ 3 addends, each is 5

We say that the **product** of 3 and 5 is 15. The numbers 3 and 5 are called **factors.**

$$3 \times 5 \quad = \quad 15$$

Factors   Product

Rectangular Arrays

The multiplication 3×5 corresponds to this rectangular array:

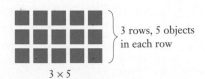

3 rows, 5 objects in each row

3×5

When you write a multiplication corresponding to a real-world situation, you should think of either a rectangular array or repeated addition. In some cases, it may help to think both ways.

We have used an " $\times$ " to denote multiplication. A dot " $\cdot$ " is also commonly used. It was invented by the German mathematician Leibniz in 1698. Parentheses are also used to denote multiplication. For example, $(3)(5) = 15.$

OBJECTIVES

After finishing Section 1.3, you should be able to:

a Determine what multiplication corresponds to a situation.

b Multiply whole numbers.

c Write a division that corresponds to a situation.

d Given a division sentence, write a related multiplication sentence; and given a multiplication sentence, write two related division sentences.

e Divide whole numbers.

FOR EXTRA HELP

Tape 1E, 1F

Write a multiplication that corresponds to the situation.

1. A jogger runs 4 mi on each of 8 days. How many miles are run in all?

2. A lab technician pours 75 mL (milliliters) of acid into each of 10 beakers. How much acid is poured in all?

3. A band is arranged rectangularly in 12 rows with 20 members in each row. How many people are in the band?

4. What is the area of this region?

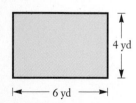

▶ **EXAMPLES** Write a multiplication that corresponds to each situation.

1. It is known that Americans drink 23 million gal of soft drinks per day (*per day* means *each day*). What quantity of soft drinks is consumed every 5 days?

   We draw a picture or at least visualize the situation. Repeated addition fits best in this case.

5 · 23 million gallons = 115 million gallons

2. One side of a building has 6 floors with 7 windows on each floor. How many windows are there on that side of the building?

   We have a rectangular array and can easily draw a sketch.

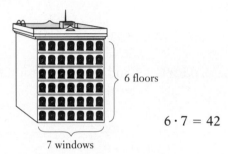

$6 \cdot 7 = 42$ ◀

Area

The area of a rectangular region is often considered to be the number of square units needed to fill it.

▶ **EXAMPLE 3** Write a multiplication that corresponds to the following situation. A rectangular rug is 4 ft long and 3 ft wide. Find its area.

   We draw a picture.

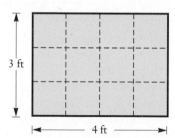

If we think of filling the rectangle with square feet, we have a rectangular array. It takes 12 square feet (ft^2) to fill it. We have

$$A = l \cdot w = 4 \times 3 = 12 \text{ square feet} \quad (12 \text{ ft}^2).$$ ◀

DO EXERCISES 1–4.

b Multiplication of Whole Numbers

Let's find the product

$$\begin{array}{r} 5\ 4 \\ \times\ 3\ 2 \\ \hline \end{array}$$

To do this, we multiply 54 by 2, then 54 by 30, and then add.

$$\begin{array}{r} 5\ 4 \\ \times\ \ \ 2 \\ \hline 1\ 0\ 8 \end{array} \qquad \begin{array}{r} ^{1} \\ 5\ 4 \\ \times\ 3\ 0 \\ \hline 1\ 6\ 2\ 0 \end{array}$$

Since we are going to add the results, let's write the work this way.

$$\begin{array}{r} 5\ 4 \\ \times\ 3\ 2 \\ \hline 1\ 0\ 8 \\ 1\ 6\ 2\ 0 \\ \hline 1\ 7\ 2\ 8 \end{array}$$

        Multiplying by 2

        Multiplying by 30

        Adding

▶ **EXAMPLE 4** Multiply 43×57.

$$\begin{array}{r} ^{2} \\ 5\ 7 \\ \times\ 4\ 3 \\ \hline 1\ 7\ 1 \end{array}$$

    Multiplying by 3

$$\begin{array}{r} ^{2} \\ ^{2} \\ 5\ 7 \\ \times\ 4\ 3 \\ \hline 1\ 7\ 1 \\ 2\ 2\ 8\ 0 \end{array}$$

    Multiplying by 40. (We write a 0 and then multiply 57 by 4.)

> You may have learned that such a 0 does not have to be written. You may omit it if you wish. If you do omit it, remember, when multiplying by tens, to put the answer in the tens place.

$$\begin{array}{r} ^{2} \\ ^{2} \\ 5\ 7 \\ \times\ 4\ 3 \\ \hline 1\ 7\ 1 \\ 2\ 2\ 8\ 0 \\ \hline 2\ 4\ 5\ 1 \end{array}$$

    Adding ◀

DO EXERCISES 5 AND 6.

Multiply.

5.
$$\begin{array}{r} 4\ 5 \\ \times\ 2\ 3 \\ \hline \end{array}$$

6.
$$\begin{array}{r} 6\ 3 \\ \times\ 4\ 8 \\ \hline \end{array}$$

ANSWERS ON PAGE A-1

Multiply.

7.
```
    7 4 6
  ×   6 2
```

8.
```
    8 3 7
  × 2 4 5
```

Multiply.

9.
```
    4 7 2
  × 3 0 6
```

10.
```
    7 0 4
  × 4 0 8
```

11.
```
    2 3 4 4
  × 6 0 0 5
```

Multiply.

12.
```
    4 7 2
  × 3 6 0
```

13.
```
    2 3 4 4
  × 7 4 0 0
```

▶ **EXAMPLE 5**   Multiply: 457×683.

```
        5 2
      6 8 3
    × 4 5 7
    4 7 8 1     Multiplying 683 by 7
```

```
      4 1
      5 2
      6 8 3
    × 4 5 7
      4 7 8 1
    3 4 1 5 0   Multiplying 683 by 50
```

```
      3 1
      4 1
      5 2
      6 8 3
    ×   4 5 7
        4 7 8 1
      3 4 1 5 0
    2 7 3 2 0 0   Multiplying 683 by 400
    3 1 2, 1 3 1  Adding
```

DO EXERCISES 7 AND 8.

Zeros in Multiplication

▶ **EXAMPLE 6**   Multiply: 306×274.

Note that $306 = 3$ hundreds $+ 6$ ones.

```
      2 7 4
    ×  3 0 6
      1 6 4 4     Multiplying by 6
    8 2 2 0 0     Multiplying by 3 hundreds. (We write 00 and then
                  multiply 274 by 3.)
    8 3, 8 4 4    Adding
```

DO EXERCISES 9–11.

▶ **EXAMPLE 7**   Multiply: 360×274.

Note that $360 = 3$ hundreds $+ 6$ tens.

```
      2 7 4       Multiplying by 6 tens. (We write 0
    ×  3 6 0      and then multiply 274 by 6.)
    1 6 4 4 0     Multiplying by 3 hundreds. (We write 00
    8 2 2 0 0     and then multiply 274 by 3.)
    9 8, 6 4 0    Adding
```

DO EXERCISES 12 AND 13.

C Division and the Real World

Division of whole numbers corresponds to two kinds of situations. Consider the division 20 ÷ 5, read "20 divided by 5." We can think of 20 objects arranged in a rectangular array. We ask "How many rows, each with 5 objects, are there?

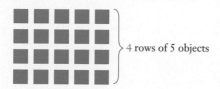

4 rows of 5 objects

Since there are 4 rows of 5 objects each, we have

$$20 \div 5 = 4.$$

We can also ask, "If we make 5 rows, how many objects will there be in each row?

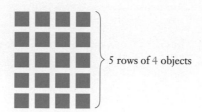

5 rows of 4 objects

Since there are 4 objects in each of the 5 rows, we have

$$20 \div 5 = 4.$$

We also write a division such as 20 ÷ 5 as

$$20/5 \quad \text{or} \quad \frac{20}{5}.$$

▶ **EXAMPLE 8** Write a division that corresponds to the following.

A parent gives $24 to 3 children, giving the same amount to each. How much does each child get?

We think of an array with 3 rows. Each row will go to a child. How many dollars will be in each row?

3 rows with 8 in each row

$24 \div 3 = 8$ ◀

Write a division that corresponds to the situation. You need not carry out the division.

14. There are 112 students in a band and they are marching with 14 in each row. How many rows are there?

▶ **EXAMPLE 9**　Write a division that corresponds to this situation. You need not carry out the division.

How many radios at $45 each can be purchased for $495?

We think of an array with $45 in each row. The money in each row will buy a radio. How many rows will there be?

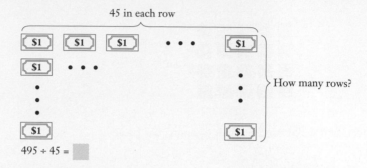

$$495 \div 45 = \boxed{}$$

◀

> **Whenever we have a rectangular array, we know the following:**
>
> **(The total number) ÷ (The number of rows) = (The number in each row).**
>
> **Also:**
>
> **(The total number) ÷ (The number in each row) = (The number of rows).**

DO EXERCISES 14 AND 15.

15. A marching band is in a rectangular array. There are 112 students in the band, and they are marching in 8 rows. How many students are there in each row?

d　**Related Sentences**

By looking at rectangular arrays, we can see how multiplication and division are related. The following array shows that $4 \cdot 5 = 20$.

$4 \cdot 5 = 20$

The array also shows the following:

$$20 \div 5 = 4 \quad \text{and} \quad 20 \div 4 = 5.$$

Division is actually defined in terms of multiplication. For example, $20 \div 5$ is defined to be the number which when multiplied by 5 gives 20. Thus, for every division sentence, there is a related multiplication sentence.

$20 \div 5 = 4$　　**Division sentence**

$20 = 4 \cdot 5$　　**Related multiplication sentence**

To get the related multiplication sentence, we move the 5 to the other side and then write a multiplication.

▶ **EXAMPLE 10**   Write a related multiplication sentence: $12 \div 6 = 2$.
We have

$$12 \div 6 = 2 \quad \text{This number moves to the right.}$$

The related multiplication sentence is $12 = 2 \cdot 6$.

| By the commutative law of multiplication, there is also another multiplication sentence: $12 = 6 \cdot 2$. |

◀

DO EXERCISES 16 AND 17.

For every multiplication sentence, we can write related divisions, as we can see from the preceding array. We move one of the factors to the opposite side and then write a division.

▶ **EXAMPLE 11**   Write two related division sentences: $7 \cdot 8 = 56$.
We move a factor to the other side and then write a division:

$$7 \cdot 8 = 56 \qquad 7 \cdot 8 = 56$$
$$7 = 56 \div 8 \qquad 8 = 56 \div 7$$

◀

DO EXERCISES 18 AND 19.

With multiplication and division, we use the following words.

$$
\begin{array}{cccc}
14 & \div & 7 & = & 2 \\
\uparrow & & \uparrow & & \uparrow \\
\text{Dividend} & & \text{Divisor} & & \text{Quotient}
\end{array}
$$

$$
\begin{array}{cccc}
14 & = & 7 & \cdot & 2 \\
\uparrow & & \uparrow & & \uparrow \\
\text{Product} & & \text{Factor} & & \text{Factor}
\end{array}
$$

e   Division of Whole Numbers

Multiplication can be thought of as repeated addition. Division can be thought of as repeated subtraction. Compare.

We can make
3 rows, adding
6 each time.

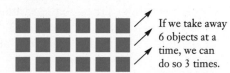

If we take away
6 objects at a
time, we can
do so 3 times.

$$18 = 6 + 6 + 6$$
$$\qquad = 3 \cdot 6$$

$$18 - 6 - 6 - 6 = 0$$

3 times
$$18 \div 6 = 3$$

Write a related multiplication sentence.
16. $15 \div 3 = 5$

17. $72 \div 8 = 9$

Write two related division sentences.
18. $6 \cdot 2 = 12$

19. $7 \cdot 6 = 42$

Divide by repeated subtraction. Then check.

20. 54 ÷ 9

21. 61 ÷ 9

22. 53 ÷ 12

23. 157 ÷ 24

To divide by repeated subtraction, we keep track of the number of times we subtract.

▶ **EXAMPLE 12**   Divide by repeated subtraction: 20 ÷ 4.

$$
\begin{array}{r}
2\ 0 \\
-\ \ 4 \longrightarrow \\
\hline
1\ 6 \\
-\ \ 4 \longrightarrow \\
\hline
1\ 2 \\
-\ \ 4 \longrightarrow \\
\hline
8 \\
-\ \ 4 \longrightarrow \\
\hline
4 \\
-\ \ 4 \longrightarrow \\
\hline
0
\end{array}
\left.\rule{0pt}{8em}\right\}
$$

We subtracted 5 times, so 20 ÷ 4 = 5.

◀

▶ **EXAMPLE 13**   Divide by repeated subtraction: 23 ÷ 5.

$$
\begin{array}{r}
2\ 3 \\
-\ \ 5 \longrightarrow \\
\hline
1\ 8 \\
-\ \ 5 \longrightarrow \\
\hline
1\ 3 \\
-\ \ 5 \longrightarrow \\
\hline
8 \\
-\ \ 5 \longrightarrow \\
\hline
\end{array}
\left.\rule{0pt}{7em}\right\}
$$

We subtracted 4 times.

3 ⟶ We have 3 left. This number is called the *remainder*. ◀

We write

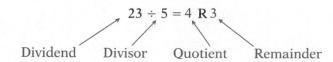

23 ÷ 5 = 4 R 3

Dividend   Divisor   Quotient   Remainder

Checking divisions.   To check a division, we multiply. Suppose we divide 98 by 2 and get 49:

$$98 \div 2 = 49.$$

To check, we think of the related sentence 49 · 2 = ▉. We multiply 49 by 2 and see if we get 98.

If there is a remainder, we add it after multiplying.

▶ **EXAMPLE 14**   Check the division in Example 6.

We found that 23 ÷ 5 = 4 R 3. To check, we multiply 5 by 4. This gives us 20. Then we add 3 to get 23. The dividend is 23, so the answer checks.

◀

DO EXERCISES 20–23.

When we use the general division process, we are doing repeated subtraction, even though we are going about it in a different way.

To divide, we start from the digit of highest place value in the dividend and work down to the lowest through the remainders. At each step we ask if there are multiples of the divisor in the quotient.

▶ **EXAMPLE 15**   Divide and check: $3642 \div 5$.

1. We start with the thousands digit in the dividend. Are there any thousands in the quotient? No; $5 \cdot 1000 = 5000$, and 5000 is larger than 3000.

2. Now we go to the hundreds place in the dividend. Are there any hundreds in the quotient? Think of the dividend as 36 hundreds. Estimate 7 hundreds. Write 7 in the hundreds place, multiply 700 by 5, write the answer below 3642, and subtract.

3. a) We go to the tens place of the first remainder. Are there any tens in the tens place of the quotient? To answer the question, think of the first remainder as 14 tens. Estimate 3 tens. When we multiply, we get 150, which is too large.
b) We lower our estimate to 2 tens. Write 2 in the tens place, multiply 20 by 5, and subtract.

4. We go to the ones place of the second remainder. Are there any ones in the ones place of the quotient? To answer the question, think of the second remainder as 42 ones. Estimate 8 ones. Write 8 in the ones place, multiply 8 by 5, and subtract.

> You may have learned to divide like this, not writing the extra zeros. You may omit them if desired.

The answer is 728 R 2. To check, we multiply 728 by 5. This gives us 3640. Then we add 2 to get 3642. The dividend is 3642, so the answer checks.   ◀

DO EXERCISES 24–26.

Divide and check.

24. $4\overline{)2\ 3\ 9}$

25. $6\overline{)8\ 8\ 5\ 5}$

26. $5\overline{)5\ 0\ 7\ 5}$

Divide.

27. 6)4 8 4 6

28. 7)7 6 1 6

Divide.

29. 2 7)9 7 2 4

30. 5 6)4 4,8 4 7

Zeros in Quotients

▶ **EXAMPLE 16**   Divide: $6341 \div 7$.

$$
\begin{array}{r}
9 \\
7 \overline{)6\ 3\ 4\ 1} \\
6\ 3\ 0\ 0 \\
\hline
4\ 1
\end{array}
$$

← *Think:* 63 hundreds ÷ 7. Estimate 9 hundreds.

$$
\begin{array}{r}
9\ 0 \\
7 \overline{)6\ 3\ 4\ 1} \\
6\ 3\ 0\ 0 \\
\hline
4\ 1
\end{array}
$$

← *Think:* 4 tens ÷ 7. There are no tens in the quotient (other than the tens in 900). We write a 0 to show this.

$$
\begin{array}{r}
9\ 0\ 5 \\
7 \overline{)6\ 3\ 4\ 1} \\
6\ 3\ 0\ 0 \\
\hline
4\ 1 \\
3\ 5 \\
\hline
6
\end{array}
$$

← *Think:* 41 ones ÷ 7. Estimate 5 ones.

The answer is 905 R 6.

DO EXERCISES 27 AND 28.

▶ **EXAMPLE 17**   Divide: $8889 \div 37$.

We round 37 to 40.

$$
\begin{array}{r}
2 \\
3\ 7 \overline{)8\ 8\ 8\ 9} \\
7\ 4\ 0\ 0 \\
\hline
1\ 4\ 8\ 9
\end{array}
$$

← *Think:* 37 ≈ 40; 88 hundreds ÷ 40. Estimate 2 hundreds.

$$
\begin{array}{r}
2\ 4 \\
3\ 7 \overline{)8\ 8\ 8\ 9} \\
7\ 4\ 0\ 0 \\
\hline
1\ 4\ 8\ 9 \\
1\ 4\ 8\ 0 \\
\hline
9
\end{array}
$$

← *Think:* 148 tens ÷ 40. Estimate 4 tens.

$$
\begin{array}{r}
2\ 4\ 0 \\
3\ 7 \overline{)8\ 8\ 8\ 9} \\
7\ 4\ 0\ 0 \\
\hline
1\ 4\ 8\ 9 \\
1\ 4\ 8\ 0 \\
\hline
9
\end{array}
$$

← *Think:* 9 ones ÷ 40. There are no ones in the quotient.

The answer is 240 R 9.

DO EXERCISES 29 AND 30.

NAME   SECTION   DATE

EXERCISE SET 1.3

 a Write a multiplication that corresponds to each situation.

1. A store sold 32 calculators at $10 each. How much money did the store receive for the calculators?

2. A beverage carton contains 8 bottles, each of which holds 16 oz. How many ounces are there in the carton?

What is the area of each region?

3.

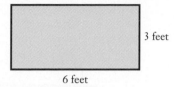

3 feet

6 feet

4.

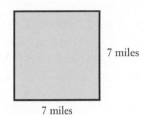

7 miles

7 miles

b Multiply.

5. $\begin{array}{r} 100 \\ \times\ 96 \\ \hline \end{array}$	**6.** $\begin{array}{r} 2340 \\ \times 1000 \\ \hline \end{array}$	**7.** $\begin{array}{r} 94 \\ \times\ 6 \\ \hline \end{array}$	**8.** $\begin{array}{r} 76 \\ \times\ 9 \\ \hline \end{array}$

9. $3 \cdot 509$ **10.** $7 \cdot 806$ **11.** $7 \cdot 9229$ **12.** $4 \cdot 7867$

13. $90 \cdot 53$ **14.** $60 \cdot 78$ **15.** $48 \cdot 65$ **16.** $34 \cdot 87$

17. $\begin{array}{r} 640 \\ \times\ 72 \\ \hline \end{array}$	**18.** $\begin{array}{r} 666 \\ \times\ 66 \\ \hline \end{array}$	**19.** $\begin{array}{r} 444 \\ \times\ 33 \\ \hline \end{array}$	**20.** $\begin{array}{r} 509 \\ \times\ 88 \\ \hline \end{array}$

21. $\begin{array}{r} 509 \\ \times 408 \\ \hline \end{array}$	**22.** $\begin{array}{r} 432 \\ \times 375 \\ \hline \end{array}$	**23.** $\begin{array}{r} 678 \\ \times 742 \\ \hline \end{array}$	**24.** $\begin{array}{r} 346 \\ \times 650 \\ \hline \end{array}$

25. $\begin{array}{r} 6428 \\ \times 3224 \\ \hline \end{array}$	**26.** $\begin{array}{r} 8928 \\ \times 3172 \\ \hline \end{array}$	**27.** $\begin{array}{r} 3482 \\ \times\ 104 \\ \hline \end{array}$	**28.** $\begin{array}{r} 6408 \\ \times 6064 \\ \hline \end{array}$

29. $\begin{array}{r} 5006 \\ \times 4008 \\ \hline \end{array}$	**30.** $\begin{array}{r} 6789 \\ \times 2330 \\ \hline \end{array}$	**31.** $\begin{array}{r} 5608 \\ \times 4500 \\ \hline \end{array}$	**32.** $\begin{array}{r} 4560 \\ \times 7890 \\ \hline \end{array}$

1. _____
2. _____
3. _____
4. _____
5. _____
6. _____
7. _____
8. _____
9. _____
10. _____
11. _____
12. _____
13. _____
14. _____
15. _____
16. _____
17. _____
18. _____
19. _____
20. _____
21. _____
22. _____
23. _____
24. _____
25. _____
26. _____
27. _____
28. _____
29. _____
30. _____
31. _____
32. _____

ANSWERS

33. _____

34. _____

35. _____

36. _____

37. _____

38. _____

39. _____

40. _____

41. _____

42. _____

43. _____

44. _____

45. _____

46. _____

47. _____

48. _____

49. _____

50. _____

51. _____

52. _____

53. _____

54. _____

55. _____

56. _____

57. _____

58. _____

59. _____

60. _____

61. _____

62. _____

63. _____

64. _____

c Write a division that corresponds to each situation. You need not carry out the division.

33. A candy factory made 176 lb (pounds) of chocolates. They put them in 4-lb boxes. How many boxes did they fill?

34. A lab technician pours 455 mL of acid into 5 beakers, putting the same amount in each. How much acid is in each beaker?

d Write a related multiplication sentence.

35. $24 \div 8 = 3$ **36.** $72 \div 9 = 8$ **37.** $22 \div 22 = 1$ **38.** $32 \div 1 = 32$

Write two related division sentences.

39. $9 \times 5 = 45$ **40.** $2 \cdot 7 = 14$ **41.** $37 \cdot 1 = 37$ **42.** $4 \cdot 12 = 48$

e Divide.

43. $277 \div 5$ **44.** $699 \div 3$ **45.** $852 \div 21$ **46.** $942 \div 23$

47. $4\overline{)1\ 2\ 2\ 8}$ **48.** $3\overline{)2\ 1\ 2\ 4}$ **49.** $8\overline{)7\ 3\ 8}$ **50.** $6\overline{)8\ 8\ 1}$

51. $5\overline{)8\ 5\ 1\ 5}$ **52.** $3\overline{)6\ 0\ 2\ 7}$ **53.** $3\ 0\overline{)8\ 7\ 5}$ **54.** $4\ 0\overline{)9\ 8\ 7}$

55. $8\ 5\overline{)7\ 6\ 7\ 2}$ **56.** $5\ 4\overline{)2\ 7\ 2\ 9}$ **57.** $1\ 1\ 1\overline{)3\ 2\ 1\ 9}$

58. $1\ 0\ 2\overline{)5\ 6\ 1\ 2}$ **59.** $2\ 4\overline{)8\ 8\ 8\ 0}$ **60.** $3\ 6\overline{)7\ 5\ 6\ 3}$

61. $2\ 8\overline{)1\ 7,0\ 6\ 7}$ **62.** $3\ 6\overline{)2\ 8,9\ 2\ 9}$

SKILL MAINTENANCE

63. Write expanded notation for 7882.

64. Use $<$ or $>$ for ■ to write a true sentence:

888 ■ 788.

1.4 Solving Equations

a Solutions

Let's find a number that we can put in the blank to make this sentence true:

$$9 = 3 + \blacksquare .$$

We are asking "9 is 3 plus what number?" The answer is 6.

$$9 = 3 + \boxed{6}$$

DO EXERCISES 1 AND 2.

A sentence with $=$ is called an **equation.** A **solution** of an equation is a number that makes the sentence true. Thus, 6 is a solution of

$$9 = 3 + \blacksquare \quad \text{because} \quad 9 = 3 + \boxed{6} \text{ is true.}$$

But 7 is not a solution of

$$9 = 3 + \blacksquare \quad \text{because} \quad 9 = 3 + \boxed{7} \text{ is false.}$$

DO EXERCISES 3 AND 4.

We can use a letter instead of a blank. For example,

$$x + 8 = 11.$$

We call x a **variable** because it can represent any number.

> A *solution* is a replacement for the letter that makes the equation true. When we find the solutions, we say that we have *solved* the equation.

▶ **EXAMPLE 1** Solve $x + 12 = 27$ by trial.

We replace x by several numbers.

If we replace x by 13, we get a false equation: $13 + 12 = 27$.
If we replace x by 14, we get a false equation: $14 + 12 = 27$.
If we replace x by 15, we get a true equation: $15 + 12 = 27$.

No other replacement makes the equation true, so the solution is 15. ◀

▶ **EXAMPLES** Solve.

2. $7 + n = 22$
(7 plus what number is 22?)
The solution is 15.

3. $8 \cdot 23 = y$
(8 times 23 is what?)
The solution is 184. ◀

Note, as in Example 3, that when the letter is alone on one side of the equation, the other side shows us what calculations to do in order to find the solution.

DO EXERCISES 5–8.

ANSWERS ON PAGE A-2

OBJECTIVES

After finishing Section 1.4, you should be able to:

a Solve simple equations by trial.

b Solve equations like $t + 28 = 54$, $28 \cdot x = 168$, and $98 \div 2 = y$.

FOR EXTRA HELP

Tape 2A

Find a number that makes the sentence true.

1. $8 = 1 + \blacksquare$

2. $\blacksquare + 2 = 7$

3. Determine whether 7 is a solution of $\blacksquare + 5 = 9$.

4. Determine whether 4 is a solution of $\blacksquare + 5 = 9$.

Solve by trial.

5. $n + 3 = 8$

6. $x - 2 = 8$

7. $45 \div 9 = y$

8. $10 + t = 32$

Solve.

9. $346 \times 65 = y$

10. $x = 2347 + 6675$

11. $4560 \div 8 = t$

12. $x = 6007 - 2346$

Solve.

13. $x + 9 = 17$

14. $77 = m + 32$

---

b   **Solving Equations**

We now begin to develop some more efficient ways to solve certain equations. When an equation has a variable alone on one side, it is easy to see the solution or to compute it. For example, the solution of

$$x = 12$$

is 12.

    When a calculation is on one side and the variable is alone on the other, we can find the solution by carrying out the calculation.

▶   **EXAMPLE 4**   Solve: $x = 245 \times 34$.

    To solve the equation, we carry out the calculation.

$$
\begin{array}{r}
2\ 4\ 5 \\
\times \quad 3\ 4 \\
\hline
9\ 8\ 0 \\
7\ 3\ 5\ 0 \\
\hline
8\ 3\ 3\ 0
\end{array}
$$

The solution is 8330.   ◀

DO EXERCISES 9–12.

    If we can get an equation in a form with the letter alone on one side, we can "see" the solution.

    Look at

$$x + 12 = 27.$$

We can get x alone by writing a related sentence:

$$x = 27 - 12 \qquad \text{12 gets subtracted to find the related subtraction.}$$
$$x = 15. \qquad \text{Doing the subtraction}$$

It is useful to think of this as "subtracting 12 *on both sides.*" Thus,

$$x + 12 - 12 = 27 - 12 \qquad \text{Subtracting 12 on both sides}$$
$$x + 0 = 15 \qquad \text{Carrying out the subtraction}$$
$$x = 15. \qquad x + 0 = x$$

> **To solve $x + a = b$, subtract a on both sides.**

▶   **EXAMPLE 5**   Solve: $t + 28 = 54$.

    We have

$$t + 28 = 54$$
$$t + 28 - 28 = 54 - 28 \qquad \text{Subtracting 28 on both sides}$$
$$t + 0 = 26$$
$$t = 26.$$

The solution is 26.   ◀

DO EXERCISES 13 AND 14.

▶ **EXAMPLE 6**   Solve: $182 = 65 + n$.
We have

$$182 = 65 + n$$
$$182 - 65 = 65 + n - 65 \qquad \text{Subtracting 65 on both sides}$$
$$117 = 0 + n \qquad \text{65 plus } n \text{ minus 65 is } 0 + n$$
$$117 = n$$

The solution is 117.   ◀

DO EXERCISE 15.

▶ **EXAMPLE 7**   Solve: $7381 + x = 8067$.
We have

$$7381 + x = 8067$$
$$7381 + x - 7381 = 8067 - 7381 \qquad \text{Subtracting 7381 on both sides}$$
$$x = 686.$$

The solution is 686.   ◀

DO EXERCISES 16 AND 17.

We now learn to solve equations like $8 \cdot n = 96$. Look at
$$8 \cdot n = 96.$$
We can get n alone by writing a related division sentence:

$$n = 96 \div 8 = \frac{96}{8} \qquad \text{We move 8 to the other side and write a division.}$$
$$n = 12. \qquad \text{Doing the division}$$

Note that $n = 12$ is easier to solve than $8 \cdot n = 96$. This is because we see easily that if we replace n on the left side by 12, we get a true sentence: $12 = 12$. The solution of $n = 12$ is 12, which is also the solution of $8 \cdot n = 96$.

It is useful to think of the preceding as "dividing by 8 *on both sides.*" Thus,

$$\frac{8 \cdot n}{8} = \frac{96}{8} \qquad \text{Dividing by 8 on both sides}$$
$$n = 12. \qquad \text{8 times } n \text{ divided by 8 is } n.$$

> **To solve $a \cdot x = b$, divide by a on both sides.**

▶ **EXAMPLE 8**   Solve: $10 \cdot x = 240$.
We have

$$10 \cdot x = 240$$
$$\frac{10 \cdot x}{10} = \frac{240}{10} \qquad \text{Dividing by 10 on both sides}$$
$$x = 24.$$

The solution is 24.   ◀

DO EXERCISES 18 AND 19.

15. Solve: $155 = t + 78$.

Solve.
16. $4566 + x = 7877$

17. $8172 = h + 2058$

Solve.
18. $8 \cdot x = 64$

19. $144 = 9 \cdot n$

ANSWERS ON PAGE A-2

20. Solve: $5152 = 8 \cdot t$.

▶ **EXAMPLE 9**　Solve: $5202 = 9 \cdot t$.

We have

$$5202 = 9 \cdot t$$

$$\frac{5202}{9} = \frac{9 \cdot t}{9} \qquad \text{Dividing by 9 on both sides}$$

$$578 = t.$$

The solution is 578.　　　　　　　　　　　　　　◀

DO EXERCISE 20.

▶ **EXAMPLE 10**　Solve: $14 \cdot y = 1092$.

We have

$$14 \cdot y = 1092$$

$$\frac{14 \cdot y}{14} = \frac{1092}{14} \qquad \text{Dividing by 14 on both sides}$$

$$y = 78.$$

21. Solve: $18 \cdot y = 1728$.

The solution is 78.　　　　　　　　　　　　　　◀

DO EXERCISE 21.

▶ **EXAMPLE 11**　Solve: $n \cdot 56 = 4648$.

We have

$$n \cdot 56 = 4648$$

$$\frac{n \cdot 56}{56} = \frac{4648}{56} \qquad \text{Dividing by 56 on both sides}$$

$$n = 83.$$

The solution is 83.　　　　　　　　　　　　　　◀

DO EXERCISE 22.

22. Solve: $n \cdot 48 = 4512$.

NAME   SECTION   DATE

EXERCISE SET 1.4

a Solve by trial.

1. $x + 0 = 14$ **2.** $x - 7 = 18$ **3.** $y \cdot 17 = 0$ **4.** $56 \div m = 7$

b Solve.

5. $13 + x = 42$ **6.** $15 + t = 22$ **7.** $12 = 12 + m$

8. $16 = t + 16$ **9.** $3 \cdot x = 24$ **10.** $6 \cdot x = 42$

11. $112 = n \cdot 8$ **12.** $162 = 9 \cdot m$ **13.** $45 \times 23 = x$

14. $23 \times 78 = y$ **15.** $t = 125 \div 5$ **16.** $w = 256 \div 16$

17. $p = 908 - 458$ **18.** $9007 - 5667 = m$ **19.** $x = 12{,}345 + 78{,}555$

20. $5678 + 9034 = t$ **21.** $3 \cdot m = 96$ **22.** $4 \cdot y = 96$

23. $715 = 5 \cdot z$ **24.** $741 = 3 \cdot t$ **25.** $10 + x = 89$

26. $20 + x = 57$ **27.** $61 = 16 + y$ **28.** $53 = 17 + w$

29. $6 \cdot p = 1944$ **30.** $4 \cdot w = 3404$ **31.** $5 \cdot x = 3715$

32. $9 \cdot x = 1269$ **33.** $47 + n = 84$ **34.** $56 + p = 92$

1.
2.
3.
4.
5.
6.
7.
8.
9.
10.
11.
12.
13.
14.
15.
16.
17.
18.
19.
20.
21.
22.
23.
24.
25.
26.
27.
28.
29.
30.
31.
32.
33.
34.

Copyright © 1993 Addison-Wesley Publishing Co., Inc.

ANSWERS

35.

36.

37.

38.

39.

40.

41.

42.

43.

44.

45.

46.

47.

48.

49.

50.

51.

52.

53.

54.

55.

56.

57.

58.

59.

60.

61.

35. $x + 78 = 144$

36. $z + 67 = 133$

37. $165 = 11 \cdot n$

38. $660 = 12 \cdot n$

39. $624 = t \cdot 13$

40. $784 = y \cdot 16$

41. $x + 214 = 389$

42. $x + 221 = 333$

43. $567 + x = 902$

44. $438 + x = 807$

45. $18 \cdot x = 1872$

46. $19 \cdot x = 6080$

47. $40 \cdot x = 1800$

48. $20 \cdot x = 1500$

49. $2344 + y = 6400$

50. $9281 = 8322 + t$

51. $8322 + 9281 = x$

52. $9281 - 8322 = y$

53. $234 \times 78 = y$

54. $10{,}534 \div 458 = q$

55. $58 \cdot m = 11{,}890$

56. $233 \cdot x = 22{,}135$

57. $x \cdot 198 = 10{,}890$

SKILL MAINTENANCE

58. Write two related subtraction sentences: $7 + 8 = 15$.

59. Write two related division sentences: $6 \cdot 8 = 48$.

Use $>$ or $<$ for ■ to write a true sentence.

60. 123 ■ 789

61. 342 ■ 339

1.5 Solving Problems

a   To solve a problem using the operations on the whole numbers, we first look at the situation. We try to translate the problem to an equation. Then we solve the equation. We check to see if the solution of the equation is a solution to the original problem. We are using the following five-step strategy.

Problem Solving Tips

1. *Familiarize* yourself with the situation. If it is described in words, as in a textbook, *read carefully*. In any case, think about the situation. Draw a picture whenever it makes sense to do so. Choose a letter, or *variable*, to represent the unknown quantity to be solved for.
2. *Translate* the problem to an equation.
3. *Solve* the equation.
4. *Check* the answer in the original wording of the problem.
5. *State* the answer to the problem clearly with appropriate units.

▶ **EXAMPLE 1**   There are 87 boxcars on a freight train. A train behind it has 112 boxcars, and a third train has 98 boxcars. The trains are put together to make one long train. How many boxcars are there on the long train?

1. *Familiarize.* We can make a drawing or at least visualize the situation.

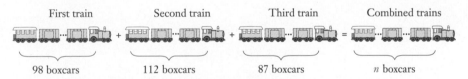

First train   Second train   Third train   Combined trains

98 boxcars   112 boxcars   87 boxcars n boxcars

Since we are combining objects, addition can be used. To define the unknown, we let n = the total number of boxcars on the train.

2. *Translate.* We translate to an equation that corresponds to the situation:

$$98 + 112 + 87 = n.$$

3. *Solve.* We solve the equation by carrying out the addition.

$$
\begin{array}{r}
\overset{1\ 1}{} \\
9\,8 \\
1\,1\,2 \\
+\ \ 8\,7 \\
\hline
2\,9\,7
\end{array}
$$

> Note that even if we did not make one long train, the total number of boxcars would still be 297.

Thus, $297 = n$, or $n = 297$.

4. *Check.* We check 297 boxcars in the original problem. There are many ways to check. We can repeat the calculation. (We leave this to the student.) We can also check the reasonableness of the answer. We would expect our answer to be larger than any of the separate trains, which it is. We can also find an estimated answer by rounding:

$$87 + 112 + 98 \approx 90 + 100 + 100 = 290 \approx 297.$$

1. In a tournament, a professional bowler rolled games of 212, 198, and 249. What was the total?

2. On a long four-day trip a family bought the following amounts of gasoline:

23 gallons, 24 gallons,
26 gallons, 25 gallons.

How much gasoline did they buy in all?

3. The area of the state of Kansas is 82,056 sq mi. The area of the state of Nebraska is 76,522 sq mi. What is the total area of the two states?

4. It takes 109 kilowatt-hours (kWh) to operate a record player for a year. It takes 440 kWh to operate a TV for a year. How much energy is needed for both?

If we had gotten an estimate like 1290 or 850, we might be suspicious that our calculated answer is incorrect. Since our estimated answer is close to our calculation, we are further convinced that our answer checks.

5. *State.* The answer is that there are 297 boxcars altogether. ◀

DO EXERCISES 1 AND 2.

> In the real world, problems are not usually given in words. You must still become familiar with the situation before you can solve the problem.

▶ **EXAMPLE 2** The John Hancock Building in Chicago is 1107 ft tall. It has two 342-ft antennas on top. How far are the tops of the antennas from the ground?

1. *Familiarize.* We first make a drawing.

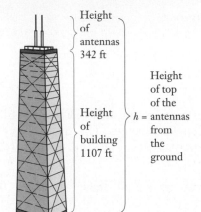

Since we are combining lengths, addition can be used. To define the unknown, we let h = the height of the top of the antennas from the ground.

2. *Translate.* We translate the problem to the following equation:

$$1107 + 342 = h.$$

3. *Solve.* To solve the equation, we carry out the addition.

$$\begin{array}{r} 1\,1\,0\,7 \\ +\ \ 3\,4\,2 \\ \hline 1\,4\,4\,9 \end{array}$$

Thus, $1449 = h$, or $h = 1449$.

4. *Check.* We check the height of 1449 ft in the original problem. We can repeat the calculation. We can also check the reasonableness of the answer. We would expect our answer to be larger than either of the heights, which it is. We can also find an estimated answer by rounding:

$$1107 + 342 \approx 1100 + 300 = 1400 \approx 1449.$$

The answer checks.

5. *State.* The height of the top of the antennas from the ground is 1449 ft. ◀

DO EXERCISES 3 AND 4.

▶ **EXAMPLE 3**   A farm contains 2679 acres. If the owner sells 1884 acres, how many acres are left?

1. *Familiarize.* We first draw a picture or at least visualize the situation. We let A = the number of acres left.

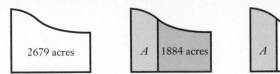

2. *Translate.* We see that this is a "take-away" situation. We translate to an equation.

Area of large farm	minus	Area of part sold	is	Number of acres left
2679	–	1884	=	A

3. *Solve.* This sentence tells us what to do. We subtract.

$$\begin{array}{r} \overset{\scriptstyle 15}{} \\ 1\ \overset{5}{\cancel{6}}\ 17 \\ 2\ \cancel{6}\ \cancel{7}\ 9 \\ -\ 1\ 8\ 8\ 4 \\ \hline 7\ 9\ 5 \end{array}$$

Thus, 795 = A, or A = 795.

4. *Check.* We check 795 acres. We can repeat the calculation. We note that the answer should be less than the original acreage, 2679 acres, which it is. We can add the answer, 795, to the number being subtracted, 1884: 1884 + 795 = 2679. We can also estimate:

$$2679 - 1884 \approx 2700 - 1900 = 800 \approx 795.$$

The answer checks.

5. *State.* There are 795 acres left.   ◀

DO EXERCISES 5 AND 6.

▶ **EXAMPLE 4**   It is 1154 mi from Indianapolis to Denver. A driver has traveled 685 mi of that distance. How much farther is it to Denver?

1. *Familiarize.* We first make a drawing or at least visualize the situation. We let x = the remaining distance to Denver.

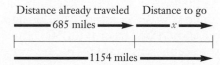

2. *Translate.* We see that this is a "how-much-more" situation. We translate to an equation.

Distance already traveled	plus	Distance to go	is	Total distance of trip
685	+	x	=	1154

5. A person has $948 in a checking account. A check is written for $427. How much is left in the checking account?

6. An oil company has 7890 gal of gasoline in a tank. It drains out 5630 gal into another tank. How much is left in the original tank?

ANSWERS ON PAGE A-2

7. Gold has a melting point of 1063° C. Silver has a melting point of 960° C. How much higher is the melting point of gold?

3. *Solve.* We solve the equation.

$$685 + x = 1154$$
$$685 + x - 685 = 1154 - 685 \qquad \text{\textbf{Subtracting 685 on both sides}}$$
$$x = 469$$

$$
\begin{array}{r}
\overset{10\ \ 14}{\overset{0\ \ \cancel{0}\ \ \cancel{4}\ \ \cancel{4}}{\cancel{1}\ \cancel{1}\ \cancel{5}\ \cancel{4}}} \\
-\ \ 6\ 8\ 5 \\
\hline
4\ 6\ 9
\end{array}
$$

4. *Check.* We check 469 mi in the original problem. This number should be less than the total distance, 1154 mi, which it is. We can repeat the calculation. We add the result, 469, to the number being subtracted, 685: 685 + 469 = 1154. We can also estimate as follows:

$$1154 - 685 \approx 1200 - 700 = 500 \approx 469.$$

This can be handy if you were using a calculator. The answer checks.

5. *State.* It is 469 mi to Denver.　　　　　　　◀

DO EXERCISES 7 AND 8.

8. Annual income in Washington, D.C., is $16,845 per person. In New Jersey it is $15,285. How much greater is the income in Washington, D.C.?

▶ **EXAMPLE 5**　A ream of paper contains 500 sheets. How many sheets are in 9 reams?

1. *Familiarize.* We first draw a picture or at least visualize the situation. We can think of this situation as a stack of reams. We let n = the total number of sheets in 9 reams.

2. *Translate.* Then we translate and solve as follows.

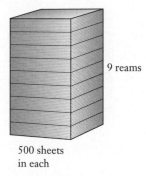

9 reams

500 sheets in each

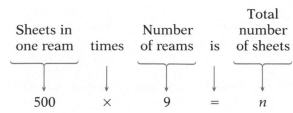

Sheets in one ream	times	Number of reams	is	Total number of sheets
500	×	9	=	n

9. A certain type of shelf can hold 40 books. How many books can 70 shelves hold?

3. *Solve.* To solve the equation, we multiply: 500 × 9 = 4500. Thus, 4500 = n, or n = 4500.

4. *Check.* An estimated answer is almost a repeated calculation. Certainly our answer should be larger than 500, since we are multiplying, so the answer seems reasonable. The answer checks.

5. *State.* There are 4500 sheets in 9 reams.　　　　◀

DO EXERCISE 9.

▶ **EXAMPLE 6**　What is the cost of 5 television sets at $145 each?

1. *Familiarize.* We first draw a picture or at least visualize the situation. We let n = the total cost of 5 television sets. Repeated addition works well here.

10. An electronics firm sells 324 calculators one month, each at a price of $16. How much money did it receive from the calculators?

2. *Translate.* We translate to an equation and solve.

Number of TV sets	times	Cost of each set	is	Total cost
5	×	145	=	n

3. *Solve.* This sentence tells us what to do. We multiply.

$$\begin{array}{r} \overset{2}{1}\,\overset{2}{4}\,5 \\ \times \qquad 5 \\ \hline 7\,2\,5 \end{array}$$ Thus, $n = 725$.

4. *Check.* We have an answer that is much larger than the cost of any individual television, which is reasonable. We can repeat our calculation. We can also check by estimating as follows:

$$5 \times 145 \approx 5 \times 150 = 750 \approx 725.$$

5. *State.* The cost of 5 television sets is $725. ◀

DO EXERCISE 10.

▶ **EXAMPLE 7** The state of Colorado is 270 mi by 380 mi. What is its area?

1. *Familiarize.* We first make a drawing. We let A = the area.

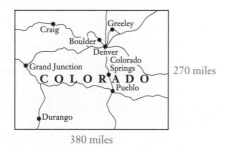

270 miles

380 miles

2. *Translate.* Using a formula for area, we have $A = l \cdot w = 380 \cdot 270$.

3. *Solve.* We carry out the multiplication.

$$\begin{array}{r} 3\,8\,0 \\ \times \qquad 2\,7\,0 \\ \hline 2\,6\,6\,0\,0 \\ 7\,6\,0\,0\,0 \\ \hline 1\,0\,2\,6\,0\,0 \end{array}$$ Thus, $A = 102{,}600$.

4. *Check.* We repeat our calculation. We also note that the answer is larger than either the length or the width, which it should be. (This might not be the case, if we were using decimals.) The answer checks.

5. *State.* The area is 102,600 sq mi. ◀

ANSWER ON PAGE A-2

11. The state of Wyoming is 275 mi by 365 mi. What is its area?

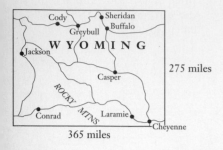

275 miles

365 miles

12. There are 60 minutes in an hour. How many minutes are there in 72 hours?

DO EXERCISE 11.

▶ **EXAMPLE 8**   There are 24 hours in a day and 7 days in a week. How many hours are there in a week?

1. *Familiarize.* We first make a drawing. We let y = the number of hours in a week. Repeated addition works well here.

2. *Translate.* We translate to a number sentence.

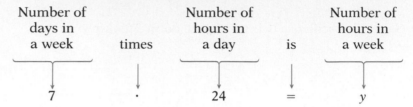

Number of days in a week	times	Number of hours in a day	is	Number of hours in a week
7	·	24	=	y

3. *Solve.* To solve the equation, we carry out the multiplication.

$$\begin{array}{r} \overset{2}{2}\,4 \\ \times\ \ 7 \\ \hline 1\,6\,8 \end{array}$$ Thus, $y = 168$.

4. *Check.* We check our answer by estimating:

$$7 \times 24 \approx 7 \times 30 = 210 \approx 168.$$

We can also check by repeating our calculation. We note that there are more hours in a week than in a day, which we would expect.

5. *State.* There are 168 hours in a week.   ◀

DO EXERCISE 12.

▶ **EXAMPLE 9**   A beverage company produces 2269 bottles of soda. How many 6-bottle cartons can be filled? How many bottles will be left over?

1. *Familiarize.* We first draw a picture. We let n = the number of 6-bottle cartons to be filled.

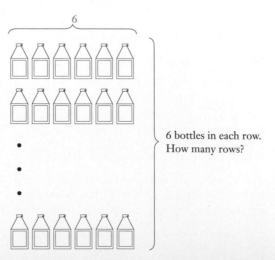

6 bottles in each row. How many rows?

2.,3. *Translate* and *Solve*. We translate to an equation and solve as follows:

$$2269 \div 6 = n.$$

$$
\begin{array}{r}
3\ 7\ 8 \\
6\,)\overline{2\ 2\ 6\ 9} \\
1\ 8\ 0\ 0 \\
\hline
4\ 6\ 9 \\
4\ 2\ 0 \\
\hline
4\ 9 \\
4\ 8 \\
\hline
1
\end{array}
$$

4. *Check*. We can check by multiplying the number of cartons by 6 and adding the remainder of 1:

$$6 \cdot 378 = 2268, \qquad 2268 + 1 = 2269.$$

5. *State*. Thus, 378 six-bottle cartons can be filled. There will be 1 bottle left over.   ◄

DO EXERCISE 13.

▶ **EXAMPLE 10**   An automobile with a 5-speed transmission gets 27 mi to the gallon in city driving. How many gallons will it take to travel 7020 mi of city driving?

1. *Familiarize*. We first draw a picture. It is often helpful to be descriptive about how you define a variable. In this example, we let g = the number of gallons (g comes from "gallons").

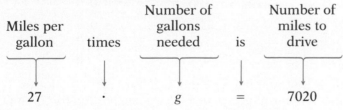

7020 miles to drive

2. *Translate*. Repeated addition applies here. Thus the following multiplication corresponds to the situation.

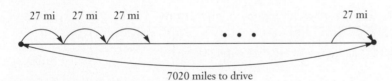

Miles per gallon	times	Number of gallons needed	is	Number of miles to drive
27	·	g	=	7020

3. *Solve*. To solve the equation, we divide on both sides by 27.

$$27 \cdot g = 7020$$
$$\frac{27 \cdot g}{27} = \frac{7020}{27}$$
$$g = 260$$

$$
\begin{array}{r}
2\ 6\ 0 \\
27\,)\overline{7\ 0\ 2\ 0} \\
5\ 4\ 0\ 0 \\
\hline
1\ 6\ 2\ 0 \\
1\ 6\ 2\ 0 \\
\hline
0
\end{array}
$$

4. *Check*. To check, we multiply 260 by 27: $27 \cdot 260 = 7020$.

5. *State*. Thus, 260 gal will be needed.   ◄

DO EXERCISE 14.

13. A beverage company produces 2205 bottles of soda. How many 8-bottle cartons can be filled? How many bottles will be left over?

14. An automobile with a 5-speed transmission gets 33 mi to the gallon in city driving. How many gallons will it take to drive 1485 mi?

15. Use the information in the table in Example 11. How long do you have to swim in order to lose one pound?

16. There are 27 bones in each human hand and 26 bones in each human foot. How many bones are there in all in the hands and feet?

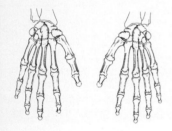

Multistep Problems

Sometimes we must use more than one operation to solve a problem. We do so in the following example.

▶ **EXAMPLE 11**   To lose one pound, you must burn off about 3500 calories.

> **To burn off 100 calories, you have to:**
> * **Run for 8 min at a brisk pace, or**
> * **Swim for 2 min at a brisk pace, or**
> * **Bicycle for 15 min at 9 mph, or**
> * **Do aerobic exercises for 15 min.**

How long do you have to run in order to lose one pound?

1. *Familiarize.* We first draw a picture.

One pound				
3500 calories				
100 cal	100 cal		...	100 cal
8 min	8 min		...	8 min

2. *Translate.* Repeated addition applies here. Thus the following multiplication corresponds to the situation. We must find out how many 100's there are in 3500. We let x = the number of 100's in 3500.

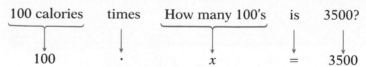

100 calories	times	How many 100's	is	3500?
100	·	x	=	3500

3. *Solve.* To solve the equation, we divide on both sides by 100.

$$100 \cdot x = 3500$$
$$\frac{100 \cdot x}{100} = \frac{3500}{100}$$
$$x = 35$$

```
         3 5
100 ) 3 5 0 0
      3 0 0 0
        5 0 0
        5 0 0
            0
```

We know that running for 8 min will burn off 100 calories. To do this 35 times will burn off a pound, so we need to run for 35 times 8 minutes in order to burn off one pound. We let t = the time it takes to run off a pound.

$$35 \times 8 = t$$
$$280 = t$$

```
     3 5
  ×    8
   2 8 0
```

4. *Check.* Suppose you run for 280 minutes. If we divide 280 by 8, we get 35, and 35 times 100 is 3500, the number of calories it takes to lose one pound.

5. *State.* It will take 280 min, or 4 hr 40 min, of running to lose one pound.   ◀

DO EXERCISES 15 AND 16.

EXERCISE SET 1.5

a Solve.

1. Ty Cobb hit 3052 singles in his career. Stan Musial hit 2641. How many did they hit together?

2. In the Revolutionary War, there were 4435 battle deaths. In the War of 1812, there were 2260. How many battle deaths were there in both wars?

3. The Empire State building is 381 m (meters) tall. It has a 68-m antenna on top. How far is the top of the antenna from the ground?

4. In a recent year, 1,580,000 people visited the United States from Japan. In addition, 1,200,000 came from England, 800,000 from Mexico, and 510,000 from West Germany. How many, in all, came from these countries?

5. A medical researcher poured first 2340 cubic centimeters of water and then 655 cubic centimeters of alcohol into a beaker. How much liquid was poured?

6. A person's water loss each day includes 400 cubic centimeters from the lungs and 500 cubic centimeters from the skin. How much is lost from both?

7. In Exercise 6, how much more water is lost from the skin than from the lungs?

8. It takes Venus 225 days to rotate about the sun. It takes the earth 365 days. How much longer does it take the earth?

9. In the Tokyo–Yokohama area, there are 17,317,000 people. In the New York–northeastern New Jersey area, there are 17,013,000 people. How many more people are there in the Tokyo–Yokohama area?

10. O'Hare International Airport is the busiest in the world, handling 45,700,000 passengers each year. Hartsfield Atlanta International is the second busiest, handling 39,000,000 passengers. How many more passengers does O'Hare handle than Hartsfield?

1. _____

2. _____

3. _____

4. _____

5. _____

6. _____

7. _____

8. _____

9. _____

10. _____

11. You wrote checks of $45, $78, and $32. Your balance before that was $246. What is your new balance?

12. A family bought a house for $108,900. They spent $16,500 for an extra room. They then sold the house for $137,780. How much did they make on the house?

11. _____

13. Playing golf for an hour burns 133 calories. How many calories would be burned in 5 hours?

14. Each day 200 people in the United States become millionaires. How many people become millionaires in one year? (Use 365 days for one year.)

12. _____

13. _____

15. There are 60 seconds in a minute and 60 minutes in an hour. How many seconds are there in an hour?

16. The average heartbeat is 73 beats per minute. How many beats are there in one hour? one day? one year?

14. _____

15. _____

17. A standard-sized tennis court is 36 ft by 78 ft. What is the area of a tennis court?

18. A rectangular field measures 48 m by 85 m. What is the area of the field?

16. _____

17. _____

19. The diameter of a circle is the length of a line through its center. The diameter of Jupiter is about 85,965 mi. The diameter of Jupiter is about 11 times the diameter of the earth. What is the diameter of the earth?

20. Sound travels at a speed of about 1087 ft per second (*per* means *for each*). How long does it take the sound of an airplane engine to reach your ear when the plane is 9783 ft overhead?

18. _____

19. _____

20. _____

21. A customer buys 8 suits at $195 each and 3 shirts at $26 each. How much is spent?

22. What is the cost of 11 radios at $27 each and 6 television sets at $736 each?

23. A college has a vacant rectangular lot that is 324 yd by 25 yd. On the lot students dug a garden that was 165 yd by 18 yd. How much area was left over?

24. A college student pays $107 a month for rent and $88 for food during 9 months at college. What is the total cost?

25. How many 16-oz bottles can be filled with 608 oz of catsup?

26. How many 24-can cases can be filled with 768 cans of beans?

27. There are 225 members in a band, and they are marching with 15 in each row. How many rows are there?

28. There are 225 members in a band, and they are marching in 5 rows. How many band members are there in each row?

29. A loan of $324 will be paid off in 12 monthly payments. How much is each payment?

30. A loan of $1404 will be paid off in 36 monthly payments. How much is each payment?

ANSWERS

21. _____

22. _____

23. _____

24. _____

25. _____

26. _____

27. _____

28. _____

29. _____

30. _____

ANSWERS

31. _____

32. _____

33. _____

34. _____

35. _____

36. _____

37. _____

38. _____

39. _____

40. _____

41. _____

42. _____

31. How many 23-kg (kilogram) bags can be filled by 885 kg of sand? How many kilograms of sand will be left over?

32. A vial contains 50 cubic centimeters of penicillin. How many 3-cubic-centimeter injections can be filled from the vial? How much will be left over?

33. A student bought 5 coats at $64 each and paid for them with $20 bills. How many $20 bills did it take?

34. How many $10 bills would it take to buy the 5 coats mentioned in Exercise 33?

35. A map has a scale of 55 mi to the inch. How far apart *on the map* are two cities that, in reality, are 605 mi apart? How far apart *in reality* are two cities that are 14 in. apart on the map?

36. A map has a scale of 46 mi to the inch. How far apart *in reality* are two cities that are 15 in. apart on the map? How far apart *on the map* are two cities that, in reality, are 552 mi apart?

37. A beverage company fills 640 12-oz bottles with soda. How many 16-oz bottles can be filled with the same amount of soda?

38. A rectangular piece of cardboard measures 64 in. by 15 in. Suppose the width were changed to 16 in. What would the length have to be in order to have the same area?

39. Use the information from the table in Example 11. How long do you have to bicycle at 9 mph in order to lose one pound?

40. Use the information from the table in Example 11. How long do you have to do aerobic exercises in order to lose one pound?

SYNTHESIS
Any exercises marked with a ▦ are to be worked with a calculator.

41. ▦ Light travels at a speed of 8,370,000 mi in 45 sec. How far does it travel in 1 sec?

42. The thickness of paper is often measured by weights. For example, 20-lb paper is that weight of the paper for which 1000 letter-size sheets weigh 20 lb. A ream of paper is 500 sheets. How much does a ream of 70-lb paper weigh?

1.6 Exponential Notation and Order of Operations

a Exponential Notation

Consider the product $3 \cdot 3 \cdot 3 \cdot 3$. Such products occur often enough that mathematicians have found it convenient to invent a shorter notation, called **exponential notation**, explained as follows.

$$\underbrace{3 \cdot 3 \cdot 3 \cdot 3}_{\text{4 factors}} \text{ is shortened to } 3^4 \longleftarrow \text{exponent}$$

We read 3^4 as "three to the fourth power," 5^3 as "five cubed," and 5^2 as "five squared." The latter comes from the fact that a square of side s has area A given by $A = s^2$.

$A = s^2$

▶ **EXAMPLE 1** Write exponential notation for $10 \cdot 10 \cdot 10 \cdot 10 \cdot 10$.

Exponential notation is 10^5.   5 is the *exponent*.   ◀
10 is the *base*.

▶ **EXAMPLE 2** Write exponential notation for $2 \cdot 2 \cdot 2$.

Exponential notation is 2^3.   ◀

DO EXERCISES 1–4.

b Evaluating Exponential Notation

▶ **EXAMPLE 3** Evaluate: 10^3.

$$10^3 = 10 \cdot 10 \cdot 10 = 1000$$ ◀

▶ **EXAMPLE 4** Evaluate: 5^4.

$$5^4 = 5 \cdot 5 \cdot 5 \cdot 5 = 625$$ ◀

DO EXERCISES 5–8.

OBJECTIVES

After finishing Section 1.6, you should be able to:

a Write exponential notation for products such as $4 \cdot 4 \cdot 4$.

b Evaluate exponential notation.

c Simplify expressions using the rules for order of operations.

d Remove parentheses within parentheses.

FOR EXTRA HELP

Tape 2C

Write exponential notation.

1. $5 \cdot 5 \cdot 5 \cdot 5$

2. $5 \cdot 5 \cdot 5 \cdot 5 \cdot 5$

3. $10 \cdot 10$

4. $10 \cdot 10 \cdot 10 \cdot 10$

Evaluate.

5. 10^4

6. 10^2

7. 8^3

8. 2^5

ANSWERS ON PAGE A-2

Simplify.

9. $93 - 14 \cdot 3$

10. $104 \div 4 + 4$

11. $25 \cdot 26 - (56 + 10)$

12. $75 \div 5 + (83 - 14)$

Simplify and compare.

13. $64 \div (32 \div 2)$ and $(64 \div 32) \div 2$

14. $(28 + 13) + 11$ and $28 + (13 + 11)$

c　Simplifying Expressions

Suppose we have a calculation like the following:

$$8 \cdot 6 - 1.$$

How do we find the answer? Do we subtract 1 from 6 and then multiply by 8, or do we multiply 8 by 6 and then subtract 1? In the first case, the answer is 40. In the second case, the answer is 47.

Consider the calculation

$$7 \cdot 14 - (12 + 18).$$

What do the parentheses mean? To deal with these questions, we must make some agreement regarding the order in which we perform operations. The rules are as follows.

Rules for Order of Operations
1. **Do all calculations within parentheses before operations outside.**
2. **Evaluate all exponential expressions.**
3. **Do all multiplications and divisions in order from left to right.**
4. **Do all additions and subtractions in order from left to right.**

It is worth noting that these are the rules that a computer uses to do computations. In order to program a computer, one must know these rules.

▶ **EXAMPLE 5** Simplify: $8 \cdot 6 - 1$.

There are no parentheses or exponents, so we start with the third step.

$$8 \cdot 6 - 1 = 48 - 1 \quad \text{Doing all multiplications and divisions in order from left to right}$$
$$= 47 \quad \text{Doing all additions and subtractions in order from left to right}$$

◀

▶ **EXAMPLE 6** Simplify: $7 \cdot 14 - (12 + 18)$.

$$7 \cdot 14 - (12 + 18) = 7 \cdot 14 - 30 \quad \text{Carrying out operations inside parentheses}$$
$$= 98 - 30 \quad \text{Doing all multiplications and divisions}$$
$$= 68 \quad \text{Doing all additions and subtractions}$$

◀

DO EXERCISES 9–12.

▶ **EXAMPLE 7** Simplify and compare:

$$23 - (10 - 9) \quad \text{and} \quad (23 - 10) - 9.$$

We have

$$23 - (10 - 9) = 23 - 1 = 22;$$
$$(23 - 10) - 9 = 13 - 9 = 4.$$

We can see that $23 - (10 - 9)$ and $(23 - 10) - 9$ represent different numbers.

◀

DO EXERCISES 13 AND 14.

▶ **EXAMPLE 8**   Simplify: $7 \cdot 2 - (12 + 0) \div 3 - (5 - 2)$.

$7 \cdot 2 - (12 + 0) \div 3 - (5 - 2) = 7 \cdot 2 - 12 \div 3 - 3$ **Carrying out operations inside parentheses**

$\qquad\qquad\qquad\qquad\qquad = 14 - 4 - 3$ **Doing all multiplications and divisions in order from left to right**

$\qquad\qquad\qquad\qquad\qquad = 7$ **Doing all additions and subtractions in order from left to right** ◀

DO EXERCISE 15.

▶ **EXAMPLE 9**   Simplify: $15 \div 3 \cdot 2 \div (10 - 8)$.

$15 \div 3 \cdot 2 \div (10 - 8) = 15 \div 3 \cdot 2 \div 2$ **Carrying out operations inside parentheses**

$\qquad\qquad\qquad\qquad = 5 \cdot 2 \div 2$ **Doing all multiplications and divisions in order from left to right**

$\qquad\qquad\qquad\qquad = 10 \div 2$

$\qquad\qquad\qquad\qquad = 5$ ◀

DO EXERCISES 16–18.

▶ **EXAMPLE 10**   Simplify and compare: $(3 + 5)^2$ and $3^2 + 5^2$.

We have

$$(3 + 5)^2 = 8^2 = 64;$$
$$3^2 + 5^2 = 9 + 25 = 34.$$

We see that $(3 + 5)^2$ and $3^2 + 5^2$ do not represent the same numbers. ◀

DO EXERCISE 19.

▶ **EXAMPLE 11**   Simplify: $6^3 \div (10 - 8)^2$.

$6^3 \div (10 - 8)^2 = 6^3 \div 2^2$ **Carrying out operations inside parentheses first**

$\qquad\qquad\qquad = 216 \div 4$ **Evaluating exponential expressions second**

$\qquad\qquad\qquad = 54$ **Dividing** ◀

▶ **EXAMPLE 12**   Simplify: $2^4 + 51 \cdot 4 - 2 \cdot (37 + 23 \cdot 2)$.

$2^4 + 51 \cdot 4 - 2 \cdot (37 + 23 \cdot 2)$

$\qquad = 2^4 + 51 \cdot 4 - 2 \cdot (37 + 46)$ **Carrying out operations inside parentheses. To do this, we first multiply 23 by 2.**

$\qquad = 2^4 + 51 \cdot 4 - 2 \cdot 83$ **Completing the addition inside parentheses**

$\qquad = 16 + 51 \cdot 4 - 2 \cdot 83$ **Evaluating exponential expressions**

$\qquad = 16 + 204 - 166$ **Doing the multiplications**

$\qquad = 220 - 166$ ⎫
$\qquad\qquad\qquad\quad$ **Doing the additions and subtractions in order from left to right**
$\qquad = 54$ ⎭ ◀

DO EXERCISES 20–22.

---

15. Simplify:
$$9 \times 4 - (20 + 4) \div 8 - (6 - 2).$$

Simplify.

16. $5 \cdot 5 \cdot 5 + 26 \cdot 71 - (16 + 25 \cdot 3)$

17. $4 \cdot 4 \cdot 4 + 10 \cdot 20 + 8 \cdot 8 - 23$

18. $95 - 2 \cdot 2 \cdot 2 \cdot 5 \div (24 - 4)$

19. Simplify and compare:
$$(4 + 6)^2 \text{ and } 4^2 + 6^2.$$

Simplify.

20. $5^3 + 26 \cdot 71 - (16 + 25 \cdot 3)$

21. $(1 + 3)^3 + 10 \cdot 20 + 8^2 - 23$

22. $95 - 2^3 \cdot 5 \div (24 - 4)$

ANSWERS ON PAGE A-2

Simplify.

23. $9 \times 5 + \{6 \div [14 - (5 + 3)]\}$

24. $[18 - (2 + 7) \div 3] - (31 - 10 \times 2)$

---

d	**Parentheses Within Parentheses**

When parentheses occur within parentheses, we can make them different shapes, such as [ ] (also called "brackets") and { } (also called "braces"). All of these have the same meaning. When parentheses occur within parentheses, computations in the innermost ones are to be done first.

▶ **EXAMPLE 13**   Simplify: $16 \div 2 + \{40 - [13 - (4 + 2)]\}$.

$$16 \div 2 + \{40 - [13 - (4 + 2)]\}$$
$$= 16 \div 2 + \{40 - [13 - 6]\} \quad \text{Doing the calculations in the innermost parentheses first}$$
$$= 16 \div 2 + \{40 - 7\} \quad \text{Again, doing the calculations in the innermost parentheses}$$
$$= 16 \div 2 + 33$$
$$= 8 + 33 \quad \text{Doing all multiplications and divisions in order from left to right}$$
$$= 41 \quad \text{Doing all additions and subtractions in order from left to right}$$ ◀

▶ **EXAMPLE 14**   Simplify: $[25 - (4 + 3) \times 3] \div (11 - 7)$.

$$[25 - (4 + 3) \times 3] \div (11 - 7) = [25 - 7 \times 3] \div (11 - 7)$$
$$= [25 - 21] \div (11 - 7)$$
$$= 4 \div 4$$
$$= 1$$ ◀

DO EXERCISES 23 AND 24.

❖ SIDELIGHTS

From time to time you will find a *"Sidelights"* like the one at the right. These are optional, but you may find them helpful and of interest. They will include such topics as study tips, career opportunities involving mathematics, applications, computer-calculator exercises, or other mathematical topics.

Palindrome Numbers

Words like "radar" and "toot" read the same backward and forward. A number that reads the same backward and forward is called a *palindrome*. For example,

$$11, \quad 121, \quad 202, \quad \text{and} \quad 34543$$

are palindrome numbers. Many numbers can be transformed to palindromes by reversing the digits and adding, and so on. For example,

$$
\begin{array}{ll}
257 & \longleftarrow \text{Not palindrome} \\
\underline{752} & \longleftarrow \text{Reverse digits} \\
1009 & \longleftarrow \text{Add} \\
\underline{9001} & \longleftarrow \text{Reverse digits} \\
10010 & \longleftarrow \text{Add} \\
\underline{01001} & \longleftarrow \text{Reverse digits and add} \\
11011 & \longleftarrow \text{Palindrome}
\end{array}
$$

EXERCISES

To what palindrome can the number be transformed?

1. 356   **2.** 471

EXERCISE SET 1.6

a Write exponential notation.

1. $3 \cdot 3 \cdot 3 \cdot 3$ **2.** $2 \cdot 2 \cdot 2 \cdot 2 \cdot 2$ **3.** $5 \cdot 5$ **4.** $13 \cdot 13 \cdot 13$

5. $7 \cdot 7 \cdot 7 \cdot 7 \cdot 7$ **6.** $10 \cdot 10$ **7.** $10 \cdot 10 \cdot 10$ **8.** $1 \cdot 1 \cdot 1 \cdot 1$

b Evaluate.

9. 7^2 **10.** 5^3 **11.** 9^3 **12.** 10^2

13. 12^4 **14.** 10^5 **15.** 11^2 **16.** 6^3

c Simplify.

17. $12 + (6 + 4)$ **18.** $(12 + 6) + 18$ **19.** $52 - (40 - 8)$

20. $(52 - 40) - 8$ **21.** $1000 \div (100 \div 10)$ **22.** $(1000 \div 100) \div 10$

23. $(256 \div 64) \div 4$ **24.** $256 \div (64 \div 4)$ **25.** $(2 + 5)^2$

26. $2^2 + 5^2$ **27.** $2 + 5^2$ **28.** $2^2 + 5$

29. $16 \cdot 24 + 50$ **30.** $23 + 18 \cdot 20$ **31.** $83 - 7 \cdot 6$

32. $10 \cdot 7 - 4$ **33.** $10 \cdot 10 - 3 \cdot 4$ **34.** $90 - 5 \cdot 5 \cdot 2$

35. $4^3 \div 8 - 4$ **36.** $8^2 - 8 \cdot 2$ **37.** $17 \cdot 20 - (17 + 20)$

38. $1000 \div 25 - (15 + 5)$ **39.** $6 \cdot 10 - 4 \cdot 10$ **40.** $3 \cdot 8 + 5 \cdot 8$

ANSWERS

1.
2.
3.
4.
5.
6.
7.
8.
9.
10.
11.
12.
13.
14.
15.
16.
17.
18.
19.
20.
21.
22.
23.
24.
25.
26.
27.
28.
29.
30.
31.
32.
33.
34.
35.
36.
37.
38.
39.
40.

ANSWERS

41. _____

42. _____

43. _____

44. _____

45. _____

46. _____

47. _____

48. _____

49. _____

50. _____

51. _____

52. _____

53. _____

54. _____

55. _____

56. _____

57. _____

58. _____

59. _____

60. _____

61. _____

62. _____

63. _____

64. _____

41. $300 \div 5 + 10$

42. $144 \div 4 - 2$

43. $3 \cdot (2 + 8)^2 - 5 \cdot (4 - 3)^2$

44. $7 \cdot (10 - 3)^2 - 2 \cdot (3 + 1)^2$

45. $4^2 + 8^2 \div 2^2$

46. $6^2 - 3^4 \div 3^3$

47. $10^3 - 10 \cdot 6 - (4 + 5 \cdot 6)$

48. $7^2 + 20 \cdot 4 - (28 + 9 \cdot 2)$

49. $6 \cdot 11 - (7 + 3) \div 5 - (6 - 4)$

50. $8 \times 9 - (12 - 8) \div 4 - (10 - 7)$

51. $120 - 3^3 \cdot 4 \div (30 - 24)$

52. $80 - 2^4 \cdot 15 \div (35 - 15)$

d   Simplify.

53. $8 \times 13 + \{42 \div [18 - (6 + 5)]\}$

54. $72 \div 6 - \{2 \times [9 - (4 \times 2)]\}$

55. $[14 - (3 + 5) \div 2] - [18 \div (8 - 2)]$

56. $[92 \times (6 - 4) \div 8] + [7 \times (8 - 3)]$

57. $(82 - 14) \times [(10 + 45 \div 5) - (6 \cdot 6 - 5 \cdot 5)]$

58. $(18 \div 2) \cdot \{[(9 \cdot 9 - 1) \div 2] - [5 \cdot 20 - (7 \cdot 9 - 2)]\}$

59. $4 \times \{(200 - 50 \div 5) - [(35 \div 7) \cdot (35 \div 7) - 4 \times 3]\}$

60. $\{[18 - 2 \cdot 6] - [40 \div (17 - 9)]\} + \{48 - 13 \times 3 + [(50 - 7 \cdot 5) + 2]\}$

SYNTHESIS

Each of the expressions in Exercises 61–63 is incorrect. First find the correct answer. Then place as many parentheses as needed in the expression in order to make the incorrect answer correct.

61. $1 + 5 \cdot 4 + 3 = 36$

62. $12 \div 4 + 2 \cdot 3 - 2 = 2$

63. $12 \div 4 + 2 \cdot 3 - 2 = 4$

64. Use any grouping symbols and one occurrence each of 1, 2, 3, 4, 5, 6, 7, 8, and 9 to represent 100.

1.7 Factorizations

In Chapter 2, we will begin our work with fractions. Certain skills make such work easier. For example, in order to simplify

$$\frac{12}{32},$$

it is important that we be able to *factor* the 12 and the 32:

$$\frac{12}{32} = \frac{4 \cdot 3}{4 \cdot 8}.$$

Then we "remove" a factor of 1:

$$\frac{4 \cdot 3}{4 \cdot 8} = \frac{4}{4} \cdot \frac{3}{8} = 1 \cdot \frac{3}{8} = \frac{3}{8}.$$

Thus factoring is an important skill in working with fractions.

a   Factors and Factorization

Here and in Section 1.8, we consider only the **natural numbers** 1, 2, 3, and so on.

Let's look at the product $3 \cdot 4 = 12$. We say that 3 and 4 are **factors** of 12. Since $12 = 12 \cdot 1$, we also know that 12 and 1 are factors of 12.

> A *factor* of a given number is a number multiplied in a product.
> A *factorization* of a number is an equation that expresses the number as a product of natural numbers.

For example, each of the following is a factorization of 12.

$12 = 4 \cdot 3$ ⟵ **This factorization shows that 4 and 3 are factors of 12.**

$12 = 12 \cdot 1$ ⟵ **This factorization shows that 12 and 1 are factors of 12.**

$12 = 6 \cdot 2$ ⟵ **This factorization shows that 6 and 2 are factors of 12.**

$12 = 2 \cdot 3 \cdot 2$ ⟵ **This factorization shows that 2 and 3 are factors of 12.**

Since $n = n \cdot 1$, every number has a factorization and every number has factors even if its only factors are itself and 1.

▶ **EXAMPLE 1**   Find all the factors of 24.

We first find some factorizations.

$$24 = 1 \cdot 24 \qquad 24 = 3 \cdot 8$$
$$24 = 2 \cdot 12 \qquad 24 = 4 \cdot 6$$

Note that all but one of the factors of a natural number are *less* than the number.

Factors: 1, 2, 3, 4, 6, 8, 12, 24.   ◀

DO EXERCISES 1–4.

OBJECTIVES

After finishing Section 1.7, you should be able to:

a Find the factors of a number.

b Find some multiples of a number, and determine whether a number is divisible by another.

c Given a number from 1 to 50, tell whether it is prime, composite, or neither.

d Find the prime factorization of a composite number.

FOR EXTRA HELP

Tape 3A

Find all the factors of the number. (*Hint:* Find some factorizations of the number.)

1. 6

2. 8

3. 10

4. 32

ANSWERS ON PAGE A-2

5. Show that each of the numbers 5, 45, and 100 is a multiple of 5.

6. Show that each of the numbers 10, 60, and 110 is a multiple of 10.

7. Multiply by 1, 2, 3, and so on, to find ten multiples of 5.

8. Determine whether 16 is divisible by 2.

9. Determine whether 125 is divisible by 5.

10. Determine whether 125 is divisible by 6.

b Multiples and Divisibility

A **multiple** of a natural number is a product of it and some natural number. For example, some multiples of 2 are:

2 (because $2 = 1 \cdot 2$);
4 (because $4 = 2 \cdot 2$);
6 (because $6 = 3 \cdot 2$);
8 (because $8 = 4 \cdot 2$);
10 (because $10 = 5 \cdot 2$).

> Note that all but one of the multiples of a number are *larger* than the number.

We find multiples of 2 by counting by twos: 2, 4, 6, 8, and so on. We can find multiples of 3 by counting by threes: 3, 6, 9, 12, and so on.

▶ **EXAMPLE 2** Show that each of the numbers 3, 6, 9, and 15 is a multiple of 3.

$$3 = 1 \cdot 3 \qquad 9 = 3 \cdot 3$$
$$6 = 2 \cdot 3 \qquad 15 = 5 \cdot 3$$
◀

DO EXERCISES 5 AND 6.

▶ **EXAMPLE 3** Multiply by 1, 2, 3, and so on, to find ten multiples of 7.

$$1 \cdot 7 = 7 \qquad 6 \cdot 7 = 42$$
$$2 \cdot 7 = 14 \qquad 7 \cdot 7 = 49$$
$$3 \cdot 7 = 21 \qquad 8 \cdot 7 = 56$$
$$4 \cdot 7 = 28 \qquad 9 \cdot 7 = 63$$
$$5 \cdot 7 = 35 \qquad 10 \cdot 7 = 70$$
◀

DO EXERCISE 7.

> A number b is said to be *divisible* by another number a if b is a multiple of a.

Thus,

4 is divisible by 2 because 4 is a multiple of 2 ($4 = 2 \cdot 2$);
27 is divisible by 3 because 27 is a multiple of 3 ($27 = 9 \cdot 3$);
100 is divisible by 25 because 100 is a multiple of 25 ($100 = 4 \cdot 25$).

> A number b is divisible by another number a if division of b by a results in a remainder of zero. We sometimes say that a divides b "evenly."

▶ **EXAMPLE 4** Determine whether 24 is divisible by 3.
We divide 24 by 3:

$$\begin{array}{r} 8 \\ 3\overline{)24} \\ \underline{24} \\ 0 \end{array}$$

Since the remainder is 0, 24 is divisible by 3.   ◀

DO EXERCISES 8–10.

c Prime and Composite Numbers

> A natural number that has exactly two different factors, itself and 1, is called a *prime number*.

▶ **EXAMPLE 5** Tell whether the numbers 2, 3, 5, 7, and 11 are prime.

The number 2 is prime. It has only the factors 1 and 2.

The number 5 is prime. It has only the factors 1 and 5.

The numbers 3, 7, and 11 are also prime. ◀

Some numbers are not prime.

▶ **EXAMPLE 6** Tell whether the numbers 4, 6, 8, 10, 63, and 1 are prime.

The number 4 is not prime. It has the factors 1, 2, and 4.

The numbers 6, 8, 10, and 63 are not prime. Each has more than two different factors.

The number 1 is not prime. It does not have two *different* factors. ◀

> A natural number, other than 1, that is not prime is called *composite*.

In other words, if a number can be factored into a product of natural numbers, some of which are not the number itself or 1, it is composite. Thus,

2, 3, 5, 7, and 11 are prime;

4, 6, 8, 10, and 63 are composite;

1 is neither prime nor composite.

DO EXERCISE 11.

d Prime Factorizations

To factor a composite number into a product of primes is to find a **prime factorization** of the number. To do this, we consider the primes

2, 3, 5, 7, 11, 13, 17, 19, 23, and so on,

and determine whether a given number is divisible by the primes.

▶ **EXAMPLE 7** Find the prime factorization of 39.

a) We divide by the first prime, 2.

$$\begin{array}{r} 19 \\ 2\,\overline{)39} \end{array} \quad R = 1$$

Since the remainder is not 0, 2 is not a factor of 39.

b) We divide by the next prime, 3.

$$\begin{array}{r} 13 \\ 3\,\overline{)39} \end{array} \quad R = 0$$

Since 13 is prime, we are finished. The prime factorization is

$$39 = 3 \cdot 13.$$ ◀

11. Tell whether each number is prime, composite, or neither.

1, 4, 6, 8, 13, 19, 41

ANSWER ON PAGE A-2

Find the prime factorization of the number.

12. 6

13. 12

14. 45

15. 98

16. 126

17. 144

▶ **EXAMPLE 8** Find the prime factorization of 76.

a) We divide by the first prime, 2.

$$
\begin{array}{r} 38 \\ 2\overline{)76} \end{array} \quad R = 0
$$

b) Since 38 is composite, we start with 2 again:

$$
\begin{array}{r} 19 \\ 2\overline{)38} \end{array} \quad R = 0
$$

Because 19 is a prime, we are finished. The prime factorization is

$$76 = 2 \cdot 2 \cdot 19.$$

We abbreviate our procedure as follows.

$$
\begin{array}{r} 19 \\ 2\overline{)38} \\ 2\overline{)76} \end{array}
$$

$$76 = 2 \cdot 2 \cdot 19, \quad \text{or } 2^2 \cdot 19 \qquad ◀$$

  Multiplication is commutative so a factorization such as $2 \cdot 2 \cdot 19$ could also be expressed as $2 \cdot 19 \cdot 2$ or $19 \cdot 2 \cdot 2$, but the prime factors are still the same. For this reason, we agree that any of these is "the" prime factorization of 76.

Every number has just one (unique) prime factorization.

▶ **EXAMPLE 9** Find the prime factorization of 72.

$$
\begin{array}{r} 3 \\ 3\overline{)9} \\ 2\overline{)18} \\ 2\overline{)36} \\ 2\overline{)72} \end{array}
$$

$$72 = 2 \cdot 2 \cdot 2 \cdot 3 \cdot 3, \quad \text{or } 2^3 \cdot 3^2 \qquad ◀$$

▶ **EXAMPLE 10** Find the prime factorization of 189.

We can use a string of successive divisions:

$$
\begin{array}{r} 7 \\ 3\overline{)21} \\ 3\overline{)63} \\ 3\overline{)189} \end{array}
$$
  189 is not divisible by 2. We move to 3.
63 is not divisible by 2. We move to 3.
21 is not divisible by 2. We move to 3.

$$189 = 3 \cdot 3 \cdot 3 \cdot 7, \quad \text{or } 3^3 \cdot 7 \qquad ◀$$

▶ **EXAMPLE 11** Find the prime factorization of 65.

We can use a string of successive divisions.

$$
\begin{array}{r} 13 \\ 5\overline{)65} \end{array}
$$
  65 is not divisible by 2 or 3. We move to 5.

$$65 = 5 \cdot 13 \qquad ◀$$

DO EXERCISES 12–17.

NAME   SECTION   DATE

EXERCISE SET 1.7

a Find all the factors of the number.

1. 16   **2.** 18   **3.** 54   **4.** 48

5. 4   **6.** 9   **7.** 7   **8.** 11

9. 1   **10.** 3   **11.** 98   **12.** 100

b Multiply by 1, 2, 3, and so on, to find ten multiples of the number.

13. 4   **14.** 14   **15.** 20   **16.** 50

                                                                    450, 500
17. 3   **18.** 5   **19.** 12   **20.** 17

21. 10   **22.** 6   **23.** 9   **24.** 11

25. Determine whether 26 is divisible by 6.

26. Determine whether 29 is divisible by 9.

27. Determine whether 1880 is divisible by 8.

28. Determine whether 4227 is divisible by 3.

29. Determine whether 256 is divisible by 16.

30. Determine whether 102 is divisible by 4.

31. Determine whether 4227 is divisible by 9.

32. Determine whether 200 is divisible by 25.

33. Determine whether 8650 is divisible by 16.

34. Determine whether 4143 is divisible by 7.

ANSWERS

1. _____
2. _____
3. _____
4. _____
5. _____
6. _____
7. _____
8. _____
9. _____
10. _____
11. _____
12. _____
13. _____
14. _____
15. _____
16. _____
17. _____
18. _____
19. _____
20. _____
21. _____
22. _____
23. _____
24. _____
25. _____
26. _____
27. _____
28. _____
29. _____
30. _____
31. _____
32. _____
33. _____
34. _____

ANSWERS

35. _____

36. _____

37. _____

38. _____

39. _____

40. _____

41. _____

42. _____

43. _____

44. _____

45. _____

46. _____

47. _____

48. _____

49. _____

50. _____

51. _____

52. _____

53. _____

54. _____

55. _____

56. _____

57. _____

58. _____

59. _____

60. _____

61. _____

62. _____

63. _____

64. _____

65. _____

66. _____

67. _____

68. _____

69. _____

70. _____

71. _____

72. _____

c Determine whether the number is prime, composite, or neither.

35. 1   **36.** 2   **37.** 9   **38.** 19

39. 11   **40.** 27   **41.** 29   **42.** 49

d Find the prime factorization of the number.

43. 8   **44.** 16   **45.** 14   **46.** 15

47. 22   **48.** 32   **49.** 25   **50.** 40

51. 50   **52.** 62   **53.** 169   **54.** 140

55. 100   **56.** 110   **57.** 35   **58.** 70

59. 72   **60.** 86   **61.** 77   **62.** 99

63. 112   **64.** 142   **65.** 300   **66.** 175

SKILL MAINTENANCE

Multiply.

67. $2 \cdot 13$ **68.** $17 \cdot 25$

Divide.

69. $0 \div 22$ **70.** $22 \div 22$

SYNTHESIS

71. Describe an arrangement of 54 objects that corresponds to the factorization $54 = 6 \times 9$.

72. Describe an arrangement of 24 objects that corresponds to the factorization $24 = 2 \cdot 3 \cdot 4$.

1.8 Divisibility

Suppose you are asked to find the simplest fractional notation for

$$\frac{117}{225}.$$

Since the numbers are quite large, you might feel that the task is difficult. However, both the numerator and the denominator have 9 as a factor. If you knew this, you could factor and simplify quickly as follows:

$$\frac{117}{225} = \frac{9 \cdot 13}{9 \cdot 25} = \frac{9}{9} \cdot \frac{13}{25} = 1 \cdot \frac{13}{25} = \frac{13}{25}.$$

How did we know that both numbers have 9 as a factor? There are fast tests for such determinations. If the sum of the digits of a number is divisible by 9, then the number is divisible by 9; that is, it has 9 as a factor. Since $1 + 1 + 7 = 9$ and $2 + 2 + 5 = 9$, both numbers have 9 as a factor.

a Rules for Divisibility

In this section we learn fast ways of determining whether numbers are divisible by 2, 3, 4, 5, 6, 8, 9, and 10. This will make simplifying with fractional notation much easier.

Divisibility by 2

You may already know the test for divisibility by 2.

> **A number is divisible by 2 (is *even*) if it has a ones digit of 0, 2, 4, 6, or 8 (that is, it has an even ones digit).**

Let's see why. Consider 354, which is

$$3 \text{ hundreds} + 5 \text{ tens} + 4.$$

Hundreds and tens are both multiples of 2. If the last digit is a multiple of 2, the entire number is.

▶ **EXAMPLES** Determine whether the number is divisible by 2.

1. 355 is not a multiple of 2; 5 is *not* even.
2. 4786 is a multiple of 2; 6 is even.
3. 8990 is a multiple of 2; 0 is even.
4. 4261 is not a multiple of 2; 1 is *not* even. ◀

DO EXERCISES 1–4.

OBJECTIVE

After finishing Section 1.8, you should be able to:

a Determine whether a number is divisible by 2, 3, 4, 5, 6, 8, 9, or 10.

Determine whether the number is divisible by 2.

1. 84

2. 59

3. 998

4. 2225

ANSWERS ON PAGE A-2

Determine whether the number is divisible by 9.

5. 16

6. 117

7. 930

8. 29,223

Determine whether the number is divisible by 3.

9. 111

10. 1111

11. 309

12. 17,216

Determine whether the number is divisible by 4.

13. 216

14. 217

15. 5865

16. 23,524

Divisibility by 9

> **A number is divisible by 9 if the sum of the digits is divisible by 9.**

▶ **EXAMPLE 5**   The number 6984 is divisible by 9 because

$$6 + 9 + 8 + 4 = 27$$

and 27 is divisible by 9.   ◀

▶ **EXAMPLE 6**   The number 322 is *not* divisible by 9 because

$$3 + 2 + 2 = 7$$

and 7 is not divisible by 9.   ◀

DO EXERCISES 5–8.

Divisibility by 3

The test for divisibility by 3 is similar to the test for divisibility by 9.

> **A number is divisible by 3 if the sum of the digits is divisible by 3.**

▶ **EXAMPLES**   Determine whether the number is divisible by 3.

7. 18 $1 + 8 = 9$ ⎫
8. 93 $9 + 3 = 12$ ⎬ All divisible by 3 because the sums of their digits are divisible by 3.
9. 201 $2 + 0 + 1 = 3$ ⎭
10. 256 $2 + 5 + 6 = 13$ The sum is not divisible by 3, so 256 is not divisible by 3.   ◀

DO EXERCISES 9–12.

Divisibility by 4

The test for divisibility by 4 is similar to the test for divisibility by 2.

> **A number is divisible by 4 if the number named by the last *two* digits is divisible by 4.**

▶ **EXAMPLES**   Determine whether the number is divisible by 4.

11. 8212   is divisible by 4 because 12 is divisible by 4.
12. 5216   is divisible by 4 because 16 is divisible by 4.
13. 8211   is *not* divisible by 4 because 11 is *not* divisible by 4.
14. 7515   is *not* divisible by 4 because 15 is *not* divisible by 4.   ◀

To see why the test for divisibility by 4 works, consider 516:

$$516 = 5 \text{ hundreds} + 16.$$

Hundreds are multiples of 4. If the number named by the last two digits is a multiple of 4, then the entire number is a multiple of 4.

Divisibility by 8

The test for divisibility by 8 is an extension of the tests for divisibility by 2 and 4.

> **A number is divisible by 8 if the number named by the last *three* digits is divisible by 8.**

▶ **EXAMPLES** Determine whether each number is divisible by 8.

15. 5648 is divisible by 8 because 648 is divisible by 8.

16. 96,088 is divisible by 8 because 88 is divisible by 8.

17. 7324 is *not* divisible by 8 because 324 is *not* divisible by 8.

18. 13,420 is *not* divisible by 8 because 420 is *not* divisible by 8. ◀

DO EXERCISES 17–20.

Divisibility by 6

A number divisible by 6 is a multiple of 6. But $6 = 2 \cdot 3$, so the number is also a multiple of 2 and 3. Thus:

> **In order for a number to be divisible by 6, the sum of the digits must be divisible by 3 and the ones digit must be 0, 2, 4, 6, or 8 (even).**

▶ **EXAMPLES** Determine whether the number is divisible by 6.

19. 720

Since 720 is even, it is divisible by 2. Also, $7 + 2 + 0 = 9$, so 720 is divisible by 3. Thus, 720 is divisible by 6.

$$720 \qquad 7 + 2 + 0 = 9$$

Even   Divisible by 3

20. 73

73 is *not* divisible by 6 because it is *not* divisible by 2.

$$7 3$$

Not even

21. 256

256 is *not* divisible by 6 because the sum of the digits is *not* divisible by 3.

$$2 + 5 + 6 = 13$$

Not divisible by 3 ◀

DO EXERCISES 21–24.

Determine whether the number is divisible by 8.

17. 7564

18. 7864

19. 17,560

20. 25,716

Determine whether the number is divisible by 6.

21. 420

22. 106

23. 321

24. 444

Determine whether the number is divisible by 10.

25. 305

26. 300

27. 847

28. 8760

Determine whether the number is divisible by 5.

29. 5780

30. 3427

31. 34,678

32. 7775

Divisibility by 10

> **A number is divisible by 10 if the ones digit is 0.**

We know that this test works because the product of 10 and *any* number has a ones digit of 0.

▶ **EXAMPLES** Determine whether the number is divisible by 10.

22. 3440   is divisible by 10 because the ones digit is 0.

23. 3447   is *not* divisible by 10 because the ones digit is not 0. ◀

DO EXERCISES 25–28.

Divisibility by 5

> **A number is divisible by 5 if the ones digit is 0 or 5.**

▶ **EXAMPLES** Determine whether the number is divisible by 5.

24.   220   is divisible by 5 because the ones digit is 0.

25.   475   is divisible by 5 because the ones digit is 5.

26. 6514   is *not* divisible by 5 because the ones digit is neither a 0 nor a 5. ◀

DO EXERCISES 29–32.

Let's see why the test for 5 works. Consider 7830:

$$7830 = 10 \cdot 783 = 5 \cdot 2 \cdot 783.$$

Since 7830 is divisible by 10 and 5 is a factor of 10, 7830 is divisible by 5. Consider 6734:

$$6734 = 673 \text{ tens} + 4.$$

Tens are multiples of 5, so the only number that must be checked is the ones digit. If the last digit is a multiple of 5, the entire number is: 4 is not a multiple of 5, so 6734 is not divisible by 5.

A Note About Divisibility by 7

There are several tests for divisibility by 7, but all of them are more complicated than simply dividing by 7. So if you want to test for divisibility by 7, divide by 7.

EXERCISE SET 1.8

a To answer Exercises 1–8, consider the following numbers.

46	300	85
224	36	711
19	45,270	13,251
555	4444	254,765

1. Which of the above are divisible by 2?

2. Which of the above are divisible by 3?

3. Which of the above are divisible by 4?

4. Which of the above are divisible by 5?

5. Which of the above are divisible by 6?

6. Which of the above are divisible by 8?

7. Which of the above are divisible by 9?

8. Which of the above are divisible by 10?

To answer Exercises 9–16, consider the following numbers.

56	200	75
324	42	812
784	501	2345
55,555	3009	2001

9. Which of the above are divisible by 3?

10. Which of the above are divisible by 2?

ANSWERS

1. _____

2. _____

3. _____

4. _____

5. _____

6. _____

7. _____

8. _____

9. _____

10. _____

Copyright © 1993 Addison-Wesley Publishing Co., Inc.

ANSWERS

11. _____

12. _____

13. _____

14. _____

15. _____

16. _____

17. _____

18. _____

19. _____

20. _____

21. _____

22. _____

23. _____

24. _____

11. Which of the above are divisible by 5?

12. Which of the above are divisible by 4?

13. Which of the above are divisible by 9?

14. Which of the above are divisible by 6?

15. Which of the above are divisible by 10?

16. Which of the above are divisible by 8?

SKILL MAINTENANCE

Solve.

17. $56 + x = 194$

18. $24 \cdot m = 624$

19. Find the total cost of 12 shirts at $37 each and 4 pairs of trousers at $59 each.

20. Divide: $4\,5\,\overline{)1\,8\,0{,}1\,3\,5.}$

SYNTHESIS

Use the tests of divisibility to find the prime factorization of the number.

21. 7800

22. 2520

23. 2772

24. 1998

1.9 Least Common Multiples

a Finding Least Common Multiples

> The *least common multiple*, or LCM, of two natural numbers is the smallest number that is a multiple of both.

▶ **EXAMPLE 1** Find the LCM of 20 and 30.

a) First list some multiples of 20 by multiplying 20 by 1, 2, 3, and so on:

20, 40, 60, 80, 100, 120, 140, 160, 180, 200, 220, 240, ...

b) Then list some multiples of 30 by multiplying 30 by 1, 2, 3, and so on:

30, 60, 90, 120, 150, 180, 210, 240, ...

c) Now list the numbers *common* to both lists, the common multiples:

60, 120, 180, 240, ...

d) These are the common multiples of 20 and 30. What is the smallest? The LCM of 20 and 30 is 60. ◀

DO EXERCISE 1.

Below we develop two efficient methods for finding LCMs. You may choose to learn either method (consult with your instructor), or both, but if you are going on to a study of algebra, you should definitely learn method 2.

Method 1: Finding LCMs Using One List of Multiples

> *Method 1:* **To find the LCM of a set of numbers (9, 12):**
>
> **a)** Determine whether the greatest number is a multiple of the others. If it is, it is the LCM. If one number is a factor of another, the LCM is the greater number.
>
> (12 is not a multiple of 9)
>
> **b)** If not, check multiples of the largest number until you get one that is a multiple of the others.
>
> (2 · 12 = 24, not a multiple of 9)
>
> (3 · 12 = 36, a multiple of 9)
>
> **c)** That number is the LCM.
>
> **LCM = 36**

▶ **EXAMPLE 2** Find the LCM of 12 and 15.

a) 15 is not a multiple of 12.

b) Check multiples:

$$2 \cdot 15 = 30, \quad \text{Not a multiple of 12}$$
$$3 \cdot 15 = 45, \quad \text{Not a multiple of 12}$$
$$4 \cdot 15 = 60. \quad \text{A multiple of 12}$$

c) The LCM = 60. ◀

DO EXERCISE 2.

OBJECTIVE

After finishing Section 1.9, you should be able to:

a Find the LCM of two or more numbers using a list of multiples or factorizations.

FOR EXTRA HELP

Tape 4A

1. By examining lists of multiples, find the LCM of 9 and 15.

2. By examining lists of multiples, find the LCM of 8 and 10.

Find the LCM.
3. 10, 15

▶ **EXAMPLE 3**   Find the LCM of 4 and 6.

a) 6 is not a multiple of 4.
b) Check multiples:

$$2 \cdot 6 = 12. \quad \text{A multiple of 4}$$

c) The LCM = 12.   ◀

DO EXERCISES 3 AND 4.

▶ **EXAMPLE 4**   Find the LCM of 4 and 8.

a) 8 is a multiple of 4, so it is the LCM.
c) The LCM = 8.   ◀

▶ **EXAMPLE 5**   Find the LCM of 10, 100, and 1000.

a) 1000 is a multiple of 10 and 100, so it is the LCM.
c) The LCM = 1000.   ◀

DO EXERCISES 5 AND 6.

4. 6, 8

Find the LCM.
5. 5, 10

Method 2: Finding LCMs Using Factorizations

A second method for finding LCMs uses prime factorizations. Consider again 20 and 30. Their prime factorizations are

$$20 = 2 \cdot 2 \cdot 5 \quad \text{and} \quad 30 = 2 \cdot 3 \cdot 5.$$

Let's look at these prime factorizations in order to find the LCM. Any multiple of 20 will have to have *two* 2's as factors and *one* 5 as a factor. Any multiple of 30 will have to have *one* 2, *one* 3, and *one* 5 as factors. The smallest number satisfying these conditions is

Two 2's, one 5; makes 20 a factor
$$2 \cdot 2 \cdot 3 \cdot 5.$$
One 2, one 3, one 5; makes 30 a factor

The LCM must have all the factors of 20 and all the factors of 30, but the factors need not be repeated when they are common to both numbers.

The greatest number of times a 2 occurs as a factor of either 20 or 30 is two, and the LCM has 2 as a factor twice. The greatest number of times a 3 occurs as a factor of either 20 or 30 is one, and the LCM has 3 as a factor once. The greatest number of times 5 occurs as a factor of either 20 or 30 is one, and the LCM has 5 as a factor once.

6. 20, 40, 80

Use prime factorizations to find the LCM.

7. 8, 10

> **Method 2. To find the LCM of a set of numbers using prime factorizations:**
>
> a) **Find the prime factorization of each number.**
>
> b) **Create a product of factors, using each factor the greatest number of times it occurs in any one factorization.**

▶ **EXAMPLE 6**   Find the LCM of 6 and 8.

a) Find the prime factorization of each number.

$$6 = 2 \cdot 3, \qquad 8 = 2 \cdot 2 \cdot 2$$

b) Create a product by writing factors, using each the greatest number of times it occurs in any one factorization.

Consider the factor 2. The greatest number of times 2 occurs in any one factorization is three. We write 2 as a factor three times.

$$2 \cdot 2 \cdot 2 \cdot ?$$

Consider the factor 3. The greatest number of times 3 occurs in any one factorization is one. We write 3 as a factor one time.

$$2 \cdot 2 \cdot 2 \cdot 3 \cdot ?$$

Since there are no other prime factors in either factorization, the

$$\text{LCM is } 2 \cdot 2 \cdot 2 \cdot 3, \text{ or } 24. \qquad ◀$$

▶ **EXAMPLE 7**   Find the LCM of 24 and 36.

a) Find the prime factorization of each number.

$$24 = 2 \cdot 2 \cdot 2 \cdot 3, \qquad 36 = 2 \cdot 2 \cdot 3 \cdot 3$$

b) Create a product by writing factors, using each the greatest number of times it occurs in any one factorization.

Consider the factor 2. The greatest number of times 2 occurs in any one factorization is three. We write 2 as a factor three times:

$$2 \cdot 2 \cdot 2 \cdot ?$$

Consider the factor 3. The greatest number of times 3 occurs in any one factorization is two. We write 3 as a factor two times:

$$2 \cdot 2 \cdot 2 \cdot 3 \cdot 3 \cdot ?$$

Since there are no other prime factors in either factorization, the

$$\text{LCM is } 2 \cdot 2 \cdot 2 \cdot 3 \cdot 3, \text{ or } 72. \qquad ◀$$

DO EXERCISES 7 AND 8.

▶ **EXAMPLE 8**   Find the LCM of 27, 90, and 84.

a) Find the prime factorization of each number.

$$27 = 3 \cdot 3 \cdot 3, \qquad 90 = 2 \cdot 3 \cdot 3 \cdot 5, \qquad 84 = 2 \cdot 2 \cdot 3 \cdot 7$$

b) Create a product by writing factors, using each the greatest number of times it occurs in any one factorization.

8. 18, 40

9. Find the LCM of 24, 35, and 45.

Find the LCM.

10. 3, 18

11. 12, 24

Find the LCM.

12. 4, 9

13. 5, 6, 7

Consider the factor 2. The greatest number of times 2 occurs in any one factorization is two. We write 2 as a factor two times:

$$2 \cdot 2 \cdot ?$$

Consider the factor 3. The greatest number of times 3 occurs in any one factorization is three. We write 3 as a factor three times:

$$2 \cdot 2 \cdot 3 \cdot 3 \cdot 3 \cdot ?$$

Consider the factor 5. The greatest number of times 5 occurs in any one factorization is one. We write 5 as a factor one time:

$$2 \cdot 2 \cdot 3 \cdot 3 \cdot 3 \cdot 5 \cdot ?$$

Consider the factor 7. The greatest number of times 7 occurs in any one factorization is one. We write 7 as a factor one time:

$$2 \cdot 2 \cdot 3 \cdot 3 \cdot 3 \cdot 5 \cdot 7 \cdot ?$$

Since no other prime factors are possible in any of the factorizations, the

LCM is $2 \cdot 2 \cdot 3 \cdot 3 \cdot 3 \cdot 5 \cdot 7$, or 3780.   ◀

DO EXERCISE 9.

▶ **EXAMPLE 9**   Find the LCM of 7 and 21.

Note that 7 is a factor of 21. We stated earlier that if one number is a factor of the other, the LCM is the larger of the numbers. Thus the LCM is 21. When you notice this at the outset, you can find the LCM quickly without using factorizations.   ◀

DO EXERCISES 10 AND 11.

▶ **EXAMPLE 10**   Find the LCM of 8 and 9.

The two numbers 8 and 9 have no common prime factor. When this happens, the LCM is just the product of the two numbers. Thus the LCM is $8 \cdot 9$, or 72.   ◀

DO EXERCISES 12 AND 13.

Let's compare the two methods considered for finding LCMs: the multiples method and the factorization method.

Method 1, the **multiples method,** can be longer than the factorization method when the LCM is large or when there are more than two numbers. But this method is faster and easier to use mentally for two numbers.

Method 2, the **factorization method,** works well for several numbers. It is just like a method used in algebra. If you are going to study algebra, you should definitely learn the factorization method.

NAME   SECTION   DATE

EXERCISE SET 1.9

a Find the LCM of each set of numbers. Do so mentally, if possible.

1. 2, 4   **2.** 3, 10   **3.** 10, 25   **4.** 3, 15

5. 20, 40   **6.** 8, 12   **7.** 18, 27   **8.** 9, 11

9. 30, 50   **10.** 24, 36   **11.** 30, 40   **12.** 13, 23

13. 18, 24   **14.** 12, 18   **15.** 60, 70   **16.** 35, 45

17. 16, 36   **18.** 18, 20   **19.** 32, 36   **20.** 36, 48

21. 2, 3, 5   **22.** 7, 18, 3   **23.** 3, 5, 7   **24.** 6, 12, 18

25. 24, 36, 12   **26.** 8, 16, 22   **27.** 5, 12, 15   **28.** 12, 18, 40

29. 9, 12, 6   **30.** 8, 16, 12   **31.** 3, 6, 8   **32.** 12, 8, 4

1. _____
2. _____
3. _____
4. _____
5. _____
6. _____
7. _____
8. _____
9. _____
10. _____
11. _____
12. _____
13. _____
14. _____
15. _____
16. _____
17. _____
18. _____
19. _____
20. _____
21. _____
22. _____
23. _____
24. _____
25. _____
26. _____
27. _____
28. _____
29. _____
30. _____
31. _____
32. _____

ANSWERS

33. _____

34. _____

35. _____

36. _____

37. _____

38. _____

39. _____

40. _____

41. _____

42. _____

43. _____

44. _____

45. _____

46. _____

47. _____

48. a) _____

b) _____

c) _____

d) _____

49. _____

50. _____

51. _____

33. 8, 48　　　　**34.** 16, 32　　　　**35.** 5, 50　　　　**36.** 12, 72

37. 11, 13　　　　**38.** 13, 14　　　　**39.** 12, 35　　　　**40.** 23, 25

41. 54, 63　　　　**42.** 56, 72　　　　**43.** 81, 90　　　　**44.** 75, 100

SKILL MAINTENANCE

45. An auditorium was sold out for a performance. It contains seats selling for $13 each. Total receipts were $3250. How many seats does this auditorium contain?

46. Multiply:　　$\begin{array}{r} 3\ 4\ 5 \\ \times\ \ 2\ 3 \\ \hline \end{array}$　　　　**47.** Subtract:　　$\begin{array}{r} 1\ 0,0\ 0\ 1 \\ -\ \ 8,0\ 3\ 7 \\ \hline \end{array}$

SYNTHESIS

48. Consider 8 and 12. Determine whether each of the following is the LCM of 8 and 12. Tell why or why not.

　a) $2 \cdot 2 \cdot 3 \cdot 3$
　b) $2 \cdot 2 \cdot 3$
　c) $2 \cdot 3 \cdot 3$
　d) $2 \cdot 2 \cdot 2 \cdot 3$

49. A cigar company uses two sizes of boxes, 6 in. and 8 in. long. These are packed in bigger cartons to be shipped. What is the shortest length carton that will accommodate boxes of either size without any room left over? (Each carton can contain only boxes of one size; no mixing is allowed.)

▥ Use your calculator and the multiples method to find the LCM of each pair of numbers.

50. 288, 324　　　　　　　　　　　　**51.** 2700, 7800

SUMMARY AND REVIEW EXERCISES: CHAPTER 1

The review exercises that follow are for practice. Answers are at the back of the book. If you miss an exercise, restudy the section and objective indicated alongside the answer.

1. Write expanded notation: 2793.

2. Write a word name: 2,781,427.

3. What does the digit 7 mean in 4,678,952?

4. Write standard notation for the number in this sentence: The gross national product is two trillion, six hundred twenty-six billion, one hundred million dollars.

Add.

5.
$$\begin{array}{r} 3\,8\,4\,7 \\ +\,2\,1\,3\,2 \\ \hline \end{array}$$

6.
$$\begin{array}{r} 2\,7{,}6\,0\,9 \\ +\,3\,8{,}4\,1\,5 \\ \hline \end{array}$$

7.
$$\begin{array}{r} 2\,7\,4\,3 \\ 4\,1\,2\,5 \\ 6\,2\,7\,4 \\ +\,8\,9\,5\,6 \\ \hline \end{array}$$

8.
$$\begin{array}{r} 9\,1{,}4\,2\,6 \\ +\ \ 7{,}4\,9\,5 \\ \hline \end{array}$$

Subtract.

9.
$$\begin{array}{r} 8\,4\,6\,5 \\ -\,7\,3\,1\,2 \\ \hline \end{array}$$

10.
$$\begin{array}{r} 3\,7\,4\,3 \\ -\,2\,5\,9\,6 \\ \hline \end{array}$$

11.
$$\begin{array}{r} 6\,0\,0\,3 \\ -\,3\,7\,2\,9 \\ \hline \end{array}$$

12.
$$\begin{array}{r} 3\,7{,}4\,0\,5 \\ -\,1\,9{,}6\,4\,8 \\ \hline \end{array}$$

13. 678 − 234

14. 6000 − 1234

Multiply.

15.
$$\begin{array}{r} 7\,0\,0 \\ \times\,6\,0\,0 \\ \hline \end{array}$$

16.
$$\begin{array}{r} 7\,8\,4\,6 \\ \times\ \ 8\,0\,0 \\ \hline \end{array}$$

17.
$$\begin{array}{r} 7\,6 \\ \times\ \ 9 \\ \hline \end{array}$$

18.
$$\begin{array}{r} 6\,3\,9\,4 \\ \times\ \ \ \ \ 7 \\ \hline \end{array}$$

19.
$$\begin{array}{r} 7\,4 \\ \times\,4\,6 \\ \hline \end{array}$$

20.
$$\begin{array}{r} 7\,2\,6 \\ \times\,6\,9\,8 \\ \hline \end{array}$$

21.
$$\begin{array}{r} 5\,8\,7 \\ \times\ \ 4\,7 \\ \hline \end{array}$$

22.
$$\begin{array}{r} 3\,4\,5\,6 \\ \times\,1\,0\,0\,0 \\ \hline \end{array}$$

Divide.

23. 80 ÷ 16

24. 63 ÷ 5

25. 7)5 6 0

26. 4)8 3 0

27. 8)3 0 7 3

28. 6 0)2 8 6

29. 7 9)4 2 6 6

30. 3 8)1 7,1 7 6

31. 1 4)7 0,1 1 2

32. 1 2)5 2,6 6 8

Solve.

33. $47 + x = 92$

34. $x = 782 - 236$

35. $46 \cdot n = 368$

Solve.

36. In 1909 the first "Lincoln-head" pennies were minted. Seventy-three years later, these pennies were first minted with a decreased copper content. In what year was the copper content reduced?

37. A family budgets $4950 yearly for food and clothing and an additional $3585 for entertainment. The yearly income of the family was $28,283. How much of this income remained after these two allotments?

38. A student buys 8 books at $25 each and pays for them with $20 bills. How many $20 bills does it take?

39. A certain cottage cheese contains 113 calories per ounce. A bulk container of this cheese contains 25 ounces. What is the caloric content of this container?

40. A sweater costs $28 and a coat costs $37. Find the total cost of 6 sweaters and 9 coats.

41. A chemist has 2753 L (liters) of acid. How many 18-L beakers can be filled? How much will be left over?

Use $<$ or $>$ for ■ to write a true sentence.

42. 67 ■ 56

43. 1 ■ 23

44. Write exponential notation: $8 \cdot 8 \cdot 8$.

45. Evaluate: 2^4.

Simplify.

46. $8 \times 6 + 17$

47. $7 + (4 + 3)^2$

48. $7 + 4^2 + 3^2$

49. $10 \times 24 - (18 + 2) \div 4 - (9 - 7)$

50. $(80 \div 16) \times [(20 - 56 \div 8) + (8 \cdot 8 - 5 \cdot 5)]$

Find the prime factorization of the number.

51. 70   **52.** 30   **53.** 45   **54.** 150

55. Determine whether 2432 is divisible by 6.

56. Determine whether 182 is divisible by 4.

57. Determine whether 4344 is divisible by 8.

58. Determine whether 4344 is divisible by 9.

59. Determine whether 37 is prime, composite, or neither.

Find the LCM.

60. 12 and 18   **61.** 18 and 45   **62.** 3, 6, and 30

❖ THINKING IT THROUGH

1. Discuss the difference between a "take away" problem situation and a "how much more" situation in subtraction.

2. Describe two ways in which multiplication can occur in the real world.

3. Describe two ways in which division can occur in the real world.

TEST: CHAPTER 1

1. Write expanded notation: 8843.

2. Write a word name: 38,403,277.

3. In the number 546,789, which digit tells the number of hundred thousands?

Add.

4.
```
  6 8 1 1
+ 3 1 7 8
```

5.
```
  4 5,8 8 9
+ 1 7,9 0 2
```

6.
```
  1 2
    8
    3
    7
+   4
```

7.
```
  6 2 0 3
+ 4 3 1 2
```

Subtract.

8.
```
  7 9 8 3
- 4 3 5 3
```

9.
```
  2 9 7 4
- 1 9 3 5
```

10.
```
  8 9 0 7
- 2 0 5 9
```

11.
```
  2 3,0 6 7
- 1 7,8 9 2
```

Multiply.

12.
```
  4 5 6 8
×       9
```

13.
```
  8 8 7 6
×   6 0 0
```

14.
```
  6 5
× 3 7
```

15.
```
  6 7 8
× 7 8 8
```

Divide.

16. $15 \div 4$

17. $420 \div 6$

18. $8\,9\overline{)8\ 6\ 3\ 3}$

19. $4\,4\overline{)3\ 5,4\ 2\ 8}$

Solve.

20. James Dean was 24 years old when he died. He was born in 1931. In what year did he die?

21. A beverage company produces 739 cans of soda. How many 8-can packages can be filled? How many cans will be left over?

22. A customer buys 15 pieces of lumber at $12 each and pays for them with $10 bills. How many $10 bills does it take?

23. A rectangular lot measures 200 m by 600 m. What is the area of the lot?

24. A sack of oranges weighs 27 lb. A sack of apples weighs 32 lb. Find the total weight of 16 bags of oranges and 43 bags of apples.

25. A box contains 5000 staples. How many staplers can be filled from the box if each stapler holds 250 staples?

1. _____
2. _____
3. _____
4. _____
5. _____
6. _____
7. _____
8. _____
9. _____
10. _____
11. _____
12. _____
13. _____
14. _____
15. _____
16. _____
17. _____
18. _____
19. _____
20. _____
21. _____
22. _____
23. _____
24. _____
25. _____

Copyright © 1993 Addison-Wesley Publishing Co., Inc.

ANSWERS

26. _____

27. _____

28. _____

29. _____

30. _____

31. _____

32. _____

33. _____

34. _____

35. _____

36. _____

37. _____

38. _____

39. _____

40. _____

41. _____

42. _____

43. _____

44. _____

45. _____

46. _____

26. The area of Vermont is 9609 sq mi. The area of New Hampshire is 9304 sq mi. How much more area does Vermont have?

27. A professional bowler rolled a game of 245. Then the bowler rolled a game of 189. How much higher was the first game?

28. Listed below are the areas, in square miles, of the New England states. What is the total area of New England?

Maine	33,215
Massachusetts	8,093
New Hampshire	9,304
Vermont	9,609
Connecticut	5,009
Rhode Island	1,214

29. You have $345 in a checking account. You write checks for $45 and $29. How much money is left in the checking account?

Solve.

30. $28 + x = 74$

31. $169 \div 13 = n$

32. $38 \cdot y = 532$

Use < or > for ■ to write a true sentence.

33. 34 ■ 17

34. 117 ■ 157

35. Write exponential notation: $12 \cdot 12 \cdot 12 \cdot 12$.

36. Evaluate: 7^3.

Simplify.

37. $(10 - 2)^2$

38. $10^2 - 2^2$

39. $(25 - 15) \div 5$

40. $8 \times \{(20 - 11) \cdot [(12 + 48) \div 6 - (9 - 2)]\}$

41. $2^4 + 24 \div 12$

Find the prime factorization of the number.

42. 18

43. 60

44. Determine whether 1784 is divisible by 8.

45. Determine whether 784 is divisible by 9.

46. Find the LCM of 12 and 16.

INTRODUCTION In this chapter, addition, subtraction, multiplication, and division using fractional notation are considered. Also discussed are addition, subtraction, multiplication, and division using mixed numerals. All these operations are then applied to problem solving.

The review sections to be used in addition to the material in this chapter are 1.2, 1.3, 1.4, and 1.5. ❖

Fractional Notation

2

AN APPLICATION

Business people have determined that $\frac{1}{4}$ of the items on a mailing list will change in one year. A business has a mailing list of 2500 people. After one year, how many addresses on that list will be incorrect?

THE MATHEMATICS

Let a = the number of addresses. Then the problem can be translated to this equation:

$$\underbrace{\frac{1}{4} \cdot 2500}_{} = a.$$

This multiplication using fractional notation occurs in problem solving.

Area of a Rectangle: $A = l \cdot w$
Area of a Square: $A = s^2$

PRETEST: CHAPTER 2

Simplify.

1. $\dfrac{57}{57}$

2. $\dfrac{68}{1}$

3. $\dfrac{0}{50}$

4. $\dfrac{8}{32}$

5. Use $<$ or $>$ for ▧ to write a true sentence:

$$\dfrac{7}{9} \ ▧ \ \dfrac{4}{5}.$$

6. Find the reciprocal: $\dfrac{7}{8}$.

7. Convert to fractional notation: $7\dfrac{5}{8}$.

8. Convert to a mixed numeral: $\dfrac{11}{2}$.

9. Add. Write a mixed numeral for the answer.

$$8\dfrac{11}{12}$$
$$+ \ 2\dfrac{3}{5}$$

10. Subtract. Write a mixed numeral for the answer.

$$14$$
$$- \ 7\dfrac{5}{6}$$

11. Multiply. Write a mixed numeral for the answer.

$$6\dfrac{2}{3} \cdot 3\dfrac{1}{4}$$

12. Divide. Write a mixed numeral for the answer.

$$35 \div 5\dfrac{5}{6}$$

Solve.

13. $\dfrac{2}{3} + x = \dfrac{8}{9}$

14. $\dfrac{7}{10} \cdot x = 21$

15. A cook bought 100 lb of potatoes and used $78\frac{3}{4}$ lb. How many pounds were left?

16. A piece of rope $\frac{5}{8}$ m long is to be cut into 15 pieces of the same length. What is the length of each piece?

17. A traveler drove $214\frac{3}{10}$ km one day and $136\frac{9}{10}$ km the next. How far did she travel in all?

18. A cake recipe calls for $3\frac{3}{4}$ cups of flour. How much flour would be used to make 6 cakes?

2.1 Fractional Notation and Simplifying

The study of arithmetic begins with the set of whole numbers

$$0, 1, 2, 3, 4, 5, 6, 7, 8, 9, 10, 11, \text{ and so on.}$$

The need soon arises for fractional parts of numbers such as halves, thirds, fourths, and so on. Here are some examples:

For $\frac{1}{10}$ of the people in the United States, English is not the primary language.

$\frac{16}{177}$ of the outdoor drive-in theaters in this country are in California.

The following are some additional examples of fractions:

$$\frac{1}{2}, \quad \frac{3}{4}, \quad \frac{8}{5}, \quad \frac{11}{23}.$$

This way of writing number names is called **fractional notation.** The top number is called the **numerator** and the bottom number is called the **denominator.**

a | Fractions and the Real World

▶ **EXAMPLE 1** What part is shaded?

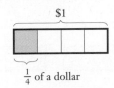

$\frac{1}{4}$ of a dollar

When an object is divided into 4 parts of the same size, each of these parts is $\frac{1}{4}$ of the object. Thus, $\frac{1}{4}$ (*one-fourth*) is shaded. ◀

DO EXERCISES 1–4.

▶ **EXAMPLE 2** What part is shaded?

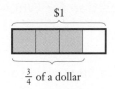

$\frac{3}{4}$ of a dollar

The object is divided into 4 parts of the same size, and 3 of them are shaded. This is $3 \cdot \frac{1}{4}$, or $\frac{3}{4}$. Thus, $\frac{3}{4}$ (*three-fourths*) of the object is shaded. ◀

OBJECTIVES

After finishing Section 2.1, you should be able to:

a | Write fractional notation for part of an object or part of a set of objects.

b | Simplify fractional notation like n/n to 1, $0/n$ to 0, and $n/1$ to n.

c | Multiply using fractional notation.

d | Find another name for a number, but having a new denominator. Use multiplying by 1.

e | Simplify fractional notation.

FOR EXTRA HELP

Tape 3B, 3C

What part is shaded?

1.

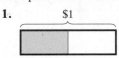

2. 1 mile

3.

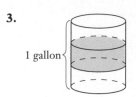

1 gallon

4.

ANSWERS ON PAGE A-2

What part is shaded?

5.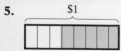

6.

7.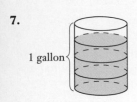

8.

What part is shaded?

9.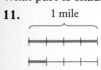

10.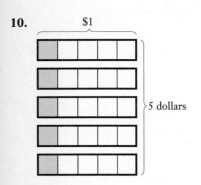

What part is shaded?

11.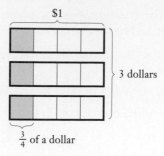

12.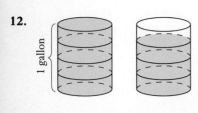

The fraction $\frac{3}{4}$ corresponds to another situation. We take 3 objects, divide them into fourths, and take $\frac{1}{4}$ of the entire amount. This is $\frac{1}{4} \cdot 3$, or $\frac{3}{4}$, or $3 \div 4$.

▶ **EXAMPLE 3**   What part is shaded?

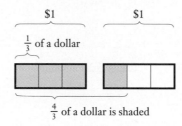

Thus, $\$\frac{3}{4}$ is shaded.   ◀

DO EXERCISES 5–10.

Fractions greater than 1 correspond to situations like the following.

▶ **EXAMPLE 4**   What part is shaded?

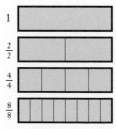

We divide the two objects into 3 parts each and take 4 of those parts. We have more than one whole object. In this case, it is $4 \cdot \frac{1}{3}$, or $\frac{4}{3}$.   ◀

DO EXERCISES 11 AND 12.

b   Some Fractional Notation for Whole Numbers

Fractional Notation for 1

The number 1 corresponds to situations like the following.

If we divide an object into n parts and take n of them, we get all of the object (1 whole object).

$$\frac{n}{n} = 1, \quad \text{for any whole number } n \text{ that is not 0.}$$

▶ **EXAMPLES**   Simplify.

5. $\frac{5}{5} = 1$ **6.** $\frac{9}{9} = 1$ **7.** $\frac{23}{23} = 1$ ◀

DO EXERCISES 13–18.

Other Whole Numbers

Consider $\frac{4}{1}$. This corresponds to taking 4 objects and dividing them into 1 part. (We do not divide them.) We have 4 objects.

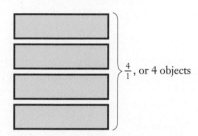

$\frac{4}{1}$, or 4 objects

> **Any whole number divided by 1 is the whole number.** That is,
>
> $$\frac{n}{1} = n, \quad \text{for any whole number } n.$$

▶ **EXAMPLES**   Simplify.

8. $\frac{2}{1} = 2$ **9.** $\frac{9}{1} = 9$ **10.** $\frac{34}{1} = 34$ ◀

DO EXERCISES 19–22.

Fractional Notation for 0

Consider $\frac{0}{4}$. This corresponds to dividing an object into 4 parts and taking none of them. We get 0.

> $$\frac{0}{n} = 0, \quad \text{for any whole number } n \text{ that is not 0.}$$

▶ **EXAMPLES**   Simplify.

11. $\frac{0}{1} = 0$ **12.** $\frac{0}{9} = 0$ **13.** $\frac{0}{23} = 0$ ◀

DO EXERCISES 23–26.

Simplify.

13. $\frac{1}{1}$ **14.** $\frac{4}{4}$

15. $\frac{34}{34}$ **16.** $\frac{100}{100}$

17. $\frac{2347}{2347}$ **18.** $\frac{103}{103}$

Simplify.

19. $\frac{8}{1}$ **20.** $\frac{10}{1}$

21. $\frac{346}{1}$ **22.** $\frac{24 - 1}{23}$

Simplify.

23. $\frac{0}{1}$ **24.** $\frac{0}{8}$

25. $\frac{0}{107}$ **26.** $\frac{4 - 4}{567}$

Divide, if possible. If not possible, write "not defined."

27. $\dfrac{8}{4}$ **28.** $\dfrac{5}{0}$

29. $\dfrac{0}{5}$ **30.** $\dfrac{0}{0}$

31. $12 \div 0$ **32.** $100 \div 10$

33. $\dfrac{5}{3-3}$ **34.** $\dfrac{8-8}{4}$

Multiply.

35. $\dfrac{3}{8} \cdot \dfrac{5}{7}$

36. $\dfrac{4}{3} \times \dfrac{8}{5}$

37. $\dfrac{3}{10} \cdot \dfrac{1}{10}$

38. $7 \cdot \dfrac{2}{3}$

Division by Zero

Why can't we divide by 0? Suppose the number 4 could be divided by 0. Then if $\square$ were the answer,

$$4 \div 0 = \square \quad \text{and this would mean} \quad 4 = \square \cdot 0 = 0. \quad \text{False!}$$

Suppose 12 could be divided by 0. If $\square$ were the answer,

$$12 \div 0 = \square \quad \text{and this would mean} \quad 12 = \square \cdot 0 = 0. \quad \text{False!}$$

Thus, $a \div 0$ would be some number $\square$ such that $a = 0 \cdot \square = 0$. So the only possible number that could be divided by 0 would be 0 itself. But such a division would give us any number we wish, for

$$\left.\begin{array}{l} 0 \div 0 = 8 \quad \text{because} \quad = 8 \cdot 0; \\ 0 \div 0 = 3 \quad \text{because} \quad = 3 \cdot 0; \\ 0 \div 0 = 7 \quad \text{because} \quad = 7 \cdot 0. \end{array}\right\} \quad \text{All true!}$$

We avoid the preceding difficulties by agreeing to exclude division by 0.

> **Division by 0 is not defined. (We agree not to divide by 0.)**

DO EXERCISES 27–34.

C   Multiplication Using Fractional Notation

We find a product such as $\frac{9}{7} \cdot \frac{3}{4}$ as follows.

> **To multiply,**
> **a) multiply the numerators, and**
> $$\frac{9}{7} \cdot \frac{3}{4} = \frac{9 \cdot 3}{7 \cdot 4} = \frac{27}{28}$$
> **b) multiply the denominators.**

▶ **EXAMPLES**   Multiply.

14. $\dfrac{5}{6} \times \dfrac{7}{4} = \dfrac{5 \times 7}{6 \times 4} = \dfrac{35}{24}$

> Skip this step whenever you can.

15. $\dfrac{3}{5} \cdot \dfrac{7}{8} = \dfrac{3 \cdot 7}{5 \cdot 8} = \dfrac{21}{40}$

16. $\dfrac{3}{5} \cdot \dfrac{3}{4} = \dfrac{9}{20}$ **17.** $\dfrac{1}{4} \cdot \dfrac{1}{3} = \dfrac{1}{12}$ **18.** $6 \cdot \dfrac{4}{5} = \dfrac{6}{1} \cdot \dfrac{4}{5} = \dfrac{24}{5}$ ◀

DO EXERCISES 35–38.

Unless one of the factors is a whole number, multiplication does not correspond to repeated addition. Let us see how multiplication of fractions corresponds to situations in the real world. We consider the multiplication

$$\frac{3}{5} \cdot \frac{3}{4}.$$

We first consider some object and take $\frac{3}{4}$ of it. We divide it into 4 parts and take 3 of them. That is shown in the shading below.

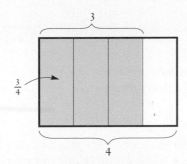

Next, we take $\frac{3}{5}$ of the result. We divide the shaded part into 5 parts and take 3 of them. That is shown below.

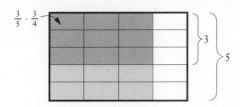

The entire object has been divided into 20 parts, and we have shaded 9 of them for a second time:

$$\frac{3}{5} \cdot \frac{3}{4} = \frac{3 \cdot 3}{5 \cdot 4} = \frac{9}{20}.$$

The figure above shows a rectangular array inside a rectangular array. The number of pieces in the entire array is $5 \cdot 4$ (the product of the denominators). The number of pieces doubly shaded is $3 \cdot 3$ (the product of the numerators). For the answer, we take 9 pieces out of a set of 20 to get $\frac{9}{20}$.

DO EXERCISE 39.

39. Draw diagrams like those in the text to show how the multiplication $\frac{1}{3} \cdot \frac{4}{5}$ corresponds to a real-world situation.

ANSWER ON PAGE A-2

Multiply.

40. $\dfrac{1}{2} \cdot \dfrac{8}{8}$

41. $\dfrac{3}{5} \cdot \dfrac{10}{10}$

42. $\dfrac{13}{25} \cdot \dfrac{4}{4}$

43. $\dfrac{8}{3} \cdot \dfrac{25}{25}$

Find another name for the number, but with the denominator indicated. Use multiplying by 1.

44. $\dfrac{4}{3} = \dfrac{?}{9}$

45. $\dfrac{3}{4} = \dfrac{?}{24}$

46. $\dfrac{9}{10} = \dfrac{?}{100}$

47. $\dfrac{3}{15} = \dfrac{?}{45}$

48. $\dfrac{8}{7} = \dfrac{?}{49}$

---

d   Multiplying by 1

Recall the following:

$$1 = \frac{1}{1} = \frac{2}{2} = \frac{3}{3} = \frac{4}{4} = \frac{10}{10} = \frac{45}{45} = \frac{100}{100} = \frac{n}{n}.$$

Any nonzero number divided by itself is 1.

> **When we multiply a number by 1, we get the same number.**
>
> $$\frac{3}{5} \cdot 1 = \frac{3}{5} \cdot \frac{4}{4} = \frac{12}{20}$$

Since $\frac{3}{5} \cdot 1 = \frac{12}{20}$, we know that $\frac{3}{5}$ and $\frac{12}{20}$ are two names for the same number. We also say that $\frac{3}{5}$ and $\frac{12}{20}$ are **equivalent.**

DO EXERCISES 40–43.

Suppose we want to find a name for $\frac{2}{3}$, but one that has a denominator of 9. We can multiply by 1 to find equivalent fractions:

$$\frac{2}{3} = \frac{2}{3} \cdot \frac{3}{3} = \frac{2 \cdot 3}{3 \cdot 3} = \frac{6}{9}.$$

We chose $\frac{3}{3}$ for 1 in order to get a denominator of 9.

▶ **EXAMPLE 19**   Find a name for $\frac{1}{4}$ with a denominator of 24.

Since $4 \cdot 6 = 24$, we multiply by $\frac{6}{6}$:

$$\frac{1}{4} = \frac{1}{4} \cdot \frac{6}{6} = \frac{1 \cdot 6}{4 \cdot 6} = \frac{6}{24}. \qquad ◀$$

▶ **EXAMPLE 20**   Find a name for $\frac{2}{5}$ with a denominator of 35.

Since $5 \cdot 7 = 35$, we multiply by $\frac{7}{7}$:

$$\frac{2}{5} = \frac{2}{5} \cdot \frac{7}{7} = \frac{2 \cdot 7}{5 \cdot 7} = \frac{14}{35}. \qquad ◀$$

DO EXERCISES 44–48.

e   Simplifying

All of the following are names for three-fourths:

$$\frac{3}{4}, \quad \frac{6}{8}, \quad \frac{9}{12}, \quad \frac{12}{16}, \quad \frac{15}{20}.$$

We say that $\frac{3}{4}$ is **simplest** because it has the smallest numerator and denominator.

To simplify, we reverse the process of "multiplying by 1."

$$\frac{12}{18} = \frac{2 \cdot 6}{3 \cdot 6}$$ ← Factor the numerator.
← Factor the denominator.

Remove the greatest common factor of the numerator and the denominator.

$$= \frac{2}{3} \cdot \frac{6}{6}$$ ← Factor the fraction.

$$= \frac{2}{3} \cdot 1$$ ← $\frac{6}{6} = 1$

$$= \frac{2}{3}$$ ← Removing a factor of 1: $\frac{2}{3} \cdot 1 = \frac{2}{3}$

▶ **EXAMPLES** Simplify.

21. $\frac{8}{20} = \frac{2 \cdot 4}{5 \cdot 4} = \frac{2}{5} \cdot \frac{4}{4} = \frac{2}{5}$

22. $\frac{2}{6} = \frac{1 \cdot 2}{3 \cdot 2} = \frac{1}{3} \cdot \frac{2}{2} = \frac{1}{3}$

The number 1 allows for pairing of factors in the numerator and the denominator.

23. $\frac{30}{6} = \frac{5 \cdot 6}{1 \cdot 6} = \frac{5}{1} \cdot \frac{6}{6} = \frac{5}{1} = 5$

We could also simplify $\frac{30}{6}$ by doing the division $30 \div 6$. That is, $\frac{30}{6} = 30 \div 6 = 5$.

◀

DO EXERCISES 49–52.

The use of prime factorizations can be helpful for larger numbers.

▶ **EXAMPLE 24** Simplify: $\frac{90}{84}$.

$$\frac{90}{84} = \frac{2 \cdot 3 \cdot 3 \cdot 5}{2 \cdot 2 \cdot 3 \cdot 7}$$ Factoring the numerator and the denominator into primes

$$= \frac{2 \cdot 3 \cdot 3 \cdot 5}{2 \cdot 3 \cdot 2 \cdot 7}$$ Changing the order so that like primes are above and below each other

$$= \frac{2}{2} \cdot \frac{3}{3} \cdot \frac{3 \cdot 5}{2 \cdot 7}$$ Factoring the fraction

$$= 1 \cdot 1 \cdot \frac{3 \cdot 5}{2 \cdot 7}$$

$$= \frac{3 \cdot 5}{2 \cdot 7}$$ Removing factors of 1

$$= \frac{15}{14}$$

◀

We could have shortened the preceding example had we recalled our tests for divisibility (Section 1.8) and noted that 6 is a factor of both the numerator and the denominator. Then

$$\frac{90}{84} = \frac{6 \cdot 15}{6 \cdot 14} = \frac{6}{6} \cdot \frac{15}{14} = \frac{15}{14}.$$

The tests for divisibility are very helpful in simplifying.

Simplify.

49. $\frac{2}{8}$

50. $\frac{10}{12}$

51. $\frac{40}{8}$

52. $\frac{24}{18}$

ANSWERS ON PAGE A-2

Simplify.

53. $\dfrac{35}{40}$

54. $\dfrac{801}{702}$

55. $\dfrac{24}{21}$

56. $\dfrac{75}{300}$

▶ **EXAMPLE 25**   Simplify: $\dfrac{603}{207}$.

At first glance this looks difficult. But note, using the test for divisibility by 9 (sum of digits divisible by 9), that both the numerator and the denominator are divisible by 9. Thus we can factor 9 from both numbers:

$$\frac{603}{207} = \frac{9 \cdot 67}{9 \cdot 23} = \frac{9}{9} \cdot \frac{67}{23} = \frac{67}{23}. \qquad ◀$$

DO EXERCISES 53–56.

CANCELING. Canceling is a shortcut that you may have used for removing a factor of 1 when working with fractional notation. With *great* concern, we mention it as a possibility of speeding up your work. Canceling may be done only when removing common factors in numerators and denominators. Each common factor allows us to remove a factor of 1 in a product. Canceling may not be done in sums. Our concern is that canceling be done with care and understanding. In effect, slashes are used to indicate factors of 1 that have been removed. Example 24 might have been done faster as follows:

$$\frac{90}{84} = \frac{2 \cdot 3 \cdot 3 \cdot 5}{2 \cdot 2 \cdot 3 \cdot 7} \qquad \text{Factoring the numerator and the denominator}$$

$$= \frac{\cancel{2} \cdot \cancel{3} \cdot 3 \cdot 5}{2 \cdot \cancel{2} \cdot \cancel{3} \cdot 7} \qquad \begin{array}{l}\text{When a factor of 1 is noted,}\\ \text{it is "canceled" as shown: } \frac{2 \cdot 3}{2 \cdot 3} = 1.\end{array}$$

$$= \frac{3 \cdot 5}{2 \cdot 7} = \frac{15}{14}.$$

CAUTION! The difficulty with canceling is that it is often applied incorrectly in situations like the following:

$$\underbrace{\frac{\cancel{2} + 3}{\cancel{2}} = 3;}_{\uparrow} \qquad \underbrace{\frac{\cancel{4} + 1}{\cancel{4} + 2} = \frac{1}{2};}_{\uparrow} \qquad \underbrace{\frac{1\cancel{5}}{5\cancel{4}} = \frac{1}{4}.}_{\uparrow}$$

      Wrong!   Wrong!   Wrong!

The correct answers are

$$\frac{2 + 3}{2} = \frac{5}{2}; \qquad \frac{4 + 1}{4 + 2} = \frac{5}{6}; \qquad \frac{15}{54} = \frac{5}{18}.$$

In each situation, the number canceled was *not* a factor of 1. Factors are parts of products. For example, in $2 \cdot 3$, 2 and 3 are factors, but in $2 + 3$, 2 and 3 are *not* factors.

If you cannot factor, do not cancel! If in doubt, do not cancel!

NAME　　　　　　　SECTION　　　DATE

EXERCISE SET 2.1

a What part of each object or set of objects is shaded?

1.　$1

2.　$1

3.
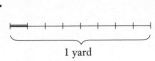

4. 1 gold bar
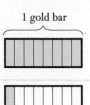

5.
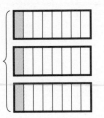
1 quart

6.
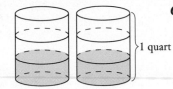

7.
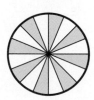

8.
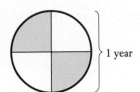
1 year

9.
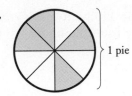
1 pie

10.
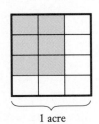

11.
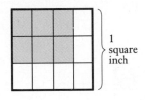
1 acre

12.
1 square inch

b Simplify.

13. $\frac{0}{1}$　　**14.** $\frac{56}{56}$　　**15.** $\frac{234}{1}$　　**16.** $\frac{0}{5}$

17. $\frac{234}{234}$　　**18.** $\frac{7}{1}$　　**19.** $\frac{0}{234}$　　**20.** $\frac{3}{3}$

Divide, if possible. If not possible, write "not defined."

21. $48 \div 0$　　**22.** $\frac{0}{99}$　　**23.** $\frac{0}{0}$　　**24.** $0 \div 55$

ANSWERS

1.
2.
3.
4.
5.
6.
7.
8.
9.
10.
11.
12.
13.
14.
15.
16.
17.
18.
19.
20.
21.
22.
23.
24.

c Multiply.

25. $\frac{1}{2} \cdot \frac{1}{3}$ **26.** $\frac{1}{4} \cdot \frac{1}{5}$ **27.** $5 \times \frac{1}{6}$ **28.** $4 \times \frac{1}{7}$

29. $\frac{2}{3} \times \frac{1}{5}$ **30.** $\frac{3}{5} \times \frac{1}{5}$ **31.** $\frac{2}{5} \cdot \frac{2}{3}$ **32.** $\frac{3}{4} \cdot \frac{3}{5}$

33. $\frac{3}{4} \cdot \frac{3}{4}$ **34.** $\frac{3}{7} \cdot \frac{4}{5}$ **35.** $\frac{2}{3} \cdot \frac{7}{13}$ **36.** $\frac{3}{11} \cdot \frac{4}{5}$

37. $7 \cdot \frac{3}{4}$ **38.** $7 \cdot \frac{2}{5}$ **39.** $\frac{7}{8} \cdot \frac{7}{8}$ **40.** $\frac{4}{5} \cdot \frac{4}{5}$

d Find another name for the given number, but with the denominator indicated. Use multiplying by 1.

41. $\frac{1}{2} = \frac{?}{10}$ **42.** $\frac{1}{6} = \frac{?}{12}$ **43.** $\frac{3}{4} = \frac{?}{48}$ **44.** $\frac{2}{9} = \frac{?}{18}$

45. $\frac{5}{3} = \frac{?}{45}$ **46.** $\frac{11}{5} = \frac{?}{30}$ **47.** $\frac{7}{22} = \frac{?}{132}$ **48.** $\frac{10}{21} = \frac{?}{126}$

e Simplify.

49. $\frac{6}{8}$ **50.** $\frac{9}{12}$ **51.** $\frac{3}{15}$ **52.** $\frac{8}{10}$

53. $\frac{24}{8}$ **54.** $\frac{36}{4}$ **55.** $\frac{18}{24}$ **56.** $\frac{42}{48}$

57. $\frac{14}{16}$ **58.** $\frac{15}{25}$ **59.** $\frac{19}{76}$ **60.** $\frac{17}{51}$

SYNTHESIS

61. A college student earned $2700 one summer. During the following year, the student spent $1200 for tuition, $540 for rent, and $360 for food. The rest went for miscellaneous expenses. What part of the income went for tuition? rent? food? miscellaneous expenses?

2.2 Multiplication and Division

a Simplifying After Multiplying

We usually simplify after we multiply. To make such simplifying easier, it is generally best not to carry out the products in the numerator and the denominator, but to factor and simplify. Consider the product

$$\frac{3}{8} \cdot \frac{4}{9}.$$

We proceed as follows:

$$\frac{3}{8} \cdot \frac{4}{9} = \frac{3 \cdot 4}{8 \cdot 9}$$ We write the products in the numerator and the denominator but we do not carry them out.

$$= \frac{3 \cdot 2 \cdot 2}{2 \cdot 2 \cdot 2 \cdot 3 \cdot 3}$$ Factoring the numerator and the denominator

$$= \frac{3 \cdot 2 \cdot 2}{3 \cdot 2 \cdot 2} \cdot \frac{1}{2 \cdot 3}$$ Factoring the fraction

$$= 1 \cdot \frac{1}{2 \cdot 3}$$

$$= \frac{1}{2 \cdot 3}$$ Removing a factor of 1

$$= \frac{1}{6}.$$

The procedure could have been shortened had we noticed that 4 is a factor of the 8 in the denominator:

$$\frac{3}{8} \cdot \frac{4}{9} = \frac{3 \cdot 4}{8 \cdot 9} = \frac{3 \cdot 4}{4 \cdot 2 \cdot 3 \cdot 3} = \frac{3 \cdot 4}{3 \cdot 4} \cdot \frac{1}{2 \cdot 3} = 1 \cdot \frac{1}{2 \cdot 3} = \frac{1}{2 \cdot 3} = \frac{1}{6}.$$

> **To multiply and simplify:**
> a) **Write the products in the numerator and the denominator, but do not carry out the products.**
> b) **Factor the numerator and the denominator.**
> c) **Factor the fraction to remove factors of 1.**
> d) **Carry out the remaining products.**

▶ **EXAMPLES** Multiply and simplify.

1. $\dfrac{2}{3} \cdot \dfrac{9}{4} = \dfrac{2 \cdot 9}{3 \cdot 4} = \dfrac{2 \cdot 3 \cdot 3}{3 \cdot 2 \cdot 2} = \dfrac{2 \cdot 3}{2 \cdot 3} \cdot \dfrac{3}{2} = 1 \cdot \dfrac{3}{2} = \dfrac{3}{2}$

2. $\dfrac{6}{7} \cdot \dfrac{5}{3} = \dfrac{6 \cdot 5}{7 \cdot 3} = \dfrac{3 \cdot 2 \cdot 5}{7 \cdot 3} = \dfrac{3}{3} \cdot \dfrac{2 \cdot 5}{7} = 1 \cdot \dfrac{2 \cdot 5}{7} = \dfrac{2 \cdot 5}{7} = \dfrac{10}{7}$

3. $40 \cdot \dfrac{7}{8} = \dfrac{40 \cdot 7}{8} = \dfrac{8 \cdot 5 \cdot 7}{8 \cdot 1} = \dfrac{8}{8} \cdot \dfrac{5 \cdot 7}{1} = 1 \cdot \dfrac{5 \cdot 7}{1} = \dfrac{5 \cdot 7}{1} = 35$ ◀

OBJECTIVES

After finishing Section 2.2, you should be able to:

a Multiply and simplify using fractional notation.

b Find the reciprocal of a number.

c Divide and simplify, using fractional notation.

d Solve equations of the type $a \cdot x = b$ and $x \cdot a = b$, where a and b may be fractions.

FOR EXTRA HELP

Tape 3D, 3E

Multiply and simplify.

1. $\dfrac{2}{3} \cdot \dfrac{7}{8}$

2. $\dfrac{4}{5} \cdot \dfrac{5}{12}$

3. $16 \cdot \dfrac{3}{8}$

4. $\dfrac{5}{8} \cdot 4$

Find the reciprocal.

5. $\dfrac{2}{5}$

6. $\dfrac{10}{7}$

7. 9

8. $\dfrac{1}{5}$

> **CAUTION!** Canceling can be used as follows for these examples.
>
> **1.** $\dfrac{2}{3} \cdot \dfrac{9}{4} = \dfrac{2 \cdot 9}{3 \cdot 4} = \dfrac{\cancel{2} \cdot 3 \cdot 3}{\cancel{3} \cdot \cancel{2} \cdot 2} = \dfrac{3}{2}$ Removing a factor of 1: $\dfrac{2 \cdot 3}{2 \cdot 3} = 1$
>
> **2.** $\dfrac{6}{7} \cdot \dfrac{5}{3} = \dfrac{6 \cdot 5}{7 \cdot 3} = \dfrac{\cancel{3} \cdot 2 \cdot 5}{7 \cdot \cancel{3}} = \dfrac{2 \cdot 5}{7} = \dfrac{10}{7}$ Removing a factor of 1: $\dfrac{3}{3} = 1$
>
> **3.** $40 \cdot \dfrac{7}{8} = \dfrac{40 \cdot 7}{8} = \dfrac{\cancel{8} \cdot 5 \cdot 7}{\cancel{8} \cdot 1} = \dfrac{5 \cdot 7}{1} = 35$ Removing a factor of 1: $\dfrac{8}{8} = 1$
>
> Remember, if you can't factor, you can't cancel!

DO EXERCISES 1–4.

b   Reciprocals

Look at these products:

$$8 \cdot \dfrac{1}{8} = \dfrac{8 \cdot 1}{8} = \dfrac{8}{8} = 1; \qquad \dfrac{2}{3} \cdot \dfrac{3}{2} = \dfrac{2 \cdot 3}{3 \cdot 2} = \dfrac{6}{6} = 1.$$

> **If the product of two numbers is 1, we say that they are *reciprocals* of each other. To find a reciprocal, interchange the numerator and the denominator:**
>
> Number $\longrightarrow \dfrac{3}{4} \qquad \dfrac{4}{3} \cdot \longleftarrow$ Reciprocal

▶ **EXAMPLES**   Find the reciprocal.

4. The reciprocal of $\dfrac{4}{5}$ is $\dfrac{5}{4}$.

5. The reciprocal of $\dfrac{8}{7}$ is $\dfrac{7}{8}$.

6. The reciprocal of 8 is $\dfrac{1}{8}$.   Think of 8 as $\dfrac{8}{1}$.

7. The reciprocal of $\dfrac{1}{3}$ is 3.   ◀

DO EXERCISES 5–8.

Does 0 have a reciprocal? If it did, it would have to be a number x such that

$$0 \cdot x = 1.$$

But 0 times any number is 0. Thus,

> **The number 0, or $\dfrac{0}{n}$, has no reciprocal! (Recall that $\dfrac{n}{0}$ is not defined.)**

C Division

Recall that $a \div b$ is that number which when multiplied by b gives a. Consider the division $\frac{3}{4} \div \frac{1}{8}$. We are asking how many $\frac{1}{8}$'s are in $\frac{3}{4}$. We can answer this by looking at the figure below.

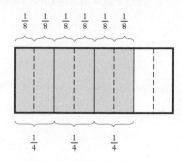

We see that there are six $\frac{1}{8}$'s in $\frac{3}{4}$. Thus,

$$\frac{3}{4} \div \frac{1}{8} = 6.$$

We can check this by multiplying:

$$6 \cdot \frac{1}{8} = \frac{6}{8} = \frac{3}{4}.$$

Here is a faster way to divide.

> **To divide, multiply the dividend by the reciprocal of the divisor:**
> $$\frac{2}{5} \div \frac{3}{4} = \frac{2}{5} \cdot \frac{4}{3} = \frac{2 \cdot 4}{5 \cdot 3} = \frac{8}{15}.$$
>
> **Multiply by the reciprocal of the divisor.**

▶ **EXAMPLES** Divide and simplify.

8. $\frac{5}{6} \div \frac{2}{3} = \frac{5}{6} \cdot \frac{3}{2} = \frac{5 \cdot 3}{6 \cdot 2} = \frac{5 \cdot 3}{3 \cdot 2 \cdot 2} = \frac{3}{3} \cdot \frac{5}{2 \cdot 2} = \frac{5}{2 \cdot 2} = \frac{5}{4}$

9. $\frac{3}{4} \div \frac{1}{8} = \frac{3}{4} \cdot 8 = \frac{3 \cdot 8}{4} = \frac{3 \cdot 4 \cdot 2}{4 \cdot 1} = \frac{4}{4} \cdot \frac{3 \cdot 2}{1} = \frac{3 \cdot 2}{1} = 6$

10. $\frac{2}{5} \div 6 = \frac{2}{5} \cdot \frac{1}{6} = \frac{2 \cdot 1}{5 \cdot 6} = \frac{2 \cdot 1}{5 \cdot 2 \cdot 3} = \frac{2}{2} \cdot \frac{1}{5 \cdot 3} = \frac{1}{5 \cdot 3} = \frac{1}{15}$

11. $\frac{3}{5} \div \frac{1}{2} = \frac{3}{5} \cdot 2 = \frac{3 \cdot 2}{5} = \frac{6}{5}$ ◀

CAUTION! Canceling can be used as follows for Examples 8–10.

8. $\frac{5}{6} \div \frac{2}{3} = \frac{5}{6} \cdot \frac{3}{2} = \frac{5 \cdot 3}{6 \cdot 2} = \frac{5 \cdot \cancel{3}}{\cancel{3} \cdot 2 \cdot 2} = \frac{5}{2 \cdot 2} = \frac{5}{4}$ Removing a factor of 1: $\frac{3}{3} = 1$

9. $\frac{3}{4} \div \frac{1}{8} = \frac{3}{4} \cdot 8 = \frac{3 \cdot 8}{4} = \frac{3 \cdot \cancel{4} \cdot 2}{\cancel{4} \cdot 1} = \frac{3 \cdot 2}{1} = 6$ Removing a factor of 1: $\frac{4}{4} = 1$

10. $\frac{2}{5} \div 6 = \frac{2}{5} \cdot \frac{1}{6} = \frac{2 \cdot 1}{5 \cdot 6} = \frac{\cancel{2} \cdot 1}{5 \cdot \cancel{2} \cdot 3} = \frac{1}{5 \cdot 3} = \frac{1}{15}$ Removing a factor of 1: $\frac{2}{2} = 1$

Remember, if you can't factor, you can't cancel!

Divide and simplify.

9. $\frac{6}{7} \div \frac{3}{4}$

10. $\frac{2}{3} \div \frac{1}{4}$

11. $\frac{4}{5} \div 8$

12. $60 \div \frac{3}{5}$

13. $\frac{3}{5} \div \frac{3}{5}$

ANSWERS ON PAGE A-2

14. Divide by multiplying by 1:

$$\frac{\frac{4}{5}}{\frac{6}{7}}.$$

Solve.

15. $\frac{5}{6} \cdot y = \frac{2}{3}$

16. $\frac{3}{4} \cdot n = 24$

Why do we multiply by a reciprocal when dividing? To see this, let's consider $\frac{2}{3} \div \frac{7}{5}$. We will multiply by 1. The name for 1 that we will use is $\frac{5/7}{5/7}$. Then we multiply as follows:

$$\frac{2}{3} \div \frac{7}{5} = \frac{\frac{2}{3}}{\frac{7}{5}} \qquad \text{Writing fractional notation for the division}$$

$$= \frac{\frac{2}{3}}{\frac{7}{5}} \cdot 1 \qquad \text{Multiplying by 1}$$

$$= \frac{\frac{2}{3}}{\frac{7}{5}} \cdot \frac{\frac{5}{7}}{\frac{5}{7}} \qquad \text{Multiplying by 1; } \frac{5}{7} \text{ is the reciprocal of } \frac{7}{5} \text{ and } \frac{\frac{5}{7}}{\frac{5}{7}} = 1$$

$$= \frac{\frac{2}{3} \cdot \frac{5}{7}}{\frac{7}{5} \cdot \frac{5}{7}} \qquad \text{Multiplying the numerators and the denominators}$$

$$= \frac{\frac{2}{3} \cdot \frac{5}{7}}{1} = \frac{2}{3} \cdot \frac{5}{7} = \frac{10}{21}$$

After we multiplied, we got 1 for the denominator. The numerator (in color) shows the multiplication by the reciprocal.

DO EXERCISE 14.

d | Solving Equations

Now let us solve equations $a \cdot x = b$ and $x \cdot a = b$, where a and b may be fractions. Proceeding as we have before, we divide on both sides by a.

▶ **EXAMPLE 12**   Solve: $\frac{4}{3} \cdot x = \frac{6}{7}$.

$$\frac{4}{3} \cdot x = \frac{6}{7}$$

$$x = \frac{6}{7} \div \frac{4}{3} \qquad \text{Dividing on both sides by } \frac{4}{3}$$

$$= \frac{6}{7} \cdot \frac{3}{4} \qquad \text{Multiplying by the reciprocal}$$

$$= \frac{2 \cdot 3 \cdot 3}{7 \cdot 2 \cdot 2} = \frac{2}{2} \cdot \frac{3 \cdot 3}{7 \cdot 2} = \frac{3 \cdot 3}{7 \cdot 2} = \frac{9}{14}$$

The solution is $\frac{9}{14}$.   ◀

▶ **EXAMPLE 13**   Solve: $t \cdot \frac{4}{5} = 80$.

Dividing on both sides by $\frac{4}{5}$, we get

$$t = 80 \div \frac{4}{5} = 80 \cdot \frac{5}{4} = \frac{80 \cdot 5}{4} = \frac{4 \cdot 20 \cdot 5}{4 \cdot 1} = \frac{4}{4} \cdot \frac{20 \cdot 5}{1} = \frac{20 \cdot 5}{1} = 100.$$

The solution is 100.   ◀

DO EXERCISES 15 AND 16.

ANSWERS ON PAGE A-2

NAME   SECTION   DATE

EXERCISE SET 2.2

a Multiply and simplify. | Don't forget to simplify! |

1. $\frac{2}{3} \cdot \frac{1}{2}$ **2.** $\frac{4}{5} \cdot \frac{1}{4}$ **3.** $\frac{1}{4} \cdot \frac{2}{3}$ **4.** $\frac{3}{6} \cdot \frac{1}{6}$

5. $\frac{12}{5} \cdot \frac{9}{8}$ **6.** $\frac{16}{15} \cdot \frac{5}{4}$ **7.** $\frac{10}{9} \cdot \frac{7}{5}$ **8.** $\frac{25}{12} \cdot \frac{4}{3}$

9. $9 \cdot \frac{1}{9}$ **10.** $4 \cdot \frac{1}{4}$ **11.** $\frac{7}{5} \cdot \frac{5}{7}$ **12.** $\frac{2}{11} \cdot \frac{11}{2}$

13. $15 \cdot \frac{1}{3}$ **14.** $14 \cdot \frac{1}{2}$ **15.** $12 \cdot \frac{3}{4}$ **16.** $18 \cdot \frac{5}{6}$

17. $\frac{7}{10} \cdot 28$ **18.** $\frac{5}{8} \cdot 34$ **19.** $240 \cdot \frac{1}{8}$ **20.** $150 \cdot \frac{1}{5}$

21. $\frac{4}{10} \cdot \frac{5}{10}$ **22.** $\frac{7}{10} \cdot \frac{34}{150}$ **23.** $\frac{8}{10} \cdot \frac{45}{100}$ **24.** $\frac{3}{10} \cdot \frac{8}{10}$

25. $\frac{11}{24} \cdot \frac{3}{5}$ **26.** $\frac{15}{22} \cdot \frac{4}{7}$ **27.** $\frac{10}{21} \cdot \frac{3}{4}$ **28.** $\frac{17}{18} \cdot \frac{3}{5}$

b Find the reciprocal.

29. $\frac{5}{6}$ **30.** $\frac{3}{8}$ **31.** 6   **32.** 2

33. $\frac{1}{6}$ **34.** $\frac{1}{4}$ **35.** $\frac{10}{3}$ **36.** $\frac{12}{5}$

ANSWERS

1. _____
2. _____
3. _____
4. _____
5. _____
6. _____
7. _____
8. _____
9. _____
10. _____
11. _____
12. _____
13. _____
14. _____
15. _____
16. _____
17. _____
18. _____
19. _____
20. _____
21. _____
22. _____
23. _____
24. _____
25. _____
26. _____
27. _____
28. _____
29. _____
30. _____
31. _____
32. _____
33. _____
34. _____
35. _____
36. _____

Copyright © 1993 Addison-Wesley Publishing Co., Inc.

ANSWERS

37. _____

38. _____

39. _____

40. _____

41. _____

42. _____

43. _____

44. _____

45. _____

46. _____

47. _____

48. _____

49. _____

50. _____

51. _____

52. _____

53. _____

54. _____

55. _____

56. _____

57. _____

58. _____

59. _____

60. _____

61. _____

62. _____

63. _____

64. _____

65. _____

66. _____

67. _____

68. _____

69. _____

70. _____

71. _____

72. _____

c Divide and simplify. | Don't forget to simplify! |

37. $\frac{3}{5} \div \frac{3}{4}$ **38.** $\frac{2}{3} \div \frac{3}{4}$ **39.** $\frac{3}{5} \div \frac{9}{4}$ **40.** $\frac{6}{7} \div \frac{3}{5}$

41. $\frac{4}{3} \div \frac{1}{3}$ **42.** $\frac{10}{9} \div \frac{1}{2}$ **43.** $\frac{1}{3} \div \frac{1}{6}$ **44.** $\frac{1}{4} \div \frac{1}{5}$

45. $\frac{3}{8} \div 3$ **46.** $\frac{5}{6} \div 5$ **47.** $\frac{12}{7} \div 4$ **48.** $\frac{16}{5} \div 2$

49. $12 \div \frac{3}{2}$ **50.** $24 \div \frac{3}{8}$ **51.** $28 \div \frac{4}{5}$ **52.** $40 \div \frac{2}{3}$

53. $\frac{5}{8} \div \frac{5}{8}$ **54.** $\frac{2}{5} \div \frac{2}{5}$ **55.** $\frac{8}{15} \div \frac{4}{5}$ **56.** $\frac{6}{13} \div \frac{3}{26}$

57. $\frac{9}{5} \div \frac{4}{5}$ **58.** $\frac{5}{12} \div \frac{25}{36}$ **59.** $120 \div \frac{5}{6}$ **60.** $360 \div \frac{8}{7}$

d Solve.

61. $\frac{4}{5} \cdot x = 60$ **62.** $\frac{3}{2} \cdot t = 90$ **63.** $\frac{5}{3} \cdot y = \frac{10}{3}$ **64.** $\frac{4}{9} \cdot m = \frac{8}{3}$

65. $x \cdot \frac{25}{36} = \frac{5}{12}$ **66.** $p \cdot \frac{4}{5} = \frac{8}{15}$ **67.** $n \cdot \frac{8}{7} = 360$ **68.** $y \cdot \frac{5}{6} = 120$

SKILL MAINTENANCE

Solve.

69. $48 \cdot t = 1680$ **70.** $456 + x = 9002$

Subtract.

71. $\begin{array}{r} 9\ 0\ 6\ 0 \\ -\ 4\ 3\ 8\ 7 \end{array}$ **72.** $\begin{array}{r} 7\ 8\ 0\ 0 \\ -\ 2\ 4\ 6\ 2 \end{array}$

2.3 Addition and Subtraction; Order

a Like Denominators

Addition using fractional notation still corresponds to combining or putting like things together, even though we may not be adding whole numbers.

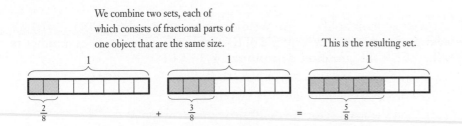

We combine two sets, each of which consists of fractional parts of one object that are the same size.

This is the resulting set.

$$\frac{2}{8} + \frac{3}{8} = \frac{5}{8}$$

2 eighths + 3 eighths = 5 eighths,

or

$$2 \cdot \frac{1}{8} + 3 \cdot \frac{1}{8} = 5 \cdot \frac{1}{8},$$

or

$$\frac{2}{8} + \frac{3}{8} = \frac{5}{8}.$$

DO EXERCISE 1.

> **To add when denominators are the same,**
> a) add the numerators,
> b) keep the denominator, and
> c) simplify, if possible.
>
> $$\frac{2}{6} + \frac{5}{6} = \frac{2+5}{6} = \frac{7}{6}$$

▶ **EXAMPLES** Add and simplify.

1. $\frac{2}{4} + \frac{1}{4} = \frac{2+1}{4} = \frac{3}{4}$ No simplifying is possible.

2. $\frac{11}{6} + \frac{3}{6} = \frac{11+3}{6} = \frac{14}{6} = \frac{2 \cdot 7}{2 \cdot 3} = \frac{2}{2} \cdot \frac{7}{3} = 1 \cdot \frac{7}{3} = \frac{7}{3}$ Here we simplified.

3. $\frac{3}{12} + \frac{5}{12} = \frac{3+5}{12} = \frac{8}{12} = \frac{4 \cdot 2}{4 \cdot 3} = \frac{4}{4} \cdot \frac{2}{3} = 1 \cdot \frac{2}{3} = \frac{2}{3}$ ◀

DO EXERCISES 2–4.

b Addition Using the LCD: Different Denominators

What do we do when denominators are different? We try to find a common denominator. We can do this by multiplying by 1. Consider adding $\frac{1}{6}$ and $\frac{3}{4}$. There are several common denominators that can be obtained. Let's look at two possibilities.

OBJECTIVES

After finishing Section 2.3, you should be able to:

a Add with fractional notation when denominators are the same.

b Add with fractional notation when denominators are different, by multiplying by 1 to find the least common denominator.

c Subtract using fractional notation.

d Use < or > to write a true sentence.

e Solve equations of the type $a + x = b$ and $x + a = b$, where a and b may be fractions.

FOR EXTRA HELP

Tape 4B, 4C

1. Find $\frac{1}{5} + \frac{3}{5}$.

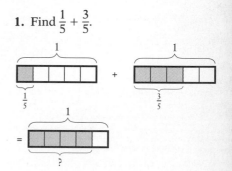

Add and simplify.

2. $\frac{1}{3} + \frac{2}{3}$

3. $\frac{5}{12} + \frac{1}{12}$

4. $\frac{9}{16} + \frac{3}{16}$

ANSWERS ON PAGE A-2

5. Add. Find the least common denominator.

$$\frac{2}{3} + \frac{1}{6}$$

A. $\frac{1}{6} + \frac{3}{4} = \frac{1}{6} \cdot 1 + \frac{3}{4} \cdot 1$

$= \frac{1}{6} \cdot \frac{4}{4} + \frac{3}{4} \cdot \frac{6}{6}$

$= \frac{4}{24} + \frac{18}{24}$

$= \frac{22}{24}$

$= \frac{11}{12}$

B. $\frac{1}{6} + \frac{3}{4} = \frac{1}{6} \cdot 1 + \frac{3}{4} \cdot 1$

$= \frac{1}{6} \cdot \frac{2}{2} + \frac{3}{4} \cdot \frac{3}{3}$

$= \frac{2}{12} + \frac{9}{12}$

$= \frac{11}{12}$

We had to simplify in (A). We didn't have to simplify in (B). In (B) we used the least common multiple of the denominators, 12. That number is called the **least common denominator,** or LCD.

> **To add when denominators are different:**
>
> a) **Find the least common multiple of the denominators. That number is the least common denominator, LCD.**
>
> b) **Multiply by 1, using an appropriate notation, *n/n*, to obtain the LCD for each number.**
>
> c) **Add and simplify, if appropriate.**

▶ **EXAMPLE 4**   Add: $\frac{3}{4} + \frac{1}{8}$.

The LCD is 8.   4 is a factor of 8 so the LCM of 4 and 8 is 8.

$\frac{3}{4} + \frac{1}{8} = \frac{3}{4} \cdot 1 + \frac{1}{8}$ ← **This fraction already has the LCD as its denominator.**

$= \frac{3}{4} \cdot \frac{2}{2} + \frac{1}{8}$ — *Think*: $4 \times \blacksquare = 8$. The answer is 2, so we multiply by 1, using $\frac{2}{2}$.

$= \frac{6}{8} + \frac{1}{8}$

$= \frac{7}{8}$ ◀

DO EXERCISE 5.

6. Add: $\frac{3}{8} + \frac{5}{6}$.

▶ **EXAMPLE 5**   Add: $\frac{1}{9} + \frac{5}{6}$.

The LCD is 18. $9 = 3 \cdot 3$ and $6 = 2 \cdot 3$, so the LCM of 9 and 6 is $2 \cdot 3 \cdot 3$, or 18.

$\frac{1}{9} + \frac{5}{6} = \frac{1}{9} \cdot 1 + \frac{5}{6} \cdot 1 = \frac{1}{9} \cdot \frac{2}{2} + \frac{5}{6} \cdot \frac{3}{3}$ — *Think:* $6 \times \blacksquare = 18$. The answer is 3, so we multiply by 1 using $\frac{3}{3}$.

— *Think:* $9 \times \blacksquare = 18$. The answer is 2, so we multiply by 1, using $\frac{2}{2}$.

$= \frac{2}{18} + \frac{15}{18}$

$= \frac{17}{18}$ ◀

DO EXERCISE 6.

▶ **EXAMPLE 6** Add: $\frac{5}{9} + \frac{11}{18}$.

The LCD is 18.

$$\frac{5}{9} + \frac{11}{18} = \frac{5}{9} \cdot \frac{2}{2} + \frac{11}{18}$$

$$= \frac{10}{18} + \frac{11}{18}$$

$$= \frac{21}{18}$$

$$= \frac{7}{6}$$

> We may still have to simplify, but it is usually easier if we have used the LCD.

◀

DO EXERCISE 7.

▶ **EXAMPLE 7** Add: $\frac{1}{10} + \frac{3}{100} + \frac{7}{1000}$.

Since 10 and 100 are factors of 1000, the LCD is 1000. Then

$$\frac{1}{10} + \frac{3}{100} + \frac{7}{1000} = \frac{1}{10} \cdot \frac{100}{100} + \frac{3}{100} \cdot \frac{10}{10} + \frac{7}{1000}$$

$$= \frac{100}{1000} + \frac{30}{1000} + \frac{7}{1000}$$

$$= \frac{137}{1000}.$$

Look back over this example. Try to think it out so that you can do it mentally. ◀

▶ **EXAMPLE 8** Add: $\frac{13}{70} + \frac{11}{21} + \frac{6}{15}$.

We have

$$\frac{13}{70} + \frac{11}{21} + \frac{6}{15} = \frac{13}{2 \cdot 5 \cdot 7} + \frac{11}{3 \cdot 7} + \frac{6}{3 \cdot 5}. \quad \text{Factoring denominators}$$

The LCD is $2 \cdot 3 \cdot 5 \cdot 7$, or 210. Then

$$\frac{13}{70} + \frac{11}{21} + \frac{6}{15} = \frac{13}{2 \cdot 5 \cdot 7} \cdot \frac{3}{3} + \frac{11}{3 \cdot 7} \cdot \frac{2 \cdot 5}{2 \cdot 5} + \frac{6}{3 \cdot 5} \cdot \frac{7 \cdot 2}{7 \cdot 2}$$

$$= \frac{13 \cdot 3}{2 \cdot 5 \cdot 7 \cdot 3} + \frac{11 \cdot 2 \cdot 5}{3 \cdot 7 \cdot 2 \cdot 5} + \frac{6 \cdot 7 \cdot 2}{3 \cdot 5 \cdot 7 \cdot 2}$$

$$= \frac{39}{3 \cdot 5 \cdot 7 \cdot 2} + \frac{110}{3 \cdot 5 \cdot 7 \cdot 2} + \frac{84}{3 \cdot 5 \cdot 7 \cdot 2}$$

$$= \frac{233}{3 \cdot 5 \cdot 7 \cdot 2}$$

$$= \frac{233}{210} \quad \text{We left 210 factored until we knew we could not simplify.}$$

In each case, we multiply by 1 to obtain the LCD. In other words, look at the prime factorization of the LCD. Multiply each number by 1 to obtain what is missing in the LCD. ◀

DO EXERCISES 8–10.

7. Add: $\frac{1}{6} + \frac{7}{18}$.

Add.

8. $\frac{4}{10} + \frac{1}{100} + \frac{3}{1000}$

9. $\frac{7}{10} + \frac{5}{100} + \frac{9}{1000}$
(Try to do this one mentally.)

10. $\frac{7}{10} + \frac{2}{21} + \frac{1}{7}$

Subtract and simplify.

11. $\dfrac{7}{8} - \dfrac{3}{8}$

C | **Subtraction**

Like Denominators

The difference $\dfrac{4}{8} - \dfrac{3}{8}$ can be considered as it was before, either "take away" or "how much more." Let us consider "take away."

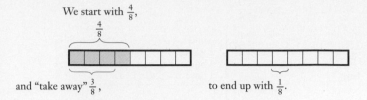

We start with $\dfrac{4}{8}$,

and "take away" $\dfrac{3}{8}$,   to end up with $\dfrac{1}{8}$.

We start with 4 eighths, and take away 3 eighths:

$$4\text{ eighths} - 3\text{ eighths} = 1\text{ eighth},$$

or

$$4 \cdot \dfrac{1}{8} - 3 \cdot \dfrac{1}{8} = \dfrac{1}{8},$$

or

$$\dfrac{4}{8} - \dfrac{3}{8} = \dfrac{1}{8}.$$

12. $\dfrac{10}{16} - \dfrac{4}{16}$

To subtract when denominators are the same,

a) subtract the numerators,

b) keep the denominator, and

c) simplify, if possible.

$$\dfrac{7}{10} - \dfrac{4}{10} = \dfrac{7 - 4}{10} = \dfrac{3}{10}$$

Answers should be simplified, if possible.

▶ **EXAMPLES** Subtract and simplify.

9. $\dfrac{7}{10} - \dfrac{3}{10} = \dfrac{7-3}{10} = \dfrac{4}{10} = \dfrac{2 \cdot 2}{5 \cdot 2} = \dfrac{2}{5} \cdot \dfrac{2}{2} = \dfrac{2}{5} \cdot 1 = \dfrac{2}{5}$

13. $\dfrac{8}{10} - \dfrac{3}{10}$

10. $\dfrac{8}{9} - \dfrac{2}{9} = \dfrac{8-2}{9} = \dfrac{6}{9} = \dfrac{2 \cdot 3}{3 \cdot 3} = \dfrac{2}{3} \cdot \dfrac{3}{3} = \dfrac{2}{3} \cdot 1 = \dfrac{2}{3}$

11. $\dfrac{32}{12} - \dfrac{25}{12} = \dfrac{32-25}{12} = \dfrac{7}{12}$ ◀

DO EXERCISES 11–13.

Different Denominators

To subtract when denominators are different:

a) **Find the least common multiple of the denominators. That number is the least common denominator, LCD.**

b) **Multiply by 1, using an appropriate notation, *n/n*, to obtain the LCD for each number.**

c) **Subtract and simplify, if appropriate.**

▶ **EXAMPLE 12**   Subtract: $\frac{2}{5} - \frac{3}{8}$.

The LCM of 5 and 8 is 40. The LCD is 40.

$$\frac{2}{5} - \frac{3}{8} = \frac{2}{5} \cdot \frac{8}{8} - \frac{3}{8} \cdot \frac{5}{5}$$ ⟵ *Think:* 8 × ▨ = 40. The answer is 5, so we multiply by 1, using $\frac{5}{5}$.

⬑ *Think:* 5 × ▨ = 40. The answer is 8, so we multiply by 1, using $\frac{8}{8}$.

$$= \frac{16}{40} - \frac{15}{40}$$

$$= \frac{16 - 15}{40} = \frac{1}{40}$$ ◀

DO EXERCISE 14.

▶ **EXAMPLE 13**   Subtract: $\frac{5}{6} - \frac{7}{12}$.

Since 6 is a factor of 12, the LCM of 6 and 12 is 12. The LCD is 12.

$$\frac{5}{6} - \frac{7}{12} = \frac{5}{6} \cdot \frac{2}{2} - \frac{7}{12}$$

$$= \frac{10}{12} - \frac{7}{12} = \frac{10 - 7}{12} = \frac{3}{12}$$

$$= \frac{3 \cdot 1}{3 \cdot 4} = \frac{3}{3} \cdot \frac{1}{4} = \frac{1}{4}$$ ◀

DO EXERCISES 15 AND 16.

d   Order

We see that $\frac{4}{5} > \frac{3}{5}$. That is, $\frac{4}{5}$ is greater than $\frac{3}{5}$.

$\frac{4}{5}$ ▭▭▭▭▭

$\frac{3}{5}$ ▭▭▭▭▭

To determine which of two numbers is greater when there is a common denominator, compare the numerators:

$$\frac{4}{5}, \frac{3}{5} \qquad 4 > 3 \qquad \frac{4}{5} > \frac{3}{5}.$$

DO EXERCISES 17 AND 18.

14. Subtract: $\frac{3}{4} - \frac{2}{3}$.

Subtract.

15. $\frac{5}{6} - \frac{1}{9}$

16. $\frac{4}{5} - \frac{3}{10}$

17. Use $<$ or $>$ for ▨ to write a true sentence.

$$\frac{3}{8} \ \blacksquare \ \frac{5}{8}$$

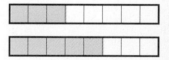

18. Use $<$ or $>$ for ▨ to write a true sentence.

$$\frac{7}{10} \ \blacksquare \ \frac{6}{10}$$

Use < or > for ■ to write a true sentence.

19. $\frac{2}{3}$ ■ $\frac{5}{8}$

20. $\frac{3}{4}$ ■ $\frac{8}{12}$

21. $\frac{5}{6}$ ■ $\frac{7}{8}$

Solve.

22. $x + \frac{2}{3} = \frac{5}{6}$

23. $\frac{3}{5} + t = \frac{7}{8}$

When denominators are different, we multiply by 1 to make the denominators the same.

▶ **EXAMPLE 14**   Use < or > for ■ to write a true sentence.

$$\frac{2}{5} \ ■ \ \frac{3}{4}$$

We have

$$\frac{2}{5} \cdot \frac{4}{4} = \frac{8}{20};$$ **We choose $\frac{4}{4}$ by looking at the denominator of $\frac{3}{4}$.**

$$\frac{3}{4} \cdot \frac{5}{5} = \frac{15}{20}.$$ **We choose $\frac{5}{5}$ by looking at the denominator of $\frac{2}{5}$.**

Since $8 < 15$, it follows that $\frac{8}{20} < \frac{15}{20}$, so

$$\frac{2}{5} < \frac{3}{4}.$$ ◀

▶ **EXAMPLE 15**   Use < or > for ■ to write a true sentence.

$$\frac{9}{10} \ ■ \ \frac{89}{100}$$

The LCD is 100.

$$\frac{9}{10} \cdot \frac{10}{10} = \frac{90}{100}$$ **We multiply by $\frac{10}{10}$ to get the LCD.**

Since $90 > 89$, it follows that $\frac{90}{100} > \frac{89}{100}$, so

$$\frac{9}{10} > \frac{89}{100}.$$ ◀

DO EXERCISES 19–21.

e   Solving Equations

Now let us solve equations of the form $x + a = b$ or $a + x = b$, where a and b may be fractions. Proceeding as we have before, we subtract a on both sides of the equation.

▶ **EXAMPLE 16**   Solve: $x + \frac{1}{4} = \frac{3}{5}$.

$$x + \frac{1}{4} = \frac{3}{5}$$

$$x + \frac{1}{4} - \frac{1}{4} = \frac{3}{5} - \frac{1}{4}$$ **Subtracting $\frac{1}{4}$ on both sides**

$$x + 0 = \frac{3}{5} \cdot \frac{4}{4} - \frac{1}{4} \cdot \frac{5}{5}$$ **The LCD is 20. We multiply by 1 to get the LCD.**

$$x = \frac{12}{20} - \frac{5}{20} = \frac{7}{20}$$

The solution is $\frac{7}{20}$.   ◀

DO EXERCISES 22 AND 23.

NAME   SECTION   DATE

EXERCISE SET 2.3

a , **b** Add and simplify.

1. $\dfrac{2}{3}+\dfrac{5}{6}$ **2.** $\dfrac{1}{4}+\dfrac{5}{6}$ **3.** $\dfrac{1}{8}+\dfrac{1}{6}$ **4.** $\dfrac{4}{5}+\dfrac{7}{10}$

5. $\dfrac{3}{20}+\dfrac{3}{4}$ **6.** $\dfrac{2}{15}+\dfrac{2}{5}$ **7.** $\dfrac{5}{6}+\dfrac{7}{9}$ **8.** $\dfrac{5}{8}+\dfrac{5}{6}$

9. $\dfrac{3}{10}+\dfrac{1}{100}$ **10.** $\dfrac{9}{10}+\dfrac{3}{100}$ **11.** $\dfrac{5}{12}+\dfrac{4}{15}$ **12.** $\dfrac{3}{16}+\dfrac{1}{12}$

13. $\dfrac{9}{10}+\dfrac{99}{100}$ **14.** $\dfrac{3}{10}+\dfrac{27}{100}$ **15.** $\dfrac{7}{8}+\dfrac{0}{1}$ **16.** $\dfrac{0}{1}+\dfrac{5}{6}$

17. $\dfrac{3}{8}+\dfrac{1}{6}$ **18.** $\dfrac{7}{8}+\dfrac{1}{6}$ **19.** $\dfrac{5}{12}+\dfrac{7}{24}$ **20.** $\dfrac{1}{18}+\dfrac{7}{12}$

21. $\dfrac{8}{10}+\dfrac{7}{100}+\dfrac{4}{1000}$ **22.** $\dfrac{1}{10}+\dfrac{2}{100}+\dfrac{3}{1000}$ **23.** $\dfrac{3}{8}+\dfrac{5}{12}+\dfrac{8}{15}$

24. $\dfrac{1}{2}+\dfrac{3}{8}+\dfrac{1}{4}$ **25.** $\dfrac{15}{24}+\dfrac{7}{36}+\dfrac{91}{48}$ **26.** $\dfrac{5}{7}+\dfrac{25}{52}+\dfrac{7}{4}$

c Subtract and simplify.

27. $\dfrac{5}{6}-\dfrac{1}{6}$ **28.** $\dfrac{11}{12}-\dfrac{2}{12}$ **29.** $\dfrac{2}{3}-\dfrac{1}{9}$ **30.** $\dfrac{1}{8}-\dfrac{1}{12}$

1. _____
2. _____
3. _____
4. _____
5. _____
6. _____
7. _____
8. _____
9. _____
10. _____
11. _____
12. _____
13. _____
14. _____
15. _____
16. _____
17. _____
18. _____
19. _____
20. _____
21. _____
22. _____
23. _____
24. _____
25. _____
26. _____
27. _____
28. _____
29. _____
30. _____

Copyright © 1993 Addison-Wesley Publishing Co., Inc.

ANSWERS

31. _____
32. _____
33. _____
34. _____
35. _____
36. _____
37. _____
38. _____
39. _____
40. _____
41. _____
42. _____
43. _____
44. _____
45. _____
46. _____
47. _____
48. _____
49. _____
50. _____
51. _____
52. _____
53. _____
54. _____
55. _____
56. _____
57. _____
58. _____
59. _____
60. _____
61. _____
62. _____
63. _____
64. _____

31. $\frac{4}{3} - \frac{5}{6}$ **32.** $\frac{7}{8} - \frac{1}{16}$ **33.** $\frac{3}{4} - \frac{3}{28}$ **34.** $\frac{2}{5} - \frac{2}{15}$

35. $\frac{5}{12} - \frac{2}{15}$ **36.** $\frac{9}{10} - \frac{11}{16}$ **37.** $\frac{6}{10} - \frac{7}{100}$ **38.** $\frac{9}{10} - \frac{3}{100}$

39. $\frac{7}{15} - \frac{3}{25}$ **40.** $\frac{18}{25} - \frac{4}{35}$ **41.** $\frac{99}{100} - \frac{9}{10}$ **42.** $\frac{78}{100} - \frac{11}{20}$

d Use < or > for ■ to write a true sentence.

43. $\frac{5}{8}$ ■ $\frac{6}{8}$ **44.** $\frac{7}{9}$ ■ $\frac{5}{9}$ **45.** $\frac{1}{3}$ ■ $\frac{1}{4}$ **46.** $\frac{1}{8}$ ■ $\frac{1}{6}$

47. $\frac{2}{3}$ ■ $\frac{5}{7}$ **48.** $\frac{3}{5}$ ■ $\frac{4}{7}$ **49.** $\frac{4}{5}$ ■ $\frac{5}{6}$ **50.** $\frac{3}{2}$ ■ $\frac{7}{5}$

51. $\frac{19}{20}$ ■ $\frac{4}{5}$ **52.** $\frac{5}{6}$ ■ $\frac{13}{16}$ **53.** $\frac{19}{20}$ ■ $\frac{9}{10}$ **54.** $\frac{3}{4}$ ■ $\frac{11}{15}$

e Solve.

55. $x + \frac{1}{30} = \frac{1}{10}$ **56.** $y + \frac{9}{12} = \frac{11}{12}$ **57.** $\frac{2}{3} + t = \frac{4}{5}$

58. $\frac{2}{3} + p = \frac{7}{8}$ **59.** $m + \frac{5}{6} = \frac{9}{10}$ **60.** $x + \frac{1}{3} = \frac{5}{6}$

SKILL MAINTENANCE

61. Divide: $3\,5\overline{)7\,1\,4\,0}$ **62.** What does the digit 6 mean in 4,678,952?

Solve.

63. A playing field is 78 ft long and 64 ft wide. What is its area?   **64.** A landscaper buys 13 maple trees and 17 oak trees for a project. A maple costs $23 and an oak costs $37. How much is spent for all the trees?

2.4 Mixed Numerals

a What Is a Mixed Numeral?

A symbol like $2\frac{3}{4}$ is called a **mixed numeral**.

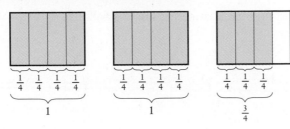

$$2\frac{3}{4} \quad \text{means} \quad 2 + \frac{3}{4}$$

This is a whole number.   This is a number less than 1.

▶ **EXAMPLES**   Convert to a mixed numeral.

1. $7 + \frac{2}{5} = 7\frac{2}{5}$

2. $4 + \frac{3}{10} = 4\frac{3}{10}$ ◀

DO EXERCISES 1–3.

The notation $2\frac{3}{4}$ has a plus sign left out. To aid in understanding, we sometimes write the missing plus sign.

▶ **EXAMPLES**   Convert to fractional notation.

3. $2\frac{3}{4} = 2 + \frac{3}{4}$ **Inserting the missing plus sign**

$= \frac{2}{1} + \frac{3}{4}$ $2 = \frac{2}{1}$

$= \frac{2}{1} \cdot \frac{4}{4} + \frac{3}{4}$ **Finding a common denominator**

$= \frac{8}{4} + \frac{3}{4}$

$= \frac{11}{4}$

4. $4\frac{3}{10} = 4 + \frac{3}{10} = \frac{4}{1} + \frac{3}{10} = \frac{4}{1} \cdot \frac{10}{10} + \frac{3}{10} = \frac{40}{10} + \frac{3}{10} = \frac{43}{10}$ ◀

DO EXERCISES 4 AND 5.

> **To convert from a mixed numeral to fractional notation:**
> ① **Multiply:** $4 \cdot 10 = 40.$
> ② **Add:** $40 + 3 = 43.$
> ③ **Keep the denominator.**
>
>
> $4\frac{3}{10} = \frac{43}{10}$

OBJECTIVES

After finishing Section 2.4, you should be able to:

a Convert from mixed numerals to fractional notation, and vice versa.

b Add using mixed numerals.

c Subtract using mixed numerals.

d Multiply using mixed numerals.

e Divide using mixed numerals.

FOR EXTRA HELP

Tape 5A, 5B, 5C

1. $1 + \frac{2}{3} = \boxed{}$ — Convert to a mixed numeral.

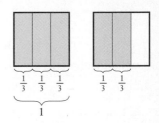

Convert to a mixed numeral.

2. $8 + \frac{3}{4}$

3. $12 + \frac{2}{3}$

Convert to fractional notation.

4. $4\frac{2}{5}$

5. $6\frac{1}{10}$

ANSWERS ON PAGE A-2

Convert to fractional notation. Use the faster way.

6. $4\frac{5}{6}$

7. $9\frac{1}{4}$

8. $20\frac{2}{3}$

Convert to a mixed numeral.

9. $\frac{7}{3}$

10. $\frac{11}{10}$

11. $\frac{110}{6}$

▶ **EXAMPLES**   Convert to fractional notation.

5. $6\frac{2}{3} = \frac{20}{3}$ **6.** $8\frac{2}{9} = \frac{74}{9}$ **7.** $10\frac{7}{8} = \frac{87}{8}$ ◀

DO EXERCISES 6–8.

We can find a mixed numeral for $\frac{5}{3}$ as follows:

$$\frac{5}{3} = \frac{3}{3} + \frac{2}{3} = 1 + \frac{2}{3} = 1\frac{2}{3}.$$

Fractional symbols like $\frac{5}{3}$ also indicate division. Let's divide.

$$3\overline{)5} \quad 1\frac{2}{3}$$
$$\underline{3}$$
$$2 \longleftarrow 3\overline{)2} \text{ or } 2 \div 3 = \frac{2}{3}$$

Thus, $\frac{5}{3} = 1\frac{2}{3}$.

In terms of objects, we can think of $\frac{5}{3}$ as 5 objects, each divided into 3 equal parts, as shown below.

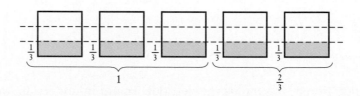

To convert from fractional notation to a mixed numeral, divide.

$$\frac{13}{5} \qquad 5\overline{)13} \quad \begin{array}{l} 2 \text{ ——— The quotient} \\ \underline{10} \\ 3 \text{ ——— The remainder} \end{array} \qquad 2\frac{3}{5}$$

▶ **EXAMPLES**   Convert to a mixed numeral.

8. $\frac{8}{5}$ $5\overline{)8}$ $\begin{array}{l} 1 \\ \underline{5} \\ 3 \end{array}$ $\frac{8}{5} = 1\frac{3}{5}$

> A fraction larger than 1, such as $\frac{8}{5}$, is sometimes referred to as an "improper" fraction. We have intentionally avoided such terminology. The use of such notation, simplified, as $\frac{8}{5}$, $\frac{69}{10}$, and so on, is quite proper and very common in algebra.

9. $\frac{69}{10}$ $10\overline{)69}$ $\begin{array}{l} 6 \\ \underline{60} \\ 9 \end{array}$ $\frac{69}{10} = 6\frac{9}{10}$

10. $\frac{122}{8}$ $8\overline{)122}$ $\begin{array}{l} 15 \\ \underline{8} \\ 42 \\ \underline{40} \\ 2 \end{array}$ $\frac{122}{8} = 15\frac{2}{8} = 15\frac{1}{4}$ ◀

DO EXERCISES 9–11.

b Addition

To find the sum $1\frac{5}{8} + 3\frac{1}{8}$, we add the fractions. Then we add the whole numbers.

$$
\begin{array}{rl}
1 & \dfrac{5}{8} = \\[2mm]
+\,3 & \dfrac{1}{8} = \\[2mm]
\hline
& \dfrac{6}{8}
\end{array}
\qquad\qquad
\begin{array}{rl}
1 & \dfrac{5}{8} \\[2mm]
+\,3 & \dfrac{1}{8} \\[2mm]
\hline
4 & \dfrac{6}{8} = 4\dfrac{3}{4}
\end{array}
$$

Add the fractions.   Add the whole numbers.

DO EXERCISE 12.

▶ **EXAMPLE 11** Add: $5\frac{2}{3} + 3\frac{5}{6}$. Write a mixed numeral for the answer.
The LCD is 6.

$$
\begin{array}{rl}
5 & \dfrac{2}{3}\cdot\dfrac{2}{2} = \quad 5\dfrac{4}{6} \\[2mm]
+\,3 & \dfrac{5}{6} = +3\dfrac{5}{6} \\[2mm]
\hline
& 8\dfrac{9}{6} = 8 + \dfrac{9}{6} \\[3mm]
& \qquad\;\; = 8 + 1\dfrac{1}{2} \\[3mm]
& \qquad\;\; = 9\dfrac{1}{2}
\end{array}
$$

To find a mixed numeral for $\frac{9}{6}$, we divide:

$$
\begin{array}{r}
1 \\
6\overline{)9} \\
6 \\
\hline
3
\end{array}
\qquad \frac{9}{6} = 1\frac{3}{6} = 1\frac{1}{2}
$$

$\frac{19}{2}$ is also a correct answer, but it is not a mixed numeral, which is what we are working with in Section 2.4. ◀

DO EXERCISE 13.

▶ **EXAMPLE 12** Add: $10\frac{5}{6} + 7\frac{3}{8}$.
The LCD is 24.

$$
\begin{array}{rl}
10 & \dfrac{5}{6}\cdot\dfrac{4}{4} = \quad 10\dfrac{20}{24} \\[2mm]
+\,7 & \dfrac{3}{8}\cdot\dfrac{3}{3} = +7\dfrac{9}{24} \\[2mm]
\hline
& 17\dfrac{29}{24} = 18\dfrac{5}{24}
\end{array}
$$
◀

DO EXERCISE 14.

12. Add.

$$
\begin{array}{r}
2\dfrac{3}{10} \\[2mm]
+\,5\dfrac{1}{10} \\[2mm]
\hline
\end{array}
$$

13. Add.

$$
\begin{array}{r}
8\dfrac{2}{5} \\[2mm]
+\,3\dfrac{7}{10} \\[2mm]
\hline
\end{array}
$$

14. Add.

$$
\begin{array}{r}
9\dfrac{3}{4} \\[2mm]
+\,3\dfrac{5}{6} \\[2mm]
\hline
\end{array}
$$

ANSWERS ON PAGE A-2

15. Subtract.

$$10\frac{7}{8}$$
$$-\ 9\frac{3}{8}$$

C   Subtraction

▶ **EXAMPLE 13**   Subtract: $7\frac{3}{4} - 2\frac{1}{4}$.

$$
\begin{array}{r}
7\ \dfrac{3}{4} = \\[4pt]
-\ 2\ \dfrac{1}{4} = \\[4pt]
\hline
\dfrac{2}{4}
\end{array}
\qquad
\begin{array}{r}
7\ \dfrac{3}{4} \\[4pt]
-\ 2\ \dfrac{1}{4} \\[4pt]
\hline
5\ \dfrac{2}{4} = 5\dfrac{1}{2}
\end{array}
$$

Subtract the fractions.   Subtract the whole numbers. ◀

DO EXERCISE 15.

▶ **EXAMPLE 14**   Subtract: $9\frac{4}{5} - 3\frac{1}{2}$.
The LCD is 10.

$$
\begin{array}{r}
9\ \dfrac{4}{5}\cdot\dfrac{2}{2} = \\[6pt]
-\ 3\ \dfrac{1}{2}\cdot\dfrac{5}{5} = \\[6pt]
\hline
\end{array}
\qquad
\begin{array}{r}
9\dfrac{8}{10} \\[6pt]
-\ 3\dfrac{5}{10} \\[6pt]
\hline
6\dfrac{3}{10}
\end{array}
$$

DO EXERCISE 16.

16. Subtract.

$$8\frac{2}{3}$$
$$-5\frac{1}{2}$$

▶ **EXAMPLE 15**   Subtract: $7\frac{1}{6} - 2\frac{1}{4}$.
The LCD is 12.

$$
\left.
\begin{array}{r}
7\ \dfrac{1}{6}\cdot\dfrac{2}{2} = \quad 7\dfrac{2}{12} \\[6pt]
-\ 2\ \dfrac{1}{4}\cdot\dfrac{3}{3} = -2\dfrac{3}{12}
\end{array}
\right\}
$$

We cannot subtract $\frac{3}{12}$ from $\frac{2}{12}$. We borrow 1, or $\frac{12}{12}$, from 7:
$7\frac{2}{12} = 6 + 1 + \frac{2}{12} = 6 + \frac{12}{12} + \frac{2}{12} = 6\frac{14}{12}$.

We can write this as

$$
\begin{array}{r}
7\dfrac{2}{12} = \quad 6\dfrac{14}{12} \\[6pt]
-\ 2\dfrac{3}{12} = -\ 2\dfrac{3}{12} \\[6pt]
\hline
4\dfrac{11}{12}
\end{array}
$$
◀

DO EXERCISE 17.

17. Subtract.

$$5\frac{1}{12}$$
$$-1\frac{3}{4}$$

▶ **EXAMPLE 16**   Subtract: $12 - 9\frac{3}{8}$.

$$
\begin{array}{r}
12 = \quad 11\dfrac{8}{8} \\[6pt]
-\ 9\dfrac{3}{8} = -\ 9\dfrac{3}{8} \\[6pt]
\hline
2\dfrac{5}{8}
\end{array}
$$

$\longleftarrow\ 12 = 11 + 1 = 11 + \frac{8}{8} = 11\frac{8}{8}$

◀

18. Subtract.

$$5$$
$$-1\frac{1}{3}$$

DO EXERCISE 18.

d Multiplication

To carry out addition and subtraction with mixed numerals, it is easiest to leave them as mixed numerals. With multiplication and division, however, it is easiest to convert them first to fractional notation.

> **To multiply using mixed numerals, first convert to fractional notation. Then multiply with fractional notation and convert the answer back to a mixed numeral, if appropriate.**

▶ **EXAMPLE 17** Multiply: $6 \cdot 2\frac{1}{2}$.

$$6 \cdot 2\frac{1}{2} = \frac{6}{1} \cdot \frac{5}{2} = \frac{6 \cdot 5}{1 \cdot 2} = \frac{2 \cdot 3 \cdot 5}{2 \cdot 1} = \frac{2}{2} \cdot \frac{3 \cdot 5}{1} = 15$$ ◀

Here we write fractional notation.

DO EXERCISE 19.

▶ **EXAMPLE 18** Multiply: $3\frac{1}{2} \cdot \frac{3}{4}$.

$$3\frac{1}{2} \cdot \frac{3}{4} = \frac{7}{2} \cdot \frac{3}{4} = \frac{21}{8} = 2\frac{5}{8}$$

Note here that we need fractional notation to carry out the multiplication.

◀

DO EXERCISE 20.

▶ **EXAMPLE 19** Multiply: $8 \cdot 4\frac{2}{3}$.

$$8 \cdot 4\frac{2}{3} = \frac{8}{1} \cdot \frac{14}{3} = \frac{112}{3} = 37\frac{1}{3}$$ ◀

DO EXERCISE 21.

▶ **EXAMPLE 20** Multiply: $2\frac{1}{4} \cdot 3\frac{2}{5}$.

$$2\frac{1}{4} \cdot 3\frac{2}{5} = \frac{9}{4} \cdot \frac{17}{5} = \frac{153}{20} = 7\frac{13}{20}$$ ◀

> CAUTION! $2\frac{1}{4} \cdot 3\frac{2}{5} \neq 6\frac{2}{20}$. A common error is to just multiply the whole numbers and then the fractions. This does not give the correct answer, $7\frac{13}{20}$, which is found by converting first to fractional notation.

DO EXERCISE 22.

19. Multiply: $6 \cdot 3\frac{1}{3}$.

20. Multiply: $2\frac{1}{2} \cdot \frac{3}{4}$.

21. Multiply: $2 \cdot 6\frac{2}{5}$.

22. Multiply: $3\frac{1}{3} \cdot 2\frac{1}{2}$.

ANSWERS ON PAGE A-2

23. Divide: $84 \div 5\frac{1}{4}$.

24. Divide: $26 \div 3\frac{1}{2}$.

Divide.

25. $2\frac{1}{4} \div 1\frac{1}{5}$

26. $1\frac{3}{4} \div 2\frac{1}{2}$

ANSWERS ON PAGE A-2

e   Division

The division $1\frac{1}{2} \div \frac{1}{6}$ is shown here.

$$1\frac{1}{2} \div \frac{1}{6} = \frac{3}{2} \div \frac{1}{6}$$

$$= \frac{3}{2} \cdot 6 = \frac{3 \cdot 6}{2} = \frac{3 \cdot 3 \cdot 2}{2 \cdot 1} = \frac{3 \cdot 3}{1} \cdot \frac{2}{2} = \frac{3 \cdot 3}{1} \cdot 1 = 9$$

> **To divide using mixed numerals, first write fractional notation. Then divide with fractional notation and convert the answer back to a mixed numeral, if appropriate.**

▶ **EXAMPLE 21**   Divide: $32 \div 3\frac{1}{5}$.

$$32 \div 3\frac{1}{5} = \frac{32}{1} \div \frac{16}{5}$$

$$= \frac{32}{1} \cdot \frac{5}{16} = \frac{32 \cdot 5}{1 \cdot 16} = \frac{2 \cdot 16 \cdot 5}{1 \cdot 16} = \frac{16}{16} \cdot \frac{2 \cdot 5}{1} = 10 \quad ◀$$

Remember to multiply by the reciprocal.

DO EXERCISE 23.

▶ **EXAMPLE 22**   Divide: $35 \div 4\frac{1}{3}$.

$$35 \div 4\frac{1}{3} = \frac{35}{1} \div \frac{13}{3} = \frac{35}{1} \cdot \frac{3}{13} = \frac{105}{13} = 8\frac{1}{13} \quad ◀$$

> CAUTION! The reciprocal of $4\frac{1}{3}$ is *not* $3\frac{1}{4}$!

DO EXERCISE 24.

▶ **EXAMPLE 23**   Divide: $2\frac{1}{3} \div 1\frac{3}{4}$.

$$2\frac{1}{3} \div 1\frac{3}{4} = \frac{7}{3} \div \frac{7}{4} = \frac{7}{3} \cdot \frac{4}{7} = \frac{7 \cdot 4}{7 \cdot 3} = \frac{7}{7} \cdot \frac{4}{3} = 1 \cdot \frac{4}{3} = \frac{4}{3} = 1\frac{1}{3} \quad ◀$$

▶ **EXAMPLE 24**   Divide: $1\frac{3}{5} \div 3\frac{1}{3}$.

$$1\frac{3}{5} \div 3\frac{1}{3} = \frac{8}{5} \div \frac{10}{3} = \frac{8}{5} \cdot \frac{3}{10} = \frac{2 \cdot 4 \cdot 3}{5 \cdot 2 \cdot 5} = \frac{2}{2} \cdot \frac{4 \cdot 3}{5 \cdot 5} = 1 \cdot \frac{4 \cdot 3}{5 \cdot 5} = \frac{12}{25} \quad ◀$$

DO EXERCISES 25 AND 26.

NAME   SECTION   DATE

EXERCISE SET 2.4

a Convert to fractional notation.

1. $6\frac{1}{4}$ **2.** $8\frac{1}{2}$ **3.** $9\frac{5}{6}$ **4.** $8\frac{7}{8}$ **5.** $15\frac{2}{3}$ **6.** $33\frac{1}{3}$

Convert to a mixed numeral.

7. $\frac{14}{3}$ **8.** $\frac{30}{9}$ **9.** $\frac{57}{10}$ **10.** $\frac{50}{8}$ **11.** $\frac{345}{8}$ **12.** $\frac{223}{4}$

b Add. Write mixed numerals for the answers.

13. $\begin{array}{r} 2\frac{7}{8} \\ + 3\frac{5}{8} \\ \hline \end{array}$ **14.** $\begin{array}{r} 4\frac{5}{6} \\ + 3\frac{5}{6} \\ \hline \end{array}$ **15.** $\begin{array}{r} 1\frac{1}{4} \\ + 1\frac{2}{3} \\ \hline \end{array}$ **16.** $\begin{array}{r} 4\frac{1}{3} \\ + 5\frac{2}{9} \\ \hline \end{array}$

17. $\begin{array}{r} 8\frac{3}{4} \\ + 5\frac{5}{6} \\ \hline \end{array}$ **18.** $\begin{array}{r} 4\frac{3}{8} \\ + 6\frac{5}{12} \\ \hline \end{array}$ **19.** $\begin{array}{r} 3\frac{2}{5} \\ + 8\frac{7}{10} \\ \hline \end{array}$ **20.** $\begin{array}{r} 5\frac{1}{2} \\ + 3\frac{7}{10} \\ \hline \end{array}$

21. $\begin{array}{r} 14\frac{5}{8} \\ + 13\frac{1}{4} \\ \hline \end{array}$ **22.** $\begin{array}{r} 16\frac{1}{4} \\ + 15\frac{7}{8} \\ \hline \end{array}$ **23.** $\begin{array}{r} 7\frac{1}{8} \\ 9\frac{2}{3} \\ + 10\frac{3}{4} \\ \hline \end{array}$ **24.** $\begin{array}{r} 45\frac{2}{3} \\ 31\frac{3}{5} \\ + 12\frac{1}{4} \\ \hline \end{array}$

c Subtract. Write mixed numerals for the answers.

25. $\begin{array}{r} 4\frac{1}{5} \\ - 2\frac{3}{5} \\ \hline \end{array}$ **26.** $\begin{array}{r} 5\frac{1}{8} \\ - 2\frac{3}{8} \\ \hline \end{array}$ **27.** $\begin{array}{r} 6\frac{3}{5} \\ - 2\frac{1}{2} \\ \hline \end{array}$ **28.** $\begin{array}{r} 7\frac{2}{3} \\ - 6\frac{1}{2} \\ \hline \end{array}$

ANSWERS

1. _____
2. _____
3. _____
4. _____
5. _____
6. _____
7. _____
8. _____
9. _____
10. _____
11. _____
12. _____
13. _____
14. _____
15. _____
16. _____
17. _____
18. _____
19. _____
20. _____
21. _____
22. _____
23. _____
24. _____
25. _____
26. _____
27. _____
28. _____

29. $\begin{array}{r} 34\frac{1}{3} \\ -\ 12\frac{5}{8} \\ \hline \end{array}$

30. $\begin{array}{r} 23\frac{5}{16} \\ -\ 16\frac{3}{4} \\ \hline \end{array}$

31. $\begin{array}{r} 21 \\ -\ 8\frac{3}{4} \\ \hline \end{array}$

32. $\begin{array}{r} 42 \\ -\ 3\frac{7}{8} \\ \hline \end{array}$

33. $\begin{array}{r} 14\frac{1}{8} \\ -\ \ \frac{3}{4} \\ \hline \end{array}$

34. $\begin{array}{r} 28\frac{1}{6} \\ -\ \ \frac{2}{3} \\ \hline \end{array}$

35. $\begin{array}{r} 25\frac{1}{9} \\ -\ 13\frac{5}{6} \\ \hline \end{array}$

36. $\begin{array}{r} 23\frac{5}{16} \\ -\ 14\frac{7}{12} \\ \hline \end{array}$

d Multiply. Write a mixed numeral for the answer.

37. $8 \cdot 2\frac{5}{6}$

38. $5 \cdot 3\frac{3}{4}$

39. $3\frac{5}{8} \cdot \frac{2}{3}$

40. $6\frac{2}{3} \cdot \frac{1}{4}$

41. $3\frac{1}{2} \cdot 2\frac{1}{3}$

42. $4\frac{1}{5} \cdot 5\frac{1}{4}$

43. $3\frac{2}{5} \cdot 2\frac{7}{8}$

44. $2\frac{3}{10} \cdot 4\frac{2}{5}$

45. $4\frac{7}{10} \cdot 5\frac{3}{10}$

46. $6\frac{3}{10} \cdot 5\frac{7}{10}$

47. $20\frac{1}{2} \cdot 10\frac{1}{5}$

48. $21\frac{1}{3} \cdot 11\frac{1}{3}$

e Divide. Write a mixed numeral for the answer.

49. $20 \div 3\frac{1}{5}$

50. $18 \div 2\frac{1}{4}$

51. $8\frac{2}{5} \div 7$

52. $3\frac{3}{8} \div 3$

53. $4\frac{3}{4} \div 1\frac{1}{3}$

54. $5\frac{4}{5} \div 2\frac{1}{2}$

55. $1\frac{7}{8} \div 1\frac{2}{3}$

56. $4\frac{3}{8} \div 2\frac{5}{6}$

57. $5\frac{1}{10} \div 4\frac{3}{10}$

58. $4\frac{1}{10} \div 2\frac{1}{10}$

59. $20\frac{1}{4} \div 90$

60. $12\frac{1}{2} \div 50$

2.5   Solving Problems

a We solve problems using fractional notation and mixed numerals in the same way as for whole numbers. The five problem-solving tips on page 35 should be reviewed.

Most problems that can be solved by multiplying fractions can be thought of in terms of rectangular arrays.

▶ **EXAMPLE 1**   A farmer owns a square mile of land. He gives $\frac{4}{5}$ of it to his daughter and she gives $\frac{2}{3}$ of her share to her son. How much land goes to the son?

1. *Familiarize.* We draw a picture to help solve the problem. The land may not be square. It could be in a shape like A or B below, or it could even be in more than one piece. But to think out the problem, we can think of it as a square, as shown by shape C.

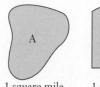

1 square mile   1 square mile   1 square mile

The daughter gets $\frac{4}{5}$ of the land. We shade $\frac{4}{5}$.

Her son gets $\frac{2}{3}$ of her part. We shade that.

2. *Translate.* We let n = the part of the land that goes to the son. We are taking "two-thirds of four-fifths." The word "of" corresponds to multiplication. Thus the following multiplication sentence corresponds to the situation:

$$\frac{2}{3} \cdot \frac{4}{5} = n.$$

3. *Solve.* The number sentence tells us what to do. We multiply:

$$\frac{2}{3} \cdot \frac{4}{5} = \frac{8}{15}.$$

4. *Check.* We can check partially by noting that the answer is smaller than the original area, 1, which we expect since the farmer is giving parts of the land away. Thus, $\frac{8}{15}$ is a reasonable answer.

5. *State.* The son gets $\frac{8}{15}$ of a square mile of land.   ◀

DO EXERCISE 1.

OBJECTIVES

After finishing Section 2.5, you should be able to:

a Solve problems involving addition, subtraction, multiplication, and division using fractional notation and mixed numerals.

FOR EXTRA HELP

Tape 3B, 3D, 3E, 4B,
     4C, 5B, 5C

1. A family uses $\frac{3}{4}$ of its land for a play area. Of that, $\frac{1}{2}$ is used for a swimming pool. What part of the land is used for the swimming pool?

2. The length of a key on a calculator is $\frac{9}{10}$ of a centimeter. The width is $\frac{7}{10}$ of a centimeter. What is the area?

Example 1 and the preceding discussion indicate that the area of a rectangular region can be found by multiplying length by width. That is true whether length and width are whole numbers or not. Remember, the area of a rectangular region is given by the formula

$$A = l \cdot w.$$

▶ **EXAMPLE 2** The length of a rectangular button on a calculator is $\frac{7}{10}$ of a centimeter. The width is $\frac{3}{10}$ of a centimeter. What is the area?

1. *Familiarize.* Recall that area is length times width. We draw a picture, letting A = the area of the calculator button.

2. *Translate.* Then we translate.

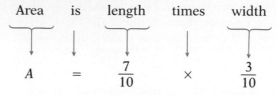

| Area | is | length | times | width |

$$A \quad = \quad \frac{7}{10} \quad \times \quad \frac{3}{10}$$

3. *Solve.* The sentence tells us what to do. We multiply:

$$\frac{7}{10} \cdot \frac{3}{10} = \frac{7 \cdot 3}{10 \cdot 10} = \frac{21}{100}.$$

4. *Check.* We check by repeating the calculation. This is left to the student.

5. *State.* The area is $\frac{21}{100}$ square centimeter.   ◀

DO EXERCISE 2.

3. Each loop in a spring takes $\frac{3}{8}$ in. of wire. How many loops can be made from 120 in. of wire?

▶ **EXAMPLE 3** How many test tubes, each containing $\frac{3}{5}$ mL, can be filled from a container of 60 mL?

1. *Familiarize.* Repeated addition will apply here. We let n = the number of test tubes in all. We draw a picture.

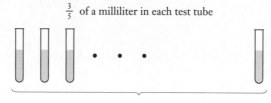

$\frac{3}{5}$ of a milliliter in each test tube

n test tubes in all

2. *Translate.* The multiplication that corresponds to the situation is

$$n \cdot \frac{3}{5} = 60.$$

3. *Solve.* We solve the equation by dividing on both sides by $\frac{3}{5}$ and carrying out the division:

$$n = 60 \div \frac{3}{5} = 60 \cdot \frac{5}{3} = \frac{60 \cdot 5}{3} = \frac{3 \cdot 20 \cdot 5}{3 \cdot 1} = \frac{3}{3} \cdot \frac{20 \cdot 5}{1} = 100.$$

4. *Check.* We check by repeating the calculation.

5. *State.* Thus, 100 test tubes can be filled.   ◀

DO EXERCISE 3.

▶ **EXAMPLE 4**   After driving 210 mi, $\frac{5}{6}$ of a trip was completed. How long was the total trip?

1. *Familiarize*. We first draw a picture or at least visualize the situation. We let n = the length of the trip.

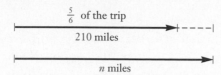

2. *Translate*. We translate to an equation.

Fraction of trip completed	times	Total length of trip	is	Amount already traveled
$\frac{5}{6}$	$\cdot$	n	$=$	210

3. *Solve*. The equation that corresponds to the situation is

$$\frac{5}{6} \cdot n = 210.$$

We solve the equation by dividing on both sides by $\frac{5}{6}$ and carrying out the division:

$$n = 210 \div \frac{5}{6} = 210 \cdot \frac{6}{5} = \frac{210 \cdot 6}{5} = \frac{5 \cdot 42 \cdot 6}{5 \cdot 1} = \frac{5}{5} \cdot \frac{42 \cdot 6}{1} = 252.$$

4. *Check*. We check by repeating the calculation.

5. *State*. The total trip was 252 mi.   ◀

DO EXERCISE 4.

▶ **EXAMPLE 5**   One jogger ran $\frac{4}{5}$ of a mile and another ran $\frac{1}{10}$ of a mile. How far did they run in all?

1. *Familiarize*. We first draw a picture. We let D = the distance run in all.

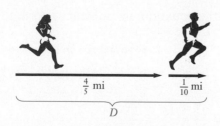

2. *Translate*. The problem can be translated to an equation as follows.

Distance of first jogger	plus	Distance of second jogger	is	Total distance
$\frac{4}{5}$	$+$	$\frac{1}{10}$	$=$	D

4. A tank had 175 gal of oil when it was $\frac{7}{8}$ full. How much could it hold?

ANSWER ON PAGE A-2

5. A consumer bought $\frac{1}{2}$ lb of peanuts and $\frac{3}{5}$ lb of cashews. How many pounds of nuts were bought altogether?

3. *Solve.* To solve the equation, we carry out the addition. The LCM of the denominators is 10 because 5 is a factor of 10. We multiply by 1 in order to obtain the LCD.

$$\frac{4}{5} \cdot \frac{2}{2} + \frac{1}{10} = D$$

$$\frac{8}{10} + \frac{1}{10} = D$$

$$\frac{9}{10} = D$$

4. *Check.* We check by repeating the calculation. We also note that the sum should be larger than either of the individual distances, which it is. This gives us a partial check on the reasonableness of the answer.

5. *State.* In all, the joggers ran $\frac{9}{10}$ of a mile.   ◀

DO EXERCISE 5.

▶ **EXAMPLE 6** A jogger has run $\frac{2}{3}$ mi and will stop running when she has run $\frac{7}{8}$ mi. How much farther does the jogger have to go?

1. *Familiarize.* We first draw a picture or at least visualize the situation. We let $d =$ the distance to go.

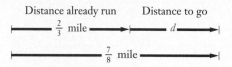

6. There is $\frac{1}{4}$ cup of cooking oil in a pitcher. How much oil must be added so there will be $\frac{4}{5}$ cup of oil in the pitcher?

2. *Translate.* We see that this is a "how much more" situation. Now we translate to an equation.

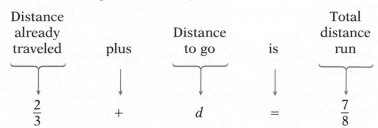

3. *Solve.* To solve the equation, we subtract $\frac{2}{3}$ on both sides.

$$\frac{2}{3} + d \ - \frac{2}{3} = \frac{7}{8} - \frac{2}{3} \qquad \text{Subtracting } \tfrac{2}{3} \text{ on both sides}$$

$$d + 0 = \frac{7}{8} \cdot \frac{3}{3} - \frac{2}{3} \cdot \frac{8}{8} \qquad \text{The LCD is 24. We multiply by 1 to obtain the LCD.}$$

$$d = \frac{21}{24} - \frac{16}{24} = \frac{5}{24}$$

4. *Check.* To check, we return to the original problem and add:

$$\frac{2}{3} + \frac{5}{24} = \frac{2}{3} \cdot \frac{8}{8} + \frac{5}{24} = \frac{16}{24} + \frac{5}{24} = \frac{21}{24} = \frac{7}{8} \cdot \frac{3}{3} = \frac{7}{8}.$$

This checks.

5. *State.* The jogger has $\frac{5}{24}$ mi to go.   ◀

DO EXERCISE 6.

▶ **EXAMPLE 7** On two business days, a salesperson drove $144\frac{9}{10}$ km and $87\frac{1}{4}$ km. What was the total distance driven?

1. *Familiarize.* We let d = the total distance driven.

2. *Translate.* We translate as follows.

$$
\underbrace{\text{Distance driven}}_{144\frac{9}{10}} + \underbrace{\text{Distance driven}}_{87\frac{1}{4}} = \underbrace{\text{Total distance}}_{d}
$$

3. *Solve.* The sentence tells us what to do. We add. The LCD is 20.

$$
144\frac{9}{10} = \quad 144\ \boxed{\frac{9}{10}\cdot\frac{2}{2}} = \quad 144\frac{18}{20}
$$

$$
+\ 87\frac{1}{4} = +\ 87\ \boxed{\frac{1}{4}\cdot\frac{5}{5}} = +\ 87\frac{5}{20}
$$

$$
231\frac{23}{20} = 232\frac{3}{20}
$$

Thus, $d = 232\frac{3}{20}$.

4. *Check.* We check by repeating the calculation. We also note that the answer is larger than any of the distances driven, which gives us a partial check of the reasonableness of the answer.

5. *State.* The total distance driven was $232\frac{3}{20}$ km. ◀

DO EXERCISE 7.

▶ **EXAMPLE 8** On a recent day, the stock of Ohio Edison opened at $\$19\frac{7}{8}$ and closed at $\$19\frac{1}{2}$. How much did it drop?

1. *Familiarize.* We let d = the amount of money the stock dropped.

2. *Translate.* We translate as follows.

$$
\underbrace{\text{Amount at}}_{19\frac{7}{8}} - \underbrace{\text{Amount at}}_{19\frac{1}{2}} = \underbrace{\text{Amount of}}_{d}
$$

3. *Solve.* To solve the equation, we carry out the subtraction. The LCD is 8.

$$
19\frac{7}{8} = \quad 19\ \frac{7}{8} = \quad 19\frac{7}{8}
$$

$$
-\ 19\frac{1}{2} = -\ 19\ \boxed{\frac{1}{2}\cdot\frac{4}{4}} = -\ 19\frac{4}{8}
$$

$$
\frac{3}{8}
$$

Thus, $d = \frac{3}{8}$.

7. A fabric store sold two pieces of burlap $6\frac{1}{4}$ yd and $10\frac{5}{6}$ yd long. What was the total length of the burlap?

ANSWER ON PAGE A-2

8. A $6\frac{1}{2}$-m pole was set $2\frac{3}{4}$ m in the ground. How much was above the ground?

4. *Check.* To check, we add the amount that the stock dropped to the closing price:

$$\frac{3}{8} + 19\frac{1}{2} = \frac{3}{8} + 19\frac{4}{8} = 19\frac{7}{8}. \qquad \text{This checks.}$$

5. *State.* The stock dropped $\$\frac{3}{8}$. ◄

DO EXERCISE 8.

▶ **EXAMPLE 9** Find the total area of a rectangle that is $8\frac{1}{2}$ by 11 in. and one that is $6\frac{1}{2}$ by $7\frac{1}{2}$ in.

1. *Familiarize.* We draw a picture of the situation. We let $a =$ the total area.

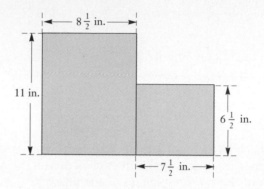

2. *Translate.* The total area is the sum of the areas of the two rectangles. This gives us the following equation:

$$a = \left(8\frac{1}{2}\right) \cdot (11) + \left(7\frac{1}{2}\right) \cdot \left(6\frac{1}{2}\right).$$

3. *Solve.* This is a multistep problem. We can carry it out doing each multiplication and then add. This follows our rules for order of operations:

$$a = \left(8\frac{1}{2}\right) \cdot (11) + \left(7\frac{1}{2}\right) \cdot \left(6\frac{1}{2}\right) = \frac{17}{2} \cdot 11 + \frac{15}{2} \cdot \frac{13}{2} = \frac{17 \cdot 11}{2} + \frac{15 \cdot 13}{2 \cdot 2}$$

$$= 93\frac{1}{2} + 48\frac{3}{4} = 93\frac{2}{4} + 48\frac{3}{4} = 141\frac{5}{4} = 141 + 1 + \frac{1}{4} + 142\frac{1}{4}.$$

4. *Check.* We check by repeating the calculation.

5. *State.* The total area of the rectangles is $142\frac{1}{4}$ sq in. ◄

DO EXERCISE 9.

9. A car travels on an interstate highway at 65 mph for $3\frac{1}{2}$ hr. How far does it travel?

EXERCISE SET 2.5

1. Business people have determined that $\frac{1}{4}$ of the items on a mailing list will change in one year. A business has a mailing list of 2500 people. After one year, how many addresses on that list will be incorrect?

2. Sociologists have determined that $\frac{2}{5}$ of the people in the world are shy. A sales manager is interviewing 650 people for an aggressive sales position. How many of these people might be shy?

1. _____

2. _____

3. A recipe calls for $\frac{2}{3}$ of a cup of flour. A chef is making an amount that is $\frac{1}{2}$ of the recipe. How much flour should the chef use?

4. Of the students in the freshman class, $\frac{2}{5}$ have cameras; $\frac{1}{4}$ of these students also join the college photography club. What fraction of the students in the freshman class join the photography club?

3. _____

4. _____

5. On a map, 1 in. represents 240 mi. How much does $\frac{2}{3}$ in. represent?

6. On a map, 1 in. represents 120 mi. How much does $\frac{3}{4}$ in. represent?

5. _____

6. _____

7. A child's teeshirt requires $\frac{3}{4}$ yd of fabric. How many shirts can be made from 24 yd of fabric?

8. A child's shirt requires $\frac{5}{6}$ yd of fabric. How many shirts can be made from 25 yd of fabric?

7. _____

8. _____

9. After driving 180 km, $\frac{5}{8}$ of a trip was completed. How long was the total trip? How many kilometers were left to drive?

10. After driving 240 km, $\frac{3}{5}$ of a trip was completed. How long was the total trip? How many kilometers were left to drive?

9. _____

10. _____

11. _____

12. _____

13. _____

14. _____

15. _____

16. _____

17. _____

18. _____

19. _____

20. _____

21. _____

22. _____

11. A student walked $\frac{7}{6}$ mi to a friend's house, and then $\frac{3}{4}$ mi to class. How far did the student walk?

12. A student walked $\frac{7}{8}$ mi to a friend's house, and then $\frac{2}{5}$ mi to class. How far did the student walk?

13. A board $\frac{9}{10}$ cm thick is glued to a board $\frac{8}{10}$ cm thick. The glue is $\frac{3}{100}$ cm thick. How thick is the result?

14. A baker used $\frac{1}{2}$ lb of flour for rolls, $\frac{1}{4}$ lb for donuts, and $\frac{1}{3}$ lb for cookies. How much flour was used?

15. A business was owned by three people. One owned $\frac{7}{12}$ of the business and the second owned $\frac{1}{6}$. How much did the third person own?

16. A parent died and left an estate to four children. One got $\frac{1}{4}$ of the estate, the second got $\frac{1}{16}$, and the third got $\frac{3}{8}$. How much did the fourth get?

17. A woman is $168\frac{1}{4}$ cm tall and her son is $150\frac{7}{10}$ cm tall. How much taller is the woman?

18. A man is $187\frac{1}{10}$ cm tall and his daughter is $180\frac{3}{4}$ cm tall. How much taller is the man?

19. The standard pencil is $16\frac{9}{10}$ cm wood and $1\frac{9}{10}$ cm eraser. What is the length of the standard pencil?

20. A plumber uses pipes of length $10\frac{5}{16}$ ft and $8\frac{3}{4}$ ft in the installation of a sink. How much pipe was used?

21. On a recent day, the stock of International Business Machines Corporation opened at $\$104\frac{5}{8}$ and dropped $\$1\frac{1}{4}$ during the course of the day. What was the closing price?

22. On a recent day, the stock of Shearson-Lehman-Hutton Corporation opened at $\$26\frac{7}{8}$ and closed at $\$27\frac{1}{4}$. How much did it gain that day?

23. Find the distance around this figure.

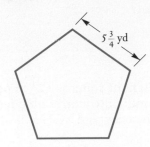

24. Find the distance around this figure.

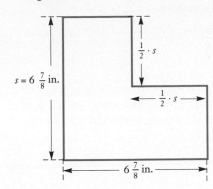

25. A painter had $3\frac{1}{2}$ gal of paint. It took $2\frac{3}{4}$ gal for a family room. It was estimated that it would take $2\frac{1}{4}$ gal to paint the living room. How much more paint was needed?

26. A person worked $10\frac{1}{2}$ hr over a three-day period. If the person worked $2\frac{1}{2}$ hr the first day and $4\frac{1}{5}$ hr the second, how many hours were worked the third day?

27. Find the length d in this figure.

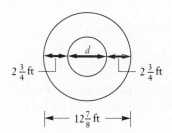

28. Find the length d in this figure.

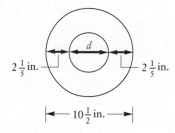

29. The weight of water is $62\frac{1}{2}$ lb per cubic foot. What is the weight of $5\frac{1}{2}$ cubic feet of water?

30. The weight of water is $62\frac{1}{2}$ lb per cubic foot. What is the weight of $2\frac{1}{4}$ cubic feet of water?

31. Fahrenheit temperature can be obtained from Celsius (centigrade) temperature by multiplying by $1\frac{4}{5}$ and adding 32°. What Fahrenheit temperature corresponds to a Celsius temperature of 20°?

32. Fahrenheit temperature can be obtained from Celsius (centigrade) temperature by multiplying by $1\frac{4}{5}$ and adding 32°. What Fahrenheit temperature corresponds to the Celsius temperature of boiling water, which is 100°?

23. _____

24. _____

25. _____

26. _____

27. _____

28. _____

29. _____

30. _____

31. _____

32. _____

33. _____

34. _____

35. _____

36. _____

37. _____

38. _____

39. _____

40. _____

41. _____

42. _____

43. _____

44. _____

45. _____

46. _____

33. A car traveled 213 mi on $14\frac{2}{10}$ gal of gas. How many miles per gallon did it get?

34. A car traveled 385 mi on $15\frac{4}{10}$ gal of gas. How many miles per gallon did it get?

35. The weight of water is $62\frac{1}{2}$ lb per cubic foot. How many cubic feet would be occupied by 250 lb of water?

36. The weight of water is $62\frac{1}{2}$ lb per cubic foot. How many cubic feet would be occupied by 375 lb of water?

37. Find the area of the shaded region.

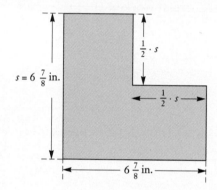

38. Find the area of the shaded region.

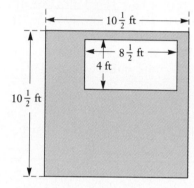

39. A rectangular lot has dimensions of $302\frac{1}{2}$ by $205\frac{1}{4}$ m. A building with dimensions of 100 by $25\frac{1}{2}$ m is built on the lot. How much area is left over?

40. Find the total area of 3 squares, each of which is $5\frac{2}{3}$ yd on a side.

SKILL MAINTENANCE

41. Divide: $986 \div 17$.

42. Subtract: $2904 - 598$.

43. Solve: $23 + y = 490$.

44. What is the total cost of 9 books at $29 each and 6 calculators at $112 each?

SYNTHESIS

45. A post is placed through some water into the mud at the bottom of the lake. Half of the post is in the mud, $\frac{1}{3}$ is in the water, and the part above water is $5\frac{1}{2}$ ft long. How long is the post?

46. Solve: $47\frac{2}{3} + n = 56\frac{1}{4}$.

SUMMARY AND REVIEW EXERCISES: CHAPTER 2

Beginning with this chapter, material from certain sections of preceding chapters will be covered on the chapter tests. Accordingly, the review exercises and the chapter tests will contain skill maintenance exercises. The review sections and objectives to be tested in addition to the material in this chapter are [1.2f], [1.3e], [1.4b], and [1.5a].

What part is shaded?

1.

2.

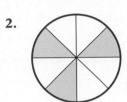

Simplify.

3. $\dfrac{0}{4}$

4. $\dfrac{23}{23}$

5. $\dfrac{48}{1}$

6. $\dfrac{48}{8}$

7. $\dfrac{10}{15}$

8. $\dfrac{7}{28}$

9. $\dfrac{12}{30}$

10. $\dfrac{9}{27}$

Multiply and simplify.

11. $4 \cdot \dfrac{3}{8}$

12. $\dfrac{6}{5} \cdot 20$

13. $\dfrac{3}{4} \cdot \dfrac{8}{9}$

14. $\dfrac{5}{7} \cdot \dfrac{1}{10}$

Find the reciprocal.

15. $\dfrac{4}{5}$

16. 3

17. $\dfrac{1}{9}$

18. $\dfrac{47}{36}$

Divide and simplify.

19. $180 \div \dfrac{3}{5}$

20. $\dfrac{3}{14} \div \dfrac{6}{7}$

21. $\dfrac{23}{25} \div \dfrac{23}{25}$

22. $\dfrac{2}{3} \div \dfrac{3}{2}$

Add and simplify.

23. $\dfrac{6}{5} + \dfrac{3}{8}$

24. $\dfrac{5}{16} + \dfrac{1}{12}$

25. $\dfrac{6}{5} + \dfrac{11}{15}$

26. $\dfrac{5}{16} + \dfrac{3}{24}$

Subtract and simplify.

27. $\dfrac{5}{9} - \dfrac{2}{9}$

28. $\dfrac{7}{8} - \dfrac{3}{4}$

29. $\dfrac{11}{27} - \dfrac{2}{9}$

30. $\dfrac{5}{6} - \dfrac{2}{9}$

Use $<$ or $>$ for ■ to write a true sentence.

31. $\dfrac{4}{7}$ ■ $\dfrac{5}{9}$

32. $\dfrac{8}{9}$ ■ $\dfrac{11}{13}$

Convert to fractional notation.

33. $7\frac{1}{2}$ **34.** $8\frac{3}{8}$

Convert to a mixed numeral.

35. $\frac{7}{3}$ **36.** $\frac{27}{4}$

Add, subtract, multiply, or divide. Write a mixed numeral for the answer.

37. $\begin{array}{r} 5\frac{3}{5} \\ + 4\frac{4}{5} \\ \hline \end{array}$ **38.** $\begin{array}{r} 8\frac{1}{3} \\ + 3\frac{2}{5} \\ \hline \end{array}$ **39.** $\begin{array}{r} 12 \\ - 4\frac{2}{9} \\ \hline \end{array}$ **40.** $\begin{array}{r} 9\frac{3}{5} \\ - 4\frac{13}{15} \\ \hline \end{array}$

41. $6 \cdot 2\frac{2}{3}$ **42.** $5\frac{1}{4} \cdot \frac{2}{3}$ **43.** $2\frac{2}{5} \div 1\frac{7}{10}$ **44.** $3\frac{1}{4} \div 26$

Solve.

45. $\frac{5}{4} \cdot t = \frac{3}{8}$ **46.** $x \cdot \frac{2}{3} = 160$ **47.** $x + \frac{2}{5} = \frac{7}{8}$ **48.** $\frac{1}{2} + y = \frac{9}{10}$

Solve.

49. After driving 60 km, $\frac{3}{8}$ of a trip is complete. How long is the trip?

50. A recipe calls for $\frac{4}{5}$ of a cup of sugar. In making $\frac{1}{2}$ of this recipe, how much sugar should be used?

51. A person usually earns $42 for working a full day. How much is received for working $\frac{1}{7}$ of a day?

52. How many $\frac{2}{3}$-cup sugar bowls can be filled from 12 cups of sugar?

53. On the first day of trading on the stock market, stock in General Mills opened at $67\frac{3}{4}$ and rose by $2\frac{5}{8}$ at the close of trading. What was the stock's closing price?

54. A wedding cake recipe requires 12 cups of shortening. Being calorie conscious, the wedding couple decides to reduce the shortening by $3\frac{5}{8}$ cups. How many cups of shortening are used in their new recipe?

SKILL MAINTENANCE

55. Divide: $3\,6\overline{)1\,4,6\,9\,7}$.

56. Solve: $765 + t = 1234$.

57. Subtract: $\begin{array}{r} 5\,6\,0\,4 \\ -1\,9\,9\,7 \\ \hline \end{array}$

58. You wrote checks for $78, $97, and $102. Your balance before that was $789. What is your new balance?

❖ **THINKING IT THROUGH**

1. Describe the process of simplifying when using fractional notation.

2. Explain why $2\frac{1}{4} \cdot 3\frac{2}{5} \neq 6\frac{2}{20}$.

3. Discuss the role of least common multiples in adding and subtracting with fractional notation.

NAME   SECTION   DATE

TEST: CHAPTER 2

1. What part is shaded?

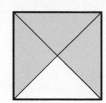

2. Use $<$ or $>$ for ▨ to write a true sentence.

$$\frac{6}{7} \ \blacksquare \ \frac{21}{25}$$

Simplify.

3. $\frac{26}{1}$ **4.** $\frac{12}{12}$ **5.** $\frac{0}{16}$ **6.** $\frac{2}{28}$

Add and simplify.

7. $\frac{1}{2} + \frac{5}{2}$ **8.** $\frac{7}{8} + \frac{2}{3}$ **9.** $\frac{7}{10} + \frac{9}{100}$

Subtract and simplify.

10. $\frac{5}{6} - \frac{3}{6}$ **11.** $\frac{5}{6} - \frac{3}{4}$ **12.** $\frac{17}{24} - \frac{5}{8}$

Multiply and simplify.

13. $\frac{4}{3} \cdot 24$ **14.** $\frac{2}{3} \cdot \frac{15}{4}$ **15.** $\frac{3}{5} \cdot \frac{1}{6}$

Find the reciprocal.

16. $\frac{5}{8}$ **17.** 18

Divide and simplify.

18. $\frac{3}{8} \div \frac{5}{4}$ **19.** $\frac{1}{5} \div \frac{1}{8}$ **20.** $12 \div \frac{2}{3}$

Solve.

21. $\frac{7}{8} \cdot x = 56$ **22.** $x + \frac{2}{3} = \frac{11}{12}$

1. _____

2. _____

3. _____

4. _____

5. _____

6. _____

7. _____

8. _____

9. _____

10. _____

11. _____

12. _____

13. _____

14. _____

15. _____

16. _____

17. _____

18. _____

19. _____

20. _____

21. _____

22. _____

ANSWERS

23. _____

24. _____

25. _____

26. _____

27. _____

28. _____

29. _____

30. _____

31. _____

32. _____

33. _____

34. _____

35. _____

36. _____

37. _____

38. _____

39. _____

23. Convert to a mixed numeral: $\frac{74}{9}$.

24. Convert to fractional notation: $3\frac{1}{2}$.

Write a mixed numeral for the answer in Exercises 25–28.

25. Add: $\quad 6\frac{2}{5}$
$$+7\frac{4}{5}$$

26. Subtract: $\quad 10\frac{1}{6}$
$$-\ 5\frac{7}{8}$$

27. Multiply: $6\frac{3}{4} \cdot \frac{2}{3}$.

28. Divide: $2\frac{1}{3} \div 1\frac{1}{6}$.

Solve.

29. It takes $\frac{7}{8}$ lb of salt to use in the ice of one batch of homemade ice cream. How much salt would it take for 32 batches?

30. A board $\frac{9}{10}$ m long is cut into 12 equal pieces. What is the length of each piece?

31. A fruitcake recipe calls for $3\frac{1}{2}$ cups of diced fruit. How much diced fruit is needed for 5 recipes?

32. An order of books for a math course weighs 220 lb. Each book weighs $2\frac{3}{4}$ lb. How many books are in the order?

33. The weights of two students are $83\frac{2}{3}$ kg and $76\frac{3}{4}$ kg. What is their total weight?

34. A standard piece of paper is $8\frac{1}{2}$ in. by 11 in. By how much does the length exceed the width?

SKILL MAINTENANCE

Solve.

35. $x + 198 = 2003$

36. $47 \cdot t = 4747$

37. It is 2060 mi from San Francisco to Winnipeg, Canada. It is 1575 mi from Winnipeg to Atlanta. What is the total length of a route from San Francisco to Winnipeg to Atlanta?

38. Divide: $2\ 4\overline{)9\ 1\ 2\ 7}$

39. Subtract: $\quad\quad 8\ 0\ 0\ 1$
$$-\ 3\ 5\ 6\ 7$$

INTRODUCTION In this chapter, the meaning of decimal notation is considered. Also discussed are rounding and estimating, addition, subtraction, multiplication, and division using decimal notation, equation solving, and problem solving. Finally, conversion from fractional notation to decimal notation is presented.

The review sections to be tested in addition to the material in this chapter are 1.7, 1.9, 2.1, and 2.4. ❖

Decimal Notation

3

AN APPLICATION

A driver filled the gasoline tank and noted that the odometer read 67,507.8. After the next filling, the odometer read 68,006.1. It took 16.5 gal to fill the tank the second time. How many miles per gallon did the driver get?

THE MATHEMATICS

This is a two-step problem, First, we let n = the number of miles driven between fillups. We find n by solving the following equation:

$$67,507.8 + n = 68,006.1$$
$$n = 68,006.1 - 67,507.8$$
$$n = 498.3.$$

We let m = the number of miles per gallon. We find m as follows:

$$498.3 \div 16.5 = m.$$

This is division using decimal notation.

Skills of Adding, Subtracting, Multiplying, and Dividing with Whole Numbers
Skill of Comparing Numbers Using Fractional Notation

PRETEST: CHAPTER 3

1. Write a word name, as on a check, for $3264.78.

Which number is larger?

2. 3.2,   0.321

3. 0.099,   0.091

4. Write fractional notation: 5.408.

5. Write decimal notation: $\dfrac{539}{10,000}$.

Add, subtract, multiply, or divide.

6.
$$\begin{array}{r} 4\,0.0 \\ -\ \ 0.9\,0\,9\,9 \\ \hline \end{array}$$

7.
$$\begin{array}{r} 4\,7 \\ \times\,0.8\,2 \\ \hline \end{array}$$

8. $102.4 + 10.24 + 1.024$

9.
$$\begin{array}{r} 3\,2\,4.5\,6 \\ \times\ \ \ 0.0\,0\,1 \\ \hline \end{array}$$

10.
$$\begin{array}{r} 0.8\,3\,5 \\ \times\ \ \ 0.7\,4 \\ \hline \end{array}$$

11. $2\,5\overline{)3\,3}$

12. $6.6\overline{)2\,0\,0.6\,4}$

13. $\dfrac{0.004653}{100}$

Solve.

14. $x + 2.33 = 5.6$

15. $9.6 \cdot y = 808.896$

Find decimal notation. Use multiplying by 1.

16. $\dfrac{7}{5}$

17. $\dfrac{23}{16}$

Find decimal notation. Use division.

18. $\dfrac{7}{9}$

19. $\dfrac{29}{7}$

Round 6156.0448 to the nearest:

20. Tenth.

21. Hundred.

22. Thousandth.

23. Estimate the product 6.92×32.458 by rounding to the nearest one.

24. Estimate the quotient $74.882209 \div 15.03$ by rounding to the nearest ten.

Solve.

25. A checking account contained $434.19. After a $148.24 check was drawn, how much was left in the account?

26. On a three-day trip, a traveler drove the following distances: 432.6 mi, 179.2 mi, and 469.8 mi. What is the total number of miles driven?

27. What is the cost of 6 compact discs at $14.95 each?

28. A person walked 10.85 km in 5 hr. How far did the person walk in 1 hr?

3.1 Decimal Notation

The set of **arithmetic numbers,** or **nonnegative rational numbers,** consists of the whole numbers

$$0, 1, 2, 3, 4, 5, 6, 7, 8, 9, 10, \text{ and so on,}$$

and fractions like

$$\frac{1}{2}, \frac{2}{3}, \frac{7}{8}, \frac{17}{10}, \text{ and so on.}$$

We studied the use of fractional notation for arithmetic numbers in Chapter 2. In Chapter 3, we will study the use of *decimal notation*. We are still considering the same set of numbers, but we are using different notation. For example, instead of using fractional notation for $\frac{7}{8}$, we use decimal notation, 0.875.

In this chapter, we will learn the meaning of decimal notation. We will also study rounding, estimating, addition, subtraction, multiplication, division, equation solving, and problem solving involving decimal notation.

a Decimal Notation and Word Names

Decimal notation for the women's shotput record is

$$69.675 \text{ ft.}$$

To understand what 69.675 means, we use a **place-value chart.** The value of each place is $\frac{1}{10}$ as large as the one to its left.

Place-Value Chart							
Hundreds	Tens	Ones	Tenths	Hundredths	Thousandths	Ten Thousandths	Hundred Thousandths
100	10	1	$\frac{1}{10}$	$\frac{1}{100}$	$\frac{1}{1000}$	$\frac{1}{10,000}$	$\frac{1}{100,000}$
	6	9 •	6	7	5		

The decimal notation 69.675 means

6 tens + 9 ones + 6 tenths + 7 hundredths + 5 thousandths,

or

$$6 \cdot 10 + 9 \cdot 1 + 6 \cdot \frac{1}{10} + 7 \cdot \frac{1}{100} + 5 \cdot \frac{1}{1000},$$

or

$$60 + 9 + \frac{6}{10} + \frac{7}{100} + \frac{5}{1000}.$$

A mixed numeral for 69.675 is $69\frac{675}{1000}$. We read 69.675 as "sixty-nine and six hundred seventy-five thousandths." When we come to the decimal point, we read "and." We can also read 69.675 as "six nine *point* six seven five."

OBJECTIVES

After finishing Section 3.1, you should be able to:

a Given decimal notation, write a word name, and write a word name for an amount of money.

b Convert from decimal notation to fractional notation.

c Convert from fractional notation to decimal notation.

FOR EXTRA HELP

Tape 6A

Write a word name for the number.

1. Each person in this country consumes an average of 27.3 gallons of coffee per year.

2. The racehorse *Swale* won the Belmont Stakes in a time of 2.4533 minutes.

3. 245.89

4. 31,479.764

Write a word name as on a check.

5. $4217.56

6. $13.98

To write a word name from decimal notation:

a) write a word name for the whole number (the number named to the left of the decimal point),

 397**.685** → Three hundred ninety-seven

b) write the word "and" for the decimal point, and

 397**.**685 → Three hundred ninety-seven and

c) write a word name for the number named to the right of the decimal point, followed by the place value of the last digit.

 397**.685** → Three hundred ninety-seven and six hundred eighty-five *thousandths*.

▶ **EXAMPLE 1**　Write a word name for the number in this sentence: Each person in this country consumes an average of 43.7 gallons of soft drinks per year.

Forty-three and seven tenths　◀

▶ **EXAMPLE 2**　Write a word name for 413.87.

Four hundred thirteen and eighty-seven hundredths　◀

▶ **EXAMPLE 3**　Write a word name for the number in this sentence: The world record in the men's marathon is 2.2525 hours.

Two and two thousand five hundred twenty-five ten thousandths　◀

▶ **EXAMPLE 4**　Write a word name for 1788.405.

One thousand, seven hundred eighty-eight and four hundred five thousandths.　◀

DO EXERCISES 1–4.

　　Decimal notation is also used with money. It is common on a check to write "and ninety-five cents" as "and $\frac{95}{100}$ dollars."

▶ **EXAMPLE 5**　Write a word name for the amount on the check, $5876.95.

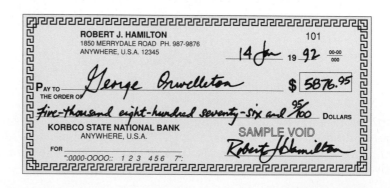

Five thousand, eight hundred seventy-six and $\frac{95}{100}$ dollars　◀

DO EXERCISES 5 AND 6.

b   Converting from Decimal Notation to Fractional Notation

We can find fractional notation as follows:

$$9.875 = 9 + \frac{8}{10} + \frac{7}{100} + \frac{5}{1000}$$

$$= 9 \cdot \frac{1000}{1000} + \frac{8}{10} \cdot \frac{100}{100} + \frac{7}{100} \cdot \frac{10}{10} + \frac{5}{1000}$$

$$= \frac{9000}{1000} + \frac{800}{1000} + \frac{70}{1000} + \frac{5}{1000} = \frac{9875}{1000}.$$

Note the following:

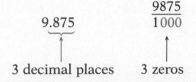

$$9.875 \qquad \frac{9875}{1000}$$

3 decimal places   3 zeros

To convert from decimal to fractional notation:

a) count the number of decimal places,   **4.98**

                2 places

b) move the decimal point that many places to the right, and   **4.98.** Move **2 places**

c) write the answer over a denominator with that number of zeros. $\dfrac{498}{100}$ **2 zeros**

▶ **EXAMPLE 6**   Write fractional notation for 0.876. Do not simplify.

$$0.876 \qquad 0.876. \qquad 0.876 = \frac{876}{1000} \qquad ◀$$

3 places

CAUTION! For a number like 0.876, we normally write a 0 before the decimal to avoid forgetting or omitting the decimal point.

▶ **EXAMPLE 7**   Write fractional notation for 56.23. Do not simplify.

$$56.23 \qquad 56.23. \qquad 56.23 = \frac{5623}{100} \qquad ◀$$

2 places

▶ **EXAMPLE 8**   Write fractional notation for 1.5018. Do not simplify.

$$1.5018 \qquad 1.5018. \qquad 1.5018 = \frac{15,018}{10,000} \qquad ◀$$

4 places

DO EXERCISES 7–10.

Write fractional notation.

7. 0.896

8. 23.78

9. 5.6789

10. 1.9

Write decimal notation.

11. $\frac{743}{100}$

12. $\frac{406}{1000}$

13. $\frac{67,089}{10,000}$

14. $\frac{9}{10}$

C **Converting from Fractional Notation to Decimal Notation**

If fractional notation has a denominator that is a power of ten, such as 10, 100, 1000, and so on, we reverse the procedure we used before.

> To convert from fractional notation to decimal notation when the denominator is 10, 100, 1000, and so on,
>
> a) count the number of zeros, and
>
> $$\frac{8679}{1000}$$
>
> 3 zeros
>
> b) move the decimal point that number of places to the left. Leave off the denominator.
>
> 8 679.
>
> Move 3 places

▶ **EXAMPLE 9** Write decimal notation for $\frac{47}{10}$.

$$\frac{47}{10}$$

1 zero

4.7.

$$\frac{47}{10} = 4.7$$ ◀

▶ **EXAMPLE 10** Write decimal notation for $\frac{123,067}{10,000}$.

$$\frac{123,067}{10,000}$$

4 zeros

12 3067.

$$\frac{123,067}{10,000} = 12.3067$$ ◀

DO EXERCISES 11–14.

When denominators are numbers other than 10, 100, and so on, we will use another method for conversion. It will be considered in Section 3.3.

NAME   SECTION   DATE

EXERCISE SET 3.1

a Write a word name for the number.

1. The average age of a bride is 23.2 years.

2. The world record in the woman's marathon was 2.6693 hours.

3. Recently one dollar was worth 135.87 Japanese yen.

4. Each day the average person spends $3.50 on health care.

5. 34.891

6. 12.345

Write a word name as on a check.

7. $326.48   **8.** $125.99   **9.** $0.67   **10.** $3.25

b Write fractional notation.

11. 6.8   **12.** 7.2   **13.** 0.17   **14.** 0.89

15. 1.46   **16.** 2.78   **17.** 204.6   **18.** 314.8

19. 3.142   **20.** 1.732   **21.** 46.03   **22.** 53.81

23. 0.00013   **24.** 0.0109   **25.** 20.003   **26.** 1000.3

27. 1.0008   **28.** 2.0114   **29.** 4567.2   **30.** 0.1104

ANSWERS

1. _____
2. _____
3. _____
4. _____
5. _____
6. _____
7. _____
8. _____
9. _____
10. _____
11. _____
12. _____
13. _____
14. _____
15. _____
16. _____
17. _____
18. _____
19. _____
20. _____
21. _____
22. _____
23. _____
24. _____
25. _____
26. _____
27. _____
28. _____
29. _____
30. _____

c Write decimal notation.

31. $\dfrac{8}{10}$ **32.** $\dfrac{1}{10}$ **33.** $\dfrac{92}{100}$ **34.** $\dfrac{4}{100}$

35. $\dfrac{93}{10}$ **36.** $\dfrac{67}{10}$ **37.** $\dfrac{889}{100}$ **38.** $\dfrac{694}{100}$

39. $\dfrac{2508}{10}$ **40.** $\dfrac{6701}{10}$ **41.** $\dfrac{3798}{1000}$ **42.** $\dfrac{78}{1000}$

43. $\dfrac{78}{10,000}$ **44.** $\dfrac{904}{10,000}$ **45.** $\dfrac{56,788}{100,000}$ **46.** $\dfrac{19}{100,000}$

47. $\dfrac{2173}{100}$ **48.** $\dfrac{6743}{100}$ **49.** $\dfrac{66}{100}$ **50.** $\dfrac{178}{100}$

51. $\dfrac{3417}{100}$ **52.** $\dfrac{9563}{100}$ **53.** $\dfrac{376,193}{1,000,000}$ **54.** $\dfrac{8,953,073}{1,000,000}$

SKILL MAINTENANCE

55. Find the LCM of 18, 27, and 54.   **56.** Subtract and simplify: $24 - 17\dfrac{2}{5}$.

57. A container has 8570 oz of beverage with which to fill 16-oz bottles. How many of these bottles can be filled? How much beverage will be left over?

SYNTHESIS

Write decimal notation.

58. $99\dfrac{44}{100}$ **59.** $4\dfrac{909}{1000}$

3.2 Addition and Subtraction with Decimals; Order

a Addition

Adding with decimal notation is similar to adding whole numbers. First we line up the decimal points. Then we add digits from the right. For example, we add the thousandths, and then the hundredths, carrying if necessary. Then we go on to the tenths, then the ones, and so on. If desired, we can add extra zeros to the right of the decimal point so that the number of places is the same.

▶ **EXAMPLE 1** Add: 56.314 + 17.78.

```
  5 6 . 3 1 4     Lining up the decimal points in order to add
+ 1 7 . 7 8 0     Adding an extra zero to the right of the decimal point
```

```
  5 6 . 3 1 4     Adding thousandths
+ 1 7 . 7 8 0
          4
```

```
  5 6 . 3 1 4     Adding hundredths
+ 1 7 . 7 8 0
        9 4
```

```
        1
  5 6 . 3 1 4     Adding tenths
+ 1 7 . 7 8 0     Write a decimal point in the answer.
      . 0 9 4     We get 10 tenths = 1 one + 0 tenths, so we carry the 1 to
                  the ones column.
```

```
    1 1
  5 6 . 3 1 4     Adding ones
+ 1 7 . 7 8 0
    4 . 0 9 4     We get 14 ones = 1 ten + 4 ones, so we carry the 1 to the
                  tens column.
```

```
  1 1
  5 6 . 3 1 4     Adding tens
+ 1 7 . 7 8 0
  7 4 . 0 9 4                                                        ◀
```

DO EXERCISES 1 AND 2.

If we want, we can write extra zeros to the right of the decimal point to get the same number of decimal places.

▶ **EXAMPLE 2** Add: 3.42 + 0.237 + 14.1.

```
    3.4 2 0     Writing extra zeros
    0.2 3 7
+ 1 4.1 0 0
  1 7.7 5 7     Adding                                               ◀
```

DO EXERCISES 3–5.

OBJECTIVES

After finishing Section 3.2, you should be able to:

a Add using decimal notation.

b Subtract using decimal notation.

c Solve equations of the type $x + a = b$ and $a + x = b$, where a and b may be in decimal notation.

d Given a pair of numbers named by decimal notation, tell which is larger.

FOR EXTRA HELP

Tape 6B, 6C

Add.

1.
```
    0.8 4 7
+ 1 0.0 7
```

2.
```
    2.1
    0.7 3 9
+ 3 1.3 6 8 9
```

Add.

3. 0.02 + 4.3 + 0.649

4. 0.12 + 3.006 + 0.4357

5. 0.4591 + 0.2374 + 8.70894

Add.

6. 789 + 123.67

7. 45.78 + 2467 + 1.993

Subtract.

8. 　3 7.4 2 8
　　− 2 6.6 7 4

9. 　0.3 4 7
　　− 0.0 0 8

Consider the addition 3456 + 19.347. Keep in mind that a whole number, such as 3456, has an "unwritten" decimal point at the right with 0 fractional parts. When adding, we can always write in that decimal point and extra zeros if desired.

▶ **EXAMPLE 3**　Add: 3456 + 19.347.

$$
\begin{array}{r}
3\,4\,5\,6.0\,0\,0 \\
+\ \ \ \ \ 1\,9.3\,4\,7 \\
\hline
3\,4\,7\,5.3\,4\,7
\end{array}
$$

Writing in the decimal point and extra zeros

Lining up the decimal points in order to add

Adding　　　◀

DO EXERCISES 6 AND 7.

b　Subtraction

Subtracting with decimal notation is similar to subtracting whole numbers. First we line up the decimal points. Then we subtract digits from the right. For example, we subtract the thousandths, and then the hundredths, the tenths, and so on, borrowing if necessary.

▶ **EXAMPLE 4**　Subtract: 56.314 − 17.78.

$$
\begin{array}{r}
5\,6.3\,1\,4 \\
-1\,7.7\,8\,0 \\
\hline
\end{array}
$$

Lining up the decimal points in order to subtract

Writing an extra 0

$$
\begin{array}{r}
5\,6.3\,1\,4 \\
-1\,7.7\,8\,0 \\
\hline
4
\end{array}
$$

Subtracting thousandths

$$
\begin{array}{r}
2\ \ 11 \\
5\,6.\cancel{3}\,\cancel{1}\,4 \\
-1\,7.7\,8\,0 \\
\hline
3\ 4
\end{array}
$$

Borrowing tenths to subtract hundredths

$$
\begin{array}{r}
12 \\
5\ \cancel{2}\ 11 \\
5\,\cancel{6}.\cancel{3}\,\cancel{1}\,4 \\
-1\,7.7\,8\,0 \\
\hline
.5\ 3\ 4
\end{array}
$$

Borrowing ones to subtract tenths

Writing a decimal point

$$
\begin{array}{r}
15\ 12 \\
4\ \cancel{5}\ \cancel{2}\ 11 \\
\cancel{5}\,\cancel{6}.\cancel{3}\,\cancel{1}\,4 \\
-1\,7.7\,8\,0 \\
\hline
8.5\ 3\ 4
\end{array}
$$

Borrowing tens to subtract ones

$$
\begin{array}{r}
15\ 12 \\
4\ \cancel{5}\ \cancel{2}\ 11 \\
\cancel{5}\,\cancel{6}.\cancel{3}\,\cancel{1}\,4 \\
-1\,7.7\,8\,0 \\
\hline
3\,8.5\ 3\ 4
\end{array}
$$

Subtracting tens　　　◀

DO EXERCISES 8 AND 9.

▶ **EXAMPLE 5** Subtract: $13.07 - 9.205$.

$$
\begin{array}{r}
\overset{12}{\cancel{1}} \overset{2}{\cancel{3}}.\overset{10}{\cancel{0}} \overset{6}{7} \overset{10}{\cancel{0}} \\
- \quad 9.2\ 0\ 5 \\
\hline
3.8\ 6\ 5
\end{array}
$$

Writing an extra zero

Subtracting ◀

▶ **EXAMPLE 6** Subtract: $23.08 - 5.0053$.

$$
\begin{array}{r}
\overset{1\ 13}{\cancel{2}} \overset{}{\cancel{3}}.0\ \overset{7}{8} \overset{9}{\cancel{0}} \overset{10}{\cancel{0}} \\
- \quad 5.0\ 0\ 5\ 3 \\
\hline
1\ 8.0\ 7\ 4\ 7
\end{array}
$$

Writing two extra zeros

Subtracting ◀

DO EXERCISES 10–12.

When subtraction involves a whole number, again keep in mind that there is an "unwritten" decimal point that can be written in if desired. Extra zeros can also be written in to the right of the decimal point.

▶ **EXAMPLE 7** Subtract: $456 - 2.467$.

$$
\begin{array}{r}
4\ 5\ \overset{5}{\cancel{6}}.\overset{9}{\cancel{0}} \overset{9}{\cancel{0}} \overset{10}{\cancel{0}} \\
- \quad 2.4\ 6\ 7 \\
\hline
4\ 5\ 3.5\ 3\ 3
\end{array}
$$

Writing in the decimal point and extra zeros

Subtracting ◀

DO EXERCISES 13 AND 14.

C Solving Equations

Now let us solve equations $x + a = b$ and $a + x = b$, where a and b may be in decimal notation. Proceeding as we have before, we subtract a on both sides.

▶ **EXAMPLE 8** Solve: $x + 28.89 = 74.567$.

We have

$$x + 28.89 - 28.89 = 74.567 - 28.89$$

Subtracting 28.89 on both sides

$$x = 45.677.$$

$$
\begin{array}{r}
\overset{6}{\cancel{7}} \overset{13}{\cancel{4}}.\overset{14}{\cancel{5}} \overset{16}{\cancel{6}} 7 \\
- 2\ 8.8\ 9\ 0 \\
\hline
4\ 5.6\ 7\ 7
\end{array}
$$

The solution is 45.677. ◀

▶ **EXAMPLE 9** Solve: $0.8879 + y = 9.0026$.

We have

$$0.8879 + y - 0.8879 = 9.0026 - 0.8879$$

Subtracting 0.8879 on both sides

$$y = 8.1147.$$

$$
\begin{array}{r}
\overset{8}{\cancel{9}}.\overset{9}{\cancel{0}} \overset{9}{\cancel{0}} \overset{11}{\cancel{2}} \overset{16}{\cancel{6}} \\
- 0.8\ 8\ 7\ 9 \\
\hline
8.1\ 1\ 4\ 7
\end{array}
$$

The solution is 8.1147. ◀

DO EXERCISES 15 AND 16.

Subtract.

10. $1.2345 - 0.7$

11. $0.9564 - 0.4392$

12. $7.37 - 0.00008$

Subtract.

13. $1277 - 82.78$

14. $5 - 0.0089$

Solve.

15. $x + 17.78 = 56.314$

16. $8.906 + t = 23.07$

Which number is larger?

17. 2.04,   2.039

18. 0.06,   0.008

19. 0.5,   0.58

20. 1,   0.9999

21. 0.8989,   0.09898

22. 21.006,   21.05

d   Order

To understand how to compare numbers in decimal notation, consider 0.85 and 0.9. First note that $0.9 = 0.90$ because $\frac{9}{10} = \frac{90}{100}$. Then $0.85 = \frac{85}{100}$ and $0.90 = \frac{90}{100}$. Since $\frac{85}{100} < \frac{90}{100}$, it follows that $0.85 < 0.90$. This leads us to a quick way to compare two numbers named in decimal notation.

> To compare two numbers in decimal notation, start at the left and compare corresponding digits. When two digits differ, the number with the larger digit is the larger of the two numbers. To ease the comparison, extra zeros can be written to the right of the decimal point, if necessary, so the number of decimal places is the same.

▶ **EXAMPLE 10**   Which of 2.109 and 2.1 is larger?

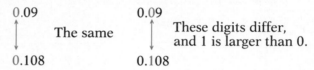

Thus, 2.109 is larger.   ◄

▶ **EXAMPLE 11**   Which of 0.09 and 0.108 is larger?

$$0.09 \quad\quad 0.09$$
The same | These digits differ, and 1 is larger than 0.
$$0.108 \quad\quad 0.108$$

Thus, 0.108 is larger.   ◄

DO EXERCISES 17–22.

NAME   SECTION   DATE

EXERCISE SET 3.2

a Add.

1.   3 1 6.2 5
        +   1 8.1 2

2.   4 1.8 2 3
        + 6 1 4.9 1 5

3.   6 5 9.4 0 3
        + 9 1 6.8 1 2

4.   3.2 5
        + 1 1 2 3.3 9

5.   0.8 0 9 6 8
        + 0.7 8 5 6 7

6.   4.1 5 2 3
        + 3.2 7 7 8

7. 0.347 + 10.04

8. 2.3 + 0.729 + 23

9. 17 + 3.24 + 0.256 + 0.3689

10.   4 7.8
          2 1 9.8 5 2
            4 3.5 9
        + 6 6 6.7 1 3

11.   2.7 0 3
             7 8.3 3
           2 8.0 0 0 9
        + 1 1 8.4 3 4 1

12.   1 3.7 2
              9.1 1 2
          6 5 4 2.7 9 0 8
        +   2 3.9 0 1

b Subtract.

13.   5.2
        − 3.9

14. 1 1.3 4 5
        −   2.1 0 5

15. 5 1.3 1
        −   2.2 9

16. 3 7.4 5
        −   6.3 2

17. 4 8.7 6
        −   3.1 5

18. 4 7.2 1
        −   3.1 5

19.   2.5
        − 0.0 0 2 5

20.   2 8.0
        −   0.2 8

1. _____

2. _____

3. _____

4. _____

5. _____

6. _____

7. _____

8. _____

9. _____

10. _____

11. _____

12. _____

13. _____

14. _____

15. _____

16. _____

17. _____

18. _____

19. _____

20. _____

ANSWERS

21. _____	
22. _____	
23. _____	
24. _____	
25. _____	
26. _____	
27. _____	
28. _____	
29. _____	
30. _____	
31. _____	
32. _____	
33. _____	
34. _____	
35. _____	
36. _____	
37. _____	
38. _____	
39. _____	
40. _____	
41. _____	
42. _____	
43. _____	
44. _____	
45. _____	
46. _____	
47. _____	

21. $2548.98 - 2.007$

22. $19 - 1.198$

23. $45 - 0.999$

24.
```
  3 2 . 7 9 7 8
-    0 . 0 5 9 2
```

25.
```
   0 . 4 9 6 3 4
- 0 . 1 2 6 7 8
```

26.
```
  6 . 0 7
- 2 . 0 0 7 8
```

c Solve.

27. $x + 0.223 = 200.12$

28. $t + 50.7 = 54.07$

29. $3.205 + m = 22.456$

30. $4.26 + q = 58.32$

d Which number is larger?

31. 0.06,　0.58

32. 0.003,　0.3

33. 0.1,　0.111

34. 31.08,　31.2

35. 0.0009,　0.001

36. 4.056,　4.043

37. 234.07,　235.07

38. 0.99999,　1.0

39. 0.4545,　0.05454

40. 0.54,　0.78

41. 0.432,　0.4325

42. 0.8437,　0.84384

SKILL MAINTENANCE

43. Multiply: $2\frac{1}{3} \cdot 4\frac{4}{5}$.

44. Divide: $2\frac{1}{3} \div 4\frac{4}{5}$.

Divide.

45. $2\ 4\overline{)8\ 2\ 0\ 8}$

46. $4\overline{)3\ 4\ 8}$

SYNTHESIS

47. A student presses the wrong button when using a calculator and adds 235.7 instead of subtracting it. The incorrect answer is 817.2. What is the correct answer?

3.3 Multiplication and Division with Decimal Notation

a Multiplication

Let's find the product

$$2.3 \times 1.12.$$

To understand how we find such products, we convert to fractional notation:

$$2.3 \times 1.12 = \frac{23}{10} \times \frac{112}{100} = \frac{23 \times 112}{10 \times 100} = \frac{2576}{1000} = 2.576.$$

We multiply the whole numbers 23 and 112, and then divide by 1000. Note the number of decimal places.

$$
\begin{array}{r}
1.1\,2 \quad \text{(2 decimal places)} \\
\times \quad 2.3 \quad \text{(1 decimal place)} \\
\hline
2.5\,7\,6 \quad \text{(3 decimal places)}
\end{array}
$$

To multiply using decimals:	0.8 × 0.43
a) Ignore the decimal points and multiply as though both factors were whole numbers.	$$\begin{array}{r} 2 \\ 0.4\,3 \\ \times \quad 0.8 \\ \hline 3\,4\,4 \end{array}$$ **Ignore the decimal points for now.**
b) Then place the decimal point in the result. The number of decimal places in the product is the sum of the numbers of places in the factors (count places from the right).	$$\begin{array}{r} 0.4\,3 \quad \text{(2 decimal places)} \\ \times \quad 0.8 \quad \text{(1 decimal place)} \\ \hline 0.3\,4\,4 \quad \text{(3 decimal places)} \end{array}$$

▶ **EXAMPLE 1** Multiply: 8.3×74.6.

a) Ignore the decimal points and multiply as though factors were whole numbers:

$$
\begin{array}{r}
3\;4 \\
1\;1 \\
7\,4.6 \\
\times \qquad 8.3 \\
\hline
2\,2\,3\,8 \\
5\,9\,6\,8\,0 \\
\hline
6\,1\,9\,1\,8
\end{array}
$$

b) Place the decimal point in the result.

$$
\begin{array}{r}
7\,4.6 \quad \text{(1 decimal place)} \\
\times \qquad 8.3 \quad \text{(1 decimal place)} \\
\hline
2\,2\,3\,8 \\
5\,9\,6\,8\,0 \\
\hline
6\,1\,9.1\,8 \quad \text{(2 decimal places)}
\end{array}
$$
◀

DO EXERCISE 1.

OBJECTIVES

After finishing Section 3.3, you should be able to:

a Multiply using decimal notation.

b Divide using decimal notation.

c Solve equations of the type $a \cdot x = b$, where a and b may be in decimal notation.

d Convert from fractional notation to decimal notation.

FOR EXTRA HELP

Tape 7A, 7B, 7C

1. Multiply.

$$
\begin{array}{r}
8\,5.4 \\
\times \qquad 6.2 \\
\hline
\end{array}
$$

ANSWER ON PAGE A-3

Multiply.

2.
```
      1 2 3 4
  × 0.0 0 4 1
```

3.
```
      4 2.6 5
  ×   0.8 0 4
```

Multiply.

4. 1000×8.415

5. 0.01×5.6

▶ **EXAMPLE 2**   Multiply: 0.0032×2148.

As we catch on to the skill, we can combine the two steps.

```
      2 1 4 8        (0 decimal places)
  × 0.0 0 3 2        (4 decimal places)
      4 2 9 6
    6 4 4 4 0
    6.8 7 3 6        (4 decimal places)        ◀
```

▶ **EXAMPLE 3**   Multiply: 0.14×0.867.

```
      0.8 6 7        (3 decimal places)
  ×       0.1 4      (2 decimal places)
        3 4 6 8
        8 6 7 0
    0.1 2 1 3 8      (5 decimal places)        ◀
```

DO EXERCISES 2 AND 3.

▶ **EXAMPLE 4**   Multiply: 100×8.415.

```
      8.4 1 5        (3 decimal places)
  ×       1 0 0      (0 decimal places)
    8 4 1.5 0 0      (3 decimal places)        ◀
```

▶ **EXAMPLE 5**   Multiply: 0.001×97.04.

```
      9 7.0 4        (2 decimal places)
  ×       0.0 0 1    (3 decimal places)
    0.0 9 7 0 4      (5 decimal places)        ◀
```

DO EXERCISES 4 AND 5.

To multiply any number by a power of ten such as 10, 100, 1000, and so on:

a) **count the number of zeros, and**

1000×34.45678

⟶ **3 zeros**

b) **move the decimal point that many places to the right.**

$1000 \times 34.45678 = 34,456.78$

Move 3 places to the right.

To multiply any number by a tenth, hundredth, or thousandth:

a) **count the number of decimal places in the tenth, hundredth, or thousandth, and**

0.001×34.45678

⟶ **3 places**

b) **move the decimal point that many places to the left.**

$0.001 \times 34.45678 = 0.034.45678$

Move 3 places to the left.

▶ **EXAMPLE 6**   Multiply: 10×0.037.

$$10 \times 0.037, \qquad 0.0\underset{\frown}{.}37, \qquad 10 \times 0.037 = 0.37$$

Move 1 place to the right.   ◀

▶ **EXAMPLE 7**   Multiply: 0.01×0.037.

$$0.01 \times 0.037, \qquad 0.00.037, \qquad 0.01 \times 0.037 = 0.00037$$

Move 2 places to the left.   ◀

DO EXERCISES 6–9.

b   Division

Whole-Number Divisors

Compare these divisions.

$$\frac{588}{7} = 84$$

$$\frac{58.8}{7} = 8.4$$

$$\frac{5.88}{7} = 0.84$$

$$\frac{0.588}{7} = 0.084$$

The number of decimal places in the quotient is the same as the number of decimal places in the dividend.

These lead us to the following method for dividing by a whole number.

To divide by a whole number:
a) **place the decimal point directly above the decimal point in the dividend, and**
b) **divide as though dividing whole numbers.**

$$
\begin{array}{r}
0.8\ 4 \\
7\overline{)5.8\ 8} \\
5\ 6\ 0 \\
\hline
2\ 8 \\
2\ 8 \\
\hline
0
\end{array}
$$

▶ **EXAMPLE 8**   Divide: $82.08 \div 24$.

Place the decimal point.

$$
\begin{array}{r}
3.4\ 2 \\
2\ 4\overline{)8\ 2.0\ 8} \\
7\ 2\ 0\ 0 \\
\hline
1\ 0\ 0\ 8 \\
9\ 6\ 0 \\
\hline
4\ 8 \\
4\ 8 \\
\hline
0
\end{array}
$$

Divide as though dividing whole numbers.   ◀

DO EXERCISES 10–12.

Multiply.
6. 100×345.906

7. 0.01×345.906

8. 0.001×0.73

9. 1000×0.73

Divide.
10. $9\overline{)5.4}$

11. $1\ 5\overline{)2\ 2.5}$

12. $8\ 2\overline{)3\ 8.5\ 4}$

Divide.

13. 2 5)8

14. 4)1 5

15. 8 6)2 1.5

Extra Zeros

Sometimes it helps to write some extra zeros to the right of the decimal point. They don't change the number.

▶ **EXAMPLES**

9. Divide: $30 \div 8$.

```
    3.7 5
8)3 0.0 0
  2 4
    6 0
    5 6
      4 0
      4 0
       0
```

10. Divide: $4 \div 25$.

```
    0.1 6
2 5)4.0 0
    2 5
    1 5 0
    1 5 0
        0
```

◀

DO EXERCISES 13–15.

Divisors That Are Not Whole Numbers

Consider the division

$$0.2\,4\overline{)8.2\,0\,8}$$

We write the division as $\dfrac{8.208}{0.24}$. Then we multiply by 1 to change to a whole-number divisor:

$$\frac{8.208}{0.24} = \frac{8.208}{0.24} \times \frac{100}{100} = \frac{820.8}{24}.$$

The divisor is now a whole number. The division

$$0.2\,4\overline{)8.2\,0\,8}$$

is the same as

$$2\,4\overline{)8\,2\,0.8}$$

To divide when the divisor is not a whole number:

a) move the decimal point (multiply by 10, 100, and so on) to make the divisor a whole number;

$$0.2\,4\overline{)8.2\,0\,8}$$

Move 2 places to the right.

b) move the decimal point (multiply the same way) in the dividend the same number of places; and

$$0.2\,4\overline{)8.2\,0\,8}$$

Move 2 places to the right.

c) place the decimal point directly above the decimal point in the dividend and divide as though dividing whole numbers.

```
       3 4.2
0.2 4)8.2 0 8
      7 2 0 0
      1 0 0 8
        9 6 0
          4 8
          4 8
           0
```

(The new decimal point in the dividend is indicated by a caret.)

▶ **EXAMPLE 11**   Divide: $5.848 \div 8.6$.

$8.6\overline{)5.8\,4\,8}$ Multiply the divisor by 10 (move the decimal point 1 place). Multiply the same way in the dividend (move 1 place).

$$8.6\overline{)5.8\,4\,8}\quad\begin{array}{r}0.6\,8\\\hline\end{array}$$

Then divide.

$$\begin{array}{r}0.6\,8\\8.6\overline{)5.8\,4\,8}\\\underline{5\,1\,6\,0}\\6\,8\,8\\\underline{6\,8\,8}\\0\end{array}$$

DO EXERCISES 16–18.

▶ **EXAMPLE 12**   Divide: $12 \div 0.64$.

$0.6\,4\overline{)1\,2.}$ Put a decimal point at the end of the whole number.

$0.6\,4\overline{)1\,2.0\,0}$ Multiply the divisor by 100 (move the decimal point 2 places). Multiply the same way in the dividend (move 2 places).

$$\begin{array}{r}1\,8.7\,5\\0.6\,4\overline{)1\,2.0\,0\,0\,0}\\\underline{6\,4\,0}\\5\,6\,0\\\underline{5\,1\,2}\\4\,8\,0\\\underline{4\,4\,8}\\3\,2\,0\\\underline{3\,2\,0}\\0\end{array}$$

Then divide.

DO EXERCISE 19.

It is often helpful to be able to divide quickly by a ten, hundred, or thousand, or by a tenth, hundredth, or thousandth. The procedure we use is based on multiplying by 1. Consider the following examples:

$$\frac{23.789}{1000} = \frac{23.789}{1000} \cdot \frac{1000}{1000} = \frac{23,789}{1,000,000} = 0.023789;$$

$$\frac{23.789}{0.01} = \frac{23.789}{0.01} \cdot \frac{100}{100} = \frac{2378.9}{1} = 2378.9.$$

We use the following procedure.

16. a) Complete.

$$\frac{3.75}{0.25} = \frac{3.75}{0.25} \times \frac{100}{100}$$
$$= \frac{(\quad)}{25}$$

b) Divide.

$$0.2\,5\overline{)3.7\,5}$$

Divide.

17. $0.8\,3\overline{)4.0\,6\,7}$

18. $3.5\overline{)4\,4.8}$

19. Divide.

$$1.6\overline{)2\,5}$$

ANSWERS ON PAGE A-3

Divide.

20. $\dfrac{0.1278}{0.01}$

21. $\dfrac{0.1278}{100}$

22. $\dfrac{98.47}{1000}$

23. $\dfrac{6.7832}{0.1}$

Solve.

24. $100 \cdot x = 78.314$

25. $0.25 \cdot y = 276.4$

To divide by a power of ten, such as 10, 100, or 1000, and so on:

a) count the number of zeros in the divisor, and

$$\dfrac{713.49}{100}$$

→ 2 zeros

b) move the decimal point that number of places to the left.

$$\dfrac{713.49}{100}, \quad 7\underset{\smile}{.}13.49 \quad \dfrac{713.49}{100} = 7.1349$$

2 places to the left

To divide by a tenth, hundredth, or thousandth:

a) count the number of decimal places in the divisor, and

$$\dfrac{713.49}{0.001}$$

→ 3 places

b) move the decimal point that number of places to the right.

$$\dfrac{713.49}{0.001}, \quad 713.490\underset{\smile}{.} \quad \dfrac{713.49}{0.001} = 713,490$$

3 places to the right

▶ **EXAMPLE 13**　Divide: $\dfrac{0.0104}{10}$.

$$\dfrac{0.0104}{10}, \quad 0\underset{\smile}{.}0.0104, \quad \dfrac{0.0104}{10} = 0.00104$$

1 place to the left to change 10 to 1　◀

▶ **EXAMPLE 14**　Divide: $\dfrac{23.738}{0.001}$.

$$\dfrac{23.738}{0.001}, \quad 23.738\underset{\smile}{.} \quad \dfrac{23.738}{0.001} = 23,738$$

3 places to the right to change 0.001 to 1　◀

DO EXERCISES 20–23.

C　Solving Equations

Now let us solve equations of the type $a \cdot x = b$, where a and b may be in decimal notation. Proceeding as we have before, we divide on both sides by a.

▶ **EXAMPLE 15**　Solve: $2.9 \times t = 0.14616$.

We have

$$\dfrac{2.9 \times t}{2.9} = \dfrac{0.14616}{2.9} \qquad \text{Dividing on both sides by 2.9}$$

$$t = 0.0504.$$

The solution is 0.0504.　◀

DO EXERCISES 24 AND 25.

d Converting from Fractional Notation to Decimal Notation

When a denominator has no prime factors other than 2's and 5's, we can find decimal notation by multiplying by 1. We multiply to get a denominator that is a power of ten like 10, 100, or 1000.

▶ **EXAMPLE 16** Find decimal notation for $\frac{3}{5}$.

$$\frac{3}{5} = \frac{3}{5} \cdot \frac{2}{2} = \frac{6}{10} = 0.6$$

We use $\frac{2}{2}$ for 1 to get a denominator of 10. ◀

▶ **EXAMPLE 17** Find decimal notation for $\frac{7}{20}$.

$$\frac{7}{20} = \frac{7}{20} \cdot \frac{5}{5} = \frac{35}{100} = 0.35$$

We use $\frac{5}{5}$ for 1 to get a denominator of 100. ◀

▶ **EXAMPLE 18** Find decimal notation for $\frac{9}{40}$.

$$\frac{9}{40} = \frac{9}{40} \cdot \frac{25}{25} = \frac{225}{1000} = 0.225$$

We use $\frac{25}{25}$ for 1 to get a denominator of 1000. ◀

▶ **EXAMPLE 19** Find decimal notation for $\frac{87}{25}$.

$$\frac{87}{25} = \frac{87}{25} \cdot \frac{4}{4} = \frac{348}{100} = 3.48$$

We use $\frac{4}{4}$ for 1 to get a denominator of 100. ◀

DO EXERCISES 26–29.

We can also divide to find decimal notation.

▶ **EXAMPLE 20** Find decimal notation for $\frac{3}{5}$.

$$\frac{3}{5} = 3 \div 5 \qquad 5\overline{)3.0} \qquad \frac{3}{5} = 0.6$$
$$\;0.6$$
$$3\,0$$
$$0$$
◀

▶ **EXAMPLE 21** Find decimal notation for $\frac{7}{8}$.

$$\frac{7}{8} = 7 \div 8 \qquad 8\overline{)7.0\,0\,0} \qquad \frac{7}{8} = 0.875$$

0.8 7 5 / 6 4 / 6 0 / 5 6 / 4 0 / 4 0 / 0 ◀

DO EXERCISES 30 AND 31.

In Examples 20 and 21, the division **terminated,** meaning that eventually we got a remainder of 0. A terminating decimal occurs when the denominator has only 2's or 5's, or both, as factors. This assumes that the fractional notation has been simplified.

Find decimal notation. Use multiplying by 1.

26. $\frac{4}{5}$

27. $\frac{9}{20}$

28. $\frac{11}{40}$

29. $\frac{33}{25}$

Find decimal notation.

30. $\frac{2}{5}$

31. $\frac{3}{8}$

ANSWERS ON PAGE A-3

Find decimal notation.

32. $\frac{1}{6}$

33. $\frac{2}{3}$

Find decimal notation.

34. $\frac{5}{11}$

35. $\frac{12}{11}$

Consider a different situation:

$$\frac{5}{6} \quad \text{or} \quad \frac{5}{2 \cdot 3}.$$

Since 6 has a 3 as a factor, the division will not terminate. We can still use division to get decimal notation, but answers will be repeating decimals, as follows.

▶ **EXAMPLE 22**   Find decimal notation for $\frac{5}{6}$.

$$\frac{5}{6} = 5 \div 6 \qquad \begin{array}{r} 0.8\ 3\ 3 \\ 6\overline{)5.0\ 0\ 0} \\ 4.8 \\ \hline 2\ 0 \\ 1\ 8 \\ \hline 2\ 0 \\ 1\ 8 \\ \hline 2 \end{array}$$

Since 2 keeps reappearing as a remainder, the digits repeat and will continue to do so; therefore,

$$\frac{5}{6} = 0.83333.\ldots$$

The dots indicate an endless sequence of digits in the quotient. When there is a repeating pattern, the dots are often replaced by a bar to indicate the repeating part—in this case, only the 3:

$$\frac{5}{6} = 0.8\overline{3}. \qquad ◀$$

DO EXERCISES 32 AND 33.

▶ **EXAMPLE 23**   Find decimal notation for $\frac{4}{11}$.

$$\frac{4}{11} = 4 \div 11 \qquad \begin{array}{r} 0.3\ 6\ 3\ 6 \\ 1\,1\overline{)4.0\ 0\ 0\ 0} \\ 3\ 3 \\ \hline 7\ 0 \\ 6\ 6 \\ \hline 4\ 0 \\ 3\ 3 \\ \hline 7\ 0 \\ 6\ 6 \\ \hline 4 \end{array}$$

Since 7 and 4 keep reappearing as remainders, the sequence of digits "36" repeats in the quotient, and

$$\frac{4}{11} = 0.363636\ldots, \quad \text{or} \quad 0.\overline{36}. \qquad ◀$$

DO EXERCISES 34 AND 35.

NAME   SECTION   DATE

EXERCISE SET 3.3

a Multiply.

1. $\begin{array}{r} 8.6 \\ \times\ \ 7 \\ \hline \end{array}$

2. $\begin{array}{r} 4\ 7 \\ \times\ 0.9 \\ \hline \end{array}$

3. $\begin{array}{r} 6.3 \\ \times\ 0.0\ 4 \\ \hline \end{array}$

4. $\begin{array}{r} 7.8 \\ \times\ 0.0\ 9 \\ \hline \end{array}$

5. $\begin{array}{r} 3\ 2.6 \\ \times\ \ \ 1\ 6 \\ \hline \end{array}$

6. $\begin{array}{r} 7.2\ 8 \\ \times\ \ \ 5.4 \\ \hline \end{array}$

7. $\begin{array}{r} 7\ 4\ 9 \\ \times\ 0.4\ 3 \\ \hline \end{array}$

8. $\begin{array}{r} 8\ 7\ 6 \\ \times\ 2\ 0.4 \\ \hline \end{array}$

9. $\begin{array}{r} 4\ 6.5\ 0 \\ \times\ \ \ \ \ 7\ 5 \\ \hline \end{array}$

10. $\begin{array}{r} 8.2\ 4 \\ \times\ 7\ 0\ 3 \\ \hline \end{array}$

11. $\begin{array}{r} 8\ 1.7 \\ \times\ 0.6\ 1\ 2 \\ \hline \end{array}$

12. $\begin{array}{r} 3\ 1.8\ 2 \\ \times\ \ \ \ 7.1\ 5 \\ \hline \end{array}$

13. $\begin{array}{r} 0.3\ 4\ 7 \\ \times\ \ \ 2.0\ 9 \\ \hline \end{array}$

14. $\begin{array}{r} 7.4\ 8\ 9 \\ \times\ \ \ \ \ \ 8.2 \\ \hline \end{array}$

15. $\begin{array}{r} 3.0\ 0\ 5 \\ \times\ 0.6\ 2\ 3 \\ \hline \end{array}$

16. $\begin{array}{r} 1\ 5\ 1.2 \\ \times\ 4.5\ 5\ 5 \\ \hline \end{array}$

17. $\begin{array}{r} 2.5\ 3\ 2 \\ \times\ 1.0\ 6\ 7 \\ \hline \end{array}$

18. $\begin{array}{r} 0.0\ 0\ 3\ 4\ 2 \\ \times\ \ \ \ \ \ \ \ 0.8\ 4 \\ \hline \end{array}$

19. $\begin{array}{r} 1\ 6.3\ 4 \\ \times\ 0.0\ 0\ 0\ 5\ 1\ 2 \\ \hline \end{array}$

20. 0.34×1000

21. 7.8×100

22. 8976.23×0.001

23. 0.1×89.23

24. 0.01×789.235

25. 0.001×97.68

26. 10×23.76

27. 100×2.8793

28. 1000×783.686852

ANSWERS

1. _____

2. _____

3. _____

4. _____

5. _____

6. _____

7. _____

8. _____

9. _____

10. _____

11. _____

12. _____

13. _____

14. _____

15. _____

16. _____

17. _____

18. _____

19. _____

20. _____

21. _____

22. _____

23. _____

24. _____

25. _____

26. _____

27. _____

28. _____

ANSWERS

29. _____

30. _____

31. _____

32. _____

33. _____

34. _____

35. _____

36. _____

37. _____

38. _____

39. _____

40. _____

41. _____

42. _____

43. _____

44. _____

45. _____

46. _____

47. _____

48. _____

49. _____

50. _____

51. _____

52. _____

53. _____

54. _____

55. _____

56. _____

57. _____

58. _____

59. _____

60. _____

61. _____

62. _____

b Divide.

29. $2\overline{)5.9\ 8}$

30. $4\overline{)9\ 5.1\ 2}$

31. $1\ 2\overline{)8\ 9.7\ 6}$

32. $2\ 1\overline{)2\ 2.8\ 9}$

33. $9.144 \div 8$

34. $3.6 \div 4$

35. $0.0\ 4\overline{)1.6\ 8}$

36. $0.1\ 2\overline{)8.4}$

37. $3.4\overline{)6\ 8}$

38. $1\ 2\overline{)1.8}$

39. $0.2\ 8\overline{)6\ 3}$

40. $0.0\ 1\ 7\overline{)1.5\ 8\ 1}$

41. $5\ 2\overline{)1\ 1\ 9.6}$

42. $0.4\ 7\overline{)0.1\ 2\ 2\ 2}$

43. $\dfrac{213.4567}{1000}$

44. $\dfrac{213.4567}{100}$

45. $\dfrac{1.0237}{0.001}$

46. $\dfrac{100.7604}{0.1}$

c Solve.

47. $4.2 \cdot x = 39.06$

48. $36 \cdot y = 14.76$

49. $1000 \cdot y = 9.0678$

50. $789.23 = 0.25 \cdot q$

d Find decimal notation.

51. $\dfrac{13}{4}$

52. $\dfrac{7}{20}$

53. $\dfrac{11}{16}$

54. $\dfrac{43}{125}$

55. $\dfrac{4}{9}$

56. $\dfrac{17}{12}$

57. $\dfrac{8}{15}$

58. $\dfrac{2}{7}$

SKILL MAINTENANCE

59. Subtract: $20 - 16\frac{3}{5}$.

60. Divide: $84 \div 8\frac{2}{5}$.

61. Find the LCM of 25 and 65.

62. Find the prime factorization of 128.

3.4 Rounding and Estimating

a Rounding

We round numbers in various situations if we do not need an exact answer. We might round to check if an answer to a problem is reasonable or to check a calculation done by hand or on a calculator. We might also round to see if we are being charged the correct amount in a store.

To understand how to round, we first look at some examples using number lines, even though this is not the way we normally do rounding.

▶ **EXAMPLE 1** Round 47 to the nearest ten.

Here is part of a number line; 47 is between 40 and 50.

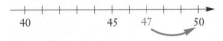

Since 47 is closer to 50, we round up to 50.   ◀

▶ **EXAMPLE 2** Round 42 to the nearest ten.
42 is between 40 and 50.

Since 42 is closer to 40, we round down to 40.   ◀

DO EXERCISES 1–4.

▶ **EXAMPLE 3** Round 45 to the nearest ten.
45 is halfway between 40 and 50.

We could round 45 down to 40 or up to 50. We agree to round up to 50.   ◀

> **When a number is halfway between rounding numbers, we agree to round up.**

DO EXERCISES 5–7.

Here is a rule for rounding.

> **To round to a certain place:**
> a) **Locate the digit in that place.**
> b) **Consider the next digit to the right.**
> c) **If the digit to the right is 5 or higher, round up; if the digit to the right is less than 5, round down.**

OBJECTIVES

After finishing Section 3.4, you should be able to:

a Round to the nearest thousandth, hundredth, tenth, one, ten, hundred, or thousand.

b Estimate sums, differences, products, and quotients by rounding.

FOR EXTRA HELP

Tape 1D, 6B, 7D

Round to the nearest ten.

1. 37

2. 52

3. 73

4. 98

Round to the nearest ten.

5. 35

6. 75

7. 85

ANSWERS ON PAGE A-3

Round to the nearest ten.

8. 137

9. 473

10. 235

11. 285

Round to the nearest hundred.

12. 641

13. 759

14. 750

15. 9325

Round to the nearest thousand.

16. 7896

17. 8459

18. 19,343

19. 68,500

▶ **EXAMPLE 4**   Round 6485 to the nearest (a) ten; (b) hundred; (c) thousand.

a) Locate the digit in the tens place. It is 8.

$$6 \ 4 \ \underset{\uparrow}{8} \ 5$$

The next digit to the right is 5, so we round up. The answer is 6490.

b) Locate the digit in the hundreds place. It is 4.

$$6 \ \underset{\uparrow}{4} \ 8 \ 5$$

The next digit to the right is 8, so we round up. The answer is 6500.

c) Locate the digit in the thousands place. It is 6.

$$\underset{\uparrow}{6} \ 4 \ 8 \ 5$$

The next digit to the right is 4, so we round down. The answer is 6000.

◀

CAUTION! 7000 is not a correct answer to Example 4(c). It is incorrect to round from the ones digit over, as follows:

$$6485, \quad 6490, \quad 6500, \quad 7000.$$

DO EXERCISES 8–19.

There are many methods of rounding. For example, in rounding 8563 to the nearest hundred, a different rule would call for us to **truncate,** meaning that we would simply change all digits to the right of the rounding location to zeros. Thus, 8563 would round to 8500, which is not the same answer that we would get using the rule in this section.

Rounding with decimal notation uses the same rule as for whole numbers. To understand, we first consider an example using a number line.

▶ **EXAMPLE 5**   Round 0.37 to the nearest tenth.

Here is part of a number line.

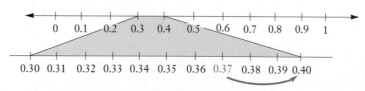

We see that 0.37 is closer to 0.40 than to 0.30. Thus, 0.37 rounded to the nearest tenth is 0.4.   ◀

▶ **EXAMPLE 6**   Round 3872.2459 to the nearest tenth.

a) Locate the digit in the tenths place.

$$3\ 8\ 7\ 2.\overset{\uparrow}{2}\ 4\ 5\ 9$$

b) Consider the next digit to the right.

$$3\ 8\ 7\ 2.2\ \overset{\uparrow}{4}\ 5\ 9$$

CAUTION! 3872.3 is not a correct answer to Example 6. It is incorrect to round from the ten thousandths digit over as follows:

3872.246,   3872.25,   3872.3.

c) Since that digit is less than 5, round down.

$$3\ 8\ 7\ 2.2 \longleftarrow \text{This is the answer.} \quad ◀$$

▶ **EXAMPLE 7**   Round 3872.2459 to the nearest hundredth.

a) Locate the digit in the hundredths place. $3\ 8\ 7\ 2.2\ \overset{\uparrow}{4}\ 5\ 9$

b) Consider the next digit to the right. $3\ 8\ 7\ 2.2\ 4\ \overset{\uparrow}{5}\ 9$

c) Since that digit is 5 or higher, round up.

$$3\ 8\ 7\ 2.2\ 5 \longleftarrow \text{This is the answer.} \quad ◀$$

▶ **EXAMPLE 8**   Round 3872.2459 to the nearest thousandth, hundredth, tenth, one, ten, hundred, and thousand.

Thousandth:	3872.246	Ten:	3870
Hundredth:	3872.25	Hundred:	3900
Tenth:	3872.2	Thousand:	4000
One:	3872		◀

▶ **EXAMPLE 9**   Round 0.008 to the nearest tenth.

a) Locate the digit in the tenths place. $0.\overset{\uparrow}{0}\ 0\ 8$

b) Consider the next digit to the right. $0.0\ \overset{\uparrow}{0}\ 8$

c) Since that digit is less than 5, round down.

The answer is 0.0, or 0.   ◀

DO EXERCISES 20–38.

Round to the nearest tenth.
20. 2.76   **21.** 13.85

22. 234.448   **23.** 7.009

Round to the nearest hundredth.
24. 0.636   **25.** 7.834

26. 34.675   **27.** 0.025

Round to the nearest thousandth.
28. 0.9434   **29.** 8.0038

30. 43.1119   **31.** 37.4005

Round 7459.3548 to the nearest:
32. Thousandth.

33. Hundredth.

34. Tenth.

35. One.

36. Ten. (*Caution:* "Tens" are not "tenths.")

37. Hundred.

38. Thousand.

ANSWERS ON PAGE A-3

39. Estimate the cost of 123 oranges at 21¢ each.

Estimate by rounding. Answers may vary.

40.
```
    6 5 0
    6 9 5
    2 4 8
 + 1 7 8
```

41.
```
    8 7.2 3
 − 3 6.8 5
```

42.
```
    6 8 3
 × 4 5 7
```

43. 14.603 ÷ 4.7

---

b   Estimating

Estimating is done to make a problem simpler so that it can be done easily or mentally. Rounding is used when estimating. There are many ways in which to estimate.

▶ **EXAMPLE 10**   Estimate the cost of 23 hammers, sold for $8.39 each. There are various ways in which we might round the numbers. Let us round the price to the nearest dollar and the number of hammers to the nearest ten. We then multiply:

$$20 \times \$8 = \$160.$$

The cost of the hammers is somewhere near $160.

We might get a closer estimate by rounding the price *down,* to $8 and rounding the number of hammers *up,* to 25. We then multiply:

$$25 \times \$8 = \$200.$$

The cost of the hammers is somewhere near $200. ◀

DO EXERCISE 39.

▶ **EXAMPLE 11**   Dick and Tom Van Arsdale are twin brothers who played professional basketball. Tom scored a total of 14,232 points in his career, and Dick scored a total of 15,079. Estimate how many points they scored in all.

One way to estimate is to round each number to the nearest thousand and then add.

```
    1 4,2 3 2        1 4,0 0 0
 + 1 5,0 7 9       + 1 5,0 0 0
                     2 9,0 0 0   ◀——— Estimated answer
```

We often use the symbol ≈ instead of = when approximating or estimating. The symbol ≈ means "is approximately equal to." In a situation such as the one in Example 11, we might write

$$14{,}232 + 15{,}079 \approx 29{,}000.$$ ◀

▶ **EXAMPLE 12**   Estimate: 4.8×52.
We have

$$5 \times 50 = 250. \quad \text{(Estimated product)}$$

We rounded 4.8 to the nearest one and 52 to the nearest ten. ◀

▶ **EXAMPLE 13**   Estimate: $82.08 \div 24$.
This is about $80 \div 20$, so the answer is about 4. ◀

DO EXERCISES 40–43.

EXERCISE SET 3.4

a Round to the nearest ten.

1. 48   **2.** 17   **3.** 67   **4.** 99

5. 731   **6.** 532   **7.** 895   **8.** 765

Round to the nearest hundred.

9. 146   **10.** 874   **11.** 957   **12.** 650

13. 3583   **14.** 4645   **15.** 2850   **16.** 4402

Round to the nearest thousand.

17. 5932   **18.** 4500   **19.** 7500   **20.** 13,855

21. 45,340   **22.** 735,562   **23.** 373,405   **24.** 2001

Round to the nearest tenth.

25. 0.11   **26.** 0.15   **27.** 2.7449   **28.** 4.78

29. 0.5794   **30.** 0.88   **31.** 123.65   **32.** 36.049

Round to the nearest hundredth.

33. 0.893   **34.** 0.675   **35.** 283.1379   **36.** 0.007

1. _____
2. _____
3. _____
4. _____
5. _____
6. _____
7. _____
8. _____
9. _____
10. _____
11. _____
12. _____
13. _____
14. _____
15. _____
16. _____
17. _____
18. _____
19. _____
20. _____
21. _____
22. _____
23. _____
24. _____
25. _____
26. _____
27. _____
28. _____
29. _____
30. _____
31. _____
32. _____
33. _____
34. _____
35. _____
36. _____

ANSWERS

37. _____

38. _____

39. _____

40. _____

41. _____

42. _____

43. _____

44. _____

45. _____

46. _____

47. _____

48. _____

49. _____

50. _____

51. _____

52. _____

53. _____

54. _____

55. _____

56. _____

57. _____

58. _____

59. _____

60. _____

61. _____

62. _____

63. _____

64. _____

37. 0.4246   **38.** 6.529   **39.** 1.435   **40.** 0.406

Round to the nearest thousandth.

41. 0.3246   **42.** 0.4278   **43.** 10.1011   **44.** 67.1006

45. 17.0015   **46.** 2.6776   **47.** 0.0009   **48.** 123.4562

Round 283.1359 to the nearest:

49. Hundred.   **50.** Tenth.   **51.** Thousandth.

52. Hundredth.   **53.** One.   **54.** Ten.

b Estimate by rounding. Remember that your way of rounding may be different from someone else's. Therefore, the answers at the back of the book may be different from yours, even though you are correct.

55.   7 6.4 8   **56.**   6 8 8 2   **57.**   7 5 6.5   **58.** 4 7.5)$\overline{1\ 5\ 2.7}$
     9 3.4 8   − 1 7 4 8   × 1 8.8
     7 8.4 2
  + 2 2.2 2

59. Estimate the cost of 2437 transistors at 31¢ each.

60. The price of a yacht is $98,032.98 and the price of an airplane is $143,899.98. Estimate the amount of money a customer will spend in buying both of them.

SKILL MAINTENANCE

61. Add: $10\frac{1}{2} + 4\frac{5}{8}$.

62. Subtract: $10\frac{1}{2} - 4\frac{5}{8}$.

63. Simplify: $\frac{36}{42}$.

64. Find the prime factorization of 162.

3.5 Solving Problems

OBJECTIVES

After finishing Section 3.5, you should be able to:

a Solve problems involving addition, subtraction, multiplication, and division with decimals.

FOR EXTRA HELP

Tape 6D, 7E

a Solving problems using decimals is like solving problems with whole numbers. We translate to an equation that corresponds to the situation. Then we solve the equation.

▶ **EXAMPLE 1** A patient was given injections of 3.68 milligrams (mg), 2.7 mg, 3.65 mg, and 5.0 mg over a 24-hr period. What was the total amount of the injections?

1. *Familiarize.* We let t = the amount of the injections.
2. *Translate.* Amounts are being combined. We translate to an equation:

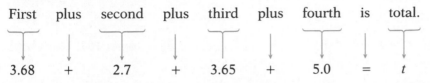

First plus second plus third plus fourth is total.

$$3.68 + 2.7 + 3.65 + 5.0 = t$$

3. *Solve.* To solve, we carry out the addition.

$$\begin{array}{r} {\scriptstyle 2\ 1} \\ 3.6\ 8 \\ 2.7\ 0 \\ 3.6\ 5 \\ +\ 5.0\ 0 \\ \hline 1\ 5.0\ 3 \end{array}$$

Thus, t = 15.03.

4. *Check.* We can check by repeating our addition. We can also see whether our answer is reasonable by first noting that it is indeed larger than any of the numbers being added. We can also check by rounding:

$$3.68 + 2.7 + 3.65 + 5.0 \approx 4.0 + 3.0 + 4.0 + 5.0 = 16 \approx 15.03.$$

If we had gotten an answer like 150.3 or 0.1503, then our estimate, 16, would have told us that we did something wrong, like not lining up the decimal points.

5. *State.* The total of the injections was 15.03 mg.   ◀

DO EXERCISE 1.

▶ **EXAMPLE 2** Normal body temperature is 98.6°F. When fevered, most people will die if their bodies reach 107°F. This is a rise of how many degrees?

1. *Familiarize.* We draw a picture or at least visualize the situation. We let n = the number of degrees of rise in temperature.

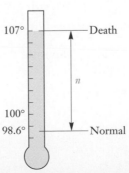

1. Each year, each of us drinks on average 43.7 gal of soft drinks, 37.3 gal of water, 27.3 gal of coffee, 21.1 gal of milk, and 8.1 gal of fruit juice. What is the total amount that each of us drinks on average?

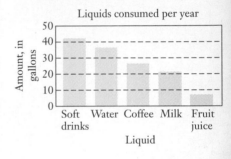

2. Coffee prices recently made a dramatic increase. The price was $2.73 per pound in May of 1990. In May of 1991, the price was $3.16. How much was the increase?

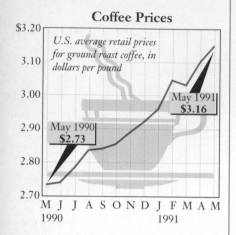

Coffee Prices

U.S. average retail prices for ground roast coffee, in dollars per pound

2. *Translate.* This is a "how-much-more" situation. We translate as follows.

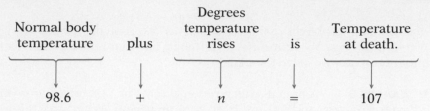

Normal body temperature	plus	Degrees temperature rises	is	Temperature at death.
98.6	+	n	=	107

3. *Solve.* We solve the equation. We subtract 98.6 on both sides.

$$98.6 + n - 98.6 = 107 - 98.6$$
$$n = 8.4$$

$$
\begin{array}{r}
16 \\
9\ 6\ 10 \\
1\ \cancel{0}\ \cancel{7}.0 \\
-\ \ 9\ 8.6 \\
\hline
8.4
\end{array}
$$

4. *Check.* We can check by adding 8.4 to 98.6, to get 107. This checks.

5. *State.* A rise of 8.4°F will cause death. ◀

DO EXERCISE 2.

▶ **EXAMPLE 3** The Internal Revenue Service allows a tax deduction of 26.5¢ per mile for mileage driven for business purposes. What deduction, in dollars, would be allowed for driving 127 miles?

1. *Familiarize.* Repeated addition fits this situation. We let d = the deduction, in dollars, allowed for driving 127 miles.

2. *Translate.* We translate as follows.

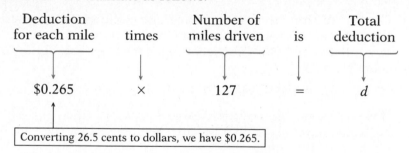

Deduction for each mile	times	Number of miles driven	is	Total deduction
$0.265	×	127	=	d

Converting 26.5 cents to dollars, we have $0.265.

3. *At a printing company, the cost of copying is 8 cents per page. How much, in dollars, would it cost to make 466 copies?*

3. *Solve.* To solve the equation, we carry out the multiplication.

$$
\begin{array}{r}
1\ 2\ 7 \\
\times\ \ 0.2\ 6\ 5 \\
\hline
3\ 3.6\ 5\ 5
\end{array}
$$

Thus, $d = 33.655$.

4. *Check.* We can obtain a partial check by rounding and estimating:

$$127 \times 0.265 \approx 130 \times 0.3 = 39 \approx 33.655.$$

5. *State.* The total deduction would be $33.66, rounded to the nearest cent. ◀

DO EXERCISE 3.

ANSWERS ON PAGE A-3

▶ **EXAMPLE 4** A loan of $7382.52 is to be paid off in 36 monthly payments. How much is each payment?

1. *Familiarize.* We let n = the amount of each payment.

2. *Translate.* The problem can be translated to the following equation, thinking that

(Total loan) ÷ (Number of payments) = (Amount of each payment)

$$\$7382.52 \div 36 = n.$$

3. *Solve.* To solve the equation, we carry out the division.

```
              2 0 5.0 7
    3 6 ) 7 3 8 2.5 2
          7 2 0 0 0 0
          ─────────────
            1 8 2 5 2
            1 8 0 0 0
          ─────────────
                2 5 2
                2 5 2
          ─────────────
                    0
```

Thus, $n = 205.07$.

4. *Check.* A partial check can be obtained by estimating the quotient: $\$7382.52 \div 36 \approx 8000 \div 40 = 200 \approx 205.07$. The estimate checks.

5. Each payment is $205.07. ◀

DO EXERCISE 4.

The area of a rectangular region is given by the formula *Area = Length · Width*, or $A = l \cdot w$. We can use this formula when numbers are named by decimals.

▶ **EXAMPLE 5** The rectangular page in a book measures 23.2 cm by 21.8 cm. Find the area.

1. *Familiarize.* We first draw a picture, letting A = the area.

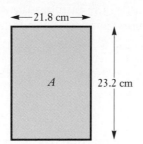

2. *Translate.* Then we use the formula $A = l \cdot w$ and translate.

$$A = 23.2 \times 21.8$$

3. *Solve.* We solve by carrying out the multiplication.

```
        2 3.2
    ×   2 1.8
    ───────────
    5 0 5.7 6
```

Thus, $A = 505.76$.

4. A loan of $4425 is to be paid off in 12 monthly payments. How much is each payment?

ANSWER ON PAGE A-3

5. A standard-size file card measures 12.7 cm by 7.6 cm. Find its area.

4. *Check.* We obtain a partial check by estimating the product:

$$23.2 \times 21.8 \approx 20 \times 22 = 440 \approx 505.76.$$

Since this estimate is not too close, we might repeat our calculation or change our estimate to be more certain. We leave this to the student. We see that 505.76 checks.

5. *State.* The area is 505.76 sq cm.   ◄

DO EXERCISE 5.

Multistep Problems

► **EXAMPLE 6** *Gas mileage.* A driver filled the gasoline tank and noted that the odometer read 67,507.8. After the next filling, the odometer read 68,006.1. It took 16.5 gal to fill the tank. How many miles per gallon did the driver get?

1. *Familiarize.* This is a two-step problem. First, we find the number of miles that have been driven between fillups. We let n = the number of miles driven.

2., 3. *Translate* and *Solve.* This is a "how-much-more" situation. We translate and solve as follows.

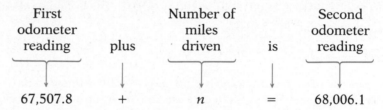

First odometer reading	plus	Number of miles driven	is	Second odometer reading
67,507.8	+	n	=	68,006.1

6. A driver filled the gasoline tank and noted that the odometer read 38,320.8. After the next filling, the odometer read 38,735.5. It took 14.5 gal to fill the tank. How many miles per gallon did the driver get?

To solve the equation, we subtract 67,507.8 on both sides:

$$n = 68,006.1 - 67,507.8$$
$$n = 498.3.$$

Second, we divide the total number of miles driven by the number of gallons. This gives us m = the number of miles per gallon—that is, the mileage. The division that corresponds to the situation is

$$498.3 \div 16.5 = m.$$

To find the number m, we divide:

$$498.3 \div 16.5 = 30.2.$$

Thus, $m = 30.2$.

4. *Check.* To check, we first multiply the number of miles per gallon times the number of gallons: $16.5 \times 30.2 = 498.3$. Then we add 498.3 to 67,507.8:

$$67,507.8 + 498.3 = 68,006.1.$$

The mileage 30.2 checks.

5. *State.* The driver gets 30.2 miles per gallon.   ◄

DO EXERCISE 6.

SUMMARY AND REVIEW EXERCISES: CHAPTER 3

The review sections and objectives to be tested in addition to the material in this chapter are [1.7d], [1.9a], [2.1e], and [2.4b, c].

Write a word name.

1. 3.47   **2.** 0.031

Write a word name as on a check.

3. $597.25   **4.** $0.98

Write fractional notation.

5. 0.09   **6.** 4.561

Write decimal notation.

7. $\dfrac{34}{1000}$ **8.** $\dfrac{2791}{100}$

Which number is larger?

9. 0.034, 0.0185   **10.** 0.91, 0.19   **11.** 0.741, 0.6943   **12.** 1.038, 1.041

Solve.

13. $x + 51.748 = 548.0275$ **14.** $3 \cdot x = 20.85$ **15.** $0.0089 + y = 5$

Add, subtract, multiply, or divide.

16. $0.41 + 4.1 + 41 + 0.091$

17.
$$\begin{array}{r} 3\,0.0 \\ -\ \ 0.7\,9\,0\,8 \\ \hline \end{array}$$

18.
$$\begin{array}{r} 2.0\,8 \\ \times\,0.1\,0\,5 \\ \hline \end{array}$$

19.
$$\begin{array}{r} 0.0\,8\,7 \\ \times\ \ \ \ 3.2 \\ \hline \end{array}$$

20. $\dfrac{13.892}{0.01}$

21.
$$\begin{array}{r} 2\,4.6\,8 \\ \times\,1\,0\,0\,0 \\ \hline \end{array}$$

22. $7.2\overline{)1\,1.5\,2}$ **23.** $2\,5\overline{)8\,0}$ **24.** $745.0109 - 59.959$

Find decimal notation.

25. $\dfrac{13}{5}$ **26.** $\dfrac{32}{25}$ **27.** $\dfrac{7}{6}$ **28.** $\dfrac{13}{4}$ **29.** $\dfrac{17}{11}$

Round 345,759.4287 to the nearest:

30. Hundred.   **31.** Ten.   **32.** Thousand.

33. Tenth.   **34.** Hundredth.   **35.** Thousandth.

36. Estimate the product 7.82 × 34.487 by rounding to the nearest one.

37. Estimate the quotient 82.304 ÷ 17.287 by rounding to the nearest ten.

38. Estimate the difference 219.875 − 4.478 by rounding to the nearest one.

39. Estimate the sum $45.78 + $78.99 by rounding to the nearest one.

Solve.

40. In the United States, there are 51.81 telephone poles for every hundred people. In Canada, there are 40.65. How many more telephone poles for every hundred people are there in the United States?

41. In 1961, the average age of a groom was 22.0. In 1984, the average age was 25.5. How much older was the average groom in 1984 than in 1961?

42. A farmer has 4 corn fields. One year the harvest in each field was 1419.3 bushels, 1761.8 bushels, 1095.2 bushels, and 2088.8 bushels. What was the year's total harvest?

43. A checking account contained $6274.53. After a $385.79 check was drawn, what was left in the account?

44. Four dresses, each costing $59.95, were bought. What was the total amount spent?

45. A train traveled 496.02 km in 6 hr. How far did it travel in 1 hr?

46. A florist sold 13 potted palms for a total of $423.65. What was the cost for each palm? Round to the nearest cent.

47. The average person drinks 3.48 cups of tea per day. How many cups of tea are drunk in a week? in a month (30 days)?

48. A student buys 6 records for $53.88. How much was each record?

SKILL MAINTENANCE

49. Add: $12\frac{1}{2} + 7\frac{3}{10}$.

50. Find the LCM of 20, 33, and 75.

51. Simplify: $\frac{28}{56}$.

52. Find the prime factorization of 192.

❖ THINKING IT THROUGH

1. Consider finding decimal notation for $\frac{44}{61}$. Discuss as many ways as you can for finding such notation and give the answer.

2. Discuss the role of estimating in calculating with decimal notation.

3. Explain how fractional notation can be used to justify multiplication with decimal notation.

TEST: CHAPTER 3

1. Write a word name for 2.34.

2. Write a word name, as on a check, for $1234.78.

Write fractional notation.

3. 0.91

4. 2.769

Write decimal notation.

5. $\dfrac{74}{100}$

6. $\dfrac{37,047}{10,000}$

Which number is larger?

7. 0.07,   0.162

8. 0.09,   0.9

9. 0.078,   0.06

Solve.

10. $x + 0.018 = 9$

11. $4.8 \cdot y = 404.448$

Add, subtract, multiply, or divide.

12.
$$\begin{array}{r} 4\ 0\ 2.3 \\ 2.8\ 1 \\ +\quad 0.1\ 0\ 9 \end{array}$$

13. $102.4 + 6.1 + 78$

14.
$$\begin{array}{r} 5\ 2.6\ 7\ 8 \\ -\quad 4.3\ 2\ 1 \end{array}$$

15. $2 - 0.0054$

16.
$$\begin{array}{r} 3\ 2 \\ \times\ 0.2\ 5 \end{array}$$

17.
$$\begin{array}{r} 0.0\ 9\ 9 \\ \times\quad 2.1 \end{array}$$

18.
$$\begin{array}{r} 2\ 1\ 3.4\ 5 \\ \times\quad 0.0\ 0\ 1 \end{array}$$

19. $2\ 5\overline{)1\ 1}$

20. $\dfrac{0.00123}{100}$

21. $3.3\overline{)1\ 0\ 0.3\ 2}$

22. $8\ 2\overline{)1\ 5.5\ 8}$

1. _____

2. _____

3. _____

4. _____

5. _____

6. _____

7. _____

8. _____

9. _____

10. _____

11. _____

12. _____

13. _____

14. _____

15. _____

16. _____

17. _____

18. _____

19. _____

20. _____

21. _____

22. _____

ANSWERS

23. _____

24. _____

25. _____

26. _____

27. _____

28. _____

29. _____

30. _____

31. _____

32. _____

33. _____

34. _____

35. _____

36. _____

37. _____

38. _____

39. _____

Find decimal notation.

23. $\dfrac{3}{4}$ 24. $\dfrac{11}{9}$ 25. $\dfrac{22}{25}$

Round 457.6783 to the nearest:

26. Ten.   27. Hundredth.   28. Thousandth.

29. Estimate the product 8.91×22.457 by rounding to the nearest one.

30. Estimate the quotient $78.2209 \div 16.09$ by rounding to the nearest ten.

Solve.

31. A student wrote checks of $123.89, $56.78, and $3446.98. How much was written in checks altogether?

32. In the 1896 Olympics, Alfred Hajos won the 100-meter freestyle in 60.37 sec. In the 1984 Olympics, Rowdy Gaines won in 49.80 sec. How much faster was Gaines?

33. A student bought 6 books at $19.95 each. How much was spent?

34. A person walked 11.85 km in 5 hr. How far did the person walk in 1 hr?

35. A consumer paid $23,456.98 for 14 acres of land. How much did it cost for 1 acre? Round to the nearest cent.

SKILL MAINTENANCE

36. Subtract and simplify: $28\dfrac{2}{3} - 2\dfrac{1}{6}$.

37. Find the LCM of 15, 36, and 40.

38. Simplify: $\dfrac{33}{54}$.

39. Find the prime factorization of 360.

INTRODUCTION This chapter introduces a new kind of notation for numbers: percent notation. It will be seen that $\frac{1}{2}$, 0.5, and 50% are all names for the same number. Finally, percent notation and equations will be used to solve problems.

The review sections to be tested in addition to the material in this chapter are 2.4, 3.1, and 3.3. ❖

Percent Notation

AN APPLICATION

Have you ever wondered why you receive so much junk mail? One reason offered by the U.S. Postal Service is that we open and read about 78% of the advertising that we receive in the mail. Suppose a business sends out 9500 advertising brochures. How many of them can it expect to be opened and read?

THE MATHEMATICS

We let a = the number opened and read. The problem can be translated to an equation and solved as follows.

This is percent notation.
↓

Restate: What number is 78% of 9500?

Translate: $a = 78\% \times 9500$.
↑

This is the kind of equation we will consider.

❖ POINTS TO REMEMBER: CHAPTER 4

      Equation-Solving Skills: Sections 2.1, 2.3, 3.2, and 3.3
      Conversion between Fractional and Decimal Notation: Sections 3.1 and 3.3

PRETEST: CHAPTER 4

Write fractional notation for the ratio.

1. 35 to 43

2. 0.079 to 1.043

3. Solve: $\dfrac{5}{6} = \dfrac{x}{27}$.

4. What is the rate in miles per gallon?

        408 miles, 16 gallons

5. Find decimal notation for 87%.

6. Find percent notation for 0.537.

7. Find percent notation for $\dfrac{3}{4}$.

8. Find fractional notation for 37%.

9. Translate to an equation. Then solve.

        What is 60% of 75?

10. Translate to a proportion. Then solve.

        What percent of 50 is 35?

Solve.

11. If 4 cans of peaches cost $1.98, how many cans of peaches can you buy for $10.89?

12. On a map, 4 in. represents 225 actual miles. If two cities are 7 in. apart on the map, how far are they actually apart?

13. The weight of muscles in a human body is 40% of total body weight. A person weighs 225 lb. What do the muscles weigh?

14. The population of a town increased from 3000 to 3600. Find the percent of increase in population.

15. The sales tax rate in Maryland is 5%. How much tax is charged on a purchase of $286? What is the total price?

16. The marked price of a stereo is $450 and is on sale at Lowland Appliances for 25% off. What are the discount and the sale price?

17. What is the simple interest on $500 at 8% for $\frac{1}{2}$ year?

18. Interest is compounded annually. Find the amount in an account if $6000 is invested at 9% for 2 years.

4.1 Ratio and Proportion

a Ratio

> **A *ratio* is the quotient of two quantities.**

For example, each day in this country about 5200 people die. Of these, 1070 die of cancer. The *ratio* of those who die of cancer to those who die is shown by the fractional notation

$$\frac{1070}{5200} \quad \text{or by the notation} \quad 1070{:}5200.$$

We read such notation as "the ratio of 1070 to 5200," listing the numerator first and the denominator second. Some other numbers whose ratio is $\frac{1070}{5200}$ are 107 and 520, 2140 and 10,400, and 10.7 and 52.

DO EXERCISE 1.

Since

$$\frac{30}{20} = \frac{3}{2} \quad \text{and} \quad \frac{6}{4} = \frac{3}{2},$$

it follows that

$$\frac{30}{20} = \frac{6}{4}.$$

We say that the pair of numbers 30 and 20 has the same ratio as the pair of numbers 6 and 4.

DO EXERCISE 2.

▶ **EXAMPLE 1** In Michigan, the ratio of lawyers to people is 2.3 per 1000. Write fractional notation for the ratio of lawyers to people.

$$\frac{2.3}{1000} \qquad \blacktriangleleft$$

▶ **EXAMPLE 2** Hank Aaron had 12,364 "at bats" in his career and 755 home runs. Write fractional notation for the ratio of at bats to home runs.

$$\frac{12,364}{755} \qquad \blacktriangleleft$$

DO EXERCISES 3–6.

▶ **EXAMPLE 3** In the triangle at the right:

a) What is the ratio of the length of the longest side to the length of the shortest side?

$$\frac{5}{3}$$

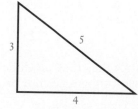

b) What is the ratio of the length of the shortest side to the longest side?

$$\frac{3}{5} \qquad \blacktriangleleft$$

OBJECTIVES

After finishing Section 4.1, you should be able to:

a Write fractional notation for ratios.

b Determine whether two pairs of numbers are proportional.

c Solve proportions.

d Give the ratio of two different kinds of measure as a rate.

e Solve problems involving proportions.

FOR EXTRA HELP

Tape 8A, 8B, 8C

1. Find three pairs of numbers whose ratio is $\frac{2}{1}$.

2. Find three pairs of numbers whose ratio is $\frac{3}{2}$.

3. Each of us drinks, on average, 182.5 gal of liquid each year. Of this, 21.1 gal is milk. Write fractional notation for the ratio of milk drunk to total amount drunk.

4. Of the 365 days in each year, it takes 107 days of work for the average person to pay his or her taxes. Write fractional notation for the ratio of days worked for taxes to total number of days worked.

Write fractional notation for the ratio.

5. 7 to 11

6. 3.4 to 0.189

ANSWERS ON PAGE A-3

For a standard television screen, there are 4 units of length for every 3 units of width.

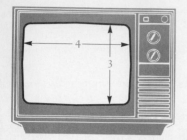

7. What is the ratio of the length to the width?

8. What is the ratio of the width to the length?

9. A family earning $11,400 per year will spend about $2964 for food. What is the ratio of food expenses to yearly income?

10. A pitcher gives up 4 earned runs in $7\frac{2}{3}$ innings of pitching. What is the ratio of earned runs to the number of innings pitched?

Determine whether the two pairs of numbers are proportional.

11. 3, 4 and 6, 8

12. 1, 4 and 10, 39

13. 1, 2 and 20, 39

DO EXERCISES 7 AND 8.

▶ **EXAMPLE 4**   A family earning $21,400 per year will spend about $3210 for car expenses. What is the ratio of car expenses to yearly income?

$$\frac{3210}{21,400}$$ ◀

DO EXERCISES 9 AND 10.

b **Proportion**

Suppose we want to compare $\frac{3}{6}$ and $\frac{2}{4}$. We find a common denominator and compare numerators. To do this, we multiply by 1:

$$\left.\begin{array}{l}\dfrac{3}{6} = \dfrac{3}{6} \cdot \dfrac{4}{4} = \dfrac{3 \cdot 4}{6 \cdot 4} = \dfrac{12}{24} \\[2mm] \dfrac{2}{4} = \dfrac{2}{4} \cdot \dfrac{6}{6} = \dfrac{2 \cdot 6}{4 \cdot 6} = \dfrac{12}{24}\end{array}\right\}\text{We see that } \dfrac{3}{6} = \dfrac{2}{4}.$$

We need only check the products $3 \cdot 4$ and $6 \cdot 2$ to test for equality.

We multiply these two numbers: $3 \cdot 4$.　$\dfrac{3}{6} \times \dfrac{2}{4}$　We multiply these two numbers: $6 \cdot 2$.

Since $3 \cdot 4 = 6 \cdot 2$, we know that $\frac{3}{6} = \frac{2}{4}$. We call $3 \cdot 4$ and $6 \cdot 2$ *cross products*.

When two pairs of numbers (such as 3, 6, and 2, 4) have the same ratio, we say that they are **proportional.** The equation

$$\frac{3}{6} = \frac{2}{4}$$

states that 3, 6 and 2, 4 are proportional. Such an equation, sometimes read as "3 is to 6 as 2 is to 4," is called a **proportion.**

▶ **EXAMPLE 5**   Determine whether 1, 2 and 3, 6 are proportional.

We can use cross-products:

$$1 \cdot 6 = 6 \quad \frac{1}{2} \times \frac{3}{6} \quad 2 \cdot 3 = 6.$$

Since the cross-products are the same, $6 = 6$, we know that $\frac{1}{2} = \frac{3}{6}$, so the numbers are proportional. ◀

▶ **EXAMPLE 6**   Determine whether 2, 5 and 4, 7 are proportional.

We can use cross-products:

$$2 \cdot 7 = 14 \quad \frac{2}{5} \times \frac{4}{7} \quad 5 \cdot 4 = 20$$

Since the cross-products are not the same, $14 \neq 20$, we know that $\frac{2}{5} \neq \frac{4}{7}$, so the numbers are not proportional. ◀

DO EXERCISES 11–13.

C Solving Proportions

Let us see how to solve proportions. Consider the proportion

$$\frac{x}{8} = \frac{3}{5}.$$

One way to solve a proportion is to use cross-products. Then we divide on both sides to get the variable alone.

$$5 \cdot x = 8 \cdot 3 \qquad \text{Finding cross-products}$$

$$x = \frac{8 \cdot 3}{5} \qquad \text{Dividing by 5 on both sides}$$

$$x = \frac{24}{5} \qquad \text{Multiplying}$$

$$x = 4.8$$

We can check that 4.8 is the solution by replacing x by 4.8 and using cross-products:

$$4.8 \cdot 5 = 24 \qquad \frac{4.8}{8} \quad \frac{3}{5} \qquad 8 \cdot 3 = 24$$

Since the cross-products are the same, it follows that $\frac{4.8}{8} = \frac{3}{5}$, so the numbers 4.8, 8 and 3, 5 are proportional, and 4.8 is the solution of the equation.

> To solve $\frac{x}{a} = \frac{c}{d}$, find cross-products and divide on both sides to get x alone.

DO EXERCISE 14.

▶ **EXAMPLE 7**   Solve: $\frac{x}{7} = \frac{5}{3}$. Write a mixed numeral for the answer.

We have

$$\frac{x}{7} = \frac{5}{3}$$

$$3 \cdot x = 7 \cdot 5 \qquad \text{Finding cross-products}$$

$$x = \frac{7 \cdot 5}{3} \qquad \text{Dividing by 3}$$

$$x = \frac{35}{3}.$$

The solution is $\frac{35}{3}$, or $11\frac{2}{3}$.   ◀

DO EXERCISE 15.

14. Solve: $\frac{x}{63} = \frac{2}{9}$.

15. Solve: $\frac{x}{9} = \frac{5}{4}$.

ANSWERS ON PAGE A-3

16. Solve: $\dfrac{21}{5} = \dfrac{n}{2.5}$.

▶ **EXAMPLE 8** Solve: $\dfrac{7.7}{15.4} = \dfrac{y}{2.2}$. Write decimal notation for the answer.

$$\frac{7.7}{15.4} = \frac{y}{2.2}$$

$$7.7 \times 2.2 = 15.4 \times y \qquad \textbf{Finding cross-products}$$

$$\frac{7.7 \times 2.2}{15.4} = y \qquad \textbf{Dividing by 15.4}$$

$$\frac{16.94}{15.4} = y \qquad \textbf{Multiplying}$$

$$1.1 = y. \qquad \textbf{Dividing:}$$

$$
\begin{array}{r}
1.1 \\
15.4\overline{)16.9_\wedge 4} \\
15\ 4\ 0 \\
\hline
1\ 5\ 4 \\
1\ 5\ 4 \\
\hline
0
\end{array}
$$

The solution is 1.1.   ◀

DO EXERCISE 16.

17. Solve: $\dfrac{2}{3} = \dfrac{6}{x}$.

▶ **EXAMPLE 9** Solve: $\dfrac{3}{x} = \dfrac{6}{4}$.

$$\frac{3}{x} = \frac{6}{4}$$

$$3 \cdot 4 = x \cdot 6 \qquad \textbf{Finding cross-products}$$

$$\frac{3 \cdot 4}{6} = x \qquad \textbf{Dividing by 6}$$

$$\frac{12}{6} = x \qquad \textbf{Multiplying}$$

$$2 = x. \qquad \textbf{Simplifying}$$

The solution is 2.   ◀

DO EXERCISE 17.

18. Solve: $\dfrac{0.4}{0.9} = \dfrac{4.8}{t}$.

▶ **EXAMPLE 10** Solve: $\dfrac{3.4}{4.93} = \dfrac{10}{n}$. Write decimal notation for the answer.

$$\frac{3.4}{4.93} = \frac{10}{n}$$

$$n \times 3.4 = 4.93 \times 10 \qquad \textbf{Finding cross-products}$$

$$n = \frac{4.93 \times 10}{3.4} \qquad \textbf{Dividing by 3.4}$$

$$n = \frac{49.3}{3.4} \qquad \textbf{Multiplying}$$

$$n = 14.5. \qquad \textbf{Dividing:}$$

$$
\begin{array}{r}
14.5 \\
3.4\overline{)49.3_\wedge 0} \\
3\ 4\ 0\ 0 \\
\hline
1\ 5\ 3\ 0 \\
1\ 3\ 6\ 0 \\
\hline
1\ 7\ 0 \\
1\ 7\ 0 \\
\hline
0
\end{array}
$$

The solution is 14.5.   ◀

DO EXERCISE 18.

d Rates

When a ratio is used to compare two different kinds of measure, we call it a **rate.** Suppose that a car is driven 200 km in 4 hr. The ratio

$$\frac{200\ km}{4\ hr}, \quad or\ 50\frac{km}{hr}, \quad or\ 50\ kilometers\ per\ hour, \quad or\ 50\ km/h$$

Recall that "per" means "division," or "for each."

is the rate traveled in kilometers per hour, which is the division of the number of kilometers by the number of hours. A ratio of distance traveled to time is also called **speed.**

▶ **EXAMPLE 11** A student drives 145 km on 2.5 L of gas. What is the rate in kilometers per liter?

$$\frac{145\ km}{2.5\ L}, \quad or\quad 58\frac{km}{L}. \quad ◀$$

▶ **EXAMPLE 12** A cook buys 10 lb of potatoes for $1.69. What is the rate in cents per pound?

$$\frac{\$1.69}{10\ lb} = \frac{169\ cents}{10\ lb}, \quad or\quad 16.9\frac{cents}{lb}. \quad ◀$$

DO EXERCISES 19–26.

e Proportion Problems

Proportions have applications in many fields such as business, chemistry, biology, health sciences, and home economics, as well as to areas of daily life.

▶ **EXAMPLE 13** If 2 shirts can be bought for $47, how many shirts can be bought for $188?

We let x = the number of shirts that can be bought for $188. Then we translate to a proportion. We make each side the ratio of the number of shirts to cost, with the number of shirts in the numerator and the cost, in dollars, in the denominator.

$$\text{Shirts} \longrightarrow \frac{2}{47} = \frac{x}{188} \longleftarrow \text{Shirts} \atop \text{Dollars}$$

Solve: $2 \cdot 188 = 47 \cdot x$ **Finding cross-products**

$\frac{2 \cdot 188}{47} = x$ **Dividing by 47 on both sides**

$\frac{2 \cdot 47 \cdot 4}{47} = x$ **Factoring**

$2 \cdot 4 = x$ **Simplifying**

$8 = x$.

Thus, 8 shirts can be bought for $188. ◀

DO EXERCISE 27.

What is the rate, or speed, in kilometers per hour?

19. 45 km, 9 hr

20. 120 km, 10 hr

21. 3 km, 10 hr

What is the rate, or speed, in meters per second?

22. 2200 m, 2 sec

23. 52 m, 13 sec

24. 232 m, 16 sec

25. A well-hit golf ball can travel 500 ft in 2 sec. What is the rate, or speed, of the golf ball in feet per second?

26. A leaky faucet can lose 14 gal of water in a week. What is the rate in gallons per day?

27. If 7 tickets cost $45.50, what is the cost of 17 tickets?

ANSWERS ON PAGE A-3

28. A car travels 700 km in 5 days. At this rate, how far will it travel in 24 days?

▶ **EXAMPLE 14** A car travels 800 km in 3 days. At this rate, how far will it travel in 15 days?

We let x = the distance traveled in 15 days. Then we translate to a proportion. We make each side the ratio of distance to time, with distance in the numerator and time in the denominator.

$$\text{Distance in 15 days} \longrightarrow \frac{x}{15} = \frac{800}{3} \longleftarrow \text{Distance in 3 days}$$
$$\text{Time} \longrightarrow \qquad\qquad\qquad \longleftarrow \text{Time}$$

Each side of the equation represents the same ratio. That is the meaning of the equation. It may be helpful in setting up a proportion to read it, in the case above, as "the unknown distance x is to 15 days, as the known distance 800 kilometers is to 3 days."

Solve: $3 \cdot x = 15 \cdot 800$ **Finding cross-products**

$x = \dfrac{15 \cdot 800}{3}$ **Dividing by 3 on both sides**

$x = \dfrac{5 \cdot 3 \cdot 800}{3}$ **Factoring**

$x = 5 \cdot 800$ **Simplifying**

$x = 4000$

Thus the car travels 4000 km in 15 days. ◀

DO EXERCISE 28.

29. Kirk McCaskill, a pitcher for the California Angels, gave up 69 earned runs in 212 innings of pitching. What was the pitcher's earned run average? Round to the nearest hundredth.

▶ **EXAMPLE 15** *Earned run average.* Dwight Gooden, a pitcher for the New York Mets, gave up 41 earned runs in 211 innings. At this rate, how many runs did he give up every 9 innings (there are 9 innings in a baseball game)?

We have the following proportion.

$$\text{Earned runs each 9 innings} \longrightarrow \frac{E}{9} = \frac{41}{211} \longleftarrow \text{Earned runs}$$
$$\text{Innings in one game} \longrightarrow \qquad\qquad \longleftarrow \text{Innings pitched}$$

Solve: $211 \cdot E = 9 \cdot 41$ **Finding cross-products**

$E = \dfrac{9 \cdot 41}{211}$ **Dividing by 211 on both sides**

$E = \dfrac{369}{211}$ **Multiplying**

$E \approx 1.75$ **Dividing and rounding to the nearest hundredth**

We know that E = the **earned run average.** Then $E = 1.75$ means that, on the average, Dwight Gooden gave up 1.75 runs every 9 innings (every game) that he pitched. ◀

DO EXERCISE 29.

NAME   SECTION   DATE

EXERCISE SET 4.1

a Write fractional notation for the ratio.

1. 4 to 5   **2.** 178 to 572   **3.** 0.4 to 12   **4.** 0.078 to 3.456

5. In a bread recipe, there are 2 cups of milk to 12 cups of flour. What is the ratio of cups of milk to cups of flour?

6. In Washington, D.C., there are 36.1 lawyers for every 1000 people. What is the ratio of lawyers to people? of people to lawyers?

b Determine whether the two pairs of numbers are proportional.

7. 5, 6 and 7, 9   **8.** 7, 5 and 6, 4   **9.** 1, 2 and 10, 20   **10.** 7, 3 and 21, 9

c Solve.

11. $\dfrac{18}{4} = \dfrac{x}{10}$ **12.** $\dfrac{x}{45} = \dfrac{20}{25}$ **13.** $\dfrac{t}{12} = \dfrac{5}{6}$ **14.** $\dfrac{12}{4} = \dfrac{x}{3}$

15. $\dfrac{2}{5} = \dfrac{8}{n}$ **16.** $\dfrac{10}{6} = \dfrac{5}{x}$ **17.** $\dfrac{16}{12} = \dfrac{24}{x}$ **18.** $\dfrac{7}{11} = \dfrac{2}{x}$

19. $\dfrac{t}{0.16} = \dfrac{0.15}{0.40}$ **20.** $\dfrac{x}{11} = \dfrac{7.1}{2}$ **21.** $\dfrac{25}{100} = \dfrac{n}{20}$ **22.** $\dfrac{35}{125} = \dfrac{7}{m}$

23. $\dfrac{1}{2} = \dfrac{7}{x}$ **24.** $\dfrac{x}{3} = \dfrac{0}{9}$ **25.** $\dfrac{\frac{1}{4}}{\frac{1}{2}} = \dfrac{\frac{1}{2}}{x}$ **26.** $\dfrac{1}{7} = \dfrac{x}{4\frac{1}{2}}$

1.
2.
3.
4.
5.
6.
7.
8.
9.
10.
11.
12.
13.
14.
15.
16.
17.
18.
19.
20.
21.
22.
23.
24.
25.
26.

27. _____

28. _____

29. _____

30. _____

31. _____

32. _____

33. _____

34. _____

35. _____

36. _____

37. _____

38. _____

39. _____

40. _____

41. _____

42. _____

d In Exercises 27 and 28, find the rate as a ratio of distance to time.

27. 120 km, 3 hr

28. 200 mi, 25 sec

29. A car is driven 500 km in 20 hr. What is the rate in kilometers per hour? in hours per kilometer?

30. A student eats 3 hamburgers in 15 min. What is the rate in hamburgers per minute? in minutes per hamburger?

31. A jet flew 2660 mi in 4.75 hr. What was its speed?

32. A turtle traveled 0.42 mi in 2.5 hr. What was its speed?

e Solve.

33. A car travels 234 km in 14 days. At this rate, how far would it travel in 42 days?

34. An automobile went 84 mi on 6.5 gal of gasoline. At this rate, how many gallons would be needed to go 126 mi?

35. If 2 sweatshirts cost $18.80, how much would 9 sweatshirts cost?

36. If 2 cans of beans cost $0.49, how many cans of beans can you buy for $6.37?

37. Tom Browning, a pitcher for the Cincinnati Reds, gave up 71 earned runs in 179 innings. What was his earned run average? Round to the nearest hundredth.

38. Bret Saberhagen, a pitcher for the Kansas City Royals, gave up 54 earned runs in 173 innings. What was his earned run average? Round to the nearest hundredth.

39. A quality-control inspector examined 200 light bulbs and found 18 defective. At this rate, how many defective bulbs would there be in a lot of 22,000?

40. On a map, $\frac{1}{4}$ in. represents 50 mi. If two cities are $3\frac{1}{4}$ in. apart on the map, how far are they apart in reality?

SYNTHESIS

41. ▦ Anne Henning set an Olympic record in speed skating with a time of 43.33 sec in the 500-m race. What was her rate, or speed, in meters per second? in seconds per meter?

42. Cy Young, one of the greatest pitchers of all time, had an earned run average of 2.63. He pitched more innings, 7356, than anyone in the history of baseball. How many earned runs did he give up?

4.2 Percent Notation

a Understanding Percent Notation

Of the people in this country, 7% claim to have seen a UFO (Unidentified Flying Object). What does this mean? It means that, on the average, out of every 100 people, 7 of them claim to have seen a UFO. Thus, 7% is a ratio of 7 to 100, or $\frac{7}{100}$.

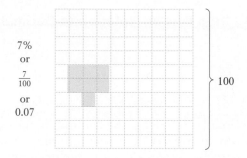

7%
or
$\frac{7}{100}$
or
0.07

100

Percent notation is used extensively in our lives. Here are some examples:

51.6% of all new marriages will end in divorce;

95% of hair spray is alcohol.

38.7% of those accidents requiring medical attention occur in the home;

23% of us go to the movies once a month;

50% of us choose pepperoni as a pizza topping;

45.8% of us sleep between 7 and 8 hours per night;

88.6% of us prefer to live in a single-family home;

7.7% financing is sometimes available on new-car loans.

The notation $n\%$ arose historically meaning "n per hundred." This leads us to the following equivalent ways of defining percent.

> **Percent notation, $n\%$, is defined**
>
> **using ratio as:** $n\% =$ the ratio of n to $100 = \frac{n}{100}$;
>
> **using fractional notation as:** $n\% = n \times \frac{1}{100}$;
>
> **using decimal notation as:** $n\% = n \times 0.01$.

▶ **EXAMPLE 1** Write three kinds of notation for 38%.

Using ratio: $38\% = \dfrac{38}{100}$ **A ratio of 38 to 100**

Using fractional notation: $38\% = 38 \times \dfrac{1}{100}$ **Replacing % by $\times \frac{1}{100}$**

Using decimal notation: $38\% = 38 \times 0.01$ **Replacing % by $\times 0.01$** ◀

OBJECTIVES

After finishing Section 4.2, you should be able to:

a Write three kinds of notation for a percent.

b Convert from percent notation to decimal notation.

c Convert from decimal notation to percent notation.

FOR EXTRA HELP

Tape 8D

Write three kinds of notation as in Examples 1 and 2.

1. 70%

2. 23.4%

3. 100%

Find decimal notation.

4. 34%

5. 78.9%

6. One year the rate of inflation was 12.08%. Find decimal notation for 12.08%.

7. The present world population growth rate is 2.1% per year. Find decimal notation for 2.1%.

▶ **EXAMPLE 2**   Write three kinds of notation for 67.8%.

Using ratio: $67.8\% = \dfrac{67.8}{100}$ **A ratio of 67.8 to 100**

Using fractional notation: $67.8\% = 67.8 \times \dfrac{1}{100}$ **Replacing % by $\times \frac{1}{100}$**

Using decimal notation: $67.8\% = 67.8 \times 0.01$ **Replacing % by $\times 0.01$**

◀

DO EXERCISES 1–3.

b   Converting from Percent Notation to Decimal Notation

Consider 78%.

$$78\% = \frac{78}{100} \quad \text{Using the definition of percent as a ratio}$$
$$= 0.78 \quad \text{Converting to decimal notation}$$

Dividing by 100 amounts to moving the decimal point two places to the left. Thus a quick way to convert from percent notation to decimal notation is to drop the percent symbol and move the decimal point two places to the left.

To convert from percent notation to decimal notation:	**36.5%**
a) drop the percent symbol, and	36.5
b) divide by 100, which means to move the decimal point two places to the left.	0 36.5 **Move 2 places to the left.** 36.5% = 0.365

▶ **EXAMPLE 3**   Find decimal notation for 99.44%.

a) Drop the percent symbol.   99.44

b) Move the decimal point two places   0 99.44
to the left.

Thus, 99.44% = 0.9944.   ◀

▶ **EXAMPLE 4**   The population growth rate of Europe is 1.1%. Find decimal notation for 1.1%.

a) Drop the percent symbol.   1.1

b) Move the decimal point two places   0 01.1
to the left.

Thus, 1.1% = 0.011.   ◀

DO EXERCISES 4–7.

c Converting from Decimal Notation to Percent Notation

Consider 0.38.

$$0.38 = \frac{38}{100} \quad \text{Converting to fractional notation}$$

$$= 38\% \quad \text{Using the definition of percent as a ratio}$$

We can convert from decimal notation to percent notation by moving the decimal point two places to the right and writing a percent symbol.

To convert from decimal notation to percent notation,	**0.675**
a) move the decimal point two places to the right, and	**0.67.5** Move 2 places to the right.
b) write a % symbol.	**67.5%**
	0.675 = 67.5%

▶ **EXAMPLE 5** Find percent notation for 1.27.

a) Move the decimal point two places to the right.   1.27

b) Write a % symbol.   127%

Thus, 1.27 = 127%.   ◀

▶ **EXAMPLE 6** Television sets are on 0.25 of the time. Find percent notation for 0.25.

a) Move the decimal point two places to the right.   0.25

b) Write a % symbol.   25%

Thus, 0.25 = 25%.   ◀

DO EXERCISES 8–12.

Find percent notation.

8. 0.24

9. 3.47

10. 1

11. Muscles make up 0.4 of a person's body. Find percent notation for 0.4.

12. Of those who buy music, 0.38 purchase prerecorded cassettes. Find percent notation for 0.38.

It is thought that the Roman Emperor Augustus began percent notation by taxing goods sold at a rate of $\frac{1}{100}$. In time, the symbol "%" evolved by interchanging the parts of the symbol "100" to "0/0" and then to "%".

ANSWERS ON PAGE A-3

❖ SIDELIGHTS

Calculator Corner:
Finding Whole-Number Remainders in Division

▶ **EXAMPLE**   Find the quotient and the whole-number remainder:

$$567 \div 13.$$

We are using a calculator with a 10-digit readout.

a) Find decimal notation for the quotient using your calculator:

$$567 \div 13 \approx 43.61538462.$$

b) Subtract the whole-number part of the answer to (a):

$$43.61538462 - 43 = 0.61538462.$$

c) Multiply the answer to (b) by the divisor, 13:

$$0.61538462 \times 13 = 8.00000006.$$

Note the rounding error on the result. This will sometimes happen when approximating using a calculator.

d) The answer is

$$43 \text{ R } 8, \quad \text{or} \quad 43\frac{8}{13}.$$

EXERCISES

Find the quotient and the whole-number remainder.

1. $478 \div 17$ **2.** $815 \div 7$

3. $824 \div 11$ **4.** $7888 \div 19$

NAME   SECTION   DATE

EXERCISE SET 4.2

a Write three kinds of notation as in Examples 1 and 2 on pp. 175–176.

1. 90%   **2.** 43.8%   **3.** 12.5%   **4.** 120%

b Find decimal notation.

5. 67%   **6.** 13%   **7.** 45.6%   **8.** 88.9%

9. 59.01%   **10.** 20.08%   **11.** 10%   **12.** 20%

13. 1%   **14.** 100%   **15.** 200%   **16.** 300%

17. 0.1%   **18.** 0.4%   **19.** 0.09%   **20.** 0.12%

21. 0.18%   **22.** 5.5%   **23.** 23.19%   **24.** 87.99%

25. Blood is 90% water. Find decimal notation for 90%.

26. Of all college football players, 2.6% play professional football. Find decimal notation for 2.6%.

27. Of those accidents requiring medical attention, 10.8% of them occur on roads. Find decimal notation for 10.8%.

28. Of all records that are purchased, 58.1% of them are pop/rock. Find decimal notation for 58.1%.

1. _____

2. _____

3. _____

4. _____

5. _____

6. _____

7. _____

8. _____

9. _____

10. _____

11. _____

12. _____

13. _____

14. _____

15. _____

16. _____

17. _____

18. _____

19. _____

20. _____

21. _____

22. _____

23. _____

24. _____

25. _____

26. _____

27. _____

28. _____

29. It is known that 45.8% percent of us sleep between 7 and 8 hours. Find decimal notation for 45.8%.

30. It is known that 23% of us go to the movies once a month. Find decimal notation for 23%.

c Find percent notation.

31. 0.47   **32.** 0.87   **33.** 0.03   **34.** 0.01

35. 1.00   **36.** 4.00   **37.** 0.334   **38.** 0.889

39. 0.75   **40.** 0.99   **41.** 0.4   **42.** 0.5

43. 0.006   **44.** 0.008   **45.** 0.017   **46.** 0.024

47. 0.2718   **48.** 0.8911   **49.** 0.0239   **50.** 0.00073

51. A person's brain is 0.025 of the body weight. Find percent notation for 0.025.

52. Of all school children, 0.95 have some tooth decay. Find percent notation for 0.95.

53. It is known that 0.24 of all children choose pizza as their favorite food. Find percent notation for 0.24.

54. It is known that 0.06 of all children choose hamburger as their favorite food. Find percent notation for 0.06.

SKILL MAINTENANCE

Convert to a mixed numeral.

55. $\dfrac{100}{3}$ **56.** $\dfrac{75}{2}$

Convert to decimal notation.

57. $\dfrac{2}{3}$ **58.** $\dfrac{1}{3}$

SYNTHESIS

59. ▦ What would you do to an entry on a calculator in order to get percent notation?

60. ▦ What would you do to percent notation on a calculator in order to get decimal notation?

4.3 Percent Notation and Fractional Notation

a Converting from Fractional Notation to Percent Notation

To convert from fractional notation to percent notation,	$\frac{3}{5}$ **Fractional notation**
a) find decimal notation by division, and	$\begin{array}{r} 0.6 \\ 5\overline{)3.0} \\ \underline{3\ 0} \\ 0 \end{array}$
b) convert the decimal notation to percent notation.	$0.6 = 0.60 = 60\%$ **Percent notation**

▶ **EXAMPLE 1** Find percent notation for $\frac{3}{8}$.

a) Find decimal notation by division.

$$\begin{array}{r} 0.3\ 7\ 5 \\ 8\overline{)3.0\ 0\ 0} \\ \underline{2\ 4} \\ 6\ 0 \\ \underline{5\ 6} \\ 4\ 0 \\ \underline{4\ 0} \\ 0 \end{array}$$

b) Convert the decimal notation to percent notation. Move the decimal point two places to the right, and write a % symbol.

$$0.37.5$$

$$\frac{3}{8} = 37.5\%, \text{ or } 37\frac{1}{2}\%$$

Don't forget the % symbol.

DO EXERCISES 1 AND 2.

OBJECTIVES

After finishing Section 4.3, you should be able to:

a Convert from fractional notation to percent notation.

b Convert from percent notation to fractional notation.

FOR EXTRA HELP

Tape 8E

Find percent notation.

1. $\frac{1}{4}$

2. $\frac{7}{8}$

ANSWERS ON PAGE A-3

3. The human body is $\frac{2}{3}$ water. Find percent notation for $\frac{2}{3}$.

▶ **EXAMPLE 2**   Of all meals, $\frac{1}{3}$ are eaten outside the home. Find percent notation for $\frac{1}{3}$.

a) Find decimal notation by division.

$$
\begin{array}{r}
0.3\ 3\ 3 \\
3 \overline{)1.0\ 0\ 0} \\
\underline{9} \\
1\ 0 \\
\underline{9} \\
1\ 0 \\
\underline{9} \\
1
\end{array}
$$

We get a repeating decimal: $0.33\overline{3}$.

b) Convert the answer to percent notation.

$$0.33.\overline{3}$$

$$\frac{1}{3} = 33.\overline{3}\%, \text{ or } 33\frac{1}{3}\% \qquad ◀$$

DO EXERCISES 3 AND 4.

4. Find percent notation: $\frac{5}{6}$.

In some cases, division is not the easiest way to convert. The following are some optional ways this might be done.

▶ **EXAMPLE 3**   Find percent notation for $\frac{69}{100}$.

We use the definition of percent as a ratio.

$$\frac{69}{100} = 69\% \qquad ◀$$

Find percent notation.

5. $\frac{57}{100}$

▶ **EXAMPLE 4**   Find percent notation for $\frac{17}{20}$.

We multiply by 1 to get 100 in the denominator. We think of what we have to multiply 20 by in order to get 100. That number is 5, so we multiply by 1 using $\frac{5}{5}$.

$$\frac{17}{20} \cdot \frac{5}{5} = \frac{85}{100} = 85\% \qquad ◀$$

DO EXERCISES 5 AND 6.

6. $\frac{19}{25}$

b   **Converting from Percent Notation to Fractional Notation**

To convert from percent notation to fractional notation,	**30%** Percent notation
a) use the definition of percent as a ratio, and	$\frac{30}{100}$
b) simplify, if possible.	$\frac{3}{10}$ Fractional notation

▶ **EXAMPLE 5**   Find fractional notation for 75%.

$$75\% = \frac{75}{100} \quad \text{Using the definition of percent}$$

$$= \frac{3 \cdot 25}{4 \cdot 25}$$

$$= \frac{3}{4} \cdot \frac{25}{25} \quad \Bigg\} \quad \text{Simplifying}$$

$$= \frac{3}{4}$$

▶ **EXAMPLE 6**   Find fractional notation for 62.5%.

$$62.5\% = \frac{62.5}{100} \quad \text{Using the definition of percent}$$

$$= \frac{62.5}{100} \times \frac{10}{10} \quad \text{Multiplying by 1 to eliminate the decimal point in the numerator}$$

$$= \frac{625}{1000}$$

$$= \frac{5 \cdot 125}{8 \cdot 125}$$

$$= \frac{5}{8} \cdot \frac{125}{125} \quad \Bigg\} \quad \text{Simplifying}$$

$$= \frac{5}{8}$$

◀

▶ **EXAMPLE 7**   Find fractional notation for $16\frac{2}{3}\%$.

$$16\frac{2}{3}\% = \frac{50}{3}\% \quad \text{Converting from the mixed numeral to fractional notation}$$

$$= \frac{50}{3} \times \frac{1}{100} \quad \text{Using the definition of percent}$$

$$= \frac{50 \cdot 1}{3 \cdot 50 \cdot 2}$$

$$= \frac{1}{6} \cdot \frac{50}{50} \quad \Bigg\} \quad \text{Simplifying}$$

$$= \frac{1}{6}$$

◀

DO EXERCISES 7–9.

Table 1 at the back of the book contains decimal, fractional, and percent equivalents that are used so often that it would speed up your work if you learned them. For example, $\frac{1}{3} = 0.\overline{3}$, so we say that the **decimal equivalent** of $\frac{1}{3}$ is $0.\overline{3}$, or that $0.\overline{3}$ has the **fractional equivalent** $\frac{1}{3}$.

DO EXERCISE 10.

Find fractional notation.

7. 60%

8. 3.25%

9. $66\frac{2}{3}\%$

10. Complete this table.

Fractional notation	$\frac{1}{5}$		
Decimal notation		$0.83\overline{3}$	
Percent notation			$37\frac{1}{2}\%$

❖ SIDELIGHTS

Applications of Ratio and Percent:
The Price-Earnings Ratio and Stock Yields

The Price-Earnings Ratio

If a company in one year has total earnings of $5,000,000 and has issued 100,000 shares of stock, the earnings per share are $50. The **price-earnings ratio, P/E,** is the price of the stock divided by the earnings per share. At one time the price per share of IBM was $263\frac{1}{8}$ and the earnings per share were $17.60. For the IBM stock, the price-earnings ratio, P/E, is given by

$$\frac{P}{E} = \frac{\text{Price of stock}}{\text{Earnings per share}}$$

$$= \frac{263\frac{1}{8}}{17.60}$$

$$= \frac{263.125}{17.60} \quad \text{Converting to decimal notation}$$

$$\approx 15.0. \quad \text{Dividing, using a calculator, and rounding to the nearest tenth}$$

Stock Yields

The price per share of IBM stock was $263\frac{1}{8}$ and the company was paying a yearly dividend of $10 per share. It is helpful to those interested in stocks to know what percent the dividend is of the price of the stock. The percent is called the **yield.** For the IBM stock the yield is given by

$$\text{Yield} = \frac{\text{Dividend}}{\text{Price per share}}$$

$$= \frac{10}{263\frac{1}{8}}$$

$$= \frac{10}{263.125} \quad \text{Converting to decimal notation}$$

$$\approx 0.038 \quad \text{Dividing and rounding to the nearest thousandth}$$

$$= 3.8\%. \quad \text{Converting to percent notation}$$

EXERCISES

Compute the price-earnings ratio and the yield for the given stock.

Stock	Price per Share	Earnings	Dividend
1. General Motors	$68\frac{5}{8}$	$11.50	$5.55
2. K-Mart	31	2.60	0.56
3. United Airlines	$18\frac{5}{8}$	4.00	0.60
4. AT&T	62	6.60	4.20

NAME   SECTION   DATE

EXERCISE SET 4.3

a Find percent notation.

1. $\frac{41}{100}$ 2. $\frac{36}{100}$ 3. $\frac{1}{100}$ 4. $\frac{5}{100}$ 5. $\frac{2}{10}$ 6. $\frac{7}{10}$

7. $\frac{3}{10}$ 8. $\frac{9}{10}$ 9. $\frac{1}{2}$ 10. $\frac{3}{4}$ 11. $\frac{5}{8}$ 12. $\frac{1}{8}$

13. $\frac{2}{5}$ 14. $\frac{4}{5}$ 15. $\frac{2}{3}$ 16. $\frac{1}{3}$ 17. $\frac{1}{6}$ 18. $\frac{5}{6}$

19. $\frac{4}{25}$ 20. $\frac{17}{25}$ 21. $\frac{1}{20}$ 22. $\frac{31}{50}$ 23. $\frac{17}{50}$ 24. $\frac{3}{20}$

25. Bread is $\frac{9}{25}$ water. Find percent notation for $\frac{9}{25}$.

26. Milk is $\frac{7}{8}$ water. Find percent notation for $\frac{7}{8}$.

b Find fractional notation.

27. 80%   28. 50%   29. 62.5%   30. 12.5%

31. $33\frac{1}{3}\%$ 32. $83\frac{1}{3}\%$ 33. $16.\overline{6}\%$ 34. $66.\overline{6}\%$

Answers:
1. ___ 2. ___ 3. ___ 4. ___ 5. ___ 6. ___ 7. ___ 8. ___ 9. ___ 10. ___ 11. ___ 12. ___ 13. ___ 14. ___ 15. ___ 16. ___ 17. ___ 18. ___ 19. ___ 20. ___ 21. ___ 22. ___ 23. ___ 24. ___ 25. ___ 26. ___ 27. ___ 28. ___ 29. ___ 30. ___ 31. ___ 32. ___ 33. ___ 34. ___

ANSWERS

35. 7.25%   **36.** 4.85%

35. _____

36. _____

37. 0.8%   **38.** 0.2%

37. _____

38. _____

39. The United States uses 35% of the world's energy. Find fractional notation for 35%.

39. _____

40. _____

41. See table.

40. The United States has 6% of the world's population. Find fractional notation for 6%.

42. _____

43. _____

44. _____

45. _____

46. _____

47. _____

41. Complete the table.

Fractional notation	Decimal notation	Percent notation
$\frac{1}{8}$		$12\frac{1}{2}\%$, or 12.5%
$\frac{1}{6}$		
		20%
	0.25	
		$33\frac{1}{3}\%$, or $33.\overline{3}\%$
		$37\frac{1}{2}\%$, or 37.5%
		40%
$\frac{1}{2}$	0.5	50%
$\frac{3}{5}$		
	0.625	
$\frac{2}{3}$		
	0.75	75%
$\frac{4}{5}$		
$\frac{5}{6}$		$83\frac{1}{3}\%$, or $83.\overline{3}\%$
$\frac{7}{8}$		$87\frac{1}{2}\%$, or 87.5%
		100%

SKILL MAINTENANCE

Solve.

42. $10 \cdot x = 725$ **43.** $15 \cdot y = 75$ **44.** $0.05 \times b = 20$ **45.** $3 = 0.16 \times b$

SYNTHESIS

Find percent notation.

46. ▥ $\frac{41}{369}$ **47.** ▥ $\frac{54}{999}$

4.4 Solving Percent Problems Using Equations

a⃝ Translating to Equations

To solve a problem involving percents, it is helpful to translate first to an equation.

▶ **EXAMPLE 1** Translate:

$$23\% \text{ of } 5 \text{ is what?}$$

$$23\% \cdot 5 = a \qquad ◀$$

> "Of" translates to "$\cdot$", or "$\times$".
> "What" translates to some letter.
> "Is" translates to "$=$".
> % translates to "$\times \frac{1}{100}$" or "$\times 0.01$".

▶ **EXAMPLE 2** Translate:

$$\text{What is } 11\% \text{ of } 49?$$

$$a = 11\% \cdot 49 \qquad ◀$$

DO EXERCISES 1 AND 2.

▶ **EXAMPLE 3** Translate:

$$3 \text{ is } 10\% \text{ of what?}$$

$$3 = 10\% \cdot b \qquad \text{Any letter can be used.} ◀$$

▶ **EXAMPLE 4** Translate:

$$45\% \text{ of what is } 23?$$

$$45\% \times b = 23 \qquad ◀$$

DO EXERCISES 3 AND 4.

▶ **EXAMPLE 5** Translate:

$$10 \text{ is what percent of } 20?$$

$$10 = n \times 20 \qquad ◀$$

▶ **EXAMPLE 6** Translate:

$$\text{What percent of } 50 \text{ is } 7?$$

$$n \cdot 50 = 7 \qquad ◀$$

DO EXERCISES 5 AND 6.

OBJECTIVES

After finishing Section 4.4, you should be able to:

a⃝ Translate percent problems to equations.

b⃝ Solve basic percent problems.

FOR EXTRA HELP

Tape 8F

Translate to an equation. Do not solve.

1. 12% of 50 is what?

2. What is 40% of 60?

Translate to an equation. Do not solve.

3. 45 is 20% of what?

4. 120% of what is 60?

Translate to an equation. Do not solve.

5. 16 is what percent of 40?

6. What percent of 84 is 10.5?

ANSWERS ON PAGE A-3

7. Solve:

What is 12% of 50?

b   **Solving Percent Problems**

In solving percent problems, we use the same strategy that we have used for solving problems throughout this text.

> To solve percent problems,
> a) translate to an equation, and
> b) solve the equation.

Percent problems are actually of three different types. Although the method we present does *not* require that you be able to identify which type we are studying, it is helpful to know them.

We know that

$$15 \text{ is } 25\% \text{ of } 60, \text{ or}$$
$$15 = 25\% \times 60.$$

We can think of this as:

> Amount = Percent number × Base.

Each of the three types of percent problems depends on which of the three pieces of information is missing.

1. Finding the amount

Example: What is 25% of 60?

Translation: $y = 25\% \cdot 60$

2. Finding the base

Example: 15 is 25% of what number?

Translation: $15 = 25\% \cdot y$

3. Finding the percent number

Example: 15 is what percent of 60?

Translation: $15 = y \cdot 60$

Finding the Amount

▶ **EXAMPLE 7**   What is 11% of 49?

Translate: $a = 11\% \times 49$.

The letter is by itself. To solve the equation, we just convert 11% to decimal notation and multiply.

```
     4 9
  × 0.1 1      11% = 0.11
     4 9
   4 9 0
a = 5.3 9
```

> A way of checking answers is by estimating as follows:
> $$11\% \times 49 \approx 10\% \times 50$$
> $$= 0.10 \times 50 = 5.$$
> Since 5 is close to 5.39, our answer is reasonable.

Thus, 5.39 is 11% of 49. The answer is 5.39.   ◀

▶ **EXAMPLE 8** 120% of $42 is what?

Translate: $120\% \times 42 = a$.

The letter is by itself. To solve the equation, we carry out the calculation.

$$
\begin{array}{r}
4\ 2 \\
\times\ 1\ .2 \\
\hline
8\ 4 \\
4\ 2\ 0 \\
\hline
a = 5\ 0\ .4
\end{array}
$$

120% = 1.20 = 1.2

Thus, 120% of $42 is $50.40. The answer is $50.40. ◀

DO EXERCISE 8.

Finding the Base

▶ **EXAMPLE 9** 5% of what is 20?

Translate: $5\% \times b = 20$.

This time the letter is *not* by itself. To solve the equation, we divide on both sides by 5%:

$b = 20 \div 5\%$ **Dividing on both sides by 5%**

$b = 20 \div 0.05$ **5% = 0.05**

$b = 400$.

$$
\begin{array}{r}
4\ 0\ 0. \\
0.0\ 5\,)\overline{2\ 0\ 0.0\ 0_{\wedge}} \\
2\ 0\ 0\ 0 \\
\hline
0
\end{array}
$$

Thus, 5% of 400 is 20. The answer is 400. ◀

DO EXERCISE 9.

▶ **EXAMPLE 10** $3 is 16% of what?

Translate: $3 is 16% of what?

$$
3\ =\ 16\%\ \times\ b.
$$

Again, the letter is not by itself. To solve the equation, we divide on both sides by 16%:

$3 \div 16\% = b$ **Dividing on both sides by 16%**

$3 \div 0.16 = b$ **16% = 0.16**

$18.75 = b$.

$$
\begin{array}{r}
1\ 8.7\ 5 \\
0.1\ 6\,)\overline{3.0\ 0_{\wedge}0\ 0} \\
1\ 6 \\
\hline
1\ 4\ 0 \\
1\ 2\ 8 \\
\hline
1\ 2\ 0 \\
1\ 1\ 2 \\
\hline
8\ 0 \\
8\ 0 \\
\hline
0
\end{array}
$$

Thus, $3 is 16% of $18.75. The answer is $18.75. ◀

DO EXERCISE 10.

8. Solve:

64% of $55 is what?

9. Solve:

20% of what is 45?

10. Solve:

$60 is 120% of what?

11. Solve:

16 is what percent of 40?

Finding the Percent Number

In solving these problems, you must remember to convert to percent notation after you have solved the equation.

▶ **EXAMPLE 11**　　10 is what percent of 20?

Translate:

$$10 \quad = \quad n \quad \times \quad 20.$$

To solve the equation, we divide on both sides by 20 and convert the result to percent notation:

$$n \cdot 20 = 10$$

$$\frac{n \cdot 20}{20} = \frac{10}{20} \qquad \text{Dividing on both sides by 20}$$

$$n = 0.50 = 50\%. \qquad \text{Converting to percent notation}$$

Thus, 10 is 50% of 20. The answer is 50%.　　◀

DO EXERCISE 11.

12. Solve:

What percent of $84 is $10.50?

▶ **EXAMPLE 12**　　What percent of $50 is $16?

Translate: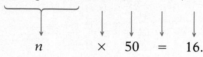

$$n \quad \times \quad 50 \quad = \quad 16.$$

To solve the equation, we divide on both sides by 50 and convert the answer to percent notation:

$$n = 16 \div 50 \qquad \text{Dividing on both sides by 50}$$

$$n = \frac{16}{50}$$

$$n = \frac{16}{50} \cdot \frac{2}{2}$$

$$n = \frac{32}{100}$$

$$n = 32\%.$$

Thus, 32% of $50 is $16. The answer is 32%.　　◀

DO EXERCISE 12.

EXERCISE SET 4.4

a Translate to an equation. Do not solve.

1. What is 41% of 89?

2. 87% of 41 is what?

3. 89 is what percent of 99?

4. What percent of 25 is 8?

5. 13 is 25% of what?

6. 21.4% of what is 20?

b Solve.

7. What is 120% of 75?

8. What is 65% of 480?

9. 150% of 30 is what?

10. 100% of 13 is what?

11. What is 5% of $300?

12. What is 3% of $45?

13. 2.1% of 50 is what?

14. $33\frac{1}{3}$% of 240 is what?
(*Hint:* $33\frac{1}{3}\% = \frac{1}{3}$.)

15. $12 is what percent of $50?

16. $15 is what percent of $60?

17. 20 is what percent of 10?

18. 90 is what percent of 30?

ANSWERS

1. _____

2. _____

3. _____

4. _____

5. _____

6. _____

7. _____

8. _____

9. _____

10. _____

11. _____

12. _____

13. _____

14. _____

15. _____

16. _____

17. _____

18. _____

19. _____

20. _____

21. _____

22. _____

23. _____

24. _____

25. _____

26. _____

27. _____

28. _____

29. _____

30. _____

31. _____

32. _____

33. _____

34. _____

35. _____

36. _____

37. _____

38. _____

39. _____

40. _____

19. What percent of $300 is $150?

20. What percent of $50 is $40?

21. What percent of 80 is 100?

22. What percent of 30 is 15?

23. 20 is 50% of what?

24. 45 is 20% of what?

25. 40% of what is $16?

26. 100% of what is $89?

27. 56.32 is 64% of what?

28. 34.32 is 44% of what?

29. 70% of what is 14?

30. 70% of what is 35?

31. What is $62\frac{1}{2}$% of 10?

32. What is $35\frac{1}{4}$% of 1200?

33. What is 8.3% of $10,200?

34. What is 9.2% of $5600?

SKILL MAINTENANCE

Write fractional notation.

35. 0.09

36. 1.79

Write decimal notation.

37. $\frac{89}{100}$

38. $\frac{7}{100}$

SYNTHESIS

Solve.

39. ▦ What is 7.75% of $10,880?

Estimate _____

Calculate _____

40. ▦ 50,951.775 is what percent of 78,995?

Estimate _____

Calculate _____

4.5 Solving Percent Problems Using Proportions*

a Translating to Proportions

A percent is a ratio of some number to 100. For example, 75% is the ratio

$\frac{75}{100}$.

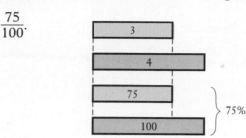

We also know that 3 and 4 have the same ratio as 75 and 100. Thus,

$$\frac{3}{4} = \frac{75}{100} = 75\%.$$

To solve a percent problem using a proportion, we translate as follows:

$$\text{Amount} \longrightarrow \frac{a}{b} = \frac{n}{100} \longleftarrow \text{Number} \atop \text{Base} \qquad\qquad \longleftarrow 100$$

You might find it helpful to read this as "part is to whole as part is to whole."

For example,

75% of 48 is 36

translates to

$$\frac{36}{48} = \frac{75}{100}.$$

A clue in translating is that the base, b, corresponds to 100 and usually follows the wording "percent of." Also, $n\%$ always translates to $n/100$. Another aid in translating is to make a comparison drawing. We usually start with the percent side. We have 0% at the top and 100% at the bottom. Then we estimate where the 75% would be located. The numbers, or quantities, that correspond are then filled in. The base—in this case, 48—always corresponds to 100% and the amount—in this case, 36—corresponds to 75%.

Percents	Quantities		Percents	Quantities		Percents	Quantities
0%	0		0%	0		0%	0
			75%			75%	36
100%			100%			100%	48

The proportion can then be read easily from the drawing.

OBJECTIVES

After finishing Section 4.5, you should be able to:

a Translate percent problems to proportions.

b Solve basic percent problems.

FOR EXTRA HELP

Tape 8F

*Note: This section presents an alternative method for solving basic percent problems. You can use either equations or proportions to solve percent problems, but you might prefer one method over the other, or your instructor may direct you to use one method over the other.

Translate to a proportion. Do not solve.

1. 12% of 50 is what?

▶ **EXAMPLE 1**   Translate to a proportion.

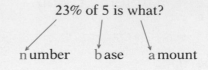

$$\frac{23}{100} = \frac{a}{5}$$

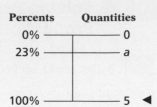

▶ **EXAMPLE 2**   Translate to a proportion.

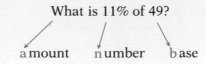

2. What is 40% of 60?

$$\frac{11}{100} = \frac{a}{49}$$

DO EXERCISES 1 AND 2.

▶ **EXAMPLE 3**   Translate to a proportion.

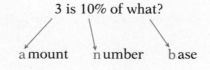

$$\frac{10}{100} = \frac{3}{b}$$

▶ **EXAMPLE 4**   Translate to a proportion.

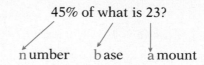

Translate to a proportion. Do not solve.

3. 45 is 20% of what?

$$\frac{45}{100} = \frac{23}{b}$$

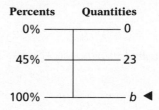

DO EXERCISES 3 AND 4.

▶ **EXAMPLE 5**   Translate to a proportion.

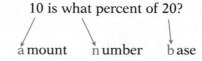

4. 120% of what is 60?

$$\frac{n}{100} = \frac{10}{20}$$

▶ **EXAMPLE 6**   Translate to a proportion.

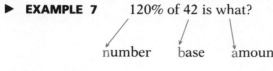

What percent of 50 is 7?

number   base   amount

$$\frac{n}{100} = \frac{7}{50}$$

Percents   Quantities

0% ——————— 0
n% ——————— 7

100% ——————— 50 ◀

DO EXERCISES 5 AND 6.

b Solving Percent Problems

▶ **EXAMPLE 7**   120% of 42 is what?

number   base   amount

Translate: $\dfrac{120}{100} = \dfrac{a}{42}$

Solve: $120 \cdot 42 = 100 \cdot a$ **Finding cross-products**

$\dfrac{120 \cdot 42}{100} = a$ **Dividing by 100**

$\dfrac{5040}{100} = a$

$50.4 = a$ **Simplifying**

Thus, 120% of 42 is 50.4. The answer is 50.4.   ◀

DO EXERCISES 7 AND 8.

Percents   Quantities

0% ——————— 0

100% ——————— 42
120% ——————— a

▶ **EXAMPLE 8**   5% of what is $20?

number   base   amount

Translate: $\dfrac{5}{100} = \dfrac{20}{b}$

Solve: $5 \cdot b = 100 \cdot 20$ **Finding cross-products**

$b = \dfrac{100 \cdot 20}{5}$ **Dividing by 5**

$b = \dfrac{5 \cdot 20 \cdot 20}{5}$ **Factoring**

$b = 400$ **Simplifying**

Thus, 5% of $400 is $20. The answer is $400.   ◀

DO EXERCISE 9.

Percents   Quantities

0% ——————— 0
5% ——————— 20

100% ——————— b

Translate to a proportion. Do not solve.

5. 16 is what percent of 40?

6. What percent of 84 is 10.5?

Solve.

7. What is 12% of 50?

8. 64% of 55 is what?

9. Solve:

     20% of what is $45?

10. Solve:

60 is 120% of what?

► **EXAMPLE 9**   3 is 16% of what?

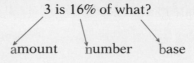

amount   number   base

Percents	Quantities
0%	0
16%	3
100%	b

Translate: $\dfrac{16}{100} = \dfrac{3}{b}$

Solve: $16 \cdot b = 100 \cdot 3$ **Finding cross-products**

$b = \dfrac{100 \cdot 3}{16}$ **Dividing by 16**

$b = \dfrac{300}{16}$

$b = 18.75$

Thus, 3 is 16% of 18.75. The answer is 18.75.   ◄

DO EXERCISE 10.

---

11. Solve:

$16 is what percent of $40?

► **EXAMPLE 10** $10 is what percent of $20?

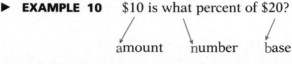

amount   number   base

Percents	Quantities
0%	0
n%	$10
100%	$20

Translate: $\dfrac{n}{100} = \dfrac{10}{20}$

Solve: $20 \cdot n = 100 \cdot 10$ **Finding cross-products**

$n = \dfrac{100 \cdot 10}{20}$ **Dividing by 20**

$n = \dfrac{20 \cdot 5 \cdot 10}{20}$

$n = 50$

Thus, $10 is 50% of $20. The answer is 50%.   ◄

DO EXERCISE 11.

---

12. Solve:

What percent of 84 is 10.5?

► **EXAMPLE 11**   What percent of 50 is 16?

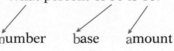

number   base   amount

Percents	Quantities
0%	0
n%	16
100%	50

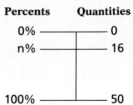

Translate: $\dfrac{n}{100} = \dfrac{16}{50}$

Solve: $50 \cdot n = 100 \cdot 16$ **Finding cross-products**

$n = \dfrac{100 \cdot 16}{50}$ **Dividing by 50**

$n = \dfrac{50 \cdot 2 \cdot 16}{50}$

$n = 32$

Thus, 32% of 50 is 16. The answer is 32%.   ◄

DO EXERCISE 12.

EXERCISE SET 4.5

a Translate to a proportion. Do not solve.

1. What is 82% of 74?

2. 58% of 65 is what?

3. 4.3 is what percent of 5.9?

4. What percent of 6.8 is 5.3?

5. 14 is 25% of what?

6. 22.3% of what is 40?

b Solve.

7. What is 84% of $50?

8. What is 78% of $90?

9. 80% of 550 is what?

10. 90% of 740 is what?

11. What is 8% of 1000?

12. What is 9% of 2000?

13. 4.8% of 60 is what?

14. 63.1% of 80 is what?

15. $24 is what percent of $96?

16. $14 is what percent of $70?

17. 102 is what percent of 100?

18. 103 is what percent of 100?

19. What percent of $480 is $120?

20. What percent of $80 is $60?

ANSWERS

1.

2.

3.

4.

5.

6.

7.

8.

9.

10.

11.

12.

13.

14.

15.

16.

17.

18.

19.

20.

21. _____

22. _____

23. _____

24. _____

25. _____

26. _____

27. _____

28. _____

29. _____

30. _____

31. _____

32. _____

33. _____

34. _____

35. _____

36. _____

21. What percent of 160 is 150?

22. What percent of 24 is 8?

23. $18 is 25% of what?

24. $75 is 20% of what?

25. 60% of what is 54?

26. 80% of what is 96?

27. 65.12 is 74% of what?

28. 63.7 is 65% of what?

29. 80% of what is 16?

30 80% of what is 10?

31. What is $62\frac{1}{2}$% of 40?

32. What is $43\frac{1}{4}$% of 2600?

33. What is 9.4% of $8300?

34. What is 8.7% of $76,000?

SYNTHESIS

Solve.

35. ▤ What is 8.85% of $12,640?

     Estimate _____

     Calculate _____

36. ▤ 78.8% of what is 9809.024?

     Estimate _____

     Calculate _____

4.6 Applications of Percent

a Percent Problems

Problems involving percent are not always stated in a manner easily translated to an equation. In such cases, it is helpful to restate the problem before translating. Sometimes it also helps to draw a picture.

▶ **EXAMPLE 1** The FBI annually receives 16,000 applications for the position of an agent. It accepts 600 of these applicants. What percent does it accept?

Method 1. Solve using an equation.

Restate: 600 is what percent of 16,000?

Translate: $600 = n \times 16,000$

To solve the equation, we divide on both sides by 16,000:

$$600 \div 16,000 = n$$
$$0.0375 = n$$
$$3.75\% = n.$$

The FBI accepts 3.75% of its applicants.

Method 2*. Solve using a proportion.

Restate: 600 is what percent of 16,000?

amount   number   base

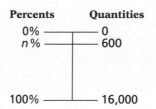

Percents	Quantities
0%	0
n%	600
100%	16,000

Translate: $\dfrac{n}{100} = \dfrac{600}{16,000}$

Solve: $16,000 \cdot n = 100 \cdot 600$ **Finding cross-products**

$n = \dfrac{100 \cdot 600}{16,000}$ **Dividing by 16,000**

$n = \dfrac{60,000}{16,000}$

$n = 3.75$

The FBI accepts 3.75% of its applicants.   ◀

DO EXERCISE 1.

Note: If you skipped Section 4.5, then you should ignore method 2.

OBJECTIVES

After finishing Section 4.6, you should be able to:

a Solve applied percent problems.

b Solve percent problems involving percent increase or decrease.

FOR EXTRA HELP

Tape 9A

1. A college basketball team won 11 of its 25 games. What percent of its games did it win?

ANSWER ON PAGE A-3

2. The weight of a human brain is 2.5% of total body weight. A person weighs 200 lb. What does the brain weigh?

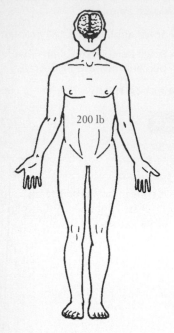

200 lb

▶ **EXAMPLE 2**   Have you ever wondered why you receive so much junk mail? One reason offered by the U.S. Postal Service is that we open and read 78% of the advertising we receive in the mail. Suppose that a business sends out 9500 advertising brochures. How many of them can it expect to be opened and read?

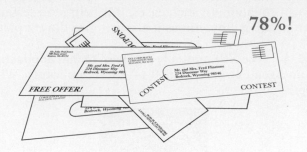

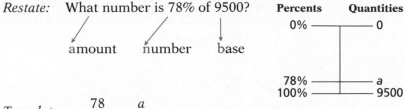

78%!

Method 1.   Solve using an equation.

Restate: What number   is   78%   of   9500?

Translate: a =   78%   ×   9500

This tells us what to do. We convert 78% to decimal notation and multiply:

$$a = 78\% \times 9500 = 0.78 \times 9500 = 7410.$$

The business can expect 7410 of its brochures to be opened and read.

Method 2.   Solve using a proportion.

Restate: What number is 78% of 9500?

      amount   number   base

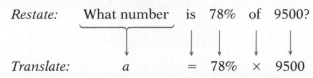

Percents	Quantities
0%	0
78%	a
100%	9500

Translate: $\dfrac{78}{100} = \dfrac{a}{9500}$

Solve: $78 \cdot 9500 = 100 \cdot a$ **Finding cross-products**

$\dfrac{78 \cdot 9500}{100} = a$ **Dividing by 100**

$\dfrac{741,000}{100} = a$

$7410 = a$

The business can expect 7410 of its brochures to be opened and read. ◀

DO EXERCISE 2.

b Percent Increase or Decrease

Percent is often used to state increases or decreases. Suppose the population of a town has *increased* 70%. This means that the increase was 70% of the former population. The population of a town is 2340 and it increases 70%. The increase is 70% of 2340, or 1638. The new population is 2340 + 1638, or 3978, which is shown below.

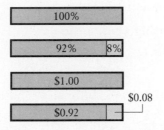

What do we mean when we say that the price of Swiss cheese has decreased 8%? If the price was $1.00 a pound and it went down to $0.92 a pound, then the decrease is $0.08, which is 8% of the original price. We can see this in the following figure.

> **To find a percent of increase or decrease, find the amount of increase or decrease and then determine what percent this is of the *original* amount.**

▶ **EXAMPLE 3**   The price of milk increased from 40 cents per liter to 45 cents per liter. What was the percent of increase?

We make a drawing.

a) First, we find the increase by subtracting.

$$\begin{array}{r} 4\ 5 \\ -\ 4\ 0 \\ \hline 5 \end{array}$$ New price
Original price
Increase

The increase is 5 cents.

3. The price of an automobile increased from $5800 to $6322. What was the percent of increase?

b) Now we ask:

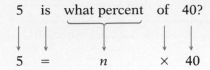

5 is what percent of 40 (the original price)?

> A common error is to use 45 instead of 40, the *original* amount.

To find out, we use either of our two methods.

    Method 1.   Solve using an equation.

$$5 \quad \text{is} \quad \underbrace{\text{what percent}} \quad \text{of} \quad 40?$$

$$5 \quad = \quad n \quad \times \quad 40$$

To solve the equation, we divide on both sides by 40:

$$5 \div 40 = n \qquad \textbf{Dividing by 40}$$
$$0.125 = n$$
$$12.5\% = n.$$

The percent of increase was 12.5%.

    Method 2.   Solve using a proportion.

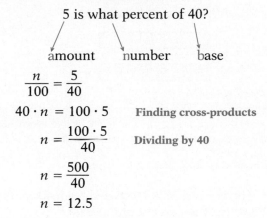

5 is what percent of 40?

$$\text{amount} \qquad \text{number} \qquad \text{base}$$

$$\frac{n}{100} = \frac{5}{40}$$
$$40 \cdot n = 100 \cdot 5 \qquad \textbf{Finding cross-products}$$
$$n = \frac{100 \cdot 5}{40} \qquad \textbf{Dividing by 40}$$
$$n = \frac{500}{40}$$
$$n = 12.5$$

The percent of increase was 12.5%.   ◀

DO EXERCISE 3.

▶ **EXAMPLE 4** By proper furnace maintenance, a family that pays a monthly fuel bill of $78.00 can reduce their bill to $70.20. What is the percent of decrease?

We make a drawing.

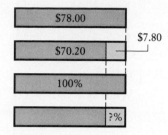

a) First, we find the decrease.

$$\begin{array}{r} 7\ 8.0\ 0 \\ -\ 7\ 0.2\ 0 \\ \hline 7.8\ 0 \end{array}\quad \begin{array}{l} \text{Original bill} \\ \text{New bill} \\ \text{Decrease} \end{array}$$

The decrease is $7.80.

b) Now we ask:

7.80 is what percent of 78.00 (the original bill)?

> A common error is to use $70.20 instead of $78.00, the *original* amount.

Method 1. Solve using an equation.

7.80   is   what percent   of   78.00?

$$7.80 \quad = \quad n \quad \times \quad 78.00$$

To solve the equation, we divide on both sides by 78:

$$7.8 \div 78 = n \qquad \textbf{Dividing by 78}$$
$$0.1 = n$$
$$10\% = n.$$

The percent of decrease is 10%.

Method 2. Solve using a proportion.

7.80 is what percent of 78.00?

amount   number   base

$$\frac{n}{100} = \frac{7.80}{78.00}$$
$$78.00 \times n = 100 \times 7.80 \qquad \textbf{Finding cross-products}$$
$$n = \frac{100 \times 7.80}{78.00} \qquad \textbf{Dividing by 78.00}$$
$$n = \frac{780}{78}$$
$$n = 10$$

The percent of decrease is 10%.

4. By using only cold water in the washing machine, a family that pays a monthly fuel bill of $78.00 can reduce their bill to $74.88. What is the percent of decrease?

DO EXERCISE 4.

ANSWER ON PAGE A-3

5. A consumer earns $9800 one year and gets a 9% raise the next. What is the new salary?

▶ **EXAMPLE 5**   A consumer earns $9700 one year and gets a 6% raise the next. What is the new salary?

We make a drawing.

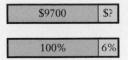

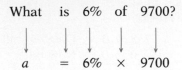

a) First, we find the increase. We ask:

What is 6% of 9700?

Method 1. Solve using an equation.

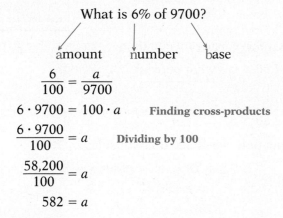

This tells us what to do. We convert 6% to decimal notation and multiply:

$$a = 0.06 \times 9700 = 582.$$

The increase is $582.00.

Method 2. Solve using a proportion.

What is 6% of 9700?

amount   number   base

$$\frac{6}{100} = \frac{a}{9700}$$

$6 \cdot 9700 = 100 \cdot a$ **Finding cross-products**

$$\frac{6 \cdot 9700}{100} = a$$ **Dividing by 100**

$$\frac{58,200}{100} = a$$

$$582 = a$$

The increase is $582.00.

b) The new salary is

$$\$9700 + \$582 = \$10,282.$$ ◀

DO EXERCISE 5.

NAME   SECTION   DATE

EXERCISE SET 4.6

a   Solve.

1. It has been determined by sociologists that 17% of the population is left-handed. Each week 160 men enter a tournament conducted by the Professional Bowlers Association. How many would you expect to be left-handed? not left-handed? Round to the nearest one.

2. A guideline commonly used by businesses is to use 5% of their operating budget for advertising. A business has an operating budget of $8000 per week. How much should it spend each week for advertising? for other expenses?

1. _____

2. _____

3. Of all moviegoers, 67% are in the 12–29 age group. A theater contained 800 people for a showing of *Teenage Ninja Mathematics Professors*. How many were in the 12–29 age group? not in this age group?

4. Deming, New Mexico, claims to have the purest drinking water in the world. It is 99.9% pure. If you had 240 L of water from Deming, how much of it, in liters, would be pure? impure?

3. _____

4. _____

5. A baseball player gets 13 hits in 40 at bats. What percent are hits? not hits?

6. On a test of 80 items, a student had 76 correct. What percent were correct? incorrect?

5. _____

6. _____

7. A lab technician has 680 mL of a solution of water and acid; 3% is acid. How many milliliters are acid? water?

8. A lab technician has 540 mL of a solution of alcohol and water; 8% is alcohol. How many milliliters are alcohol? water?

7. _____

8. _____

ANSWERS

9. Of the 8760 hours in a year, most television sets are on for 2190 hours. What percent is this?

10. In a medical study, it was determined that if 800 people kiss someone else who has a cold, only 56 will actually catch a cold. What percent is this?

9. _____

10. _____

11. A nut dealer has 1800 lb of peanuts, 1500 lb of cashews, and 700 lb of almonds. What percent are peanuts? cashews? almonds?

12. It costs an oil company $40,000 a day to operate two refineries. Refinery A takes 37.5% of the cost, and refinery B takes the rest of the cost.

   a) What is the cost of operating refinery A? refinery B?
   b) What percent of the cost does it take to run refinery B?

11. _____

12. a) _____

b) _____

b Solve.

13. The amount in a savings account increased from $200 to $216. What was the percent of increase?

14. The population of a small town increased from 840 to 882. What was the percent of increase?

13. _____

14. _____

15. During a sale, a dress decreased in price from $70 to $56. What was the percent of decrease?

16. A person on a diet goes from a weight of 125 lb to a weight of 110 lb. What is the percent of decrease?

17. A person earns $8600 one year and gets a 5% raise in salary. What is the new salary?

18. A person earns $10,400 one year and gets an 8% raise in salary. What is the new salary?

19. The value of a car typically decreases by 30% in the first year. A car is bought for $12,000. What is its value one year later?

20. One year the pilots of Pan American Airlines shocked the business world by taking an 11% pay cut. The former salary was $55,000. What was the reduced salary?

21. World population is increasing by 1.6% each year. In 1990, it was 5.2 billion. How much will it be in 1991? 1992? 1993?

22. By increasing the thermostat from 72° to 78°, a family can reduce its cooling bill by 50%. If the cooling bill was $106.00, what would the new bill be? By what percent has the temperature been increased?

ANSWERS

15. _____

16. _____

17. _____

18. _____

19. _____

20. _____

21. _____

22. _____

23. _____

24. _____

25. _____

26. _____

27. _____

28. _____

29. _____

30. _____

23. A car normally depreciates 30% of its original value in the first year. A car is worth $8750 after the first year. What was its original cost?

24. A standard or nominal "two by four" actually measures $1\frac{1}{2}$ in. by $3\frac{1}{2}$ in. The rough board is 2 in. by 4 in., but is planed and dried to the finished size. What percent of the wood is removed in planing and drying?

25. _Treadmill test._ Treadmill tests are often administered to diagnose heart ailments. A guideline in such a test is to try to get you to reach what is called your **maximal heartbeat,** in beats per minute. The maximal heartbeat is found by subtracting a person's age from 220 and then multiplying by 85%. What is the maximal heartbeat of a person of age 25? 36? 48? 60? 76? Round to the nearest one.

26. _Car depreciation._ Given normal use, an American-made car will depreciate 30% of its original cost the first year and 14% of its remaining value in the second year. What is the value of a car at the end of the second year if its original cost was $9600? $12,500? $18,400?

SYNTHESIS

27. Which is higher, if either?
   a) $1000 increased by 15%, then that amount decreased by 15%, or,
   b) $1000 decreased by 15%, then that amount increased by 15%.

28. If p is 120% of q, q is what percent of p?

29. It has been determined that at the age of 10, a girl has reached 84.4% of her final adult growth. A girl is 4 ft, 8 in. at the age of 10. What will be her final adult height?

30. It has been determined that at the age of 15 a boy has reached 96.1% of his final adult height. A boy is 6 ft, 4 in. at the age of 15. What will be his final adult height?

4.7 Consumer Applications

a Sales Tax

Percent is used in sales tax computations. The sales tax rate in Arkansas is 3%. This means that the tax is 3% of the purchase price. Suppose the purchase price on a coat is $124.45. The sales tax is then

3% of $124.45   or   0.03 × 124.45,

or

3.7335,   or about $3.73.

The total that you pay is the price plus the sales tax:

$124.45 + $3.73,   or $128.18.

$124.45

+ 3% Sales Tax

Sales tax = Sales tax rate × Purchase price
Total price = Purchase price + Sales tax

▶ **EXAMPLE 1**   The sales tax rate in California is 6%. How much tax is charged on the purchase of a coat for $124.45? What is the total price?

a) We first find the sales tax. It is

6% of $124.45,   or   0.06 × 124.45,

which is

7.467,   or about $7.47.

b) The total price is the purchase price plus the sales tax:

$124.45 + $7.47,   or $131.92.   ◀

DO EXERCISE 1.

▶ **EXAMPLE 2**   The sales tax is $32 on the purchase of a sofa for $800. What is the sales tax rate?

Think: Sales tax is what percent of purchase price?

Translate: 32   =   r   ×   800

To solve the equation, we divide on both sides by 800:

$$32 \div 800 = r$$
$$0.04 = r$$
$$4\% = r.$$

The sales tax rate is 4%.   ◀

DO EXERCISE 2.

OBJECTIVES

After finishing Section 4.7, you should be able to:

a   Solve problems involving sales tax and percent.

b   Solve problems involving commission and percent.

c   Solve problems involving discount and percent.

d   Solve problems involving simple interest and percent.

e   Solve problems involving compound interest.

FOR EXTRA HELP

Tape 9B, 9C, 9D

1. The sales tax rate in California is 6%. How much tax is charged on the purchase of a refrigerator for $368.95? What is the total price?

2. The sales tax is $33 on the purchase of a washing machine for $550. What is the sales tax rate?

3. A salesperson's commission rate is 30%. What is the commission from the sale of $18,760 worth of air conditioners?

4. A clothing salesperson's commission is 16%. A commission of $268 is received. How many dollars worth of clothing were sold?

b   Commission

When you work for a **salary,** you get the same amount of money each week or month. When you work for a **commission,** you get paid a percentage of the amount that you sell. To find commission, take a certain percentage of sales.

> **Commission = Commission rate × Sales**

▶ **EXAMPLE 3**   A salesperson's commission rate is 20%. What is the commission from the sale of $25,560 worth of vacuum cleaners?

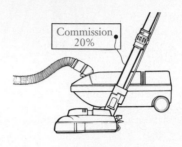
Commission 20%

$$\begin{array}{ccccc} \textit{Commission} & = & \textit{Commission rate} & \times & \textit{Sales} \\ C & = & 20\% & \times & 25{,}560 \end{array}$$

This tells us what to do. We multiply:

$$C = 20\% \times 25{,}560 = 0.2 \times 25{,}560 = 5112.$$

The commission is $5112.   ◀

DO EXERCISE 3.

▶ **EXAMPLE 4**   A motorcycle salesperson's commission rate is 25%. A commission of $425 is received. How many dollars worth of motorcycles were sold?

Commission 25%

$$\begin{array}{ccccc} \textit{Commission} & = & \textit{Commission rate} & \times & \textit{Sales} \\ 425 & = & 25\% & \times & S \end{array}$$

To solve this equation, we divide on both sides by 25%:

$$425 \div 25\% = S$$
$$425 \div 0.25 = S$$
$$1700 = S.$$

There were $1700 worth of motorcycles sold.   ◀

DO EXERCISE 4.

c Discount

The regular price of a rug is $60. It is on sale at 25% off. Since 25% of $60 is $15, the sale price is $60 − $15, or $45. We call $60 the **marked price**, 25% the **rate of discount**, $15 the **discount**, and $45 the **sale price**. These are related as follows.

> **Discount = Rate of discount × Marked price**
> **Sale price = Marked price − Discount**

▶ **EXAMPLE 5**   A rug is marked $240 and is on sale at 25% off. What is the discount? the sale price?

a) *Discount = Rate of discount × Marked price*
    D = 25% × 240

This tells us what to do. We convert 25% to decimal notation and multiply:

$$D = 0.25 \times 240 = 60.$$

The discount is $60.

b) *Sale price = Market price − Discount*
    D = 240 − 60

This tells us what to do. We subtract:

$$S = 240 - 60 = 180.$$

The sale price is $180.   ◀

DO EXERCISE 5.

d Simple Interest

You put $100 in a savings account for 1 year. The $100 is called the **principal.** The **interest rate** is 8%. This means that you get back 8% of the principal, which is

8% of $100,   or   0.08 × 100,   or $8.00,

in addition to the principal. The $8.00 is called the **interest.**

5. A suit is marked $140 and is on sale at 24% off. What is the discount? the sale price?

ANSWER ON PAGE A-3

6. What is the interest on $4300 principal at the interest rate of 14% for 1 year?

▶ **EXAMPLE 6**   What is the interest on $2500 principal at the interest rate of 6% for 1 year?

We take 6% of $2500:

$$6\% \times 2500 = 0.06 \times \$2500$$
$$= 150.$$

The interest for 1 year is $150. ◀

DO EXERCISE 6.

To find interest for a fraction t of a year, we compute the interest for 1 year and multiply by t.

▶ **EXAMPLE 7**   What is the interest on $2500 principal at the interest rate of 6% for $\frac{1}{4}$ year?

a) We find the interest for 1 year. We take 6% of $2500:

$$6\% \times 2500 = 0.06 \times 2500 = 150.$$

b) We multiply by $\frac{1}{4}$:

$$\frac{1}{4} \times 150 = \frac{150}{4} = 37.50.$$

The interest for $\frac{1}{4}$ year is $37.50. ◀

DO EXERCISE 7.

7. What is the interest on $4300 principal at the interest rate of 14% for $\frac{3}{4}$ year?

Money is often borrowed for 30, 60, or 90 days even though the interest rate is given **per year.** To simplify calculations, businesspeople consider there to be 360 days in a year. If a loan is for 30 days, it is for 30/360 of a year. The actual interest is found by finding interest for 1 year and taking 30/360 of it.

▶ **EXAMPLE 8**   What is the interest on $400 at 8% for 30 days?

We convert 30 days to a fractional part of one year.

$$\text{Interest} = (\text{Interest for 1 year}) \times \frac{30}{360}$$

$$= (8\% \times \$400) \times \frac{30}{360}$$

$$= 0.08 \times 400 \times \frac{1}{12}$$

$$= 32 \times \frac{1}{12}$$

$$= \frac{32}{12}$$

$$= \frac{8}{3}$$

$$= 2.66\overline{6}$$

$$\approx 2.67 \qquad \textbf{Rounding to the nearest hundredth}$$

The interest for 30 days is $2.67. ◀

A general formula for interest is as follows.

Interest = Rate · Principal · Time (expressed in some part of a year),
or

$$I = (r \cdot P) \cdot t, \quad \text{or, more commonly,} \quad I = P \cdot r \cdot t.$$

Interest computed in this way is called **simple interest.**

DO EXERCISE 8.

e Compound Interest

When interest is paid *on interest,* we call it **compound interest.** This type of interest is usually paid on savings accounts. Suppose you have $100 in a savings account at 6%. In 1 year, you earn

6% of $100,   or $6 interest.

Then you have $106. If you leave the interest in your account, the next year you earn interest on $106, which is

6% of $106,   or   0.06 × 106,   or $6.36.

You then have $106 + $6.36, or $112.36 in your account. When this happens, we say that interest is **compounded annually.** The interest of $6 the first year earned $0.36 the second year.

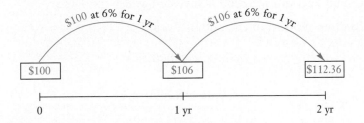

▶ **EXAMPLE 9**   Interest is compounded annually. Find the amount in an account if $2000 is invested at 8% for 2 years.

a) We find the interest at the end of 1 year:

$$I = 8\% \times \$2000$$
$$= 0.08 \times \$2000 = \$160.$$

b) We then find the new principal after 1 year:

$$\$2000 + \$160 = \$2160.$$

c) Going into the second year, the principal is $2160. We now find the interest for 1 year after that:

$$I = 8\% \times \$2160$$
$$= 0.08 \times \$2160 = \$172.80$$

d) Next we find the new principal after 2 years:

$$\$2160 + \$172.80 = \$2332.80.$$

The amount in the account after 2 years is $2332.80.   ◀

DO EXERCISE 9.

8. What is the interest on $4800 at 7% for 60 days?

9. Interest is compounded annually. Find the amount in an account if $2000 is invested at 11% for 2 years.

10. Interest is compounded semiannually. Find the amount in an account if $2000 is invested at 5% for 1 year.

Interest added to an account every half year is **compounded semiannually.** Suppose you have $100 in a savings account at 6%. In $\frac{1}{2}$ year, you earn

$$6\% \times \$100 \times \frac{1}{2}, \quad \text{or} \quad \$3 \text{ interest.}$$

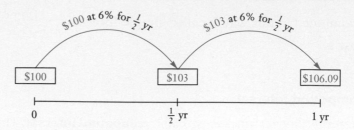

Then you have $103 if you leave the interest in your account. The last half of the year, you earn interest on $103, which is

$$6\% \times \$103 \times \frac{1}{2}, \quad \text{or} \quad \$3.09.$$

You then have $103 + $3.09, or $106.09 in your account. If interest were compounded annually, you would have $106, but with interest compounded semiannually, you have $106.09. The more often interest is compounded, the more interest your money earns.

▶ **EXAMPLE 10**　Interest is compounded semiannually. Find the amount in an account if $2000 is invested at 8% for 1 year.

a) We find the interest at the end of $\frac{1}{2}$ year:

$$I = 8\% \times \$2000 \times \frac{1}{2}$$
$$= 0.08 \times \$2000 \times \frac{1}{2}$$
$$= \$160 \times \frac{1}{2}$$
$$= \$80.$$

b) We then find the new principal after $\frac{1}{2}$ year:

$$\$2000 + \$80 = \$2080.$$

c) Going into the last half of the year, the principal is $2080. Now we find the interest for $\frac{1}{2}$ year after that:

$$I = 8\% \times \$2080 \times \frac{1}{2}$$
$$= 0.08 \times \$2080 \times \frac{1}{2}$$
$$= \$166.40 \times \frac{1}{2}$$
$$= \$83.20.$$

d) Next we find the new principal after 1 year:

$$\$2080 + \$83.20 = \$2163.20.$$

The amount in the account after 1 year is $2163.20.　◀

EXERCISE SET 4.7

a Solve.

1. The sales tax rate in New York City is 8.25%. How much tax is charged on a purchase of $248? What is the total price?

2. The sales tax rate in Indiana is 5%. How much tax is charged on a purchase of $586? What is the total price?

3. The sales tax rate in Pennsylvania is 6%. How much tax is charged on a purchase of $189.95? What is the total price?

4. The sales tax rate in Nevada is 5.75%. How much tax is charged on a purchase of $220.99? What is the total price?

5. The sales tax is $48 on a purchase of $960. What is the sales tax rate?

6. The sales tax is $35.80 on a purchase of $895. What is the sales tax rate?

7. The sales tax is $1030.40 on an automobile purchase of $18,400. What is the sales tax rate?

8. The sales tax is $15 on the purchase of a diamond ring for $500. What is the sales tax rate?

9. The sales tax on a car is $168 and the sales tax rate is 6%. Find the purchase price (the price before taxes are added).

10. The sales tax on a purchase is $66 and the sales tax rate is 5.5%. Find the purchase price.

11. The sales tax rate in Dallas is 1% for the city and 4% for the state. How much tax is charged on a purchase of $665?

12. The sales tax rate in Omaha is 1.5% for the city and 3.5% for the state. How much tax is charged on a purchase of $780?

b Solve.

13. A salesperson's commission rate is 20%. What is the commission from the sale of $18,450 worth of furnaces?

14. A salesperson's commission rate is 32%. What is the commission from the sale of $12,500 worth of dictionaries?

15. A salesperson earns $120 selling $2400 worth of television sets. What is the commission rate?

16. A salesperson earns $408 selling $3400 worth of stereos. What is the commission rate?

17. A sweeper salesperson's commission rate is 40%. A commission of $392 is received. How many dollars worth of sweepers were sold?

18. A real estate agent's commission rate is 7%. A commission of $2800 is received on the sale of a home. How much did the home sell for?

19. A real estate commission is 7%. What is the commission on the sale of a $98,000 home?

20. A real estate commission is 8%. What is the commission on the sale of a piece of land for $68,000?

21. An encyclopedia salesperson earns a salary of $500 a month, plus a 2% commission on sales. One month $990 worth of encyclopedias were sold. What were the wages that month?

22. Some salespersons have their commission increased according to how much they sell. A salesperson gets a commission of 5% for the first $2000 and 8% on the amount over $2000. What is the total commission on sales of $6000?

c Solve.

23. Find the discount and the rate of discount for the ring in this ad.

1/2 CARAT T.W. DIAMOND, 14K GOLD LADY'S BRIDAL SET WAS $1275.00
$888

24. What is the mathematical error in this ad?

Water-Resistant Watch With 24-Hour Alarm

Cut 30%

6⁹⁵ Reg. 9.95

Resists water to 100 feet! Calendar, chime. #63-5058

Find what is missing.

25.

Marked price	Rate of discount	Discount	Sale price
$300	10%		

25. _____

26.

$20.00	25%		

26. _____

27.

$125.00	10%		

27. _____

28.

	15%	$65.70	

28. _____

29.

$600		$240	

29. _____

30.

$12,800		$1920	

30. _____

31. _____

d Find the *simple* interest.

	Principal	Rate of interest	Time
31.	$200	13%	1 year
32.	$450	18%	1 year
33.	$2000	12.4%	1 year
34.	$4400	9.4%	1 year
35.	$200	7.7%	$\frac{1}{2}$ year
36.	$4300	14%	$\frac{1}{4}$ year
37.	$2000	15%	30 days
38.	$5000	14.5%	60 days

32. _____

33. _____

34. _____

35. _____

36. _____

37. _____

38. _____

e Interest is compounded annually. Find the amount in the account after the given time. Round to the nearest cent.

Principal	Rate of interest	Time
39. $400	10%	2 years
40. $400	7.7%	2 years
41. $200	8.8%	2 years
42. $1000	15%	2 years

Interest is compounded semiannually. Find the amount in the account after the given time. Round to the nearest cent.

Principal	Rate of interest	Time
43. $400	16%	1 year
44. $1000	18%	1 year
45. $2000	9%	1 year
46. $5000	7%	1 year

SKILL MAINTENANCE

47. Write fractional notation: 0.93.

48. Solve: $2.3 \times y = 85.1$.

49. Convert to decimal notation: $\frac{13}{11}$.

50. Convert to a mixed numeral: $\frac{29}{11}$.

SYNTHESIS

51. ▤ The sales tax rate on a purchase is 5.4%. How much tax is charged on a purchase of $96,568.95?

52. ▤ The sales tax is $3811.88 on a purchase of $58,644.24. What is the sales tax rate?

53. ▤ What is the simple interest on $24,680 at 7.75% for $\frac{3}{4}$ year?

54. ▤ Which gives the most interest, $1000 \times 8\% \times \frac{30}{360}$, or $1000 \times 8\% \times \frac{30}{365}$?

39. _____

40. _____

41. _____

42. _____

43. _____

44. _____

45. _____

46. _____

47. _____

48. _____

49. _____

50. _____

51. _____

52. _____

53. _____

54. _____

SUMMARY AND REVIEW EXERCISES: CHAPTER 4

The review sections and objectives to be tested in addition to the material in this chapter are [2.4a], [3.1b], and [3.3c, d].

Write fractional notation for the ratio.

1. 47 to 84   **2.** 46 to 1.27   **3.** 83 to 100   **4.** 0.72 to 197

Solve.

5. $\dfrac{8}{9} = \dfrac{x}{36}$ **6.** $\dfrac{120}{\frac{3}{7}} = \dfrac{7}{x}$ **7.** $\dfrac{6}{x} = \dfrac{48}{56}$ **8.** $\dfrac{4.5}{120} = \dfrac{0.9}{x}$

9. What is the rate in dollars per kilogram?

$355.04,   14 kilograms

10. A lawn requires 319 gal of water for every 500 sq ft. What is the rate in gallons per square foot?

Find percent notation.

11. 0.483   **12.** 0.36   **13.** $\dfrac{3}{8}$ **14.** $\dfrac{1}{3}$

Find decimal notation.

15. 73.5%   **16.** $6\frac{1}{2}\%$

Find fractional notation.

17. 24%   **18.** 6.3%

Translate to an equation. Then solve.

19. 30.6 is what percent of 90?   **20.** 63 is 84 percent of what?   **21.** What is $38\frac{1}{2}\%$ of 168?

Translate to a proportion. Then solve.

22. 24 percent of what is 16.8?   **23.** 22.2 is what percent of 30?   **24.** What is $38\frac{1}{2}\%$ of 168?

Solve.

25. If 3 dozen eggs cost $2.67, how much will 5 dozen eggs cost?

26. Fifteen acres are required to produce 54 bushels of tomatoes. At this rate, how many acres would be required to produce 97.2 bushels of tomatoes?

27. In Michigan, there are 2.3 lawyers for every 1000 people. The population of Detroit is 1,140,000. How many lawyers are there in Detroit?

28. Under typical conditions, $1\frac{1}{2}$ ft of snow will melt to 2 in. of water. To how many inches of water will $4\frac{1}{2}$ ft of snow melt?

29. A college has a student body with 960 students. Of these, 17.5% are seniors. How many students are seniors?

30. The price of a color television set was reduced from $350 to $308. Find the percent of decrease in price.

31. A county has a population that is increasing 3% each year. This year the population is 80,000. What will it be next year?

32. The price of a box of cookies increased from 85 cents to $1.02. What was the percent of increase in the price?

33. In a certain state, a sales tax of $378 is collected on the purchase of a car for $7560. What is the sales tax rate?

34. A salesperson earns $753.50 selling $6850 worth of televisions. What is the commission rate?

35. An item has a marked price of $350. It is placed on sale at 12% off. What are the discount and the sale price?

36. An insurance salesperson receives a 7% commission. If $420 worth of insurance is sold, what is the commission?

37. What is the simple interest on $220 principal at the interest rate of 14.5% for 1 year?

38. What is the simple interest on $250 at 12.2% for $\frac{1}{2}$ year?

39. Interest is compounded annually. Find the amount in an account if $150 is invested at 12% for 2 years.

40. Interest is compounded semiannually. Find the amount in an account if $200 is invested at 12% for 1 year.

SKILL MAINTENANCE

Solve.

41. $10.4 \times y = 665.6$ **42.** $100 \times x = 761.23$

Write fractional notation.

43. 12.03   **44.** 0.033

Convert to decimal notation.

45. $\frac{11}{3}$ **46.** $\frac{11}{7}$

Convert to a mixed numeral.

47. $\frac{11}{3}$ **48.** $\frac{121}{7}$

❖ **THINKING IT THROUGH**

1. Discuss as many daily uses of percent as you can.

2. Describe each method used for solving basic percent problems.

3. Explain percent increase and percent decrease and a common error when doing such problems.

NAME   SECTION   DATE

TEST: CHAPTER 4

Write fractional notation for the ratio.

1. 85 to 97

2. 0.34 to 124

1. _____

2. _____

Solve.

3. $\dfrac{9}{4} = \dfrac{27}{x}$

4. $\dfrac{150}{2.5} = \dfrac{x}{6}$

3. _____

4. _____

5. What is the rate in meters per second?

10 meters, 16 seconds

6. A 12-lb shankless ham contains 16 servings. What is the rate in servings per pound?

5. _____

6. _____

7. Find decimal notation for 89%.

8. Find percent notation for 0.674.

7. _____

9. Find percent notation for $\dfrac{7}{8}$.

10. Find fractional notation for 65%.

8. _____

9. _____

11. Translate to an equation. Then solve.

What is 40% of 55?

12. Translate to a proportion. Then solve.

What percent of 80 is 65?

10. _____

11. _____

12. _____

ANSWERS

13. _____

14. _____

15. _____

16. _____

17. _____

18. _____

19. _____

20. _____

21. _____

22. _____

23. _____

24. _____

25. _____

26. _____

Solve.

13. A person traveled 432 km in 12 hr. At this rate, how far would the person go in 42 hr?

14. If 2 cans of apricots cost $1.19, how many cans of apricots can you buy for $26.18?

15. A watch loses 2 min in 10 hr. At this rate, how much would it lose in 24 hr?

16. The weight of muscles in a human body is 40% of total body weight. A person weighs 125 lb. What do the muscles weigh?

17. The population of a town increased from 2000 to 2400. Find the percent of increase in population.

18. The sales tax rate in Maryland is 5%. How much tax is charged on a purchase of $324? What is the total price?

19. A salesperson's commission rate is 15%. What is the commission from the sale of $4200 worth of merchandise?

20. The marked price of an item is $200 and is on sale at 20% off. What are the discount and the sale price?

21. What is the simple interest on $100 at 8.6% for $\frac{1}{2}$ year?

22. Interest is compounded annually. Find the amount in an account if $100 is invested at 13% for 2 years.

SKILL MAINTENANCE

23. Solve: $8.4 \times y = 1864.8$.

24. Write fractional notation: 0.007.

25. Convert to decimal notation: $\frac{17}{12}$.

26. Convert to a mixed numeral: $\frac{153}{44}$.

INTRODUCTION There are many ways in which to analyze or describe data. One is to look at certain numbers or *statistics* related to the data. We will consider three kinds of statistics, the *average,* the *median,* and the *mode.* Another way is to make graphs. We will consider several types of graphs, pictographs, bar graphs, line graphs, and circle graphs.

The review sections to be tested in addition to the material in this chapter are 2.2, 4.1, 4.4, 4.5, and 4.6. ❖

Descriptive Statistics

AN APPLICATION

Hollis Stacy, shown in the photograph here, won a recent U.S. Women's Open with scores of 74, 72, 75, and 69. What was her average score?

THE MATHEMATICS

We add the scores and divide by the number of addends. The average is as follows:

$$\text{Average} = \frac{74 + 72 + 75 + 69}{4}$$

PRETEST: CHAPTER 5

Find the (a) average, (b) median, and (c) mode.

1. 46, 50, 53, 55

2. 5, 4, 3, 2, 1

3. 4, 17, 4, 18, 4, 17, 18, 20

4. A car traveled 660 km in 12 hr. What was the average number of kilometers per hour?

5. To get a C in chemistry, a student must average 70 on four tests. Scores on the first three tests were 68, 71, and 65. What is the lowest score that the student can make on the last test and still get a C?

6. The following data show the percentage of women selecting a particular reason for exercising. Make a circle graph to show the data.

Health: 51%

Lose weight: 38%

Relieve stress: 11%

7. The following table shows the comparison of the cost of a $100,000 life insurance policy for female smokers and nonsmokers at certain ages.

a) How much does it cost a female smoker, age 32, for insurance?

b) How much does it cost a female nonsmoker, age 32, for insurance?

c) How much more does it cost a female smoker, age 35, than a nonsmoker at the same age?

8. Using the data in Exercise 7, draw a vertical bar graph showing the cost of insurance for a female smoker at various ages. Use age on the horizontal scale and cost on the vertical scale.

	Life Insurance: Female	
Age	**Cost (Smoker)**	**Cost (Nonsmoker)**
31	$294	$170
32	298	172
33	302	176
34	310	178
35	316	182

The line graph below shows the number of first-year students enrolled in law school for various years.

9. In what year was enrollment largest?

10. How many more were in law school in 1988 than in 1965?

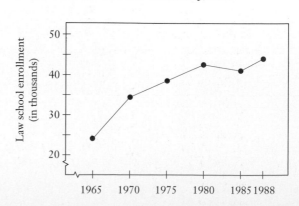

5.1 Averages, Medians, and Modes

a Averages

A **statistic** is a number that describes a set of data. One way to describe or examine data is to look for a number or *"center point"* that characterizes the data. The most common kind of center point is the *mean* or *average* of the set of numbers.

Suppose a student made the following scores on four tests.

Test 1: 78
Test 2: 81
Test 3: 82
Test 4: 79

What is the *average* of the scores? First we add the scores:

$$78 + 81 + 82 + 79 = 320.$$

Second, we divide by the number of addends:

$$\frac{320}{4} = 80.$$

Note that $78 + 81 + 82 + 79 = 320$, and that

$$80 + 80 + 80 + 80 = 320.$$

The number 80 is called the **average** of the set of test scores. It's also called the **arithmetic mean** or, simply, the **mean.**

> To find the *average* of a set of numbers, add them. Then divide by the number of addends.

▶ **EXAMPLE 1** On a four-day trip, a car was driven the following number of kilometers each day: 240, 302, 280, 320. What was the average number of kilometers per day?

$$\frac{240 + 302 + 280 + 320}{4} = \frac{1142}{4}, \text{ or } 285.5$$

The car was driven an average of 285.5 km per day. The average is such that if the car had been driven exactly 285.5 km each day, it would have completed the trip in 4 days. ◀

DO EXERCISES 1–4.

▶ **EXAMPLE 2** Hank Aaron holds the record for the most home runs in a career, with 755. He played for 22 seasons. What was the average number of home runs he hit per year? Round to the nearest tenth.

We already have the sum of the home runs. It is 755. We divide the total, 755, by the number of seasons, 22, and round:

$$\frac{755}{22} \approx 34.3.$$

Hank Aaron hit an average of 34.3 home runs per year. ◀

DO EXERCISE 5.

Find the average.

1. 14, 175, 36

2. 75, 36.8, 95.7, 12.1

3. A student made the following scores on five tests: 68, 85, 82, 74, 96. What was the average score?

4. In the first five games, a basketball player scored points as follows: 26, 21, 13, 14, 23. Find the average number of points scored per game.

5. O. J. Simpson set an NFL rushing record, gaining 2003 yd in a 14-game season. What was the average number of yards he gained per game? Round to the nearest tenth.

ANSWERS ON PAGE A-3

6. According to EPA estimates in a recent year, a Honda Civic was expected to travel 700 mi (city) on 25 gal of gasoline. What was the average number of miles expected per gallon?

▶ **EXAMPLE 3**   According to EPA estimates in a recent year, a Chevrolet Corvette was expected to travel 375 mi (city) on 25 gal of gasoline. What was the average number of miles expected per gallon?

We divide the total number of miles, 375, by the number of gallons, 25:

$$\frac{375}{25} = 15.$$

The average was 15 miles per gallon.   ◄

DO EXERCISE 6.

▶ **EXAMPLE 4**   *Grade point average, GPA.* In most colleges students are assigned grade point values for grades obtained. The **grade point average,** or **GPA,** is the average of the grade point values for each hour taken. Suppose at a certain college grade point values are assigned as follows:

A: 4.00   D: 1.00
B: 3.00   F: 0.00
C: 2.00

A student obtained the following grades for one semester. What was the student's grade point average?

Course	Grade	Number of credit hours in course
Accounting	B	4
Calculus	A	5
English	A	5
French	C	3
Physical education	F	1

7. A student obtained the following grades one semester.

Grade	Number of credit hours in course
B	3
C	4
C	4
A	2

What was the student's grade point average? Assume that the grade point values are 4.00 for an A, 3.00 for a B, and so on.

To find the GPA, we first add all the grade point values for each hour taken. We do this by first multiplying the grade point value (in color below) by the number of hours in the course and then adding as follows:

Accounting $3.00 \cdot 4 = 12$
Calculus $4.00 \cdot 5 = 20$
English $4.00 \cdot 5 = 20$
French $2.00 \cdot 3 =\ \ 6$
Physical education $0.00 \cdot 1 =\ \ \underline{0}$
                          58 (Total)

The total number of hours taken is $4 + 5 + 5 + 3 + 1$, or 18. We divide 58 by 18 and round to the nearest hundredth:

$$\frac{58}{18} \approx 3.22.$$

The student's grade point average was 3.22.   ◄

DO EXERCISE 7.

▶ **EXAMPLE 5** To get a B in math, a student must score an average of 80 on the tests. On the first four tests, the scores were 79, 88, 64, and 78. What is the lowest score that the student can get on the last test and still get a B?

We can find the total of the five scores needed as follows:

$$80 + 80 + 80 + 80 + 80 = 5 \cdot 80, \quad \text{or} \quad 400.$$

The total of the scores on the first four tests is

$$79 + 88 + 64 + 78 = 309.$$

Thus the student needs to get at least

$$400 - 309, \quad \text{or} \quad 91$$

to get a B. We can check this as follows:

$$\frac{79 + 88 + 64 + 78 + 91}{5} = \frac{400}{5}, \quad \text{or} \quad 80. \quad \blacktriangleleft$$

DO EXERCISE 8.

b   Medians

Another kind of center point is a *median.* Suppose a student made the following scores on five tests.

Test 1:   78
Test 2:   81
Test 3:   82
Test 4:   76
Test 5:   84

Let's first list the scores in order from smallest to largest:

$$76, \quad 78, \quad 81, \quad 82, \quad 84.$$

The middle score is called the **median.** Thus, 81 is the median of the scores.

▶ **EXAMPLE 6** What is the median of this set of numbers?

$$99, \quad 870, \quad 91, \quad 98, \quad 106, \quad 90, \quad 98$$

We first rearrange the numbers in order from smallest to largest. Then we locate the middle number, 98.

$$90, \quad 91, \quad 98, \quad 98, \quad 99, \quad 106, \quad 870$$

Middle number

The median is 98.   ◀

DO EXERCISES 9–11.

8. To get an A in math, a student must score an average of 90 on the tests. On the first three tests, the scores were 80, 100, and 86. What is the lowest score that the student can get on the last test and still get an A?

Find the median.
9. 17, 13, 18, 14, 19

10. 20, 14, 13, 19, 16, 18, 17

11. 78, 81, 83, 91, 103, 102, 122, 119, 88

The *median* of a set of data is the middle number if there is an odd number of numbers. If there is an even number of numbers, then there are two numbers in the middle and the *median* is the number that is halfway between the two middle numbers.

ANSWERS ON PAGE A-3

Find the median.

12. 13, 20, 19, 16, 18, 14

13. 68, 34, 67, 69, 34, 70

Find the mode.

14. 23, 45, 45, 45, 78

15. 34, 34, 67, 67, 68, 70

16. 13, 24, 27, 28, 67, 89

17. A student received the following tests scores:

74, 86, 96, 67, 82.

a) What is the median score?
b) What is the mean?
c) What is the mode?

▶ **EXAMPLE 7**   What is the median of this set of numbers?

69,   80,   61,   63,   62,   65

We first rearrange the numbers in order from smallest to largest. There is an even number of numbers. We look for the middle two, which are 63 and 65. The median is halfway between 63 and 65. It is 64.

61,   62,   63,   65,   69,   80
↑
Median 64

Note that the number halfway between two numbers is their average. In this example, the number halfway between 63 and 65 is found as follows:

$$\text{Median} = \frac{63 + 65}{2} = \frac{128}{2} = 64. \quad ◀$$

▶ **EXAMPLE 8**   What is the median of this set of numbers?

25,   26,   24,   23

We first rearrange the numbers in order from smallest to largest. There is an even number of numbers. The two middle numbers are 24 and 25. The median is halfway between 24 and 25. We find it as follows:

23,   24,   25,   26
↑
Median 24.5

$$\text{Median} = \frac{24 + 25}{2} = \frac{49}{2} = 24.5. \quad ◀$$

DO EXERCISES 12 AND 13.

C   **Modes**

The final type of center point sometimes used to analyze data is the **mode**.

> The *mode* of a set of data is the number or numbers that occur most often.

▶ **EXAMPLE 9**   Find the mode of this set of data.

13,   14,   17,   17,   18,   19

The number that occurs most often is 17. Thus the mode is 17.   ◀

A set of data has just one mean and just one median, but it can have more than one mode. If no number repeats, then each number in the set is a mode.

▶ **EXAMPLE 10**   Find the mode, or modes, of this set of data.

33,   34,   34,   34,   35,   36,   37,   37,   37,   38,   39,   40

There are two numbers that occur most often, 34 and 37. Thus the modes are 34 and 37.   ◀

DO EXERCISES 14–17.

NAME   SECTION   DATE

EXERCISE SET 5.1

a , **b** , **c** For each set of numbers, find the average, the median, and the mode.

1. 8, 7, 15, 15, 15, 12   **2.** 72, 83, 85, 88, 92   **3.** 5, 10, 15, 20, 25, 30, 35

1. _____

4. 13, 13, 25, 27, 32   **5.** 1.2, 4.3, 5.7, 7.4, 7.4   **6.** 13.4, 13.4, 12.6, 42.9

2. _____

7. 234, 228, 234, 229, 234, 278   **8.** $29.95, $28.79, $30.95, $29.95

3. _____

The following are the weights of the defensive linemen of the Dallas Cowboys. Use the data for Exercises 9 and 10.

9. What are the average, median, and mode of the weights in pounds?

4. _____

5. _____

Weight (lb)	Weight (kg)
250	113
255	116
260	118
260	118

10. What are the average, median, and mode of the weights in kilograms?

6. _____

11. The following temperatures were recorded for seven days:

43°, 40°, 23°, 38°, 54°, 35°, 47°.

What was the average temperature? the median? the mode?

12. Hollis Stacy, a professional golfer, scored 74, 72, 75, and 69 to win the U.S. Women's Open in a recent year. What was the average score? the median? the mode?

7. _____

8. _____

9. _____

13. According to EPA estimates in a recent year, a Triumph TR-7 was expected to get 522 mi (highway) on 18 gal of gasoline. What was the average number of miles per gallon?

14. According to EPA estimates in a recent year, a Ford Wagon was expected to get 432 mi (highway) on 24 gal of gasoline. What was the average number of miles per gallon?

10. _____

11. _____

In Exercises 15 and 16 are the grades of a student for one semester. In each case find the grade point average. Assume that the grade point values are 4.00 for an A, 3.00 for a B, and so on.

12. _____

13. _____

15.

Grades	Number of credit hours in course
B	4
B	5
B	3
C	4

16.

Grades	Number of credit hours in course
A	5
B	4
B	3
C	5

14. _____

15. _____

16. _____

ANSWERS

17. _____

18. _____

19. _____

20. _____

21. _____

22. _____

23. _____

24. _____

25. _____

26. _____

27. _____

17. The following prices per pound of steak were found at five supermarkets:

$9.79, $9.59, $9.69, $9.79, $9.89.

What was the average price per pound of steak? the median price? the mode?

18. The following prices per pound of ground beef were found at five supermarkets:

$2.39, $2.29, $2.49, $2.09, $1.99.

What was the average price per pound of ground beef? the median price? the mode?

19. To get a B in math, a student must average 80 on five tests. Scores on the first four tests were 80, 74, 81, and 75. What is the lowest score that the student can get on the last test and still get a B?

20. To get an A in math, a student must average 90 on five tests. Scores on the first four tests were 90, 91, 81, and 92. What is the lowest score that the student can get on the last test and still get an A?

21. The following are the salaries of the employees at the Suitemup Clothing Store. What is the average salary?

Number	Type	Salary
1	Owner	$29,200
5	Salesperson	19,600
3	Secretary	14,800
1	Custodian	13,000

SKILL MAINTENANCE

Multiply.

22. $14 \cdot 14$ **23.** $\dfrac{2}{3} \cdot \dfrac{2}{3}$ **24.** 1.4×1.4 **25.** 1.414×1.414

SYNTHESIS

▤ *Bowling averages.* Computing a bowling average involves a special kind of rounding. In effect, we never round up. For example, suppose a bowler gets a total of 599 for 3 games. To find the average, we divide 599 by 3 and drop the amount to the right of the decimal point:

$$\frac{599}{3} \approx 199.67. \qquad \text{The bowler's average is 199.}$$

In each case, find the bowling average.

26. 547 pins in 3 games   **27.** 4621 in 27 games

5.2 Tables, Charts, and Pictographs

a Tables and Charts

Another way to analyze data is to present it first in a **table** or **chart.**

▶ **EXAMPLE 1** The following chart is a sample rate schedule for dialing direct, long-distance, and interstate telephone calls.

		MON	TUE	WED	THU	FRI	SAT	SUN
8 A.M.	Weekday			Full rate				
5 P.M.	Evening		45% discount from full rate					
11 P.M. 8 A.M.	Night and Weekend		60% discount from full rate					

a) Which would be less expensive: placing a call at 9 P.M. on Wednesday or 7 A.M. on Friday?

b) On which days of the week is an 11 A.M. call less expensive than on other days?

c) What discount from the full rate will you get if you call at 6 P.M. on Sunday?

Careful attention to the chart will give us the answers.

a) Placing a call at 9 P.M. puts us in the evening-rate portion of the chart. We then read across the chart to Wednesday and find that we will receive a 45% discount. Placing a call at 7 A.M. puts us in the night-and-weekend portion of the chart. Again, we read across the chart, this time to Friday, and we find a discount of 60%. It is less expensive to place the call on Friday.

b) Calling at 11 A.M. puts us in the weekday rate (full rate) on Monday through Friday. On Saturday and Sunday, however, an 11 A.M. call places us in the night-and-weekend rate (60% discount). Thus calling on Saturday and Sunday at 11 A.M. is less expensive than on other days at the same time.

c) A call at 6 P.M. puts us in the evening-rate schedule. When we read across the chart to Sunday (passing over the lightly shaded area on Saturday), we find that we are still using the evening rate between 5 P.M. and 11 P.M. Therefore, we would receive a 45% discount. ◀

DO EXERCISES 1–3.

OBJECTIVES

After finishing Section 5.2, you should be able to:

a Read and interpret data from tables and charts.

b Read and interpret data from pictographs.

c Draw simple pictographs.

FOR EXTRA HELP

Tape 10B

Use the chart in Example 1 to answer each of the following.

1. Which of the following times has the lowest rate: 10 P.M. on Wednesday, 10 A.M. on Tuesday, or 2 P.M. on Sunday?

2. Suppose the full rate to call an out-of-state friend is $0.50 for the first minute and $0.34 for each additional minute. You decide to call your friend at midnight on Saturday and you talk for 7 min. What is the cost of the call?

3. When, during the weekdays, is the rate the highest?

Use the table in Example 2 to answer each of the following.

4. In which cities will you have to pay $50 or more, per week, for family day care?

▶ **EXAMPLE 2** According to the U.S. Bureau of Labor Statistics, 56% of women with children under the age of 6, or about 9 million women, work outside the home. The following table shows the weekly cost ranges, per child, for several day-care programs in seven major U.S. cities.

	Family day care		Day-care center		Caregiver comes to child's home
	Age	Cost	Age	Cost	
Boston	0–2	$45–160	0–2	$90–150	$260–340
	2–5	$40–160	2–5	$75–110	
New York	0–2	$35–140	0–2	$60–150	$165–300
	2–5	$40–160	2–5	$75–110	
Atlanta	0–2	$30–60	0–2	$35–70	$165–230
	2–5	$30–55	2–5	$50–70	
St. Louis	0–2	$45–50	0–2	$65–80	$165 and up
	2–5	$40–160	2–5	$75–110	
Dallas	0–2	$50–70	0–2	$60–90	$165–200
	2–5	$50–70	2–5	$50–70	
Denver	0–2	$65–105	0–2	$65–105	$165–200
	2–5	$55–105	2–5	$55–105	
San Francisco	0–2	$55–90	0–2	$90–120	$165–200
	2–5	$55–85	2–5	$65–90	

5. If you live in St. Louis, what will be the combined weekly cost range to place your 1-year-old and your 3-year-old in a day-care center?

a) In which city is it most expensive to have the caregiver come to your home?

b) How much will it cost you each week to have your 4-year-old child cared for in a day-care center in New York?

c) What is the maximum, per child, that you would expect to pay for a 4-year-old child cared for in family day care in Atlanta?

We look at the table to answer the questions.

a) We go to the last column, since the caregiver will come to your home, and read down the column, looking for the greatest entry. When we find it ($260–$340), we read back across, all the way to the left of that entry, and find that that is the rate in Boston.

b) This time we find New York in the first column. We then read across to the column under the heading "Day-Care Center." Since your child is 4 years old, we select the 2–5 age range, and the corresponding cost entry is $75–$110.

6. In which cities are you sure to spend under $150 per week for your child to be cared for in your own home?

c) Locating Atlanta on the left, we read across to the column headed "Family Day Care." Since the range indicated is $30–$55, the maximum that you would expect to pay is $55. ◀

DO EXERCISES 4–6.

b   Reading and Interpreting Pictographs

Pictographs (or picture graphs) are another way to show information. Instead of actually listing the amounts to be considered, a pictograph uses visually appropriate symbols to represent the amounts. In addition, a *key* is given telling what each symbol represents, so there is no need to read from a second scale.

▶ **EXAMPLE 3**   This pictograph shows an approximation of the number of productive oil wells in eight Middle-Eastern countries. Just below the graph, there is a key that tells you that each symbol represents 50 oil wells.

Productive Oil Wells in the Middle East	
Iran	🛢🛢🛢🛢🛢🛢🛢🛢🛢🛢🛢
Iraq	🛢🛢🛢🛢🛢🛢
Israel	🛢
Kuwait	🛢🛢🛢🛢🛢🛢🛢🛢🛢🛢🛢
Oman	🛢🛢🛢🛢🛢🛢🛢🛢🛢
Saudi Arabia	🛢🛢🛢🛢🛢🛢🛢🛢🛢🛢🛢
Syria	🛢🛢🛢🛢🛢🛢🛢🛢🛢🛢🛢🛢
Turkey	🛢🛢🛢🛢🛢🛢🛢🛢

🛢 = 50 wells

a) How many productive oil wells are there in Saudi Arabia?

b) How many more productive oil wells does Oman have than Turkey?

c) What is the total number of productive oil wells in the top four oil-producing countries?

We can compute the answers by first reading the pictograph.

a) Saudi Arabia's wells are represented by 11 symbols. Since each symbol stands for 50 wells, we can multiply 11 × 50 and get 550 oil wells.

b) Oman has 9 symbols representing about 450 oil wells (9 × 50). Turkey has about 400 oil wells, as shown by 8 symbols (8 × 50). Therefore, Oman has approximately 50 more wells than Turkey does.

c) By counting the symbols, you can see that Iran (11 symbols), Kuwait (11 symbols), Saudi Arabia (11 symbols), and Syria (12 symbols) are the top four oil-producing countries. The total number of symbols for these countries is 45, which represents a total of 2250 oil wells (45 × 50).   ◀

DO EXERCISES 7–9.

Use the pictograph in Example 3 to answer each of the following.

7. How many productive oil wells are there in Syria?

8. Turkey has more productive oil wells than which two countries combined?

9. What is the average number of productive oil wells for these 8 countries?

ANSWERS ON PAGE A-3

Use the graph in Example 4 to answer each of the following.

10. India has a greater population than the combined populations of which other countries?

You should realize by now that, although pictographs seem to be very easy to read, they are difficult to draw accurately because whole symbols reflect loose approximations due to significant rounding. In pictographs, you also need to use some mathematics to find the actual amounts.

▶ **EXAMPLE 4**   This pictograph shows fairly recent estimates of the population of five countries.

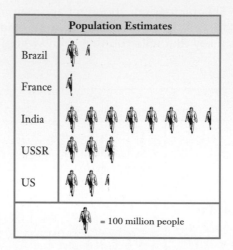

11. Which two countries are closest in population?

Give the approximate population of each country.

Brazil's population is represented by 1 whole symbol (100 million people) and about $\frac{1}{3}$ of another symbol (33 million people) for a total of 133 million people.

France's population is shown by about $\frac{1}{2}$ of a symbol, representing a total of 50 million people.

For India, we have 7 whole symbols (7 × 100 million people) and $\frac{1}{2}$ of another (50 million people), giving a total of 750 million people.

The population of the USSR is represented by 2 whole symbols (2 × 100 million people) and about $\frac{3}{4}$ of another (75 million people) for a total of 275 million people.

12. Which two countries have the greatest difference in population?

The population of the United States is shown by 2 whole symbols (2 × 100 million people) and about $\frac{1}{3}$ of another (33 million people), giving a total of 233 million people.   ◀

One advantage of pictographs is that the appropriate choice of a symbol will tell you, at a glance, the kind of measurement being made. Another advantage is that the comparison of amounts represented in the graph can be expressed more easily by just counting symbols. For instance, in Example 3, the ratio of Iraq's oil wells to Saudi Arabia's oil wells is 6:11.

One disadvantage of pictographs is that, to make a pictograph easy to read, the amounts must be rounded significantly to the unit that a symbol represents. This makes it difficult to accurately represent an amount. Another problem is that it is difficult to determine very accurately how much a partial symbol represents. A third disadvantage is that you must use some mathematics to finally compute the amount represented, since there is usually no explicit statement of the amount.

DO EXERCISES 10–12.

EXERCISE SET 5.2

a The following table gives information about various types of nails. Use the table for Exercises 1–10.

NAIL SIZES				
		Approximate number per pound		
Penny number	**Length (inches)**	**Common nails**	**Box nails**	**Finishing nails**
4	$1\frac{1}{2}$	316	437	548
6	2	181	236	309
8	$2\frac{1}{2}$	106	145	189
10	3	69	94	121
12	$3\frac{1}{4}$	64	87	113
16	$3\frac{1}{2}$	49	71	90
20	4	31	52	62
30	$4\frac{1}{2}$	20		
40	5			
50	$5\frac{1}{2}$			

1. How long is a 20-penny nail?

2. What penny number is given to a nail that is $2\frac{1}{2}$ in. long?

3. How many 10-penny box nails are there in a pound?

4. What type of nail comes 309 to the pound?

5. How many more 16-penny finishing nails can you get in a pound than 10-penny common nails?

6. How many fewer 8-penny common nails will you get in a pound than 6-penny common nails?

7. How many 30-penny box nails will you get in a pound?

8. What type of nail comes 40 to the pound?

9. How many nails will you get if you buy 5 pounds of 4-penny finishing nails?

10. You need approximately 448 12-penny common nails. How many pounds should you buy?

This table shows the number of calories burned in 30 min of exercise for various types of activities and several weight categories. Use the table for Exercises 11–22.

Activity	Calories burned in 30 min		
	110 lb	132 lb	154 lb
Aerobic dance	201	237	282
Calisthenics	216	261	351
Racquetball	213	252	294
Tennis	165	192	222
Moderate bicycling	138	171	198
Moderate jogging	321	378	453
Moderate walking	111	132	159

11. _____

11. How many calories are burned by a 154-lb person after 30 min of racquetball?

12. How many calories are burned by a 132-lb person after 30 min of moderate jogging?

12. _____

13. _____

13. What activity burns 216 calories in 30 min for a 110-lb person?

14. What activity burns calories at the rate of 132 every 30 min for a 132-lb person?

14. _____

15. _____

15. Which burns more calories in 30 min for a 154-lb person: aerobic dance or tennis?

16. Which burns more calories in 30 min: moderate bicycling or moderate walking?

16. _____

17. _____

17. How many calories will have been burned by a 110-lb person after 2 hr of tennis?

18. How many minutes of moderate walking will it take for a 110-lb person to burn as many calories as a 154-lb person will burn playing 30 min of tennis?

18. _____

19. _____

19. Which activity burns the least number of calories for a 132-lb person?

20. A 110-lb person needs to burn at least 215 calories every 30 min. What activities will provide at least that rate of burn?

20. _____

21. _____

21. How many calories would you expect a 120-lb person to burn during 30 min of moderate walking?

22. How many calories would you expect a 143-lb person to burn during 30 min of calisthenics?

22. _____

b This pictograph shows sales of shampoo for a soap company for six consecutive years. Use the pictograph for Exercises 23–30.

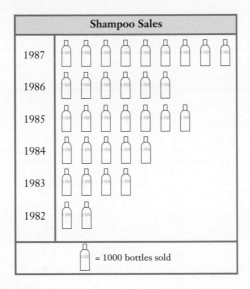

23. In which year was the greatest number of bottles sold?

24. Between what two consecutive years was there the greatest growth?

25. Between what two years was the amount of positive growth the least?

26. How many sales does one bottle represent?

27. How many bottles were sold in 1985?

28. How many more bottles were sold in 1987 than in 1983?

29. In which year was there actually a decline in the number of bottles sold?

30. The sales for 1987 were how many times the sales for 1982?

23. _____

24. _____

25. _____

26. _____

27. _____

28. _____

29. _____

30. _____

This pictograph shows a baseball player's "at-bats" in one month. Use the pictograph for Exercises 31–38.

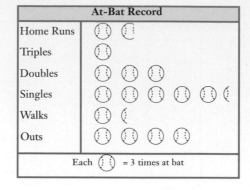

At-Bat Record	
Home Runs	⚾ ⚾
Triples	⚾
Doubles	⚾ ⚾ ⚾
Singles	⚾ ⚾ ⚾ ⚾ ⚾ ⚾
Walks	⚾ ⚾
Outs	⚾ ⚾ ⚾ ⚾

Each ⚾ = 3 times at bat

31. _____

31. How many times at bat does one baseball symbol represent?

32. How many of the player's hits were home runs?

32. _____

33. _____

33. How many hits were singles?

34. How many more doubles than home runs did the player hit?

34. _____

35. How many fewer triples than singles did the player hit?

36. What was the total number of hits for the month?

35. _____

37. What happened exactly 12 times to the batter?

38. What did the player do most during the month?

36. _____

C **39.** Draw a pictograph representing the number of U.S. automobile registrations shown by the information below. Be sure to put in all of the appropriate labels. Use a license plate symbol to represent 10,000,000 cars.

1960:	62.5 million cars
1965:	75.0 million cars
1970:	90.0 million cars
1975:	110.0 million cars
1980:	135.0 million cars
1985:	157.5 million cars

37. _____

U.S. Automobile Registrations	
1960	
412CNG =	

38. _____

39. See chart.

Copyright © 1993 Addison-Wesley Publishing Co., Inc.

SKILL MAINTENANCE

Solve.

40. _____

40. A football team has won 3 out of its first 4 games. At this rate, how many games will it win in a 16-game season?

41. The state of Maine is 90% forest. The area of Maine is 30,955 sq mi. How many square miles of Maine are forest?

41. _____

5.3 Bar Graphs and Line Graphs

A **bar graph** is convenient for showing comparisons because you can tell at a glance which amount represents the largest or smallest quantity. Of course, since bar graphs are a more abstract form of pictographs, this is true of pictographs as well. However, with bar graphs, a *second scale* is usually included so that a more accurate determination of the amount can be made.

a Reading and Interpreting Bar Graphs

▶ **EXAMPLE 1**   A recent National Assessment of Educational Progress Survey showed these reasons given by students for dropping out of high school.

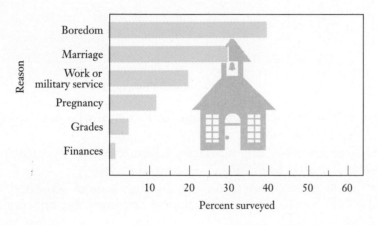

a) Approximately how many in the survey dropped out because of pregnancy?

b) What reason was given least often for dropping out?

c) What reason was given by about 30% for dropping out?

We look at the graph to answer the questions.

a) We go to the right end of the bar representing pregnancy and then go down to the percent scale. We can read, fairly accurately, that approximately 12% dropped out because of pregnancy.

b) We look for the shortest bar and find that it represents finances.

c) We go to the right on the percent scale to find the 30% mark and then up until we reach a bar that ends at approximately 30%. We then go across to the left and read the reason. The reason given by about 30% was marriage.   ◀

DO EXERCISES 1–3.

OBJECTIVES

After finishing Section 5.3, you should be able to:

a Read and interpret data from bar graphs.

b Draw bar graphs.

c Read and interpret data from line graphs.

d Draw simple line graphs.

FOR EXTRA HELP

Tape 10C

Use the bar graph in Example 1 to answer each of the following.

1. What reason was given most often for dropping out?

2. What reason was given by about 20% for dropping out?

3. How many in the survey dropped out because of grades?

Use the bar graph in Example 2 to answer each of the following.

4. What is the average annual income for a person who has completed only high school?

5. What is the greatest average annual income for a person who doesn't finish high school?

6. How much more can you expect to earn annually if you complete high school than if you complete only the 8th grade?

Of course, the bars can be drawn vertically as well.

▶ **EXAMPLE 2** A recent survey of 2000 individuals produced the following information on average income based on years of schooling.

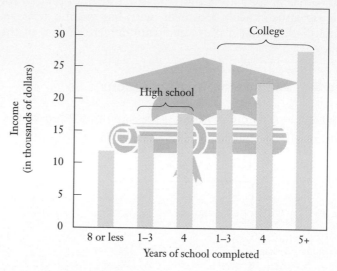

a) What is the average annual income for a person who has completed two years of high school?

b) How many years of schooling does it take to expect an average annual income of at least $20,000?

c) How much more income, on the average, can be expected after completing three years of college than after completing only one year of college?

Interpreting the graph carefully will give us the answers.

a) We go to the right, across the bottom, to the bar representing income for a person with 1–3 years of high school. We then go up to the top of the bar and, from there, back to the left to read approximately $14,000 on the income scale.

b) We go up the left-hand scale of the graph to the $20,000 mark and read to the right, until we come to a bar crossing our path. Moving down on that bar, we find that at least 4 years of college are needed.

c) There is only one bar representing 1–3 years of college. Therefore, this graph shows no difference in income between the two groups, though it may exist. ◀

DO EXERCISES 4–6.

b Drawing Bar Graphs

▶ **EXAMPLE 3** Make a vertical bar graph to show the following information about the number of cricket chirps per minute as that relates to the temperature.

56°F: 69 chirps per minute
59°F: 76 chirps per minute
62°F: 88 chirps per minute
65°F: 100 chirps per minute

First, we indicate on the base or horizontal scale the different degree markings. (See the figure at the left below.)

Then we label the marks on the vertical scale appropriately by 10's to represent the number of cricket chirps (see the graph at the left below). The jagged lines at the start of the horizontal and vertical scales indicate that we have left out a portion of the scales (to save space) since it was not necessary in providing information.

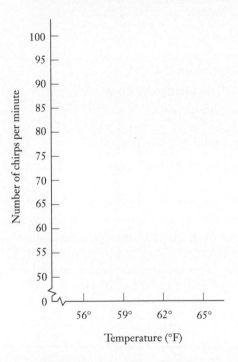
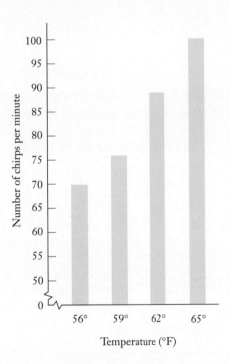

Finally, we draw vertical bars to show the number of chirps per minute for each temperature reading, as shown in the figure at the right above. ◀

DO EXERCISE 7.

7. Make a horizontal bar graph to show the loudness of various sounds listed below. (*Hint:* See Example 1.) A decibel is a measure of the loudness of sounds.

Sound	Loudness (in decibels)
Whisper	15
Tick of watch	30
Speaking aloud	60
Noisy factory	90
Moving car	80
Car horn	98
Subway	104

Use the line graph in Example 4 to answer each of the following.

8. For which week was the DJIA closing the highest?

9. For which week was the DJIA closing about 2100?

10. About how many points did the DJIA increase between weeks 1 and 6?

---

c   **Reading and Interpreting Line Graphs**

Line graphs are often used to show a change over time as well as to indicate patterns or trends.

▶ **EXAMPLE 4**   This line graph shows the closing Dow Jones Industrial Average (DJIA) for each of six weeks. Note that, again, we have a jagged line at the base of the vertical scale indicating an unnecessary portion of the scale. Note, too, that the vertical scale differs from the horizontal scale so that numbers fit reasonably.

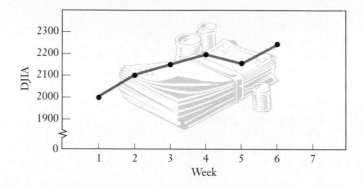

a) For which week was the DJIA closing the lowest?

b) Between which two weeks did the DJIA closing decrease?

c) For which week was the DJIA closing about 2200?

We look at the graph to find the answers.

a) For the first week, the line is at its lowest point, representing a close of about 2000.

b) Reading the graph from left to right, we see that the line went down between the 4th and 5th weeks.

c) We locate 2200 on the DJIA scale and then move to the right until we reach the point representing a closing that is closest to our position. At that point, we move down to the "Week" scale and see which week is indicated. We find that the DJIA closing was closest to 2200 for the 4th week.   ◄

DO EXERCISES 8–10.

▶ **EXAMPLE 5** The line graph below gives information from a 14-year study about the average daily cost of a semiprivate hospital room. The averages were figured every two years.

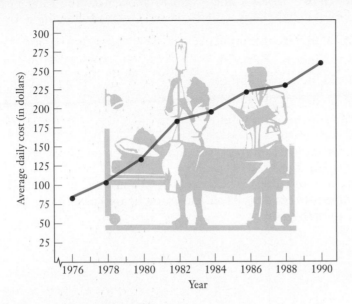

a) Give the average daily cost for a semiprivate room in 1978.

b) In which year was the average daily cost $181?

c) How much did the average daily cost increase from 1984 to 1986?

We read the graph to find the answers.

a) We find the year 1978 on the bottom scale and move up from that point to the line. We then go straight across to the left from the line and find that we are slightly above the $100 mark. A reasonable estimate would be $104.

b) Going up the left scale to a point slightly above $175, we move straight across to the right until we cross the line. At that point, we go down to the scale for "years" on the bottom and find that this occurred in 1982.

c) The graph shows an approximate average daily cost of $193 in 1984 and $218 in 1986. This gives an increase of $25 between these two years. ◀

DO EXERCISES 11–13.

Use the line graph in Example 5 to answer each of the following.

11. Between which two years did the average daily cost increase the most?

12. On the basis of the trend indicated in the graph, predict how much the average daily cost will increase from 1990 to 1994.

13. On the basis of the indicated pattern, in approximately what year did the average daily cost go over $200?

ANSWERS ON PAGE A-4

14. Draw a line graph to show how the average price per acre of farmland has changed in four years. Use the following information.

1986: $548

1987: $563

1988: $597

1989: $645

d Drawing Line Graphs

▶ **EXAMPLE 6**   Draw a line graph to show how the total number of inches of rainfall has changed in five years. Use the following information.

1982: 30 inches of rainfall

1983: 28 inches of rainfall

1984: 25 inches of rainfall

1985: 30 inches of rainfall

1986: 27 inches of rainfall

First, we indicate on the horizontal scale the different years and title it "Years." (See the following graph.)

Then we mark the vertical scale appropriately by 5's to show the number of inches of rainfall (see the graph below) and title it "Number of inches of rainfall."

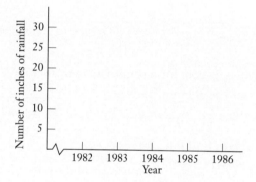

Now, we mark the points above each of the years at the appropriate level to indicate the number of inches of rainfall, and draw line segments connecting them to show the change.

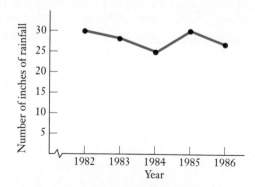

DO EXERCISE 14.

5.4 Circle Graphs

We often use **circle graphs** to show the percent of a quantity used in different categories. Circle graphs can also be used very effectively to show visually the *ratio* of one category to another. In either case, it is quite often necessary to use mathematics to find the actual amounts represented for each specific category.

a Reading and Interpreting Circle Graphs

▶ **EXAMPLE 1** This circle graph shows expenses as a percent of income in a family of four, according to a recent study of the Bureau of Labor Statistics. (*Note:* Due to rounding, the sum of the percents is 101% instead of 100%.)

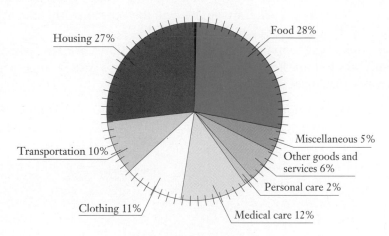

Housing 27%
Food 28%
Transportation 10%
Miscellaneous 5%
Other goods and services 6%
Personal care 2%
Clothing 11%
Medical care 12%

a) Which item accounts for the greatest expense?

b) For a family with a $2000 monthly income, how much is spent for transportation?

c) Some surveys combine medical care with personal care. What percent would be spent on those two items combined?

We look at the sections of the graph to find the answers.

a) It is immediately apparent that there are two sections that are larger than the rest. Of those two sections, the one representing food is the larger, at 28%.

b) The section of the circle representing transportation shows a 10% expense; 10% of $2000 is $200.

c) In a circle graph, we can add percents safely for problems of this type. Therefore, 12% (medical care) + 2% (personal care) = 14%. ◀

DO EXERCISES 1–3.

OBJECTIVES

After finishing Section 5.4, you should be able to:

a Read and interpret data from circle graphs.

b Draw circle graphs.

FOR EXTRA HELP

Tape 10D

Consider a family with a $2000 monthly income and use the circle graph in Example 1 to answer each of the following.

1. How much would this family typically spend on housing each month?

2. What percent of the income is spent on housing and clothing combined?

3. Compare the amount spent on medical care with the amount spent on personal care. What is the ratio?

b   Drawing Circle Graphs

▶ **EXAMPLE 2**   In a quick inventory, it was found that the types of books listed below made up the indicated percent of available books in a library. Use this information to draw a circle graph reflecting the different types of books available.

a)   History books: 25%

b)   Science books: 10%

c)   Fiction: 45%

d)   Reference books: 5%

e)   Other: 15%

We will first draw each section in a separate working circle to illustrate more clearly how each is made. We will then combine them in a single circle to show the complete graph.

Our circles will be marked off in 5-degree sections. We are providing you with circles marked off, but you could also use a protractor. (Remember that there are 360 degrees in a circle.)

a)   History books account for 25%, so they should be shown by 25% of the circle. Mathematically, this is 25% of 360° (0.25 × 360), or 90°.

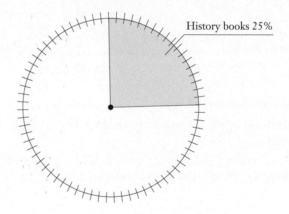

History books 25%

b)   Science books account for 10% of the books; 10% of 360° (0.10 × 360) is 36° more.

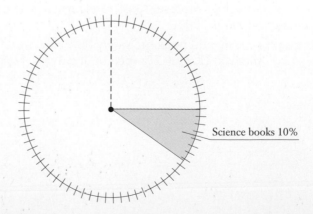

Science books 10%

c) Fiction represents 45% of the books, and 45% of 360° (0.45 × 360) is another 162°.

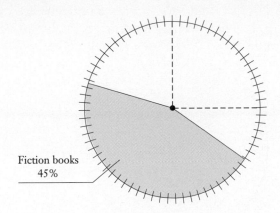

Fiction books
45%

d) Reference books represent 5% of the books; 5% of 360° (0.05 × 360) is 18° more.

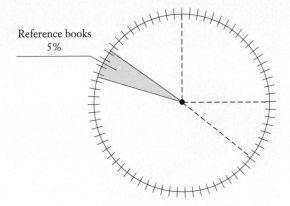

Reference books
5%

4. For each of the following uses of paper, find the number of degrees needed, to the nearest degree, to draw a circle graph. Then draw the graph.

a) Packaging: 48%

b) Writing paper: 30%

c) Tissues: 8%

d) Other: 14%

e) Draw the graph.

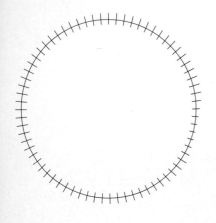

e) Other books make up the remaining 15%. We find that 15% of 360° (0.15 × 360) is 54°. Note that this last section accounts exactly for the remainder of the circle.

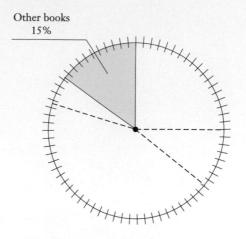

Now we can combine all of these sections in a single circle, which results in the circle graph below.

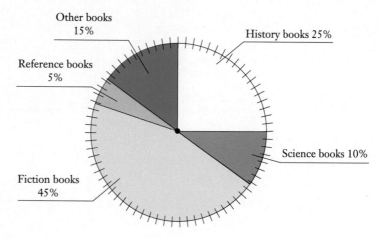

DO EXERCISE 4.

NAME   SECTION   DATE

EXERCISE SET 5.4

ANSWERS

a This circle graph, in the shape of a record, shows music preferences of customers on the basis of record store sales, according to the National Association of Recording Merchandisers.

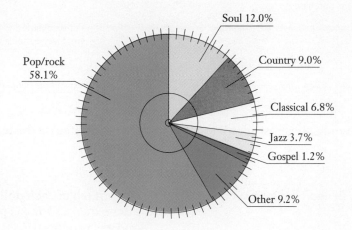

Soul 12.0%

Pop/rock 58.1%

Country 9.0%

Classical 6.8%

Jazz 3.7%

Gospel 1.2%

Other 9.2%

1. What percent of all records sold are jazz?

2. Together, what percent of all records sold are either soul or pop/rock?

3. A music store sells 3000 records a month. How many are country?

4. A music store sells 2500 records a month. How many are gospel?

5. What percent of all records sold are classical?

6. Together, what percent of all records sold are either classical or jazz?

1. _____

2. _____

3. _____

4. _____

5. _____

6. _____

ANSWERS

This circle graph shows how each customer's dollar is spent by the Indiana Gas Company on an annual basis.

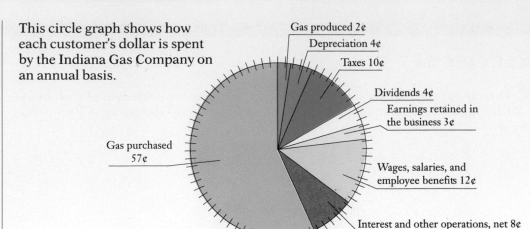

Gas produced 2¢
Depreciation 4¢
Taxes 10¢
Dividends 4¢
Earnings retained in the business 3¢
Gas purchased 57¢
Wages, salaries, and employee benefits 12¢
Interest and other operations, net 8¢

7. _____

8. _____

9. _____

7. On which item is the most spent?

8. On which item is the least spent?

10. _____

9. How much of each dollar is spent on dividends?

10. How much of each dollar is left after expenses for gas purchased and gas produced?

11. _____

11. How much of each dollar is spent on dividends, wages, salaries, and employee benefits all together?

12. The total amount spent on depreciation and dividends is the same as the amount spent on what other item?

12. _____

b

13. See graph. _____

13. Use this information on vacation expenditures to find the number of degrees required to represent each type of expenditure, and then draw and label an appropriate circle graph.

Transportation: 15%

Meals: 20%

14. _____

Lodging: 32%

Recreation: 18%

Other: 15%

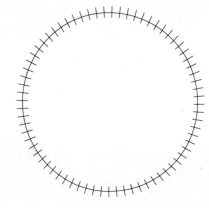

15. _____

16. _____

SKILL MAINTENANCE

Solve.

14. What is 45% of 668?

15. 16 is what percent of 64?

16. 23 is 20 percent of what?

17. Divide and simplify: $\frac{4}{7} \div \frac{16}{21}$.

17. _____

SUMMARY AND REVIEW EXERCISES: CHAPTER 5

The review sections and objectives to be tested in addition to the material in this chapter are [2.2c], [4.1e], [4.4a], [4.5a], and [4.6a].

Find the average.

1. 26, 34, 43, 51

2. 7, 11, 14, 17, 18

3. 0.2, 1.7, 1.9, 2.4

4. 700, 900, 1900, 2700, 3000

5. $2, $14, $17, $17, $21, $29

6. 20, 190, 280, 470, 470, 500

Find the median.

7. 26, 34, 43, 51

8. 7, 11, 14, 17, 18

9. 0.2, 1.7, 1.9, 2.4

10. 700, 900, 1900, 2700, 3000

11. $2, $14, $17, $17, $21, $29

12. 20, 190, 280, 470, 470, 500

Find the mode.

13. 26, 34, 43, 26, 51

14. 7, 11, 11, 14, 17, 17, 18

15. 0.2, 0.2, 0.2, 1.7, 1.9, 2.4

16. 700, 700, 800, 2700, 800

17. $2, $14, $17, $17, $21, $29

18. 20, 20, 20, 20, 20, 500

19. One summer, a student earned the following amounts over a four-week period: $102, $112, $130, and $98. What was the average amount earned? the median?

20. The following temperatures were recorded every four hours on a certain day: 63°, 58°, 66°, 72°, 71°, 67°. What was the average temperature for that day?

21. To get an A in math, a student must average 90 on four tests. Scores on the first three tests were 94, 78, and 92. What is the lowest score that the student can make on the last test and still get an A?

This table illustrates various living expenses for urban areas in several U.S. cities. Use it for Exercises 22–27.

Urban area	1800-square-foot house	Rent for 2-bedroom apartment	Dry-clean suit	Woman's shampoo/trim	1 dozen eggs	1 game bowling
Washington, D.C.	$150,277	$ 848	$6.35	$27.20	$0.86	$2.14
Springfield, Missouri	$ 70,716	$ 292	$5.75	$19.10	$0.93	$1.50
Laurel, Mississippi	$ 75,400	$ 258	$4.17	$14.84	$0.68	$1.75
Highest	$290,000 (Boston MA)	$1600 (Boston MA)	$8.68 (Fairbanks AL)	$27.20 (Washington DC)	$1.42 (Bakersfield CA)	$2.50 (Boston MA)
Lowest	$ 65,600 (Nevada MO)	$ 258 (Laurel MS)	$3.25 (Canton OH)	$6.50 (Sherman TX)	$0.50 (Kirksville MO)	$0.98 (Canton OH)

22. Where does a 2-bedroom apartment cost the most?

23. What is the lowest price that you will pay for one dozen eggs?

24. How much more will you pay to dry-clean a suit in Washington, D.C., than in Laurel, Mississippi?

25. How much does an 1800-square-foot home in Springfield, Missouri, cost?

26. Where will it cost $27.20 to get a woman's shampoo and trim?

27. Where will you pay the lowest price for one game of bowling?

This pictograph shows, for 1986, the number of space launches of several countries. Use it for Exercises 28–31.

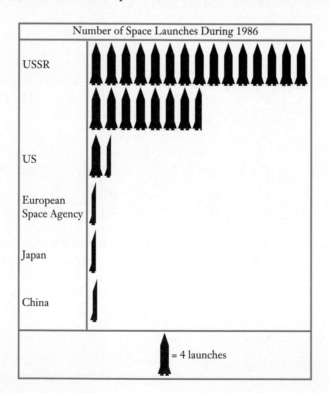

28. Which country had the most launches in 1986?

29. What was the greatest number of launches for one country?

30. What country had three times as many launches as China?

31. How many launches were made by all five countries combined?

This bar graph shows the Fast Food Price Index for several major cities. By definition for the purpose of this comparison, "fast food" consists of a quarter-pound cheeseburger, large order of fries, and medium-sized soft drink. Use it for Exercises 32–37.

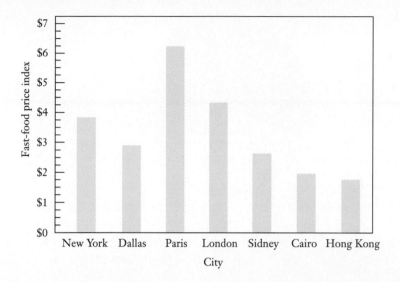

32. What is the most that you will pay for this meal?

33. Where will you pay the least for this meal?

34. In which of the given United States cities will you spend the most for this meal?

35. What is the least that you will spend for this meal considering the given U.S. cities?

36. How much more will you pay for this meal in Paris than in Hong Kong?

37. Where will you pay close to the same price for this meal that you would pay in Dallas?

This line graph shows the number of accidents per 100 drivers, by age. Use it for Exercises 38–43.

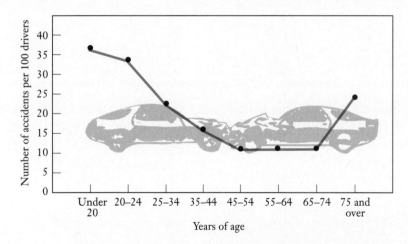

38. What age group has the most accidents per 100 drivers?

39. What is the fewest number of accidents per 100 in any age group?

40. How many more accidents do people over 75 years of age have than those in the age range of 65–74?

41. Between what ages does the number of accidents stay basically the same?

42. How many fewer accidents do persons 25–34 years of age have than those 20–24 years of age?

43. What age group has accidents more than three times as often as persons 55–64 years of age?

This circle graph shows the percent of homebuyers preferring various locations for their homes. Use it for Exercises 44–47.

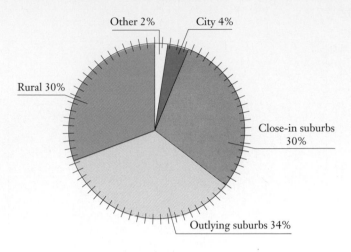

44. What percent of homebuyers prefer the rural areas?

45. What is the preference of 34% of the homebuyers?

46. What percent of homebuyers prefer to live somewhere in the suburbs?

47. Homebuyers prefer a rural area how many times more than the city?

SKILL MAINTENANCE

Solve.

48. A company car was driven 4200 miles in the first 4 months of a year. At this rate, how far will it be driven in 12 months?

49. 92% of the world population does not have a telephone. The population is about 234 million. How many do not have a telephone?

50. 789 is what percent of 355.05?

51. What percent of 98 is 49?

Divide and simplify.

52. $\dfrac{3}{4} \div \dfrac{5}{6}$

53. $\dfrac{5}{8} \div \dfrac{3}{2}$

❖ THINKING IT THROUGH

1. Compare averages, medians, and modes. Discuss why you might use one over the others to analyze a set of data.

2. Compare bar graphs and line graphs. Discuss why you might use one over the other to graph a set of data.

3. Compare bar graphs and circle graphs. Discuss why you might use one over the other to graph a set of data.

NAME   SECTION   DATE

TEST: CHAPTER 5

Find the average.

1. 45, 49, 52, 54   **2.** 1, 2, 3, 4, 5   **3.** 3, 17, 17, 18, 18, 20

1. _____

Find the median and the mode.

4. 45, 49, 52, 54   **5.** 1, 2, 3, 4, 5   **6.** 3, 17, 17, 18, 18, 20

2. _____

3. _____

7. A car went 754 km in 13 hr. What was the average number of kilometers per hour?

8. To get a C in chemistry, a student must average 70 on four tests. Scores on the first three tests were 68, 71, and 65. What is the lowest score that the student can make on the last test and still get a C?

4. _____

5. _____

Use the following table to answer the questions about the number of calories burned during various walking activities in Exercises 9–12.

6. _____

Walking activity	Calories burned in 30 min		
	110 lb	132 lb	154 lb
Walking			
Fitness (5 mph)	183	213	246
Mildly energetic (3.5 mph)	111	132	159
Strolling (2 mph)	69	84	99
Hiking			
3 mph with 20-lb load	210	249	285
3 mph with 10-lb load	195	228	264
3 mph with no load	183	213	246

7. _____

9. What activity provides the greatest benefit in burned calories for a person weighing 132 lb?

10. What is the least strenuous activity you must perform if you weigh 154 lb and you want to burn at least 250 calories every 30 min?

8. _____

9. _____

10. _____

11. How is "mildly energetic walking" defined?

12. What type of walking can a person weighing 110 lb do that will give the same benefit as some type of hiking?

13. Draw a vertical bar graph using an appropriate set of scales, showing the percent of teachers holding a master's degree for the following years. Be sure to label the scales properly.

1961:　24%

1966:　23%

1971:　28%

1976:　38%

1981:　50%

1986:　51%

11. _____

12. _____

20 ―

15 ―

0

1961

13. _____

The following pictograph shows the number of hits in a season for several professional baseball players. Use it for Exercises 14–18.

Number of Hits in a Season for 5 Professional Players

Carew

Garr

Gross

McRae

Allen

= 25 hits

14. _____

14. How many hits does each baseball symbol represent?

15. Who had the most hits?

15. _____

16. How many hits did Allen get?

17. Who got 210 hits?

18. How many more hits did Gross get than McRae?

The following line graph shows the amount of money being spent by travelers to come to the United States. Use it for Exercises 19–22.

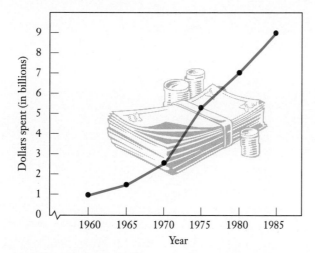

19. What trend, if any, is being shown in this graph?

20. In what five-year period was the increase the greatest?

21. How much was spent in 1960?

22. How much more was spent in 1985 than in 1980?

16. _____

17. _____

18. _____

19. _____

20. _____

21. _____

22. _____

ANSWERS

23. Use the following information to make a circle graph showing the percent of available money that people invest in certain ways. Be sure to label each section appropriately. (*Note:* The given circle is divided into 5-degree sections.)

Savings accounts: 48%

Stocks: 12%

Mutual funds: 16%

Retirement funds: 24%

23. _____

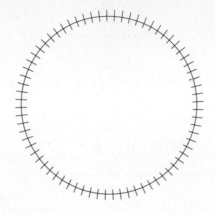

24. _____

25. _____

26. _____

SKILL MAINTENANCE

24. Divide and simplify: $\dfrac{3}{5} \div \dfrac{12}{125}$.

25. 17 is 25% of what number?

26. 78% of the television sets that are on are tuned to one of the major networks. Suppose 20,000 TV sets in a town are being watched. How many are tuned to a major network?

27. A baseball player gets 7 hits in the first 20 times at bat. At this rate, how many times at bat will it take to get 119 hits?

27. _____

INTRODUCTION This chapter introduces basic geometric figures, such as segments, rays, lines, and angles. Measures considered in this chapter are perimeter, area, and volume. Relationships between angle measures, congruent and similar triangles, and properties of parallelograms are also studied.

The review sections to be tested in addition to the material in this chapter are 1.6, 2.4, 3.3, 4.2, and 4.3. ❖

Geometry

AN APPLICATION

How "big" is one million dollars? This photo shows one million one-dollar bills assembled by the Bureau of Engraving. The width of a dollar bill is 2.3125 in., the length is 6.0625 in., and the thickness is 0.0041 in. Find the volume occupied by one million one-dollar bills.

THE MATHEMATICS

To find the volume of a single one-dollar bill, we multiply the length times the width and then by the height of thickness:

This is a formula for volume.

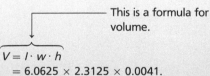

$V = l \cdot w \cdot h$
$ = 6.0625 \times 2.3125 \times 0.0041.$

Then we multiply the result by one million.

PRETEST: CHAPTER 6

1. Find the perimeter.

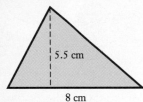

2. Find the area of the shaded region.

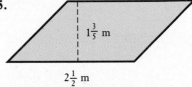

Find the area.

3.

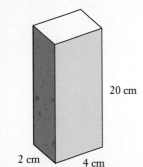

4.

5.

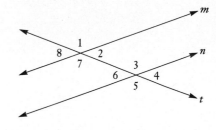

6. Find the length of a diameter of a circle with a radius of 4.8 m.

7. Find the circumference and area of the circle in Exercise 6. Use 3.14 for π.

8. Find the volume and the surface area.

9. Find the volume. Use 3.14 for π.

10. If $m \parallel n$ and $m\angle 8 = 29°$, what are the measures of the other angles?

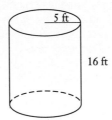

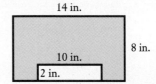

11. Given that $\triangle PQR \cong \triangle STV$, list the congruent corresponding parts.

12. Given that $\triangle MAC \sim \triangle GET$, find MA and GT.

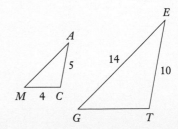

6.1 | Basic Geometric Figures

In geometry we study sets of points. A **geometric figure** (or *figure*) is simply a set of points. Thus a figure can be a set with one point, two points, or sets that look like those below.

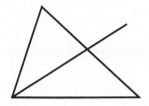  

a | Segments, Rays, and Lines

A **segment** is a geometric figure consisting of two points, called *endpoints*, and all points between them. The segment whose endpoints are A and B is shown below. It can be named $\overline{AB}$ or $\overline{BA}$.

DO EXERCISE 1.

We get an idea of a geometric figure called a ray by thinking of a ray of light. A **ray** consists of a segment, say $\overline{AB}$, and all points X such that B is between A and X: that is, $\overline{AB}$ and all points "beyond" B.

A ray is usually drawn as shown below. It has just one endpoint. The arrow indicates that it extends forever in one direction.

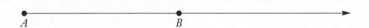

A ray is named $\overrightarrow{AB}$, where B is some point on the ray other than A. The endpoint is always listed first. Thus rays $\overrightarrow{AB}$ and $\overrightarrow{BA}$ are different.

DO EXERCISES 2–5.

The rays such as $\overrightarrow{PQ}$ and $\overrightarrow{QP}$ make up what is known as a **line**. A line can be named with a small letter m, as shown below, or it can be named by two points P and Q on the line as $\overleftrightarrow{PQ}$.

DO EXERCISES 6–11 ON THE FOLLOWING PAGE.

---

1. **a)** Draw a segment.
   b) Label its endpoints E and F.
   c) Name this segment in two ways.

2. Draw two points P and Q.

3. Draw $\overline{PQ}$.

4. Draw $\overrightarrow{PQ}$. What is its endpoint?

5. Use a colored pencil to draw $\overrightarrow{QP}$. What is its endpoint?

ANSWERS ON PAGE A-4

6. Draw two points *R* and *S*.

7. Draw $\overline{RS}$. What are its endpoints?

8. Draw $\overrightarrow{RS}$. What is its endpoint?

9. Draw $\overrightarrow{SR}$. What is its endpoint?

10. Draw $\overleftrightarrow{RS}$. What are its endpoints?

11. Name this line in seven different ways.

Name the angle in four different ways.

12.

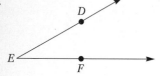

13.

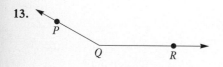

Lines in the same plane are called **coplanar.** Coplanar lines that do not intersect are called **parallel.** For example, lines *l* and *m* below are *parallel* ($l \parallel m$).

The figure below shows two lines that cross. Their *intersection* is *D*. They are also called **intersecting lines.**

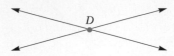

b   Angles

An **angle** is a set of points consisting of two rays with a common endpoint. The endpoint, *B*, is called the **vertex.**

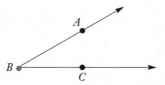

The rays are called the *sides*. The angle above can be named

angle *ABC*, $\angle ABC$, $\angle CBA$,   or $\angle B$.

Note that the name of the vertex either is in the middle or is listed by itself.

DO EXERCISES 12 AND 13.

Measuring angles is similar to measuring segments. To measure angles, we start with some arbitrary angle and assign to it a measure of 1. We call it a *unit angle*. Suppose that $\angle ABC$, below, is a unit angle. Let us then measure $\angle DEF$. If we made 3 copies of $\angle ABC$, they would "fill up" $\angle DEF$. Thus the measure of $\angle DEF$ is 3.

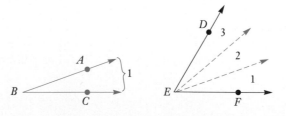

The unit most commonly used for angle measure is the degree. Below is such a unit. Its measure is 1 degree, or 1°.

Here are some other angles with their degree measures.

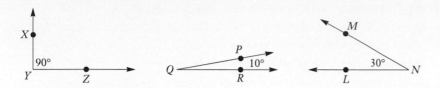

To indicate the measure of ∠ *XYZ*, we write *m* ∠ *XYZ* = 90°.

We can use a device called a *protractor* to measure angles. Note the two scales. Let us find the measure of ∠ *PQR*. We place the △ at the vertex and line up one of the sides at 0°. Then we check where the other side crosses the scale. Since 0° is on the inside scale in this case, we check where the side crosses the inside scale. Thus, *m* ∠ *PQR* = 145°.

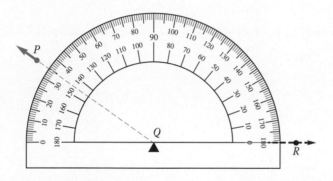

DO EXERCISE 14.

Let us find the measure of ∠ *ABC*. This time we will use the 0° on the outside scale. We see that *m* ∠ *ABC* = 42°.

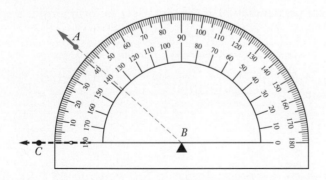

DO EXERCISE 15.

14. Use a protractor to measure this angle.

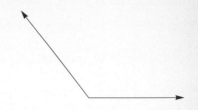

15. Use a protractor to measure this angle.

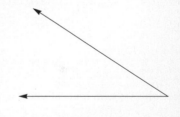

ANSWERS ON PAGE A-4

Classify the angle as right, straight, acute, or obtuse. Use your protractor if necessary.

16.   **17.**

18.

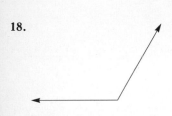

19.

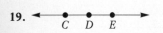

Determine whether the pair of lines is perpendicular. Use a protractor.

20.

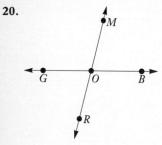

21.

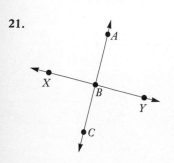

---

c **Classifying Angles**

The following are ways in which we classify angles.

> **Right angles:** Angles whose measure is 90°.
>
> **Straight angles:** Angles whose measure is 180°.
>
> **Acute angles:** Angles whose measure is greater than 0° and less than 90°.
>
> **Obtuse angles:** Angles whose measure is greater than 90° and less than 180°.

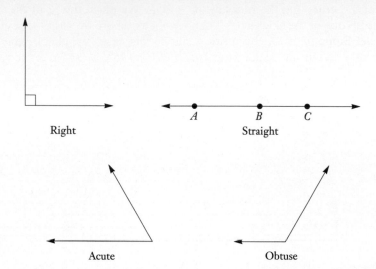

Right   Straight

Acute   Obtuse

DO EXERCISES 16–19.

d **Perpendicular Lines**

Two lines are **perpendicular** if they intersect to form a right angle.

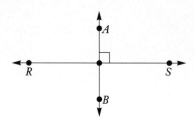

To say that $\overleftrightarrow{AB}$ is perpendicular to $\overleftrightarrow{RS}$, we write $\overleftrightarrow{AB} \perp \overleftrightarrow{RS}$. If two lines intersect to form one right angle, they form four right angles.

DO EXERCISES 20 AND 21.

e Polygons

The figures below are examples of **polygons**.

 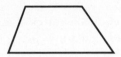

A **triangle** is a polygon made up of three segments, or sides. Consider these triangles. The triangle with vertices *A*, *B*, and *C* can be named △*ABC*.

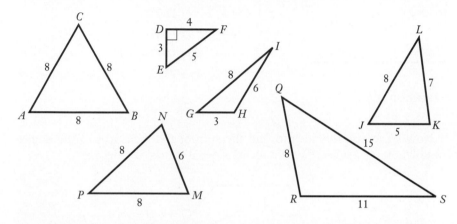

We can classify triangles according to sides and according to angles.

> *Equilateral triangle:* **All sides are the same length.**
> *Isosceles triangle:* **Two or more sides are the same length.**
> *Scalene triangle:* **All sides are of different lengths.**
> *Right triangle:* **One angle is a right angle.**
> *Obtuse triangle:* **One angle is an obtuse angle.**
> *Acute triangle:* **All three angles are acute.**

DO EXERCISES 22–25.

We can further classify polygons as follows.

Number of sides	Polygon	Number of sides	Polygon
4	Quadrilateral	8	Octagon
5	Pentagon	9	Nonagon
6	Hexagon	10	Decagon
7	Heptagon	12	Dodecagon

DO EXERCISES 26–31. (EXERCISE 31 IS ON THE FOLLOWING PAGE.)

22. Which triangles on this page are:

  a) equilateral?

  b) isosceles?

  c) scalene?

23. Are all equilateral triangles isosceles?

24. Are all isosceles triangles equilateral?

25. Which triangles on this page are:

  a) right triangles?

  b) obtuse triangles?

  c) acute triangles?

Classify the polygon by name.

26.

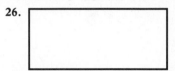

27.

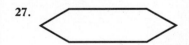

28.

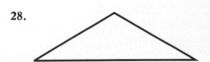

29.

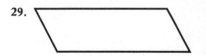

30.

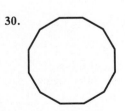

ANSWERS ON PAGE A-4

31.

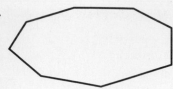

32. Find the missing angle measure.

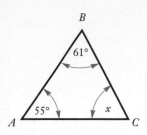

33. Consider a five-sided figure:

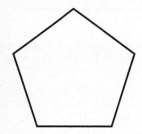

Complete.

a) The figure can be divided into _____ triangles.

b) The sum of the angle measures of each triangle is _____.

c) The sum of the angle measures of the polygon is _____ · 180°, or _____.

34. What is the sum of the angle measures of an octagon?

35. What is the sum of the angle measures of a 25-sided figure?

ANSWERS ON PAGE A-4

---

f **Sum of the Angle Measures of a Polygon**

The measures of the angles of a triangle add up to 180°. Thus if we know the measures of two angles of a triangle, we can calculate the third.

> In any triangle, the sum of the measures of the angles is 180°:
> $$m(\angle A) + m(\angle B) + m(\angle C) = 180°.$$

▶ **EXAMPLE 1** Find the missing angle measure.

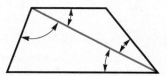

$$m(\angle A) + m(\angle B) + m(\angle C) = 180°$$
$$x + 65° + 24° = 180°$$
$$x + 89° = 180°$$
$$x = 180° - 89°$$
$$x = 91° \quad ◀$$

DO EXERCISE 32.

Now let us use this idea to find the sum of the measures of the angles of a polygon of n sides. First let us consider a four-sided figure:

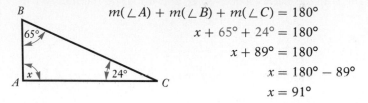

We can divide the figure into two triangles. The sum of the angle measures of each triangle is 180°. We have two triangles, so the sum of the angle measures of the figure is $2 \cdot 180°$, or 360°.

DO EXERCISE 33.

If a polygon has n sides, it can be divided into $n - 2$ triangles, each having 180° as the sum of its angle measures. Thus the sum of the angle measures of the polygon is $(n - 2) \cdot 180°$.

> If a polygon has n sides, then the sum of its angle measures is $(n - 2) \cdot 180°$.

▶ **EXAMPLE 2** What is the sum of the angle measures of a hexagon?

A hexagon has 6 sides. We use the formula $(n - 2) \cdot 180°$:

$$(n - 2) \cdot 180° = (6 - 2) \cdot 180°$$
$$= 4 \cdot 180°$$
$$= 720°. \quad ◀$$

DO EXERCISES 34 AND 35.

EXERCISE SET 6.1

a

1. Draw the segment whose endpoints are *G* and *H*. Name the segment in two ways.

•   •
G   *H*

2. Draw the segment whose endpoints are *C* and *D*. Name the segment in two ways.

•   •
C   *D*

1. _____

2. _____

3. Draw the ray with endpoint *Q*. Name the ray.

•   •
Q   *D*

4. Draw the ray with endpoint *D*. Name the ray.

•   •
Q   *D*

3. _____

5. Name this line in seven different ways.

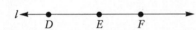

l   *D*   *E*   *F*

6. Name this line in seven different ways.

m   *J*   *K*   *T*

4. _____

5. _____

b Name the angle in four different ways.

7.

I

G   *H*

8.

R

P

Q

6. _____

7. _____

Use a protractor and measure the angle.

9.

10.

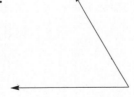

8. _____

9. _____

10. _____

ANSWERS

11. _____

12. _____

13. _____

14. _____

15. _____

16. _____

17. _____

18. _____

19. _____

20. _____

21. _____

22. _____

23. _____

24. _____

11.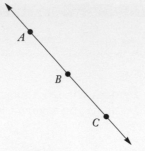

12.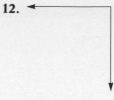

13.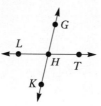

14.

c

15.–20. Classify each of the angles in Exercises 9–14 as right, straight, acute, or obtuse.

d Determine whether the pair of lines is perpendicular. Use a protractor.

21.

22.

23.

24.

e Classify the triangle as equilateral, isosceles, or scalene. Then classify it as right, obtuse, or acute.

ANSWERS

25.

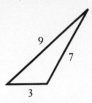

9

7

3

26.

7   7

5

27.

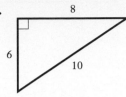

8

6

10

25. _____

26. _____

28.

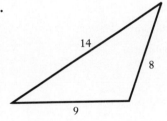

8   8

12

29.

6   6

6

30.

12   13

5

27. _____

28. _____

29. _____

31.

14

8

9

32.

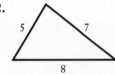

5   7

8

30. _____

31. _____

Classify the polygon by name.

33.

34.

32. _____

33. _____

35.

36.

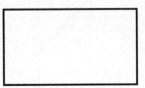

34. _____

35. _____

36. _____

ANSWERS

37. _____

38. _____

39. _____

40. _____

41. _____

42. _____

43. _____

44. _____

45. _____

46. _____

47. _____

48. _____

49. _____

50. _____

51. _____

52. _____

53. _____

54. _____

55. _____

37.

38.

39.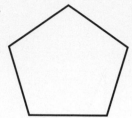

40.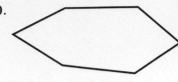

41.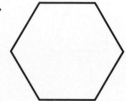

42.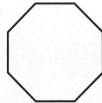

f Find the sum of the angle measures of each of the following.

43. A decagon

44. A quadrilateral

45. A 14-sided polygon

46. A 17-sided polygon

Find the missing angle measure.

47.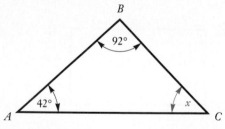

48.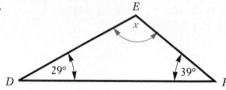

SKILL MAINTENANCE

Divide. Find decimal notation for the answer.

49. $21 \div 12$

50. $23.4 \div 10$

51. $23.4 \div 100$

52. $23.4 \div 1000$

53. Multiply 3.14×4.41. Round to the nearest hundredth.

54. Multiply: $4 \times 20\frac{1}{8}$.

55. Multiply: $48 \times \frac{1}{12}$.

6.2 Perimeter

a Finding Perimeters

A *polygon* is a geometric figure with three or more sides. The *perimeter* of a polygon is the distance around it, or the sum of the lengths of its sides.

▶ **EXAMPLE 1** Find the perimeter of this polygon.

We add the lengths of the sides. Since all the units are the same, we add the numbers, keeping meters (m) as the unit.

Perimeter = 6 m + 5 m + 4 m + 5 m + 9 m

= (6 + 5 + 4 + 5 + 9) m

= 29 m

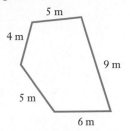

DO EXERCISES 1 AND 2.

▶ **EXAMPLE 2** Find the perimeter of a rectangle that is 3 cm by 4 cm.

Perimeter = 3 cm + 3 cm + 4 cm + 4 cm

= (3 + 3 + 4 + 4) cm = 14 cm

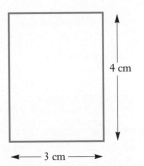

DO EXERCISE 3.

The *perimeter* of a rectangle is twice the sum of the length and the width, or 2 times the length plus 2 times the width:

$$P = 2 \cdot (l + w), \text{ or } P = 2 \cdot l + 2 \cdot w.$$

▶ **EXAMPLE 3** Find the perimeter of a rectangle that is 4.3 ft by 7.8 ft.

$P = 2 \cdot (l + w) = 2 \cdot (4.3 \text{ ft} + 7.8 \text{ ft})$

$P = 2 \cdot (12.1 \text{ ft}) = 24.2 \text{ ft}$

DO EXERCISES 4 AND 5.

A **square** is a rectangle all of whose sides have the same length.

▶ **EXAMPLE 4** Find the perimeter of a square whose sides are 9 mm long.

$P = 9 \text{ mm} + 9 \text{ mm} + 9 \text{ mm} + 9 \text{ mm}$

$P = (9 + 9 + 9 + 9) \text{ mm} = 36 \text{ mm}$

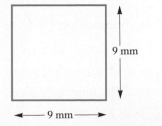

DO EXERCISE 6 ON THE FOLLOWING PAGE.

OBJECTIVES

After finishing Section 6.2, you should be able to:

a Find the perimeter of a polygon.

b Solve problems involving perimeter.

FOR EXTRA HELP

Tape 11C

Find the perimeter of the polygon.

1.

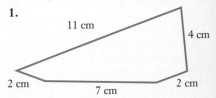

2.

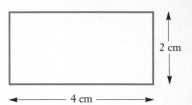

3. Find the perimeter of a rectangle that is 2 cm by 4 cm.

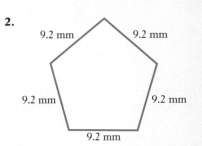

4. Find the perimeter of a rectangle that is 5.25 yd by 3.5 yd.

5. Find the perimeter of a rectangle that is 8 km by 8 km.

ANSWERS ON PAGE A-4

6. Find the perimeter of a square whose sides have length 10 km.

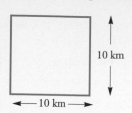

←——10 km——→

The perimeter of a *square* is four times the length of a side:

$$P = 4 \cdot s.$$

▶ **EXAMPLE 5**   Find the perimeter of a square whose sides are $20\frac{1}{8}$ in. long.

$P = 4 \cdot s$

$P = 4 \cdot 20\frac{1}{8}$ in.

$P = 4 \cdot \dfrac{161}{8}$ in.

$P = \dfrac{4 \cdot 161}{4 \cdot 2}$ in.

$P = \dfrac{161}{2} \cdot \dfrac{4}{4}$ in.

$P = 80\frac{1}{2}$ in.   ◀

7. Find the perimeter of a square whose sides have length $5\frac{1}{4}$ yd.

DO EXERCISES 7 AND 8.

b   **Solving Problems**

▶ **EXAMPLE 6**   A garden is 15 ft by 20 ft. A fence is to be built around the garden. How many feet of fence will be needed? Fencing sells for $2.95 a foot. What will the fencing cost?

1. *Familiarize.* We make a drawing. We let P = the perimeter.

8. Find the perimeter of a square whose sides have length 7.8 km.

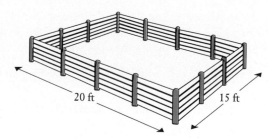

20 ft   15 ft

2. *Translate.* The perimeter of the garden is given by

$$P = 2 \cdot (l + w) = 2 \cdot (15 \text{ ft} + 20 \text{ ft}).$$

3. *Solve.* We calculate the perimeter as follows:

$$P = 2 \cdot (15 \text{ ft} + 20 \text{ ft}) = 2 \cdot (35 \text{ ft}) = 70 \text{ ft}.$$

Then we multiply by $2.95 to find the cost of the fencing:

$$\text{Cost} = \$2.95 \times \text{Perimeter} = \$2.95 \times 70 \text{ ft} = \$206.50.$$

9. A garden is 25 ft by 10 ft. A fence is to be built around the garden. How many feet of fencing will be needed? Fencing costs $4.95 a foot. What will be the cost of the fencing?

4. *Check.* The check is left to the student.

5. *State.* The fencing will cost $206.50.   ◀

DO EXERCISE 9.

NAME   SECTION   DATE

EXERCISE SET 6.2

a Find the perimeter of the polygon.

1.

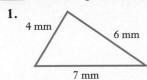

4 mm
6 mm
7 mm

2.

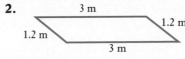

3 m
1.2 m
1.2 m
3 m

3.

3.5 cm
3.5 cm
3.5 cm
4.25 cm
0.5 cm

4.

3.4 km
5.6 km

5.

3.25 m
3.25 m

6.

Each side
$\frac{1}{6}$ km

Find the perimeter of the rectangle.

7. 5 ft by 10 ft

8. 2.5 m by 100 m

9. 34.67 cm by 4.9 cm

10. $3\frac{1}{2}$ yd by $4\frac{1}{2}$ yd

Find the perimeter of the square.

11. 22 ft on a side

12. 56.9 km on a side

13. 45.5 mm on a side

14. $3\frac{1}{8}$ yd on a side

1. _____

2. _____

3. _____

4. _____

5. _____

6. _____

7. _____

8. _____

9. _____

10. _____

11. _____

12. _____

13. _____

14. _____

b　Solve.

15. A fence is to be built around a 173-m–by–240-m field. What is the perimeter of the field? Fence wire costs $1.45 per meter. What will wire for the fence cost?

16. A standard-sized softball diamond is a square whose sides have length 65 ft. What is the perimeter of a softball diamond?

17. A standard sheet of typewriter paper is 21.6 cm by 27.9 cm. What is the perimeter of the paper?

18. A piece of flooring tile is a square 30.5 cm on a side. What is its perimeter?

19. A carpenter is to build a fence around a 9-m–by–12-m garden.

   a) The posts are 3 m apart. How many posts will be needed?
   b) The posts cost $2.40 each. How much will the posts cost?
   c) The fence will surround all but 3 m of the garden, which will be a gate. How long will the fence be?
   d) The fence costs $0.85 per meter. What will the cost of the fence be?
   e) The gate costs $9.95. What is the total cost of the materials?

20. A rain gutter is to be installed around the house shown in the figure.

   a) Find the perimeter of the house.
   b) The gutter costs $4.59 per foot. Find the total cost of the gutter.

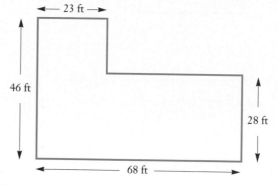

15. _____

16. _____

17. _____

18. _____

19. _____

20. _____

21. _____

22. _____

23. _____

24. _____

SKILL MAINTENANCE

21. Convert to decimal notation: 56.1%.

22. Convert to percent notation: 0.6734.

23. Evaluate: 31^2.

24. Convert to percent notation: $\dfrac{9}{8}$.

6.3 Area: Rectangles and Squares

a Rectangles

A polygon and its interior form a plane region. We can find the area of a *rectangular region* by filling it with square units. Two such units, a *square inch* and a *square centimeter,* are shown below.

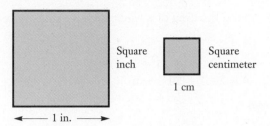

Square inch

Square centimeter

1 cm

← 1 in. →

▶ **EXAMPLE 1** What is the area of this region?

We have a rectangular array. Since the region is filled with 12 square centimeters, its area is 12 square centimeters (sq cm), or 12 cm². The number of units is 3 × 4.

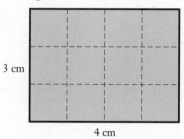

3 cm

4 cm ◀

DO EXERCISE 1.

> The area of a rectangular region is the product of the length *l* and the width *w*:
>
> $$A = l \cdot w.$$
>
>
>
> *w*
>
> *l*

▶ **EXAMPLE 2** Find the area of a rectangle that is 4 yd by 7 yd.

$$A = l \cdot w = 4 \text{ yd} \cdot 7 \text{ yd} = 4 \cdot 7 \cdot \text{yd} \cdot \text{yd} = 28 \text{ yd}^2$$

We think of yd · yd as (yd)² and denote it yd². Thus we read "28 yd²" as "28 square yards." ◀

DO EXERCISES 2 AND 3.

▶ **EXAMPLE 3** Find the area of a square whose sides are each 9 mm long.

$$A = (9 \text{ mm}) \cdot (9 \text{ mm})$$
$$A = 9 \cdot 9 \cdot \text{mm} \cdot \text{mm}$$
$$A = 81 \text{ mm}^2$$

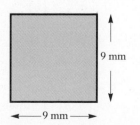

9 mm

← 9 mm → ◀

DO EXERCISE 4.

OBJECTIVES

After finishing Section 6.3, you should be able to:

a Find the area of a rectangle or square.

b Solve problems involving areas of rectangles or squares.

FOR EXTRA HELP

Tape 11D

1. What is the area of this region? Count the square centimeters.

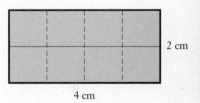

2 cm

4 cm

2. Find the area of a rectangle that is 7 km by 8 km.

3. Find the area of a rectangle that is $5\frac{1}{4}$ yd by $3\frac{1}{2}$ yd.

4. Find the area of a square whose sides have length 12 km.

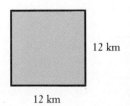

12 km

12 km

5. Find the area of a square whose sides have length 10.9 m.

The area of a square region is the square of the length of a side:

$$A = s \cdot s, \quad \text{or} \quad A = s^2.$$

▶ **EXAMPLE 4**   Find the area of a square whose sides have length 20.3 m.

$A = s \cdot s$

$A = 20.3 \text{ m} \times 20.3 \text{ m}$

$A = 20.3 \times 20.3 \times \text{m} \times \text{m} = 412.09 \text{ m}^2$ ◀

DO EXERCISES 5 AND 6.

6. Find the area of a square whose sides have length $3\frac{1}{2}$ yd.

b   Solving Problems

▶ **EXAMPLE 5**   A square sandbox 1.5 m on a side is placed on a 20-m–by–31.2-m lawn. It costs $0.04 per square meter to have the lawn mowed. What is the total cost of mowing?

1. *Familiarize.* We first draw a picture.

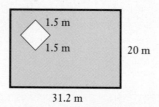

2. *Translate.* This is a two-step problem. We first find the area left over after the area of the sandbox is subtracted. Then we multiply by the cost per square meter. We let A = the area left over.

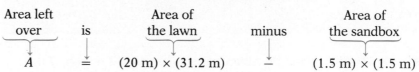

7. A square flower bed 3.5 m on a side is dug on a 30-m by 22.4-m lawn. How much area is left over? Draw a picture first.

3. *Solve.* The area of the lawn is

$$(20 \text{ m}) \times (31.2 \text{ m}) = 20 \times 31.2 \times \text{m} \times \text{m} = 624 \text{ m}^2.$$

The area of the sandbox is

$$(1.5 \text{ m}) \times (1.5 \text{ m}) = 1.5 \times 1.5 \times \text{m} \times \text{m} = 2.25 \text{ m}^2.$$

The area left over is

$$A = 624 \text{ m}^2 - 2.25 \text{ m}^2 = 621.75 \text{ m}^2.$$

Then we multiply by $0.04:

$$\$0.04 \times 621.75 = \$24.87.$$

4. *Check.* The check is left to the student.

5. *State.* The total cost of mowing the lawn is $24.87.   ◀

ANSWERS ON PAGE A-4

DO EXERCISE 7.

NAME   SECTION   DATE

EXERCISE SET 6.3

a Find the area.

1.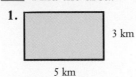
3 km
5 km

2.
1.5 m
1.5 m

3.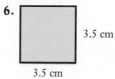
2 cm
0.7 cm

4.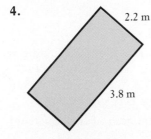
2.2 m
3.8 m

5.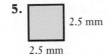
2.5 mm
2.5 mm

6.
3.5 cm
3.5 cm

7.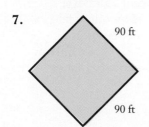
90 ft
90 ft

8.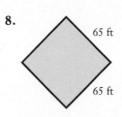
65 ft
65 ft

Find the area of the rectangle.

9. 5 ft by 10 ft

10. 14 yd by 8 yd

11. 34.67 cm by 4.9 cm

12. 2.45 km by 100 km

Find the area of the square.

13. 22 ft on a side

14. 18 yd on a side

15. 56.9 km on a side

16. 45.5 m on a side

b Solve.

17. A lot is 40 m by 36 m. A house 27 m by 9 m is built on the lot. How much area is left over?

18. A field is 240.8 m by 450.2 m. Part of the field, 160.4 m by 90.6 m, is paved for a parking lot. How much area is left over?

ANSWERS

1. _____

2. _____

3. _____

4. _____

5. _____

6. _____

7. _____

8. _____

9. _____

10. _____

11. _____

12. _____

13. _____

14. _____

15. _____

16. _____

17. _____

18. _____

19. _____

20. _____

21. a) _____

b) _____

22. a) _____

b) _____

c) _____

23. _____

24. _____

25. _____

26. _____

27. _____

28. _____

19. A sidewalk is built around two sides of a building, as shown in the figure. What is the area of the sidewalk?

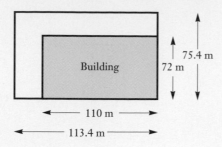

20. A standard sheet of typewriter paper is $8\frac{1}{2}$ in. by 11 in. We usually type on a $7\frac{1}{2}$-in.–by–9-in. area of the paper. What would be the area of the margin?

21. A family wants to carpet a 4.5-m–by–5.5-m room.
  a) How many square meters of carpeting will they need?
  b) The carpeting they want is $8.40 per square meter. How much will it cost?

22. A room is 4 m by 6 m. The ceiling is 3 m above the floor. There are two windows in the room, each 0.8 m by 1 m. The door is 0.8 m by 2 m.
  a) What is the area of the walls and the ceiling?
  b) A liter of paint will cover 20.2 sq m. How many liters will be needed for the room?
  c) Paint costs $2.48 a liter. How much will it cost to paint the room?

Find the area of the shaded region.

23.

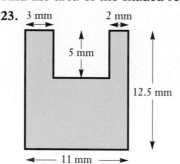

24.

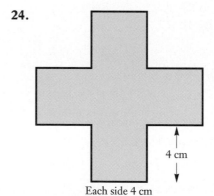

Each side 4 cm

SKILL MAINTENANCE

Convert to percent notation.

25. 0.452   **26.** $\frac{1}{3}$ **27.** $\frac{11}{20}$ **28.** $\frac{22}{25}$

6.4 Area: Parallelograms, Triangles, and Trapezoids

a

Parallelograms

A **parallelogram** is a four-sided figure with two pairs of parallel sides, as shown below.

To find the area of a parallelogram, consider the one below.

If we cut off a piece and move it to the other end, we get a rectangle.

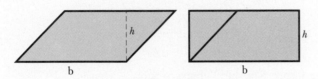

We can find the area by multiplying the length b, called a **base**, by h, called the **height.**

> The area of a parallelogram is the product of the length of a base b and the height h:
>
> $$A = b \cdot h.$$

▶ **EXAMPLE 1** Find the area of this parallelogram.

$A = b \cdot h$
$A = 7 \text{ km} \cdot 5 \text{ km}$
$A = 35 \text{ km}^2$

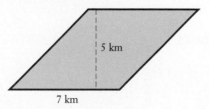

◀

OBJECTIVES

After finishing Section 6.4, you should be able to:

a Find areas of parallelograms, triangles, and trapezoids.

b Solve problems involving areas of parallelograms, triangles, and trapezoids

FOR EXTRA HELP

Tape 11E

Find the area.

1.

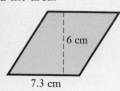

6 cm

7.3 cm

2.

5.5 km

2.25 km

▶ **EXAMPLE 2**   Find the area of this parallelogram.

$$A = b \cdot h$$
$$A = (1.2 \text{ m}) \times (6 \text{ m})$$
$$A = 7.2 \text{ m}^2$$

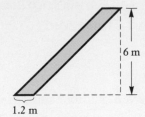

6 m

1.2 m ◀

DO EXERCISES 1 AND 2.

Triangles

To find the area of a triangle, think of cutting out another just like it.

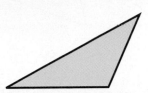

Then place the second one like this.

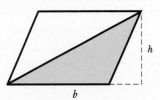

h

b

The resulting figure is a parallelogram whose area is

$$b \cdot h.$$

The triangle we started with has half the area of the parallelogram, or

$$\frac{1}{2} \cdot b \cdot h.$$

> **The area of a triangle is half the length of the base times the height:**
>
> $$A = \frac{1}{2} \cdot b \cdot h.$$

▶ **EXAMPLE 3**   Find the area of this triangle.

$$A = \frac{1}{2} \cdot b \cdot h$$

$$A = \frac{1}{2} \cdot 9 \text{ m} \cdot 6 \text{ m}$$

$$A = \frac{9 \cdot 6}{2} \text{ m}^2$$

$$A = 27 \text{ m}^2$$

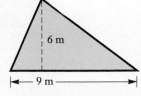

6 m

9 m

◀

▶ **EXAMPLE 4**   Find the area of this triangle.

$$A = \frac{1}{2} \cdot b \cdot h$$

$$A = \frac{1}{2} \times 6.25 \text{ cm} \times 5.5 \text{ cm}$$

$$A = 0.5 \times 6.25 \times 5.5 \text{ cm}^2$$

$$A = 17.1875 \text{ cm}^2$$

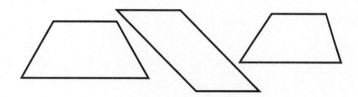

◀

DO EXERCISES 3 AND 4.

Trapezoids

A **trapezoid** is a four-sided figure with at least one pair of parallel sides, as shown below.

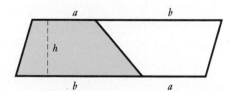

To find the area of a trapezoid, think of cutting out another just like it.

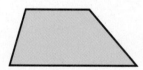

Then place the second one like this.

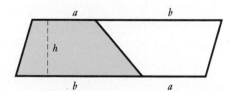

The resulting figure is a parallelogram whose area is

$$h \cdot (a + b).$$ The base is $a + b$.

The trapezoid we started with has half the area of the parallelogram, or

$$\frac{1}{2} \cdot h \cdot (a + b).$$

The area of a trapezoid is half the product of the height and the sum of the lengths of the parallel sides, or the product of the height and the average length of the bases:

$$A = \frac{1}{2} \cdot h \cdot (a + b) = h \cdot \frac{a + b}{2}.$$

Find the area.

3.

4.

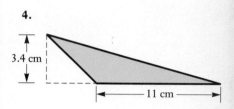

Find the area.

5.

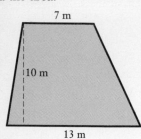

6.

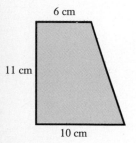

7. Find the area of the shaded region.

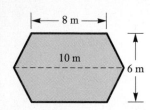

▶ **EXAMPLE 5**   Find the area of this trapezoid.

$$A = \frac{1}{2} \cdot h \cdot (a + b)$$

$$A = \frac{1}{2} \cdot 7 \text{ cm} \cdot (12 + 18) \text{ cm}$$

$$A = \frac{7 \cdot 30}{2} \cdot \text{cm}^2 = \frac{7 \cdot 15 \cdot 2}{1 \cdot 2} \text{ cm}^2$$

$$A = \frac{7 \cdot 15}{1} \cdot \frac{2}{2} \text{ cm}^2$$

$$A = 105 \text{ cm}^2$$

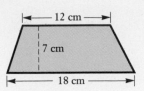

DO EXERCISES 5 AND 6.

b   **Solving Problems**

▶ **EXAMPLE 6**   Find the area of this kite.

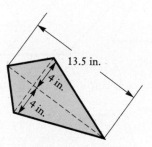

1. *Familiarize.* We look for the kinds of figures whose areas we can calculate using area formulas that we already know.

2. *Translate.* The shaded region consists of two triangles, each with a base of 13.5 in. and a height of 4 in. We can apply the formula $A = \frac{1}{2} \cdot b \cdot h$ for the area of a triangle and then multiply by 2.

3. *Solve.*

$$A = \frac{1}{2} \cdot (13.5 \text{ in.}) \cdot (4 \text{ in.}) = 27 \text{ in}^2$$

Then we multiply by 2:

$$2 \cdot 27 \text{ in}^2 = 54 \text{ in}^2.$$

4. *Check.* We can check by repeating the calculations.

5. *State.* The area of the shaded region is 54 in². ◀

DO EXERCISE 7.

NAME   SECTION   DATE

EXERCISE SET 6.4

a Find the area.

1.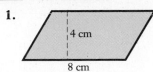
4 cm
8 cm

2.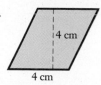
4 cm
4 cm

3.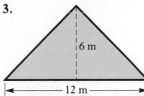
6 m
12 m

4.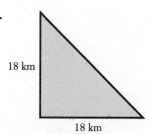
18 km
18 km

5.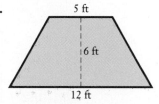
5 ft
6 ft
12 ft

6.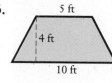
5 ft
4 ft
10 ft

7.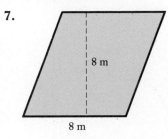
8 m
8 m

8.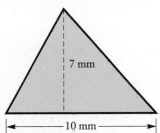
7 mm
10 mm

9.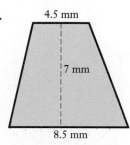
4.5 mm
7 mm
8.5 mm

10.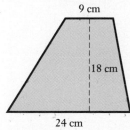
7.25 m
12 m

11.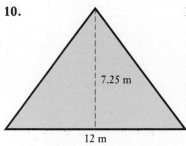
3.5 cm
2.3 cm

12.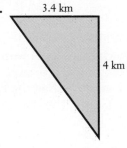
3.4 km
4 km

13.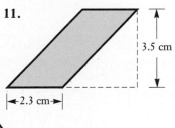
9 cm
18 cm
24 cm

14.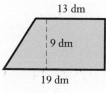
13 dm
9 dm
19 dm

15.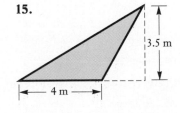
3.5 m
4 m

1. _____

2. _____

3. _____

4. _____

5. _____

6. _____

7. _____

8. _____

9. _____

10. _____

11. _____

12. _____

13. _____

14. _____

15. _____

16. _____

17. _____

18. _____

19. _____

20. _____

21. _____

22. _____

23. _____

24. _____

25. _____

26. _____

27. _____

28. _____

16.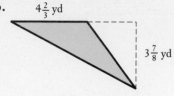
$4\frac{2}{3}$ yd

$3\frac{7}{8}$ yd

17.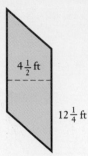
$4\frac{1}{2}$ ft

$12\frac{1}{4}$ ft

18.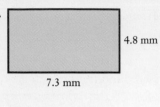
4.8 mm

7.3 mm

b Find the area of the shaded region.

19.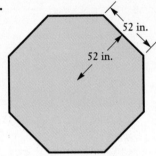
15 cm

30 cm

30 cm

20.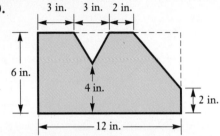
3 in.   3 in.   2 in.

6 in.

4 in.

2 in.

12 in.

21.
52 in.

52 in.

22.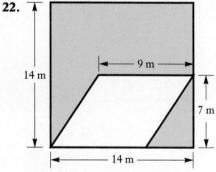
14 m

9 m

7 m

14 m

23. A lot is 36 m by 24 m. A triangular swimming pool with a height of 4.6 m and a base of 5.2 m is constructed on the lot. How much area is left over?

24. Find the total area of the sides and ends of the building.

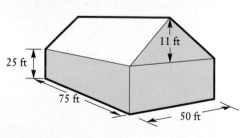
25 ft

11 ft

75 ft

50 ft

SKILL MAINTENANCE

Convert to fractional notation.

25. 9.25%

26. $87\frac{1}{2}$%

Convert to percent notation.

27. $\frac{11}{8}$

28. $\frac{2}{3}$

6.5 Circles

a Radius and Diameter

At the right is a circle with center O. Segment $\overline{AC}$ is a *diameter*. A **diameter** is a segment that passes through the center of the circle and has endpoints on the circle. Segment $\overline{OB}$ is called a *radius*. A **radius** is a segment with one endpoint on the center and the other endpoint on the circle.

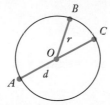

Suppose that d is the diameter of a circle and r is the radius. Then

$$d = 2 \cdot r \quad \text{and} \quad r = \frac{d}{2}.$$

▶ **EXAMPLE 1** Find the length of a radius of this circle.

$$r = \frac{d}{2}$$
$$r = \frac{12 \text{ m}}{2}$$
$$r = 6 \text{ m}$$

12 m

◀

▶ **EXAMPLE 2** Find the length of a diameter of this circle.

$$d = 2 \cdot r$$
$$d = 2 \cdot \frac{1}{4} \text{ ft}$$
$$d = \frac{1}{2} \text{ ft}$$

$\frac{1}{4}$ ft

◀

DO EXERCISES 1 AND 2.

b Circumference

The **circumference** of a circle is the distance around it and calculating it is similar to finding the perimeter of a polygon.

Take a 12-oz soft drink can and measure the circumference C of the lid with a tape measure. Then measure the diameter d. Then find the ratio C/d.

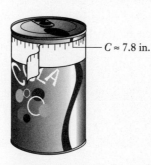

$d \approx 2.5$ in.

 $C \approx 7.8$ in.

$$\frac{C}{d} \approx \frac{7.8 \text{ in.}}{2.5 \text{ in.}} \approx 3.1$$

OBJECTIVES

After finishing Section 6.5, you should be able to:

a Find the length of a radius of a circle given the length of a diameter, and find the length of a diameter given the length of a radius.

b Find the circumference of a circle given the length of a diameter or radius.

c Find the area of a circle given the length of a radius.

d Solve problems involving circles.

FOR EXTRA HELP

Tape 12A

1. Find the length of a radius.

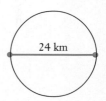

24 km

2. Find the length of a diameter.

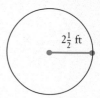

$2\frac{1}{2}$ ft

3. Find the circumference of this circle. Use 3.14 for π.

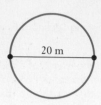

20 m

Suppose we did this with cans and circles of several sizes. We would get a number close to 3.1. For any circle, if we divide the circumference C by the diameter d, we get the same number. We call this number π (pi).

$$\frac{C}{d} = \pi \text{ or } C = \pi \cdot d. \qquad \text{The number } \pi \text{ is about 3.14, or about } \frac{22}{7}.$$

▶ **EXAMPLE 3**   Find the circumference of this circle. Use 3.14 for π.

$C = \pi \cdot d$
$C \approx 3.14 \times 6$ cm
$C = 18.84$ cm

6 cm

The circumference is about 18.84 cm.   ◀

DO EXERCISE 3.

4. Find the circumference of this circle. Use $\frac{22}{7}$ for π.

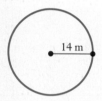

14 m

Since

$$d = 2 \cdot r,$$

where r is the length of a radius, it follows that

$$C = \pi \cdot d = \pi \cdot (2 \cdot r).$$

$$C = 2 \cdot \pi \cdot r$$

▶ **EXAMPLE 4**   Find the circumference of this circle. Use $\frac{22}{7}$ for π.

$C = 2 \cdot \pi \cdot r$

$C \approx 2 \cdot \dfrac{22}{7} \cdot 70$ m

$C = 2 \cdot 22 \cdot \dfrac{70}{7}$ m

$C = 44 \cdot 10$ m

$C = 440$ m

70 m

The circumference is about 440 m.   ◀

5. Find the circumference of this circle. Use 3.14 for π.

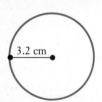

3.2 cm

▶ **EXAMPLE 5**   Find the perimeter of this figure. Use 3.14 for π.

We let $P =$ the perimeter. We have half a circle attached to a square. We add half the circumference to the lengths of the three line segments.

$P = 3 \times 9.4$ km $+ \dfrac{1}{2} \times 2 \times \pi \times 4.7$ km

≈ 28.2 km $+ 3.14 \times 4.7$ km

$= 28.2$ km $+ 14.758$ km

$= 42.958$ km

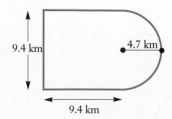

9.4 km

4.7 km

9.4 km

The perimeter is about 57.716 km.   ◀

DO EXERCISES 4 AND 5.

6. Find the area of this circle. Use $\frac{22}{7}$ for π.

C Area

Below is a circle of radius r.

6. Find the area of this circle. Use $\frac{22}{7}$ for π.

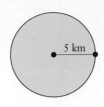

Think of cutting half the circular region into small pieces and arranging them as shown below.

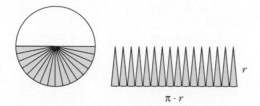

Then imagine cutting the other half of the circular region and arranging the pieces in with the others as shown below.

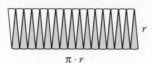

This is almost a parallelogram. The base has length $\frac{1}{2} \cdot 2 \cdot \pi \cdot r$, or $\pi \cdot r$ (half the circumference) and the height is r. Thus the area is about

$$(\pi \cdot r) \cdot r.$$

This is the area of a circle.

> **The area of a circle with radius of length r is given by**
> $$A = \pi \cdot r \cdot r, \quad \text{or} \quad A = \pi \cdot r^2.$$

▶ **EXAMPLE 6** Find the area of this circle. Use $\frac{22}{7}$ for π.

$A = \pi \cdot r \cdot r$

$A \approx \dfrac{22}{7} \cdot 14 \text{ cm} \cdot 14 \text{ cm}$

$A = \dfrac{22}{7} \cdot 196 \text{ cm}^2$

$A = 616 \text{ cm}^2$

The area is about 616 cm². ◀

DO EXERCISE 6.

7. Find the area of this circle. Use 3.14 for π.

10.4 cm

► **EXAMPLE 7**   Find the area of this circle. Use 3.14 for π. Round to the nearest hundredth.

$$A = \pi \cdot r \cdot r$$
$$A \approx 3.14 \times 2.1 \text{ m} \times 2.1 \text{ m}$$
$$A = 3.14 \times 4.41 \text{ m}^2$$
$$A = 13.8474 \text{ m}^2$$
$$A \approx 13.85 \text{ m}^2$$

2.1 m

The area is about 13.85 m^2.   ◄

DO EXERCISE 7.

d   Solving Problems

► **EXAMPLE 8**   Which is larger, and by how much: an 8-inch square cookie sheet or an 8-inch diameter circular pizza pan?

First, we draw a picture of each.

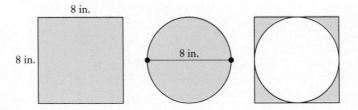

8 in.

8 in.

8 in.

Then we compute areas.
The area of the square is

$$A = s \cdot s$$
$$= 8 \text{ in.} \times 8 \text{ in.}$$
$$= 64 \text{ in}^2.$$

8. Which is larger and by how much: a 10-inch square cookie sheet or a 12-inch diameter pizza pan?

The diameter of the circle is 8 in., so the radius is 8 in./2, or 4 in. The area of the circle is

$$A = \pi \cdot r \cdot r$$
$$\approx 3.14 \times 4 \text{ in.} \times 4 \text{ in.}$$
$$= 50.24 \text{ in}^2.$$

We see that the cookie sheet is larger by about

$$64 \text{ in}^2 - 50.24 \text{ in}^2, \quad \text{or} \quad 13.76 \text{ in}^2.$$

13.76 in^2 is actually the area of the shaded region shown to the right above.   ◄

DO EXERCISE 8.

ANSWERS ON PAGE A-5

NAME   SECTION   DATE

EXERCISE SET 6.5

a Find the length of a diameter of the circle.

1.

7 cm

2.

8 m

3.

$\frac{3}{4}$ in.

4.
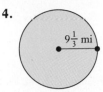
$9\frac{1}{3}$ mi

Find the length of a radius of the circle.

5.
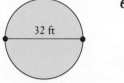
32 ft

6.

24 in.

7.

1.4 cm

8.
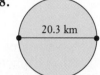
20.3 km

b Find the circumference of each circle in Exercises 1–4. Use $\frac{22}{7}$ for π.

9. Exercise 1   **10.** Exercise 2   **11.** Exercise 3   **12.** Exercise 4

Find the circumference of each circle in Exercises 5–8. Use 3.14 for π.

13. Exercise 5   **14.** Exercise 6   **15.** Exercise 7   **16.** Exercise 8

c Find the area of each circle in Exercises 1–4. Use $\frac{22}{7}$ for π.

17. Exercise 1   **18.** Exercise 2   **19.** Exercise 3   **20.** Exercise 4

Find the area of each circle in Exercises 5–8. Use 3.14 for π.

21. Exercise 5   **22.** Exercise 6   **23.** Exercise 7   **24.** Exercise 8

1. _____

2. _____

3. _____

4. _____

5. _____

6. _____

7. _____

8. _____

9. _____

10. _____

11. _____

12. _____

13. _____

14. _____

15. _____

16. _____

17. _____

18. _____

19. _____

20. _____

21. _____

22. _____

23. _____

24. _____

ANSWERS

d   Solve. Use 3.14 for π.

25. The lid of a cola can has a 6-cm diameter. What is its radius? circumference? area?

26. A penny has a 1-cm radius. What is its diameter? circumference? area?

25. _____

26. _____

27. A radio station is allowed by the FCC to broadcast over an area with a radius of 220 km. How much area is this?

28. Which is larger and by how much: a 12-inch circular pizza or a 12-inch square pizza?

27. _____

29. The trunk of an elm tree has a 1.1-m diameter. What is its circumference?

30. A silo has a 10-m diameter. What is its circumference?

28. _____

29. _____

31. The circumference of a quarter is 7.85 cm. What is the diameter? radius? area?

32. The circumference of a dime is 5.652 cm. What is the diameter? radius? area?

30. _____

31. _____

33. A circular swimming pool is surrounded by a walk that is 1 m wide. The diameter of the pool is 20 m. What is the area of the walk?

34. A roller rink is shown below. What is its area? Hardwood flooring costs $10.50 per square meter. How much would flooring cost?

32. _____

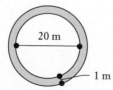

20 m

1 m

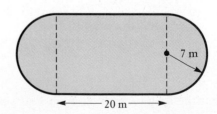

7 m

20 m

33. _____

34. _____

Find the perimeter. Use 3.14 for π.

35.

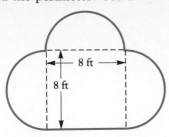

36.

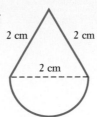

37.

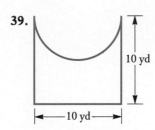

38.

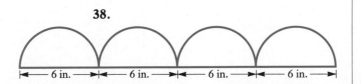

39.

40.

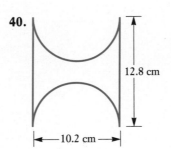

Find the area of the shaded region. Use 3.14 for π.

41.

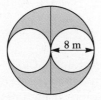

42.

35. _____

36. _____

37. _____

38. _____

39. _____

40. _____

41. _____

42. _____

43.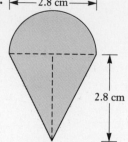

44.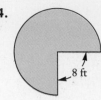

43. _____

44. _____

45. _____

45.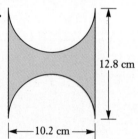

46.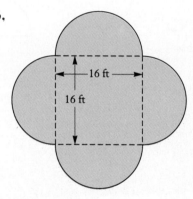

46. _____

47. _____

48. _____

49. _____

SKILL MAINTENANCE

Convert to percent notation.

47. 0.875   **48.** 0.58

49. $0.\overline{6}$ **50.** 0.4361

50. _____

51. _____

SYNTHESIS

51. ▨ $\pi \approx \frac{3927}{1250}$ is another approximation for π. Find decimal notation using your calculator. Round to the nearest thousandth.

52. ▨ The distance from Kansas City to Indianapolis is 500 mi. A car was driven this distance using tires with a radius of 14 in. How many revolutions of each tire occurred on the trip? Use $\frac{22}{7}$ for π.

52. _____

53. Tennis balls are usually packed vertically three in a can, one on top of another. Suppose the diameter of a tennis ball is d. Find the height of the stack of balls. Find the circumference of one ball. Which is greater? Explain.

53. _____

6.6 Volume and Surface Area

a Volume and Surface Area of Rectangular Solids

The **volume** of a **rectangular solid** is the number of unit cubes needed to fill it.

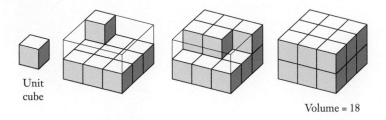

Unit cube

Volume = 18

Two other units are shown below.

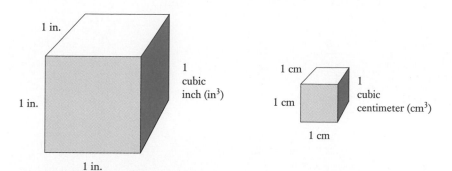

1 in.

1 cubic inch (in³)

1 cm

1 cubic centimeter (cm³)

▶ **EXAMPLE 1** Find the volume.

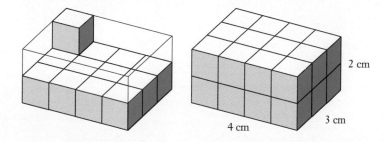

2 cm

4 cm

3 cm

The figure is made up of 2 layers of 12 cubes each, so its volume is 24 cubic centimeters (cm³). ◀

DO EXERCISE 1.

> The volume of a rectangular solid is found by multiplying length by width by height:
>
> $$V = l \cdot w \cdot h.$$

OBJECTIVES

After finishing Section 6.6, you should be able to:

a Find the volume and the surface area of a rectangular solid.

b Given the radius and the height, find the volume of a circular cylinder.

c Given the radius, find the volume of a sphere.

d Given the radius, find the volume of a circular cone.

FOR EXTRA HELP

Tape 12C, 13A

1. Find the volume.

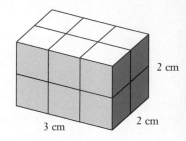

2 cm

3 cm

2 cm

2. Find the volume and the surface area.

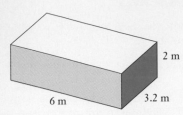

3. A cord of wood is 4 ft by 4 ft by 8 ft. What is the volume of a cord of wood?

▶ **EXAMPLE 2**   Find the volume of this solid.

$V = l \cdot w \cdot h$
$V = 10\text{ m} \cdot 8\text{ m} \cdot 7\text{ m}$
$V = 10 \cdot 56\text{ m}^3$
$V = 560\text{ m}^3$

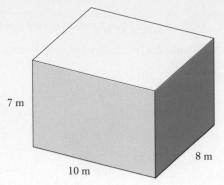

The **surface area** of a rectangular solid is the total area of the six rectangles that form the surface of the solid. For the rectangular solid below, we can show the six rectangles with a diagram.

$SA =$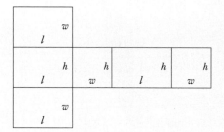

$= lw + lw + lh + wh + lh + wh$
$= 2lw + 2lh + 2wh, \quad \text{or} \quad 2(lw + lh + wh)$

> The surface area of a rectangular solid with length *l*, width *w*, and height *h* is given by the formula
>
> $$SA = 2lw + 2lh + 2wh, \quad \text{or} \quad 2(lw + lh + wh).$$

▶ **EXAMPLE 3**   Find the surface area of the rectangular solid in Example 2.

$SA = 2lw + 2lh + 2wh$
$\quad = 2 \cdot 10\text{ m} \cdot 8\text{ m} + 2 \cdot 10\text{ m} \cdot 7\text{ m} + 2 \cdot 8\text{ m} \cdot 7\text{ m}$
$\quad = 160\text{ m}^2 + 140\text{ m}^2 + 112\text{ m}^2$
$\quad = 412\text{ m}^2$ ◀

> The units used for area are square units.
> The units used for volume are cubic units.

DO EXERCISES 2 AND 3.

b Cylinders

A rectangular solid with a shaded base is shown below. Note that we can think of the volume as the product of the area of the base times the height:

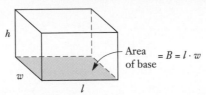

$$V = l \cdot w \cdot h$$
$$= (l \cdot w) \cdot h$$
$$= (\text{Area of the base}) \cdot h$$
$$= B \cdot h$$

where B represents the area of the base.

Like rectangular solids, **circular cylinders** have bases of equal area that lie in parallel planes. The bases of circular cylinders are circular regions.

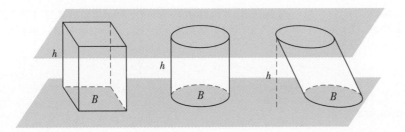

The volume of a circular cylinder is found in a manner similar to finding the volume of a rectangular solid. The volume is the product of the area of the base times the height. The height is always measured perpendicular to the base.

> The volume of a circular cylinder is the product of the area of the base *B* and the height *h*:
>
> $$V = B \cdot h, \quad \text{or} \quad V = \pi \cdot r^2 \cdot h.$$

▶ **EXAMPLE 4** Find the volume of this circular cylinder. Use 3.14 for π.

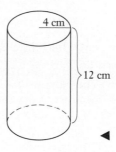

$$V = Bh = \pi \cdot r^2 \cdot h$$
$$\approx 3.14 \times 4\text{ cm} \times 4\text{ cm} \times 12\text{ cm}$$
$$= 602.88\text{ cm}^3$$

◀

DO EXERCISES 4 AND 5.

c Spheres

A **sphere** is the three-dimensional counterpart of a circle. It is the set of all points in space that are a given distance (the radius) from a given point (the center).

---

4. Find the volume of the cylinder. Use 3.14 for π.

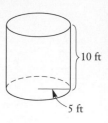

10 ft

5 ft

5. Find the volume of the cylinder. Use $\frac{22}{7}$ for π.

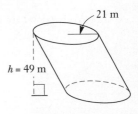

21 m

$h = 49$ m

6. Find the volume of the sphere. Use $\frac{22}{7}$ for π.

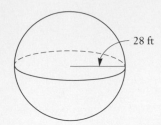

7. The radius of a standard-sized golf ball is 2.1 cm. Find its volume. Use 3.14 for π.

8. Find the volume of this cone. Use 3.14 for π.

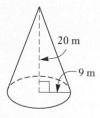

9. Find the volume of this cone. Use $\frac{22}{7}$ for π.

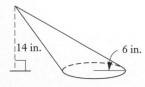

We find the volume of a sphere as follows.

> **The volume of a sphere of radius r is given by**
> $$V = \frac{4}{3} \cdot \pi \cdot r^3.$$

▶ **EXAMPLE 5** The radius of a standard-sized bowling ball is 4.2915 in. Find the volume of a bowling ball. Round to the nearest hundredth of a cubic inch. Use 3.14 for π.

$$V = \frac{4}{3} \cdot \pi \cdot r^3 \approx \frac{4}{3} \times 3.14 \times (4.2915 \text{ in.})^3$$
$$\approx 1.33 \times 3.14 \times 79.0364 \text{ in}^3 \approx 330.07 \text{ in}^3 \qquad ◀$$

DO EXERCISES 6 AND 7.

d   Cones

Consider a circle in a plane and choose any point not in the plane. The circular region, together with the set of all segments connecting P to a point on the circle, is called a **circular cone**.

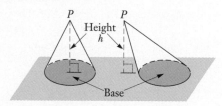

We find the volume of a cone as follows.

> **The volume of a circular cone with base radius r is one-third the product of the base area and the height:**
> $$V = \frac{1}{3} \cdot B \cdot h = \frac{1}{3} \pi \cdot r^2 \cdot h.$$

▶ **EXAMPLE 6** Find the volume of this cone. Use $\frac{22}{7}$ for π.

$$V = \frac{1}{3} \pi \cdot r^2 \cdot h$$
$$\approx \frac{1}{3} \times \frac{22}{7} \times 3 \text{ cm} \times 3 \text{ cm} \times 7 \text{ cm}$$
$$= 66 \text{ cm}^3$$

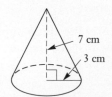

                                                  ◀

DO EXERCISES 8 AND 9.

NAME   SECTION   DATE

EXERCISE SET 6.6

a Find the volume and the surface area.

1.

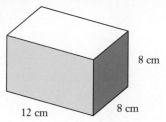

8 cm

12 cm   8 cm

2.

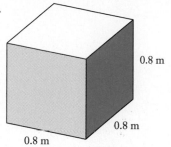

0.8 m

0.8 m

0.8 m

3.

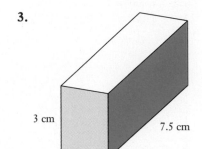

3 cm

7.5 cm

2 cm

4.

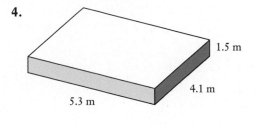

1.5 m

4.1 m

5.3 m

5.

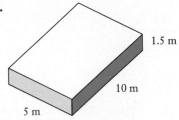

1.5 m

10 m

5 m

6.

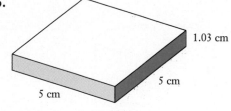

1.03 cm

5 cm

5 cm

7.

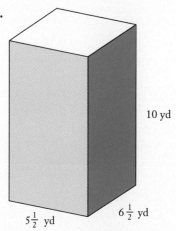

10 yd

$5\frac{1}{2}$ yd $6\frac{1}{2}$ yd

8.

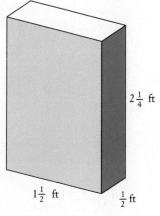

$2\frac{1}{4}$ ft

$1\frac{1}{2}$ ft $\frac{1}{2}$ ft

1. V = _____

   SA = _____

2. V = _____

   SA = _____

3. V = _____

   SA = _____

4. V = _____

   SA = _____

5. V = _____

   SA = _____

6. V = _____

   SA = _____

7. V = _____

   SA = _____

8. V = _____

   SA = _____

b Find the volume of the circular cylinder. Use 3.14 for π in Exercises 9–12. Use $\frac{22}{7}$ for π in Exercises 13–16.

9.
8 in.
4 in.

10.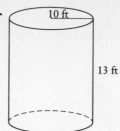
10 ft
13 ft

9. _____

10. _____

11.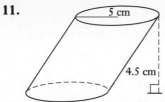
5 cm
4.5 cm

12.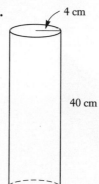
4 cm
40 cm

11. _____

12. _____

13.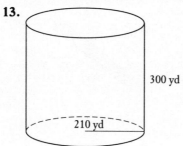
300 yd
210 yd

14.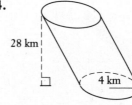
28 km
4 km

13. _____

14. _____

15.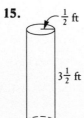
$\frac{1}{2}$ ft
$3\frac{1}{2}$ ft

16.
4.2 cm
20 cm

15. _____

16. _____

c Find the volume of the sphere. Use 3.14 for π in Exercises 17–20. Use $\frac{22}{7}$ for π in Exercises 21 and 22.

17.

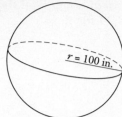

r = 100 in.

18.

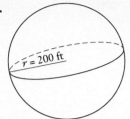

r = 200 ft

19.

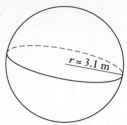

r = 3.1 m

20.

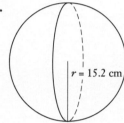

r = 15.2 cm

21.

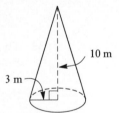

r = 7 km

22.

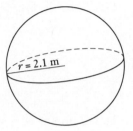

r = 2.1 m

d Find the volume of the cone. Use 3.14 for π in Exercises 23 and 24. Use $\frac{22}{7}$ for π in Exercises 25–28.

23.

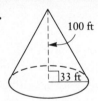

100 ft

33 ft

24.

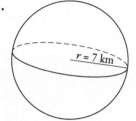

10 m

3 m

25.

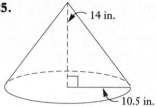

14 in.

10.5 in.

26.

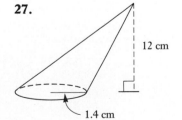

8.4 cm

5 cm

27.

12 cm

1.4 cm

28.

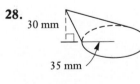

30 mm

35 mm

ANSWERS

17. _____

18. _____

19. _____

20. _____

21. _____

22. _____

23. _____

24. _____

25. _____

26. _____

27. _____

28. _____

29. _____

30. _____

31. _____

32. _____

33. _____

34. _____

35. _____

36. _____

37. _____

38. _____

39. _____

40. _____

41. _____

b , c Solve.

29. The diameter of the base of a circular cylinder is 14 m. The height is 220 m. Find the volume. Use $\frac{22}{7}$ for π.

30. A rung of a ladder is 2 in. in diameter and 16 in. long. Find the volume. Use 3.14 for π.

31. A barn silo, excluding the top, is a circular cylinder. The silo is 6 m in diameter and the height is 13 m. Find the volume. Use 3.14 for π.

32. A log of wood has a diameter of 12 cm and a height of 42 cm. Find the volume. Use 3.14 for π.

33. The diameter of a spherical gas tank is 6 m. Find the volume to the nearest tenth of a cubic meter. Use 3.14 for π.

34. The diameter of a tennis ball is 6.5 cm. Find the volume. Use 3.14 for π.

35. The diameter of the earth is 6400 km. Find the volume of the earth. Use 3.14 for π.

36. The volume of a ball is 36π cm^3. Find the dimensions of a rectangular box that is just large enough to hold the ball.

SKILL MAINTENANCE

Multiply.

37. $5 \times 22\frac{1}{2}$

38. $28 \times 13\frac{1}{4}$

Evaluate.

39. 10^3

40. 15^2

SYNTHESIS

41. Solve the problem regarding the volume of one million one-dollar bills as given on the chapter opening page. Give the answer in both cubic inches and cubic feet.

6.7 Relationships Between Angle Measures

a Complementary and Supplementary Angles

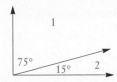

∠1 and ∠2 above are **complementary** angles.

$$m\angle 1 + m\angle 2 = 90°$$
$$75° + 15° = 90°$$

> **Two angles are *complementary* if and only if the sum of their measures is 90°. Each angle is called a complement of the other.**

If two angles are complementary, each is an acute angle.

▶ **EXAMPLE 1** Identify each pair of complementary angles.

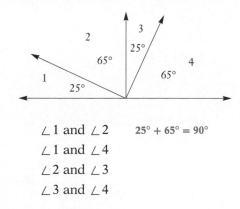

∠1 and ∠2   25° + 65° = 90°
∠1 and ∠4
∠2 and ∠3
∠3 and ∠4   ◀

DO EXERCISE 1.

▶ **EXAMPLE 2** Find the measure of a complement of an angle of 39°.

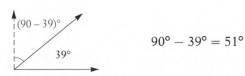

$$90° - 39° = 51°$$

The measure of a complement is 51°.   ◀

DO EXERCISES 2–4.

OBJECTIVES

After finishing Section 6.7, you should be able to:

a Identify complementary and supplementary angles and find the measure of a complement or a supplement of a given angle.

b Determine if segments are congruent and if angles are congruent.

c Use the Vertical Angle Property to find measures of angles.

d Identify pairs of corresponding angles, interior angles, and alternate interior angles and apply properties of transversals and parallel lines to find measures of angles.

1. Identify each pair of complementary angles.

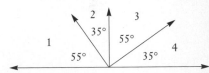

Find the measure of a complement of the angle.

2.

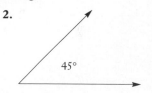

3.

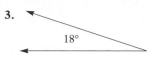

4.

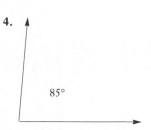

5. Identify each pair of supplementary angles.

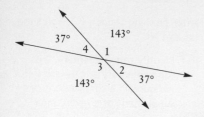

Find the measure of a supplement of
an angle with the given measure.

6. 38°

7. 157°

8. 90°

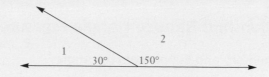

∠1 and ∠2 above are **supplementary** angles.

$$m\angle 1 + m\angle 2 = 180°$$
$$30° + 150° = 180°$$

> **Two angles are *supplementary* if and only if the sum of their measures
> is 180°. Each angle is called a supplement of the other.**

▶ **EXAMPLE 3**   Identify each pair of supplementary angles.

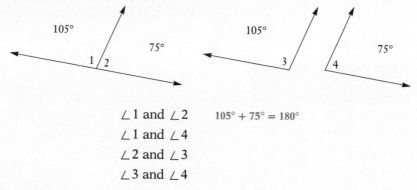

∠1 and ∠2 $105° + 75° = 180°$
∠1 and ∠4
∠2 and ∠3
∠3 and ∠4   ◀

DO EXERCISE 5.

▶ **EXAMPLE 4**   Find the measure of a supplement of an angle of 112°.

$$180° - 112° = 68°$$

Thus the measure of a supplement is 68°.   ◀

DO EXERCISES 6–8.

b Congruent Segments and Angles

Congruent figures have the same size and shape. They fit together exactly.

> **Two segments are *congruent* if and only if they have the same length.**

▶ **EXAMPLE 5** Use a ruler to show that $\overline{PQ}$ and $\overline{RS}$ are congruent.

 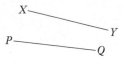

Since both segments have the same length, $\overline{PQ}$ and $\overline{RS}$ are congruent. To say that $\overline{PQ}$ and $\overline{RS}$ are congruent, we write

$$\overline{PQ} \cong \overline{RS}.$$ ◀

▶ **EXAMPLE 6** Which pairs of segments are congruent? Use a ruler.

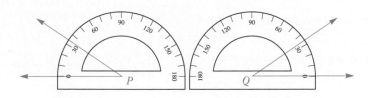

$$\overline{AB} \cong \overline{CD} \quad \text{and} \quad \overline{PQ} \cong \overline{XY}$$ ◀

DO EXERCISES 9 AND 10.

> **Two angles are *congruent* if and only if they have the same measures.**

▶ **EXAMPLE 7** Use a protractor to show that $\angle P$ and $\angle Q$ are congruent.

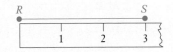 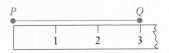

Since $m\angle P = m\angle Q = 34°$, $\angle P$ and $\angle Q$ are congruent. To say that $\angle P$ and $\angle Q$ are congruent, we write

$$\angle P \cong \angle Q.$$ ◀

Which pairs of segments are congruent? Use a ruler.

9.

10.

Which pairs of angles are congruent? Use a protractor.

11.

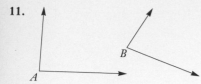

12.

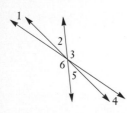

13. In the figure below, $m\angle 2 = 41°$ and $m\angle 4 = 10°$. Find $m\angle 1$, $m\angle 3$, $m\angle 5$, and $m\angle 6$.

▶ **EXAMPLE 8**   Which pairs of angles are congruent? Use a protractor.

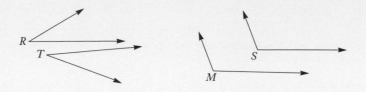

$$\angle M \cong \angle S \quad \text{since} \quad m\angle M = m\angle S = 110°. \quad ◀$$

DO EXERCISES 11 AND 12.

If two angles are congruent, then their supplements are congruent and their complements are congruent.

C   **Vertical Angles**

When $\overleftrightarrow{RT}$ intersects $\overleftrightarrow{SQ}$ at P, four angles are formed:

    $\angle SPT$

    $\angle RPQ$

    $\angle SPR$

    $\angle QPT$

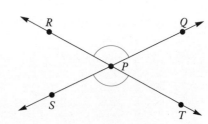

Pairs of angles such as $\angle RPQ$ and $\angle SPT$ are called **vertical angles.**

> **Two nonstraight angles are *vertical* angles if and only if their sides form two pairs of opposite rays.**

Vertical angles are supplements of the same angle. Thus they are congruent.

> The Vertical Angle Property
>
> **Vertical angles are congruent.**

▶ **EXAMPLE 9**   In the figure below, $m\angle 1 = 23°$ and $m\angle 3 = 34°$. Find $m\angle 2$, $m\angle 4$, $m\angle 5$, and $m\angle 6$.

Since $\angle 1$ and $\angle 4$ are vertical angles, $m\angle 4 = 23°$. Likewise, $\angle 3$ and $\angle 6$ are vertical angles, so $m\angle 6 = 34°$.

$$m\angle 1 + m\angle 2 + m\angle 3 = 180$$
$$23 + m\angle 2 + 34 = 180 \quad \text{Substituting}$$
$$m\angle 2 = 180 - 57$$
$$m\angle 2 = 123°$$

Since $\angle 2$ and $\angle 5$ are vertical angles, $m\angle 5 = 123°$.

DO EXERCISE 13.

d **Transversals and Angles**

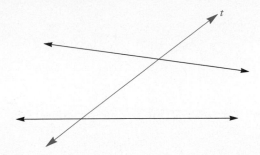

> A *transversal* is a line that intersects two or more coplanar lines in different points.

When a transversal intersects a pair of lines, eight angles are formed. Certain pairs of these angles have special names.

Corresponding Angles

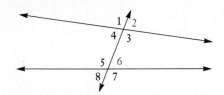

∠2 and ∠6

∠3 and ∠7

∠1 and ∠5

∠4 and ∠8

Interior Angles

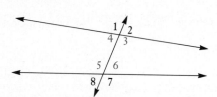

∠3, ∠4, ∠5, and ∠6

Alternate Interior Angles

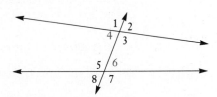

∠4 and ∠6

∠3 and ∠5

Use the following figure to answer Margin Exercises 14–16.

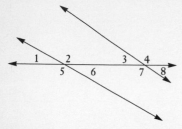

14. Identify all pairs of corresponding angles.

15. Identify all interior angles.

16. Identify all pairs of alternate interior angles.

▶ **EXAMPLE 10** Identify all pairs of corresponding angles, all interior angles, and all pairs of alternate interior angles.

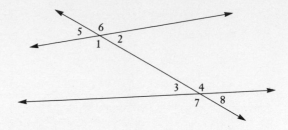

Corresponding angles:	$\angle 6$ and $\angle 4$, $\angle 2$ and $\angle 8$, $\angle 5$ and $\angle 3$, $\angle 1$ and $\angle 7$
Interior angles:	$\angle 1$, $\angle 2$, $\angle 3$, $\angle 4$
Alternate interior angles:	$\angle 1$ and $\angle 4$, $\angle 2$ and $\angle 3$

◀

DO EXERCISES 14–16.

Given a line l and a point P not on l, there is at most one line that contains P and is parallel to l.

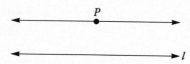

If two lines are parallel, the following relations hold between the angles.

Properties of Parallel Lines

1. If a transversal intersects two parallel lines, then the corresponding angles are congruent.

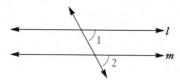

If $l \parallel m$, then $\angle 1 \cong \angle 2$.

2. If a transversal intersects two parallel lines, then the alternate interior angles are congruent.

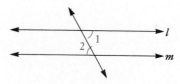

If $l \parallel m$, then $\angle 1 \cong \angle 2$.

3. In a plane, if two lines are parallel to a third line, then the two lines are parallel to each other.

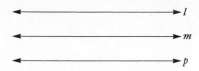

If $l \parallel p$ and $m \parallel p$, then $l \parallel m$.

4. If a transversal intersects two parallel lines, then the interior angles on the same side of the transversal are supplementary.

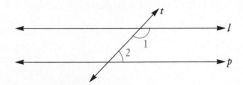

If $l \parallel p$, then $m\angle 1 + m\angle 2 = 180°$.

5. If a transversal is perpendicular to one of two parallel lines, then it is perpendicular to the other.

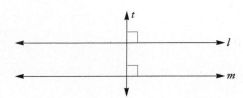

▶ **EXAMPLE 11**   If $l \parallel m$ and $m\angle 1 = 40°$, what are the measures of the other angles?

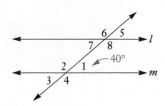

$m\angle 7 = 40°$	**Using Property 2**
$m\angle 5 = 40°$	**Using Property 1**
$m\angle 8 = 140°$	**Using Property 4**
$m\angle 3 = 40°$	$\angle 1$ and $\angle 3$ are vertical angles
$m\angle 4 = 140°$	**Using Property 1** and $m\angle 8 = 140°$
$m\angle 2 = 140°$	$\angle 2$ and $\angle 4$ are vertical angles and $m\angle 4 = 140°$
$m\angle 6 = 140°$	$\angle 6$ and $\angle 8$ are vertical angles and $m\angle 8 = 140°$

◀

DO EXERCISE 17.

17. If $l \parallel m$ and $m\angle 3 = 51°$, what are the measures of the other angles?

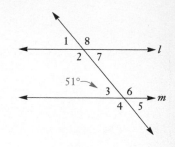

ANSWER ON PAGE A-5

18. If $\overline{AB} \parallel \overline{CD}$, which pairs of angles are congruent?

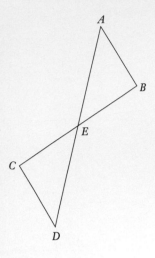

▶ **EXAMPLE 12** If $\overline{PT} \parallel \overline{SR}$, which pairs of angles are congruent?

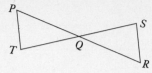

$$\angle TPQ \cong \angle SRQ \quad \text{and} \quad \angle PTQ \cong \angle RSQ \quad \text{Using Property 2}$$
$$\angle PQT \cong \angle RQS \quad \text{and} \quad \angle PQS \cong \angle RQT \quad \text{Vertical angles} \quad ◀$$

DO EXERCISE 18.

▶ **EXAMPLE 13** If $\overline{DE} \parallel \overline{BC}$, which pairs of angles are congruent?

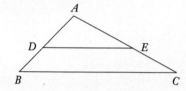

$$\angle ADE \cong \angle ABC \quad \text{and} \quad \angle AED \cong \angle ACB \quad \text{Using Property 1} \quad ◀$$

DO EXERCISE 19.

19. If $\overline{PQ} \parallel \overline{RS}$, which pairs of angles are congruent?

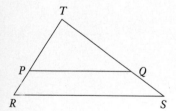

NAME   SECTION   DATE

EXERCISE SET 6.7

a Find the measure of a complement of an angle with the given measure.

1. 11°   **2.** 83°   **3.** 67°   **4.** 5°

Find the measure of a supplement of an angle with the given measure.

5. 3°   **6.** 54°   **7.** 139°   **8.** 13°

b Determine if the pair of segments is congruent. Use a ruler.

9.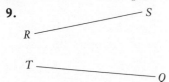

10.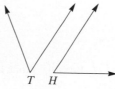

Determine if the pair of angles is congruent. Use a protractor.

11.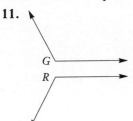

12.

c

13. In the figure, $m\angle 1 = 80°$ and $m\angle 5 = 67°$. Find $m\angle 2$, $m\angle 3$, $m\angle 4$, and $m\angle 6$.

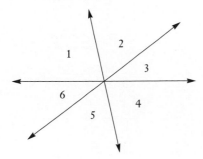

14. In the figure, $m\angle 2 = 42°$ and $m\angle 4 = 56°$. Find $m\angle 1$, $m\angle 3$, $m\angle 5$, and $m\angle 6$.

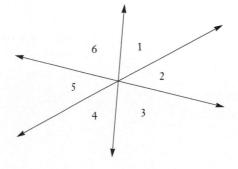

ANSWERS

1. _____

2. _____

3. _____

4. _____

5. _____

6. _____

7. _____

8. _____

9. _____

10. _____

11. _____

12. _____

13. _____

14. _____

d In Exercises 15 and 16, (a) identify all pairs of corresponding angles, (b) identify all interior angles, and (c) identify all pairs of alternate interior angles.

15.

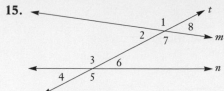

Lines *m* and *n*
Transversal *t*

16.

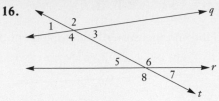

Lines *q* and *r*
Transversal *t*

15. _____

16. _____

17. If *m* ∥ *n* and *m*∠4 = 125°, what are the measures of the other angles?

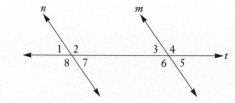

18. If *m* ∥ *n* and *m*∠8 = 34°, what are the measures of the other angles?

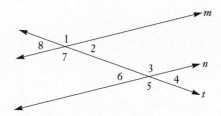

17. _____

18. _____

In each figure, $\overline{AB} \parallel \overline{CD}$. Identify pairs of congruent angles. When possible, give the measures of the angles.

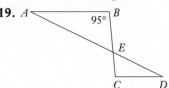

19.

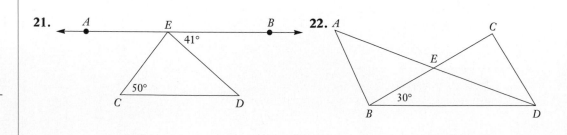

20.

19. _____

20. _____

21. _____

22. _____

6.8 Congruent Triangles and Properties of Parallelograms

OBJECTIVES

After finishing Section 6.8, you should be able to:

a Identify the corresponding parts of congruent triangles and show why triangles are congruent using SAS, SSS, and ASA.

b Use properties of parallelograms to find lengths of sides and measures of angles of parallelograms.

a Congruent Triangles

Triangles can be classified by their angles.

Acute: All angles acute
Right: One right angle
Obtuse: One obtuse angle
Equiangular: All angles congruent

Triangles can also be classified by their sides.

Equilateral: All sides congruent
Isosceles: At least two sides congruent
Scalene: No sides congruent

We know that congruent figures fit together exactly.

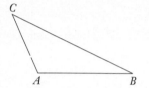 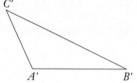

B' is read "*B* prime."

These triangles will fit together exactly if we match *A* with *A'*, *B* with *B'*, and *C* with *C'*. On the other hand, if we match *A* with *B'*, *B* with *C'*, and *C* with *A'*, the triangles will not fit together exactly. The matching of vertices determines corresponding sides and angles.

▶ **EXAMPLES**   Consider $\triangle ABC$ and $\triangle A'B'C'$ above.

1. If we match *A* with *A'*, *B* with *B'*, and *C* with *C'*, what are the corresponding sides?

$$\overline{AB} \leftrightarrow \overline{A'B'}$$
$$\overline{BC} \leftrightarrow \overline{B'C'} \qquad \leftrightarrow \text{ means "corresponds to."}$$
$$\overline{AC} \leftrightarrow \overline{A'C'}$$

2. If we match *A* with *B'*, *B* with *C'*, and *C* with *A'*, what are the corresponding angles?

$$\angle A \leftrightarrow \angle B' \qquad \angle B \leftrightarrow \angle C' \qquad \angle C \leftrightarrow \angle A'$$

If $A \leftrightarrow A'$, $B \leftrightarrow B'$, and $C \leftrightarrow C'$, then we write $ABC \leftrightarrow A'B'C'$.   ◀

> Two triangles are *congruent* if and only if their vertices can be matched so that the corresponding angles and sides are congruent.

The corresponding sides and angles of two congruent triangles are called *corresponding parts* of congruent triangles. Corresponding parts of congruent triangles are always congruent.

1. Suppose that $\triangle ABC \cong \triangle DEF$. What are the congruent corresponding parts?

We write $\triangle ABC \cong \triangle A'B'C'$ to say that $\triangle ABC$ and $\triangle A'B'C'$ are congruent. We agree that this symbol also tells us the way in which the vertices are matched.

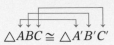

$$\triangle ABC \cong \triangle A'B'C'$$

$\triangle ABC \cong \triangle A'B'C'$ means that

$$\angle A \cong \angle A' \quad \text{and} \quad \overline{AB} \cong \overline{A'B'}$$
$$\angle B \cong \angle B' \qquad\qquad \overline{AC} \cong \overline{A'C'}$$
$$\angle C \cong \angle C' \qquad\qquad \overline{BC} \cong \overline{B'C'}.$$

▶ **EXAMPLE 3**   Suppose that $\triangle PQR \cong \triangle STV$. What are the congruent corresponding parts?

Angles	Sides
$\angle P \cong \angle S$	$\overline{PQ} \cong \overline{ST}$
$\angle Q \cong \angle T$	$\overline{PR} \cong \overline{SV}$
$\angle R \cong \angle V$	$\overline{QR} \cong \overline{TV}$

◀

DO EXERCISE 1.

▶ **EXAMPLE 4**   Name the corresponding parts of these congruent triangles.

2. Name the corresponding parts of these congruent triangles.

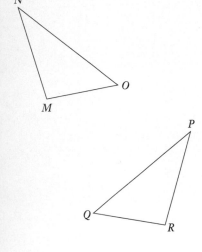

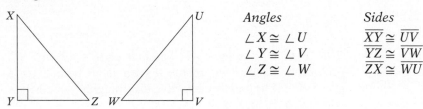

Angles	Sides
$\angle X \cong \angle U$	$\overline{XY} \cong \overline{UV}$
$\angle Y \cong \angle V$	$\overline{YZ} \cong \overline{VW}$
$\angle Z \cong \angle W$	$\overline{ZX} \cong \overline{WU}$

◀

DO EXERCISE 2.

Sometimes we can show that triangles are congruent without already knowing that all six corresponding parts are congruent.

On a full sheet of paper, draw $\triangle ABC$. On another sheet of paper, make a copy of $\angle A$. Label the copy $\angle D$. On the sides of $\angle D$, copy $\overline{AB}$ and $\overline{AC}$. Label the copy $\overline{DE}$ and $\overline{DF}$. Draw $\overline{EF}$. Cut out $\triangle DEF$ and $\triangle ABC$ and place them together. What do you conclude?

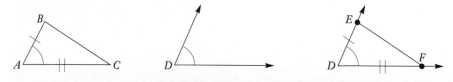

The Side–Angle–Side (SAS) Property

Two triangles are congruent if two sides and the included angle of one triangle are congruent to two sides and the included angle of the other triangle.

It is important to be able to explain why triangles are congruent.

▶ **EXAMPLE 12** In △ABC and △DEF, $\overline{AB} \cong \overline{DE}$, $\overline{AC} \cong \overline{DF}$, and $\angle A \cong \angle D$. Explain why the triangles are congruent.

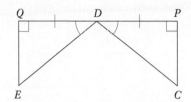

We have two sides and an included angle of △ABC congruent to the corresponding parts of △DEF. Thus, △ABC ≅ △DEF by SAS. ◄

▶ **EXAMPLE 13** In △CPD and △EQD, $\overline{CP} \perp \overline{QP}$ and $\overline{EQ} \perp \overline{QP}$. Also, $\angle QDE \cong \angle PDC$ and D is the midpoint of $\overline{QP}$. Explain why △CPD ≅ △EQD.

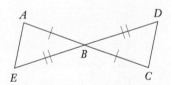

The perpendicular sides form right angles, which are congruent. Since D is the midpoint of $\overline{QP}$, we know that $\overline{QD} \cong \overline{PD}$. With $\angle QDE \cong \angle PDC$, we have △CPD ≅ △EQD by ASA. ◄

DO EXERCISE 10.

Sometimes we can conclude that angles and segments are congruent by first showing that triangles are congruent.

▶ **EXAMPLE 14** $\overline{AB} \cong \overline{BC}$ and $\overline{EB} \cong \overline{DB}$. What can you conclude?

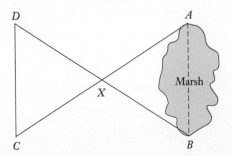

Since $\angle ABE$ and $\angle CBD$ are vertical angles, $\angle ABE \cong \angle CBD$. Thus, △ABE ≅ △CBD by SAS. As corresponding parts, $\overline{AE} \cong \overline{CD}$, $\angle A \cong \angle C$, and $\angle E \cong \angle D$. ◄

▶ **EXAMPLE 15** Explain how you can use congruent triangles to find the distance across a marsh.

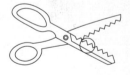

Mark off distances AX and BX. Extend $\overline{AX}$ and $\overline{BX}$ so that point X becomes the midpoint of $\overline{AC}$ and $\overline{BD}$. Then △ABX ≅ △CDX by SAS. Thus, $\overline{DC} \cong \overline{AB}$ as corresponding parts. Then we can measure $\overline{DC}$ knowing that $DC = AB$. ◄

DO EXERCISES 11 AND 12.

10. In this figure, $\overline{AB} \perp \overline{ED}$ and B is the midpoint of $\overline{ED}$. Explain why △ABD ≅ △ABE.

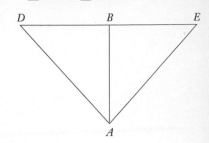

11. $\angle R \cong \angle T$, $\angle W \cong \angle V$, and $\overline{RW} \cong \overline{TV}$. What can you conclude about this figure?

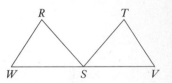

12. On a pair of pinking shears, the indicated angles and sides are congruent. How do you know that P is the midpoint of $\overline{GR}$?

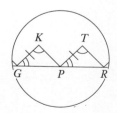

Find the measure of each angle.

13.

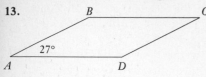

14.

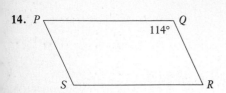

Find the length of each side.

15.

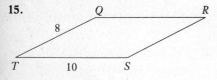

16. The perimeter of ▱*DEFG* is 68.

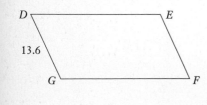

b Properties of Parallelograms

A quadrilateral is a polygon with four sides. A **diagonal** of a quadrilateral is a segment that joins two opposite vertices.

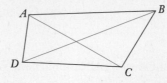

$\overline{AC}$ and $\overline{BD}$ are diagonals.

The sum of the measures of the angles of a quadrilateral is 360°.

A parallelogram is a quadrilateral with two pairs of parallel sides.

$\overline{AB} \parallel \overline{CD}$
$\overline{AC} \parallel \overline{BD}$

Draw two pairs of parallel lines to form parallelogram *ABCD*. Compare the lengths of opposite sides. Compare the measures of opposite angles. Compare the measures of consecutive angles. Draw diagonal $\overline{AC}$. How are △*ADC* and △*CBA* related? Draw diagonal $\overline{BD}$, intersecting $\overline{AC}$ at point *E*. What is special about point *E*?

Using the comparisons and the fact that corresponding parts of congruent triangles are congruent, we can list the following properties of parallelograms.

Properties of Parallelograms

1. **A diagonal of a parallelogram determines two congruent triangles.**
2. **The opposite angles of a parallelogram are congruent.**
3. **The opposite sides of a parallelogram are congruent.**
4. **Consecutive angles of a parallelogram are supplementary.**
5. **The diagonals of a parallelogram bisect each other.**

▶ **EXAMPLE 16**   If $m\angle A = 120°$, find the measures of the other angles of parallelogram *ABCD*.

$m\angle C = 120°$ **Using Property 2**

$m\angle B = 60°$ **Using Property 4**

$m\angle D = 60°$ **Using Property 2**

◀

▶ **EXAMPLE 17**   Find *AB* and *BC*.

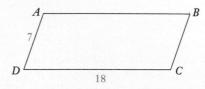

$AB = 18$ and $BC = 7$ **Using Property 3**   ◀

NAME   SECTION   DATE

EXERCISE SET 6.8

a Name the corresponding parts of these congruent triangles.

1. $\triangle ABC \cong \triangle RST$ **2.** $\triangle MNQ \cong \triangle HJK$

3. $\triangle DEF \cong \triangle GHK$ **4.** $\triangle ABC \cong \triangle ABC$

5. $\triangle XYZ \cong \triangle UVW$ **6.** $\triangle ABC \cong \triangle ACB$

Name the corresponding parts of the congruent triangles.

7. 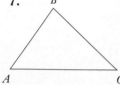   **8.**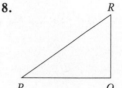

9. 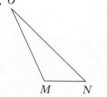   **10.**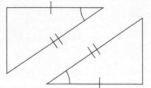

Determine whether the pair of triangles is congruent by the SAS Property.

11. 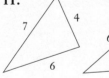   **12.** 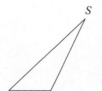   **13.**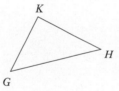

14.    **15.** 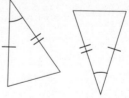   **16.**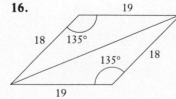

1. _____

2. _____

3. _____

4. _____

5. _____

6. _____

7. _____

8. _____

9. _____

10. _____

11. _____

12. _____

13. _____

14. _____

15. _____

16. _____

Determine whether the pair of triangles is congruent by the SSS Property.

17.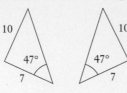

18.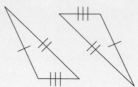

19.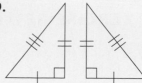

20.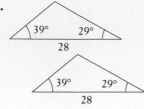

21.

22.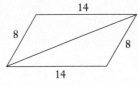

Determine whether the pair of triangles is congruent by the ASA Property.

23.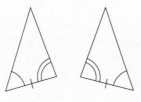

24.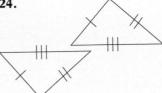

25.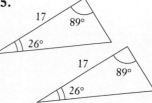

26.

27.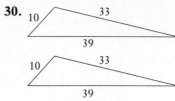

28.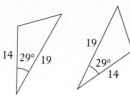

Which property (if any) should be used to show that the pair of triangles is congruent?

29.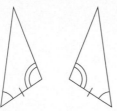

30.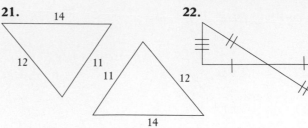

31.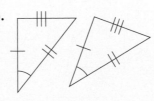

32.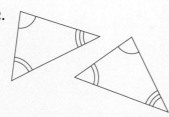

33.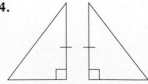

34.

Explain why the triangles indicated in parentheses are congruent.

35. R is the midpoint of both $\overline{PT}$ and $\overline{QS}$. ($\triangle PRQ \cong \triangle TRS$)

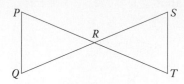

36. $\angle 1$ and $\angle 2$ are right angles, X is the midpoint of $\overline{AY}$, and $\overline{XB} \cong \overline{XY}$. ($\triangle ABX \cong \triangle XZY$)

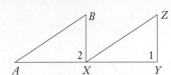

37. L is the midpoint of $\overline{KM}$ and $\overline{GL} \perp \overline{KM}$. ($\triangle KLG \cong \triangle MLG$)

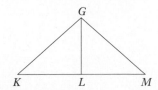

38. X is the midpoint of $\overline{QS}$ and $\overline{RP}$ with $RQ = SP$. ($\triangle RQX \cong \triangle PSX$)

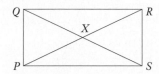

39. $\triangle AEB$ and $\triangle CDB$ are isosceles with $\overline{AE} \cong \overline{AB} \cong \overline{CB} \cong \overline{CD}$. Also, B is the midpoint of $\overline{ED}$. ($\triangle AEB \cong \triangle CDB$)

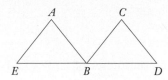

40. $\overline{AB} \perp \overline{BE}$ and $\overline{DE} \perp \overline{BE}$. $\overline{AB} \cong \overline{DE}$ and $\angle BAC \cong \angle EDC$. ($\triangle ABC \cong \triangle DEC$)

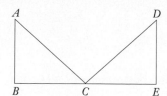

What can you conclude about each figure using the given information?

41. $\overline{GK} \perp \overline{LJ}$, $\overline{HK} \cong \overline{KJ}$, and $\overline{GK} \cong \overline{LK}$

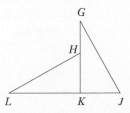

42. $\overline{AB} \cong \overline{DC}$ and $\angle BAC \cong \angle DCA$

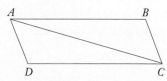

35. _____

36. _____

37. _____

38. _____

39. _____

40. _____

41. _____

42. _____

Copyright © 1993 Addison-Wesley Publishing Co., Inc.

ANSWERS

Use corresponding parts to solve Exercises 43 and 44.

43. On this national flag, the indicated segments and angles are congruent. Explain why *P* is the midpoint of $\overline{EF}$.

44. The indicated sides of a kite are congruent. Explain how you know that $\angle 1 \cong \angle 2$.

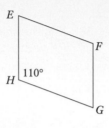

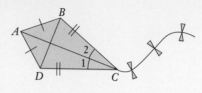

43. _____

44. _____

b Find the measures of the angles of the parallelogram.

45.   **46.**   **47.**   **48.**

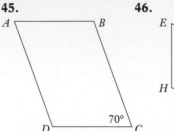

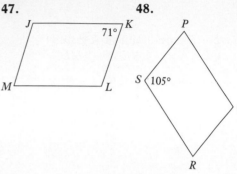

45. _____

46. _____

47. _____

Find the lengths of the sides of the parallelogram.

49.   **50.**

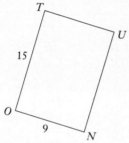

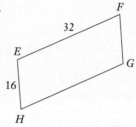

48. _____

49. _____

51. The perimeter of ▱ *JKLM* is 22.

52. The perimeter of ▱ *WXYZ* is 248.

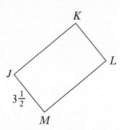

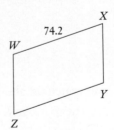

50. _____

53. *AB* = 14 and *BD* = 19. Find the length of each diagonal.

54. *EJ* = 23 and *GJ* = 13. Find the length of each diagonal.

51. _____

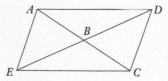

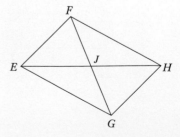

52. _____

53. _____

54. _____

6.9 Similar Triangles

a We know that congruent figures have the same shape and size. *Similar figures* have the same shape, but are not necessarily the same size.

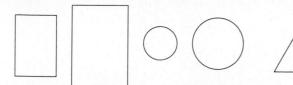

Similar figures

▶ **EXAMPLE 1** Which pairs of triangles appear to be similar?

a) 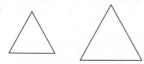   b)

c) 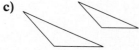   d)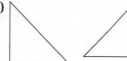

Pairs (a), (c), and (d) appear to be similar.   ◀

DO EXERCISE 1.

Similar triangles have corresponding sides and angles.

▶ **EXAMPLE 2** △*ABC* and △*DEF* are similar. Name their corresponding sides and angles.

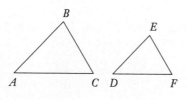

$$\overline{AB} \leftrightarrow \overline{DE} \qquad \angle A \leftrightarrow \angle D$$
$$\overline{AC} \leftrightarrow \overline{DF} \qquad \angle B \leftrightarrow \angle E$$
$$\overline{BC} \leftrightarrow \overline{EF} \qquad \angle C \leftrightarrow \angle F$$ ◀

DO EXERCISE 2.

OBJECTIVES

After finishing Section 6.9, you should be able to:

a Identify corresponding parts of similar triangles, determine which sides of a given pair of triangles have lengths that are proportional, and find lengths of sides in similar triangles.

1. Which pairs of triangles appear to be similar?

a)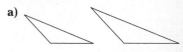

b)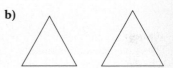

c)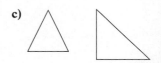

d)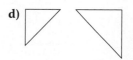

2. △*PQR* and △*GHK* are similar. Name their corresponding sides and angles.

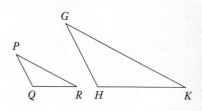

ANSWERS ON PAGE A-5

3. Suppose that $\triangle JKL \sim \triangle ABC$. Which angles are congruent? Which sides are proportional?

> Two triangles are *similar* if and only if their vertices can be matched so that the corresponding angles are congruent and the lengths of corresponding sides are proportional.

To say that $\triangle ABC$ and $\triangle DEF$ are similar, we write "$\triangle ABC \sim \triangle DEF$." We will agree that this symbol also tells us the way in which the vertices are matched.

$$\triangle ABC \sim \triangle DEF$$

Thus, $\triangle ABC \sim \triangle DEF$ means that

$$\begin{array}{l} \angle A \cong \angle D \\ \angle B \cong \angle E \\ \angle C \cong \angle F \end{array} \quad \text{and} \quad \frac{AB}{DE} = \frac{AC}{DF} = \frac{BC}{EF}.$$

▶ **EXAMPLE 3** Suppose that $\triangle PQR \sim \triangle STV$. Which angles arc congruent? Which sides are proportional?

$$\begin{array}{l} \angle P \cong \angle S \\ \angle Q \cong \angle T \\ \angle R \cong \angle V \end{array} \quad \text{and} \quad \frac{PQ}{ST} = \frac{PR}{SV} = \frac{QR}{TV} \qquad ◀$$

DO EXERCISE 3.

4. These triangles are similar. Which sides are proportional?

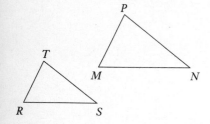

▶ **EXAMPLE 4** These triangles are similar. Which sides are proportional?

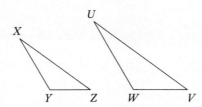

It appears that if we match X with U, Y with W, and Z with V, the corresponding angles will be congruent. Thus,

$$\frac{XY}{UW} = \frac{XZ}{UV} = \frac{YZ}{WV}. \qquad ◀$$

DO EXERCISE 4.

We can find lengths of sides in similar triangles.

▶ **EXAMPLE 5** If $\triangle RAE \sim \triangle GRL$, find RL and GL.

Since $\triangle RAE \sim \triangle GRL$, the corresponding sides are proportional. Thus,

$$\frac{6}{9} = \frac{4}{RL}$$

$$6(RL) = 9 \cdot 4 \qquad \text{Finding cross-products}$$

$$6(RL) = 36$$

$$RL = 6$$

and

$$\frac{6}{9} = \frac{7}{GL}$$

$$6(GL) = 9 \cdot 7$$

$$6(GL) = 63$$

$$GL = 10\tfrac{1}{2}.$$

DO EXERCISE 5.

▶ **EXAMPLE 6**   If $\overline{AB} \parallel \overline{CD}$, find CD.

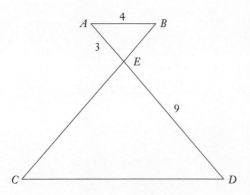

Recall that if a transversal intersects two parallel lines, then the alternate interior angles are congruent (Section 6.7). Thus,

$$\angle A \cong \angle D \quad \text{and} \quad \angle C \cong \angle B,$$

because they are pairs of alternate interior angles. Since $\angle AEB$ and $\angle DEC$ are vertical angles, they are congruent. Thus by definition

$$\triangle AEB \sim \triangle DEC$$

and the lengths of the corresponding sides are proportional. Thus,

$$\frac{AE}{DE} = \frac{AB}{CD}$$

$$\frac{3}{9} = \frac{4}{CD}$$

$$3 \cdot CD = 36$$

$$CD = 12. \qquad ◀$$

DO EXERCISE 6.

5. If $\triangle WNE \sim \triangle CBT$, find BT and CT.

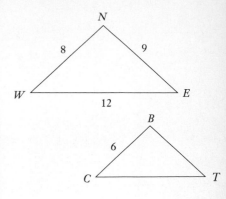

6. If $\overline{QR} \parallel \overline{ST}$, find QR.

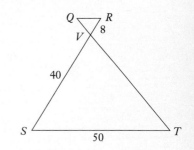

❖ SIDELIGHTS

An Application of Ratio: State Lottery Profits

The chart below shows the profits of state lotteries in a recent year. Use the information to do the exercises.

State	Profit, in millions
Arizona	$ 22.0
Colorado	32.0
Connecticut	148.8
Delaware	15.0
Illinois	517.8
Maine	4.4
Maryland	263.7
Massachusetts	284.0
Michigan	320.0
New Hampshire	4.3
New Jersey	388.0
New York	615.0
Ohio	338.0
Pennsylvania	572.6
Rhode Island	18.6
Vermont	1.2
Washington	58.8

EXERCISES

1. Which state made the most from lotteries?

2. Which state made the least from lotteries?

3. How much more did the state with the most lottery income make than the state with the least income?

4. How much, in billions, did these states make together from lotteries?

5. What is the ratio of the lottery income of New York to the entire amount taken in by lotteries? Use your calculator.

6. How much did New England take in from lotteries?

7. How much more did Ohio take in than Maryland?

8. The population of Washington is 4,300,000. At what rate, in dollars per person, did the people of Washington contribute to their lottery?

9. The population of New York is 17,667,000. At what rate, in dollars per person, did the people of New York contribute to their lottery?

10. The population of Illinois is 11,486,000. At what rate, in dollars per person, did the people of Illinois contribute to their lottery?

11. Which state, Washington, New York, or Illinois, has the highest ratio of lottery contributions per person?

EXERCISE SET 6.9

a For each pair of similar triangles, name the corresponding sides and angles.

1.

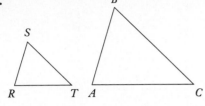

2.

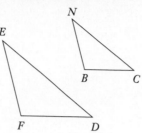

3.

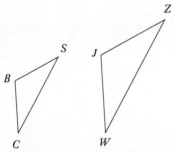

4.

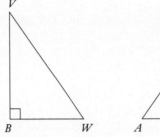

For each pair of similar triangles, name the congruent angles and proportional sides.

5. $\triangle ABC \sim \triangle RST$

6. $\triangle PQR \sim \triangle STV$

7. $\triangle MES \sim \triangle CLF$

8. $\triangle SMH \sim \triangle WLK$

1. _____

2. _____

3. _____

4. _____

5. _____

6. _____

7. _____

8. _____

Name the proportional sides in these similar triangles.

9.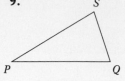

9. _____

10.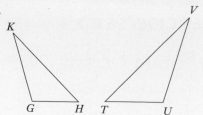

10. _____

11.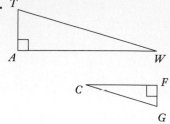

11. _____

12.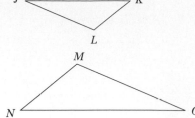

12. _____

13. If △*ABC* ~ △*PQR*, find *QR* and *PR*.

14. If △*MAC* ~ △*GET*, find *AM* and *GT*.

13. _____

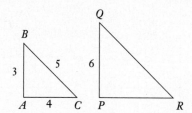

14. _____

15. _____

15. If $\overline{AD} \parallel \overline{CB}$, find *EC*.

16. If $\overline{LN} \parallel \overline{PM}$, find *QM*.

16. _____

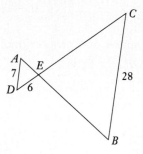

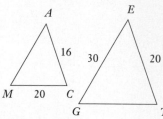

17. _____

18. _____

SKILL MAINTENANCE

17. Multiply: $17\frac{3}{4} \times 5\frac{1}{2}$.

18. Convert to decimal notation: 0.3%.   **19.** Evaluate: 6^4.

19. _____

SUMMARY AND REVIEW: CHAPTER 6

IMPORTANT PROPERTIES AND FORMULAS

Perimeter of a Rectangle: $P = 2 \cdot (l + w)$,
  or $P = 2 \cdot l + 2 \cdot w$

Perimeter of a Square: $P = 4 \cdot s$

Area of a Rectangle: $A = l \cdot w$

Area of a Square: $A = s \cdot s$, or $A = s^2$

Area of a Parallelogram: $A = b \cdot h$

Area of a Triangle: $A = \frac{1}{2}b \cdot h$

Area of a Trapezoid: $A = \frac{1}{2}h \cdot (a + b)$

Radius and Diameter of a Circle: $d = 2 \cdot r$

Circumference of a Circle: $C = 2 \cdot \pi \cdot r$

Area of a Circle: $A = \pi \cdot r \cdot r$,
  or $A = \pi \cdot r^2$

Volume of a Rectangular Solid: $V = l \cdot w \cdot h$

Volume of a Circular Cylinder: $V = \pi \cdot r^2 \cdot h$

Volume of a Sphere: $V = \frac{4}{3} \cdot \pi \cdot r^3$

Volume of a Cone: $V = \frac{1}{3} \cdot \pi \cdot r^2 \cdot h$

REVIEW EXERCISES

The review sections and objectives to be tested in addition to the material in this chapter are [1.6b], [2.4d], [3.3a], [4.2b, c], and [4.3a, b].

1. Find the perimeter.

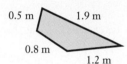

0.5 m   1.9 m
0.8 m
  1.2 m

2. The dimensions of a standard-sized tennis court are 78 ft by 36 ft. Find the perimeter of the tennis court.

Find the area.

3.

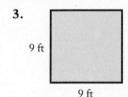

9 ft

9 ft

4.

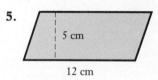

1.8 cm

7 cm

5.

5 cm

12 cm

6.   4 mm

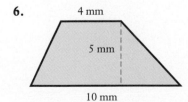

5 mm

10 mm

7.

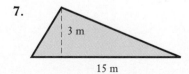

3 m

15 m

8.

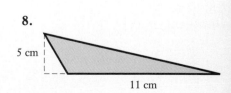

5 cm

11 cm

9. A sidewalk is built around three sides of a building and has equal width on the three sides, as shown at right. What is the area of the sidewalk?

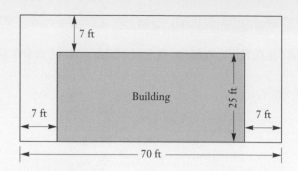

Find the length of a radius of the circle.

10.

16 m

11.

$\frac{28}{11}$ in.

Find the length of a diameter of the circle.

12.

7 ft

13.

10 cm

14. Find the circumference of the circle in Exercise 10. Use 3.14 for π.

15. Find the circumference of the circle in Exercise 11. Use $\frac{22}{7}$ for π.

16. Find the area of the circle in Exercise 10. Use 3.14 for π.

17. Find the area of the circle in Exercise 11. Use $\frac{22}{7}$ for π.

Find the volume and the surface area.

18.

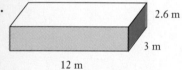

2.6 m

3 m

12 m

19.

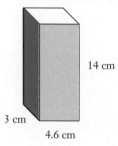

14 cm

3 cm

4.6 cm

Find the volume. Use 3.14 for π.

20.

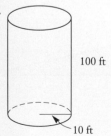

100 ft

10 ft

21.

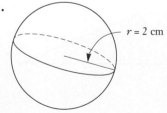

$r = 2$ cm

22.

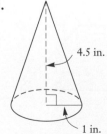

4.5 in.

1 in.

Use this figure for Questions 23–25.

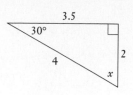

23. Find the missing angle measure.

24. Classify the triangle as equilateral, isosceles, or scalene.

25. Classify the triangle as right, obtuse, or acute.

26. Find the sum of the angle measures of a hexagon.

Find the measure of a complement of an angle with the given measure.

27. 82°

28. 5°

Find the measure of a supplement of an angle with the given measure.

29. 33°

30. 133°

31. In this figure, $m\angle 1 = 38°$ and $m\angle 5 = 105°$. Find $m\angle 2$, $m\angle 3$, $m\angle 4$, and $m\angle 6$.

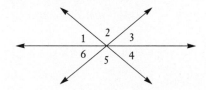

32. In this figure, identify (a) all pairs of corresponding angles, (b) all interior angles, and (c) all pairs of alternate interior angles.

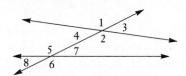

33. If $m \parallel n$ and $m\angle 4 = 135°$, what are the measures of the other angles?

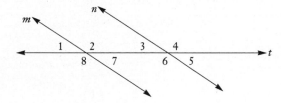

Name the corresponding parts of these congruent triangles.

34. $\triangle DHJ \cong \triangle RZK$

35.

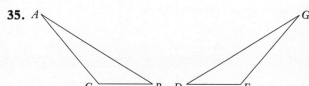

Which property (if any) should be used to show that the following pairs of triangles are congruent?

36.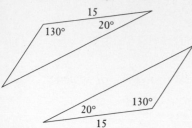

37.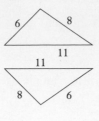

38.

39. *J* is the midpoint of $\overline{IK}$ and $\overline{HI} \parallel \overline{KL}$. Explain why $\triangle JIH \cong \triangle JKL$.

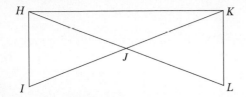

40. Find the measures of the angles and the lengths of the sides of this parallelogram.

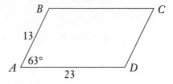

41. If $\triangle CQW \sim \triangle FAS$, name the congruent angles and the proportional sides.

42. If $\triangle NMO \sim \triangle STR$, find *MO*.

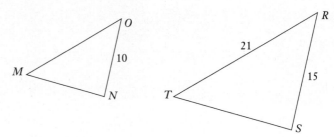

SKILL MAINTENANCE

43. Multiply: $5\frac{3}{4} \times 9\frac{1}{2}$.

Evaluate.

44. 4.7^3

45. $\left(\frac{1}{2}\right)^4$

46. Convert to fractional notation: 73%.

47. Convert to percent notation: 0.47.

48. Convert to percent notation: $\frac{23}{25}$.

❖ THINKING IT THROUGH

1. List and describe all the area formulas that you have learned in this chapter.

2. List and describe all the volume formulas that you have learned in this chapter.

TEST: CHAPTER 6

1. Find the perimeter.

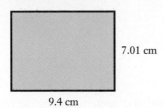

7.01 cm

9.4 cm

2. The dimensions of a doormat are $2\frac{1}{2}$ ft by $4\frac{1}{2}$ ft. Find the perimeter and the area of the mat.

Find the area.

3.

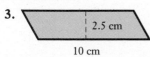

2.5 cm

10 cm

4.

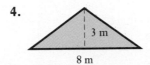

3 m

8 m

5.

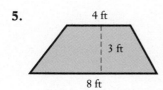

4 ft

3 ft

8 ft

6.

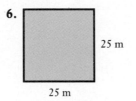

25 m

25 m

7. Find the area of the shaded region.

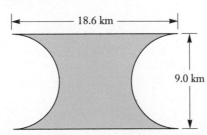

18.6 km

9.0 km

1. _____

2. _____

3. _____

4. _____

5. _____

6. _____

7. _____

8. Find the length of a diameter of this circle.

9. Find the length of a radius of this circle.

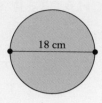

10. Find the circumference of the circle in Exercise 8. Use $\frac{22}{7}$ for π.

11. Find the area of the circle in Exercise 9. Use 3.14 for π.

12. Find the volume and the surface area.

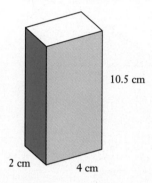

Find the volume. Use 3.14 for π.

13.

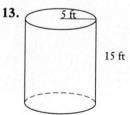

14.

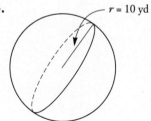

15.

8. _____

9. _____

10. _____

11. _____

12. _____

13. _____

14. _____

15. _____

Use this figure for Questions 16–18.

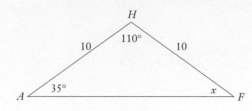

16. Find the missing angle measure.

16. _____

17. Classify the triangle as equilateral, isosceles, or scalene.

17. _____

18. Classify the triangle as right, obtuse, or acute.

18. _____

19. Find the sum of the angle measures of a pentagon.

19. _____

20. Find the measure of a supplement of an angle of 31°.

21. Find the measure of a complement of an angle of 79°.

20. _____

22. In the figure, $m \angle 1 = 62°$ and $m \angle 5 = 110°$. Find $m \angle 2$, $m \angle 3$, $m \angle 4$, and $m \angle 6$.

23. If $m \parallel n$ and $m \angle 4 = 120°$, what are the measures of the other angles?

21. _____

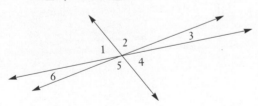

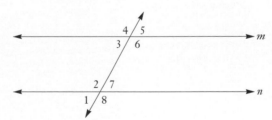

22. _____

24. Name the corresponding parts of these congruent triangles: $\triangle CWS \cong \triangle ATZ$.

23. _____

24. _____

Which property (if any) would you use to show that $\triangle RST \cong \triangle DEF$ with the given information?

25. $\overline{RS} \cong \overline{DE}$, $\overline{RT} \cong \overline{DF}$, and $\angle R \cong \angle D$

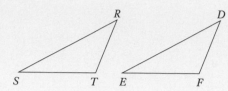

26. $\angle R \cong \angle D$, $\angle S \cong \angle E$, and $\angle T \cong \angle F$

27. $\overline{RS} \cong \overline{DE}$, $\angle R \cong \angle D$, and $\angle S \cong \angle E$

28. $\angle R \cong \angle D$, $\overline{RT} \cong \overline{DF}$, and $\overline{ST} \cong \overline{EF}$

29. The perimeter of $\square DEFG$ is 62. Find the measures of the angles and the lengths of the sides.

30. In $\square JKLM$, $JN = 3.2$ and $KN = 3$. Find the lengths of the diagonals, $\overline{LJ}$ and $\overline{KM}$.

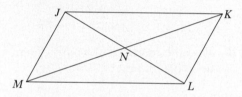

31. If $\triangle ERS \sim \triangle TGF$, name the congruent angles and the proportional sides.

32. If $\triangle GTR \sim \triangle ZEK$, find EK and ZK.

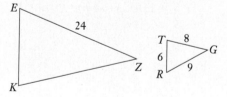

SKILL MAINTENANCE

33. Multiply: 4.6×2.31. Round to the nearest tenth.

Evaluate.

34. 10^3

35. $\left(\dfrac{1}{4}\right)^2$

36. Convert to percent notation: $\dfrac{13}{16}$.

37. Convert to decimal notation: 93.2%.

38. Convert to fractional notation: $33\frac{1}{3}\%$.

ANSWERS column:
25. ____
26. ____
27. ____
28. ____
29. ____
30. ____
31. ____
32. ____
33. ____
34. ____
35. ____
36. ____
37. ____
38. ____

INTRODUCTION In this chapter we consider the number system used most in algebra. It is called the real-number system. We will learn to add, subtract, multiply, and divide real numbers and to manipulate certain expressions. Such manipulation will be important when we solve equations and problems in Chapter 8.

The review sections to be tested in addition to the material in this chapter are 1.6, 1.7, 1.9, 2.2, 4.2, and 4.3. ❖

Introduction to Real Numbers and Algebraic Expressions

7

AN APPLICATION

In a football game, the quarterback attempted passes with the following results:

1st try: 13-yd gain;
2nd try: incomplete;
3rd try: 12-yd loss (tackled behind the line);
4th try: 21-yd gain;
5th try: 14-yd loss.

What is the total number of yards gained?

THE MATHEMATICS

We let t = the total number of yards. Then t is given by

$$t = 13 + 0 + (-12) + 21 + (-14).$$

These are *negative* numbers.

Area of a Rectangle:	$A = l \cdot w$
Area of a Square:	$A = s^2$
Area of a Triangle:	$A = \frac{1}{2}b \cdot h$
Simple-Interest Formula:	$I = P \cdot r \cdot t$

PRETEST: CHAPTER 7

1. Evaluate $x/2y$ when $x = 5$ and $y = 8$.

2. Write an algebraic expression: Seventy-eight percent of some number.

3. Find the area of a rectangle when the length is 22.5 ft and the width is 16 ft.

4. Find $-x$ when $x = -12$.

Use either $<$ or $>$ for ▨ to write a true sentence.

5. 0 ▨ -5

6. 10 ▨ -5

7. -35 ▨ -45

8. $-\dfrac{2}{3}$ ▨ $\dfrac{4}{5}$

Find the absolute value.

9. $|-12|$

10. $|2.3|$

11. $|0|$

Find the opposite, or additive inverse.

12. 5.4

13. $-\dfrac{2}{3}$

Compute and simplify.

14. $-9 + (-8)$

15. $20.2 - (-18.4)$

16. $-\dfrac{5}{6} - \dfrac{3}{10}$

17. $-11.5 + 6.5$

18. $-9(-7)$

19. $\dfrac{5}{8}\left(-\dfrac{2}{3}\right)$

20. $-19.6 \div 0.2$

21. $-56 \div (-7)$

22. $12 - (-6) + 14 - 8$

23. $20 - 10 \div 5 + 2^3$

Multiply.

24. $9(z - 2)$

25. $-2(2a + b - 5c)$

Factor.

26. $4x - 12$

27. $6y - 9z - 18$

Simplify.

28. $3y - 7 - 2(2y + 3)$

29. $\{2[3(y + 1) - 4] - [5(y - 3) - 5]\}$

30. Write an inequality with the same meaning as $x > 12$.

7.1 Introduction to Algebra

Many kinds of problems require the use of equations in order to be solved effectively. The study of algebra involves the use of equations to solve problems. Equations are constructed from algebraic expressions. The purpose of this section is to introduce you to the types of expressions encountered in algebra.

a   Algebraic Expressions

In arithmetic, you have worked with expressions such as

$$37 + 86, \quad 7 \times 8, \quad 19 - 7, \quad \text{and} \quad \frac{3}{8}.$$

In algebra, we use certain letters for numbers and work with *algebraic expressions* such as

$$x + 86, \quad 7 \times t, \quad 19 - y, \quad \text{and} \quad \frac{a}{b}.$$

Sometimes a letter can stand for various numbers. In that case we call the letter a **variable.** Sometimes a letter can stand for just one number. In that case we call the letter a **constant.** Let b = your date of birth. Then b is a constant. Let a = your age. Then a is a variable since a changes from year to year.

How do algebraic expressions arise? Most often they occur in problem-solving situations. For example, consider the following chart, which you might see in a magazine.

Starting Pay

Starting salaries of police in 1987 are up about 25% since 1982.

Police: 1982 $15,635

1987 $19,544

Suppose we wanted to know how much more the 1987 salary was than the 1982 salary.

In algebra, we translate the problem into an equation. It might be done as follows.

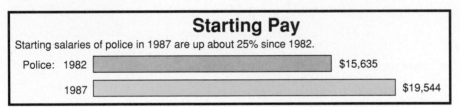

Salary in 1982	plus	How much?	is	Salary in 1987
$15,635	+	x	=	$19,544

Note that we have an algebraic expression on the left. To find the number x, we can subtract $15,635 on both sides of the equation:

$$\$15,635 + x - \$15,635 = \$19,544 - \$15,635$$
$$x = \$19,544 - \$15,635.$$

Then we carry out the subtraction and obtain the answer $3909.

In arithmetic, you probably would do this subtraction right away without considering an equation. In algebra, you will find most problems difficult without first solving an equation.

DO EXERCISE 1.

OBJECTIVES

After finishing Section 7.1, you should be able to:

a   Evaluate algebraic expressions by substitution.

b   Translate phrases to algebraic expressions.

FOR EXTRA HELP

Tape 14A

1. Translate this problem to an equation. Use the graph below. How many more flights are there on the Dallas–Houston route than on the New York–Boston route?

Taking flight in traffic
Here's how many flights are made monthly on the busiest air routes:

Dallas–Houston	2,866
Los Angeles–San Francisco	2,822
New York–Chicago	2,710
New York–Washington	2,442
New York–Boston	2,128

ANSWER ON PAGE A-5

2. Evaluate $a + b$ for $a = 38$ and $b = 26$.

An **algebraic expression** consists of variables, numerals, and operation signs. When we replace a variable by a number, we say that we are **substituting** for the variable. This process is called **evaluating the expression**.

▶ **EXAMPLE 1**   Evaluate $x + y$ for $x = 37$ and $y = 29$.

We substitute 37 for x and 29 for y and carry out the addition:

$$x + y = 37 + 29 = 66.$$

The number 66 is called the **value** of the expression.   ◀

3. Evaluate $x - y$ for $x = 57$ and $y = 29$.

Algebraic expressions involving multiplication can be written in several ways. For example, "8 times a" can be written as $8 \times a$, $8 \cdot a$, $8(a)$, or simply $8a$. Two letters written together without a symbol, such as ab, also indicates a multiplication.

▶ **EXAMPLE 2**   Evaluate $3y$ for $y = 14$.

$$3y = 3(14) = 42$$ ◀

DO EXERCISES 2–4.

4. Evaluate $4t$ for $t = 15$.

▶ **EXAMPLE 3**   The area A of a rectangle of length l and width w is given by the formula $A = lw$. Find the area when l is 24.5 in. and w is 16 in.

We substitute 24.5 in. for l and 16 in. for w and carry out the multiplication:

$$
\begin{aligned}
A = lw &= (24.5 \text{ in.})(16 \text{ in.}) \\
&= (24.5)(16)(\text{in.})(\text{in.}) \\
&= 392 \text{ in}^2, \quad \text{or } 392 \text{ square inches.}
\end{aligned}
$$

DO EXERCISE 5.

5. Find the area of a rectangle when l is 24 ft and w is 8 ft.

Algebraic expressions involving division can also be written in several ways. For example, "8 divided by t" can be written as $8 \div t$, or $\dfrac{8}{t}$, where the fraction bar is a division symbol.

▶ **EXAMPLE 4**   The time needed for a satellite to orbit the earth is determined by the height of the satellite above the earth's surface and the speed, or velocity, of the satellite. If a satellite is orbiting 300 mi above the earth's surface, it travels about 27,000 mi in one orbit. The time t, in hours, that it takes to orbit the earth one time is given by

6. Find the orbiting time of the satellite in Example 4 when the velocity is 8000 mph.

$$t = \frac{27,000}{v},$$

where v is the velocity of the satellite in miles per hour. Find the orbiting time of the satellite when the velocity v is 10,000 mph.

We substitute 10,000 for v and carry out the division:

$$t = \frac{27,000}{v} = \frac{27,000}{10,000} = 2.7 \text{ hr.}$$ ◀

DO EXERCISE 6.

► **EXAMPLE 5**   Evaluate $\dfrac{a}{b}$ for $a = 63$ and $b = 9$.

We substitute 63 for a and 9 for b and carry out the division:

$$\frac{a}{b} = \frac{63}{9} = 7. \qquad ◄$$

► **EXAMPLE 6**   Evaluate $\dfrac{12m}{n}$ for $m = 8$ and $n = 16$.

$$\frac{12m}{n} = \frac{12 \cdot 8}{16} = \frac{96}{16} = 6 \qquad ◄$$

DO EXERCISES 7 AND 8.

b   **Translating to Algebraic Expressions**

In algebra, we translate problems to equations. The different parts of an equation are translations of word phrases to algebraic expressions. It is easier to translate if we know that certain words translate to certain operation symbols.

KEY WORDS			
Addition (+)	**Subtraction (−)**	**Multiplication (·)**	**Division (÷)**
add	subtract	multiply	divide
sum	difference	product	quotient
plus	minus	times	divided by
more than	less than	twice	
increased by	decreased by	of	
	take from		

► **EXAMPLE 7**   Translate to an algebraic expression:

Twice (or two times) some number.

Think of some number, say 8. What number is twice 8? It is 16. How did you get 16? You multiplied by 2. Do the same thing using a variable. We can use any variable we wish, such as x, y, m, or n. Let's use y to stand for some number. Multiply by 2. We get an expression

$$y \times 2, \quad 2 \times y, \quad 2 \cdot y, \quad \text{or} \quad 2y. \qquad ◄$$

► **EXAMPLE 8**   Translate to an algebraic expression:

Seven less than some number.

We let

x represent the number.

Now if the number were 23, then the translation would be $23 - 7$. If we knew the number to be 345, then the translation would be $345 - 7$. If the number is x, then the translation is

$$x - 7. \qquad ◄$$

7. Evaluate a/b for $a = 200$ and $b = 8$.

8. Evaluate $10p/q$ when $p = 40$ and $q = 25$.

Translate to an algebraic expression.

9. Twelve less than some number

10. Twelve more than some number

11. Four less than some number

12. Half of some number

13. Six more than eight times some number

14. The difference of two numbers

15. Fifty-nine percent of some number

16. Two hundred less than the product of two numbers

17. The sum of two numbers

Note that $7 - x$ is *not* a correct translation of the expression in Example 8. The expression $7 - x$ is a translation of "seven minus some number" or "some number less than seven."

▶ **EXAMPLE 9**   Translate to an algebraic expression:

Eighteen more than a number.

We let

$$t = \text{the number.}$$

Now if the number were 26, then the translation would be $18 + 26$. If we knew the number to be 174, then the translation would be $18 + 174$. If the number is t, then the translation is

$$18 + t. \qquad ◀$$

▶ **EXAMPLE 10**   Translate to an algebraic expression:

A number divided by 5.

We let

$$m = \text{the number.}$$

Now if the number were 76, then the translation would be $76 \div 5$, or 76/5, or $\frac{76}{5}$. If the number were 213, then the translation would be $213 \div 5$, or 213/5, or $\frac{213}{5}$. If the number is m, then the translation is

$$m \div 5, \qquad m/5, \quad \text{or} \quad \frac{m}{5}. \qquad ◀$$

▶ **EXAMPLE 11**   Translate each of the following phrases to an algebraic expression.

Phrase	Algebraic expression
Five more than some number	$5 + n$, or $n + 5$
Half of a number	$\frac{1}{2}t$, or $\frac{t}{2}$
Five more than three times some number	$5 + 3p$, or $3p + 5$
The difference of two numbers	$x - y$
Six less than the product of two numbers	$mn - 6$
Seventy-six percent of some number	$76\%z$, or $0.76z$

◀

DO EXERCISES 9–17.

NAME   SECTION   DATE

EXERCISE SET 7.1

a Substitute to find values of the expressions.

1. Theresa is 6 yr younger than her husband Frank. Suppose the variable x stands for Frank's age. Then $x - 6$ stands for Theresa's age. How old is Theresa when Frank is 29? 34? 47?

2. Employee A took five times as long to do a job as employee B. Suppose t stands for the time it takes B to do a job. Then $5t$ stands for the time it takes A. How long did it take A if B took 30 sec? 90 sec? 2 min?

3. The area A of a parallelogram with base b and height h is given by $A = bh$. Find the area of the parallelogram when the height is 15.4 cm (centimeters) and the base is 6.5 cm.

4. The area A of a triangle with base b and height h is given by $A = \frac{1}{2}bh$. Find the area when $b = 45$ m (meters) and $h = 86$ m.

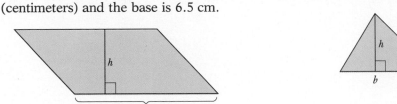

5. A driver who drives at a speed of r mph for t hr will travel a distance d mi given by $d = rt$ mi. How far will a driver travel at a speed of 55 mph for 4 hr?

6. *Simple interest.* The simple interest I on a principal of P dollars at interest rate r for time t, in years, is given by $I = Prt$. Find the simple interest on a principal of $4800 at 9% for 2 yr. (*Hint:* 9% = 0.09.)

Evaluate.

7. $6x$ for $x = 7$

8. $7y$ for $y = 7$

9. $\dfrac{x}{y}$ for $x = 9$ and $y = 3$

10. $\dfrac{m}{n}$ for $m = 14$ and $n = 2$

11. $\dfrac{3p}{q}$ for $p = 2$ and $q = 6$

12. $\dfrac{5y}{z}$ for $y = 15$ and $z = 25$

13. $\dfrac{x + y}{5}$ for $x = 10$ and $y = 20$

14. $\dfrac{p + q}{2}$ for $p = 2$ and $q = 16$

15. $\dfrac{x - y}{8}$ for $x = 20$ and $y = 4$

16. $\dfrac{m - n}{5}$ for $m = 16$ and $n = 6$

1. _____

2. _____

3. _____

4. _____

5. _____

6. _____

7. _____

8. _____

9. _____

10. _____

11. _____

12. _____

13. _____

14. _____

15. _____

16. _____

b Translate to an algebraic expression.

17. 6 more than b **18.** 8 more than t **19.** 9 less than c

20. 4 less than d **21.** 6 increased by q **22.** 11 increased by z

23. b more than a **24.** c more than d **25.** x less than y

26. c less than h **27.** x added to w **28.** s added to t

29. m subtracted from n **30.** p subtracted from q **31.** The sum of r and s

32. The sum of d and f **33.** Twice x **34.** Three times p

35. 5 multiplied by t **36.** The product of 3 and b

37. The product of 97% and some number   **38.** 43% of some number

39. A student had d dollars before going to the bookstore. The student bought a book for $29.95. How much did the student have after the purchase?   **40.** A driver drove at a speed of 65 mph for t hr. How far did the driver go?

SKILL MAINTENANCE

Find the prime factorization.

41. 54   **42.** 192

Find the LCM.

43. 6, 18   **44.** 6, 24, 32

SYNTHESIS

Translate to an algebraic expression.

45. Some number x plus three times y **46.** Some number a plus 2 plus b

47. A number that is 3 less than twice x **48.** Your age in 5 years, if you are a years old now

7.2 The Real Numbers

A **set** is a collection of objects. For our purposes we will most often be considering sets of numbers. One way to name a set uses what is called **roster notation.** For example, the set containing the numbers 0, 2, and 5 can be named {0, 2, 5}.

Sets that are part of other sets are called **subsets.** In this section, we become acquainted with the set of *real numbers* and its various subsets.

Two important subsets of the real numbers are listed below using roster notation.

> **Natural numbers = {1, 2, 3, . . .}. These are the numbers used for counting.**
>
> **Whole numbers = {0, 1, 2, 3, . . .}. This is the set of natural numbers with 0 included.**

We can represent these sets on a number line. The natural numbers are those to the right of 0.

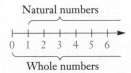

We create a new set, called the *integers*, by starting with the whole numbers, 0, 1, 2, 3, and so on. For each natural number 1, 2, 3, and so on, we obtain a new number to the left of 0 on the number line:

For the number 1, there will be an *opposite* number −1 (negative 1).

For the number 2, there will be an *opposite* number −2 (negative 2).

For the number 3, there will be an *opposite* number −3 (negative 3), and so on.

The **integers** consist of the whole numbers and these new numbers. We picture them on a number line as follows.

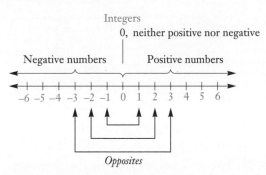

We call the newly obtained numbers **negative integers.** The natural numbers are called **positive integers.** Zero is neither positive nor negative. We call −1 and 1 opposites of each other. Similarly, −2 and 2 are opposites, −3 and 3 are opposites, −100 and 100 are opposites, and 0 is its own opposite. This gives us the set of integers, which extends infinitely on the number line to the left and right of 0.

> **The set of integers = {. . . , −5, −4, −3, −2, −1, 0, 1, 2, 3, 4, 5, . . .}.**

OBJECTIVES

After finishing Section 7.2, you should be able to:

a Tell which integers correspond to a real-world situation.

b Graph rational numbers on a number line.

c Convert from fractional· notation to decimal notation for a rational number.

d Determine which of two real numbers is greater and indicate which, using < or >; given an inequality like $a < b$, write another inequality with the same meaning. Determine whether an inequality like $-3 \leq 5$ is true or false.

e Find the absolute value of a real number.

FOR EXTRA HELP

Tape 14B

Tell which integers correspond to the given situation.

1. The halfback gained 8 yd on the first down. The quarterback was sacked for a 5-yd loss on second down.

2. The highest temperature ever recorded in the United States was 134° in Death Valley on July 10, 1913. The coldest temperature ever recorded in the United States was 76° below zero in Tanana, Alaska, in January of 1886.

3. At 10 sec before liftoff, ignition occurs. At 148 sec after liftoff, the first stage is detached from the rocket.

4. A student owes $137 to the bookstore. The student has $289 in a savings account.

a | **Integers and the Real World**

Integers can be associated with many real-world problems and situations. The following examples will help you get ready to translate problem situations to mathematical language.

▶ **EXAMPLE 1**   Tell which integer corresponds to this situation: The temperature is 3 degrees below zero.

3° below zero is −3°

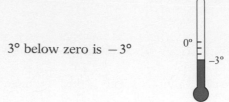

◀

▶ **EXAMPLE 2**   Tell which integer corresponds to this situation: Losing 21 points in a card game.

Losing 21 points in a card game gives you −21 points.

◀

▶ **EXAMPLE 3**   Tell which integer corresponds to this situation: Death Valley is 280 ft below sea level.

The integer −280 corresponds to the situation. The elevation is −280 ft.

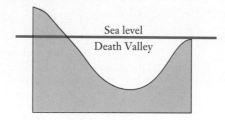

◀

▶ **EXAMPLE 4**   Tell which integers correspond to this situation: A salesperson made $78 on Monday, but lost $57 on Tuesday.

The integers 78 and −57 correspond to the situation. The integer 78 corresponds to the profit on Monday and −57 corresponds to the loss on Tuesday.   ◀

DO EXERCISES 1–4.

b | **The Rational Numbers**

We created the set of integers by obtaining a negative number for each natural number. To create a larger number system, called the set of **rational numbers,** we consider quotients of integers with nonzero divisors. The following are rational numbers.

$$\frac{2}{3}, \quad -\frac{2}{3}, \quad \frac{7}{1}, \quad 4, \quad -3, \quad 0, \quad \frac{23}{-8}, \quad 2.4, \quad -0.17.$$

The number $-\frac{2}{3}$ (read "negative two-thirds") can also be named $\frac{2}{-3}$ or $\frac{-2}{3}$. The number 2.4 can be named $\frac{24}{10}$ or $\frac{12}{5}$, and -0.17 can be named $-\frac{17}{100}$.

Note that this new set of numbers, the rational numbers, contains the whole numbers, the integers, and the numbers of arithmetic (also called the nonnegative rational numbers). We can describe the set of rational numbers using set notation as follows.

The set of rational numbers $= \left\{ \dfrac{a}{b} \middle| a \text{ and } b \text{ are integers and } b \neq 0 \right\}.$

$\left(\text{This is read "the set of numbers } \dfrac{a}{b}, \text{ where } a \text{ and } b \text{ are integers and } b \neq 0." \right)$

We picture the rational numbers on a number line as follows. There is a point on the line for every rational number.

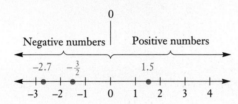

To **graph** a number means to find and mark its point on the line. Some numbers are graphed in the preceding figure.

▶ **EXAMPLE 5**   Graph: $\frac{5}{2}$.

The number $\frac{5}{2}$ can be named $2\frac{1}{2}$, or 2.5. Its graph is halfway between 2 and 3.

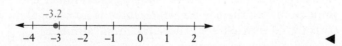   ◀

▶ **EXAMPLE 6**   Graph: -3.2.

The graph of -3.2 is $\frac{2}{10}$ of the way from -3 to -4.

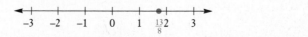   ◀

▶ **EXAMPLE 7**   Graph: $\frac{13}{8}$.

The number $\frac{13}{8}$ can be named $1\frac{5}{8}$, or 1.625. The graph is about $\frac{6}{10}$ of the way from 1 to 2.

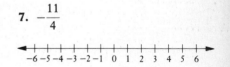   ◀

DO EXERCISES 5–7.

ANSWERS ON PAGE A-5

Graph on a number line.

5. $-\dfrac{7}{2}$

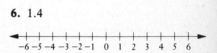

6. 1.4

7. $-\dfrac{11}{4}$

Convert to decimal notation.

8. $-\dfrac{3}{8}$

9. $-\dfrac{6}{11}$

10. $\dfrac{4}{3}$

c   Notation for Rational Numbers

The rational numbers can be named using fractional or decimal notation.

▶ **EXAMPLE 8**   Convert to decimal notation: $-\frac{5}{8}$.

We first find decimal notation for $\frac{5}{8}$. Since $\frac{5}{8}$ means $5 \div 8$, we divide.

$$
\begin{array}{r}
0.6\ 2\ 5 \\
8\overline{)5.0\ 0\ 0} \\
4\ 8 \\
\hline
2\ 0 \\
1\ 6 \\
\hline
4\ 0 \\
4\ 0 \\
\hline
0
\end{array}
$$

Thus, $\frac{5}{8} = 0.625$, so $-\frac{5}{8} = -0.625$. ◄

Decimal notation for $-\frac{5}{8}$ is -0.625. We consider -0.625 to be a **terminating decimal.** Decimal notation for some numbers repeats.

▶ **EXAMPLE 9**   Convert to decimal notation: $\frac{7}{11}$.

We divide.

$$
\begin{array}{r}
0.6\ 3\ 6\ 3\ldots \\
11\overline{)7.0\ 0\ 0\ 0} \\
6\ 6 \\
\hline
4\ 0 \\
3\ 3 \\
\hline
7\ 0 \\
6\ 6 \\
\hline
4\ 0 \\
3\ 3 \\
\hline
7
\end{array}
$$

$$\frac{7}{11} = 0.\overline{63}$$

We can abbreviate repeating decimal notation by writing a bar over the repeating part, in this case, $0.\overline{63}$. ◄

DO EXERCISES 8–10.

d   The Real Numbers and Order

Every rational number has a point on the number line. However, there are some points on the line for which there is no rational number. These points correspond to what are called **irrational numbers.**

What kinds of numbers correspond to points that are irrational numbers? One example is the number π, which is used in finding the area and circumference of a circle: $A = \pi r^2$ and $C = 2\pi r$.

Another example of an irrational number is the square root of 2, named $\sqrt{2}$.

It is the length of the diagonal of a square with sides of length 1. It is also the number that when multiplied by itself gives 2. There is no rational number that can be multiplied by itself to get 2. But the following are rational *approximations*:

1.4 is an approximation of $\sqrt{2}$ because $(1.4)^2 = 1.96$;

1.41 is a better approximation because $(1.41)^2 = 1.988$;

1.4142 is an even better approximation because $(1.4142)^2 = 1.99996164$.

We can find rational approximations for square roots using a calculator.

Decimal notation for rational numbers *either* terminates *or* repeats. Decimal notation for irrational numbers *neither* terminates *nor* repeats. Some other examples of irrational numbers are π, $\sqrt{3}$, $-\sqrt{8}$, $\sqrt{11}$, and $0.121221222122221\ldots$. Whenever we take the square root of a number that is not a perfect square we will get an irrational number.

The rational numbers and the irrational numbers together correspond to all the points on a number line and make up what is called the **real-number system.**

> **The set of real numbers = The set of all numbers corresponding to points on the number line.**

The real numbers consist of the rational numbers and the irrational numbers. The following figure shows the relationship between various kinds of numbers.

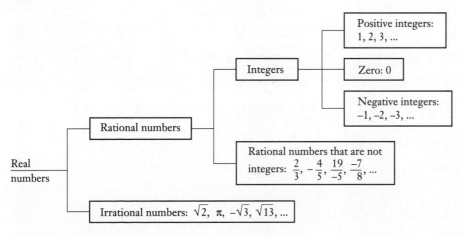

Use either < or > for ▨ to write a true sentence.

11. −3 ▨ 7

12. −8 ▨ −5

13. 7 ▨ −10

14. 3.1 ▨ −9.5

15. −$\frac{2}{3}$ ▨ −1

16. −$\frac{11}{8}$ ▨ $\frac{23}{15}$

17. −$\frac{2}{3}$ ▨ −$\frac{5}{9}$

18. −4.78 ▨ −5.01

▶ **EXAMPLE 10**   Graph the real number $\sqrt{3}$ on a number line.

We use a calculator or Table 2 at the back of the book and approximate $\sqrt{3} \approx 1.732$ ("≈" means "approximately equal to"). Then we locate this number on a number line.

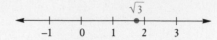

◀

Real numbers are named in order on the number line, with larger numbers named further to the right. For any two numbers on the line, the one to the left is less than the one to the right.

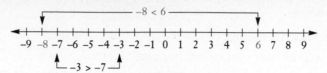

We use the symbol **<** to mean "**is less than.**" The sentence −8 < 6 means "−8 is less than 6." The symbol **>** means "**is greater than.**" The sentence −3 > −7 means "−3 is greater than −7."

▶ **EXAMPLES**   Use either < or > for ▨ to write a true sentence.

11. 2 ▨ 9   Since 2 is to the left of 9, 2 is less than 9, so 2 < 9.

12. −7 ▨ 3   Since −7 is to the left of 3, we have −7 < 3.

13. 6 ▨ −12   Since 6 is to the right of −12, then 6 > −12.

14. −18 ▨ −5   Since −18 is to the left of −5, we have −18 < −5.

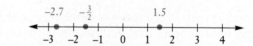

15. −2.7 ▨ −$\frac{3}{2}$ The answer is −2.7 < −$\frac{3}{2}$.

16. 1.5 ▨ −2.7   The answer is 1.5 > −2.7.

17. 1.38 ▨ 1.83   The answer is 1.38 < 1.83.

18. −3.45 ▨ 1.32   The answer is −3.45 < 1.32.

19. $\frac{5}{8}$ ▨ $\frac{7}{11}$ We convert to decimal notation: $\frac{5}{8}$ = 0.625 and $\frac{7}{11}$ = 0.6363 . . . . Thus, $\frac{5}{8}$ < $\frac{7}{11}$.   ◀

DO EXERCISES 11–18.

ANSWERS ON PAGE A-5

Note that both $-8 < 6$ and $6 > -8$ are true. These are **inequalities.** Every true inequality yields another true inequality when we interchange the numbers or variables and reverse the direction of the inequality sign.

$a < b$ also has the meaning $b > a$.

▶ **EXAMPLES**   Write another inequality with the same meaning.

20. $a < -5$ The inequality $-5 > a$ has the same meaning.

21. $-3 > -8$ The inequality $-8 < -3$ has the same meaning.   ◀

A helpful mental device is to think of an inequality sign as an "arrow" with the arrow pointing to the smaller number.

DO EXERCISES 19 AND 20.

Note that all positive real numbers are greater than zero and all negative real numbers are less than zero.

If x is a positive real number, then $x > 0$.
If x is a negative real number, then $x < 0$.

Expressions like $a \le b$ and $b \ge a$ are also inequalities. We read $a \le b$ as "**a is less than or equal to b.**" We read $a \ge b$ as "**a is greater than or equal to b.**"

▶ **EXAMPLES**   Write true or false for each statement.

22. $-3 \le 5$ True since $-3 < 5$ is true

23. $-3 \le -3$ True since $-3 = -3$ is true

24. $-5 \ge 4$ False since neither $-5 > 4$ nor $-5 = 4$ is true   ◀

DO EXERCISES 21–23.

e ▪ Absolute Value

From the number line, we see that numbers like 4 and -4 are the same distance from zero. Distance is always a nonnegative number. We call the distance from zero on a number line the **absolute value** of the number.

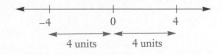

The *absolute value* of a number is its distance from zero on a number line. We use the symbol $|x|$ to represent the absolute value of a number x.

Write another inequality with the same meaning.

19. $-5 < 7$

20. $x > 4$

Write true or false.

21. $-4 \le -6$

22. $7 \ge 7$

23. $-2 \le 3$

ANSWERS ON PAGE A-5

Find the absolute value.

24. $|8|$

To find absolute value:
1. **If a number is negative, make it positive.**
2. **If a number is positive or zero, leave it alone.**

▶ **EXAMPLES**   Find the absolute value.

25. $|-7|$ The distance of -7 from 0 is 7, so $|-7|$ is 7.

26. $|12|$ The distance of 12 from 0 is 12, so $|12|$ is 12.

27. $|0|$ The distance of 0 from 0 is 0, so $|0|$ is 0.

25. $|0|$

28. $\left|\frac{3}{2}\right| = \frac{3}{2}$

29. $|-2.73| = 2.73$ ◀

DO EXERCISES 24–28.

26. $|-9|$

27. $\left|-\frac{2}{3}\right|$

28. $|5.6|$

NAME   SECTION   DATE

EXERCISE SET 7.2

	ANSWERS

a Tell which real numbers correspond to the situation.

1. The temperature on Wednesday was 18° above zero. On Thursday it was 2° below zero.

2. The Dead Sea, between Jordan and Israel, is 1286 ft below sea level, whereas Mt. Everest is 29,028 ft above sea level.

3. A student deposited $750 in a savings account. Two weeks later, the student withdrew $125.

4. During a certain time period, the United States had a deficit of $3 million in foreign trade.

5. During a video game, a player intercepted a missile worth 20 points, lost a starship worth 150 points, and captured a base worth 300 points.

6. 3 seconds before liftoff of a rocket occurs. 128 seconds after the liftoff of a rocket occurs.

b Graph the number on the number line.

7. $\dfrac{10}{3}$

8. $-\dfrac{17}{5}$

9. -4.3

10. 3.87

Write an inequality with the same meaning.

11. $-6 > x$ **12.** $x < 8$ **13.** $-10 \le y$ **14.** $12 \ge t$

c Convert to decimal notation.

15. $-\dfrac{3}{8}$ **16.** $-\dfrac{1}{8}$ **17.** $\dfrac{5}{3}$ **18.** $\dfrac{5}{6}$

19. $\dfrac{7}{6}$ **20.** $\dfrac{5}{12}$ **21.** $\dfrac{2}{3}$ **22.** $\dfrac{1}{4}$

23. $-\dfrac{1}{2}$ **24.** $\dfrac{5}{8}$ **25.** $\dfrac{1}{10}$ **26.** $-\dfrac{7}{20}$

ANSWERS

1. _____

2. _____

3. _____

4. _____

5. _____

6. _____

7. See graph.

8. See graph.

9. See graph.

10. See graph.

11. _____

12. _____

13. _____

14. _____

15. _____

16. _____

17. _____

18. _____

19. _____

20. _____

21. _____

22. _____

23. _____

24. _____

25. _____

26. _____

Copyright © 1993 Addison-Wesley Publishing Co., Inc.

ANSWERS

27.

28.

29.

30.

31.

32.

33.

34.

35.

36.

37.

38.

39.

40.

41.

42.

43.

44.

45.

46.

47.

48.

49.

50.

51.

52.

53.

54.

55.

56.

57.

58.

59.

60.

61.

62.

63.

64.

d Use either $<$ or $>$ for ▨ to write a true sentence.

27. 5 ▨ 0

28. 9 ▨ 0

29. -9 ▨ 5

30. 8 ▨ -8

31. -6 ▨ 6

32. 0 ▨ -7

33. -8 ▨ -5

34. -4 ▨ -3

35. -5 ▨ -11

36. -3 ▨ -4

37. -6 ▨ -5

38. -10 ▨ -14

39. 2.14 ▨ 1.24

40. -3.3 ▨ -2.2

41. -14.5 ▨ 0.011

42. 17.2 ▨ -1.67

43. -12.88 ▨ -6.45

44. -14.34 ▨ -17.88

45. $\dfrac{5}{12}$ ▨ $\dfrac{11}{25}$

46. $-\dfrac{14}{17}$ ▨ $-\dfrac{27}{35}$

Write true or false.

47. $-3 \geq -11$

48. $5 \leq -5$

49. $0 \geq 8$

50. $-5 \leq 7$

e Find the absolute value.

51. $|-3|$

52. $|-7|$

53. $|10|$

54. $|11|$

55. $|0|$

56. $|-4|$

57. $|-24|$

58. $|325|$

59. $\left|-\dfrac{2}{3}\right|$

60. $\left|-\dfrac{10}{7}\right|$

61. $\left|\dfrac{0}{4}\right|$

62. $|14.8|$

SYNTHESIS

List in order from the least to the greatest.

63. $-\dfrac{2}{3}, \quad \dfrac{1}{2}, \quad -\dfrac{3}{4}, \quad -\dfrac{5}{6}, \quad \dfrac{3}{8}, \quad \dfrac{1}{6}$

64. $7^1, \quad -5, \quad |-6|, \quad 4, \quad |3|, \quad -100, \quad 0, \quad 1^7, \quad \dfrac{14}{4}$

7.3 Addition of Real Numbers

In this section, we consider addition of real numbers. First, to gain an under-standing, we add using a number line. Then we consider rules for addition.

Addition of numbers can be illustrated on a number line. To do the addition $a + b$, we start at a, and then move according to b.

a) If b is positive, we move to the right.

b) If b is negative, we move to the left.

c) If b is 0, we stay at a.

▶ **EXAMPLE 1** Add: $3 + (-5)$.

$3 + (-5) = -2$

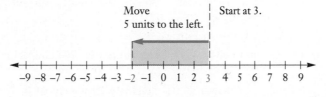

◀

▶ **EXAMPLE 2** Add: $-4 + (-3)$.

$-4 + (-3) = -7$

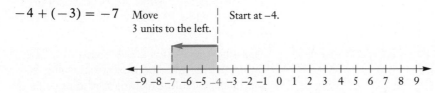

◀

▶ **EXAMPLE 3** Add: $-4 + 9$.

$-4 + 9 = 5$

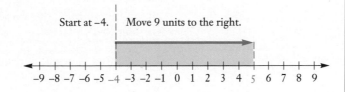

◀

▶ **EXAMPLE 4** Add: $-5.2 + 0$.

$-5.2 + 0 = -5.2$

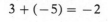

◀

DO EXERCISES 1–6.

OBJECTIVES

After finishing Section 7.3, you should be able to:

a Add real numbers without using a number line.

b Find the additive inverse, or opposite, of a real number.

FOR EXTRA HELP

Tape 14C

Add using a number line.

1. $0 + (-8)$

2. $1 + (-4)$

3. $-3 + (-5)$

4. $-3 + 7$

5. $-5.4 + 5.4$

6. $-\dfrac{5}{2} + \dfrac{1}{2}$

ANSWERS ON PAGE A-5

Add without using a number line.

7. $-5 + (-6)$ **8.** $-9 + (-3)$

9. $-4 + 6$ **10.** $-7 + 3$

11. $5 + (-7)$ **12.** $-20 + 20$

13. $-11 + (-11)$ **14.** $10 + (-7)$

15. $-0.17 + 0.7$ **16.** $-6.4 + 8.7$

17. $-4.5 + (-3.2)$ **18.** $-8.6 + 2.4$

19. $\dfrac{5}{9} + \left(-\dfrac{7}{9}\right)$ **20.** $-\dfrac{1}{5} + \left(-\dfrac{3}{4}\right)$

a   Adding Without a Number Line

You may have noticed some patterns in the preceding examples. These lead us to rules for adding without using a number line that are more efficient for adding larger or more complicated numbers.

> **Rules for Addition of Real Numbers**
>
> 1. *Positive numbers:* Add the same as numbers of arithmetic. The answer is positive.
> 2. *Negative numbers:* Add absolute values. The answer is negative.
> 3. *A positive and a negative number:* Subtract absolute values. Then:
>   a) If the positive number has the greater absolute value, the answer is positive.
>   b) If the negative number has the greater absolute value, the answer is negative.
>   c) If the numbers have the same absolute value, the answer is 0.
> 4. *One number is zero:* The sum is the other number.

Rule 4 is known as the **Identity Property of 0.** It says that for any real number a, $a + 0 = a$.

▶ **EXAMPLES**   Add without using a number line.

5. $-12 + (-7) = -19$ Two negatives. *Think:* Add the absolute values, getting 19. Make the answer *negative*, -19.

6. $-1.4 + 8.5 = 7.1$ The absolute values are 1.4 and 8.5. The difference is 7.1. The positive number has the larger absolute value, so the answer is *positive*, 7.1.

7. $-36 + 21 = -15$ The absolute values are 36 and 21. The difference is 15. The negative number has the larger absolute value, so the answer is *negative*, -15.

8. $1.5 + (-1.5) = 0$ The numbers have the same absolute value. The sum is 0.

9. $-\dfrac{7}{8} + 0 = -\dfrac{7}{8}$ One number is zero. The sum is $-\frac{7}{8}$.

10. $-9.2 + 3.1 = -6.1$

11. $-\dfrac{3}{2} + \dfrac{9}{2} = \dfrac{6}{2} = 3$

12. $-\dfrac{2}{3} + \dfrac{5}{8} = -\dfrac{16}{24} + \dfrac{15}{24} = -\dfrac{1}{24}$ ◀

DO EXERCISES 7–20.

Suppose we want to add several numbers, some positive and some negative, as follows. How can we proceed?

$$15 + (-2) + 7 + 14 + (-5) + (-12)$$

We can change grouping and order as we please when adding. For instance, we can group the positive numbers together and the negative numbers together and add them separately. Then we add the two results.

▶ **EXAMPLE 13**   Add: $15 + (-2) + 7 + 14 + (-5) + (-12)$.

a) $15 + 7 + 14 = 36$ Adding the positive numbers

b) $-2 + (-5) + (-12) = -19$ Adding the negative numbers

c) $36 + (-19) = 17$ Adding the results

We can also add the numbers in any other order we wish, say from left to right as follows:

$$
\begin{aligned}
15 + (-2) + 7 + 14 + (-5) + (-12) &= 13 + 7 + 14 + (-5) + (-12) \\
&= 20 + 14 + (-5) + (-12) \\
&= 34 + (-5) + (-12) \\
&= 29 + (-12) \\
&= 17 \quad ◀
\end{aligned}
$$

DO EXERCISES 21–24.

b   Opposites and Additive Inverses

Suppose we add two numbers that are opposites, such as 6 and -6. The result is 0. When opposites are added, the result is always 0. Such numbers are also called **opposites**, or **additive inverses.** Every real number has an opposite.

> **Two numbers whose sum is 0 are called *opposites,* or *additive inverses*** **of each other.**

▶ **EXAMPLES**   Find the opposite of each number.

14. 34   The opposite of 34 is -34 because $34 + (-34) = 0$.

15. -8 The opposite of -8 is 8 because $-8 + 8 = 0$.

16. 0   The opposite of 0 is 0 because $0 + 0 = 0$.

17. $-\dfrac{7}{8}$ The opposite of $-\dfrac{7}{8}$ is $\dfrac{7}{8}$ because $-\dfrac{7}{8} + \dfrac{7}{8} = 0$.   ◀

DO EXERCISES 25–30.

To name the opposite, we use the symbol $-$, as follows.

> **The opposite, or additive inverse, of a number *a* can be named $-a$** **(read ''the opposite of *a*'' or ''the additive inverse of *a*'').**

Note that if we take a number, say 8, and find its opposite, -8, and then find the opposite of the result, we will have the original number, 8, again.

Add.

21. $(-15) + (-37) + 25 + 42 + (-59) + (-14)$

22. $42 + (-81) + (-28) + 24 + 18 + (-31)$

23. $-2.5 + (-10) + 6 + (-7.5)$

24. -35
17
14
-27
31
-12

Find the opposite.

25. -4 **26.** 8.7

27. -7.74 **28.** $-\dfrac{8}{9}$

29. 0   **30.** 12

ANSWERS ON PAGE A-5

Find $-x$ and $-(-x)$ when x is:

31. 14   **32.** 1

33. -19 **34.** -1.6

35. $\dfrac{2}{3}$ **36.** $-\dfrac{9}{8}$

Change the sign. (Find the opposite.)

37. -4 **38.** -13.4

39. 0   **40.** $\dfrac{1}{4}$

> The opposite of the opposite of a number is the number itself. The additive inverse of the additive inverse of a number is the number itself. That is, for any number a,
>
> $$-(-a) = a.$$

▶ **EXAMPLE 18**   Find $-x$ and $-(-x)$ when $x = 16$.

a) If $x = 16$, then $-x = -16$.   The opposite of 16 is -16.

b) If $x = 16$, then $-(-x) = -(-16) = 16$.   The opposite of the opposite of 16 is 16. ◀

▶ **EXAMPLE 19**   Find $-x$ and $-(-x)$ when $x = -3$.

a) If $x = -3$, then $-x = -(-3) = 3$.

b) If $x = -3$, then $-(-x) = -(-(-3)) = -3$. ◀

Note in Example 19 that an extra set of parentheses is used to show that we are substituting the negative number -3 for x. Symbolism like $--x$ is not considered meaningful.

DO EXERCISES 31–36.

A symbol such as -8 is usually read "negative 8." It could be read "the additive inverse of 8," because the additive inverse of 8 is negative 8. It could also be read "the opposite of 8," because the opposite of 8 is -8. Thus a symbol like -8 can be read in more than one way. A symbol like $-x$, which has a variable, should be read "the opposite of x" or "the additive inverse of x" and *not* "negative x," because we do not know whether x represents a positive number, a negative number, or 0. Check this out by referring to the preceding examples.

We can use the symbolism $-a$ to restate the definition of opposite, or additive inverse.

> For any real number a, the *opposite*, or *additive inverse*, of a, $-a$, is such that
>
> $$a + (-a) = (-a) + a = 0.$$

Signs of Numbers

A negative number is sometimes said to have a "negative sign." A positive number is said to have a "positive sign." When we replace a number by its opposite, we can say that we have "changed its sign."

▶ **EXAMPLES**   Change the sign. (Find the opposite.)

20. -3 $-(-3) = 3$ The opposite of -3 is 3.

21. -10 $-(-10) = 10$

22. 0 $-(0) = 0$

23. 14 $-(14) = -14$ ◀

DO EXERCISES 37–40.

EXERCISE SET 7.3

a Add. Do not use a number line except as a check.

1. $-9 + 2$ **2.** $2 + (-5)$ **3.** $-10 + 6$ **4.** $8 + (-3)$

5. $-8 + 8$ **6.** $6 + (-6)$ **7.** $-3 + (-5)$ **8.** $-4 + (-6)$

9. $-7 + 0$ **10.** $-13 + 0$ **11.** $0 + (-27)$ **12.** $0 + (-35)$

13. $17 + (-17)$ **14.** $-15 + 15$ **15.** $-17 + (-25)$ **16.** $-24 + (-17)$

17. $18 + (-18)$ **18.** $-13 + 13$ **19.** $-18 + 18$ **20.** $11 + (-11)$

21. $8 + (-5)$ **22.** $-7 + 8$ **23.** $-4 + (-5)$ **24.** $10 + (-12)$

25. $13 + (-6)$ **26.** $-3 + 14$ **27.** $-25 + 25$ **28.** $40 + (-40)$

29. $63 + (-18)$ **30.** $85 + (-65)$ **31.** $-6.5 + 4.7$ **32.** $-3.6 + 1.9$

33. $-2.8 + (-5.3)$ **34.** $-7.9 + (-6.5)$ **35.** $-\dfrac{3}{5} + \dfrac{2}{5}$ **36.** $-\dfrac{4}{3} + \dfrac{2}{3}$

ANSWERS

1. _____
2. _____
3. _____
4. _____
5. _____
6. _____
7. _____
8. _____
9. _____
10. _____
11. _____
12. _____
13. _____
14. _____
15. _____
16. _____
17. _____
18. _____
19. _____
20. _____
21. _____
22. _____
23. _____
24. _____
25. _____
26. _____
27. _____
28. _____
29. _____
30. _____
31. _____
32. _____
33. _____
34. _____
35. _____
36. _____

ANSWERS

37. _____
38. _____
39. _____
40. _____
41. _____
42. _____
43. _____
44. _____
45. _____
46. _____
47. _____
48. _____
49. _____
50. _____
51. _____
52. _____
53. _____
54. _____
55. _____
56. _____
57. _____
58. _____
59. _____
60. _____
61. _____
62. _____
63. _____
64. _____
65. _____
66. _____
67. _____
68. _____
69. _____
70. _____

37. $-\frac{3}{7}+\left(-\frac{5}{7}\right)$ 38. $-\frac{4}{9}+\left(-\frac{6}{9}\right)$ 39. $-\frac{5}{8}+\frac{1}{4}$ 40. $-\frac{5}{6}+\frac{2}{3}$

41. $-\frac{3}{7}+\left(-\frac{2}{5}\right)$ 42. $-\frac{5}{8}+\left(-\frac{1}{3}\right)$ 43. $-\frac{7}{16}+\frac{7}{8}$ 44. $-\frac{3}{28}+\frac{5}{42}$

45. $75+(-14)+(-17)+(-5)$ 46. $28+(-44)+17+31+(-94)$

47. $-44+\left(-\frac{3}{8}\right)+95+\left(-\frac{5}{8}\right)$ 48. $24+3.1+(-44)+(-8.2)+63$

49. $98+(-54)+113+(-998)+44+(-612)$

50. $-455+(-123)+1026+(-919)+213$

b Find the opposite, or additive inverse.

51. 24 52. −64 53. −26.9 54. 48.2

Find $-x$ when x is:

55. 9 56. −26 57. $-\frac{14}{3}$ 58. $\frac{1}{328}$

Find $-(-x)$ when x is:

59. −65 60. 29 61. $\frac{5}{3}$ 62. −9.1

Change the sign. (Find the opposite.)

63. −14 64. −22.4 65. 10 66. $-\frac{7}{8}$

SYNTHESIS

67. For what numbers x is $-x$ negative? 68. For what numbers x is $-x$ positive?

Tell whether the sum is positive, negative, or zero.

69. If n is positive and m is negative, $-n+m$ is _____.

70. If $n=m$ and n and m are negative, $-n+(-m)$ is _____.

b Problem Solving

Let us see how we can use subtraction of real numbers to solve problems.

▶ **EXAMPLE 12**   The lowest point in Asia is the Dead Sea, which is 400 m below sea level. The lowest point in the United States is Death Valley, which is 86 m below sea level. How much higher is Death Valley than the Dead Sea?

It is helpful to draw a picture of the situation.

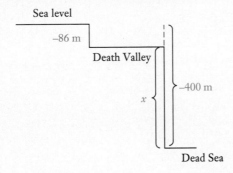

We see that −86 is the higher altitude at Death Valley and −400 is the lower altitude at the Dead Sea. To find how much higher Death Valley is, we subtract:

$$-86 - (-400) = -86 + 400 = 314.$$

Death Valley is 314 m higher than the Dead Sea.   ◀

DO EXERCISES 22 AND 23.

Solve.

22. A small business made a profit of $18 on Monday. There was a loss of $7 on Tuesday. On Wednesday there was a loss of $5, and on Thursday there was a profit of $11. Find the total profit or loss.

23. In Churchill, Manitoba, Canada, the average daily low temperature in January is −31°C. The average daily low temperature in Key West, Florida, is 19°C. How much higher is the average daily low temperature in Key West, Florida?

ANSWERS ON PAGE A-5

❖ SIDELIGHTS

Careers and Their Uses of Mathematics

Students typically ask the question "Why do we have to study mathematics?" This is a question with a complex set of answers. Certainly, one answer is that you will use this mathematics in the next course. While it is a correct answer, it sometimes frustrates students, because this answer can be given in the next mathematics course, and the next one, and so on. Sometimes an answer can be given by applications like those you have seen or will see in this book. Another answer is that you are living in a society in which mathematics becomes more and more critical with each passing day. Evidence of this was provided recently by a nationwide symposium sponsored by the National Research Council's Mathematical Sciences Education Board. Results showed that "Other than demographic factors, the *strongest* predictor of earnings nine years after high school is the number of mathematics courses taken." This is a significant testimony to the need for you to take as many mathematics courses as possible.

We try to provide other answers to "Why do we have to study mathematics?" in what follows. We have listed several occupations that are attractive and popular to students. Below each occupation are listed various kinds of mathematics that are useful in that occupation.

Doctor	Lawyer
Equations	Equations
Percent notation	Percent notation
Graphing	Graphing
Statistics	Probability
Geometry	Statistics
Measurement	Ratio and proportion
Estimation	Area and volume
Exponents	Negative numbers
Logic	Formulas
	Calculator skills

Pilot	Firefighter
Equations	Percent notation
Percent notation	Graphing
Graphing	Estimation
Trigonometry	Formulas
Angles and geometry	Angles and geometry
Calculator skills	Probability
Computer skills	Statistics
Ratio and proportion	Area and geometry
Vectors	Square roots
	Exponents
	Pythagorean theorem

Accountant and businessperson	Travel agent
Computer skills	Whole-number skills
Calculator skills	Fraction/decimal skills
Equations	Estimation
Systems of equations	Percent notation
Formulas	Equations
Probability	Calculator skills
Statistics	Computer skills
Ratio and proportion	
Percent notation	
Estimation	

Librarian	Machinist
Whole-number skills	Whole-number skills
Fraction/decimal skills	Fraction/decimal skills
Estimation	Estimation
Percent notation	Percent notation
Ratio and proportion	Length, area, volume, and perimeter
Area and perimeter	Angle measures
Formulas	Geometry
Calculator skills	Pythagorean theorem
Computer skills	Square roots
	Equations
	Formulas
	Graphing
	Calculator skills
	Computer skills

Nurse	Police officer
Whole-number skills	Whole-number skills
Fraction/decimal skills	Fraction/decimal skills
Estimation	Estimation
Percent notation	Percent notation
Ratio and proportion	Ratio and proportion
Equations	Geometry
English/Metric measurement	Negative numbers
Probability	Probability
Statistics	Statistics
Formulas	Calculator skills
Exponents and scientific notation	
Calculator skills	
Computer skills	

NAME   SECTION   DATE

EXERCISE SET 7.4

a   Subtract.

1. $3 - 7$ **2.** $4 - 9$ **3.** $0 - 7$ **4.** $0 - 10$

5. $-8 - (-2)$ **6.** $-6 - (-8)$ **7.** $-10 - (-10)$ **8.** $-6 - (-6)$

9. $12 - 16$ **10.** $14 - 19$ **11.** $20 - 27$ **12.** $30 - 4$

13. $-9 - (-3)$ **14.** $-7 - (-9)$ **15.** $-40 - (-40)$ **16.** $-9 - (-9)$

17. $7 - 7$ **18.** $9 - 9$ **19.** $7 - (-7)$ **20.** $4 - (-4)$

21. $8 - (-3)$ **22.** $-7 - 4$ **23.** $-6 - 8$ **24.** $6 - (-10)$

25. $-4 - (-9)$ **26.** $-14 - 2$ **27.** $2 - 9$ **28.** $2 - 8$

29. $-6 - (-5)$ **30.** $-4 - (-3)$ **31.** $8 - (-10)$ **32.** $5 - (-6)$

33. $0 - 5$ **34.** $0 - 6$ **35.** $-5 - (-2)$ **36.** $-3 - (-1)$

ANSWERS

1. _____
2. _____
3. _____
4. _____
5. _____
6. _____
7. _____
8. _____
9. _____
10. _____
11. _____
12. _____
13. _____
14. _____
15. _____
16. _____
17. _____
18. _____
19. _____
20. _____
21. _____
22. _____
23. _____
24. _____
25. _____
26. _____
27. _____
28. _____
29. _____
30. _____
31. _____
32. _____
33. _____
34. _____
35. _____
36. _____

37. _____

38. _____

39. _____

40. _____

41. _____

42. _____

43. _____

44. _____

45. _____

46. _____

47. _____

48. _____

49. _____

50. _____

51. _____

52. _____

53. _____

54. _____

55. _____

56. _____

57. _____

58. _____

59. _____

60. _____

61. _____

62. _____

63. _____

64. _____

65. _____

66. _____

67. _____

68. _____

37. $-7 - 14$

38. $-9 - 16$

39. $0 - (-5)$

40. $0 - (-1)$

41. $-8 - 0$

42. $-9 - 0$

43. $7 - (-5)$

44. $8 - (-3)$

45. $2 - 25$

46. $18 - 63$

47. $-42 - 26$

48. $-18 - 63$

49. $-71 - 2$

50. $-49 - 3$

51. $24 - (-92)$

52. $48 - (-73)$

53. $-50 - (-50)$

54. $-70 - (-70)$

55. $\dfrac{3}{8} - \dfrac{5}{8}$

56. $\dfrac{3}{9} - \dfrac{9}{9}$

57. $\dfrac{3}{4} - \dfrac{2}{3}$

58. $\dfrac{5}{8} - \dfrac{3}{4}$

59. $-\dfrac{3}{4} - \dfrac{2}{3}$

60. $-\dfrac{5}{8} - \dfrac{3}{4}$

61. $-\dfrac{5}{8} - \left(-\dfrac{3}{4}\right)$

62. $-\dfrac{3}{4} - \left(-\dfrac{2}{3}\right)$

63. $6.1 - (-13.8)$

64. $1.5 - (-3.5)$

65. $-3.2 - 5.8$

66. $-2.7 - 5.9$

67. $0.99 - 1$

68. $0.87 - 1$

69. $-79 - 114$ **70.** $-197 - 216$ **71.** $0 - (-500)$ **72.** $500 - (-1000)$

73. $-2.8 - 0$ **74.** $6.04 - 1.1$ **75.** $7 - 10.53$ **76.** $8 - (-9.3)$

77. $\dfrac{1}{6} - \dfrac{2}{3}$ **78.** $-\dfrac{3}{8} - \left(-\dfrac{1}{2}\right)$ **79.** $-\dfrac{4}{7} - \left(-\dfrac{10}{7}\right)$ **80.** $\dfrac{12}{5} - \dfrac{12}{5}$

81. $-\dfrac{7}{10} - \dfrac{10}{15}$ **82.** $-\dfrac{4}{18} - \left(-\dfrac{2}{9}\right)$ **83.** $\dfrac{1}{13} - \dfrac{1}{12}$ **84.** $-\dfrac{1}{7} - \left(-\dfrac{1}{6}\right)$

Simplify.

85. $18 - (-15) - 3 - (-5) + 2$ **86.** $22 - (-18) + 7 + (-42) - 27$

87. $-31 + (-28) - (-14) - 17$ **88.** $-43 - (-19) - (-21) + 25$

89. $-34 - 28 + (-33) - 44$ **90.** $39 + (-88) - 29 - (-83)$

91. $-93 - (-84) - 41 - (-56)$ **92.** $84 + (-99) + 44 - (-18) - 43$

93. $-5 - (-30) + 30 + 40 - (-12)$ **94.** $14 - (-50) + 20 - (-32)$

95. $132 - (-21) + 45 - (-21)$ **96.** $81 - (-20) - 14 - (-50) + 53$

ANSWERS

69. _____
70. _____
71. _____
72. _____
73. _____
74. _____
75. _____
76. _____
77. _____
78. _____
79. _____
80. _____
81. _____
82. _____
83. _____
84. _____
85. _____
86. _____
87. _____
88. _____
89. _____
90. _____
91. _____
92. _____
93. _____
94. _____
95. _____
96. _____

Copyright © 1993 Addison-Wesley Publishing Co., Inc.

ANSWERS

97. _____

98. _____

99. _____

100. _____

101. _____

102. _____

103. _____

104. _____

105. _____

106. _____

107. _____

108. _____

109. _____

110. _____

111. _____

112. _____

b Solve.

97. Your total assets are $619.46. You borrow $950 for the purchase of a stereo system. What are your total assets now?

98. You owe a friend $420. The friend decides to cancel $156 of the debt. How much do you owe now?

99. You are in debt $215.50. How much money will you need to make your total assets y dollars?

100. On a winter night, the temperature dropped from $-5°C$ to $-12°C$. How many degrees did it drop?

101. The lowest point in Africa is Lake Assal, which is 156 m below sea level. The lowest point in South America is the Valdes Peninsula, which is 40 m below sea level. How much lower is Lake Assal than the Valdes Peninsula?

102. The deepest point in the Pacific Ocean is the Marianas Trench with a depth of 10,415 m. The deepest point in the Atlantic Ocean is the Puerto Rico Trench with a depth of 8648 m. How much higher is the Puerto Rico Trench than the Marianas Trench?

SKILL MAINTENANCE

103. Evaluate: 5^3.

104. Find the prime factorization of 864.

SYNTHESIS

Subtract.

105. ▥ $123,907 - 433,789$

106. ▥ $23,011 - (-60,432)$

Tell whether the statement is true or false for all integers m and n. If false, give a counterexample.

107. $n - 0 = 0 - n$

108. $0 - n = n$

109. If $m \neq n$, then $m - n \neq 0$.

110. If $m = -n$, then $m + n = 0$.

111. If $m + n = 0$, then m and n are additive inverses.

112. If $m - n = 0$, then $m = -n$.

7.5 Multiplication of Real Numbers

a Multiplication

Multiplication of real numbers is very much like multiplication of numbers of arithmetic. The only difference is that we must determine whether the answer is positive or negative.

Multiplication of a Positive Number and a Negative Number

To see how to multiply a positive number and a negative number, consider the pattern of the following.

This number decreases → 4 · 5 =   20 ← This number decreases
by 1 each time.   3 · 5 =   15   by 5 each time.
$$3 \cdot 5 = 15$$
$$2 \cdot 5 = 10$$
$$1 \cdot 5 = 5$$
$$0 \cdot 5 = 0$$
$$-1 \cdot 5 = -5$$
$$-2 \cdot 5 = -10$$
$$-3 \cdot 5 = -15$$

DO EXERCISE 1.

According to this pattern, it looks as though the product of a negative number and a positive number is negative. That is the case, and we have the first part of the rule for multiplying numbers.

> To multiply a positive number and a negative number, multiply their absolute values. The answer is negative.

▶ **EXAMPLES** Multiply.

1. $8(-5) = -40$

2. $-\dfrac{1}{3} \cdot \dfrac{5}{7} = -\dfrac{5}{21}$

3. $(-7.2)5 = -36$ ◀

DO EXERCISES 2–7.

Multiplication of Two Negative Numbers

How do we multiply two negative numbers? Again, we look for a pattern.

This number decreases → 4 · (−5) = −20 ← This number increases
by 1 each time.   3 · (−5) = −15   by 5 each time.
$$3 \cdot (-5) = -15$$
$$2 \cdot (-5) = -10$$
$$1 \cdot (-5) = -5$$
$$0 \cdot (-5) = 0$$
$$-1 \cdot (-5) = 5$$
$$-2 \cdot (-5) = 10$$
$$-3 \cdot (-5) = 15$$

DO EXERCISE 8.

OBJECTIVE

After finishing Section 7.5, you should be able to:

a Multiply real numbers.

FOR EXTRA HELP

Tape 15B

1. Complete, as in the example.
$$4 \cdot 10 = 40$$
$$3 \cdot 10 = 30$$
$$2 \cdot 10 =$$
$$1 \cdot 10 =$$
$$0 \cdot 10 =$$
$$-1 \cdot 10 =$$
$$-2 \cdot 10 =$$
$$-3 \cdot 10 =$$

Multiply.

2. $-3 \cdot 6$

3. $20 \cdot (-5)$

4. $4 \cdot (-20)$

5. $-\dfrac{2}{3} \cdot \dfrac{5}{6}$

6. $-4.23(7.1)$

7. $\dfrac{7}{8}\left(-\dfrac{4}{5}\right)$

8. Complete, as in the example.
$$3 \cdot (-10) = -30$$
$$2 \cdot (-10) = -20$$
$$1 \cdot (-10) =$$
$$0 \cdot (-10) =$$
$$-1 \cdot (-10) =$$
$$-2 \cdot (-10) =$$
$$-3 \cdot (-10) =$$

Multiply.

9. $-3 \cdot (-4)$

10. $-16 \cdot (-2)$

11. $-7 \cdot (-5)$

12. $-\dfrac{4}{7}\left(-\dfrac{5}{9}\right)$

13. $-\dfrac{3}{2}\left(-\dfrac{4}{9}\right)$

14. $-3.25(-4.14)$

Multiply.

15. $5(-6)$

16. $(-5)(-6)$

17. $(-3.2) \cdot 0$

18. $\left(-\dfrac{4}{5}\right)\left(\dfrac{10}{3}\right)$

According to the pattern, it appears that the product of two negative numbers is positive. That is actually so, and we have the second part of the rule for multiplying real numbers.

> **To multiply two negative numbers, multiply their absolute values. The answer is positive.**

DO EXERCISES 9–14.

The following is an alternative way to consider the rules we have for multiplication.

> **To multiply two real numbers:**
> 1. **Multiply the absolute values.**
> 2. **If the signs are the same, the answer is positive.**
> 3. **If the signs are different, the answer is negative.**

Multiplication by Zero

The only case that we have not considered is multiplying by zero. As with other numbers, the product of any real number and 0 is 0.

> ### The Multiplicative Property of Zero
>
> **For any real number a,**
> $$a \cdot 0 = 0.$$
> **(The product of 0 and any real number is 0.)**

▶ **EXAMPLES** Multiply.

4. $(-3)(-4) = 12$

5. $-1.6(2) = -3.2$

6. $-19 \cdot 0 = 0$

7. $\left(-\dfrac{5}{6}\right)\left(-\dfrac{1}{9}\right) = \dfrac{5}{54}$ ◀

DO EXERCISES 15–18.

Multiplying More Than Two Numbers

When multiplying more than two real numbers, we can choose order and grouping as we please.

▶ **EXAMPLES** Multiply.

8. $-8 \cdot 2(-3) = -16(-3)$ Multiplying the first two numbers
$= 48$ Multiplying the results

9. $-8 \cdot 2(-3) = 24 \cdot 2$ Multiplying the negatives. Every pair of negative numbers gives a positive product.
$= 48$

10. $-3(-2)(-5)(4) = 6(-5)(4)$ Multiplying the first two numbers
$= (-30)4$
$= -120$

11. $\left(-\frac{1}{2}\right)(8)\left(-\frac{2}{3}\right)(-6) = (-4)4$ Multiplying the first two numbers and the last two numbers

$$= -16$$

12. $-5 \cdot (-2) \cdot (-3) \cdot (-6) = 10 \cdot 18$
$$= 180$$

13. $(-3)(-5)(-2)(-3)(-6) = (-30)(18) = -540$ ◄

We can see the following pattern in the results of Examples 12 and 13.

The product of an even number of negative numbers is positive.
The product of an odd number of negative numbers is negative.

DO EXERCISES 19–24.

▶ **EXAMPLE 14**   Evaluate $(-x)^2$ and $-x^2$ when $x = 5$.

$(-x)^2 = (-5)^2 = (-5)(-5) = 25;$ Substitute 5 for x. Then evaluate the power.

$-x^2 = -(5)^2 = -25$ Substitute 5 for x. Evaluate the power. Then find the opposite.   ◄

Note that the expressions $(-x)^2$ and $-x^2$ are *not* equivalent. That is, they do not have the same value for every replacement of the variable by a real number. To find $(-x)^2$, we take the opposite and then square. To find $-x^2$, we find the square and then take the opposite.

▶ **EXAMPLE 15**   Evaluate $2x^2$ when $x = 3$ and $x = -3$.

$$2x^2 = 2(3)^2 = 2(9) = 18;$$

$$2x^2 = 2(-3)^2 = 2(9) = 18$$ ◄

DO EXERCISES 25–27.

Multiply.

19. $5 \cdot (-3) \cdot 2$

20. $-3 \times (-4.1) \times (-2.5)$

21. $-\frac{1}{2} \cdot \left(-\frac{4}{3}\right) \cdot \left(-\frac{5}{2}\right)$

22. $-2 \cdot (-5) \cdot (-4) \cdot (-3)$

23. $(-4)(-5)(-2)(-3)(-1)$

24. $(-1)(-1)(-2)(-3)(-1)(-1)$

25. Evaluate $(-x)^2$ and $-x^2$ when $x = 2$.

26. Evaluate $(-x)^2$ and $-x^2$ when $x = 3$.

27. Evaluate $3x^2$ when $x = 4$ and $x = -4$.

ANSWERS ON PAGE A-5

❖ SIDELIGHTS

Study Tips: Studying for Tests and Making the Most of Tutoring Sessions

As has been stated, we will often present some tips and guidelines to enhance your learning abilities. Sometimes these tips will be focused on mathematics, but sometimes they will be more general, as is the case here where we consider test preparation and tutoring.

TEST-TAKING TIPS

Many test-taking tips have been covered on the *To the student* page at the beginning of the book. If you have not read that material, do so now. We now provide some other test-taking tips.

- *Make up your own test questions as you study.* You have probably noted by now the section and objective codes that appear throughout the book. After you have done your homework over a particular objective, write one or two questions on your own that you think might be on a test. You will be amazed at the insight this will provide. You are actually carrying out a task similar to what a teacher does in preparing an exam.

- *Ask former students for old exams.* Working such exams can be very helpful and allows you to see what various professors think is important.

- *When taking a test, read each question carefully and try to do all the questions the first time through, but pace yourself.* Answer all the questions, and mark those to recheck if you have time at the end. Very often your first hunch will be correct.

- *Try to write your test in a neat and orderly manner.* Very often your instructor tries to give you partial credit when grading an exam. If your test paper is sloppy and disorderly, it is difficult to verify the partial credit. Doing your homework in a neat and orderly manner can ease such a task on an exam. Try using an erasable pen to make your writing darker and therefore more readable.

MAKING THE MOST OF TUTORING AND HELP SESSIONS

Often you will determine that a tutoring session may be helpful. The following comments may help you to make the most of such situations.

- *Work on the topics before you go to the help or tutoring session. Do not go to such sessions with the view of yourself as an empty cup and the tutor as a magician who will instantly pour in the learning.* The primary source of your ability to learn is within you. We have seen so many students over the years go to help or tutoring sessions with no advanced preparation. You are often wasting your time and perhaps your money if you are paying for such sessions. Go to class, study the textbook, and mark trouble spots. Then use the help and tutoring sessions to deal with these difficulties most efficiently.

- *Do not be afraid to ask questions in these help and tutoring sessions!* The more you relate to your tutor, the more the tutor can help you with your difficulties.

- *Try being a tutor yourself.* Explaining a topic to someone else is often the best way to learn it.

- *What about the student who says "I could do the work at home, but on the test I made silly mistakes"?* Yes, all of us, including instructors, make silly computational mistakes in class, on homework, and on tests. But your instructor, if he or she has taught for some time, is probably aware that 90% of students who make such comments in truth do not have the depth of knowledge of the subject matter, and such silly mistakes very often are a sign that the student has not mastered the material. There is no way we can make that analysis for you. It will have to be unraveled by some careful soul searching on your part or by a conference with your instructor.

NAME   SECTION   DATE

EXERCISE SET 7.5

a   Multiply.

1. $-8 \cdot 2$ **2.** $-2 \cdot 5$ **3.** $-7 \cdot 6$ **4.** $-9 \cdot 2$

5. $8 \cdot (-3)$ **6.** $9 \cdot (-5)$ **7.** $-9 \cdot 8$ **8.** $-10 \cdot 3$

9. $-8 \cdot (-2)$ **10.** $-2 \cdot (-5)$ **11.** $-7 \cdot (-6)$ **12.** $-9 \cdot (-2)$

13. $15 \cdot (-8)$ **14.** $-12 \cdot (-10)$ **15.** $-14 \cdot 17$ **16.** $-13 \cdot (-15)$

17. $-25 \cdot (-48)$ **18.** $39 \cdot (-43)$ **19.** $-3.5 \cdot (-28)$ **20.** $97 \cdot (-2.1)$

21. $9 \cdot (-8)$ **22.** $7 \cdot (-9)$ **23.** $4 \cdot (-3.1)$ **24.** $3 \cdot (-2.2)$

25. $-6 \cdot (-4)$ **26.** $-5 \cdot (-6)$ **27.** $-7 \cdot (-3.1)$ **28.** $-4 \cdot (-3.2)$

29. $\dfrac{2}{3} \cdot \left(-\dfrac{3}{5}\right)$ **30.** $\dfrac{5}{7} \cdot \left(-\dfrac{2}{3}\right)$ **31.** $-\dfrac{3}{8} \cdot \left(-\dfrac{2}{9}\right)$ **32.** $-\dfrac{5}{8} \cdot \left(-\dfrac{2}{5}\right)$

33. -6.3×2.7 **34.** -4.1×9.5 **35.** $-\dfrac{5}{9} \cdot \dfrac{3}{4}$

36. $-\dfrac{8}{3} \cdot \dfrac{9}{4}$ **37.** $7 \cdot (-4) \cdot (-3) \cdot 5$ **38.** $9 \cdot (-2) \cdot (-6) \cdot 7$

39. $-\dfrac{2}{3} \cdot \dfrac{1}{2} \cdot \left(-\dfrac{6}{7}\right)$ **40.** $-\dfrac{1}{8} \cdot \left(-\dfrac{1}{4}\right) \cdot \left(-\dfrac{3}{5}\right)$ **41.** $-3 \cdot (-4) \cdot (-5)$

ANSWERS
1.
2.
3.
4.
5.
6.
7.
8.
9.
10.
11.
12.
13.
14.
15.
16.
17.
18.
19.
20.
21.
22.
23.
24.
25.
26.
27.
28.
29.
30.
31.
32.
33.
34.
35.
36.
37.
38.
39.
40.
41.

42. $-2 \cdot (-5) \cdot (-7)$ **43.** $-2 \cdot (-5) \cdot (-3) \cdot (-5)$ **44.** $-3 \cdot (-5) \cdot (-2) \cdot (-1)$

45. $\dfrac{1}{5}\left(-\dfrac{2}{9}\right)$ **46.** $-\dfrac{3}{5}\left(-\dfrac{2}{7}\right)$ **47.** $-7 \cdot (-21) \cdot 13$

48. $-14 \cdot (34) \cdot 12$ **49.** $-4 \cdot (-1.8) \cdot 7$ **50.** $-8 \cdot (-1.3) \cdot (-5)$

51. $-\dfrac{1}{9}\left(-\dfrac{2}{3}\right)\left(\dfrac{5}{7}\right)$ **52.** $-\dfrac{7}{2}\left(-\dfrac{5}{7}\right)\left(-\dfrac{2}{5}\right)$

53. $4 \cdot (-4) \cdot (-5) \cdot (-12)$ **54.** $-2 \cdot (-3) \cdot (-4) \cdot (-5)$

55. $0.07 \cdot (-7) \cdot 6 \cdot (-6)$ **56.** $80 \cdot (-0.8) \cdot (-90) \cdot (-0.09)$

57. $\left(-\dfrac{5}{6}\right)\left(\dfrac{1}{8}\right)\left(-\dfrac{3}{7}\right)\left(-\dfrac{1}{7}\right)$ **58.** $\left(\dfrac{4}{5}\right)\left(-\dfrac{2}{3}\right)\left(-\dfrac{15}{7}\right)\left(\dfrac{1}{2}\right)$

59. $(-14) \cdot (-27) \cdot 0$ **60.** $7 \cdot (-6) \cdot 5 \cdot (-4) \cdot 3 \cdot (-2) \cdot 1 \cdot 0$

61. $(-8)(-9)(-10)$ **62.** $(-7)(-8)(-9)(-10)$

63. $(-6)(-7)(-8)(-9)(-10)$ **64.** $(-5)(-6)(-7)(-8)(-9)(-10)$

65. Evaluate $(-3x)^2$ and $-3x^2$ when $x = 7$.

66. Evaluate $(-2x)^2$ and $-2x^2$ when $x = 3$.

67. Evaluate $5x^2$ when $x = 2$ and $x = -2$.

68. Evaluate $2x^2$ when $x = 5$ and $x = -5$.

SYNTHESIS

Simplify. Keep in mind the rules for order of operations in Section 1.6.

69. $-6[(-5) + (-7)]$ **70.** $-3[(-8) + (-6)]\left(-\dfrac{1}{7}\right)$

71. $-(3^5) \cdot [-(2^3)]$ **72.** $4(2^4) \cdot [-(3^3)] \cdot 6$

73. $|(-2)^3 + 4^2| - (2 - 7)^2$ **74.** $|-11(-3)^2 - 5^3 - 6^2 - (-4)^2|$

75. What must be true of m and n if $-mn$ is to be (a) positive? (b) zero? (c) negative?

76. Evaluate $-6(3x - 5y) + z$ when $x = -2$, $y = -4$, and $z = 5$.

7.6 Division of Real Numbers

We now consider division of real numbers. The definition of division results in rules for division very much like those for multiplication.

a Division of Integers

> The quotient $\dfrac{a}{b}$ (or $a \div b$) is the number, if there is one, that when multiplied by b gives a.

Let us use the definition to divide integers.

▶ **EXAMPLES** Divide, if possible. Check your answer.

1. $14 \div (-7) = -2$ — We look for a number that when multiplied by -7 gives 14. That number is -2. *Check:* $(-2)(-7) = 14$.

2. $\dfrac{-32}{-4} = 8$ — We look for a number that when multiplied by -4 gives -32. That number is 8. *Check:* $8(-4) = -32$.

3. $\dfrac{-10}{7} = -\dfrac{10}{7}$ — We look for a number that when multiplied by 7 gives -10. That number is $-\frac{10}{7}$. *Check:* $-\frac{10}{7} \cdot 7 = -10$.

4. $\dfrac{-17}{0}$ is **undefined.** — We look for a number that when multiplied by 0 gives -17. There is no such number because the product of 0 and *any* number is 0.   ◀

The rules for division are the same as those for multiplication. We state them together.

> **To multiply or divide two real numbers:**
> 1. **Multiply or divide the absolute values.**
> 2. **If the signs are the same, the answer is positive.**
> 3. **If the signs are different, the answer is negative.**

DO EXERCISES 1–8.

Division by Zero

Example 4 shows why we cannot divide -17 by 0. We can use the same argument to show why we cannot divide any nonzero number b by 0. Consider $b \div 0$. We look for a number that when multiplied by 0 gives b. There is no such number because the product of 0 and any number is 0. Thus we cannot divide a nonzero number b by 0.

On the other hand, if we divide 0 by 0, we look for a number r such that $0 \cdot r = 0$. But, $0 \cdot r = 0$ for any number r. Thus it appears that $0 \div 0$ could be any number we choose. Getting any answer we want when we divide 0 by 0 would be very confusing. Thus we agree that division by zero is undefined.

> **Division by zero is undefined.** That is, $a \div 0$ is undefined for all real numbers a. But, $0 \div a = 0$, when a is nonzero. That is, 0 divided by a nonzero number is 0.

Divide.

1. $6 \div (-3)$

2. $\dfrac{-15}{-3}$

3. $-24 \div 8$

4. $\dfrac{-32}{-4}$

5. $\dfrac{30}{-5}$

6. $\dfrac{30}{-7}$

7. $\dfrac{-5}{0}$

8. $\dfrac{0}{-3}$

Find the reciprocal.

9. $\dfrac{2}{3}$

10. $-\dfrac{5}{4}$

11. -3

12. $-\dfrac{1}{5}$

13. 5.78

14. $\dfrac{1}{2/3}$

b   Reciprocals

When two numbers like $\frac{1}{2}$ and 2 are multiplied, the result is 1. Such numbers are called **reciprocals** of each other. Every nonzero real number has a reciprocal, also called a **multiplicative inverse**.

> Two numbers whose product is 1 are called *reciprocals* of each other.

▶ **EXAMPLES**   Find the reciprocal of each number.

5. $\dfrac{7}{8}$ The reciprocal of $\dfrac{7}{8}$ is $\dfrac{8}{7}$ because $\dfrac{7}{8} \cdot \dfrac{8}{7} = 1.$

6. -5 The reciprocal of -5 is $-\dfrac{1}{5}$ because $-5\left(-\dfrac{1}{5}\right) = 1.$

7. 3.9 The reciprocal of 3.9 is $\dfrac{1}{3.9}$ because $3.9\left(\dfrac{1}{3.9}\right) = 1.$

8. $-\dfrac{1}{2}$ The reciprocal of $-\dfrac{1}{2}$ is -2 because $\left(-\dfrac{1}{2}\right)(-2) = 1.$

9. $-\dfrac{2}{3}$ The reciprocal of $-\dfrac{2}{3}$ is $-\dfrac{3}{2}$ because $\left(-\dfrac{2}{3}\right)\left(-\dfrac{3}{2}\right) = 1.$

10. $\dfrac{1}{3/4}$ The reciprocal of $\dfrac{1}{3/4}$ is $\dfrac{3}{4}$ because $\left(\dfrac{1}{3/4}\right)\left(\dfrac{3}{4}\right) = 1.$ ◀

> For $a \neq 0$, the reciprocal of a can be named $\dfrac{1}{a}$ and the reciprocal of $\dfrac{1}{a}$ is a.
>
> The reciprocal of a nonzero number $\dfrac{a}{b}$ can be named $\dfrac{b}{a}$.
>
> The number 0 has no reciprocal.

DO EXERCISES 9–14.

The reciprocal of a positive number is also a positive number, because their product must be the positive number 1. The reciprocal of a negative number is also a negative number, because their product must be the positive number 1.

> The reciprocal of a number has the same sign as the number itself.

It is important *not* to confuse *opposite* with *reciprocal*. Keep in mind that the opposite, or additive inverse, of a number is what we add to the number to get 0, whereas a reciprocal is what we multiply the number by to get 1. Compare the following.

Number	Opposite (Change the sign.)	Reciprocal (Invert but do not change the sign.)
$-\dfrac{3}{8}$	$\dfrac{3}{8}$	$-\dfrac{8}{3}$
19	-19	$\dfrac{1}{19}$
$\dfrac{18}{7}$	$-\dfrac{18}{7}$	$\dfrac{7}{18}$
-7.9	7.9	$-\dfrac{1}{7.9}$, or $-\dfrac{10}{79}$
0	0	Undefined

$\left(-\dfrac{3}{8}\right)\left(-\dfrac{8}{3}\right) = 1$

$-\dfrac{3}{8} + \dfrac{3}{8} = 0$

DO EXERCISE 15.

C   Division of Real Numbers

We know that we can subtract by adding an opposite. Similarly, we can divide by multiplying by a reciprocal.

> **For any real numbers a and b, $b \neq 0$,**
> $$\frac{a}{b} = a \cdot \frac{1}{b}.$$
> **(To divide, we can multiply by the reciprocal of the divisor.)**

▶ **EXAMPLES**   Rewrite each division as a multiplication.

11. $-4 \div 3$ $-4 \div 3$ is the same as $-4 \cdot \dfrac{1}{3}$

12. $\dfrac{6}{-7}$ $\dfrac{6}{-7} = 6\left(-\dfrac{1}{7}\right)$

13. $\dfrac{x + 2}{5}$ $\dfrac{x + 2}{5} = (x + 2)\dfrac{1}{5}$ **Parentheses are necessary here.**

14. $\dfrac{-17}{1/b}$ $\dfrac{-17}{1/b} = -17 \cdot b$

15. $\dfrac{3}{5} \div \left(-\dfrac{9}{7}\right)$ $\dfrac{3}{5} \div \left(-\dfrac{9}{7}\right) = \dfrac{3}{5}\left(-\dfrac{7}{9}\right)$ ◀

DO EXERCISES 16–20.

When actually doing division calculations, we sometimes multiply by a reciprocal and we sometimes divide directly. With fractional notation, it is usually better to multiply by a reciprocal. With decimal notation, it is usually better to divide directly.

15. Complete the following table.

Number	Opposite	Reciprocal
$\dfrac{2}{3}$		
$-\dfrac{5}{4}$		
0		
1		
-4.5		

Rewrite the division as a multiplication.

16. $\dfrac{4}{7} \div \left(-\dfrac{3}{5}\right)$

17. $\dfrac{5}{-8}$

18. $\dfrac{a - b}{7}$

19. $\dfrac{-23}{1/a}$

20. $-5 \div 7$

ANSWERS ON PAGE A-6

Divide by multiplying by the reciprocal of the divisor.

21. $\dfrac{4}{7} \div \left(-\dfrac{3}{5}\right)$

22. $-\dfrac{8}{5} \div \dfrac{2}{3}$

23. $-\dfrac{12}{7} \div \left(-\dfrac{3}{4}\right)$

24. $21.7 \div (-3.1)$

Find two equal expressions for the number with negative signs in different places.

25. $\dfrac{-5}{6}$

26. $-\dfrac{8}{7}$

27. $\dfrac{10}{-3}$

▶ **EXAMPLES**　Divide by multiplying by the reciprocal of the divisor.

16. $\dfrac{2}{3} \div \left(-\dfrac{5}{4}\right) = \dfrac{2}{3} \cdot \left(-\dfrac{4}{5}\right) = -\dfrac{8}{15}$

17. $-\dfrac{5}{6} \div \left(-\dfrac{3}{4}\right) = -\dfrac{5}{6} \cdot \left(-\dfrac{4}{3}\right) = \dfrac{20}{18} = \dfrac{10 \cdot 2}{9 \cdot 2} = \dfrac{10}{9} \cdot \dfrac{2}{2} = \dfrac{10}{9}$

> Be careful not to change the sign when taking a reciprocal!

18. $-\dfrac{3}{4} \div \dfrac{3}{10} = -\dfrac{3}{4} \cdot \left(\dfrac{10}{3}\right) = -\dfrac{30}{12} = -\dfrac{5}{2} \cdot \dfrac{6}{6} = -\dfrac{5}{2}$　◀

With decimal notation, it is easier to carry out long division than to multiply by the reciprocal.

▶ **EXAMPLES**　Divide.

19. $-27.9 \div (-3) = \dfrac{-27.9}{-3} = 9.3$　　Do the long division $3\overline{)27.9}$. The answer is positive.　$\overset{9.3}{}$

20. $-6.3 \div 2.1 = -3$　　Do the long division $2.1\overline{)6.30}$. The answer is negative.　$\overset{3.0}{}$　◀

DO EXERCISES 21–24.

Consider the following:

$$\frac{2}{3} = \frac{2}{3} \cdot 1 = \frac{2}{3} \cdot \frac{-1}{-1} = \frac{2(-1)}{3(-1)} = \frac{-2}{-3},$$

$$-\frac{2}{3} = -1 \cdot \frac{2}{3} = \frac{-1}{1} \cdot \frac{2}{3} = \frac{-1 \cdot 2}{1 \cdot 3} = \frac{-2}{3},$$

and

$$\frac{-2}{3} = \frac{-2}{3} \cdot 1 = \frac{-2}{3} \cdot \frac{-1}{-1} = \frac{-2(-1)}{3(-1)} = \frac{2}{-3}.$$

We can use the following properties to make sign changes in fractional notation.

> **For any numbers a and b, $b \neq 0$:**
>
> **1.**　　　　$\dfrac{-a}{b} = \dfrac{a}{-b} = -\dfrac{a}{b}$
>
> (The opposite of a number a divided by another number b is the same as the number a divided by the opposite of another number b, and both are the same as the opposite of a *divided by b*.)
>
> **2.**　　　　$\dfrac{-a}{-b} = \dfrac{a}{b}$
>
> (The opposite of a number a divided by the opposite of another number b is the same as the quotient of the two numbers a and b.)

DO EXERCISES 25–27.

NAME   SECTION   DATE

EXERCISE SET 7.6

a Divide, if possible. Check each answer.

1. $36 \div (-6)$

2. $\dfrac{28}{-7}$

3. $\dfrac{26}{-2}$

4. $26 \div (-13)$

5. $\dfrac{-16}{8}$

6. $-22 \div (-2)$

7. $\dfrac{-48}{-12}$

8. $-63 \div (-9)$

9. $\dfrac{-72}{9}$

10. $\dfrac{-50}{25}$

11. $-100 \div (-50)$

12. $\dfrac{-200}{8}$

13. $-108 \div 9$

14. $\dfrac{-64}{-7}$

15. $\dfrac{200}{-25}$

16. $-300 \div (-13)$

17. $\dfrac{75}{0}$

18. $\dfrac{0}{-5}$

19. $\dfrac{88}{-9}$

20. $\dfrac{-145}{-5}$

b Find the reciprocal.

21. $\dfrac{15}{7}$

22. $\dfrac{3}{8}$

23. $-\dfrac{47}{13}$

24. $-\dfrac{31}{12}$

25. 13

26. -10

27. 4.3

28. -8.5

29. $-\dfrac{1}{7.1}$

30. $\dfrac{1}{-4.9}$

31. $\dfrac{p}{q}$

32. $\dfrac{s}{t}$

33. $\dfrac{1}{4y}$

34. $\dfrac{-1}{8a}$

35. $\dfrac{2a}{3b}$

36. $\dfrac{-4y}{3x}$

1. _____
2. _____
3. _____
4. _____
5. _____
6. _____
7. _____
8. _____
9. _____
10. _____
11. _____
12. _____
13. _____
14. _____
15. _____
16. _____
17. _____
18. _____
19. _____
20. _____
21. _____
22. _____
23. _____
24. _____
25. _____
26. _____
27. _____
28. _____
29. _____
30. _____
31. _____
32. _____
33. _____
34. _____
35. _____
36. _____

c Rewrite the division as a multiplication.

37. $3 \div 19$

38. $4 \div (-9)$

39. $\dfrac{6}{-13}$

40. $-\dfrac{12}{41}$

41. $\dfrac{13.9}{-1.5}$

42. $-\dfrac{47.3}{21.4}$

43. $\dfrac{x}{\frac{1}{y}}$

44. $\dfrac{13}{x}$

45. $\dfrac{3x+4}{5}$

46. $\dfrac{4y-8}{-7}$

47. $\dfrac{5a-b}{5a+b}$

48. $\dfrac{2x+x^2}{x-5}$

Divide.

49. $\dfrac{3}{4} \div \left(-\dfrac{2}{3}\right)$

50. $\dfrac{7}{8} \div \left(-\dfrac{1}{2}\right)$

51. $-\dfrac{5}{4} \div \left(-\dfrac{3}{4}\right)$

52. $-\dfrac{5}{9} \div \left(-\dfrac{5}{6}\right)$

53. $-\dfrac{2}{7} \div \left(-\dfrac{4}{9}\right)$

54. $-\dfrac{3}{5} \div \left(-\dfrac{5}{8}\right)$

55. $-\dfrac{3}{8} \div \left(-\dfrac{8}{3}\right)$

56. $-\dfrac{5}{8} \div \left(-\dfrac{6}{5}\right)$

57. $-6.6 \div 3.3$

58. $-44.1 \div (-6.3)$

59. $\dfrac{-11}{-13}$

60. $\dfrac{-1.9}{20}$

61. $\dfrac{48.6}{-3}$

62. $\dfrac{-17.8}{3.2}$

63. $\dfrac{-9}{17-17}$

64. $\dfrac{-8}{-5+5}$

SKILL MAINTENANCE

65. Simplify: $\dfrac{264}{468}$.

66. Convert to decimal notation: 47.7%.

67. Simplify: $2^3 - 5 \cdot 3 + 8 \cdot 10 \div 2$.

68. Add and simplify: $\dfrac{2}{3} + \dfrac{5}{6}$.

SYNTHESIS

69. ▦ Find the reciprocal of -10.5.

70. Determine those real numbers that are their own reciprocals.

71. Determine those real numbers a for which the additive inverse of a is the same as the reciprocal of a.

72. ▦ What should happen if you enter a number on a calculator and press the reciprocal key twice? Why?

Tell whether the expression represents a positive number or a negative number when m and n are negative.

73. $\dfrac{-n}{m}$

74. $\dfrac{-n}{-m}$

75. $-\left(\dfrac{-n}{m}\right)$

76. $-\left(\dfrac{n}{-m}\right)$

77. $-\left(\dfrac{-n}{-m}\right)$

7.7 Properties of Real Numbers

a Equivalent Expressions

In solving equations and doing other kinds of work in algebra, we manipulate expressions in various ways. For example, instead of

$$x + x,$$

we might write

$$2x,$$

knowing that the two expressions represent the same number for any meaningful replacement of x. In that sense, the expressions $x + x$ and $2x$ are **equivalent.**

> Two expressions that have the same value for all meaningful replacements are called *equivalent.*

The expressions $x + 3x$ and $5x$ are *not* equivalent.

DO EXERCISES 1 AND 2.

We will consider several laws of real numbers in this section which will allow us to find equivalent expressions. The first two laws are *identity properties of 0 and 1.*

> The Identity Property of 0
>
> **For any real number a, $a + 0 = 0 + a = a$. (The number 0 is the *additive identity*.)**
>
> The Identity Property of 1
>
> **For any real number a, $a \cdot 1 = 1 \cdot a = a$. (The number 1 is the *multiplicative identity*.)**

We often refer to the use of the identity property of 1 as "multiplying by 1."

▶ **EXAMPLE 1** Use multiplying by 1 to find an expression equivalent to $\frac{2}{3}$ with a denominator of $3x$.

We multiply by 1, using x/x as a name for 1:

$$\frac{2}{3} = \frac{2}{3} \cdot 1 = \frac{2}{3} \cdot \frac{x}{x} = \frac{2x}{3x}.$$ ◀

Note that the expressions $2/3$ and $2x/3x$ are equivalent. They have the same value for any meaningful expression. Note that 0 is not a meaningful replacement in $2x/3x$, but for all nonzero real numbers the expressions $2/3$ and $2x/3x$ have the same value.

DO EXERCISE 3.

OBJECTIVES

After finishing Section 7.7, you should be able to:

a Find equivalent fractional expressions and simplify fractional expressions by multiplying by 1.

b Use the commutative and associative laws to find equivalent expressions.

c Use the distributive laws to multiply expressions like 8 and $x - y$.

d Use the distributive laws to factor expressions like $4x - 12$.

e Collect like terms.

FOR EXTRA HELP

Tape 16A

Complete each of the following tables by evaluating each expression for the given values.

1.

	$x + x$	$2x$
$x = 3$		
$x = -6$		
$x = 4.8$		

2.

	$x + 3x$	$5x$
$x = 2$		
$x = -6$		
$x = 4.8$		

3. Use multiplying by 1 to find an expression equivalent to $\frac{3}{4}$ with a denominator of $4y$.

ANSWERS ON PAGE A-6

Simplify.

4. $\dfrac{3y}{4y}$

5. $-\dfrac{16m}{12m}$

6. Evaluate $x + y$ and $y + x$ when $x = -2$ and $y = 3$.

7. Evaluate xy and yx when $x = -2$ and $y = 5$.

In algebra, we consider an expression like 2/3 to be "simplified" from $2x/3x$. To find such simplified expressions, we use the identity property of 1 to remove a factor of 1.

▶ **EXAMPLE 2** Simplify: $-\dfrac{20x}{12x}$.

$$-\frac{20x}{12x} = -\frac{5 \cdot 4x}{3 \cdot 4x} \qquad \text{We look for the largest common factor of the numerator and the denominator and factor each.}$$

$$= -\frac{5}{3} \cdot \frac{4x}{4x} \qquad \text{Factoring the fractional expression}$$

$$= -\frac{5}{3} \cdot 1 \qquad \frac{4x}{4x} = 1$$

$$= -\frac{5}{3} \qquad \text{Removing a factor of 1 using the identity property of 1} \quad ◀$$

DO EXERCISES 4 AND 5.

b　**The Commutative and Associative Laws**

The Commutative Laws

Let us examine the expressions $x + y$ and $y + x$, as well as xy and yx.

▶ **EXAMPLE 3** Evaluate $x + y$ and $y + x$ for $x = 4$ and $y = 3$.
We substitute 4 for x and 3 for y in both expressions:

$$x + y = 4 + 3 = 7; \qquad y + x = 3 + 4 = 7. \quad ◀$$

▶ **EXAMPLE 4** Evaluate xy and yx for $x = 23$ and $y = 12$.
We substitute 23 for x and 12 for y in both expressions:

$$xy = 23 \cdot 12 = 276; \qquad yx = 12 \cdot 23 = 276. \quad ◀$$

DO EXERCISES 6 AND 7.

Note that the expressions

$$x + y \quad \text{and} \quad y + x$$

have the same values no matter what the variables stand for. Thus they are equivalent. Therefore, when we add two numbers, the order in which we add does not matter. Similarly, the expressions xy and yx are equivalent. They also have the same values, no matter what the variables stand for. Therefore, when we multiply two numbers, the order in which we multiply does not matter.

The following are examples of general patterns or laws.

The Commutative Laws

Addition.   **For any numbers *a* and *b*,**

$$a + b = b + a.$$

(We can change the order when adding without affecting the answer.)

Multiplication.   **For any numbers *a* and *b*,**

$$ab = ba.$$

(We can change the order when multiplying without affecting the answer.)

Using a commutative law, we know that $x + 2$ and $2 + x$ are equivalent. Similarly, $3x$ and $x(3)$ are equivalent. Thus, in an algebraic expression, we can replace one by the other and the result will be equivalent to the original expression.

▶ **EXAMPLE 5**   Use the commutative laws to write an expression equivalent to $y + 5$, xy, and $7 + ab$.

An expression equivalent to $y + 5$ is $5 + y$ by the commutative law of addition.

An expression equivalent to xy is yx by the commutative law of multiplication.

An expression equivalent to $7 + ab$ is $ab + 7$ by the commutative law of addition. Another expression equivalent to $7 + ab$ is $7 + ba$ by the commutative law of multiplication.   ◀

DO EXERCISES 8–10.

The Associative Laws

Now let us examine the expressions $a + (b + c)$ and $(a + b) + c$. Note that these expressions involve parentheses as *grouping* symbols, and they also involve three numbers. Calculations within parentheses are to be done first.

▶ **EXAMPLE 6**   Calculate and compare: $3 + (8 + 5)$ and $(3 + 8) + 5$.

$$3 + (8 + 5) = 3 + 13 \qquad \text{Calculating within parentheses first;}$$
$$\text{adding the 8 and 5}$$
$$= 16;$$
$$(3 + 8) + 5 = 11 + 5 \qquad \text{Calculating within parentheses first;}$$
$$\text{adding the 3 and 8}$$
$$= 16 \qquad ◀$$

Use a commutative law to write an equivalent expression.

8. $x + 9$

9. pq

10. $xy + t$

ANSWERS ON PAGE A-6

11. Calculate and compare:
$8 + (9 + 2)$ and $(8 + 9) + 2$.

12. Calculate and compare:
$10 \cdot (5 \cdot 3)$ and $(10 \cdot 5) \cdot 3$.

Use an associative law to write an equivalent expression.

13. $a + (b + 2)$

14. $3(vw)$

The two expressions in Example 6 name the same number. Moving the parentheses to group the additions differently did not affect the value of the expression.

▶ **EXAMPLE 7**　Calculate and compare: $3 \cdot (4 \cdot 2)$ and $(3 \cdot 4) \cdot 2$.

$$3 \cdot (4 \cdot 2) = 3 \cdot 8 \qquad (3 \cdot 4) \cdot 2 = 12 \cdot 2$$
$$= 24; \qquad\qquad = 24 \qquad ◀$$

DO EXERCISES 11 AND 12.

You may have noted that when only addition is involved, parentheses can be placed any way we please without affecting the answer. When only multiplication is involved, parentheses also can be placed any way we please without affecting the answer.

> The Associative Laws
>
> *Addition.*　For any numbers a, b, and c,
> $$a + (b + c) = (a + b) + c.$$
> (Numbers can be grouped in any manner for addition.)
> *Multiplication.*　For any numbers a, b, and c,
> $$a \cdot (b \cdot c) = (a \cdot b) \cdot c.$$
> (Numbers can be grouped in any manner for multiplication.)

The associative laws say parentheses may be placed any way we please when only additions or only multiplications are involved. So we often omit them. For example,

$$x + (y + 2) \quad \text{means} \quad x + y + 2, \quad \text{and} \quad (lw)h \text{ means } lwh.$$

▶ **EXAMPLE 8**　Use an associative law to write an expression equivalent to $(y + z) + 3$.

An equivalent expression is

$$y + (z + 3)$$

by the associative law of addition.　◀

▶ **EXAMPLE 9**　Use an associative law to write an expression equivalent to $8(xy)$.

An equivalent expression is

$$(8x)y$$

by the associative law of multiplication.　◀

DO EXERCISES 13 AND 14.

Using the Commutative and Associative Laws Together

► **EXAMPLE 10**   Use the commutative and associative laws to write at least three expressions equivalent to $(x + 5) + y$.

a) $(x + 5) + y = x + (5 + y)$ Using the associative law first and then using the commutative law

   $ = x + (y + 5)$

b) $(x + 5) + y = y + (x + 5)$ Using the commutative law first and then the commutative law again

   $ = y + (5 + x)$

c) $(x + 5) + y = 5 + (x + y)$ Using the commutative law first and then the associative law ◄

► **EXAMPLE 11**   Use the commutative and associative laws to write at least three expressions equivalent to $(3x)y$.

a) $(3x)y = 3(xy)$ Using the associative law first and then using the commutative law

   $ = 3(yx)$

b) $(3x)y = y(x3)$ Using the commutative law twice

c) $(3x)y = x(y3)$ Using the commutative law, and then the associative law, and then the commutative law again ◄

DO EXERCISES 15 AND 16.

C   The Distributive Laws

The *distributive laws* are the basis of many procedures in both arithmetic and algebra. These are probably the most important laws that we use to manipulate algebraic expressions. The distributive law of multiplication over addition involves two operations: addition and multiplication.

Let us begin by considering a multiplication problem from arithmetic:

$$
\begin{array}{r}
4\ 5 \\
\times\quad 7 \\
\hline
3\ 5 \\
2\ 8\ 0 \\
\hline
3\ 1\ 5
\end{array}
$$

$3\ 5 \leftarrow$ This is $7 \cdot 5$.
$2\ 8\ 0 \leftarrow$ This is $7 \cdot 40$.
$3\ 1\ 5 \leftarrow$ This is the sum $7 \cdot 40 + 7 \cdot 5$.

To carry out the multiplication, we actually added two products. That is,

$$7 \cdot 45 = 7(40 + 5) = 7 \cdot 40 + 7 \cdot 5.$$

Let us examine this further. If we wish to multiply a sum of several numbers by a factor, we can either add and then multiply, or multiply and then add.

Use the commutative and associative laws to write at least three equivalent expressions.

15. $4(tu)$

16. $r + (2 + s)$

ANSWERS ON PAGE A-6

17. **a)** $7 \cdot (3 + 6)$

 b) $(7 \cdot 3) + (7 \cdot 6)$

18. **a)** $2 \cdot (10 + 30)$

 b) $(2 \cdot 10) + (2 \cdot 30)$

19. **a)** $(2 + 5) \cdot 4$

 b) $(2 \cdot 4) + (5 \cdot 4)$

Calculate.

20. **a)** $4(5 - 3)$

 b) $4 \cdot 5 - 4 \cdot 3$

21. **a)** $-2 \cdot (5 - 3)$

 b) $-2 \cdot 5 - (-2) \cdot 3$

22. **a)** $5 \cdot (2 - 7)$

 b) $5 \cdot 2 - 5 \cdot 7$

What are the terms of the expression?

23. $5x - 4y + 3$

24. $-4y - 2x + 3z$

▶ **EXAMPLE 12**   Compute in two ways: $5 \cdot (4 + 8)$.

a) $5 \cdot (4 + 8)$ Adding within parentheses first, and then multiplying

$= 5 \cdot \quad 12$
$= 60$

b) $(5 \cdot 4) + (5 \cdot 8)$ Distributing the multiplication to terms within parentheses first and then adding

$= \quad 20 \quad + \quad 40$
$= \quad 60$ ◀

DO EXERCISES 17–19.

> ### The Distributive Law of Multiplication Over Addition
>
> **For any numbers *a*, *b*, and *c*,**
> $$a(b + c) = ab + ac.$$

In the statement of the distributive law, we know that in an expression such as $ab + ac$, the multiplications are to be done first according to our rules for order of operations. So, instead of writing $(4 \cdot 5) + (4 \cdot 7)$, we can write $4 \cdot 5 + 4 \cdot 7$. However, in $a(b + c)$, we cannot omit the parentheses. If we did, we would have $ab + c$, which means $(ab) + c$. For example, $3(4 + 2) = 18$, but $3 \cdot 4 + 2 = 14$.

There is another distributive law that relates multiplication and subtraction. This law says that to multiply by a difference, we can either subtract and then multiply or multiply and then subtract.

> ### The Distributive Law of Multiplication Over Subtraction
>
> **For any numbers *a*, *b*, and *c*,**
> $$a(b - c) = ab - ac.$$

We often refer to "*the* distributive law" when we mean *either* of these laws.

DO EXERCISES 20–22.

What do we mean by the *terms* of an expression? **Terms** are separated by addition signs. If there are subtraction signs, we can find an equivalent expression that uses addition signs.

▶ **EXAMPLE 13**   What are the terms of $3x - 4y + 2z$?
We have

$$3x - 4y + 2z = 3x + (-4y) + 2z. \quad \text{Separating parts with + signs}$$

The terms are $3x$, $-4y$, and $2z$.   ◀

DO EXERCISES 23 AND 24.

The distributive laws are a basis for a procedure in algebra called **multiplying**. In an expression like $8(a + 2b - 7)$, we multiply each term inside the parentheses by 8:

$$8(a + 2b - 7) = 8 \cdot a + 8 \cdot 2b - 8 \cdot 7 = 8a + 16b - 56.$$

▶ **EXAMPLES**   Multiply.

14. $9(x - 5) = 9x - 9(5)$ Using the distributive law of multiplication over subtraction
$$= 9x - 45$$

15. $\frac{4}{3}(s - t + w) = \frac{4}{3}s - \frac{4}{3}t + \frac{4}{3}w$ Using both distributive laws

16. $-4(x - 2y + 3z) = -4 \cdot x - (-4)(2y) + (-4)(3z)$
$$= -4x - (-8y) + (-12z)$$
$$= -4x + 8y - 12z$$

We can also do this problem by first finding an equivalent expression with all plus signs and then multiplying:

$$-4(x - 2y + 3z) = -4[x + (-2y) + 3z]$$
$$= -4 \cdot x + (-4)(-2y) + (-4)(3z)$$
$$= -4x + 8y - 12z. \quad ◀$$

DO EXERCISES 25–28.

d   Factoring

Factoring is the reverse of multiplying. To factor, we can use the distributive laws in reverse: $ab + ac = a(b + c)$ and $ab - ac = a(b - c)$.

> To *factor* an expression is to find an equivalent expression that is a product.

Look at Example 14. To *factor* $9x - 45$, we find an equivalent expression that is a product, $9(x - 5)$. When all the terms of an expression have a factor in common, we can "factor it out" using the distributive laws. Note the following.

   $9x$ has the factors $9, -9, 3, -3, 1, -1, x, -x, 3x, -3x, 9x, -9x$;
   -45 has the factors $1, -1, 3, -3, 5, -5, 9, -9, 15, -15, 45, -45$

We usually remove the largest common factor. In this case, that factor is 9.
   Remember that an expression is factored when we find an equivalent expression that is a product.

▶ **EXAMPLES**   Factor.

17. $5x - 10 = 5 \cdot x - 5 \cdot 2$ Try to do this step mentally.
$$= 5(x - 2)$$ You can check by multiplying.

18. $ax - ay + az = a(x - y + z)$

Multiply.

25. $3(x - 5)$

26. $5(x - y + 4)$

27. $-2(x - 3)$

28. $-5(x - 2y + 4z)$

Factor.

29. $6x - 12$

30. $3x - 6y + 9$

31. $bx + by - bz$

32. $16a - 36b + 42$

33. $\frac{3}{8}x - \frac{5}{8}y + \frac{7}{8}$

34. $-12x + 32y - 16z$

Collect like terms.

35. $6x - 3x$

36. $7x - x$

37. $x - 9x$

38. $x - 0.41x$

39. $5x + 4y - 2x - y$

40. $3x - 7x - 11 + 8y + 4 - 13y$

19. $9x + 27y - 9 = 9 \cdot x + 9 \cdot 3y - 9 \cdot 1$
$$= 9(x + 3y - 1) \qquad \blacktriangleleft$$

> **CAUTION!** Note that $3(3x + 9y - 3)$ is also equivalent to $9x + 27y - 9$, but it is *not* the desired form. However, we can complete the process by factoring out another factor of 3: $9x + 27y - 9 = 3(3x + 9y - 3) = 3 \cdot 3(x + 3y - 1) = 9(x + 3y - 1)$. Remember to factor out the largest common factor.

▶ **EXAMPLES**   Factor. Try to write just the answer if you can.

20. $5x - 5y = 5(x - y)$

21. $-3x + 6y - 9z = -3(x - 2y + 3z)$

We might also factor the expression in Example 21 as follows:
$$-3x + 6y - 9z = 3(-x + 2y - 3z).$$

We usually factor out a negative when the first term is negative. The way we factor can depend on the situation in which we are working.

22. $18z - 12x - 24 = 6(3z - 2x - 4)$

23. $\frac{1}{2}x + \frac{3}{2}y - \frac{1}{2} = \frac{1}{2}(x + 3y - 1)$

> *Remember:* An expression is factored when it is written as a product.

$\blacktriangleleft$

DO EXERCISES 29–34.

e Collecting Like Terms

Terms such as $5x$ and $-4x$, whose variable factors are exactly the same, are called **like terms.** Similarly, $3y^2$ and $9y^2$ are like terms because the variables are raised to the same power. Terms such as $4y$ and $5y^2$ are not like terms, and $7x$ and $2y$ are not like terms.

The process of **collecting like terms** is also based on the distributive laws. We can apply the distributive law "on the right" because of the commutative law of multiplication.

▶ **EXAMPLES**   Collect like terms. Try to write just the answer if you can.

24. $4x + 2x = (4 + 2)x = 6x$ Factoring out the x using a distributive law

25. $2x + 3y - 5x - 2y = 2x - 5x + 3\,y - 2\,y$
$$= (2 - 5)x + (3 - 2)\,y = -3x + y$$

26. $3x - x = (3 - 1)x = 2x$

27. $x - 0.24x = 1 \cdot x - 0.24x = (1 - 0.24)x = 0.76x$

28. $x - 6x = 1 \cdot x - 6 \cdot x = (1 - 6)x = -5x$

29. $4x - 7y + 9x - 5 + 3y - 8 = 13x - 4y - 13$ $\blacktriangleleft$

DO EXERCISES 35–40.

NAME   SECTION   DATE

EXERCISE SET 7.7

a Find an equivalent expression with the given denominator.

1. $\dfrac{2}{5}$; $5x$ **2.** $\dfrac{5}{6}$; $6t$ **3.** $\dfrac{2}{3}$; $15y$ **4.** $\dfrac{7}{8}$; $16x$

Simplify.

5. $-\dfrac{24a}{16a}$ **6.** $-\dfrac{42t}{18t}$ **7.** $-\dfrac{42ab}{36ab}$ **8.** $-\dfrac{64pq}{48pq}$

b Write an equivalent expression. Use a commutative law.

9. $y + 8$ **10.** $x + 3$ **11.** mn **12.** ab

13. $9 + xy$ **14.** $11 + ab$ **15.** $ab + c$ **16.** $rs + t$

Write an equivalent expression. Use an associative law.

17. $a + (b + 2)$ **18.** $3(vw)$ **19.** $(8x)y$ **20.** $(y + z) + 7$

21. $(a + b) + 3$ **22.** $(5 + x) + y$ **23.** $3(ab)$ **24.** $(6x)y$

Use the commutative and associative laws to write three equivalent expressions.

25. $(a + b) + 2$ **26.** $(3 + x) + y$ **27.** $5 + (v + w)$ **28.** $6 + (x + y)$

29. $(xy)3$ **30.** $(ab)5$ **31.** $7(ab)$ **32.** $5(xy)$

1. _____
2. _____
3. _____
4. _____
5. _____
6. _____
7. _____
8. _____
9. _____
10. _____
11. _____
12. _____
13. _____
14. _____
15. _____
16. _____
17. _____
18. _____
19. _____
20. _____
21. _____
22. _____
23. _____
24. _____
25. _____
26. _____
27. _____
28. _____
29. _____
30. _____
31. _____
32. _____

c   Multiply.

33. $2(b + 5)$ **34.** $4(x + 3)$ **35.** $7(1 + t)$ **36.** $4(1 + y)$

37. $6(5x + 2)$ **38.** $9(6m + 7)$ **39.** $7(x + 4 + 6y)$ **40.** $4(5x + 8 + 3p)$

41. $7(4 - 3)$ **42.** $15(8 - 6)$ **43.** $-3(3 - 7)$ **44.** $1.2(5 - 2.1)$

45. $4.1(6.3 - 9.4)$ **46.** $-\dfrac{8}{9}\left(\dfrac{2}{3} - \dfrac{5}{3}\right)$ **47.** $7(x - 2)$ **48.** $5(x - 8)$

49. $-7(y - 2)$ **50.** $-9(y - 7)$

51. $-9(-5x - 6y + 8)$ **52.** $-7(-2x - 5y + 9)$

53. $-4(x - 3y - 2z)$ **54.** $8(2x - 5y - 8z)$

55. $3.1(-1.2x + 3.2y - 1.1)$ **56.** $-2.1(-4.2x - 4.3y - 2.2)$

Give the terms of the expression.

57. $4x + 3z$ **58.** $8x - 1.4y$

59. $7x + 8y - 9z$ **60.** $8a + 10b - 18c$

d   Factor. Check by multiplying.

61. $2x + 4$ **62.** $5y + 20$ **63.** $30 + 5y$ **64.** $7x + 28$

65. $14x + 21y$

66. $18a + 24b$

67. $5x + 10 + 15y$

68. $9a + 27b + 81$

69. $8x - 24$

70. $10x - 50$

71. $32 - 4y$

72. $24 - 6m$

73. $8x + 10y - 22$

74. $9a + 6b - 15$

75. $ax - a$

76. $by - 9b$

77. $ax - ay - az$

78. $cx + cy - cz$

79. $18x - 12y + 6$

80. $-14x + 21y + 7$

e Collect like terms.

81. $9a + 10a$

82. $12x + 2x$

83. $10a - a$

84. $-16x + x$

85. $2x + 9z + 6x$

86. $3a - 5b + 7a$

87. $7x + 6y^2 + 9y^2$

88. $12m^2 + 6q + 9m^2$

89. $41a + 90 - 60a - 2$

90. $42x - 6 - 4x + 2$

91. $23 + 5t + 7y - t - y - 27$

92. $45 - 90d - 87 - 9d + 3 + 7d$

ANSWERS

65. _____

66. _____

67. _____

68. _____

69. _____

70. _____

71. _____

72. _____

73. _____

74. _____

75. _____

76. _____

77. _____

78. _____

79. _____

80. _____

81. _____

82. _____

83. _____

84. _____

85. _____

86. _____

87. _____

88. _____

89. _____

90. _____

91. _____

92. _____

93. $\dfrac{1}{2}b + \dfrac{1}{2}b$

94. $\dfrac{2}{3}x + \dfrac{1}{3}x$

95. $2y + \dfrac{1}{4}y + y$

96. $\dfrac{1}{2}a + a + 5a$

97. $11x - 3x$

98. $9t - 17t$

99. $6n - n$

100. $10t - t$

101. $y - 17y$

102. $3m - 9m + 4$

103. $-8 + 11a - 5b + 6a - 7b + 7$

104. $8x - 5x + 6 + 3y - 2y - 4$

105. $9x + 2y - 5x$

106. $8y - 3z + 4y$

107. $11x + 2y - 4x - y$

108. $13a + 9b - 2a - 4b$

109. $2.7x + 2.3y - 1.9x - 1.8y$

110. $6.7a + 4.3b - 4.1a - 2.9b$

111. $\dfrac{1}{5}x + \dfrac{4}{5}y + \dfrac{2}{5}x - \dfrac{1}{5}y$

112. $\dfrac{7}{8}x + \dfrac{5}{8}y + \dfrac{1}{8}x - \dfrac{3}{8}y$

SKILL MAINTENANCE

113. Add and simplify: $\dfrac{11}{12} + \dfrac{15}{16}$.

114. Subtract and simplify: $\dfrac{7}{8} - \dfrac{2}{3}$.

115. Find the LCM for 16, 18, and 24.

116. Convert to percent notation: $\dfrac{3}{10}$.

SYNTHESIS

Tell whether the following expressions are equivalent. Also, tell why.

117. $3t + 5$ and $3 \cdot 5 + t$

118. $4x$ and $x + 4$

119. $5m + 6$ and $6 + 5m$

120. $(x + y) + z$ and $z + (x + y)$

Collect like terms if possible and factor the result.

121. $q + qr + qrs + qrst$

122. $21x + 44xy + 15y - 16x - 8y - 38xy + 2y + xy$

7.8 Simplifying Expressions; Order of Operations

We now expand our ability to manipulate expressions by first considering opposites of sums and differences. Then we simplify expressions involving parentheses.

a Inverses of Sums

What happens when we multiply a real number by -1? Consider the following products:

$$-1(7) = -7, \qquad -1(-5) - 5, \qquad -1(0) = 0.$$

From these examples, it appears that when we multiply a number by -1, we get the additive inverse, or opposite, of that number.

> **The Property of -1**
>
> **For any real number a,**
> $$-1 \cdot a = -a.$$
> (Negative one times a is the opposite of a.)
> **(Negative one times a is the opposite of a.)**
> **(Negative one times a is the additive inverse of a.)**

The property of -1 enables us to find certain expressions equivalent to opposites of sums.

▶ **EXAMPLES** Find an equivalent expression without parentheses.

1. $-(3 + x) = -1(3 + x)$ Using the property of -1
$$= -1 \cdot 3 + (-1)x \qquad \text{Using a distributive law, multiplying each term by } -1$$
$$= -3 + (-x) \qquad \text{Using the property of } -1$$
$$= -3 - x$$

2. $-(3x + 2y + 4) = -1(3x + 2y + 4)$ Using the property of -1
$$= -1(3x) + (-1)(2y) + (-1)4 \qquad \text{Using a distributive law}$$
$$= -3x - 2y - 4 \qquad \text{Using the property of } -1 \qquad ◀$$

DO EXERCISES 1 AND 2.

Suppose we want to remove parentheses in an expression like

$$-(x - 2y + 5).$$

We can first find an equivalent expression in which the inside expression is separated by plus signs. Then taking the opposite of each term we get

$$-(x - 2y + 5) = -[x + (-2y) + 5]$$
$$= -x + 2y - 5.$$

The most efficient method for this is to replace each term in the parentheses by its opposite ("change the sign of every term"). Doing so for $-(x - 2y + 5)$, we obtain $-x + 2y - 5$ as an equivalent expression.

OBJECTIVES

After finishing Section 7.8, you should be able to:

a Find an equivalent expression for an opposite without parentheses, where an expression has several terms.

b Simplify expressions by removing parentheses and collecting like terms.

c Simplify expressions with parentheses inside parentheses.

d Simplify expressions using rules for order of operations.

FOR EXTRA HELP

Tape 16B

Find an equivalent expression without parentheses.

1. $-(x + 2)$

2. $-(5x + 2y + 8)$

Find an equivalent expression without parentheses. Try to do this in one step.

3. $-(6 - t)$

4. $-(x - y)$

5. $-(-4a + 3t - 10)$

6. $-(18 - m - 2n + 4z)$

Remove parentheses and simplify.

7. $5x - (3x + 9)$

8. $5y - 2 - (2y - 4)$

Remove parentheses and simplify.

9. $6x - (4x + 7)$

10. $8y - 3 - (5y - 6)$

11. $(2a + 3b - c) - (4a - 5b + 2c)$

▶ **EXAMPLES**   Find an equivalent expression without parentheses.

3. $-(5 - y) = -5 + y$ Changing the sign of each term

4. $-(2a - 7b - 6) = -2a + 7b + 6$

5. $-(-3x + 4y + z - 7w - 23) = 3x - 4y - z + 7w + 23$ ◀

DO EXERCISES 3–6.

b   Removing Parentheses and Simplifying

When a sum is added, as in $5x + (2x + 3)$, we can simply remove, or drop, the parentheses and collect like terms because of the associative law of addition:

$$5x + (2x + 3) = 5x + 2x + 3 = 7x + 3.$$

On the other hand, when a sum is subtracted, as in $3x - (4x + 2)$, no "associative" law applies. However, we can subtract by adding an opposite. We then remove parentheses by changing the sign of each term inside the parentheses and collecting like terms.

▶ **EXAMPLE 6**   Remove parentheses and simplify.

$$3x - (4x + 2) = 3x + [-(4x + 2)]$$ Adding the opposite of $(4x + 2)$

$$= 3x + (-4x - 2)$$ Changing the sign of each term inside the parentheses

$$= 3x - 4x - 2$$

$$= -x - 2$$ Collecting like terms   ◀

DO EXERCISES 7 AND 8.

In practice, the first three steps of Example 6 are usually combined by changing the sign of each term in parentheses and then collecting like terms.

▶ **EXAMPLES**   Remove parentheses and simplify.

7. $5y - (3y + 4) = 5y - 3y - 4$ Removing parentheses by changing the sign of every term inside the parentheses

$$= 2y - 4$$ Collecting like terms

8. $3y - 2 - (2y - 4) = 3y - 2 - 2y + 4$

$$= y + 2$$

9. $(3a + 4b - 5) - (2a - 7b + 4c - 8) = 3a + 4b - 5 - 2a + 7b - 4c + 8$

$$= a + 11b - 4c + 3$$ ◀

DO EXERCISES 9–11.

Next, consider subtracting an expression consisting of several terms preceded by a number other than 1 or -1.

▶ **EXAMPLE 10** Remove parentheses and simplify.

$$
\begin{aligned}
x - 3(x + y) &= x + [-3(x + y)] && \text{Adding the opposite of } 3(x + y) \\
&= x + [-3x - 3y] && \text{Multiplying } x + y \text{ by } -3 \\
&= x - 3x - 3y \\
&= -2x - 3y && \text{Collecting like terms} && ◀
\end{aligned}
$$

In practice, the first three steps of Example 10 are usually combined by multiplying each term in parentheses by -3 and then collecting like terms.

▶ **EXAMPLES** Remove parentheses and simplify.

11. $3y - 2(4y - 5) = 3y - 8y + 10$ Multiplying each term in parentheses by -2
$$\qquad\qquad\qquad = -5y + 10$$

12. $(2a + 3b - 7) - 4(-5a - 6b + 12) = 2a + 3b - 7 + 20a + 24b - 48$
$$\qquad\qquad\qquad\qquad\qquad\qquad = 22a + 27b - 55 \qquad ◀$$

DO EXERCISES 12–14.

C Parentheses Within Parentheses

Some expressions contain more than one kind of grouping symbol such as brackets [ ] and braces { }.

> When more than one kind of grouping symbol occurs, do the computations in the innermost ones first. Then work from the inside out.

▶ **EXAMPLES** Simplify.

13. $[3 - (7 + 3)] = [3 - 10]$ Computing $7 + 3$
$$\qquad\qquad\qquad = -7$$

14. $\{8 - [9 - (12 + 5)]\} = \{8 - [9 - 17]\}$ Computing $12 + 5$
$$\qquad\qquad\qquad\qquad = \{8 - [-8]\} \quad \text{Computing } 9 - 17$$
$$\qquad\qquad\qquad\qquad = 8 + 8$$
$$\qquad\qquad\qquad\qquad = 16$$

15. $[(-4) \div (-\tfrac{1}{4})] \div \tfrac{1}{4} = [(-4) \cdot (-4)] \div \tfrac{1}{4}$ Working with the innermost parentheses first: computing $(-4) \div (-\tfrac{1}{4})$
$$\qquad\qquad\qquad\qquad = 16 \div \tfrac{1}{4}$$
$$\qquad\qquad\qquad\qquad = 16 \cdot 4$$
$$\qquad\qquad\qquad\qquad = 64$$

16. $4(2 + 3) - \{7 - [4 - (8 + 5)]\}$
$$= 4 \cdot 5 - \{7 - [4 - 13]\} \quad \text{Working with the innermost parentheses first}$$
$$= 20 - \{7 - [-9]\} \quad \text{Computing } 4 \cdot 5 \text{ and } 4 - 13$$
$$= 20 - 16 \quad \text{Computing } 7 - [-9]$$
$$= 4 \qquad ◀$$

DO EXERCISES 15–18.

Remove parentheses and simplify.

12. $y - 9(x + y)$

13. $5a - 3(7a - 6)$

14. $4a - b - 6(5a - 7b + 8c)$

Simplify.

15. $12 - (8 + 2)$

16. $\{9 - [10 - (13 + 6)]\}$

17. $[24 \div (-2)] \div (-2)$

18. $5(3 + 4) - \{8 - [5 - (9 + 6)]\}$

ANSWERS ON PAGE A-6

19. Simplify:

$[3(x + 2) + 2x] - [4(y + 2) - 3(y - 2)]$

▶ **EXAMPLE 17**   Simplify.

$[5(x + 2) - 3x] - [3(y + 2) - 7(y - 3)]$

$= [5x + 10 - 3x] - [3y + 6 - 7y + 21]$ Working with the innermost parentheses first

$= [2x + 10] - [-4y + 27]$ Collecting like terms within brackets

$= 2x + 10 + 4y - 27$ Removing brackets

$= 2x + 4y - 17$ Collecting like terms   ◀

DO EXERCISE 19.

d   Order of Operations

When several operations are to be done in a calculation or a problem, we apply the same rules that we did in Section 1.6. We repeat them here for review. (If you did not study that section earlier, you should do so now.)

> **Rules for Order of Operations**
>
> 1. **Do all calculations within parentheses before operations outside.**
> 2. **Evaluate all exponential expressions.**
> 3. **Do all multiplications and divisions in order from left to right.**
> 4. **Do all additions and subtractions in order from left to right.**

These rules are consistent with the way in which most computers perform calculations.

Simplify.

20. $23 - 42 \cdot 30$

▶ **EXAMPLE 18**   Simplify: $-34 \cdot 56 - 17$.

There are no parentheses or powers so we start with the third step.

$-34 \cdot 56 - 17 = -1904 - 17$ Carrying out all multiplications and divisions in order from left to right

$= -1921$ Carrying out all additions and subtractions in order from left to right   ◀

▶ **EXAMPLE 19**   Simplify: $2^4 + 51 \cdot 4 - (37 + 23 \cdot 2)$.

$2^4 + 51 \cdot 4 - (37 + 23 \cdot 2)$

$= 2^4 + 51 \cdot 4 - (37 + 46)$ Carrying out all operations inside parentheses first, multiplying 23 by 2, and following the rules for order of operations within the parentheses

21. $52 \cdot 5 + 5^3 - (4^2 - 48 \div 4)$

$= 2^4 + 51 \cdot 4 - 83$ Completing the addition inside parentheses

$= 16 + 51 \cdot 4 - 83$ Evaluating exponential expressions

$= 16 + 204 - 83$ Doing all multiplications

$= 220 - 83$ Doing all additions and subtractions in order from left to right

$= 137$ ◀

DO EXERCISES 20 AND 21.

EXERCISE SET 7.8

a Find an equivalent expression without parentheses.

1. $-(2x + 7)$

2. $-(3x + 5)$

3. $-(5x - 8)$

4. $-(6x - 7)$

5. $-(4a - 3b + 7c)$

6. $-(5x - 2y - 3z)$

7. $-(6x - 8y + 5)$

8. $-(8x + 3y + 9)$

9. $-(3x - 5y - 6)$

10. $-(6a - 4b - 7)$

11. $-(-8x - 6y - 43)$

12. $-(-2a + 9b - 5c)$

b Remove parentheses and simplify.

13. $9x - (4x + 3)$

14. $7y - (2y + 9)$

15. $2a - (5a - 9)$

16. $11n - (3n - 7)$

17. $2x + 7x - (4x + 6)$

18. $3a + 2a - (4a + 7)$

19. $2x - 4y - 3(7x - 2y)$

20. $3a - 7b - 1(4a - 3b)$

21. $15x - y - 5(3x - 2y + 5z)$

22. $4a - b - 4(5a - 7b + 8c)$

ANSWERS
1.
2.
3.
4.
5.
6.
7.
8.
9.
10.
11.
12.
13.
14.
15.
16.
17.
18.
19.
20.
21.
22.

23. _____

24. _____

25. _____

26. _____

27. _____

28. _____

29. _____

30. _____

31. _____

32. _____

33. _____

34. _____

35. _____

36. _____

37. _____

38. _____

39. _____

40. _____

41. _____

42. _____

43. _____

44. _____

23. $(3x + 2y) - 2(5x - 4y)$

24. $(-6a - b) - 3(4b + a)$

25. $(12a - 3b + 5c) - 5(-5a + 4b - 6c)$

26. $(-8x + 5y - 12) - 6(2x - 4y - 10)$

c Simplify.

27. $[9 - 2(5 - 4)]$

28. $[6 - 5(8 - 4)]$

29. $8[7 - 6(4 - 2)]$

30. $10[7 - 4(7 - 5)]$

31. $[4(9 - 6) + 11] - [14 - (6 + 4)]$

32. $[7(8 - 4) + 16] - [15 - (7 + 3)]$

33. $[10(x + 3) - 4] + [2(x - 1) + 6]$

34. $[9(x + 5) - 7] + [4(x - 12) + 9]$

35. $[7(x + 5) - 19] - [4(x - 6) + 10]$

36. $[6(x + 4) - 12] - [5(x - 8) + 11]$

37. $3\{[7(x - 2) + 4] - [2(2x - 5) + 6]\}$

38. $4\{[8(x - 3) + 9] - [4(3x - 7) + 2]\}$

39. $4\{[5(x - 3) + 2] - 3[2(x + 5) - 9]\}$

40. $3\{[6(x - 4) + 5] - 2[5(x + 8) - 10]\}$

d Simplify.

41. $8 - 2 \cdot 3 - 9$

42. $8 - (2 \cdot 3 - 9)$

43. $(8 - 2 \cdot 3) - 9$

44. $(8 - 2)(3 - 9)$

45. $[(-24) \div (-3)] \div (-\frac{1}{2})$

46. $[32 \div (-2)] \div (-2)$

47. $16 \cdot (-24) + 50$

48. $10 \cdot 20 - 15 \cdot 24$

49. $2^4 + 2^3 - 10$

50. $40 - 3^2 - 2^3$

51. $5^3 + 26 \cdot 71 - (16 + 25 \cdot 3)$

52. $4^3 + 10 \cdot 20 + 8^2 - 23$

53. $4 \cdot 5 - 2 \cdot 6 + 4$

54. $4 \cdot (6 + 8)/(4 + 3)$

55. $4^3/8$

56. $5^3 - 7^2$

57. $8(-7) + 6(-5)$

58. $10(-5) + 1(-1)$

59. $19 - 5(-3) + 3$

60. $14 - 2(-6) + 7$

61. $9 \div (-3) + 16 \div 8$

62. $-32 - 8 \div 4 - (-2)$

63. $6 - 4^2$

64. $(2 - 5)^2$

65. $(3 - 8)^2$

66. $3 - 3^2$

ANSWERS

45. _____

46. _____

47. _____

48. _____

49. _____

50. _____

51. _____

52. _____

53. _____

54. _____

55. _____

56. _____

57. _____

58. _____

59. _____

60. _____

61. _____

62. _____

63. _____

64. _____

65. _____

66. _____

ANSWERS

67. _____

68. _____

69. _____

70. _____

71. _____

72. _____

73. _____

74. _____

75. _____

76. _____

77. _____

78. _____

79. _____

80. _____

81. _____

82. _____

83. _____

84. _____

85. _____

86. _____

87. _____

88. _____

89. _____

90. _____

67. $12 - 20^3$

68. $20 + 4^3 \div (-8)$

69. $2 \times 10^3 - 5000$

70. $-7(3^4) + 18$

71. $6[9 - (3 - 4)]$

72. $8[(6 - 13) - 11]$

73. $-1000 \div (-100) \div 10$

74. $256 \div (-32) \div (-4)$

75. $8 - (7 - 9)$

76. $(8 - 7) - 9$

77. $\dfrac{10 - 6^2}{9^2 + 3^2}$

78. $\dfrac{5^2 - 4^3 - 3}{9^2 - 2^2 - 1^5}$

79. $\dfrac{3(6 - 7) - 5 \cdot 4}{6 \cdot 7 - 8(4 - 1)}$

80. $\dfrac{20(8 - 3) - 4(10 - 3)}{10(2 - 6) - 2(5 + 2)}$

81. $\dfrac{2^3 - 3^2 + 12 \cdot 5}{-32 \div (-16) \div (-4)}$

82. $\dfrac{|3 - 5|^2 - |7 - 13|}{|12 - 9| + |11 - 14|}$

SYNTHESIS

Find an equivalent expression by enclosing the last three terms in parentheses preceded by a minus sign.

83. $6y + 2x - 3a + c$ **84.** $x - y - a - b$ **85.** $6m + 3n - 5m + 4b$

Simplify.

86. $z - \{2z - [3z - (4z - 5z) - 6z] - 7z\} - 8z$

87. $\{x - [f - (f - x)] + [x - f]\} - 3x$

88. $x - \{x - 1 - [x - 2 - (x - 3 - \{x - 4 - [x - 5 - (x - 6)]\})]\}$

89. Determine whether it is true that, for any real numbers a and b, $ab = (-a)(-b)$. Explain why or why not.

90. Determine whether it is true that, for any real numbers a and b, $-(ab) = (-a)b = a(-b)$. Explain why or why not.

SUMMARY AND REVIEW: CHAPTER 7

IMPORTANT PROPERTIES AND FORMULAS

Properties of the Real-Number System

Commutative Laws: $a + b = b + a,$ $ab = ba$

Associative Laws: $a + (b + c) = (a + b) + c,$ $a(bc) = (ab)c$

Identity Properties: For every real number a, $a + 0 = a$ and $a \cdot 1 = a$.

Opposite Properties: For each real number a, there is an opposite $-a$, such that $a + (-a) = 0$.

For each nonzero real number a, there is a reciprocal $\dfrac{1}{a}$, such that $a\left(\dfrac{1}{a}\right) = 1$.

Distributive Laws: $a(b + c) = ab + ac,$ $a(b - c) = ab - ac$

REVIEW EXERCISES

The review sections and objectives to be tested in addition to the material in this chapter are [1.6b, c], [1.7d], [1.9a], [2.2c], [4.2b], and [4.3a].

1. Evaluate $\dfrac{x - y}{3}$ when $x = 17$ and $y = 5$.

2. Translate to an algebraic expression: Nineteen percent of some number.

3. Tell which integers correspond to this situation: Mike has a debt of $45 and Joe has $72 in his savings account.

4. Find: $|-38|$.

Graph the number on a number line.

5. -2.5

6. $\dfrac{8}{9}$

Use either $<$ or $>$ for ▮ to write a true sentence.

7. -3 ▮ 10

8. -1 ▮ -6

9. 0.126 ▮ -12.6

10. $-\dfrac{2}{3}$ ▮ $-\dfrac{1}{10}$

Find the opposite.

11. 3.8

12. $-\dfrac{3}{4}$

Find the reciprocal.

13. $\dfrac{3}{8}$

14. -7

15. Find $-x$ when x is -34.

16. Find $-(-x)$ when x is 5.

Compute and simplify.

17. $4 + (-7)$

18. $6 + (-9) + (-8) + 7$

19. $-3.8 + 5.1 + (-12) + (-4.3) + 10$

20. $-3 - (-7)$

21. $-\dfrac{9}{10} - \dfrac{1}{2}$

22. $-3.8 - 4.1$

23. $-9 \cdot (-6)$

24. $-2.7(3.4)$

25. $\frac{2}{3} \cdot \left(-\frac{3}{7}\right)$

26. $3 \cdot (-7) \cdot (-2) \cdot (-5)$

27. $35 \div (-5)$

28. $-5.1 \div 1.7$

29. $-\frac{3}{5} \div \left(-\frac{4}{5}\right)$

30. $|-3.4 - 12.2| - 8(-7)$

31. $|-12(-3) - 2^3 - (-9)(-10)|$

Solve.

32. On the first, second, and third downs, a football team had these gains and losses: 5-yd gain, 12-yd loss, and 15-yd gain. Find the total gain (or loss).

33. Your total assets are $170. You borrow $300. What are your total assets now?

Multiply.

34. $5(3x - 7)$

35. $-2(4x - 5)$

36. $10(0.4x + 1.5)$

37. $-8(3 - 6x)$

Factor.

38. $2x - 14$

39. $6x - 6$

40. $5x + 10$

41. $12 - 3x$

Collect like terms.

42. $11a + 2b - 4a - 5b$

43. $7x - 3y - 9x + 8y$

44. $6x + 3y - x - 4y$

45. $-3a + 9b + 2a - b$

Remove parentheses and simplify.

46. $2a - (5a - 9)$

47. $3(b + 7) - 5b$

48. $3[11 - 3(4 - 1)]$

49. $2[6(y - 4) + 7]$

50. $[8(x + 4) - 10] - [3(x - 2) + 4]$

51. $5\{[6(x - 1) + 7] - [3(3x - 4) + 8]\}$

Write true or false.

52. $-9 \leq 11$

53. $-11 \geq -3$

54. Write another inequality with the same meaning as $-3 < x$.

SKILL MAINTENANCE

55. Divide and simplify: $\frac{11}{12} \div \frac{7}{10}$.

56. Compute and simplify: $\frac{5^3 - 2^4}{5 \cdot 2 + 2^3}$.

57. Find the prime factorization of 648.

58. Convert to percent notation: $\frac{5}{8}$.

59. Convert to decimal notation: 5.67%.

60. Find the LCM of 15, 27, and 30.

SYNTHESIS

61. Simplify: $-\left|\frac{7}{8} - \left(-\frac{1}{2}\right) - \frac{3}{4}\right|$.

62. Simplify: $(|2.7 - 3| + 3^2 - |-3|) \div (-3)$.

❖ THINKING IT THROUGH

1. List three examples of rational numbers that are not integers.

2. Explain at least three uses of the distributive laws considered in this chapter.

TEST: CHAPTER 7

ANSWERS

1. Evaluate $\dfrac{3x}{y}$ when $x = 10$ and $y = 5$.

2. Write an algebraic expression: Nine less than some number.

3. Find the area of a triangle when the height h is 30 ft and the base b is 16 ft.

Use either $<$ or $>$ for ▨ to write a true sentence.

4. -4 ▨ 0

5. -3 ▨ -8

6. -0.78 ▨ -0.87

7. $-\dfrac{1}{8}$ ▨ $\dfrac{1}{2}$

Find the absolute value.

8. $|-7|$

9. $\left|\dfrac{9}{4}\right|$

10. $|-2.7|$

Find the opposite.

11. $\dfrac{2}{3}$

12. -1.4

13. Find $-x$ when x is -8.

Find the reciprocal.

14. -2

15. $\dfrac{4}{7}$

Compute and simplify.

16. $3.1 - (-4.7)$

17. $-8 + 4 + (-7) + 3$

18. $-\dfrac{1}{5} + \dfrac{3}{8}$

19. $2 - (-8)$

20. $3.2 - 5.7$

21. $\dfrac{1}{8} - \left(-\dfrac{3}{4}\right)$

1. _____

2. _____

3. _____

4. _____

5. _____

6. _____

7. _____

8. _____

9. _____

10. _____

11. _____

12. _____

13. _____

14. _____

15. _____

16. _____

17. _____

18. _____

19. _____

20. _____

21. _____

22. $4 \cdot (-12)$

23. $-\dfrac{1}{2} \cdot \left(-\dfrac{3}{8}\right)$

24. $-45 \div 5$

25. $-\dfrac{3}{5} \div \left(-\dfrac{4}{5}\right)$

26. $4.864 \div (-0.5)$

27. $-2(16) - |2(-8) - 5^3|$

28. Wendy has $143 in her savings account. She withdraws $25. Then she makes a deposit of $30. How much is now in her savings account?

Multiply.

29. $3(6 - x)$

30. $-5(y - 1)$

Factor.

31. $12 - 22x$

32. $7x + 21 + 14y$

Simplify.

33. $6 + 7 - 4 - (-3)$

34. $5x - (3x - 7)$

35. $4(2a - 3b) + a - 7$

36. $4\{3[5(y - 3) + 9] + 2(y + 8)\}$

37. $256 \div (-16) \div 4$

38. $2^3 - 10[4 - (-2 + 18)3]$

39. Write an inequality with the same meaning as $x \leq -2$.

SKILL MAINTENANCE

40. Evaluate: $(1.2)^3$.

41. Convert to percent notation: $\dfrac{1}{8}$.

42. Find the prime factorization of 280.

43. Find the LCM of 16, 20, and 30.

SYNTHESIS

44. Simplify: $|-27 - 3(4)| - |-36| + |-12|$.

45. Simplify: $a - \{3a - [4a - (2a - 4a)]\}$.

INTRODUCTION In this chapter we use the manipulations discussed in Chapter 7 to solve equations and inequalities. We then solve problems using equations and inequalities.

The review sections to be tested in addition to the material in this chapter are 3.1, 3.2, 3.3, 7.1, 7.3, and 7.8. ❖

Solving Equations and Inequalities

AN APPLICATION

The state of Colorado is in the shape of a rectangle whose perimeter is 1300 mi. The length is 110 mi more than the width. Find the dimensions.

THE MATHEMATICS

Let $w =$ the width of the state of Colorado. The problem can be translated to the following *equation:*

$$2(w + 110) + 2w = 1300.$$

Identity Properties of 0 and 1: $a + 0 = a, \quad a \cdot 1 = a$
Simple-Interest Formula: $I = Prt$
Sum of the Angles of a Triangle $= 180°$
Perimeter of a Rectangle: $P = 2l + 2w$
Consecutive Integers: $x, \quad x + 1, \quad x + 2, \quad x + 3$, etc.
Consecutive Even Integers: $x, \quad x + 2, \quad x + 4, \quad x + 6$, etc.
Consecutive Odd Integers: $x, \quad x + 2, \quad x + 4, \quad x + 6$, etc.

PRETEST: CHAPTER 8

Solve.

1. $-7x = 49$

2. $4y + 9 = 2y + 7$

3. $6a - 2 = 10$

4. $4 + x = 12$

5. $7 - 3(2x - 1) = 40$

6. $\dfrac{4}{9}x - 1 = \dfrac{7}{8}$

7. $1 + 2(a + 3) = 3(2a - 1) + 6$

8. $-3x \le 18$

9. $y + 5 > 1$

10. $5 - 2a < 7$

11. $3x + 4 \ge 2x + 7$

12. $8y < -18$

13. Solve for G: $P = 3KG$.

14. Solve for a: $A = \dfrac{3a - b}{b}$.

Solve.

15. The perimeter of a rectangular field is 146 m. The width is 5 m less than the length. Find the dimensions.

16. Money is invested in a savings account at 9% simple interest. After one year, there is $708.50 in the account. How much was originally invested?

17. The sum of three consecutive integers is 246. Find the integers.

18. When 18 is added to six times a number, the result is less than 120. For what numbers is this possible?

Graph on a number line.

19. $x > -3$

20. $x \le 4$

8.1 Solving Equations: The Addition Principle

a Equations and Solutions

In order to solve problems, we must learn to solve equations.

> An *equation* is a number sentence that says that the expressions on either side of the equals sign, =, represent the same number.

Here are some examples:

$$3 + 2 = 5, \qquad 14 - 10 = 1 + 3, \qquad x + 6 = 13, \qquad 3x - 2 = 7 - x.$$

Equations have expressions on each side of the equals sign. The sentence "$14 - 10 = 1 + 3$" asserts that the expressions $14 - 10$ and $1 + 3$ name the same number.

Some equations are true. Some are false. Some are neither true nor false.

▶ **EXAMPLES** Determine whether the equation is true, false, or neither.

1. $3 + 2 = 5$ The equation is *true*.

2. $7 - 2 = 4$ The equation is *false*.

3. $x + 6 = 13$ The equation is *neither* true nor false, because we do not know what number x represents.   ◀

DO EXERCISES 1–3.

> Any replacement for the variable that makes an equation true is called a *solution* of the equation. To solve an equation means to find *all* of its solutions.

One way to determine whether a number is a solution of an equation is to evaluate the algebraic expression on each side of the equation by substitution. If the values are the same, then the number is a solution.

▶ **EXAMPLE 4** Determine whether 7 is a solution of $x + 6 = 13$.

We have

$$
\begin{array}{c|c}
x + 6 = 13 & \text{Writing the equation} \\
\hline
7 + 6 & 13 \qquad \text{Substituting 7 for } x \\
13 & \text{TRUE}
\end{array}
$$

Since the left-hand and the right-hand sides are the same, we have a solution. No other number makes the equation true, so the only solution is the number 7.   ◀

OBJECTIVES

After finishing Section 8.1, you should be able to:

a Determine whether a given number is a solution of a given equation.

b Solve equations using the addition principle.

FOR EXTRA HELP

Tape 17A

Determine whether the equation is true, false, or neither.

1. $5 - 8 = -4$

2. $12 + 6 = 18$

3. $x + 6 = 7 - x$

Determine whether the given number is a solution of the given equation.

4. 8; $x + 4 = 12$

5. 0; $x + 4 = 12$

6. -3; $7 + x = -4$

▶ **EXAMPLE 5** Determine whether 19 is a solution of $7x = 141$.

We have

$$
\begin{array}{rl}
7x = 141 & \text{Writing the equation} \\
\overline{7(19) \mid 141} & \text{Substituting 19 for } x \\
133 \mid & \text{FALSE}
\end{array}
$$

Since the left-hand and the right-hand sides are not the same, we do not have a solution. ◀

DO EXERCISES 4–6.

b Using the Addition Principle

Consider the equation

$$x = 7.$$

We can easily see that the solution of this equation is 7. If we replace x by 7, we get

$$7 = 7, \quad \text{which is true.}$$

Now consider the equation of Example 4:

$$x + 6 = 13.$$

In Example 4, we discovered that the solution of this equation is also 7, but the fact that 7 is the solution is not as obvious. We now begin to consider principles that allow us to start with an equation and end up with an equation like $x = 7$, in which the variable is alone on one side and for which the solution is easy to find. The equations $x + 6 = 13$ and $x = 7$ are **equivalent.**

> **Equations with the same solutions are called *equivalent equations.***

One of the principles that we use in solving equations concerns adding. An equation $a = b$ says that a and b stand for the same number. Suppose this is true, and we add a number c to the number a. We get the same answer if we add c to b, because a and b are the same number.

> **The Addition Principle**
>
> If an equation $a = b$ is true, then
>
> $$a + c = b + c$$
>
> is true for any number c.

When we use the addition principle, we sometimes say that we "add the same number on both sides of an equation." This is also true for subtraction, since we can express every subtraction as an addition. That is, since

$$a - c = b - c \quad \text{means} \quad a + (-c) = b + (-c),$$

the addition principle tells us that we can "subtract the same number on both sides of an equation."

ANSWERS ON PAGE A-6

▶ **EXAMPLE 4**   Solve: $-x = 9$.

$$-x = 9$$
$$-1 \cdot x = 9 \qquad \text{Using the property of } -1$$
$$-1 \cdot (-1 \cdot x) = -1 \cdot 9 \qquad \begin{array}{l}\text{Multiplying on both sides by } -1, \text{ the} \\ \text{reciprocal of itself, or dividing by } -1\end{array}$$
$$1 \cdot x = -9$$
$$x = -9$$

Check:

$$\begin{array}{c|c} -x = 9 \\ \hline -(-9) & 9 \\ 9 & \text{TRUE} \end{array}$$

The solution is -9.

DO EXERCISE 5.

5. Solve: $-x = -10$.

Now we solve an equation with a division using the multiplication principle. Consider an equation like $-y/9 = 14$. In Chapter 1, we learned that a division can be expressed as multiplication by the reciprocal of the divisor. Thus,

$$\frac{-y}{9} = \frac{1}{9}(-y).$$

The reciprocal of $\frac{1}{9}$ is 9. Then, using the multiplication principle, we multiply on both sides by 9. This is shown in the following example.

▶ **EXAMPLE 5**   Solve: $\dfrac{-y}{9} = 14$.

$$\frac{-y}{9} = 14$$

$$\frac{1}{9}(-y) = 14$$

$$9 \cdot \frac{1}{9}(-y) = 9 \cdot 14 \qquad \text{Multiplying by 9 on both sides}$$

$$-y = 126$$

$$y = -126 \qquad \text{Multiplying by } -1 \text{ on both sides}$$

Check:

$$\begin{array}{c|c} \dfrac{-y}{9} = 14 \\ \hline \dfrac{-(-126)}{9} & 14 \\ \dfrac{126}{9} & \\ 14 & \text{TRUE} \end{array}$$

The solution is -126.

DO EXERCISE 6.

6. Solve: $-14 = \dfrac{-y}{2}$.

ANSWERS ON PAGE A-6

Solve.

7. $1.12x = 8736$

▶ **EXAMPLE 6**   Solve: $1.16y = 9744$.

$$1.16y = 9744$$

$$\frac{1.16y}{1.16} = \frac{9744}{1.16} \qquad \text{Dividing by 1.16}$$

$$y = \frac{9744}{1.16}$$

$$y = 8400$$

Check:

$$\begin{array}{c|c} 1.16y = 9744 \\ \hline 1.16(8400) & 9744 \\ 9744 & \text{TRUE} \end{array}$$

The solution is 8400.   ◀

DO EXERCISES 7 AND 8.

Note that equations are reversible. That is, if $a = b$ is true, then $b = a$ is true. Thus, when we solve $15 = 3x$, we can reverse it and solve $3x = 15$ if we wish.

8. $6.3 = -2.1y$

NAME   SECTION   DATE

EXERCISE SET 8.2

a Solve using the multiplication principle. Don't forget to check!

1. $6x = 36$ **2.** $3x = 39$ **3.** $5x = 45$

4. $9x = 72$ **5.** $84 = 7x$ **6.** $56 = 8x$

7. $-x = 40$ **8.** $100 = -x$ **9.** $-x = -1$

10. $-68 = -r$ **11.** $7x = -49$ **12.** $9x = -36$

13. $-12x = 72$ **14.** $-15x = 105$ **15.** $-21x = -126$

16. $-13x = -104$ **17.** $\dfrac{t}{7} = -9$ **18.** $\dfrac{y}{-8} = 11$

19. $\dfrac{3}{4}x = 27$ **20.** $\dfrac{4}{5}x = 16$ **21.** $\dfrac{-t}{3} = 7$

22. $\dfrac{-x}{6} = 9$ **23.** $-\dfrac{m}{3} = \dfrac{1}{5}$ **24.** $\dfrac{1}{9} = -\dfrac{z}{7}$

1. _____

2. _____

3. _____

4. _____

5. _____

6. _____

7. _____

8. _____

9. _____

10. _____

11. _____

12. _____

13. _____

14. _____

15. _____

16. _____

17. _____

18. _____

19. _____

20. _____

21. _____

22. _____

23. _____

24. _____

Copyright © 1993 Addison-Wesley Publishing Co., Inc.

ANSWERS

25. _____

26. _____

27. _____

28. _____

29. _____

30. _____

31. _____

32. _____

33. _____

34. _____

35. _____

36. _____

37. _____

38. _____

39. _____

40. _____

41. _____

42. _____

43. _____

44. _____

45. _____

46. _____

47. _____

48. _____

49. _____

50. _____

25. $-\dfrac{3}{5}r = \dfrac{9}{10}$ **26.** $\dfrac{2}{5}y = -\dfrac{4}{15}$ **27.** $-\dfrac{3}{2}r = -\dfrac{27}{4}$

28. $-\dfrac{5}{7}x = -\dfrac{10}{14}$ **29.** $6.3x = 44.1$ **30.** $2.7y = 54$

31. $-3.1y = 21.7$ **32.** $-3.3y = 6.6$ **33.** $38.7m = 309.6$

34. $29.4m = 235.2$ **35.** $-\dfrac{2}{3}y = -10.6$ **36.** $-\dfrac{9}{7}y = 12.06$

SKILL MAINTENANCE

Collect like terms.

37. $3x + 4x$ **38.** $6x + 5 - 7x$

Remove parentheses and simplify.

39. $3x - (4 + 2x)$ **40.** $2 - 5(x + 5)$

SYNTHESIS

Solve.

41. ▤ $-0.2344m = 2028.732$ **42.** $0 \cdot x = 0$

43. $0 \cdot x = 9$ **44.** $4|x| = 48$ **45.** $2|x| = -12$

Solve for x.

46. $ax = 5a$ **47.** $3x = \dfrac{b}{a}$ **48.** $cx = a^2 + 1$ **49.** $\dfrac{a}{b}x = 4$

50. A student makes a calculation and gets an answer of 22.5. On the last step, the student multiplies by 0.3 when a division by 0.3 should have been done. What should the correct answer be?

8.3 Using the Principles Together

a Applying Both Principles

Consider the equation $3x + 4 = 13$. It is more complicated than those we discussed in the preceding two sections. In order to solve such an equation, we first isolate the x-term, $3x$, using the addition principle. Then we apply the multiplication principle to get x by itself.

▶ **EXAMPLE 1** Solve: $3x + 4 = 13$.

$$3x + 4 = 13$$

$$3x + 4 - 4 = 13 - 4 \qquad \text{Using the addition principle: subtracting 4 on both sides}$$

$$3x = 9 \qquad \text{Simplifying}$$

$$\frac{3x}{3} = \frac{9}{3} \qquad \text{Using the multiplication principle: dividing on both sides by 3}$$

$$x = 3 \qquad \text{Simplifying}$$

Check:

$$\begin{array}{c|c} 3x + 4 = 13 \\ \hline 3 \cdot 3 + 4 & 13 \\ 9 + 4 & \\ 13 & \text{TRUE} \end{array}$$

We use our rules for order of operations to carry out the check. We find the product $3 \cdot 3$. Then we add 4.

The solution is 3. ◀

DO EXERCISE 1.

▶ **EXAMPLE 2** Solve: $-5x - 6 = 16$.

$$-5x - 6 = 16$$

$$-5x - 6 + 6 = 16 + 6 \qquad \text{Adding 6 on both sides}$$

$$-5x = 22$$

$$\frac{-5x}{-5} = \frac{22}{-5} \qquad \text{Dividing on both sides by } -5$$

$$x = -\frac{22}{5}, \quad \text{or} \quad -4\frac{2}{5} \qquad \text{Simplifying}$$

Check:

$$\begin{array}{c|c} -5x - 6 = 16 \\ \hline -5\left(-\dfrac{22}{5}\right) - 6 & 16 \\ 22 - 6 & \\ 16 & \text{TRUE} \end{array}$$

The solution is $-\dfrac{22}{5}$. ◀

DO EXERCISES 2 AND 3.

OBJECTIVES

After finishing Section 8.3, you should be able to:

a Solve equations using both the addition and the multiplication principles.

b Solve equations in which like terms may need to be collected.

c Solve equations by first removing parentheses and collecting like terms.

FOR EXTRA HELP

Tape 18A

1. Solve: $9x + 6 = 51$.

Solve.

2. $8x - 4 = 28$

3. $-\dfrac{1}{2}x + 3 = 1$

4. Solve: $-18 - x = -57$.

Solve.

5. $-4 - 8x = 8$

6. $41.68 = 4.7 - 8.6y$

Solve.

7. $4x + 3x = -21$

8. $x - 0.09x = 728$

▶ **EXAMPLE 3**   Solve: $45 - x = 13$.

$$45 - x = 13$$
$$-45 + 45 - x = -45 + 13 \qquad \text{Adding } -45 \text{ on both sides}$$
$$-x = -32$$
$$-1 \cdot x = -32 \qquad \text{Using the property of } -1: -x = -1 \cdot x$$
$$\frac{-1 \cdot x}{-1} = \frac{-32}{-1} \qquad \begin{array}{l}\text{Dividing on both sides by } -1 \text{ (You could have}\\ \text{multiplied on both sides by } -1 \text{ instead. That}\\ \text{would also change the sign on both sides.)}\end{array}$$
$$x = 32$$

The number 32 checks and is the solution.   ◀

DO EXERCISE 4.

As we improve our equation-solving skills, we begin to shorten some of our writing. Thus we may not always write a number being added, subtracted, multiplied, or divided on both sides. We simply write it on the opposite side.

▶ **EXAMPLE 4**   Solve: $16.3 - 7.2y = -8.18$.

$$16.3 - 7.2y = -8.18$$
$$-7.2y = -16.3 + (-8.18) \qquad \begin{array}{l}\text{Adding } -16.3 \text{ on both sides. We write the}\\ \text{addition of } -16.3 \text{ on the right side.}\end{array}$$
$$-7.2y = -24.48$$
$$y = \frac{-24.48}{-7.2} \qquad \begin{array}{l}\text{Dividing by } -7.2 \text{ on both sides. We write}\\ \text{the division by } -7.2 \text{ on the right side.}\end{array}$$
$$y = 3.4$$

Check:

$$\begin{array}{c|c} 16.3 - 7.2y = -8.18 \\ \hline 16.3 - 7.2(3.4) & -8.18 \\ 16.3 - 24.48 & \\ -8.18 & \text{TRUE} \end{array}$$

The solution is 3.4.   ◀

DO EXERCISES 5 AND 6.

b   **Collecting Like Terms**

If there are like terms on one side of the equation, we collect them before using the addition or the multiplication principle.

▶ **EXAMPLE 5**   Solve: $3x + 4x = -14$.

$$3x + 4x = -14$$
$$7x = -14 \qquad \text{Collecting like terms}$$
$$x = \frac{-14}{7} \qquad \text{Dividing by 7 on both sides}$$
$$x = -2$$

The number -2 checks, so the solution is -2.   ◀

DO EXERCISES 7 AND 8.

If there are like terms on opposite sides of the equation, we get them on the same side by using the addition principle. Then we collect them. In other words, we get all terms with a variable on one side and all numbers on the other.

▶ **EXAMPLE 6** Solve: $2x - 2 = -3x + 3$.

$$2x - 2 = -3x + 3$$
$$2x - 2 + 2 = -3x + 3 + 2 \qquad \text{Adding 2}$$
$$2x = -3x + 5 \qquad \text{Collecting like terms}$$
$$2x + 3x = -3x + 3x + 5 \qquad \text{Adding } 3x$$
$$5x = 5 \qquad \text{Simplifying}$$
$$\frac{5x}{5} = \frac{5}{5} \qquad \text{Dividing by 5}$$
$$x = 1 \qquad \text{Simplifying}$$

Check:

$$
\begin{array}{c|c}
\multicolumn{2}{c}{2x - 2 = -3x + 3} \\
\hline
2 \cdot 1 - 2 & -3 \cdot 1 + 3 \\
2 - 2 & -3 + 3 \\
0 & 0 \qquad \text{TRUE}
\end{array}
$$

The solution is 1. ◀

DO EXERCISE 9.

In Example 6, we used the addition principle to get all terms with a variable on one side and all numbers on the other side. Then we collected like terms and proceeded as before. If there are like terms on one side at the outset, they should be collected before proceeding.

▶ **EXAMPLE 7** Solve: $6x + 5 - 7x = 10 - 4x + 3$.

$$6x + 5 - 7x = 10 - 4x + 3$$
$$-x + 5 = 13 - 4x \qquad \text{Collecting like terms}$$
$$4x - x + 5 = 13 - 4x + 4x \qquad \text{Adding } 4x$$
$$3x + 5 = 13 \qquad \text{Simplifying}$$
$$3x + 5 - 5 = 13 - 5 \qquad \text{Subtracting 5}$$
$$3x = 8 \qquad \text{Simplifying}$$
$$\frac{3x}{3} = \frac{8}{3} \qquad \text{Dividing by 3}$$
$$x = \frac{8}{3} \qquad \text{Simplifying}$$

The number $\frac{8}{3}$ checks, so it is the solution. ◀

DO EXERCISES 10–12.

9. Solve: $7y + 5 = 2y + 10$.

Solve.

10. $5 - 2y = 3y - 5$

11. $7x - 17 + 2x = 2 - 8x + 15$

12. $3x - 15 = 5x + 2 - 4x$

ANSWERS ON PAGE A-6

13. Solve: $\dfrac{7}{8}x - \dfrac{1}{4} + \dfrac{1}{2}x = \dfrac{3}{4} + x.$

Clearing of Fractions and Decimals

We have stated that we generally use the addition principle first. There are, however, some situations in which it is to our advantage to use the multiplication principle first. Consider, for example,

$$\frac{1}{2}x = \frac{3}{4}.$$

If we multiply by 4 on both sides, we get $2x = 3$, which has no fractions. We have "cleared of fractions." Consider

$$2.3x = 5.$$

If we multiply by 10 on both sides, we get $23x = 50$, which has no decimal points. We have "cleared of decimals." The equations are then easier to solve. It is your choice whether to clear of the fractions or decimals, but doing so often eases computations.

In what follows, we use the multiplication principle first to "clear of" or "eliminate" fractions or decimals. For fractions, the number we multiply by is the **least common multiple of all the denominators.**

▶ **EXAMPLE 8**   Solve:

$$\frac{2}{3}x - \frac{1}{6} + \frac{1}{2}x = \frac{7}{6} + 2x.$$

The number 6 is the least common multiple of all the denominators. We multiply by 6 on both sides.

$$6\left(\tfrac{2}{3}x - \tfrac{1}{6} + \tfrac{1}{2}x\right) = 6\left(\tfrac{7}{6} + 2x\right) \qquad \text{Multiplying by 6 on both sides}$$

$$6 \cdot \tfrac{2}{3}x - 6 \cdot \tfrac{1}{6} + 6 \cdot \tfrac{1}{2}x = 6 \cdot \tfrac{7}{6} + 6 \cdot 2x \qquad \begin{array}{l}\text{Using the distributive laws (\textit{Caution!}}\\ \text{Be sure to multiply all the terms by 6.)}\end{array}$$

$$4x - 1 + 3x = 7 + 12x \qquad \begin{array}{l}\text{Simplifying. Note that the fractions}\\ \text{are cleared.}\end{array}$$

$$7x - 1 = 7 + 12x \qquad \text{Collecting like terms}$$

$$7x - 12x = 7 + 1 \qquad \begin{array}{l}\text{Subtracting 12\textit{x} and adding 1 to get all}\\ \text{terms with variables on one side and}\\ \text{all constant terms on the other side}\end{array}$$

$$-5x = 8 \qquad \text{Collecting like terms}$$

$$x = -\tfrac{8}{5} \qquad \text{Multiplying by } -\tfrac{1}{5} \text{ or dividing by } -5$$

The number $-\tfrac{8}{5}$ checks and is the solution.   ◀

DO EXERCISE 13.

ANSWER ON PAGE A-6

Here is a procedure for solving the types of equation discussed in this section.

> An Equation-Solving Procedure
>
> 1. **Multiply on both sides to clear the equation of fractions or decimals. (This is optional, but it can ease computations.)**
> 2. **Collect like terms on each side, if necessary.**
> 3. **Get all terms with variables on one side and all constant terms on the other side, using the addition principle.**
> 4. **Collect like terms again, if necessary.**
> 5. **Multiply or divide to solve for the variable, using the multiplication principle.**
> 6. **Check all possible solutions in the original equation.**

We illustrate this by repeating Example 4, but we clear the equation of decimals first.

▶ **EXAMPLE 9**   Solve: $16.3 - 7.2y = -8.18$.

The greatest number of decimal places in any one number is *two*. Multiplying by 100, which has *two* 0's, will clear of decimals.

$$100(16.3 - 7.2y) = 100(-8.18) \quad \text{Multiplying by 100 on both sides}$$
$$100(16.3) - 100(7.2y) = 100(-8.18) \quad \text{Using a distributive law}$$
$$1630 - 720y = -818 \quad \text{Simplifying}$$
$$-720y = -818 - 1630 \quad \text{Subtracting 1630 on both sides}$$
$$-720y = -2448 \quad \text{Collecting like terms}$$
$$y = \frac{-2448}{-720} = 3.4 \quad \text{Dividing by } -720 \text{ on both sides}$$

The number 3.4 checks and is the solution.   ◀

DO EXERCISE 14.

C   Equations Containing Parentheses

To solve certain kinds of equations that contain parentheses, we use the distributive laws to first remove the parentheses. Then we proceed as before.

▶ **EXAMPLE 10**   Solve: $4x = 2(12 - 2x)$.

$$4x = 2(12 - 2x)$$
$$4x = 24 - 4x \quad \text{Using a distributive law to multiply and remove parentheses}$$
$$4x + 4x = 24 \quad \text{Adding } 4x \text{ to get all } x\text{-terms on one side}$$
$$8x = 24 \quad \text{Collecting like terms}$$
$$\frac{8x}{8} = \frac{24}{8} \quad \text{Dividing by 8}$$
$$x = 3$$

14. Solve: $41.68 = 4.7 - 8.6y$.

ANSWER ON PAGE A-6

Solve.

15. $2(2y + 3) = 14$

16. $5(3x - 2) = 35$

Solve.

17. $3(7 + 2x) = 30 + 7(x - 1)$

18. $4(3 + 5x) - 4 = 3 + 2(x - 2)$

Check:

$$
\begin{array}{c|c}
\multicolumn{2}{c}{4x = 2(12 - 2x)} \\
\hline
4 \cdot 3 & 2(12 - 2 \cdot 3) \\
12 & 2(12 - 6) \\
 & 2 \cdot 6 \\
 & 12 \qquad \text{TRUE}
\end{array}
$$

We use the rules for order of operations to carry out the calculations on each side of the equation.

The solution is 3. ◀

DO EXERCISES 15 AND 16.

▶ **EXAMPLE 11**   Solve: $2 - 5(x + 5) = 3(x - 2) - 1$.

$$2 - 5(x + 5) = 3(x - 2) - 1$$

$$2 - 5x - 25 = 3x - 6 - 1 \qquad \text{Using the distributive laws to multiply and remove parentheses}$$

$$-5x - 23 = 3x - 7 \qquad \text{Simplifying}$$

$$-23 + 7 = 3x + 5x \qquad \text{Adding } 5x \text{ and } 7 \text{ to get all } x\text{-terms on one side and all other terms on the other side}$$

$$-16 = 8x \qquad \text{Simplifying}$$

$$-2 = x \qquad \text{Dividing by 8}$$

Check:

$$
\begin{array}{c|c}
\multicolumn{2}{c}{2 - 5(x + 5) = 3(x - 2) - 1} \\
\hline
2 - 5(-2 + 5) & 3(-2 - 2) - 1 \\
2 - 5(3) & 3(-4) - 1 \\
2 - 15 & -12 - 1 \\
-13 & -13 \qquad \text{TRUE}
\end{array}
$$

The solution is -2. ◀

Note that the solution of $-2 = x$ is -2, which is also the solution of $x = -2$.

DO EXERCISES 17 AND 18.

EXERCISE SET 8.3

a Solve. Don't forget to check!

1. $5x + 6 = 31$

2. $3x + 6 = 30$

3. $8x + 4 = 68$

4. $7z + 9 = 72$

5. $4x - 6 = 34$

6. $6x - 3 = 15$

7. $3x - 9 = 33$

8. $5x - 7 = 48$

9. $7x + 2 = -54$

10. $5x + 4 = -41$

11. $-45 = 3 + 6y$

12. $-91 = 9t + 8$

13. $-4x + 7 = 35$

14. $-5x - 7 = 108$

15. $-7x - 24 = -129$

16. $-6z - 18 = -132$

b Solve.

17. $5x + 7x = 72$

18. $4x + 5x = 45$

19. $8x + 7x = 60$

20. $3x + 9x = 96$

21. $4x + 3x = 42$

22. $6x + 19x = 100$

23. $-6y - 3y = 27$

24. $-4y - 8y = 48$

25. $-7y - 8y = -15$

ANSWERS

1. _____

2. _____

3. _____

4. _____

5. _____

6. _____

7. _____

8. _____

9. _____

10. _____

11. _____

12. _____

13. _____

14. _____

15. _____

16. _____

17. _____

18. _____

19. _____

20. _____

21. _____

22. _____

23. _____

24. _____

25. _____

ANSWERS

26.

27.

28.

29.

30.

31.

32.

33.

34.

35.

36.

37.

38.

39.

40.

41.

42.

43.

44.

45.

46.

47.

48.

49.

50.

26. $-10y - 3y = -39$

27. $10.2y - 7.3y = -58$

28. $6.8y - 2.4y = -88$

29. $x + \dfrac{1}{3}x = 8$

30. $x + \dfrac{1}{4}x = 10$

31. $8y - 35 = 3y$

32. $4x - 6 = 6x$

33. $8x - 1 = 23 - 4x$

34. $5y - 2 = 28 - y$

35. $2x - 1 = 4 + x$

36. $5x - 2 = 6 + x$

37. $6x + 3 = 2x + 11$

38. $5y + 3 = 2y + 15$

39. $5 - 2x = 3x - 7x + 25$

40. $10 - 3x = 2x - 8x + 40$

41. $4 + 3x - 6 = 3x + 2 - x$

42. $5 + 4x - 7 = 4x - 2 - x$

43. $4y - 4 + y + 24 = 6y + 20 - 4y$

44. $5y - 7 + y = 7y + 21 - 5y$

Solve. Clear of fractions or decimals first.

45. $\dfrac{7}{2}x + \dfrac{1}{2}x = 3x + \dfrac{3}{2} + \dfrac{5}{2}x$

46. $\dfrac{7}{8}x - \dfrac{1}{4} + \dfrac{3}{4}x = \dfrac{1}{16} + x$

47. $\dfrac{2}{3} + \dfrac{1}{4}t = \dfrac{1}{3}$

48. $-\dfrac{3}{2} + x = -\dfrac{5}{6} - \dfrac{4}{3}$

49. $\dfrac{2}{3} + 3y = 5y - \dfrac{2}{15}$

50. $\dfrac{1}{2} + 4m = 3m - \dfrac{5}{2}$

51. $\dfrac{5}{3} + \dfrac{2}{3}x = \dfrac{25}{12} + \dfrac{5}{4}x + \dfrac{3}{4}$

52. $1 - \dfrac{2}{3}y = \dfrac{9}{5} - \dfrac{y}{5} + \dfrac{3}{5}$

53. $2.1x + 45.2 = 3.2 - 8.4x$

54. $0.96y - 0.79 = 0.21y + 0.46$

55. $1.03 - 0.62x = 0.71 - 0.22x$

56. $1.7t + 8 - 1.62t = 0.4t - 0.32 + 8$

57. $\dfrac{2}{7}x - \dfrac{1}{2}x = \dfrac{3}{4}x + 1$

58. $\dfrac{5}{16}y + \dfrac{3}{8}y = 2 + \dfrac{1}{4}y$

c Solve.

59. $3(2y - 3) = 27$

60. $4(2y - 3) = 28$

61. $40 = 5(3x + 2)$

62. $9 = 3(5x - 2)$

63. $2(3 + 4m) - 9 = 45$

64. $3(5 + 3m) - 8 = 88$

65. $5r - (2r + 8) = 16$

66. $6b - (3b + 8) = 16$

67. $6 - 2(3x - 1) = 2$

68. $10 - 3(2x - 1) = 1$

69. $5(d + 4) = 7(d - 2)$

70. $3(t - 2) = 9(t + 2)$

71. $8(2t + 1) = 4(7t + 7)$

72. $7(5x - 2) = 6(6x - 1)$

ANSWERS

51. _____

52. _____

53. _____

54. _____

55. _____

56. _____

57. _____

58. _____

59. _____

60. _____

61. _____

62. _____

63. _____

64. _____

65. _____

66. _____

67. _____

68. _____

69. _____

70. _____

71. _____

72. _____

ANSWERS

73. _____
74. _____
75. _____
76. _____
77. _____
78. _____
79. _____
80. _____
81. _____
82. _____
83. _____
84. _____
85. _____
86. _____
87. _____
88. _____
89. _____
90. _____
91. _____
92. _____
93. _____
94. _____
95. _____
96. _____
97. _____
98. _____
99. _____
100. _____
101. _____

73. $3(r - 6) + 2 = 4(r + 2) - 21$

74. $5(t + 3) + 9 = 3(t - 2) + 6$

75. $19 - (2x + 3) = 2(x + 3) + x$

76. $13 - (2c + 2) = 2(c + 2) + 3c$

77. $\frac{1}{3}(6x + 24) - 20 = -\frac{1}{4}(12x - 72)$

78. $\frac{1}{4}(8y + 4) - 17 = -\frac{1}{2}(4y - 8)$

79. $2[4 - 2(3 - x)] - 1 = 4[2(4x - 3) + 7] - 25$

80. $5[3(7 - t) - 4(8 + 2t)] - 20 = -6[2(6 + 3t) - 4]$

81. $\frac{2}{3}(2x - 1) = 10$

82. $\frac{4}{5}(3x + 4) = 20$

83. $\frac{3}{4}\left(3x - \frac{1}{2}\right) - \frac{2}{3} = \frac{1}{3}$

84. $\frac{2}{3}\left(\frac{7}{8} - 4x\right) - \frac{5}{8} = \frac{3}{8}$

85. $0.7(3x + 6) = 1.1 - (x + 2)$

86. $0.9(2x + 8) = 20 - (x + 5)$

87. $a + (a - 3) = (a + 2) - (a + 1)$

88. $0.8 - 4(b - 1) = 0.2 + 3(4 - b)$

SKILL MAINTENANCE

89. Divide: $-22.1 \div 3.4$.

90. Factor: $7x - 21 - 14y$.

91. Use $<$ or $>$ for ■ to write a true sentence: -15 ■ -13.

92. Find $-(-x)$ when $x = -14$.

SYNTHESIS

Solve.

93. ▦ $0.008 + 9.62x - 42.8 = 0.944x + 0.0083 - x$.

94. $\frac{y - 2}{3} = \frac{2 - y}{5}$

95. $0 = y - (-14) - (-3y)$

96. $3x = 4x$

97. $\frac{5 + 2y}{3} = \frac{25}{12} + \frac{5y + 3}{4}$

98. ▦ $0.05y - 1.82 = 0.708y - 0.504$

99. $-2y + 5y = 6y$

100. $\frac{4 - 3x}{7} = \frac{2 + 5x}{49} - \frac{x}{14}$

101. Solve the equation $4x - 8 = 32$ by first using the addition principle. Then solve it by first using the multiplication principle.

8.4 Solving Problems

a Five Steps for Solving Problems

We have studied many new equation-solving tools in this chapter. We now apply them to problem solving. The following five-step strategy can be very helpful in solving problems.

Five Steps for Problem Solving in Algebra

1. *Familiarize* yourself with the problem situation.
2. *Translate* the problem to an equation.
3. *Solve* the equation.
4. *Check* the answer in the original problem.
5. *State* the answer to the problem clearly.

Of the five steps, the most important is probably the first one: becoming familiar with the problem situation. Here are some hints for familiarization.

To familiarize yourself with the problem situation:

1. If a problem is given in words, read it carefully.
2. Reread the problem, perhaps aloud. Try to verbalize the problem to yourself.
3. List the information given and the questions to be answered. Choose a variable (or variables) to represent the unknown and clearly state what the variable represents. Be descriptive! For example, let L = length, d = distance, and so on.
4. Find further information. Look up a formula on the inside frontcover of this book or in a reference book. Talk to a reference librarian or an expert in the field.
5. Make a table of the given information and the information you have collected. Look for patterns that may help in the translation to an equation.
6. Make a drawing and label it with known information. Also, indicate unknown information, using specific units if given.
7. Guess or estimate the answer.

▶ **EXAMPLE 1** A 72-in. board is cut into two pieces. One piece is twice as long as the other. How long are the pieces?

1. *Familiarize.* We first draw a picture. We let

$$x = \text{the length of the shorter piece.}$$

Then $\qquad 2x$ = the length of the longer piece.

(We can also let y = the length of the longer piece. Then $\frac{1}{2}y$ = the length of the shorter piece. This, however, introduces fractions and will make the solution somewhat more difficult.)

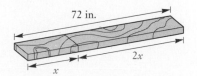

OBJECTIVE

After finishing Section 8.4, you should be able to:

a Solve problems by translating to equations.

FOR EXTRA HELP

Tape 18B

1. A 58-in. board is cut into two pieces. One piece is 2 in. longer than the other. How long are the pieces?

We can further familiarize ourselves with the problem by making some guesses. Suppose $x = 31$ in. Then $2x = 62$ in. and $x + 2x = 93$ in. This is not correct but does help us to become familiar with the problem.

2. *Translate.* From the figure, we can see that the lengths of the two pieces add up to 72 in. This gives us our translation.

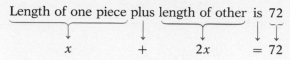

$$\text{Length of one piece plus length of other is 72}$$
$$x \qquad + \qquad 2x \qquad = 72$$

3. *Solve.* We solve the equation:

$$x + 2x = 72$$
$$3x = 72 \qquad \text{Collecting like terms}$$
$$x = 24. \qquad \text{Dividing by 3}$$

4. *Check.* Do we have an answer to the *problem*? If one piece is 24 in. long, the other, to be twice as long, must be 48 in. long. The lengths of the pieces add up to 72 in. This checks.

5. *State.* One piece is 24 in. long, and the other is 48 in. long. ◄

DO EXERCISE 1.

► **EXAMPLE 2** Five plus three more than a number is nineteen. What is the number?

1. *Familiarize.* Let $x =$ the number. Then "three more than the number" translates to $x + 3$ and "5 more than $x + 3$" translates to $5 + (x + 3)$.

2. If 5 is subtracted from three times a certain number, the result is 10. What is the number?

2. *Translate.* The familiarization leads us to the following translation:

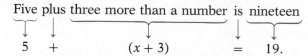

$$\text{Five plus three more than a number is nineteen}$$
$$5 \quad + \qquad (x + 3) \qquad = \qquad 19.$$

3. *Solve.* We solve the equation:

$$5 + (x + 3) = 19$$
$$x + 8 = 19 \qquad \text{Collecting like terms}$$
$$x = 11. \qquad \text{Subtracting 8}$$

4. *Check.* Three more than 11 is 14. Adding 5 to 14, we get 19. This checks.

5. *State.* The number is 11. ◄

DO EXERCISE 2.

The following are examples of **consecutive integers:** 16, 17, 18, 19, 20; and $-31, -30, -29, -28$. Note that consecutive integers can be represented in the form x, $x + 1$, $x + 2$, and so on.

The following are examples of **consecutive even integers:** 16, 18, 20, 22, 24; and $-52, -50, -48, -46$. Note that consecutive even integers can be represented in the form x, $x + 2$, $x + 4$, and so on.

The following are examples of **consecutive odd integers:** 21, 23, 25, 27, 29; and $-71, -69, -67, -65$. Note that consecutive odd integers can be represented in the form x, $x + 2$, $x + 4$, and so on.

▶ **EXAMPLE 3**   A book is opened. The sum of the page numbers on the facing pages is 233. Find the page numbers.

1. *Familiarize.*   Look at your page numbers on the pages to which your book is now open. Note that they are consecutive positive integers. The numbers follow each other if we count by ones. Thus if we let $x =$ the smaller number, then $x + 1 =$ the larger number.

To become more familiar with the problem, we can make a table. How do we get the entries to the table? First, we just guess a value for x. Then we find $x + 1$. Finally, we add the two numbers and see what happens. You might actually solve the problem this way, even though you need to practice using algebra.

x	$x + 1$	Sum of x and $x + 1$
14	15	29
24	25	49
102	103	205

2. *Translate.*   We reword the problem and translate as follows.

First integer + second integer = 233   **Rewording**

$$x \quad + \quad (x + 1) \quad = 233 \qquad \text{\textbf{Translating}}$$

3. *Solve.*   We solve the equation:

$$x + (x + 1) = 233$$
$$2x + 1 = 233 \qquad \text{\textbf{Collecting like terms}}$$
$$2x = 232 \qquad \text{\textbf{Subtracting 1}}$$
$$x = 116. \qquad \text{\textbf{Dividing by 2}}$$

If x is 116, then $x + 1$ is 117.

4. *Check.*   Our possible answers are 116 and 117. These are consecutive integers. Their sum is 233, so the answers check in the *original problem*.

5. *State.*   The page numbers are 116 and 117.   ◀

DO EXERCISE 3.

3. A book is opened. The sum of the page numbers on the facing pages is 457. Find the page numbers.

ANSWER ON PAGE A-6

4. Acme also rents compact cars at a daily rate of $34.95 plus 27 cents per mile. What mileage will allow the businessperson to stay within a budget of $100?

▶ **EXAMPLE 4**   Acme Rent-A-Car rents an intermediate-size car (such as a Chevrolet, Ford, or Plymouth) at a daily rate of $44.95 plus 29 cents a mile. A salesperson can spend $100 per day on car rental. How many miles can the person drive on the $100 budget?

1. *Familiarize.*   Suppose the businessperson drives 75 mi. Then the cost is

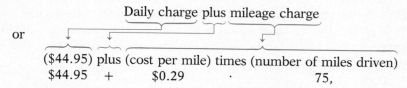

or

($44.95) plus (cost per mile) times (number of miles driven)
$44.95   + $0.29   ·   75,

which is $44.95 + $21.75, or $66.70. This familiarizes us with the way in which a calculation is made. Note that we convert 29 cents to $0.29 so that we have the same units, dollars. Otherwise, we will not get a correct answer.

Let m = the number of miles that can be driven on $100.

2. *Translate.*   We reword the problem and translate as follows.

Daily rate plus cost per mile times number of miles driven is cost

$44.95   + $0.29   · m = $100

3. *Solve.*   We solve the equation:

$$44.95 + 0.29m = 100$$
$$100(44.95 + 0.29m) = 100(100) \quad \text{Multiplying by 100 on both sides to clear of the decimals}$$
$$100(44.95) + 100(0.29m) = 10,000 \quad \text{Using a distributive law}$$
$$4495 + 29m = 10,000$$
$$29m = 5505 \quad \text{Subtracting 4495}$$
$$m = \frac{5505}{29} \quad \text{Dividing by 29}$$
$$m \approx 189.8. \quad \text{Rounding to the nearest tenth. ''} \approx \text{'' means ''approximately equal to.''}$$

4. *Check.*   We check in the original problem. We multiply 189.8 by $0.29, getting $55.042. Then we add $55.042 to $44.95 and get $99.992, which is just about the $100 allotted.

5. *State.*   The person can drive about 189.8 mi on the car rental allotment of $100.   ◀

DO EXERCISE 4.

▶ **EXAMPLE 5**   The state of Colorado is in the shape of a rectangle whose perimeter is 1300 mi. The length is 110 mi more than the width. Find the dimensions.

1. *Familiarize.*   We first draw a picture. We let

$$w = \text{the width of the rectangle.}$$

Then $w + 110 = \text{the length.}$

(We could also let $l = \text{the length and } l - 110 = \text{the width.})$

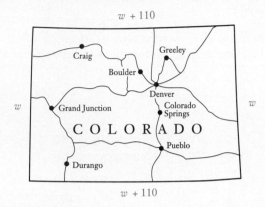

The perimeter P of a rectangle is the distance around it and is given by the formula $2l + 2w = P$, where $l = \text{the length and } w = \text{the width.}$

2. *Translate.*   To translate the problem, we substitute $w + 110$ for l and 1300 for P, as follows:

$$2l + 2w = P$$
$$2(w + 110) + 2w = 1300.$$

3. *Solve.*   We solve the equation:

$$2(w + 110) + 2w = 1300$$
$$2w + 220 + 2w = 1300$$
$$4w + 220 = 1300$$
$$4w = 1080$$
$$w = 270.$$

Possible dimensions are $w = 270$ mi and $w + 110 = 380$ mi.

4. *Check.*   If the width is 270 mi and the length is 110 mi + 270 mi, or 380 mi, the perimeter is 2(380 mi) + 2(270 mi), or 1300 mi. This checks.

5. *State.*   The width is 270 mi, and the length is 380 mi.   ◀

DO EXERCISE 5.

▶ **EXAMPLE 6**   The second angle of a triangle is twice as large as the first. The measure of the third angle is 20° greater than that of the first angle. How large are the angles?

1. *Familiarize.*   We draw a picture. We let.

$$\text{measure of 1st angle} = x.$$

Then $\text{measure of 2nd angle} = 2x,$

and $\text{measure of 3rd angle} = x + 20.$

5. A standard-sized rug has a perimeter of 42 ft. The length is 3 ft more than the width. Find the dimensions of the rug.

ANSWER ON PAGE A-6

6. The second angle of a triangle is three times as large as the first. The third angle measures 30° more than the first angle. Find the measures of the angles.

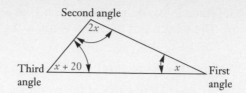

2. *Translate.* To translate we need to recall a geometric fact. (You might, as part of step 1, look it up in a geometry book or in the list of formulas at the back of this book.) The measures of the angles of any triangle add up to 180°.

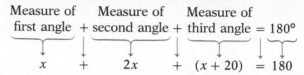

3. *Solve.* We solve:

$$x + 2x + (x + 20) = 180$$
$$4x + 20 = 180$$
$$4x = 160$$
$$x = 40.$$

Possible measures for the angles are as follows:

First angle: $x = 40°$;

Second angle: $2x = 2(40) = 80°$;

Third angle: $x + 20 = 40 + 20 = 60°.$

4. *Check.* Consider 40°, 80°, and 60°. The second is twice the first, and the third is 20° greater than the first. The sum is 180°. These numbers check.

5. *State.* The measures of the angles are 40°, 80°, and 60°.   ◄

CAUTION!   Units are important in answers.

DO EXERCISE 6.

We close this section with some other tips to aid you in problem solving.

Problem-Solving Tips

1. **To be good at problem solving, work lots of problems.**

2. **Look for patterns when solving problems. Each time you study an example in a text, you may observe a pattern for problems that you will see later in the exercise sets or some other practical situation.**

3. **When translating to an equation, or some other mathematical language, consider the dimensions of the variables and constants in the equation. The variables that represent length should all be in the same unit, those that represent money should all be in dollars or all in cents, and so on.**

NAME   SECTION   DATE

EXERCISE SET 8.4

a Solve.

1. What number added to 60 is 112?

2. Seven times what number is 2233?

1. _____

3. When 42 is multiplied by a number, the result is 2352. Find the number.

4. When 345 is added to a number, the result is 987. Find the number.

2. _____

3. _____

5. A game board has 64 squares. If you win 35 squares and your opponent wins the rest, how many does your opponent win?

6. A consultant charges $80 an hour. How many hours did the consultant work to make $53,400?

4. _____

5. _____

7. In a recent year, the cost of four 12-oz boxes of Post[R] Oat Flakes was $7.96. How much did one box cost?

8. The total amount spent on women's blouses in a recent year was $6.5 billion. This was $0.2 billion more than was spent on women's dresses. How much was spent on women's dresses?

6. _____

7. _____

8. _____

9. When 18 is subtracted from six times a certain number, the result is 96. What is the number?

10. When 28 is subtracted from five times a certain number, the result is 232. What is the number?

9. _____

11. If you double a number and then add 16, you get two fifths of the original number. What is the original number?

12. If you double a number and then add 85, you get three fourths of the original number. What is the original number?

10. _____

11. _____

12. _____

13. _____

14. _____

15. _____

16. _____

17. _____

18. _____

19. _____

20. _____

21. _____

22. _____

23. _____

24. _____

13. If you add two fifths of a number to the number itself, you get 56. What is the number?

14. If you add one third of a number to the number itself, you get 48. What is the number?

15. A 180-m rope is cut into three pieces. The second piece is twice as long as the first. The third piece is three times as long as the second. How long is each piece of rope?

16. A 480-m wire is cut into three pieces. The second piece is three times as long as the first. The third piece is four times as long as the second. How long is each piece?

17. The sum of the page numbers on the facing pages of a book is 73. What are the page numbers?

18. The sum of the page numbers on the facing pages of a book is 81. What are the page numbers?

19. The sum of two consecutive even integers is 114. What are the integers?

20. The sum of two consecutive even integers is 106. What are the integers?

21. The sum of three consecutive integers is 108. What are the integers?

22. The sum of three consecutive integers is 126. What are the integers?

23. The sum of three consecutive odd integers is 189. What are the integers?

24. Three consecutive integers are such that the first plus one-half the second plus three less than twice the third is 964. Find the integers.

25. The top of the John Hancock Building in Chicago is a rectangle whose length is 60 ft more than the width. The perimeter is 520 ft. Find the width and the length of the rectangle. Find the area of the rectangle.

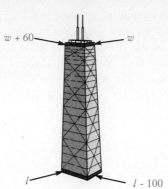

25. _____

26. The ground floor of the John Hancock Building is a rectangle whose width is 100 ft less than the length. The perimeter is 860 ft. Find the width and the length of the rectangle. Find the area of the rectangle.

26. _____

27. _____

27. The perimeter of a standard-sized piece of typewriter paper is 99 cm. The width is 6.3 cm less than the length. Find the length and the width.

28. The perimeter of the state of Wyoming is 1280 mi. The width is 90 mi less than the length. Find the width and the length.

28. _____

29. The second angle of a triangle is four times as large as the first. The third angle is 45° less than the sum of the other two angles. Find the measure of the first angle.

30. The second angle of a triangle is three times as large as the first. The third angle is 25° less than the sum of the other two angles. Find the measure of the first angle.

29. _____

30. _____

31. Badger Rent-A-Car rents an intermediate-size car at a daily rate of $34.95 plus 10 cents per mile. A businessperson is allotted $80 for car rental. How many miles can the businessperson travel on the $80 budget?

32. Badger also rents compact cars at $43.95 plus 10 cents per mile. A businessperson has a car rental allotment of $90. How many miles can the businessperson travel on the $90 budget?

31. _____

32. _____

33. _____

34. _____

35. _____

36. _____

37. _____

38. _____

39. _____

40. _____

41. _____

42. _____

43. _____

44. _____

33. The second angle of a triangle is three times as large as the first. The measure of the third angle is 40° greater than that of the first angle. How large are the angles?

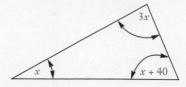

34. One angle of a triangle is 32 times as large as another. The measure of the third angle is 10° greater than that of the smallest angle. How large are the angles?

35. The equation

$$R = -0.028t + 20.8$$

can be used to predict the world record in the 200-m dash, where R stands for the record in seconds and t for the number of years since 1920. In what year will the record be 18.0 sec?

36. The equation

$$F = \frac{1}{4}N + 40$$

can be used to determine temperatures given how many times a cricket chirps per minute, where F represents temperature in degrees and N the number of chirps per minute. Determine the number of chirps per minute necessary in order for the temperature to be 80°.

SYNTHESIS

37. Abraham Lincoln's 1863 Gettysburg Address refers to the year 1776 as "Four *score* and seven years ago." Write an equation and find what number a score represents.

38. If the daily rental for a car is $18.90 plus a certain price per mile and a person must drive 190 mi and still stay within a $55.00 budget, what is the highest price per mile that the person can afford?

39. A student scored 78 on a test that had 4 seven-point fill-ins and 24 three-point multiple-choice questions. The student had one fill-in wrong. How many multiple-choice questions did the student answer correctly?

40. The width of a rectangle is three fourths of the length. The perimeter of the rectangle becomes 50 cm when the length and the width are each increased by 2 cm. Find the length and the width.

41. Apples are collected in a basket for six people. One third, one fourth, one eighth, and one fifth are given to four people, respectively. The fifth person gets ten apples with one apple remaining for the sixth person. Find the original number of apples in the basket.

42. A student has an average score of 82 on three tests. The student's average score on the first two tests is 85. What was the score on the third test?

43. A storekeeper goes to the bank to get $10 worth of change. The storekeeper requests twice as many quarters as half dollars, twice as many dimes as quarters, three times as many nickels as dimes, and no pennies or dollars. How many of each coin did the storekeeper get?

44. ▤ The area of this triangle is 2.9047 in². Find x.

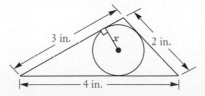

8.5 Solving Percent Problems

a   Many problems involve percents. We can use our knowledge of equations and the problem-solving process to solve such problems.

▶ **EXAMPLE 1**   What percent of 45 is 15?

1. *Familiarize.* This type of problem is stated so explicitly that we can proceed directly to the translation. We first let x = the percent.

2. *Translate.* We translate as follows:

$$\underbrace{\text{What percent}}_{x\%} \text{ of } \underbrace{45}_{\cdot \ 45} \text{ is } \underbrace{15?}_{= \ 15.}$$

3. *Solve.* We solve the equation:

$$x\% \cdot 45 = 15$$
$$x \times 0.01 \times 45 = 15$$
$$x(0.45) = 15$$
$$x = \frac{15}{0.45} \qquad \text{Dividing by 0.45}$$
$$x = \frac{15}{0.45} \times \frac{100}{100} = \frac{1500}{45}$$
$$x = 33\frac{1}{3}.$$

4. *Check.* We check by finding $33\frac{1}{3}\%$ of 45:

$$33\frac{1}{3}\% \cdot 45 = \frac{1}{3} \cdot 45 = 15. \qquad \text{See Table 1 at the back of the book.}$$

5. *State.* The answer is $33\frac{1}{3}\%$.   ◀

DO EXERCISES 1 AND 2.

▶ **EXAMPLE 2**   3 is 16 percent of what?

1. *Familiarize.* This problem is stated so explicitly that we can proceed directly to the translation. We let y = the number that we are taking 16% of.

2. *Translate.* The translation is as follows:

$$\underbrace{3}_{3} \underbrace{\text{is}}_{=} \underbrace{16}_{16} \underbrace{\text{percent}}_{\%} \underbrace{\text{of}}_{\cdot} \underbrace{\text{what?}}_{y}$$

3. *Solve.* We solve the equation:

$$3 = 16\% \cdot y$$
$$3 = 0.16y$$
$$0.16y = 3$$
$$y = \frac{3}{0.16} \qquad \text{Dividing by 0.16}$$
$$y = 18.75.$$

OBJECTIVE

After finishing Section 8.5, you should be able to:

a   Solve problems involving percent.

Solve.

1. What percent of 50 is 16?

2. 15 is what percent of 60?

ANSWERS ON PAGE A-6

Solve.

3. 45 is 20 percent of what?

4. *Check.* We check by finding 16% of 18.75:

$$16\% \times 18.75 = 0.16 \times 18.75 = 3.$$

5. *State.* The answer is 18.75.   ◄

DO EXERCISES 3 AND 4.

Perhaps you have noticed that to handle percents in problems such as those in Examples 1 and 2, you can convert to decimal notation before continuing.

4. 120 percent of what is 60?

▶ **EXAMPLE 3**   Blood is 90% water. The average adult has 5 quarts (qt) of blood. How much water is in the average adult's blood?

1. *Familiarize.* We first write down the given information.

> Blood: 90% water
>
> Adult: Body contains 5 qt of blood.

We want to find the amount of water that is in the blood of an adult. We let $x =$ the amount of water in the blood of an adult. It seems reasonable that we take 90% of 5. This leads us to the rewording and translating of the problem.

2. *Translate.*

Solve.

5. What is 23% of 48?

> *Rewording:*   90% of 5 is what?
>
> *Translating:*   90% · 5 = x

3. *Solve.* We solve the equation:

$$90\% \cdot 5 = x$$
$$0.90 \times 5 = x \qquad \text{Converting 90\% to decimal notation}$$
$$4.5 = x.$$

4. *Check.* The check is actually the computation we use to solve the equation:

$$90\% \cdot 5 = 0.90 \times 5 = 4.5.$$

5. *State.* The answer is that there are 4.5 qt of water in an adult who has 5 qt of blood.   ◄

DO EXERCISES 5 AND 6.

6. The area of Arizona is 19% of the area of Alaska. The area of Alaska is 586,400 mi² (square miles). What is the area of Arizona?

▶ **EXAMPLE 4**   An investment is made at 8% simple interest for 1 year. It grows to $783. How much was originally invested (the principal)?

1. *Familiarize.* Suppose that $100 was invested. Recalling the formula for simple interest, $I = Prt$, we know that the interest for 1 year on $100 at 8% simple interest is given by $I = \$100 \cdot 8\% \cdot 1 = \$8$. Then, at the end of the year, the *amount* in the account is found by adding principal and interest:

> Principal + Interest = Amount
>
> $100   + $8   = $108.

In this problem we are working backward. We are trying to find the principal, which is the original investment. We let $x =$ the principal.

ANSWERS ON PAGE A-6

2. *Translate.*   We reword the problem and then translate.

Rewording: Principal + Interest = Amount

Translating: x + 8%x = 783   **Interest is 8% of the principal.**

3. *Solve.*   We solve the equation:

$$x + 8\%x = 783$$
$$x + 0.08x = 783 \qquad \text{Converting}$$
$$1x + 0.08x = 783 \qquad \text{Identity property of 1}$$
$$1.08x = 783 \qquad \text{Collecting like terms}$$
$$x = \frac{783}{1.08} \qquad \text{Dividing by 1.08}$$
$$x = 725.$$

4. *Check.*   We check by taking 8% of $725 and adding it to $725:

$$8\% \times \$725 = 0.08 \times 725 = \$58.$$

Then $725 + $58 = $783, so $725 checks.

5. *State.*   The original investment was $725.   ◄

DO EXERCISE 7.

▶ **EXAMPLE 5**   The price of an automobile was decreased to a sale price of $13,559. This was a 9% reduction. What was the former price?

1. *Familiarize.*   Suppose that the former price was $16,000. A 9% reduction can be found by taking 9% of $16,000, that is,

$$9\% \text{ of } \$16,000 = 0.09(\$16,000) = \$1440.$$

Then the sale price is found by subtracting the amount of the reduction:

Former price − Reduction = Sale price

$16,000   − $1440   = $14,560.

Our guess of $16,000 was too high, but we are becoming familiar with the problem. We let x = the former price of the automobile. It is reduced by 9%. So the sale price $= x - 9\%x$.

2. *Translate.*   We reword and then translate:

Former price − Reduction = Sale price   **Rewording**

x −   9%x = $13,559.   **Translating**

ANSWER ON PAGE A-6

---

7. An investment is made at 7% simple interest for 1 year. It grows to $8988. How much was originally invested (the principal)?

8. The price of a suit was decreased to a sale price of $526.40. This was a 20% reduction. What was the former price?

3. *Solve.* We solve the equation:

$$x - 9\%x = 13,559$$
$$x - 0.09x = 13,559 \qquad \text{Converting to decimal notation}$$
$$1x - 0.09x = 13,559$$
$$(1 - 0.09)x = 13,559 \qquad \text{Factoring out the } x$$
$$0.91x = 13,559 \qquad \text{Collecting like terms}$$
$$x = \frac{13,559}{0.91} \qquad \text{Dividing by 0.91}$$
$$x = 14,900.$$

4. *Check.* To check, we find 9% of $14,900 and subtract:

$$9\% \times \$14,900 = 0.09 \times \$14,900 = \$1341$$
$$\$14,900 - \$1341 = \$13,559.$$

Since we get the sale price, $13,559, the $14,900 checks.

5. *State.* The former price was $14,900.   ◀

This problem is easy with algebra. Without algebra it is not. A common error in a problem like this is to take 9% of the sale price and subtract or add. Note that 9% of the original price is not equal to 9% of the sale price!

DO EXERCISE 8.

NAME   SECTION   DATE

EXERCISE SET 8.5

a Solve.

1. What percent of 68 is 17?

2. What percent of 75 is 36?

3. What percent of 125 is 30?

4. What percent of 300 is 57?

5. 45 is 30% of what number?

6. 20.4 is 24% of what number?

7. 0.3 is 12% of what number?

8. 7 is 175% of what number?

9. What number is 65% of 840?

10. What number is 1% of one million?

11. What percent of 80 is 100?

12. What percent of 10 is 205?

13. What is 2% of 40?

14. What is 40% of 2?

15. 2 is what percent of 40?

16. 40 is 2% of what number?

17. The FBI annually receives 16,000 applicants to become agents. It accepts 600 of these applicants. What percent does it accept?

18. The U.S. Postal Service reports that we open and read 78% of the junk mail that we receive. A business sends out 9500 advertising brochures. How many of them can it expect to be opened and read?

19. It has been determined by sociologists that 17% of the population is left-handed. Each week 160 men enter a tournament conducted by the Professional Bowlers Association. How many of them would you expect to be left-handed? Round to the nearest one.

20. In a medical study, it was determined that if 800 people kiss someone else who has a cold, only 56 will actually catch the cold. What percent is this?

21. On a test of 88 items, a student got 76 correct. What percent were correct?

22. A baseball player had 13 hits in 25 times at bat. What percent were hits?

1. _____

2. _____

3. _____

4. _____

5. _____

6. _____

7. _____

8. _____

9. _____

10. _____

11. _____

12. _____

13. _____

14. _____

15. _____

16. _____

17. _____

18. _____

19. _____

20. _____

21. _____

22. _____

ANSWERS

23. _____

24. _____

25. _____

26. _____

27. _____

28. _____

29. _____

30. _____

31. _____

32. _____

33. _____

34. _____

35. _____

36. _____

37. _____

38. _____

39. _____

23. The cost of a Navy F-14 Tomcat jet is $24 million. Eventually each jet will need to be renovated at 2% of its original cost. How much is that cost?

24. The cost of a Navy A-6 Intruder attack bomber is $30 million. Eventually each bomber will need to be renovated at 2% of its original cost. How much is that cost?

25. A family spent $208 one month for food. This was 26% of its income. What was their monthly income?

26. The sales tax rate in New York City is 8%. How much would be charged on a purchase of $428.86? How much will the total cost of the purchase be?

27. Water volume increases 9% when water freezes. If 400 cubic centimeters of water is frozen, how much will its volume increase? What will be the volume of the ice?

28. An investment is made at 9% simple interest for 1 year. It grows to $8502. How much was originally invested?

29. Money is borrowed at 10% simple interest. After 1 year, $7194 pays off the loan. How much was originally borrowed?

30. Due to inflation the price of an item increased 12¢. This was an 8% increase. What was the old price? the new price?

31. After a 40% price reduction, a shirt is on sale at $9.60. What was the original price (that is, the price before reduction)?

32. After a 34% price reduction, a blouse is on sale at $9.24. What was the original price?

SYNTHESIS

33. In a basketball league, the Falcons won 15 of their first 20 games. How many more games will they have to play where they win only half the time in order to win 60% of the total number of games?

34. One number is 25% of another. The larger number is 12 more than the smaller. What are the numbers?

35. In one city, a sales tax of 9% was added to the price of gasoline as registered on the pump. Suppose a driver asked for $10 worth of gas. The attendant filled the tank until the pump read $9.10 and charged the driver $10. Something was wrong. Use algebra to correct the error.

36. The weather report is "a 60% chance of showers during the day, 30% tonight, and 5% tomorrow morning." What are the chances it won't rain during the day? tonight? tomorrow morning?

37. Twenty-seven people make a certain amount of money at a sale. What percentage does each receive if they share the profit equally?

38. If x is 160% of y, y is what percent of x?

39. Which of the following is higher, if cithcr?

A. x is increased by 25%; then that amount is decreased by 25%.
B. x is decreased by 25%; then that amount is increased by 25%.

Explain.

8.6 Formulas

a Solving Formulas

A **formula** is a "recipe" for doing a certain type of calculation. Formulas are often given as equations. Here is an example of a formula that has to do with weather: $M = \frac{1}{5}n$. You see a flash of lightning. After a few seconds you hear the thunder associated with that flash. How far away was the lightning?

Your distance from the storm is M miles. You can find that distance by counting the number of seconds n that it takes the sound of the thunder to reach you and then multiplying by $\frac{1}{5}$.

▶ **EXAMPLE 1** Consider the formula $M = \frac{1}{5}n$. It takes 10 sec for the sound of thunder to reach you after you have seen a flash of lightning. How far away is the storm?

We substitute 10 for n and calculate M: $M = \frac{1}{5}n = \frac{1}{5}(10) = 2$. The storm is 2 mi away. ◀

DO EXERCISE 1.

Suppose that we know how far we are from the storm and want to calculate the number of seconds it would take the sound of the thunder to reach us. We could substitute a number for M, say 2, and solve for n:

$$2 = \frac{1}{5}n$$
$$10 = n. \qquad \text{Multiplying by 5}$$

However, if we wanted to do this repeatedly, it might be easier to solve for n by getting it alone on one side. We "solve" the formula for n.

▶ **EXAMPLE 2** Solve for n: $M = \frac{1}{5}n$.

We have

$$M = \frac{1}{5}n \qquad \text{We want this letter alone.}$$
$$5 \cdot M = 5 \cdot \frac{1}{5}n \qquad \text{Multiplying on both sides by 5}$$
$$5M = n.$$

In the above situation for $M = 2$, $n = 5(2)$, or 10. ◀

DO EXERCISE 2.

To see how the addition and multiplication principles apply to formulas, compare the following.

A. Solve.

$$5x + 2 = 12$$
$$5x = 12 - 2$$
$$5x = 10$$
$$x = \frac{10}{5} = 2$$

B. Solve.

$$5x + 2 = 12$$
$$5x = 12 - 2$$
$$x = \frac{12 - 2}{5}$$

C. Solve for x.

$$ax + b = c$$
$$ax = c - b$$
$$x = \frac{c - b}{a}$$

In (A) we solved as we did before. In (B) we did not carry out the calculations. In (C) we could not carry out the calculations because we had unknown numbers.

OBJECTIVE

After finishing Section 8.6, you should be able to:

a Solve a formula for a specified letter.

FOR EXTRA HELP

Tape 19A

1. Suppose that it takes the sound of thunder 14 sec to reach you. How far away is the storm?

2. Solve for I: $E = IR$.

   (This is a formula from electricity relating voltage E, current I, and resistance R.)

3. Solve for D: $C = \pi D$.

(This is a formula for the circumference C of a circle of diameter D.)

4. Solve for c:

$$A = \frac{a + b + c + d}{4}.$$

5. Solve for I:

$$E = \frac{9R}{I}.$$

(This is a formula for computing the earned run average E of a pitcher who has given up R earned runs in I innings of pitching.)

▶ **EXAMPLE 3**   Solve for r: $C = 2\pi r$.

This is a formula for the circumference C of a circle of radius r.

$$C = 2\pi r \qquad \text{We want this letter alone.}$$

$$\frac{C}{2\pi} = \frac{2\pi r}{2\pi} \qquad \text{Dividing by } 2\pi$$

$$\frac{C}{2\pi} = r$$

> *Caution!* Remember, formulas are equations. Use the same principles in solving that you use for any other equation.

◀

DO EXERCISE 3.

    With the formulas in this section, we can use a procedure like that described in Section 8.3.

> **To solve a formula for a given letter, identify the letter, and:**
> 1. **Multiply on both sides to clear of fractions or decimals, if that is needed.**
> 2. **Collect like terms on each side, if necessary.**
> 3. **Get all terms with the letter to be solved for on one side of the equation and all other terms on the other side.**
> 4. **Collect like terms again, if necessary.**
> 5. **Solve for the letter in question.**

▶ **EXAMPLE 4**   Solve for a: $A = \dfrac{a + b + c}{3}$.

This is a formula for the average A of three numbers a, b, and c.

$$A = \frac{a + b + c}{3} \qquad \text{We want the letter } a \text{ alone.}$$

$$3A = a + b + c \qquad \text{Multiplying by 3 to clear of the fraction}$$

$$3A - b - c = a$$

◀

DO EXERCISE 4.

▶ **EXAMPLE 5**   Solve for C: $Q = \dfrac{100M}{C}$.

This is a formula used in psychology for intelligence quotient Q, where M is mental age and C is chronological, or actual, age.

$$Q = \frac{100M}{C} \qquad \text{We want the letter } C \text{ alone.}$$

$$CQ = 100M \qquad \text{Multiplying by } C \text{ to clear of the fraction}$$

$$C = \frac{100M}{Q} \qquad \text{Dividing by } Q$$

◀

DO EXERCISE 5.

NAME   SECTION   DATE

EXERCISE SET 8.6

a Solve for the given letter.

1. $A = bh$, for b
   (Area of a parallelogram with base b
   and height h)

2. $A = bh$, for h

3. $d = rt$, for r
   (A distance formula, where d is
   distance, r is speed, and t is time)

4. $d = rt$, for t

5. $I = Prt$, for P
   (Simple-interest formula, where I is
   interest, P is principal, r is interest
   rate, and t is time)

6. $I = Prt$, for t

7. $F = ma$, for a
   (A physics formula, where F is force,
   m is mass, and a is acceleration)

8. $F = ma$, for m

9. $P = 2l + 2w$, for w
   (Perimeter of a rectangle of length l
   and width w)

10. $P = 2l + 2w$, for l

11. $A = \pi r^2$, for r^2
    (Area of a circle with radius r)

12. $A = \pi r^2$, for π

13. $A = \dfrac{1}{2}bh$, for b
    (Area of a triangle with base b and
    height h)

14. $A = \dfrac{1}{2}bh$, for h

15. $E = mc^2$, for m
    (A relativity formula)

16. $E = mc^2$, for c^2

17. $Q = \dfrac{c + d}{2}$, for d

18. $Q = \dfrac{p - q}{2}$, for p

19. $A = \dfrac{a + b + c}{3}$, for b

20. $A = \dfrac{a + b + c}{3}$, for c

1. _____

2. _____

3. _____

4. _____

5. _____

6. _____

7. _____

8. _____

9. _____

10. _____

11. _____

12. _____

13. _____

14. _____

15. _____

16. _____

17. _____

18. _____

19. _____

20. _____

21. $v = \dfrac{3k}{t}$, for t

22. $P = \dfrac{ab}{c}$, for c

23. $Ax + By = C$, for y

24. $Ax + By = C$, for x

25. $A = \dfrac{1}{2}ah + \dfrac{1}{2}bh$, for b; for h

26. $A = \dfrac{1}{2}ah - \dfrac{1}{2}bh$, for a; for h

27. $Q = 3a + 5ca$, for a

28. $P = 4m + 7mn$, for m

29. The formula

$$H = \dfrac{D^2 N}{2.5}$$

is used to find the horsepower H of an N-cylinder engine. Solve for D^2.

30. Solve for N:

$$H = \dfrac{D^2 N}{2.5}.$$

31. The area of a sector of a circle is given by

$$A = \dfrac{\pi r^2 S}{360},$$

where r is the radius and S is the angle measure of the sector. Solve for S.

32. Solve for r^2:

$$A = \dfrac{\pi r^2 S}{360}.$$

33. The formula

$$R = -0.0075t + 3.85$$

can be used to estimate the world record in the 1500-m run t years after 1930. Solve for t.

34. The formula

$$F = \dfrac{9}{5}C + 32$$

can be used to convert from Celsius, or Centigrade, temperature C to Fahrenheit temperature F. Solve for C.

SKILL MAINTENANCE

35. Convert to decimal notation: $\dfrac{23}{25}$.

36. Add: $-23 + (-67)$.

37. Subtract: $-45.8 - (-32.6)$.

38. Remove parentheses and simplify:

$$4a - 8b - 5(5a - 4b).$$

SYNTHESIS

39. In $A = lw$, l and w both double. What is the effect on A?

40. In $P = 2a + 2b$, P doubles. Do a and b necessarily both double?

41. In $A = \frac{1}{2}bh$, b increases by 4 units and h does not change. What happens to A?

42. Solve for F:

$$D = \dfrac{1}{E + F}.$$

8.7 Solving Inequalities

We now extend our equation-solving principles to the solving of inequalities.

a Solutions of Inequalities

In Section 1.2, we defined the symbols > (greater than), < (less than), ≥ (greater than or equal to), and ≤ (less than or equal to). For example, $3 \leq 4$ and $3 \leq 3$ are both true, but $-3 \leq -4$ and $0 \geq 2$ are both false.

An **inequality** is a number sentence with >, <, ≥, or ≤ as its verb—for example,

$$-4 > t, \quad x < 3, \quad 2x + 5 \geq 0, \quad \text{and} \quad -3y + 7 \leq -8.$$

Some replacements for a variable in an inequality make it true and some make it false. A replacement that makes an inequality true is called a **solution.** The set of all solutions is called the **solution set.** When we have found the set of all solutions of an inequality, we say that we have **solved** the inequality.

▶ **EXAMPLES**   Determine whether the number is a solution of $x < 2$.

1. -2 Since $-2 < 2$ is true, -2 is a solution.

2. 2   Since $2 < 2$ is false, 2 is not a solution.   ◀

▶ **EXAMPLES**   Determine whether the number is a solution of $y \geq 6$.

3. 6   Since $6 \geq 6$ is true, 6 is a solution.

4. -4 Since $-4 \geq 6$ is false, -4 is not a solution.   ◀

DO EXERCISES 1 AND 2.

b Graphs of Inequalities

Some solutions of $x < 2$ are 0.45, -8.9, $-\pi$, and so on. In fact, there are infinitely many real numbers that are solutions. Because we cannot list them all individually, it is helpful to make a drawing that represents all the solutions.

A **graph** of an inequality is a drawing that represents its solutions. An inequality in one variable can be graphed on a number line. An inequality in two variables can be graphed on a coordinate plane.

We first graph inequalities in one variable on a number line.

▶ **EXAMPLE 5**   Graph: $x < 2$.

The solutions of $x < 2$ are those numbers less than 2. They are shown on the graph by shading all points to the left of 2. The open circle at 2 indicates that 2 is not part of the graph.

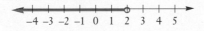   ◀

Determine whether each number is a solution of the inequality.

1. $x > 3$

   a) 2   **b)** 0

   c) -5 **d)** 15

   e) 3

2. $x \leq 6$

   a) 6   **b)** 0

   c) -4 **d)** 25

   e) -6

Graph.

3. $x < 4$

4. $y \geq -2$

5. $-2 \leq x < 4$

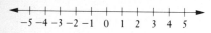

► **EXAMPLE 6**   Graph: $y \geq -3$.

The solutions of $y \geq -3$ are shown on the number line by shading the point for -3 and all points to the right of -3. The closed circle at -3 indicates that -3 *is* part of the graph.

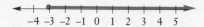   ◄

► **EXAMPLE 7**   Graph: $-2 < x \leq 3$.

The inequality $-2 < x \leq 3$ is read "-2 is less than x *and* x is less than or equal to 3," or "x is greater than -2 and less than or equal to 3." To be a solution of this inequality, a number must be a solution of both $-2 < x$ and $x \leq 3$. The number 1 is a solution, as are -0.5, 2, 2.5, and 3. The solution set is graphed as follows:

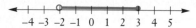

The open circle at -2 means that -2 is not part of the graph. The closed circle at 3 means that 3 is part of the graph. The other solutions are shaded.   ◄

DO EXERCISES 3–5.

C Solving Inequalities Using the Addition Principle

Consider the true inequality

$$3 < 7.$$

If we add 2 on both sides, we get another true inequality:

$$3 + 2 < 7 + 2, \quad \text{or} \quad 5 < 9.$$

Similarly, if we add -3 on both sides, we get another true inequality:

$$3 + (-3) < 7 + (-3), \quad \text{or} \quad 0 < 4.$$

> **The Addition Principle for Inequalities**
>
> **If the same number is added on both sides of a true inequality, we get another true inequality.**

Let's see how we use the addition principle to solve inequalities.

► **EXAMPLE 8**   Solve: $x + 2 > 8$. Then graph.

We use the addition principle, subtracting 2 on both sides:

$$x + 2 - 2 > 8 - 2$$
$$x > 6.$$

Using the addition principle, we get an inequality for which we can determine the solutions easily.

Any number greater than 6 makes the last sentence true and is a solution of that sentence. Any such number is also a solution of the original sentence. Thus the inequality is solved. The graph is as follows:

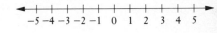

We cannot check all the solutions of an inequality by substitution, as we can check solutions of equations, because there are too many of them. A partial check can be done by substituting a number greater than 6, say 7, into the original inequality:

$$\frac{\begin{array}{c|c} x + 2 > 8 \\ \hline 7 + 2 & 8 \\ 9 & \text{TRUE} \end{array}}{}$$

Since $9 > 8$ is true, 7 is a solution. Any number greater than 6 is a solution.

◄

When two inequalities have the same solutions, we say that they are **equivalent.** Whenever we use the addition principle with inequalities, the first and last sentences will be equivalent.

► **EXAMPLE 9** Solve: $3x + 1 \le 2x - 3$. Then graph.

We have

$$3x + 1 \le 2x - 3$$
$$3x + 1 - 1 \le 2x - 3 - 1 \qquad \text{Subtracting 1}$$
$$3x \le 2x - 4 \qquad \text{Simplifying}$$
$$3x - 2x \le 2x - 4 - 2x \qquad \text{Subtracting } 2x$$
$$x \le -4. \qquad \text{Simplifying}$$

The graph is as follows:

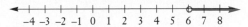

Any number less than or equal to -4 is a solution. The following are some solutions:

$$-4, \quad -5, \quad -6, \quad -4.1, \quad -2045, \quad \text{and} \quad -18\pi.$$

Besides drawing a graph, we can also describe all the solutions of an inequality using **set notation.** We could just begin to list them in a set as follows:

$$\{-4, -5, -6, -4.1, -2045, -18\pi, \ldots\}.$$

We can never list them all this way, however. Seeing this set without knowing the inequality makes it difficult for us to know what real numbers we are considering. There is another kind of notation used. It is

$$\{x \mid x \le -4\},$$

which is read:

"The set of all x such that x is less than or equal to -4."

This shorter notation for sets is called **set-builder notation.** From now on, you should use this notation when solving inequalities. ◄

DO EXERCISES 6–8.

ANSWERS ON PAGE A-6

Solve. Then graph.

6. $x + 3 > 5$

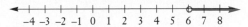

7. $x - 1 \le 2$

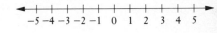

8. $5x + 1 < 4x - 2$

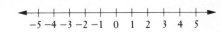

Solve.

9. $x + \dfrac{2}{3} \geq \dfrac{4}{5}$

▶ **EXAMPLE 10**   Solve: $x + \frac{1}{3} > \frac{5}{4}$.

We have

$$x + \tfrac{1}{3} > \tfrac{5}{4}$$

$$x + \tfrac{1}{3} - \tfrac{1}{3} > \tfrac{5}{4} - \tfrac{1}{3} \qquad \text{Subtracting } \tfrac{1}{3}$$

$$x > \tfrac{5}{4} \cdot \tfrac{3}{3} - \tfrac{1}{3} \cdot \tfrac{4}{4} \qquad \begin{array}{l}\text{Multiplying by 1 to obtain a} \\ \text{common denominator}\end{array}$$

$$x > \tfrac{15}{12} - \tfrac{4}{12}$$

$$x > \tfrac{11}{12}.$$

Any number greater than $\frac{11}{12}$ is a solution. The solution set is

$$\{x \mid x > \tfrac{11}{12}\},$$

which is read: "The set of all x such that x is greater than $\frac{11}{12}$."   ◀

When solving inequalities, you may obtain an answer like $7 < x$. Recall from Chapter 7 that this has the same meaning as $x > 7$. Thus the solution set can be described as $\{x \mid 7 < x\}$ or as $\{x \mid x > 7\}$. The latter is used most often.

DO EXERCISES 9 AND 10.

10. $5y + 2 \leq -1 + 4y$

d   Solving Inequalities Using the Multiplication Principle

There is a multiplication principle for inequalities similar to that for equations, but it must be modified when multiplying on both sides by a negative number. Consider the true inequality

$$3 < 7.$$

If we multiply on both sides by a positive number 2, we get another true inequality:

$$3 \cdot 2 < 7 \cdot 2,$$

or $\qquad\qquad\qquad\qquad 6 < 14.$ True

If we multiply on both sides by a negative number -3, we get the false inequality

$$3 \cdot (-3) < 7 \cdot (-3),$$

or $\qquad\qquad\qquad\qquad -9 < -21.$ False

However, if we reverse the inequality symbol, we get a true inequality:

$$-9 > -21.$$ True

Summarizing these results, we obtain the multiplication principle for inequalities.

> **The Multiplication Principle for Inequalities**
>
> **If we multiply (or divide) on both sides of a true inequality by a positive number, we get another true inequality. If we multiply (or divide) by a negative number and reverse the inequality symbol, we get another true inequality.**

▶ **EXAMPLE 11**   Solve: $4x < 28$. Then graph.
We have

$$\frac{4x}{4} < \frac{28}{4}$$ Dividing by 4
        └── The symbol stays the same.

$$x < 7.$$ Simplifying

The solution set is $\{x \mid x < 7\}$. The graph is as follows:

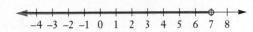

DO EXERCISES 11 AND 12.

▶ **EXAMPLE 12**   Solve: $-2y < 18$. Then graph.
We have

$$\frac{-2y}{-2} > \frac{18}{-2}$$ Dividing by -2
         └── The symbol must be reversed!

$$y > -9.$$ Simplifying

The solution set is $\{y \mid y > -9\}$. The graph is as follows:

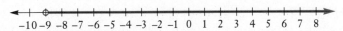

DO EXERCISES 13 AND 14.

e   **Using the Principles Together**

We use the addition and multiplication principles together in solving inequalities in much the same way as in solving equations. We generally use the addition principle first.

▶ **EXAMPLE 13**   Solve: $6 - 5y > 7$.
We have

$$-6 + 6 - 5y > -6 + 7$$ Adding -6

$$-5y > 1$$ Simplifying

$$\frac{-5y}{-5} < \frac{1}{-5}$$ Dividing by -5
        └── The symbol must be reversed.

$$y < -\frac{1}{5}$$ Simplifying

The solution set is $\{y \mid y < -\frac{1}{5}\}$.

DO EXERCISE 15.

Solve. Then graph.

11. $8x < 64$

12. $5y \geq 160$

Solve.

13. $-4x \leq 24$

14. $-5y > 13$

15. Solve: $7 - 4x < 8$.

ANSWERS ON PAGE A-6

16. Solve: $24 - 7y \le 11y - 14$.

▶ **EXAMPLE 14**   Solve: $8y - 5 > 17 - 5y$.
We have

$$-17 + 8y - 5 > -17 + 17 - 5y \qquad \text{Adding } -17$$
$$8y - 22 > -5y \qquad \text{Simplifying}$$
$$-8y + 8y - 22 > -8y - 5y \qquad \text{Adding } -8y$$
$$-22 > -13y \qquad \text{Simplifying}$$
$$\frac{-22}{-13} < \frac{-13y}{-13} \qquad \text{Dividing by } -13$$

The symbol must be reversed.

$$\frac{22}{13} < y.$$

The solution set is $\{y | \frac{22}{13} < y\}$. Since $\frac{22}{13} < y$ has the same meaning as $y > \frac{22}{13}$, we can also describe the solution set as $\{y | y > \frac{22}{13}\}$. That is, $\frac{22}{13} < y$ and $y > \frac{22}{13}$ are equivalent. Answers are generally written, however, with the variable on the left.   ◀

We can often solve inequalities in such a way as to avoid having to reverse the inequality symbol. We add so that after like terms have been collected, the coefficient of the variable term is positive. We show this by solving the inequality in Example 15 a different way.

17. Solve. Use a method like the one used in Example 15.

$$24 - 7y \le 11y - 14$$

▶ **EXAMPLE 15**   Solve: $8y - 5 > 17 - 5y$.
We note that if we add $5y$ on both sides, the coefficient of the y-term will be positive after like terms have been collected.

$$8y - 5 + 5y > 17 - 5y + 5y \qquad \text{Adding } 5y \text{ on both sides}$$
$$13y - 5 > 17 \qquad \text{Simplifying}$$
$$13y - 5 + 5 > 17 + 5 \qquad \text{Adding 5 on both sides}$$
$$13y > 22 \qquad \text{Simplifying}$$
$$\frac{13y}{13} > \frac{22}{13} \qquad \text{Dividing by 13 on both sides}$$
$$y > \frac{22}{13}$$

The solution set is $\{y | y > \frac{22}{13}\}$.   ◀

DO EXERCISES 16 AND 17.

18. Solve:

$$3(7 + 2x) \le 30 + 7(x - 1).$$

▶ **EXAMPLE 16**   Solve: $3(x - 2) - 1 < 2 - 5(x + 6)$.

$$3(x - 2) - 1 < 2 - 5(x + 6)$$
$$3x - 6 - 1 < 2 - 5x - 30 \qquad \text{Using the distributive laws to multiply and remove parentheses}$$
$$3x - 7 < -5x - 28 \qquad \text{Simplifying}$$
$$3x + 5x < -28 + 7 \qquad \text{Adding } 5x \text{ and 7 to get all } x\text{-terms on one side and all other terms on the other side}$$
$$8x < -21 \qquad \text{Simplifying}$$
$$x < \frac{-21}{8}, \quad \text{or} \quad -\frac{21}{8} \qquad \text{Dividing by 8}$$

The solution set is $\{x | x < -\frac{21}{8}\}$.   ◀

DO EXERCISE 18.

EXERCISE SET 8.7

a Determine whether each number is a solution of the given inequality.

1. $x > -4$
  a) 4
  b) 0
  c) -4
  d) 6
  e) 5.6

2. $y < 5$
  a) 0
  b) 5
  c) -1
  d) -5
  e) $7\frac{1}{4}$

3. $x \geq 6$
  a) -6
  b) 0
  c) 6
  d) 8
  e) $-3\frac{1}{2}$

4. $x \leq 10$
  a) 4
  b) -10
  c) 0
  d) 11
  e) -4.7

b Graph on a number line.

5. $x > 4$

6. $y < 0$

7. $t < -3$

8. $y > 5$

9. $m \geq -1$

10. $p \leq 3$

11. $-3 < x \leq 4$

12. $-5 \leq x < 2$

13. $0 < x < 3$

14. $-5 \leq x \leq 0$

c Solve using the addition principle. Then graph.

15. $x + 7 > 2$

16. $x + 6 > 3$

17. $x + 8 \leq -10$

18. $x + 9 \leq -12$

Solve using the addition principle.

19. $y - 7 > -12$

20. $y - 10 > -16$

21. $2x + 3 > x + 5$

22. $2x + 4 > x + 7$

23. $3x + 9 \leq 2x + 6$

24. $3x + 10 \leq 2x + 8$

25. $5x - 6 < 4x - 2$

26. $6x - 8 < 5x - 9$

27. $-7 + c > 7$

ANSWERS

1.
2.
3.
4.
5. See graph.
6. See graph.
7. See graph.
8. See graph.
9. See graph.
10. See graph.
11. See graph.
12. See graph.
13. See graph.
14. See graph.
15.
16.
17.
18.
19.
20.
21.
22.
23.
24.
25.
26.
27.

28. $-9 + c > 9$

29. $y + \dfrac{1}{4} \le \dfrac{1}{2}$

30. $y + \dfrac{1}{3} \le \dfrac{5}{6}$

31. $x - \dfrac{1}{3} > \dfrac{1}{4}$

32. $x - \dfrac{1}{8} > \dfrac{1}{2}$

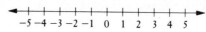 Solve using the multiplication principle. Then graph.

33. $5x < 35$

34. $8x \ge 32$

35. $-12x > -36$

36. $-16x > -64$

Solve using the multiplication principle.

37. $5y \ge -2$

38. $7x > -4$

39. $-2x \le 12$

40. $-3y \le 15$

41. $-4y \ge -16$

42. $-7x < -21$

43. $-3x < -17$

44. $-5y > -23$

45. $-2y > \dfrac{1}{7}$

46. $-4x \le \dfrac{1}{9}$

47. $-\dfrac{6}{5} \le -4x$

48. $-\dfrac{7}{8} > -56t$

e Solve using the addition and multiplication principles.

49. $4 + 3x < 28$

50. $5 + 4y < 37$

51. $3x - 5 \le 13$

52. $5y - 9 \le 21$

53. $13x - 7 < -46$

54. $8y - 4 < -52$

55. $30 > 3 - 9x$

56. $40 > 5 - 7y$

57. $4x + 2 - 3x \leq 9$

58. $15x + 3 - 14x \leq 7$

59. $-3 < 8x + 7 - 7x$

60. $-5 < 9x + 8 - 8x$

61. $6 - 4y > 4 - 3y$

62. $7 - 8y > 5 - 7y$

63. $5 - 9y \leq 2 - 8y$

64. $6 - 13y \leq 4 - 12y$

65. $19 - 7y - 3y < 39$

66. $18 - 6y - 9y < 63$

67. $2.1x + 45.2 > 3.2 - 8.4x$

68. $0.96y - 0.79 \leq 0.21y + 0.46$

69. $\dfrac{x}{3} - 2 \leq 1$

70. $\dfrac{2}{3} - \dfrac{x}{5} < \dfrac{4}{15}$

71. $\dfrac{y}{5} + 1 \leq \dfrac{2}{5}$

72. $\dfrac{3x}{4} + \dfrac{7}{8} \geq -15$

73. $3(2y - 3) < 27$

74. $4(2y - 3) > 28$

75. $2(3 + 4m) - 9 \geq 45$

76. $3(5 + 3m) - 8 \leq 88$

ANSWERS

55. _____

56. _____

57. _____

58. _____

59. _____

60. _____

61. _____

62. _____

63. _____

64. _____

65. _____

66. _____

67. _____

68. _____

69. _____

70. _____

71. _____

72. _____

73. _____

74. _____

75. _____

76. _____

ANSWERS

77. _____

78. _____

79. _____

80. _____

81. _____

82. _____

83. _____

84. _____

85. _____

86. _____

87. _____

88. _____

89. _____

90. _____

91. _____

92. _____

93. _____

94. _____

95.   See graph. _____

96. _____

97. _____

98. _____

99. _____

77. $8(2t + 1) > 4(7t + 7)$

78. $7(5x - 2) < 6(6x - 1)$

79. $3(r - 6) + 2 < 4(r + 2) - 21$

80. $5(t + 3) + 9 > 3(t - 2) + 6$

81. $\frac{1}{4}(8y + 4) - 17 > -\frac{1}{2}(4y - 8)$

82. $\frac{1}{3}(6x + 24) - 20 < -\frac{1}{4}(12x - 72)$

83. $\frac{2}{3}(2x - 1) \geq 10$

84. $\frac{4}{5}(3x + 4) \leq 20$

85. $0.8(3x + 6) \geq 1.1 - (x + 2)$

86. $0.4(2x + 8) \geq 20 - (x + 5)$

87. $a + (a - 1) < (a + 2) - (a + 1)$

88. $0.8 - 4(b - 1) > 0.2 + 3(4 - b)$

SKILL MAINTENANCE

Add.

89. $-56 + (-18)$ **90.** $-2.3 + 7.1$ **91.** $-\frac{3}{4} + \frac{1}{8}$ **92.** $8.12 - 9.23$

SYNTHESIS

93. Suppose that $2x - 5 \geq 9$ is true for some value of x. Determine whether $2x - 5 \geq 8$ is true for that same value of x.

94. Determine whether each number is a solution of the inequality $|x| < 3$.
   a) 0   **b)** -2
   c) -3 **d)** 4
   e) 3   **f)** 1.7
   g) -2.8

95. Graph $|x| < 3$ on a number line.

96. Determine whether each number is a solution of the inequality $|x| \geq 4$.
   a) 0   **b)** -5
   c) 6   **d)** -3
   e) 3   **f)** -8
   g) 9.7

Solve.

97. $x + 3 \leq 3 + x$

98. $x + 4 < 3 + x$

99. Suppose we are considering *only* integer solutions to $x > 5$. Find an equivalent inequality involving $\geq$.

8.8 Solving Problems Using Inequalities

We can use inequalities to solve certain kinds of problems.

a Translating to Inequalities

Let us first practice translating sentences to inequalities.

▶ **EXAMPLES** Translate to an inequality.

1. A number is less than 5.

$$x < 5$$

2. A number is greater than or equal to $3\frac{1}{2}$.

$$y \geq 3\frac{1}{2}$$

3. My salary is at most $34,000.

$$S \leq \$34,000$$

4. The number of compact disc players is at least 2700.

$$C \geq 2700$$

5. 12 more than twice a number is less than 37.

$$12 + 2x < 37$$ ◀

DO EXERCISES 1–5.

b Solving Problems

▶ **EXAMPLE 6** A student is taking an introductory algebra course in which four tests are to be given. To get an A, the student must average at least 90 on the four tests. The student got scores of 91, 86, and 89 on the first three tests. Determine (in terms of an inequality) what scores on the last test will allow the student to get an A.

1. *Familiarize.* Let us try some guessing. Suppose the student gets a 92 on the last test. The average of the four scores is their sum divided by the number of tests, 4, and is given by

$$\frac{91 + 86 + 89 + 92}{4} = 89.5.$$

For this average to be *at least* 90, it must be greater than or equal to 90. In this case, we have $89.5 \geq 90$, which is not true. But there are scores that will give the A. To find them, we translate to an inequality and solve. Let $x = $ the student's score on the last test.

2. *Translate.* The average of the four scores must be *at least* 90. This means that it must be greater than or equal to 90. Thus we can translate the problem to the inequality

$$\frac{91 + 86 + 89 + x}{4} \geq 90.$$

OBJECTIVES

After finishing Section 8.8, you should be able to:

a Translate number sentences to inequalities.

b Solve problems using inequalities.

Translate.

1. A number is less than or equal to 8.

2. A number is greater than -2.

3. The speed of that car is at most 180 mph.

4. The price of that car is at least $5800.

5. Twice a number minus 32 is greater than 5.

6. A student is taking a literature course in which four tests are to be given. To get a B, the student must average at least 80 on the four tests. The student got scores of 82, 76, and 78 on the first three tests. Determine (in terms of an inequality) what scores on the last test will allow the student to get at least a B.

3. *Solve.* We solve the inequality. We first multiply by 4 to clear of fractions.

$$4\left(\frac{91 + 86 + 89 + x}{4}\right) \geq 4 \cdot 90 \qquad \text{Multiplying by 4}$$

$$91 + 86 + 89 + x \geq 360$$

$$266 + x \geq 360 \qquad \text{Collecting like terms}$$

$$x \geq 94$$

The solution set is $\{x \mid x \geq 94\}$.

4. *Check.* We can obtain a partial check by substituting a number greater than or equal to 94. We leave it to the student to try 95 in a manner similar to what was done in the familiarization step.

5. *State.* Any score that is at least 94 will give the student an A in the course. ◄

DO EXERCISE 6.

▶ **EXAMPLE 7**   Butter stays solid at Fahrenheit temperatures below 88°. The formula

$$F = \tfrac{9}{5}C + 32$$

can be used to convert Celsius temperatures C to Fahrenheit temperatures F. Determine (in terms of an inequality) those Celsius temperatures for which butter stays solid.

1. *Familiarize.* Suppose we guess to see how we might consider a solution. We try a Celsius temperature of 40°. We substitute and find F:

$$F = \tfrac{9}{5}C + 32 = \tfrac{9}{5}(40) + 32 = 72 + 32 = 104°.$$

This is higher than 88°, so 40° is *not* a solution. To find the solutions, we need to solve an inequality.

7. Gold stays solid at Fahrenheit temperatures below 1945.4°. Determine (in terms of an inequality) those Celsius temperatures for which gold stays solid. Use the formula given in Example 7.

2. *Translate.* The Fahrenheit temperature F is to be less than 88. We have the inequality

$$F < 88.$$

To find the Celsius temperatures C that satisfy this condition, we substitute $\tfrac{9}{5}C + 32$ for F, which gives us the following inequality:

$$\tfrac{9}{5}C + 32 < 88.$$

3. *Solve.* We solve the inequality:

$$\tfrac{9}{5}C + 32 < 88$$

$$5(\tfrac{9}{5}C + 32) < 5(88) \qquad \text{Multiplying by 5 to clear of fractions}$$

$$5(\tfrac{9}{5}C) + 5(32) < 440 \qquad \text{Using a distributive law}$$

$$9C + 160 < 440 \qquad \text{Simplifying}$$

$$9C < 280 \qquad \text{Subtracting 160}$$

$$C < \frac{280}{9} \qquad \text{Dividing by 9}$$

$$C < 31.1. \qquad \text{Dividing and rounding to the nearest tenth}$$

The solution set of the inequality is $\{C \mid C < 31.1°\}$.

4. *Check.* The check is left to the student.

5. *State.* Butter stays solid at Celsius temperatures below 31.1°. ◄

     DO EXERCISE 7.

NAME   SECTION   DATE

EXERCISE SET 8.8

a Translate to an inequality.

1. A number is greater than 4.

2. A number is less than 7.

3. A number is less than or equal to −6.

4. A number is greater than or equal to 13.

5. The number of people is at least 1200.

6. The cost is at most $3457.95.

7. The amount of acid is not to exceed 500 liters.

8. The cost of gasoline is no less than 94 cents per gallon.

9. Two more than three times a number is less than 13.

10. Five less than one-half a number is greater than 17.

b Solve.

11. Your quiz grades are 73, 75, 89, and 91. Determine (in terms of an inequality) those scores that you can obtain on the last quiz in order to receive an average quiz grade of at least 85.

12. A human body is considered to be fevered when its temperature is higher than 98.6°F. Using the formula given in Example 7, determine (in terms of an inequality) those Celsius temperatures for which the body is fevered.

13. The formula
$$R = -0.075t + 3.85$$
can be used to predict the world record in the 1500-m run t years after 1930. Determine (in terms of an inequality) those years for which the world record will be less than 3.5 min.

14. The formula
$$R = -0.028t + 20.8$$
can be used to predict the world record in the 200-m dash t years after 1920. Determine (in terms of an inequality) those years for which the world record will be less than 19.0 sec.

15. Acme rents station wagons at a daily rate of $42.95 plus $0.46 per mile. A family wants to rent a wagon one day while on vacation, but must stay within a budget of $200. Determine (in terms of an inequality) those mileages that will allow the family to stay within budget. Round to the nearest tenth of a mile.

16. Atlas rents an intermediate-size car at a daily rate of $44.95 plus $0.39 per mile. A businessperson is not to exceed a daily car rental budget of $250. Determine (in terms of an inequality) those mileages that will allow the businessperson to stay within budget. Round to the nearest tenth of a mile.

ANSWERS

1. _____

2. _____

3. _____

4. _____

5. _____

6. _____

7. _____

8. _____

9. _____

10. _____

11. _____

12. _____

13. _____

14. _____

15. _____

16. _____

Copyright © 1993 Addison-Wesley Publishing Co., Inc.

ANSWERS

17. _____

18. _____

19. _____

20. _____

21. _____

22. _____

23. _____

24. _____

25. _____

26. _____

27. _____

28. _____

29. _____

30. _____

17. Find all numbers such that the sum of the number and 15 is less than four times the number.

18. Find all numbers such that three times the number minus ten times the number is greater than or equal to eight times the number.

19. The width of a rectangle is fixed at 4 cm. Determine (in terms of an inequality) those lengths for which the area will be less than 86 cm².

20. The width of a rectangle is fixed at 16 yd. Determine (in terms of an inequality) those lengths for which the area will be greater than or equal to 264 yd².

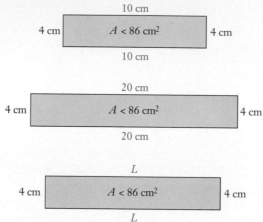

21. One side of a triangle is 2 cm shorter than the base. The other side is 3 cm longer than the base. What lengths of the base will allow the perimeter to be greater than 19 cm?

22. The perimeter of a rectangular swimming pool is not to exceed 70 ft. The length is to be twice the width. What widths will meet these conditions?

23. A salesperson made 18 customer calls last week and 22 calls this week. How many calls must be made next week in order to maintain an average of at least 20 for the three-week period?

24. George and Joan do volunteer work at a hospital. Joan worked 3 hr more than George, and together they worked more than 27 hr. What possible number of hours did each work?

25. A student is shopping for a new pair of jeans and two sweaters of the same kind. He is determined to spend no more than $120.00 for the outfit. He buys jeans for $21.95. What is the most the student can spend for each sweater?

26. The medium-size box of dog food weighs 1 lb more than the small size. The large size weighs 2 lb more than the small size. The total weight of the three boxes is at most 30 lb. What are the possible weights of the small box?

27. The width of a rectangle is 32 km. What lengths will make the area at least 2048 km²?

28. The height of a triangle is 20 cm. What lengths of the base will make the area at most 40 cm²?

SYNTHESIS

29. The area of a square can be no more than 64 cm². What lengths of a side will allow this?

30. The sum of two consecutive odd integers is less than 100. What is the largest possible pair of such integers?

SUMMARY AND REVIEW: CHAPTER 8

IMPORTANT PROPERTIES AND FORMULAS

The Addition Principles: If $a = b$ is true, then $a + c = b + c$ is true for any real number c. If the same number is added on both sides of an inequality, we get another true inequality.

The Multiplication Principles: If $a = b$ is true, then $ac = bc$ is true for any real number c. If we multiply on both sides of a true inequality by a positive number, we get another true inequality. If we multiply by a negative number and reverse the inequality symbol, we get another true inequality.

REVIEW EXERCISES

The review sections and objectives to be tested in addition to the material in this chapter are [3.1b], [3.2a, b], [3.3a, b], [7.1a, b], [7.3a], and [7.8b].

Solve.

1. $x + 5 = -17$

2. $-8x = -56$

3. $-\dfrac{x}{4} = 48$

4. $n - 7 = -6$

5. $15x = -35$

6. $x - 11 = 14$

7. $-\dfrac{2}{3} + x = -\dfrac{1}{6}$

8. $\dfrac{4}{5}y = -\dfrac{3}{16}$

9. $y - 0.9 = 9.09$

10. $5 - x = 13$

11. $5t + 9 = 3t - 1$

12. $7x - 6 = 25x$

13. $\dfrac{1}{4}x - \dfrac{5}{8} = \dfrac{3}{8}$

14. $14y = 23y - 17 - 10$

15. $0.22y - 0.6 = 0.12y + 3 - 0.8y$

16. $\dfrac{1}{4}x - \dfrac{1}{8}x = 3 - \dfrac{1}{16}x$

17. $4(x + 3) = 36$

18. $3(5x - 7) = -66$

19. $8(x - 2) = 5(x + 4)$

20. $-5x + 3(x + 8) = 16$

Determine whether the given number is a solution of the inequality $x \le 4$.

21. -3

22. 7

23. 4

Solve. Write set notation for the answers.

24. $y + \dfrac{2}{3} \ge \dfrac{1}{6}$

25. $9x \ge 63$

26. $2 + 6y > 14$

27. $7 - 3y \ge 27 + 2y$

28. $3x + 5 < 2x - 6$

29. $-4y < 28$

30. $3 - 4x < 27$

31. $4 - 8x < 13 + 3x$

32. $-3y \ge -21$

33. $-4x \le \dfrac{1}{3}$

Graph on a number line.

34. $4x - 6 < x + 3$

35. $-2 < x \le 5$

36. $y > 0$

Solve.

37. $C = \pi d$, for d

38. $V = \dfrac{1}{3}Bh$, for B

39. $A = \dfrac{a + b}{2}$, for a

40. A color television sold for $629 in May. This was $38 more than the cost in January. Find the cost in January.

41. Selma gets a $4 commission for each appliance that she sells. One week she got $108 in commissions. How many appliances did she sell?

42. An 8-m board is cut into two pieces. One piece is 2 m longer than the other. How long are the pieces?

43. If 14 is added to three times a certain number, the result is 41. Find the number.

44. The sum of two consecutive odd integers is 116. Find the integers.

45. The perimeter of a rectangle is 56 cm. The width is 6 cm less than the length. Find the width and the length.

46. After a 30% reduction, an item is on sale for $154. What was the marked price (the price before reducing)?

47. A businessperson's salary is $30,000. That is a 15% increase over the previous year's salary. What was the previous salary (to the nearest dollar)?

48. The measure of the second angle of a triangle is 50° more than that of the first. The measure of the third angle is 10° less than twice the first. Find the measures of the angles.

49. Your quiz grades are 71, 75, 82, and 86. What is the lowest grade you can get on the next quiz and still have an average of at least 80?

50. The length of a rectangle is 43 cm. What widths will make the perimeter greater than 120 cm?

SKILL MAINTENANCE

51. Convert to decimal notation: $\frac{17}{12}$.

52. Divide: $12.42 \div 5.4$.

53. Add: $-12 + 10 + (-19) + (-24)$.

54. Remove parentheses and simplify: $5x - 8(6x - y)$.

SYNTHESIS

55. The total length of the Nile and Amazon Rivers is 13,108 km. If the Amazon were 234 km longer, it would be as long as the Nile. Find the length of each river.

56. Consumer experts advise us never to pay the sticker price for a car. A rule of thumb is to pay the sticker price minus 20% of the sticker price, plus $200. A car is purchased for $11,520 using the rule. What was the sticker price?

Solve.

57. $2|n| + 4 = 50$

58. $|3n| = 60$

59. $y = 2a - ab + 3$, for a

❖ THINKING IT THROUGH

Explain all possible errors in each of the following.

1. Solve: $4 - 3x = 5$
$$3x = 9$$
$$x = 3.$$

2. Solve: $2(x - 5) = 7$
$$2x - 5 = 7$$
$$2x = 12$$
$$x = 6.$$

3. Explain the difference in using the multiplication principle for solving equations and for solving inequalities.

NAME   SECTION   DATE

TEST: CHAPTER 8

Solve.

1. $x + 7 = 15$

2. $t - 9 = 17$

3. $3x = -18$

4. $-\dfrac{4}{7}x = -28$

5. $3t + 7 = 2t - 5$

6. $\dfrac{1}{2}x - \dfrac{3}{5} = \dfrac{2}{5}$

7. $8 - y = 16$

8. $-\dfrac{2}{5} + x = -\dfrac{3}{4}$

9. $3(x + 2) = 27$

10. $-3x + 6(x + 4) = 9$

11. $0.4p + 0.2 = 4.2p - 7.8 - 0.6p$

Solve. Write set notation for the answers.

12. $x + 6 \le 2$

13. $14x + 9 > 13x - 4$

14. $12x \le 60$

15. $-2y \ge 26$

16. $-4y \le -32$

17. $-5x \ge \dfrac{1}{4}$

18. $4 - 6x > 40$

19. $5 - 9x \ge 19 + 5x$

1. _____

2. _____

3. _____

4. _____

5. _____

6. _____

7. _____

8. _____

9. _____

10. _____

11. _____

12. _____

13. _____

14. _____

15. _____

16. _____

17. _____

18. _____

19. _____

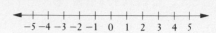

ANSWERS

20. _____

21. _____

22. _____

23. _____

24. _____

25. _____

26. _____

27. _____

28. _____

29. _____

30. _____

31. _____

32. _____

33. _____

34. _____

35. _____

36. _____

37. _____

Graph on a number line.

20. $y \leq 9$

$$\longleftarrow\!\!\!\!+\!\!\!\longrightarrow$$
$$\quad -12 \quad -8 \quad -4 \quad 0 \quad 4 \quad 8 \quad 12$$

21. $6x - 3 < x + 2$

$$\longleftarrow\!\!\!+\!\!\!+\!\!\!+\!\!\!+\!\!\!+\!\!\!+\!\!\!+\!\!\!+\!\!\!+\!\!\!+\!\!\!+\!\!\!\longrightarrow$$
$$-5\,-4\,-3\,-2\,-1\;\;0\;\;1\;\;2\;\;3\;\;4\;\;5$$

22. $-2 \leq x \leq 2$

$$\longleftarrow\!\!\!+\!\!\!+\!\!\!+\!\!\!+\!\!\!+\!\!\!+\!\!\!+\!\!\!+\!\!\!+\!\!\!+\!\!\!+\!\!\!\longrightarrow$$
$$-5\,-4\,-3\,-2\,-1\;\;0\;\;1\;\;2\;\;3\;\;4\;\;5$$

Solve.

23. The perimeter of a rectangle is 36 cm. The length is 4 cm greater than the width. Find the width and the length.

24. If you triple a number and then subtract 14, you get two thirds of the original number. What is the original number?

25. The sum of three consecutive odd integers is 249. Find the integers.

26. Money is invested in a savings account at 12% simple interest. After 1 year, there is $840 in the account. How much was originally invested?

Solve the formulas for the given letter.

27. Solve $A = 2\pi rh$, for r.

28. Solve $w = \dfrac{P - 2l}{2}$, for l.

Solve.

29. Find all numbers such that six times the number is greater than the number plus 30.

30. The width of a rectangle is 96 yd. Find all possible lengths so that the perimeter of the rectangle will be at least 540 yd.

SKILL MAINTENANCE

31. Add: $\dfrac{2}{3} + \left(-\dfrac{8}{9}\right)$.

32. Evaluate $\dfrac{4x}{y}$ when $x = 2$ and $y = 3$.

33. Translate to an algebraic expression: Seventy-three percent of p.

34. Simplify: $2x - 3y - 5(4x - 8y)$.

SYNTHESIS

35. Solve $c = \dfrac{1}{a - d}$, for d.

36. Solve: $3|w| - 8 = 37$.

37. A movie theater had a certain number of tickets to give away. Five people got the tickets. The first got one third of the tickets, the second got one fourth of the tickets, and the third got one fifth of the tickets. The fourth person got eight tickets, and there were five tickets left for the fifth person. Find the total number of tickets given away.

INTRODUCTION   Algebraic expressions like $16t^2$, seen below, and $3x^2 - 7x + 5$ are called *polynomials*. One of the most important parts of introductory algebra is the study of polynomials. In this chapter, we learn to add, subtract, multiply, and divide polynomials.

Of particular importance in this chapter is the study of fast ways to find special products of polynomials, which will be helpful not only in this text but also in more advanced mathematics.

The review sections to be tested in addition to the material in this chapter are 7.4, 7.7, 8.3, and 8.4. ❖

Polynomials: Operations

9

AN APPLICATION

The distance s, in feet, traveled by a body falling freely from rest in t seconds is approximated by

$$16t^2.$$

An object is dropped and takes 3 sec to hit the ground. From what height was it dropped?

THE MATHEMATICS

To solve the problem, we substitute 3 for t and evaluate:

$$\underline{16t^2} = 16(3)^2 = 144 \text{ ft.}$$
$\uparrow$

This is a *polynomial*.

Distributive Laws: $a(b + c) = ab + ac, \quad a(b - c) = ab - ac$
Definition of Exponents, $n \geq 2$: $a^n = \underbrace{a \cdot a \cdot a \cdots a}_{n \text{ factors}}$

PRETEST: CHAPTER 9

1. Multiply: $x^{-3}x^5$.

2. Divide: $\dfrac{x^{-2}}{x^5}$.

3. Simplify: $(-4x^2y^{-3})^2$.

4. Express using a positive exponent: p^{-3}.

5. Convert to scientific notation: 0.000347.

6. Convert to decimal notation: 3.4×10^6.

7. Identify the degree of each term and the degree of the polynomial:
$$2x^3 - 4x^2 + 3x - 5.$$

8. Collect like terms:
$$2a^3b - a^2b^2 + ab^3 + 9 - 5a^3b - a^2b^2 + 12b^3.$$

9. Add:
$$(5x^2 - 7x + 8) + (6x^2 + 11x - 19).$$

10. Subtract:
$$(5x^2 - 7x + 8) - (6x^2 + 11x - 19).$$

Multiply.

11. $5x^2(3x^2 - 4x + 1)$

12. $(x + 5)^2$

13. $(x - 5)(x + 5)$

14. $(x^3 + 6)(4x^3 - 5)$

15. $(2x - 3y)(2x - 3y)$

16. Divide: $(x^3 - x^2 + x + 2) \div (x - 2)$.

▶ **EXAMPLE 7** Evaluate $5x^3$ when $x = -2$.

$$5x^3 = 5 \cdot (-2)^3 \quad \text{Substituting}$$
$$= 5(-8) \quad \text{Evaluating the power first}$$
$$= -40 \qquad \blacktriangleleft$$

Recall that two expressions are equivalent if they have the same value for all meaningful replacements. Note that Examples 6 and 7 show that $(5x)^3$ and $5x^3$ are *not* equivalent.

DO EXERCISES 9–13.

d **Multiplying Powers with Like Bases**

There are several rules for manipulating exponential notation to obtain equivalent expressions. We first consider multiplying powers with like bases:

$$a^3 \cdot a^2 = \underbrace{(a \cdot a \cdot a)}_{3 \text{ factors}}\underbrace{(a \cdot a)}_{2 \text{ factors}} = \underbrace{a \cdot a \cdot a \cdot a \cdot a}_{5 \text{ factors}} = a^5.$$

Since an integer exponent greater than 1 tells how many times we use a base as a factor, then $(a \cdot a \cdot a)(a \cdot a) = a \cdot a \cdot a \cdot a \cdot a = a^5$ by the associative law. Note that the exponent in a^5 is the sum of those in $a^3 \cdot a^2$. That is, $3 + 2 = 5$. Likewise,

$$b^4 \cdot b^3 = (b \cdot b \cdot b \cdot b)(b \cdot b \cdot b) = b^7, \quad \text{where} \quad 4 + 3 = 7.$$

Adding the exponents gives the correct result.

> **The Product Rule**
>
> For any number a and any positive integers m and n,
>
> $$a^m \cdot a^n = a^{m+n}.$$
>
> **(When multiplying with exponential notation, if the bases are the same, keep the base and add the exponents.)**

▶ **EXAMPLES** Multiply and simplify. By simplify, we mean write as one number to a nonnegative power.

8. $8^4 \cdot 8^3 = 8^{4+3}$ Adding exponents: $a^m \cdot a^n = a^{m+n}$
$\qquad = 8^7$

9. $x^2 \cdot x^9 = x^{2+9}$
$\qquad = x^{11}$

10. $m^5 m^{10} m^3 = m^{5+10+3}$
$\qquad\qquad = m^{18}$

11. $x \cdot x^8 = x^1 \cdot x^8 = x^{1+8}$
$\qquad\qquad\qquad = x^9$

12. $(a^3 b^2)(a^3 b^5) = (a^3 a^3)(b^2 b^5)$
$\qquad\qquad\qquad = a^6 b^7 \qquad \blacktriangleleft$

DO EXERCISES 14–18.

e **Dividing Powers with Like Bases**

The following suggests a rule for dividing powers with like bases, such as a^5/a^2:

$$\frac{a^5}{a^2} = \frac{a \cdot a \cdot a \cdot a \cdot a}{a \cdot a} = \frac{a \cdot a \cdot a \cdot a \cdot a}{1 \cdot a \cdot a} = \frac{a \cdot a \cdot a}{1} \cdot \frac{a \cdot a}{a \cdot a} = \frac{a \cdot a \cdot a}{1} \cdot 1$$
$$= a \cdot a \cdot a = a^3.$$

9. Evaluate t^3 when $t = 5$.

10. Find the area of a circle when $r = 32$ cm. Use 3.14 for π.

11. Evaluate $200 - a^4$ when $a = 3$.

12. Evaluate $t^1 - 4$ and $t^0 - 4$ when $t = 7$.

13. a) Evaluate $(4t)^2$ when $t = -3$.

b) Evaluate $4t^2$ when $t = -3$.

c) Determine whether $(4t)^2$ and $4t^2$ are equivalent.

Multiply and simplify.

14. $3^5 \cdot 3^5$

15. $x^4 \cdot x^6$

16. $p^4 p^{12} p^8$

17. $x \cdot x^4$

18. $(a^2 b^3)(a^7 b^5)$

ANSWERS ON PAGE A-7

Divide and simplify.

19. $\dfrac{4^5}{4^2}$

Note that the exponent in a^3 is the difference of those in $a^5 \div a^2$. If we subtract exponents, we get $5 - 2$, which is 3.

> **The Quotient Rule**
>
> **For any nonzero number a and any positive integers m and n,**
>
> $$\frac{a^m}{a^n} = a^{m-n}.$$
>
> **(When dividing with exponential notation, if the bases are the same, keep the base and subtract the exponent of the denominator from the exponent of the numerator.)**

▶ **EXAMPLES**   Divide and simplify. By simplify, we mean write as one number to a nonnegative power.

20. $\dfrac{y^6}{y^2}$

13. $\dfrac{6^5}{6^3} = 6^{5-3}$ Subtracting exponents

   $= 6^2$

14. $\dfrac{x^8}{x^2} = x^{8-2}$

   $= x^6$

15. $\dfrac{t^{12}}{t} = t^{12-1}$

   $= t^{11}$

16. $\dfrac{p^5 q^7}{p^2 q^5} = p^{5-2} q^{7-5}$

   $= p^3 q^2$ ◀

The quotient rule can also be used to explain the definition of 0 as an exponent. Consider the expression a^4/a^4, where a is nonzero:

$$\frac{a^4}{a^4} = \frac{a \cdot a \cdot a \cdot a}{a \cdot a \cdot a \cdot a} = 1.$$

21. $\dfrac{p^{10}}{p}$

This is true because the numerator and the denominator are the same. Now suppose we apply the rule for dividing powers with the same base:

$$\frac{a^4}{a^4} = a^{4-4} = a^0 = 1.$$

Since both expressions for a^4/a^4 are equivalent to 1, it follows that $a^0 = 1$, when $a \neq 0$.

We can explain why we do not define 0^0 using the quotient rule. We know that 0^0 is 0^{1-1}. But 0^{1-1} is also equal to $0/0$. We have already seen that division by 0 is undefined, so we also have 0^0 undefined.

DO EXERCISES 19–22.

22. $\dfrac{a^7 b^6}{a^3 b^4}$

f   **Negative Integers as Exponents**

We can use the rule for dividing powers with like bases to lead us to a definition of exponential notation when the exponent is a negative integer. Consider $5^3/5^7$ and first simplify it using procedures we have learned for working with fractions:

$$\frac{5^3}{5^7} = \frac{5 \cdot 5 \cdot 5}{5 \cdot 5 \cdot 5 \cdot 5 \cdot 5 \cdot 5 \cdot 5} = \frac{5 \cdot 5 \cdot 5 \cdot 1}{5 \cdot 5 \cdot 5 \cdot 5 \cdot 5 \cdot 5 \cdot 5}$$

$$= \frac{5 \cdot 5 \cdot 5}{5 \cdot 5 \cdot 5} \cdot \frac{1}{5 \cdot 5 \cdot 5 \cdot 5} = \frac{1}{5^4}.$$

Now we apply the rule for dividing powers with the same bases. Then

$$\frac{5^3}{5^7} = 5^{3-7} = 5^{-4}.$$

From these two expressions for $5^3/5^7$, it follows that

$$5^{-4} = \frac{1}{5^4}.$$

This leads to our definition of negative exponents:

> **For any real number a that is nonzero and any integer n,**
>
> $$a^{-n} = \frac{1}{a^n}.$$
>
> **(The numbers a^{-n} and a^n are reciprocals.)**

▶ **EXAMPLES**   Express using positive exponents. Then simplify.

17. $4^{-2} = \dfrac{1}{4^2} = \dfrac{1}{16}$

18. $(-3)^{-2} = \dfrac{1}{(-3)^2} = \dfrac{1}{(-3)(-3)} = \dfrac{1}{9}$

19. $m^{-3} = \dfrac{1}{m^3}$

20. $ab^{-1} = a\left(\dfrac{1}{b^1}\right) = a\left(\dfrac{1}{b}\right) = \dfrac{a}{b}$

21. $3c^{-5} = 3\left(\dfrac{1}{c^5}\right) = \dfrac{3}{c^5}$

22. $\dfrac{1}{x^{-3}} = x^3$ (x^{-3} and x^3 are reciprocals.)   ◀

CAUTION!   Note in Example 17 that

$$4^{-2} \neq 4(-2) \quad \text{and} \quad \frac{1}{4^2} \neq 4(-2).$$

Similarly, in Example 18,

$$(-3)^{-2} \neq (-3)(-2) \quad \text{and} \quad \frac{1}{(-3)^2} \neq (-3)(-2).$$

In particular, $a^{-n} \neq a(-n)$. The negative exponent also does not mean to multiply in the denominator. That is

$$4^{-2} = \frac{1}{16}, \quad not \quad \frac{1}{-16}.$$

DO EXERCISES 23–28.

The rules for multiplying and dividing powers with like bases still hold when exponents are 0 or negative. We will state them in a summary at the end of this section.

Express with positive exponents. Then simplify.

23. 4^{-3}

24. 5^{-2}

25. 2^{-4}

26. $(-2)^{-3}$

27. $4p^{-3}$

28. $\dfrac{1}{x^{-2}}$

ANSWERS ON PAGE A-7

Simplify.

29. $5^{-2} \cdot 5^4$

▶ **EXAMPLES**   Simplify. By simplify, we mean write as one number to a nonnegative power.

23. $7^{-3} \cdot 7^6 = 7^{-3+6}$ Adding   **24.** $x^4 \cdot x^{-3} = x^{4+(-3)} = x^1 = x$
                    $= 7^3$ exponents

25. $\dfrac{5^4}{5^{-2}} = 5^{4-(-2)}$ Subtracting   **26.** $\dfrac{x}{x^7} = x^{1-7} = x^{-6} = \dfrac{1}{x^6}$
                         exponents

          $= 5^{4+2} = 5^6$

30. $x^{-3} \cdot x^{-4}$

27. $\dfrac{b^{-4}}{b^{-5}} = b^{-4-(-5)} = b^1 = b$ ◀

In Examples 23–27, it may help to think as follows: After writing the base, write the top exponent. Then write a subtraction sign. Then write the bottom exponent. Then do the subtraction by adding the opposite. For example,

$$\frac{x^{-3}}{x^{-5}} = x^{-3-(-5)} = x^{-3+5} = x^2$$

(1) Write the base.
(2) Write the top exponent.
(3) Write a subtraction sign.
(4) Write the bottom exponent.

DO EXERCISES 29–33.

31. $\dfrac{7^{-2}}{7^3}$

The following is another way to explain the definition of negative exponents.

On this side, we divide by 5 at each step.	$5 \cdot 5 \cdot 5 \cdot 5 = 5^4$	On this side, the exponents decrease by 1.
	$5 \cdot 5 \cdot 5 = 5^3$	
	$5 \cdot 5 = 5^2$	
	$5 = 5^1$	
	$1 = 5^0$	
	$\dfrac{1}{5} = 5^?$	
	$\dfrac{1}{25} = 5^?$	

32. $\dfrac{b^{-2}}{b^{-3}}$

To continue the pattern, it should follow that

$$\frac{1}{5} = \frac{1}{5^1} = 5^{-1} \quad \text{and} \quad \frac{1}{25} = \frac{1}{5^2} = 5^{-2}.$$

The following is a summary of the definitions and rules for exponents that we have considered in this section.

33. $\dfrac{t}{t^{-5}}$

Definitions and Rules for Exponents

For any integers m and n,

1 as an exponent: $a^1 = a,$

0 as an exponent: $a^0 = 1, a \neq 0$

Negative integers as exponents: $a^{-n} = \dfrac{1}{a^n}$

Product Rule: $a^m \cdot a^n = a^{m+n}$

Quotient Rule: $\dfrac{a^m}{a^n} = a^{m-n}$

ANSWERS ON PAGE A-7

NAME   SECTION   DATE

EXERCISE SET 9.1

a What is the meaning of each of the following?

1. 2^4 **2.** 5^3 **3.** $(1.4)^5$ **4.** m^6

5. $(7p)^2$ **6.** $(11c)^3$ **7.** $(19k)^4$ **8.** $(10pq)^2$

b Evaluate.

9. $t^0, \ t \neq 0$ **10.** $a^0, \ a \neq 0$ **11.** a^1 **12.** q^1

13. 9.68^0 **14.** 9.68^1 **15.** $(ab)^1$ **16.** $(ab)^0$

c Evaluate.

17. m^3 when $m = 3$ **18.** x^6 when $x = 2$

19. p^1 when $p = 19$ **20.** x^{19} when $x = 0$

21. x^4 when $x = 4$ **22.** y^{15} when $y = 1$

23. $y^2 - 7$ when $y = -10$ **24.** $z^5 + 5$ when $z = -2$

ANSWERS

1. _____

2. _____

3. _____

4. _____

5. _____

6. _____

7. _____

8. _____

9. _____

10. _____

11. _____

12. _____

13. _____

14. _____

15. _____

16. _____

17. _____

18. _____

19. _____

20. _____

21. _____

22. _____

23. _____

24. _____

25. _____

26. _____

27. _____

28. _____

29. _____

30. _____

31. _____

32. _____

33. _____

34. _____

35. _____

36. _____

37. _____

38. _____

39. _____

40. _____

41. _____

42. _____

43. _____

44. _____

45. _____

46. _____

47. _____

48. _____

49. _____

50. _____

25. Find the area of a circle when $r = 34$ ft. Use 3.14 for π.

26. The area A of a square with sides of length s is given by $A = s^2$. Find the area of a square with sides of length 24 m (meters).

f Express using positive exponents. Then simplify.

27. 3^{-2} **28.** 2^{-3} **29.** 10^{-4} **30.** 5^{-6}

31. 7^{-3} **32.** 5^{-2} **33.** a^{-3} **34.** x^{-2}

35. $\dfrac{1}{y^{-4}}$ **36.** $\dfrac{1}{t^{-7}}$ **37.** $\dfrac{1}{z^{-n}}$ **38.** $\dfrac{1}{h^{-n}}$

Express using negative exponents.

39. $\dfrac{1}{4^3}$ **40.** $\dfrac{1}{5^2}$ **41.** $\dfrac{1}{x^3}$ **42.** $\dfrac{1}{y^2}$

d , **f** Multiply and simplify.

43. $2^4 \cdot 2^3$ **44.** $3^5 \cdot 3^2$ **45.** $8^5 \cdot 8^9$ **46.** $n^3 \cdot n^{20}$

47. $x^4 \cdot x^3$ **48.** $y^7 \cdot y^9$ **49.** $9^{17} \cdot 9^{21}$ **50.** $t^0 \cdot t^{16}$

51. $(3y)^4(3y)^8$

52. $(2t)^8(2t)^{17}$

53. $(7y)^1(7y)^{16}$

54. $(8x)^0(8x)^1$

55. $3^{-5} \cdot 3^8$

56. $5^{-8} \cdot 5^9$

57. $x^{-2} \cdot x$

58. $x \cdot x^{-1}$

59. $x^4 \cdot x^3$

60. $x^9 \cdot x^4$

61. $x^{-7} \cdot x^{-6}$

62. $y^{-5} \cdot y^{-8}$

63. $t^8 \cdot t^{-8}$

64. $m^{10} \cdot m^{-10}$

e , **f** Divide and simplify.

65. $\dfrac{7^5}{7^2}$

66. $\dfrac{4^7}{4^3}$

67. $\dfrac{8^{12}}{8^6}$

68. $\dfrac{9^{14}}{9^2}$

69. $\dfrac{y^9}{y^5}$

70. $\dfrac{x^{12}}{x^{11}}$

71. $\dfrac{16^2}{16^8}$

72. $\dfrac{5^4}{5^{10}}$

73. $\dfrac{m^6}{m^{12}}$

74. $\dfrac{p^4}{p^5}$

75. $\dfrac{(8x)^6}{(8x)^{10}}$

76. $\dfrac{(9t)^4}{(9t)^{11}}$

ANSWERS

51. _____

52. _____

53. _____

54. _____

55. _____

56. _____

57. _____

58. _____

59. _____

60. _____

61. _____

62. _____

63. _____

64. _____

65. _____

66. _____

67. _____

68. _____

69. _____

70. _____

71. _____

72. _____

73. _____

74. _____

75. _____

76. _____

Copyright © 1993 Addison-Wesley Publishing Co., Inc.

ANSWERS

77. _____

78. _____

79. _____

80. _____

81. _____

82. _____

83. _____

84. _____

85. _____

86. _____

87. _____

88. _____

89. _____

90. _____

91. _____

92. _____

93. _____

94. _____

95. _____

96. _____

97. _____

98. _____

99. _____

100. _____

101. _____

102. _____

103. _____

104. _____

105. _____

106. _____

107. _____

108. _____

109. _____

77. $\dfrac{18^9}{18^9}$ **78.** $\dfrac{(6y)^7}{(6y)^7}$ **79.** $\dfrac{x}{x^{-1}}$ **80.** $\dfrac{x^6}{x}$

81. $\dfrac{x^7}{x^{-2}}$ **82.** $\dfrac{t^8}{t^{-3}}$ **83.** $\dfrac{z^{-6}}{z^{-2}}$ **84.** $\dfrac{y^{-7}}{y^{-3}}$

85. $\dfrac{x^{-5}}{x^{-8}}$ **86.** $\dfrac{y^{-4}}{y^{-9}}$ **87.** $\dfrac{m^{-9}}{m^{-9}}$ **88.** $\dfrac{x^{-8}}{x^{-8}}$

Simplify.

89. 8^2, 8^{-2}, $\left(\dfrac{1}{8}\right)^2$, $\left(\dfrac{1}{8}\right)^{-2}$, -8^2,   and $(-8)^2$

90. 5^2, 5^{-2}, $\left(\dfrac{1}{5}\right)^2$, $\left(\dfrac{1}{5}\right)^{-2}$, -5^2,   and $(-5)^2$

SKILL MAINTENANCE

91. Translate to an algebraic expression: Sixty-four percent of t.

92. Evaluate $3x/y$ when $x = 4$ and $y = 12$.

93. Divide: $1555.2 \div 24.3$.

94. Add: $1555.2 + 24.3$.

SYNTHESIS

95. Determine whether $(5y)^0$ and $5y^0$ are equivalent expressions.

Simplify.

96. $(y^{2x})(y^{3x})$ **97.** $a^{5k} \div a^{3k}$ **98.** $\dfrac{a^{6t}(a^{7t})}{a^{9t}}$

99. $\dfrac{\left(\dfrac{1}{2}\right)^4}{\left(\dfrac{1}{2}\right)^5}$ **100.** $\dfrac{(0.4)^5}{(0.4)^3(0.4)^2}$

101. Determine whether $(a + b)^2$ and $a^2 + b^2$ are equivalent. (*Hint:* Choose values for x and y and evaluate.)

Use $>$, $<$, or $=$ for ▨ to write a true sentence.

102. 3^5 ▨ 3^4 **103.** 4^2 ▨ 4^3 **104.** 4^3 ▨ 5^3 **105.** 4^3 ▨ 3^4

Find a value of the variable that shows that the two expressions are *not* equivalent.

106. $3x^2$; $(3x)^2$ **107.** $(a + 3)^2$; $a^2 + 3^2$

108. $\dfrac{x + 2}{2}$; x **109.** $\dfrac{y^6}{y^3}$; y^2

9.2 Exponents and Scientific Notation

We now enhance our ability to manipulate exponential expressions by considering three more rules. The rules are also applied to a new way to name numbers called *scientific notation*.

a Raising Powers to Powers

Consider an expression like $(3^2)^4$. We are raising 3^2 to the fourth power:

$$(3^2)^4 = (3^2)(3^2)(3^2)(3^2)$$
$$= (3 \cdot 3)(3 \cdot 3)(3 \cdot 3)(3 \cdot 3)$$
$$= 3 \cdot 3 \cdot 3 \cdot 3 \cdot 3 \cdot 3 \cdot 3 \cdot 3$$
$$= 3^8.$$

Note that in this case we could have multiplied the exponents:

$$(3^2)^4 = 3^{2 \cdot 4} = 3^8.$$

Likewise, $(y^8)^3 = (y^8)(y^8)(y^8) = y^{24}$. Once again, we get the same result if we multiply the exponents:

$$(y^8)^3 = y^{8 \cdot 3} = y^{24}.$$

> **The Power Rule**
>
> **For any real number a and any integers m and n,**
> $$(a^m)^n = a^{mn}.$$
> **(To raise a power to a power, multiply the exponents.)**

▶ **EXAMPLES** Simplify.

1. $(3^5)^4 = 3^{5 \cdot 4}$ Multiplying exponents
    $= 3^{20}$

2. $(2^2)^5 = 2^{2 \cdot 5} = 2^{10}$

3. $(y^{-5})^7 = y^{-5 \cdot 7} = y^{-35} = \dfrac{1}{y^{35}}$

4. $(x^4)^{-2} = x^{4(-2)} = x^{-8} = \dfrac{1}{x^8}$

5. $(a^{-4})^{-6} = a^{(-4)(-6)} = a^{24}$ ◀

DO EXERCISES 1–4.

b Raising a Product or a Quotient to a Power

When an expression inside parentheses is raised to a power, the inside expression is the base. Let us compare $2a^3$ and $(2a)^3$:

$2a^3 = 2 \cdot a \cdot a \cdot a;$ The base is a.

$(2a)^3 = (2a)(2a)(2a)$ The base is $2a$.

    $= (2 \cdot 2 \cdot 2)(a \cdot a \cdot a)$ Using the associative law of multiplication

    $= 2^3 a^3$

    $= 8a^3.$

We see that $2a^3$ and $(2a)^3$ are *not* equivalent. We also see that we can evaluate the power $(2a)^3$ by raising each factor to the power 3. This leads us to the following rule for raising a product to a power.

OBJECTIVES

After finishing Section 9.2, you should be able to:

a Use the power rule to raise powers to powers.

b Raise a product to a power and a quotient to a power.

c Convert between scientific notation and decimal notation.

d Multiply and divide using scientific notation.

e Solve problems using scientific notation.

Simplify.

1. $(3^4)^5$

2. $(x^{-3})^4$

3. $(y^{-5})^{-3}$

4. $(x^{-4})^8$

ANSWERS ON PAGE A-7

Simplify.

5. $(2x^5y^{-3})^4$

6. $(5x^5y^{-6}z^{-3})^2$

7. $[(-x)^{37}]^2$

8. $(3y^{-2}x^{-5}z^8)^3$

Simplify.

9. $\left(\dfrac{x^6}{5}\right)^2$

10. $\left(\dfrac{2t^5}{w^4}\right)^3$

11. $\left(\dfrac{x^4}{3}\right)^{-2}$

> #### Raising a Product to a Power
>
> **For any real numbers a and b and any integer n,**
> $$(ab)^n = a^nb^n.$$
> **(To raise a product to the nth power, raise each factor to the nth power.)**

▶ **EXAMPLES**

6. $(4x^2)^3 = 4^3 \cdot (x^2)^3$ Raising each factor to the third power
$$= 64x^6$$

7. $(5x^3y^5z^2)^4 = 5^4(x^3)^4(y^5)^4(z^2)^4$ Raising each factor to the fourth power
$$= 625x^{12}y^{20}z^8$$

8. $(-5x^4y^3)^3 = (-5)^3(x^4)^3(y^3)^3$
$$= -125x^{12}y^9$$

9. $[(-x)^{25}]^2 = (-x)^{50}$
$$= (-1 \cdot x)^{50}$$ Using the property of -1 (Section 7.8)
$$= (-1)^{50}x^{50}$$
$$= 1 \cdot x^{50}$$ The product of an even number of negative factors is positive.
$$= x^{50}$$

10. $(5x^2y^{-2})^3 = 5^3(x^2)^3(y^{-2})^3 = 125x^6y^{-6}$ Be careful to raise *each* factor to the third power.
$$= \frac{125x^6}{y^6}$$

11. $(3x^3y^{-5}z^2)^4 = 3^4(x^3)^4(y^{-5})^4(z^2)^4$
$$= 81x^{12}y^{-20}z^8$$
$$= \frac{81x^{12}z^8}{y^{20}}$$

◀

DO EXERCISES 5–8.

There is a similar rule for raising a quotient to a power.

> #### Raising a Quotient to a Power
>
> **For any real numbers a and b, $b \neq 0$, and any integer n,**
> $$\left(\frac{a}{b}\right)^n = \frac{a^n}{b^n}.$$
> **(To raise a quotient to a power, raise the numerator to the power and divide by the denominator to the power.)**

▶ **EXAMPLES**   Simplify.

12. $\left(\dfrac{x^2}{4}\right)^3 = \dfrac{(x^2)^3}{4^3} = \dfrac{x^6}{64}$

13. $\left(\dfrac{3a^4}{b^3}\right)^2 = \dfrac{(3a^4)^2}{(b^3)^2} = \dfrac{3^2(a^4)^2}{b^{3 \cdot 2}} = \dfrac{9a^8}{b^6}$

14. $\left(\dfrac{y^3}{5}\right)^{-2} = \dfrac{(y^3)^{-2}}{5^{-2}} = \dfrac{y^{-6}}{5^{-2}} = \dfrac{\dfrac{1}{y^6}}{\dfrac{1}{5^2}} = \dfrac{1}{y^6} \div \dfrac{1}{5^2} = \dfrac{1}{y^6} \cdot \dfrac{5^2}{1} = \dfrac{25}{y^6}$

◀

DO EXERCISES 9–11.

c Scientific Notation

There are many kinds of symbols, or notation, for numbers. You are already familiar with fractional notation, decimal notation, and percent notation. Now we study another, **scientific notation,** which is especially useful when calculations involve very large or very small numbers. The following are examples of scientific notation:

The distance from the earth to the sun:

$$9.3 \times 10^7 \text{ mi} = 93,000,000 \text{ mi}$$

The mass of a hydrogen atom:

$$1.7 \times 10^{-24} \text{ gm} = 0.0000000000000000000000017 \text{ gm}$$

> *Scientific notation* **for a number is an expression of the type**
>
> $$N \times 10^n,$$
>
> **where 1 is less than or equal to N and N is less than 10 ($1 \leq N < 10$), and N is expressed in decimal notation. 10^n is also considered to be scientific notation when $N = 1$.**

You should try to make conversions to scientific notation mentally as much as possible. Here is a handy mental device.

> A positive exponent indicates a large number (greater than one) and a negative exponent indicates a small number (less than one).

▶ **EXAMPLES**

15. $78,000 = 7.8 \times 10^4$ $\qquad$ 7.8 000.

$\qquad\qquad\qquad\qquad\qquad\qquad$ 4 places

Large number, so the exponent is positive.

16. $0.0000057 = 5.7 \times 10^{-6}$ $\qquad$ 0.000005.7

$\qquad\qquad\qquad\qquad\qquad\qquad\qquad$ 6 places

Small number, so the exponent is negative. ◀

Each of the following is *not* scientific notation.

$$\underline{12.46} \times 10^7 \qquad\qquad \underline{0.347} \times 10^{-5}$$

$\qquad\uparrow\qquad\qquad\qquad\qquad\qquad\uparrow$

This number is greater than 10.   This number is less than 1.

DO EXERCISES 12 AND 13.

▶ **EXAMPLES** Convert mentally to decimal notation.

17. $7.893 \times 10^5 = 789,300$ $\qquad$ 7.89300.

$\qquad\qquad\qquad\qquad\qquad\qquad\qquad$ 5 places

Positive exponent, so the answer is a large number.

18. $4.7 \times 10^{-8} = 0.000000047$ $\qquad$ 0.00000004.7

$\qquad\qquad\qquad\qquad\qquad\qquad\qquad$ 8 places

Negative exponent, so the answer is a small number. ◀

DO EXERCISES 14 AND 15.

Convert to scientific notation.

12. 0.000517

13. 523,000,000

Convert to decimal notation.

14. 6.893×10^{11}

15. 5.67×10^{-5}

ANSWERS ON PAGE A-7

Multiply and write scientific notation for the result.

16. $(1.12 \times 10^{-8})(5 \times 10^{-7})$

When using a calculator, we can express a number like 260,000,000 using scientific notation in a form like

$$2.6 \, E \, 8, \quad \text{or} \quad 2.6 \quad 8,$$

or perhaps in other forms, depending on your calculator.

d   Multiplying and Dividing Using Scientific Notation

Multiplying

Consider the product

$$400 \cdot 2000 = 800,000.$$

In scientific notation, this would be

$$(4 \times 10^2) \cdot (2 \times 10^3) = (4 \cdot 2)(10^2 \cdot 10^3) = 8 \times 10^5.$$

By applying the commutative and associative laws, we can find this product by multiplying $4 \cdot 2$, to get 8, and $10^2 \cdot 10^3$, to get 10^5 (we do this by adding the exponents).

▶   **EXAMPLE 19**   Multiply: $(1.8 \times 10^6) \cdot (2.3 \times 10^{-4})$.

We apply the commutative and associative laws to get

$$\begin{aligned}
(1.8 \times 10^6) \cdot (2.3 \times 10^{-4}) &= (1.8 \cdot 2.3) \times (10^6 \cdot 10^{-4}) \\
&= 4.14 \times 10^{6+(-4)} \quad \text{\textbf{Adding exponents}} \\
&= 4.14 \times 10^2.
\end{aligned}$$
◀

17. $(9.1 \times 10^{-17})(8.2 \times 10^3)$

▶   **EXAMPLE 20**   Multiply: $(3.1 \times 10^5) \cdot (4.5 \times 10^{-3})$.

We have

$$\begin{aligned}
(3.1 \times 10^5) \cdot (4.5 \times 10^{-3}) &= (3.1 \times 4.5)(10^5 \cdot 10^{-3}) \\
&= 13.95 \times 10^2.
\end{aligned}$$

The answer at this stage is

$$13.95 \times 10^2,$$

but this is *not* scientific notation, because 13.95 is not a number between 1 and 10. To find scientific notation, we convert 13.95 to scientific notation and simplify:

$$\begin{aligned}
13.95 \times 10^2 &= (1.395 \times 10^1) \times 10^2 \quad \text{\textbf{Substituting } 1.395 \times 10^1 \text{ for } 13.95} \\
&= 1.395 \times (10^1 \times 10^2) \quad \text{\textbf{Associative law}} \\
&= 1.395 \times 10^3. \quad \text{\textbf{Adding exponents}}
\end{aligned}$$

The answer is

$$1.395 \times 10^3.$$
◀

DO EXERCISES 16 AND 17.

Dividing

Consider the quotient

$$800,000 \div 400 = 2000.$$

In scientific notation, this is

$$(8 \times 10^5) \div (4 \times 10^2) = \frac{8 \times 10^5}{4 \times 10^2} = 2 \times 10^3.$$

We can find this product by dividing 8 by 4, to get 2, and 10^5 by 10^2, to get 10^3 (we do this by subtracting the exponents).

▶ **EXAMPLE 21**   Divide: $(3.41 \times 10^5) \div (1.1 \times 10^{-3})$.

$$\begin{aligned} (3.41 \times 10^5) \div (1.1 \times 10^{-3}) &= \frac{3.41 \times 10^5}{1.1 \times 10^{-3}} \\ &= \frac{3.41}{1.1} \times \frac{10^5}{10^{-3}} \\ &= 3.1 \times 10^{5-(-3)} \\ &= 3.1 \times 10^8 \qquad ◀ \end{aligned}$$

▶ **EXAMPLE 22**   Divide: $(6.4 \times 10^{-7}) \div (8.0 \times 10^6)$.
We have

$$\begin{aligned} (6.4 \times 10^{-7}) \div (8.0 \times 10^6) &= \frac{6.4 \times 10^{-7}}{8.0 \times 10^6} \\ &= \frac{6.4}{8.0} \times \frac{10^{-7}}{10^6} \\ &= 0.8 \times 10^{-7-6} \\ &= 0.8 \times 10^{-13}. \end{aligned}$$

The answer at this stage is

$$0.8 \times 10^{-13},$$

but this is *not* scientific notation, because 0.8 is not a number between 1 and 10. To find scientific notation, we convert 0.8 to scientific notation and simplify:

$$\begin{aligned} 0.8 \times 10^{-13} &= (8.0 \times 10^{-1}) \times 10^{-13} \quad \text{Substituting } 8.0 \times 10^{-1} \text{ for } 0.8 \\ &= 8.0 \times (10^{-1} \times 10^{-13}) \quad \text{Associative law} \\ &= 8.0 \times 10^{-14}. \quad \text{Adding exponents} \end{aligned}$$

The answer is

$$8.0 \times 10^{-14}. \qquad ◀$$

DO EXERCISES 18 AND 19.

Solving Problems with Scientific Notation

▶ **EXAMPLE 23**   There are 3300 members in the Professional Bowlers Association. There are 244 million people in the United States. What part of the population are members of the Professional Bowlers Association? Write scientific notation for the answer.

Divide and write scientific notation for the result.

18. $\dfrac{4.2 \times 10^5}{2.1 \times 10^2}$

19. $\dfrac{1.1 \times 10^{-4}}{2.0 \times 10^{-7}}$

ANSWERS ON PAGE A-7

20. There are 300,000 words in the English language. The average person knows about 10,000 of them. What part of the total number of words does the average person know? Write scientific notation for the answer.

The part of the population that belongs to the Professional Bowlers Association is

$$\frac{3300}{244 \text{ million}}.$$

We know that 1 million = 1,000,000 = 10^6, so 244 million = 244×10^6, or 2.44×10^8. We also have 3300 = 3.3×10^3. We can now divide and write scientific notation for the answer:

$$\frac{3300}{244 \text{ million}} = \frac{3.3 \times 10^3}{2.44 \times 10^8}$$

$$\approx 1.3525 \times 10^{-5}. \qquad ◀$$

DO EXERCISE 20.

▶ **EXAMPLE 24**　Americans drink 3 million gallons of orange juice in one day. How much orange juice is consumed in this country in one year? Write scientific notation for the answer.

There are 365 days in a year, so the amount of orange juice consumed is

$$(365 \text{ days}) \cdot (3 \text{ million}) = (3.65 \times 10^2)(3 \times 10^6)$$

$$= 10.95 \times 10^8$$

$$= (1.095 \times 10^1) \times 10^8$$

$$= 1.095 \times 10^9.$$

There are 1.095×10^9 gallons of orange juice consumed in this country in one year. ◀

DO EXERCISE 21.

21. Americans eat 6.5 million gallons of popcorn each day. How much popcorn do they eat in one year? Write scientific notation for the answer.

The following is a summary of the definitions and rules for exponents that we have considered in this section and the preceding one.

Definitions and Rules for Exponents

$$a^1 = a, \qquad a^0 = 1, \qquad a \neq 0,$$

Negative exponents:　　$a^{-n} = \dfrac{1}{a^n}, \quad a \neq 0$

Product Rule:　　$a^m \cdot a^n = a^{m+n}$

Quotient Rule:　　$\dfrac{a^m}{a^n} = a^{m-n}$

Power Rule:　　$(a^m)^n = a^{mn}$

Raising a Product to a Power:　　$(ab)^n = a^n b^n$

Raising a Quotient to a Power:　　$\left(\dfrac{a}{b}\right)^n = \dfrac{a^n}{b^n}$

Scientific Notation:　　$N \times 10^n$, or 10^n, where N is a number such that $1 \leq N < 10$

NAME   SECTION   DATE

EXERCISE SET 9.2

a , b Simplify.

1. $(2^3)^2$ **2.** $(3^4)^3$ **3.** $(5^2)^{-3}$ **4.** $(9^3)^{-4}$

5. $(x^{-3})^{-4}$ **6.** $(a^{-5})^{-6}$ **7.** $(4x^3)^2$ **8.** $4(x^3)^2$

9. $(x^4y^5)^{-3}$ **10.** $(t^5x^3)^{-4}$ **11.** $(x^{-6}y^{-2})^{-4}$ **12.** $(x^{-2}y^{-7})^{-5}$

13. $(3x^3y^{-8}z^{-3})^2$ **14.** $(2a^2y^{-4}z^{-5})^3$ **15.** $\left(\dfrac{a^2}{b^3}\right)^4$ **16.** $\left(\dfrac{x^3}{y^4}\right)^5$

17. $\left(\dfrac{y^3}{2}\right)^2$ **18.** $\left(\dfrac{a^5}{3}\right)^3$ **19.** $\left(\dfrac{y^2}{2}\right)^{-3}$ **20.** $\left(\dfrac{a^4}{3}\right)^{-2}$

21. $\left(\dfrac{x^2y}{z}\right)^3$ **22.** $\left(\dfrac{m}{n^4p}\right)^3$ **23.** $\left(\dfrac{a^2b}{cd^3}\right)^{-2}$ **24.** $\left(\dfrac{2a^2}{3b^4}\right)^{-3}$

c Convert to scientific notation.

25. 78,000,000,000 **26.** 3,700,000,000,000

27. 907,000,000,000,000,000 **28.** 168,000,000,000,000

29. 0.00000374 **30.** 0.000000000275

31. 0.000000018 **32.** 0.00000000002

33. 100,000,000,000 **34.** 0.0000001

Convert to decimal notation.

35. 7.84×10^8 **36.** 1.35×10^7 **37.** 8.764×10^{-10} **38.** 9.043×10^{-3}

39. 10^8 **40.** 10^4 **41.** 10^{-4} **42.** 10^{-7}

ANSWERS
1.
2.
3.
4.
5.
6.
7.
8.
9.
10.
11.
12.
13.
14.
15.
16.
17.
18.
19.
20.
21.
22.
23.
24.
25.
26.
27.
28.
29.
30.
31.
32.
33.
34.
35.
36.
37.
38.
39.
40.
41.
42.

d Multiply or divide and write scientific notation for the result.

43. $(3 \times 10^4)(2 \times 10^5)$

44. $(1.9 \times 10^8)(3.4 \times 10^{-3})$

45. $(5.2 \times 10^5)(6.5 \times 10^{-2})$

46. $(7.1 \times 10^{-7})(8.6 \times 10^{-5})$

47. $(9.9 \times 10^{-6})(8.23 \times 10^{-8})$

48. $(1.123 \times 10^4) \times 10^{-9}$

49. $\dfrac{8.5 \times 10^8}{3.4 \times 10^{-5}}$

50. $\dfrac{5.6 \times 10^{-2}}{2.5 \times 10^5}$

51. $(3.0 \times 10^6) \div (6.0 \times 10^9)$

52. $(1.5 \times 10^{-3}) \div (1.6 \times 10^{-6})$

53. $\dfrac{7.5 \times 10^{-9}}{2.5 \times 10^{12}}$

54. $\dfrac{4.0 \times 10^{-3}}{8.0 \times 10^{20}}$

e Solve. Write scientific notation for the answer.

55. About 250,000 people die per day in the world. How many die in one year?

56. The average discharge at the mouth of the Amazon River is 4,200,000 cubic feet per second. How much water is discharged from the Amazon River in one hour? in one year?

57. There are 300,000 words in the English language. The exceptional person knows about 20,000 of them. What part of the total number of words does the exceptional person know?

58. The mass of the earth is about 5.98×10^{24} kg. The mass of the planet Saturn is about 95 times the mass of the earth. Write scientific notation for the mass of Saturn.

SYNTHESIS

59. ▦ Carry out the indicated operations. Write scientific notation for the result.

$$\dfrac{(5.2 \times 10^6)(6.1 \times 10^{-11})}{1.28 \times 10^{-3}}$$

60. Find the reciprocal and express in scientific notation.

$$(6.25 \times 10^{-3})$$

61. Write $4^3 \cdot 8 \cdot 16$ as a power of 2.

62. Write $2^8 \cdot 16^3 \cdot 64$ as a power of 4.

Simplify.

63. $\dfrac{(5^{12})^2}{5^{25}}$

64. $\dfrac{a^{22}}{(a^2)^{11}}$

65. $\dfrac{(3^5)^4}{3^5 \cdot 3^4}$

66. $\dfrac{49^{18}}{7^{35}}$

67. $\left(\dfrac{1}{a}\right)^{-n}$

68. $\dfrac{(0.4)^5}{[(0.4)^3]^2}$

(*Hint:* Study Exercise 64.)

Determine whether each of the following is true for any pairs of integers m and n and any positive numbers x and y.

69. $x^m \cdot y^n = (xy)^{mn}$

70. $x^m \cdot y^m = (xy)^{2m}$

71. $(x - y)^m = x^m - y^m$

9.3 Introduction to Polynomials

We have already learned to evaluate and to manipulate certain kinds of algebraic expressions. We will now consider algebraic expressions called *polynomials.*

The following are examples of *monomials in one variable:*

$$3x^2, \quad 2x, \quad -5, \quad 37p^4, \quad 0.$$

Each expression is a constant or a constant times some variable to a nonnegative integer power. More formally, a **monomial** is an expression of the type ax^n, where a is a real-number constant and n is a nonnegative integer.

Algebraic expressions like the following are **polynomials:**

$$\tfrac{3}{4}y^5, \quad -2, \quad 5y+3, \quad 3x^2+2x-5, \quad -7a^3+\tfrac{1}{2}a, \quad 6x, \quad 37p^4, \quad x, \quad 0.$$

> A *polynomial* is a monomial or a combination of sums and/or differences of monomials.

The following algebraic expressions are *not* polynomials:

$$\textbf{(1)} \quad \frac{x+3}{x-4}, \qquad \textbf{(2)} \quad 5x^3-2x^2+\frac{1}{x}, \qquad \textbf{(3)} \quad \frac{1}{x^3-2}.$$

Expressions (1) and (3) are not polynomials because they represent quotients, not sums. Expression (2) is not a polynomial because

$$\frac{1}{x}=x^{-1},$$

and this is not a monomial because the exponent is negative.

DO EXERCISE 1.

a Evaluating Polynomials and Applications

When we replace the variable in a polynomial by a number, the polynomial then represents a number called a **value** of the polynomial. Finding that number, or value, is called **evaluating the polynomial.** We evaluate a polynomial using our rules for order of operations (Section 1.8).

▶ **EXAMPLE 1** Evaluate the polynomial when $x=2$.

a) $3x+5=3\cdot 2+5=6+5=11$

b) $2x^2-7x+3=2\cdot 2^2-7\cdot 2+3=2\cdot 4-14+3=8-14+3=-3$ ◀

▶ **EXAMPLE 2** Evaluate the polynomial when $x=-5$.

a) $2-x^3=2-(-5)^3=2-(-125)=2+125=127$

b) $-x^2-3x+1=-(-5)^2-3(-5)+1=-25+15+1=-9$ ◀

DO EXERCISES 2–5.

Polynomials occur in many real-world situations. The following examples are two such applications.

OBJECTIVES

After finishing Section 9.3, you should be able to:

[a] Evaluate a polynomial for a given value of the variable.

[b] Identify the terms of a polynomial.

[c] Identify the like terms of a polynomial.

[d] Identify the coefficients of a polynomial.

[e] Collect the like terms of a polynomial.

[f] Arrange a polynomial in descending order, or collect the like terms and then arrange in descending order.

[g] Identify the degree of each term of a polynomial and the degree of the polynomial.

[h] Identify the missing terms of a polynomial.

[i] Classify a polynomial as a monomial, binomial, trinomial, or none of these.

FOR EXTRA HELP

Tape 20A

1. Write three polynomials.

Evaluate the polynomial for $x=3$.

2. $-4x-7$

3. $-5x^3+7x+10$

Evaluate the polynomial for $x=-4$.

4. $5x+7$

5. $2x^2+5x-4$

ANSWERS ON PAGE A-7

6. In the situation of Example 4, what is the total number of games to be played in a league of 12 teams?

7. The perimeter of a square of side x is given by the polynomial $4x$.

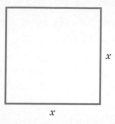

A baseball diamond is a square 90 ft on a side. Find the perimeter of a baseball diamond.

8. In the situation of Example 3, find the concentration after 3 hr.

Find an equivalent polynomial using only additions.

9. $-9x^3 - 4x^5$

10. $-2y^3 + 3y^7 - 7y$

▶   **EXAMPLE 3**   *Medical dosage.* The concentration, in parts per million, of a certain medication in the bloodstream after time t, in hours, is given by the polynomial

$$-0.05t^2 + 2t + 2.$$

Find the concentration after 2 hr.

     To find the concentration after 2 hr, we evaluate the polynomial for $t = 2$:

$$
\begin{aligned}
-0.05t^2 + 2t + 2 &= -0.05(2)^2 + 2(2) + 2 \\
&= -0.05(4) + 2(2) + 2 \\
&= -0.2 + 4 + 2 \\
&= -0.2 + 6 \\
&= 5.8.
\end{aligned}
$$

Carrying out the calculation using rules for order of operations

The concentration after 2 hr is 5.8 parts per million.   ◀

▶   **EXAMPLE 4**   *Games in a sports league.* In a sports league of n teams in which each team plays every other team twice, the total number of games to be played is given by the polynomial

$$n^2 - n.$$

A women's slow-pitch softball league has 10 teams. What is the total number of games to be played?

     We evaluate the polynomial for $n = 10$:

$$n^2 - n = 10^2 - 10 = 100 - 10 = 90.$$

The league plays 90 games.   ◀

DO EXERCISES 6–8.

b   **Identifying Terms**

As we saw in Section 7.4, subtractions can be rewritten as additions. For any polynomial that has some subtractions, we can find an equivalent polynomial using only additions.

▶   **EXAMPLES**   Find an equivalent polynomial using only additions.

5. $-5x^2 - x = -5x^2 + (-x)$

6. $4x^5 - 2x^6 - 4x + 7 = 4x^5 + (-2x^6) + (-4x) + 7$ ◀

DO EXERCISES 9 AND 10.

     When a polynomial has only additions, the monomials being added are called **terms.** In Example 5, the terms are $-5x^2$ and $-x$. In Example 6, the terms are $4x^5$, $-2x^6$, $-4x$, and 7.

▶   **EXAMPLE 7**   Identify the terms of the polynomial

$$4x^7 + 3x + 12 + 8x^3 + 5x.$$

Terms: $4x^7$, $3x$, 12, $8x^3$, and $5x$.   ◀

     If there are subtractions, you can *think* of them as additions without rewriting.

▶ **EXAMPLE 8**   Identify the terms of the polynomial

$$3t^4 - 5t^6 - 4t + 2.$$

Terms: $3t^4$, $-5t^6$, $-4t$, and 2.   ◀

DO EXERCISES 11 AND 12.

c   Like Terms

When terms have the same variable and the variable is raised to the same power, we say that they are **like terms,** or **similar terms.**

▶ **EXAMPLES**   Identify the like terms in the polynomial.

9. $4x^3 + 5x - 4x^2 + 2x^3 + x^2$

Like terms: $4x^3$ and $2x^3$ Same variable and exponent
Like terms: $-4x^2$ and x^2 Same variable and exponent

10. $6 - 3a^2 + 8 - a - 5a$

Like terms: 6 and 8   Constant terms are like terms because
$6 = 6x^0$ and $8 = 8x^0$.

Like terms: $-a$ and $-5a$ ◀

DO EXERCISES 13 AND 14.

d   Coefficients

The coefficient of the term $5x^3$ is 5. In the following polynomial, the color numbers are the **coefficients:**

$$3x^5 - 2x^3 + 5x + 4.$$

▶ **EXAMPLE 11**   Identify the coefficient of each term in the polynomial

$$3x^4 - 4x^3 + 7x^2 + x - 8.$$

The coefficient of the first term is 3.
The coefficient of the second term is -4.
The coefficient of the third term is 7.
The coefficient of the fourth term is 1.
The coefficient of the fifth term is -8.   ◀

DO EXERCISE 15.

e   Collecting Like Terms

We can often simplify polynomials by **collecting like terms,** or **combining similar terms.** To do this, we use the distributive laws. We factor out the exponential expression and add or subtract the coefficients. We try to do this mentally as much as possible.

▶ **EXAMPLES**   Collect like terms.

12. $2x^3 - 6x^3 = (2 - 6)x^3 = -4x^3$ Using a distributive law

13. $5x^2 + 7 + 4x^4 + 2x^2 - 11 - 2x^4 = (5 + 2)x^2 + (4 - 2)x^4 + (7 - 11)$
$$= 7x^2 + 2x^4 - 4 \quad ◀$$

Identify the terms of the polynomial.

11. $3x^2 + 6x + \dfrac{1}{2}$

12. $-4y^5 + 7y^2 - 3y - 2$

Identify the like terms in the polynomial.

13. $4x^3 - x^3 + 2$

14. $4t^4 - 9t^3 - 7t^4 + 10t^3$

15. Identify the coefficient of each term in the polynomial
$$2x^4 - 7x^3 - 8.5x^2 + 10x - 4.$$

ANSWERS ON PAGE A-7

Collect like terms.

16. $3x^2 + 5x^2$

17. $4x^3 - 2x^3 + 2 + 5$

18. $\frac{1}{2}x^5 - \frac{3}{4}x^5 + 4x^2 - 2x^2$

Collect like terms.

19. $24 - 4x^3 - 24$

20. $5x^3 - 8x^5 + 8x^5$

21. $-2x^4 + 16 + 2x^4 + 9 - 3x^5$

Collect like terms.

22. $7x - x$

23. $5x^3 - x^3 + 4$

24. $\frac{3}{4}x^3 + 4x^2 - x^3 + 7$

25. $8x^2 - x^2 + x^3 - 1 - 4x^2 + 10$

Arrange each polynomial in descending order.

26. $x + 3x^5 + 4x^3 + 5x^2 + 6x^7 - 2x^4$

27. $4x^2 - 3 + 7x^5 + 2x^3 - 5x^4$

28. $-14 + 7t^2 - 10t^5 + 14t^7$

Note that using the distributive laws in this manner allows us to collect like terms by adding or subtracting the coefficients. Often the middle step is omitted and we add or subtract mentally, just writing the answer. In collecting like terms, we may get 0.

▶ **EXAMPLES**   Collect like terms.

14. $5x^3 - 5x^3 = (5 - 5)x^3 = 0x^3 = 0$

15. $3x^4 + 2x^2 - 3x^4 + 8 = (3 - 3)x^4 + 2x^2 + 8$
$$= 0x^4 + 2x^2 + 8 = 2x^2 + 8 \qquad ◀$$

DO EXERCISES 16–21.

Multiplying a term of a polynomial by 1 does not change the term, but it may make the polynomial easier to factor or add and subtract.

▶ **EXAMPLES**   Collect like terms.

16. $5x^2 + x^2 = 5x^2 + 1x^2$ Replacing x^2 by $1x^2$
$$= (5 + 1)x^2 \qquad \text{Using a distributive law}$$
$$= 6x^2$$

17. $5x^4 - 6x^3 - x^4 = 5x^4 - 6x^3 - 1x^4$ $x^4 = 1x^4$
$$= (5 - 1)x^4 - 6x^3$$
$$= 4x^4 - 6x^3$$

18. $\frac{2}{3}x^4 - x^3 - \frac{1}{6}x^4 + \frac{2}{5}x^3 - \frac{3}{10}x^3 = (\frac{2}{3} - \frac{1}{6})x^4 + (-1 + \frac{2}{5} - \frac{3}{10})x^3$
$$= (\frac{4}{6} - \frac{1}{6})x^4 + (-\frac{10}{10} + \frac{4}{10} - \frac{3}{10})x^3$$
$$= \frac{3}{6}x^4 - \frac{9}{10}x^3$$
$$= \frac{1}{2}x^4 - \frac{9}{10}x^3 \qquad ◀$$

DO EXERCISES 22–25.

f   **Descending and Ascending Order**

Note in the following polynomial that the exponents decrease. We say that the polynomial is arranged in **descending order:**

$$2x^4 - 8x^3 + 5x^2 - x + 3.$$

The term with the largest exponent is first. The term with the next largest exponent is second, and so on. The associative and commutative laws allow us to arrange the terms of a polynomial in descending order.

▶ **EXAMPLES**   Arrange the polynomial in descending order.

19. $6x^5 + 4x^7 + x^2 + 2x^3 = 4x^7 + 6x^5 + 2x^3 + x^2$

20. $\frac{2}{3} + 4x^5 - 8x^2 + 5x - 3x^3 = 4x^5 - 3x^3 - 8x^2 + 5x + \frac{2}{3} \qquad ◀$

We usually arrange polynomials in descending order, but not always. The opposite order is called **ascending order.** Generally, if an exercise is written in a certain order, we give the answer in that same order.

DO EXERCISES 26–28.

▶ **EXAMPLE 21**   Collect like terms and then arrange in descending order:

$$2x^2 - 4x^3 + 3 - x^2 - 2x^3.$$

We have

$$2x^2 - 4x^3 + 3 - x^2 - 2x^3 = x^2 - 6x^3 + 3 \qquad \text{Collecting like terms}$$

$$= -6x^3 + x^2 + 3 \qquad \text{Arranging in descending order} \quad ◀$$

DO EXERCISES 29 AND 30.

g Degrees

The **degree** of a term is the exponent of the variable. The degree of the term $5x^3$ is 3.

▶ **EXAMPLE 22**   Identify the degree of each term of $8x^4 + 3x + 7$.

The degree of $8x^4$ is 4.

The degree of $3x$ is 1.   Recall that $x = x^1$.

The degree of 7 is 0.   Think of 7 as $7x^0$. Recall that $x^0 = 1$.   ◀

The **degree of a polynomial** is the largest of the degrees of the terms, unless it is the polynomial 0. The polynomial 0 is a special case. We agree that it has *no* degree either as a term or as a polynomial. This is because we can express 0 as $0 = 0x^5 = 0x^7$, and so on, using any exponent we wish.

▶ **EXAMPLE 23**   Identify the degree of the polynomial $5x^3 - 6x^4 + 7$.

We have

$$5x^3 - 6x^4 + 7. \qquad \text{The largest exponent is 4.}$$

The degree of the polynomial is 4.   ◀

DO EXERCISE 31.

Let us summarize the terminology we have learned for the polynomial

$$3x^4 - 8x^3 + 5x^2 + 7x - 6$$

Term	Coefficient	Degree of the term	Degree of the polynomial
$3x^4$	3	4	4
$-8x^3$	-8	3	
$5x^2$	5	2	
$7x$	7	1	
-6	-6	0	

Collect like terms and then arrange in descending order.

29. $3x^2 - 2x + 3 - 5x^2 - 1 - x$

30. $-x + \dfrac{1}{2} + 14x^4 - 7x - 1 - 4x^4$

31. Identify the degree of each term and the degree of the polynomial:
$$-6x^4 + 8x^2 - 2x + 9.$$

ANSWERS ON PAGE A-7

Identify the missing terms in the polynomial.

32. $2x^3 + 4x^2 - 2$

33. $-3x^4$

34. $x^3 + 1$

35. $x^4 - x^2 + 3x + 0.25$

Classify the polynomial as a monomial, binomial, trinomial, or none of these.

36. $5x^4$

37. $4x^3 - 3x^2 + 4x + 2$

38. $3x^2 + x$

39. $3x^2 + 2x - 4$

h Missing Terms

If a coefficient is 0, we usually do not write the term. We say that we have a **missing term.**

▶ **EXAMPLE 23**   Identify the missing terms in the polynomial

$$8x^5 - 2x^3 + 5x^2 + 7x + 8.$$

There is no term with x^4. We say that the x^4-term (or the *fourth-degree term*) is missing.   ◀

For certain skills or manipulations, we can write missing terms with zero coefficients or leave space. For example, we can write the polynomial $3x^2 + 9$ as

$$3x^2 + 0x + 9 \quad \text{or} \quad 3x^2 + \qquad 9.$$

DO EXERCISES 32–35.

i Classifying Polynomials

Polynomials with just one term are called **monomials.** Polynomials with just two terms are called **binomials.** Those with just three terms are called **trinomials.** Those with more than three terms are usually not specified with a name.

▶ **EXAMPLE 24**

Monomials	Binomials	Trinomials	None of these
$4x^2$	$2x + 4$	$3x^3 + 4x + 7$	$4x^3 - 5x^2 + x - 8$
9	$3x^5 + 6x$	$6x^7 - 7x^2 + 4$	
$-23x^{19}$	$-9x^7 - 6$	$4x^2 - 6x - \frac{1}{2}$	

◀

DO EXERCISES 36–39.

EXERCISE SET 9.3

ANSWERS

a Evaluate the polynomial for $x = 4$.

1. $-5x + 2$ **2.** $-3x + 1$ **3.** $2x^2 - 5x + 7$

4. $3x^2 + x + 7$ **5.** $x^3 - 5x^2 + x$ **6.** $7 - x + 3x^2$

Evaluate the polynomial for $x = -1$.

7. $3x + 5$ **8.** $6 - 2x$ **9.** $x^2 - 2x + 1$

10. $5x - 6 + x^2$ **11.** $-3x^3 + 7x^2 - 3x - 2$ **12.** $-2x^3 - 5x^2 + 4x + 3$

Daily accidents. The daily number of accidents N (average number of accidents per day) involving drivers of age a is approximated by the polynomial

$$N = 0.4a^2 - 40a + 1039.$$

13. Evaluate the polynomial for $a = 18$ to find the daily number of accidents involving 18-year-old drivers.

14. Evaluate the polynomial for $a = 20$ to find the daily number of accidents involving 20-year-old drivers.

Falling distance. The distance s, in feet, traveled by a body falling freely from rest in t seconds is approximated by the polynomial

$$s = 16t^2.$$

$s = 16t^2$

15. A stone is dropped from a cliff and takes 8 sec to hit the ground. How high is the cliff?

16. A brick is dropped from a building and takes 3 sec to hit the ground. How high is the building?

Total revenue. An electronics firm is marketing a new kind of stereo. *Total revenue* is the total amount of money taken in. The firm determines that when it sells x stereos, it will take in

$$280x - 0.4x^2 \text{ dollars.}$$

17. What is the total revenue from the sale of 75 stereos?

18. What is the total revenue from the sale of 100 stereos?

Total cost. The electronics firm determines that the total cost of producing x stereos is given by

$$5000 + 0.6x^2 \text{ dollars.}$$

19. What is the total cost of producing 500 stereos?

20. What is the total cost of producing 650 stereos?

b Identify the terms of the polynomial.

21. $2 - 3x + x^2$ **22.** $2x^2 + 3x - 4$

1. _____

2. _____

3. _____

4. _____

5. _____

6. _____

7. _____

8. _____

9. _____

10. _____

11. _____

12. _____

13. _____

14. _____

15. _____

16. _____

17. _____

18. _____

19. _____

20. _____

21. _____

22. _____

ANSWERS

23. _____

24. _____

25. _____

26. _____

27. _____

28. _____

29. _____

30. _____

31. _____

32. _____

33. _____

34. _____

35. _____

36. _____

37. _____

38. _____

39. _____

40. _____

41. _____

42. _____

43. _____

44. _____

45. _____

46. _____

47. _____

48. _____

49. _____

50. _____

51. _____

52. _____

53. _____

54. _____

c   Identify the like terms in the polynomial.

23. $5x^3 + 6x^2 - 3x^2$ **24.** $3x^2 + 4x^3 - 2x^2$

25. $2x^4 + 5x - 7x - 3x^4$ **26.** $-3t + t^3 - 2t - 5t^3$

d   Identify the coefficient of each term of the polynomial.

27. $-3x + 6$ **28.** $2x - 4$ **29.** $5x^2 + 3x + 3$

30. $3x^2 - 5x + 2$ **31.** $-7x^3 + 6x^2 + 3x + 7$ **32.** $5x^4 + x^2 - x + 2$

33. $-5x^4 + 6x^3 - 3x^2 + 8x - 2$ **34.** $7x^3 - 4x^2 - 4x + 5$

e   Collect like terms.

35. $2x - 5x$ **36.** $2x^2 + 8x^2$ **37.** $x - 9x$

38. $x - 5x$ **39.** $5x^3 + 6x^3 + 4$ **40.** $6x^4 - 2x^4 + 5$

41. $5x^3 + 6x - 4x^3 - 7x$ **42.** $3a^4 - 2a + 2a + a^4$ **43.** $6b^5 + 3b^2 - 2b^5 - 3b^2$

44. $2x^2 - 6x + 3x + 4x^2$ **45.** $\dfrac{1}{4}x^5 - 5 + \dfrac{1}{2}x^5 - 2x - 37$

46. $\dfrac{1}{3}x^3 + 2x - \dfrac{1}{6}x^3 + 4 - 16$ **47.** $6x^2 + 2x^4 - 2x^2 - x^4 - 4x^2$

48. $8x^2 + 2x^3 - 3x^3 - 4x^2 - 4x^2$ **49.** $\dfrac{1}{4}x^3 - x^2 - \dfrac{1}{6}x^2 + \dfrac{3}{8}x^3 + \dfrac{5}{16}x^3$

50. $\dfrac{1}{5}x^4 + \dfrac{1}{5} - 2x^2 + \dfrac{1}{10} - \dfrac{3}{15}x^4 + 2x^2 - \dfrac{3}{10}$

f   Arrange the polynomial in descending order.

51. $x^5 + x + 6x^3 + 1 + 2x^2$ **52.** $3 + 2x^2 - 5x^6 - 2x^3 + 3x$

53. $5y^3 + 15y^9 + y - y^2 + 7y^8$ **54.** $9p - 5 + 6p^3 - 5p^4 + p^5$

Collect like terms and then arrange in descending order.

55. $3x^4 - 5x^6 - 2x^4 + 6x^6$

56. $-1 + 5x^3 - 3 - 7x^3 + x^4 + 5$

57. $-2x + 4x^3 - 7x + 9x^3 + 8$

58. $-6x^2 + x - 5x + 7x^2 + 1$

59. $3x + 3x + 3x - x^2 - 4x^2$

60. $-2x - 2x - 2x + x^3 - 5x^3$

61. $-x + \dfrac{3}{4} + 15x^4 - x - \dfrac{1}{2} - 3x^4$

62. $2x - \dfrac{5}{6} + 4x^3 + x + \dfrac{1}{3} - 2x$

g Identify the degree of each term of the polynomial and the degree of the polynomial.

63. $2x - 4$

64. $6 - 3x$

65. $3x^2 - 5x + 2$

66. $5x^3 - 2x^2 + 3$

67. $-7x^3 + 6x^2 + 3x + 7$

68. $5x^4 + x^2 - x + 2$

69. $x^2 - 3x + x^6 - 9x^4$

70. $8x - 3x^2 + 9 - 8x^3$

71. For the polynomial $-7x^4 + 6x^3 - 3x^2 + 8x - 2$, complete the following table.

Term	Coefficient	Degree of the term	Degree of the polynomial
$6x^3$	6		
		2	
$8x$		1	
	-2		

55. _____

56. _____

57. _____

58. _____

59. _____

60. _____

61. _____

62. _____

63. _____

64. _____

65. _____

66. _____

67. _____

68. _____

69. _____

70. _____

71. _____

ANSWERS

72. _____

73. _____

74. _____

75. _____

76. _____

77. _____

78. _____

79. _____

80. _____

81. _____

82. _____

83. _____

84. _____

85. _____

86. _____

87. _____

88. _____

89. _____

90. _____

91. _____

92. _____

93. _____

72. For the polynomial $3x^2 + 8x^5 - 46x^3 + 6x - 2.4 - \frac{1}{2}x^4$, complete the following table.

Term	Coefficient	Degree of the term	Degree of the polynomial
		5	
$-\frac{1}{2}x^4$		4	
	-46		
$3x^2$		2	
	6		
-2.4			

h   Identify the missing terms in the polynomial.

73. $x^3 - 27$ **74.** $x^5 + x$ **75.** $x^4 - x$

76. $5x^4 - 7x + 2$ **77.** $2x^3 - 5x^2 + x - 3$ **78.** $-6x^3$

i   Classify the polynomial as a monomial, binomial, trinomial, or none of these.

79. $x^2 - 10x + 25$ **80.** $-6x^4$ **81.** $x^3 - 7x^2 + 2x - 4$

82. $x^2 - 9$ **83.** $4x^2 - 25$ **84.** $2x^4 - 7x^3 + x^2 + x - 6$

85. $40x$ **86.** $4x^2 + 12x + 9$

SKILL MAINTENANCE

87. Three tired campers stopped for the night. All they had to eat was a bag of apples. During the night, one awoke and ate one third of the apples. Later, a second camper awoke and ate one third of the apples that remained. Much later, the third camper awoke and ate one third of those apples yet remaining after the other two had eaten. When they got up the next morning, 8 apples were left. How many did they have to begin with?

88. A family spent $2011 to drive a car one year, during which the car was driven 7400 mi. The family spent $972 for insurance and $114 for a license registration fee. The only other cost was for gasoline. How much did gasoline cost per mile?

SYNTHESIS

Combine like terms.

89. $\frac{9}{2}x^8 + \frac{1}{9}x^2 + \frac{1}{2}x^9 + \frac{9}{2}x^1 + \frac{9}{2}x^9 + \frac{8}{9}x^2 + \frac{1}{2}x - \frac{1}{2}x^8$

90. $(3x^2)^3 + 4x^2 \cdot 4x^4 - x^4(2x)^2 + ((2x)^2)^3 - 100x^2(x^2)^2$

91. Construct a polynomial in x (meaning that x is the variable) of degree 5 with four terms and coefficients that are integers.

92. What is the degree of $(5m^5)^2$?

93. A polynomial in x has degree 3. The coefficient of x^2 is three less than the coefficient of x^3. The coefficient of x is three times the coefficient of x^2. The remaining coefficient is two more than the coefficient of x^3. The sum of the coefficients is -4. Find the polynomial.

9.4 Addition and Subtraction of Polynomials

a Addition

To add two polynomials, we can think of writing a plus sign between them and then collecting like terms. Depending on the situation, you may see polynomials written in descending order, ascending order, or neither. Generally, if an exercise is written in a particular order, we write the answer in that same order.

▶ **EXAMPLE 1** Add: $(-3x^3 + 2x - 4) + (4x^3 + 3x^2 + 2)$.

$$(-3x^3 + 2x - 4) + (4x^3 + 3x^2 + 2)$$
$$= (-3 + 4)x^3 + 3x^2 + 2x + (-4 + 2) \quad \text{Collecting like terms}$$
$$\qquad\qquad\qquad\qquad\qquad\qquad\qquad\qquad (\textit{No signs are changed.})$$
$$= x^3 + 3x^2 + 2x - 2 \qquad\qquad\qquad\qquad\qquad ◀$$

▶ **EXAMPLE 2** Add:

$$\left(\frac{2}{3}x^4 + 3x^2 - 2x + \frac{1}{2}\right) + \left(-\frac{1}{3}x^4 + 5x^3 - 3x^2 + 3x - \frac{1}{2}\right).$$

$$\left(\frac{2}{3}x^4 + 3x^2 - 2x + \frac{1}{2}\right) + \left(-\frac{1}{3}x^4 + 5x^3 - 3x^2 + 3x - \frac{1}{2}\right)$$
$$= \left(\frac{2}{3} - \frac{1}{3}\right)x^4 + 5x^3 + (3 - 3)x^2 + (-2 + 3)x + \left(\frac{1}{2} - \frac{1}{2}\right) \quad \begin{matrix}\text{Collecting}\\\text{like terms}\end{matrix}$$
$$= \frac{1}{3}x^4 + 5x^3 + x \qquad\qquad\qquad\qquad\qquad ◀$$

We can add polynomials as we do because they represent numbers. After some practice, you will be able to add mentally.

DO EXERCISES 1–4.

▶ **EXAMPLE 3** Add: $(3x^2 - 2x + 2) + (5x^3 - 2x^2 + 3x - 4)$.

$$(3x^2 - 2x + 2) + (5x^3 - 2x^2 + 3x - 4)$$
$$= 5x^3 + (3 - 2)x^2 + (-2 + 3)x + (2 - 4) \quad \text{You might do this step mentally.}$$
$$= 5x^3 + x^2 + x - 2 \qquad \text{Then you would write only this.} \qquad ◀$$

DO EXERCISES 5 AND 6.

We can also add polynomials by writing like terms in columns.

▶ **EXAMPLE 4** Add: $9x^5 - 2x^3 + 6x^2 + 3$ and $5x^4 - 7x^2 + 6$ and $3x^6 - 5x^5 + x^2 + 5$.

We arrange the polynomials with like terms in columns.

$$
\begin{array}{l}
9x^5 \qquad\quad - 2x^3 + 6x^2 + \;3 \\
\qquad\; 5x^4 \qquad\qquad - 7x^2 + \;6 \qquad \text{We leave spaces for missing terms.} \\
\underline{3x^6 - 5x^5 \qquad\qquad\quad + \;\;x^2 + \;5} \\
3x^6 + 4x^5 + 5x^4 - 2x^3 \qquad\quad + 14 \qquad \text{Adding}
\end{array}
$$

We write the answer as $3x^6 + 4x^5 + 5x^4 - 2x^3 + 14$ without the missing space. ◀

OBJECTIVES

After finishing Section 9.4, you should be able to:

a Add polynomials.

b Find the opposite of a polynomial.

c Subtract polynomials.

d Solve problems using addition and subtraction of polynomials.

FOR EXTRA HELP

Tape 20B

Add.

1. $(3x^2 + 2x - 2) + (-2x^2 + 5x + 5)$

2. $(-4x^5 + x^3 + 4) + (7x^4 + 2x^2)$

3. $(31x^4 + x^2 + 2x - 1) + (-7x^4 + 5x^3 - 2x + 2)$

4. $(17x^3 - x^2 + 3x + 4) + \left(-15x^3 + x^2 - 3x - \frac{2}{3}\right)$

Add mentally. Try to write just the answer.

5. $(4x^2 - 5x + 3) + (-2x^2 + 2x - 4)$

6. $(3x^3 - 4x^2 - 5x + 3) + \left(5x^3 + 2x^2 - 3x - \frac{1}{2}\right)$

Add.

7.
$$-2x^3 + 5x^2 - 2x + 4$$
$$x^4 \qquad + 6x^2 + 7x - 10$$
$$-9x^4 + 6x^3 + x^2 \qquad - 2$$

8. $-3x^3 + 5x + 2$ and
$x^3 + x^2 + 5$ and
$x^3 - 2x - 4$

Find two equivalent expressions for the opposite of the polynomial.

9. $12x^4 - 3x^2 + 4x$

10. $-4x^4 + 3x^2 - 4x$

11. $-13x^6 + 2x^4 - 3x^2 + x - \dfrac{5}{13}$

12. $-7y^3 + 2y^2 - y + 3$

Simplify.

13. $-(4x^3 - 6x + 3)$

14. $-(5x^4 + 3x^2 + 7x - 5)$

15. $-\left(14x^{10} - \dfrac{1}{2}x^5 + 5x^3 - x^2 + 3x\right)$

It is sometimes easier to visualize the addition if we add in columns.

DO EXERCISES 7 AND 8.

b Opposites of Polynomials

We now look at subtraction of polynomials. To do so, we first consider the opposite, or additive inverse, of a polynomial.

We know that two numbers are opposites of each other if their sum is zero. For example, 5 and -5 are opposites, since $5 + (-5) = 0$. The same definition holds for polynomials.

> **Two polynomials are *opposites*, or *additive inverses*, of each other if their sum is zero.**

To find a way to determine an opposite, look for a pattern in the following examples:

a) $2x + (-2x) = 0$;

b) $-6x^2 + 6x^2 = 0$;

c) $(5t^3 - 2) + (-5t^3 + 2) = 0$;

d) $(7x^3 - 6x^2 - x + 4) + (-7x^3 + 6x^2 + x - 4) = 0$.

Since $(5t^3 - 2) + (-5t^3 + 2) = 0$, we know that the opposite of $(5t^3 - 2)$ is $(-5t^3 + 2)$. To say the same thing with purely algebraic symbolism, consider

The opposite of $(5t^3 - 2)$ is $-5t^3 + 2.$

$$- \qquad (5t^3 - 2) \quad = \quad -5t^3 + 2.$$

> **We can find an equivalent polynomial for the opposite, or additive inverse, of a polynomial by replacing each term by its opposite—that is, *changing the sign of every term.***

▶ **EXAMPLE 5**   Find two equivalent expressions for the opposite of

$$4x^5 - 7x^3 - 8x + \dfrac{5}{6}.$$

a) $-\left(4x^5 - 7x^3 - 8x + \dfrac{5}{6}\right)$

b) $-4x^5 + 7x^3 + 8x - \dfrac{5}{6}$ Changing the sign of every term

Thus, $-(4x^5 - 7x^3 - 8x + \frac{5}{6})$ is equivalent to $-4x^3 + 7x^3 + 8x - \frac{5}{6}$, and each is the opposite of the original polynomial $4x^5 - 7x^3 - 8x + \frac{5}{6}$.   ◀

DO EXERCISES 9–12.

▶ **EXAMPLE 6**   Simplify: $-\left(-7x^4 - \dfrac{5}{9}x^3 + 8x^2 - x + 67\right)$.

$$-\left(-7x^4 - \dfrac{5}{9}x^3 + 8x^2 - x + 67\right) = 7x^4 + \dfrac{5}{9}x^3 - 8x^2 + x - 67$$ ◀

DO EXERCISES 13–15.

c   **Subtraction of Polynomials**

Recall that we can subtract a real number by adding its opposite, or additive inverse: $a - b = a + (-b)$. This allows us to find an equivalent expression for the difference of two polynomials.

▶ **EXAMPLE 7**   Subtract:

$$(9x^5 + x^3 - 2x^2 + 4) - (2x^5 + x^4 - 4x^3 - 3x^2).$$

We have

$(9x^5 + x^3 - 2x^2 + 4) - (2x^5 + x^4 - 4x^3 - 3x^2)$

$= 9x^5 + x^3 - 2x^2 + 4 + [-(2x^5 + x^4 - 4x^3 - 3x^2)]$ Adding the opposite

$= 9x^5 + x^3 - 2x^2 + 4 - 2x^5 - x^4 + 4x^3 + 3x^2$ Finding the opposite by changing the sign of *each* term

$= 7x^5 - x^4 + 5x^3 + x^2 + 4$ Collecting like terms   ◀

DO EXERCISES 16 AND 17.

As with similar work in Section 7.8, we combine steps by changing the sign of each term of the polynomial being subtracted and collecting like terms. Try to do this mentally as much as possible.

▶ **EXAMPLE 8**   Subtract: $(9x^5 + x^3 - 2x) - (-2x^5 + 5x^3 + 6)$.

$(9x^5 + x^3 - 2x) - (-2x^5 + 5x^3 + 6)$

$= 11x^5 - 4x^3 - 2x - 6$ Change signs and collect like terms. Try to do so mentally.   ◀

DO EXERCISES 18 AND 19.

We can use columns to subtract. We replace coefficients by their opposites, as shown in Example 7.

▶ **EXAMPLE 9**   Write in columns and subtract:

$$(5x^2 - 3x + 6) - (9x^2 - 5x - 3).$$

a) $\begin{aligned} 5x^2 - 3x + 6 \\ -(9x^2 - 5x - 3) \end{aligned}$ Writing similar terms in columns

b) $\begin{aligned} 5x^2 - 3x + 6 \\ -9x^2 + 5x + 3 \end{aligned}$ Changing signs

c) $\begin{aligned} 5x^2 - 3x + 6 \\ -9x^2 + 5x + 3 \\ \hline -4x^2 + 2x + 9 \end{aligned}$ Adding   ◀

If you can do so without error, you can arrange the polynomials in columns and write just the answer.

Subtract.

16. $(7x^3 + 2x + 4) - (5x^3 - 4)$

17. $(-3x^2 + 5x - 4) - (-4x^2 + 11x - 2)$

Subtract mentally. Try to write just the answer.

18. $(-6x^4 + 3x^2 + 6) - (2x^4 + 5x^3 - 5x^2 + 7)$

19. $\left(\dfrac{3}{2}x^3 - \dfrac{1}{2}x^2 + 0.3\right) - \left(\dfrac{1}{2}x^3 + \dfrac{1}{2}x^2 + \dfrac{4}{3}x + 1.2\right)$

ANSWERS ON PAGE A-7

Write in columns and subtract.

20. $(4x^3 + 2x^2 - 2x - 3) -$
$(2x^3 - 3x^2 + 2)$

21. $(2x^3 + x^2 - 6x + 2) -$
$(x^5 + 4x^3 - 2x^2 - 4x)$

22. Find a polynomial for the sum of
the areas of the rectangles.

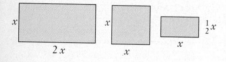

23. Find a polynomial for the shaded
area.

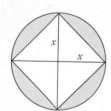

▶ **EXAMPLE 10**　Write in columns and subtract:

$$(x^3 + x^2 + 2x - 12) - (-2x^3 + x^2 - 3x).$$

We have

$$\begin{array}{r} x^3 + x^2 + 2x - 12 \\ -2x^3 + x^2 - 3x \\ \hline 3x^3 + 5x - 12. \end{array}$$　　◀

DO EXERCISES 20 AND 21.

d　**Solving Problems**

▶ **EXAMPLE 11**　Find a polynomial for the sum of the areas of these
rectangles.

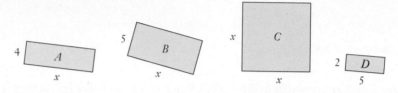

Recall that the area of a rectangle is the product of the length and the
width. The sum of the areas is a sum of products. We find these products
and then collect like terms.

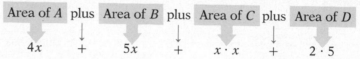

Area of A	plus	Area of B	plus	Area of C	plus	Area of D
$4x$	$+$	$5x$	$+$	$x \cdot x$	$+$	$2 \cdot 5$

We collect like terms:

$$4x + 5x + x^2 + 10 = x^2 + 9x + 10.$$　　◀

DO EXERCISE 22.

▶ **EXAMPLE 12**　A 4-ft by 4-ft sandbox is placed on a square lawn x ft on
a side. Find a polynomial for the remaining area.

We draw a picture of the situation as
shown here.

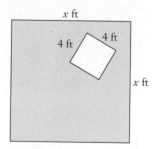

We reword the problem and write the polynomial as follows.

$$\underbrace{\text{Area of lawn}} - \underbrace{\text{Area of sandbox}} = \text{Area left over}$$

$$x \cdot x \quad - \quad 4 \cdot 4 \quad = \text{Area left over}$$

Then

$$x^2 - 16 = \text{Area left over.}$$　　◀

DO EXERCISE 23.

NAME   SECTION   DATE

EXERCISE SET 9.4

a Add.

1. $(3x + 2) + (-4x + 3)$

2. $(6x + 1) + (-7x + 2)$

3. $(-6x + 2) + (x^2 + x - 3)$

4. $(x^2 - 5x + 4) + (8x - 9)$

5. $(x^2 - 9) + (x^2 + 9)$

6. $(x^3 + x^2) + (2x^3 - 5x^2)$

7. $(3x^2 - 5x + 10) + (2x^2 + 8x - 40)$

8. $(6x^4 + 3x^3 - 1) + (4x^2 - 3x + 3)$

9. $(1.2x^3 + 4.5x^2 - 3.8x) +$
$(-3.4x^3 - 4.7x^2 + 23)$

10. $(0.5x^4 - 0.6x^2 + 0.7) +$
$(2.3x^4 + 1.8x - 3.9)$

11. $(1 + 4x + 6x^2 + 7x^3) +$
$(5 - 4x + 6x^2 - 7x^3)$

12. $(3x^4 - 6x - 5x^2 + 5) +$
$(6x^2 - 4x^3 - 1 + 7x)$

13. $(9x^8 - 7x^4 + 2x^2 + 5) +$
$(8x^7 + 4x^4 - 2x)$

14. $(4x^5 - 6x^3 - 9x + 1) +$
$(6x^3 + 9x^2 + 9x)$

15. $(\frac{1}{4}x^4 + \frac{2}{3}x^3 + \frac{5}{8}x^2 + 7) +$
$(-\frac{3}{4}x^4 + \frac{3}{8}x^2 - 7)$

16. $(\frac{1}{3}x^9 + \frac{1}{5}x^5 - \frac{1}{2}x^2 + 7) +$
$(-\frac{1}{5}x^9 + \frac{1}{4}x^4 - \frac{3}{5}x^5 + \frac{3}{4}x^2 + \frac{1}{2})$

17. $0.02x^5 - 0.2x^3 + x + 0.08$ and
$-0.01x^5 + x^4 - 0.8x - 0.02$

18. $(0.03x^6 + 0.05x^3 + 0.22x + 0.05) +$
$(\frac{7}{100}x^6 - \frac{3}{100}x^3 + 0.5)$

19. $-3x^4 + 6x^2 + 2x - 1$
$ -3x^2 + 2x + 1$

20. $-4x^3 + 8x^2 + 3x - 2$
$ -4x^2 + 3x + 2$

21.
$$\begin{array}{r}
0.15x^4 + 0.10x^3 - 0.9x^2 \\
-0.01x^3 + 0.01x^2 + x \\
1.25x^4 + 0.11x^2 + 0.01 \\
0.27x^3 + 0.99 \\
-0.35x^4 + 15x^2 - 0.03
\end{array}$$

22.
$$\begin{array}{r}
0.05x^4 + 0.12x^3 - 0.5x^2 \\
-0.02x^3 + 0.02x^2 + 2x \\
1.5x^4 + 0.01x^2 + 0.15 \\
0.25x^3 + 0.85 \\
-0.25x^4 + 10x^2 - 0.04
\end{array}$$

1. _____

2. _____

3. _____

4. _____

5. _____

6. _____

7. _____

8. _____

9. _____

10. _____

11. _____

12. _____

13. _____

14. _____

15. _____

16. _____

17. _____

18. _____

19. _____

20. _____

21. _____

22. _____

b Find two equivalent expressions for the opposite of the polynomial.

23. $-5x$

24. $x^2 - 3x$

25. $-x^2 + 10x - 2$

26. $-4x^3 - x^2 - x$

27. $12x^4 - 3x^3 + 3$

28. $4x^3 - 6x^2 - 8x + 1$

Simplify.

29. $-(3x - 7)$

30. $-(-2x + 4)$

31. $-(4x^2 - 3x + 2)$

32. $-(-6a^3 + 2a^2 - 9a + 1)$

33. $-(-4x^4 + 6x^2 + \frac{3}{4}x - 8)$

34. $-(-5x^4 + 4x^3 - x^2 + 0.9)$

c Subtract.

35. $(3x + 2) - (-4x + 3)$

36. $(6x + 1) - (-7x + 2)$

37. $(-6x + 2) - (x^2 + x - 3)$

38. $(x^2 - 5x + 4) - (8x - 9)$

39. $(x^2 - 9) - (x^2 + 9)$

40. $(x^3 + x^2) - (2x^3 - 5x^2)$

41. $(6x^4 + 3x^3 - 1) - (4x^2 - 3x + 3)$

42. $(-4x^2 + 2x) - (3x^3 - 5x^2 + 3)$

43. $(1.2x^3 + 4.5x^2 - 3.8x) - (-3.4x^3 - 4.7x^2 + 23)$

44. $(0.5x^4 - 0.6x^2 + 0.7) - (2.3x^4 + 1.8x - 3.9)$

45. $(\frac{5}{8}x^3 - \frac{1}{4}x - \frac{1}{3}) - (-\frac{1}{8}x^3 + \frac{1}{4}x - \frac{1}{3})$

46. $(\frac{1}{5}x^3 + 2x^2 - 0.1) - (-\frac{2}{5}x^3 + 2x^2 + 0.01)$

47. $(0.08x^3 - 0.02x^2 + 0.01x) - (0.02x^3 + 0.03x^2 - 1)$

48. $(0.8x^4 + 0.2x - 1) - (\frac{7}{10}x^4 + \frac{1}{5}x - 0.1)$

Subtract.

49. $x^2 + 5x + 6$
$\underline{x^2 + 2x}$

50. $x^3 \qquad + 1$
$\underline{x^3 + x^2}$

51. $5x^4 + 6x^3 - 9x^2$
$\underline{-6x^4 - 6x^3 \qquad + 8x + 9}$

52. $5x^4 \qquad + 6x^2 - 3x + 6$
$\underline{\qquad 6x^3 + 7x^2 - 8x - 9}$

53. $x^5 \qquad\qquad\qquad - 1$
$\underline{x^5 - x^4 + x^3 - x^2 + x - 1}$

54. $x^5 + x^4 - x^3 + x^2 - x + 2$
$\underline{x^5 - x^4 + x^3 - x^2 - x + 2}$

d Solve.

55. Find a polynomial for the sum of the areas of these rectangles.

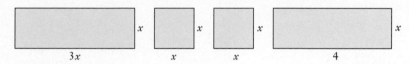

Find a polynomial for the perimeter of the figure.

56.

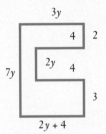

57.

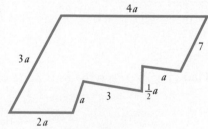

Find two algebraic expressions for the area of the figure.

58.

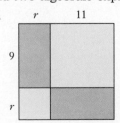

59.

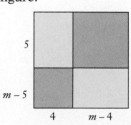

ANSWERS

49. _____

50. _____

51. _____

52. _____

53. _____

54. _____

55. _____

56. _____

57. _____

58. _____

59. _____

60. Find $(x + 3)^2$ using the four areas of the square shown here.

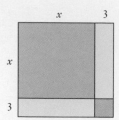

60. _____

Find a polynomial for the shaded area.

61. _____

61.

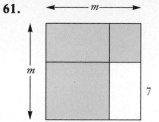

62.

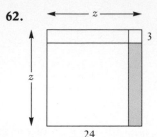

62. _____

63. _____

63.

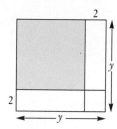

64. _____

64. Find $(y - 2)^2$ using the four parts of this square.

65. _____

66. _____

67. _____

SYNTHESIS

Simplify.

65. $(7y^2 - 5y + 6) - (3y^2 + 8y - 12) + (8y^2 - 10y + 3)$

66. $(3x^2 - 4x + 6) - (-2x^2 + 4) + (-5x - 3)$

67. $(-y^4 - 7y^3 + y^2) + (-2y^4 + 5y - 2) - (-6y^3 + y^2)$

68. _____

68. $(-4 + x^2 + 2x^3) - (-6 - x + 3x^3) - (-x^2 - 5x^3)$

9.5 Multiplication of Polynomials

We now multiply polynomials using techniques based, for the most part, on the distributive laws, but also on the associative and commutative laws. As we proceed in this chapter, we will develop special ways to find certain products.

a Multiplying Monomials

Consider $(3x)(4x)$. We multiply as follows:

$$(3x)(4x) = 3 \cdot x \cdot 4 \cdot x \qquad \text{By the associative law of multiplication}$$
$$= 3 \cdot 4 \cdot x \cdot x \qquad \text{By the commutative law of multiplication}$$
$$= (3 \cdot 4) \cdot x \cdot x \qquad \text{By the associative law}$$
$$= 12x^2. \qquad \text{Using the product rule for exponents}$$

> **To find an equivalent expression for the product of two monomials, multiply the coefficients and then multiply the variables using the product rule for exponents.**

▶ **EXAMPLES** Multiply.

1. $(5x)(6x) = (5 \cdot 6)(x \cdot x) \qquad \text{Multiplying the coefficients}$
$\qquad = 30x^2 \qquad \text{Simplifying}$

2. $(3x)(-x) = (3x)(-1x)$
$\qquad = (3)(-1)(x \cdot x)$
$\qquad = -3x^2$

3. $(-7x^5)(4x^3) = (-7 \cdot 4)(x^5 \cdot x^3)$
$\qquad = -28x^{5+3} \qquad \text{Adding the exponents}$
$\qquad = -28x^8 \qquad \text{Simplifying} \qquad ◀$

After some practice, you can do this mentally. Multiply the coefficients and then the variables by keeping the base and adding the exponents. Write only the answer.

DO EXERCISES 1–8.

b Multiplying a Monomial and Any Polynomial

To find an equivalent expression for the product of a monomial, such as $2x$, and a binomial, such as $5x + 3$, we use a distributive law.

▶ **EXAMPLE 4** Multiply: $2x$ and $5x + 3$.

$$(2x)(5x + 3) = (2x)(5x) + (2x)(3) \qquad \text{Using a distributive law}$$
$$= 10x^2 + 6x \qquad \text{Multiplying the monomials} \qquad ◀$$

OBJECTIVES

After finishing Section 9.5, you should be able to:

a Multiply monomials.

b Multiply a monomial and any polynomial.

c Multiply two binomials.

d Multiply any two polynomials.

FOR EXTRA HELP

Tape 20C

Multiply.

1. $3x$ and -5

2. $-x$ and x

3. $-x$ and $-x$

4. $-x^2$ and x^3

5. $3x^5$ and $4x^2$

6. $4y^5$ and $-2y^6$

7. $-7y^4$ and $-y$

8. $7x^5$ and 0

ANSWERS ON PAGE A-7

Multiply.

9. $4x$ and $2x + 4$

10. $3t^2(-5t + 2)$

11. $5x^3(x^3 + 5x^2 - 6x + 8)$

Multiply.

12. $x + 8$ and $x + 5$ $x^3 + 13x + 40$

13. $(x + 5)(x - 4)$

Multiply.

14. $5x + 3$ and $x - 4$

15. $(2x - 3)(3x - 5)$

▶ **EXAMPLE 5**   Multiply: $5x(2x^2 - 3x + 4)$.

$$5x(2x^2 - 3x + 4) = (5x)(2x^2) - (5x)(3x) + (5x)(4)$$
$$= 10x^3 - 15x^2 + 20x \quad ◀$$

> To multiply a monomial and a polynomial, multiply each term of the polynomial by the monomial.

▶ **EXAMPLE 6**   Multiply: $2x^2(x^3 - 7x^2 + 10x - 4)$.

$$2x^2(x^3 - 7x^2 + 10x - 4) = 2x^5 - 14x^4 + 20x^3 - 8x^2 \quad ◀$$

DO EXERCISES 9–11.

c   Multiplying Two Binomials

To find an equivalent expression for the product of two binomials, we use the distributive laws more than once. In Example 7, we use a distributive law three times.

▶ **EXAMPLE 7**   Multiply: $x + 5$ and $x + 4$.

$$(x + 5)(x + 4) = x(x + 4) + 5(x + 4) \quad \text{Using a distributive law}$$
$$= x \cdot x + x \cdot 4 + 5 \cdot x + 5 \cdot 4 \quad \text{Using a distributive law on each part}$$
$$= x^2 + 4x + 5x + 20 \quad \text{Multiplying the monomials}$$
$$= x^2 + 9x + 20 \quad \text{Collecting like terms} \quad ◀$$

DO EXERCISES 12 AND 13.

▶ **EXAMPLE 8**   Multiply: $4x + 3$ and $x - 2$.

$$(4x + 3)(x - 2) = 4x(x - 2) + 3(x - 2) \quad \text{Using a distributive law}$$
$$= 4x \cdot x - 4x \cdot 2 + 3 \cdot x - 3 \cdot 2 \quad \text{Using a distributive law on each part}$$
$$= 4x^2 - 8x + 3x - 6 \quad \text{Multiplying the monomials}$$
$$= 4x^2 - 5x - 6 \quad \text{Collecting like terms} \quad ◀$$

DO EXERCISES 14 AND 15.

ANSWERS ON PAGE A-7

d ■ Multiplying Any Polynomials

Let us consider the product of a binomial and a trinomial. We again use a distributive law three times. You may see ways to skip some steps and do the work mentally.

▶ **EXAMPLE 9** Multiply: $(x^2 + 2x - 3)(x^2 + 4)$.

$$(x^2 + 2x - 3)(x^2 + 4) = (x^2 + 2x - 3)x^2 + (x^2 + 2x - 3)4$$
$$= x^2 \cdot x^2 + 2x \cdot x^2 - 3 \cdot (x^2) + x^2(4) + 2x \cdot 4 - 3 \cdot 4$$
$$= x^4 + 2x^3 - 3x^2 + 4x^2 + 8x - 12$$
$$= x^4 + 2x^3 + x^2 + 8x - 12 \qquad ◀$$

DO EXERCISES 16 AND 17.

Perhaps you have discovered the following in the preceding examples.

> To multiply two polynomials P and Q, select one of the polynomials, say P. Then multiply each term of P by every term of Q and collect like terms.

We can use columns for long multiplications. We multiply each term at the top by every term at the bottom. We write like terms in columns, and then we add the results. Such multiplication is like multiplying with whole numbers:

$$
\begin{array}{r}
4\ 5\ 7 \\
\times \quad 6\ 3 \\
\hline
1\ 3\ 7\ 1 \\
2\ 7\ 4\ 2\ 0 \\
\hline
2\ 8\ 7\ 9\ 1
\end{array}
\qquad
\begin{array}{r}
4\ 5\ 7 \\
\times \quad\quad 6\ 3 \\
\hline
1200 + 150 + 21 \\
2400 + 3000 + 420 \\
\hline
2400 + 4200 + 570 + 21
\end{array}
$$

$= 400 + 50 + 7$
$= 60 + 3$
$= 3(457) = 3(400 + 50 + 7)$
$= 60(457) = 60(400 + 50 + 7)$
$= 28,971$

▶ **EXAMPLE 10** Multiply: $(4x^2 - 2x + 3)(x + 2)$.

$$
\begin{array}{r}
4x^2 - 2x + 3 \\
x + 2 \\
\hline
8x^2 - 4x + 6 \\
4x^3 - 2x^2 + 3x \\
\hline
4x^3 + 6x^2 - \ x + 6
\end{array}
$$

Multiplying the top row by 2
Multiplying the top row by x
Collecting like terms

Line up like terms in columns. ◀

Multiply.

16. $(x^2 + 3x - 4)(x^2 + 5)$

17. $(3y^2 - 7)(2y^3 - 2y + 5)$

ANSWERS ON PAGE A-7

Multiply.

18. $3x^2 - 2x + 4$
$ x + 5$

19. $-5x^2 + 4x + 2$
$ -4x^2 - 8$

20. Multiply.

$$3x^2 - 2x - 5$$
$$2x^2 + x - 2$$

ANSWERS ON PAGE A-7

▶ **EXAMPLE 11**　Multiply: $(5x^3 - 3x + 4)(-2x^2 - 3)$.

When missing terms occur, it helps to leave spaces for them and align like terms as we multiply.

$$
\begin{array}{r}
5x^3 \qquad - 3x + 4 \\
-2x^2 \qquad - 3 \\
\hline
-15x^3 \qquad + 9x - 12 \\
-10x^5 + 6x^3 - 8x^2 \\
\hline
-10x^5 - 9x^3 - 8x^2 + 9x - 12
\end{array}
$$

Multiplying by -3
Multiplying by $-2x^2$
Collecting like terms　◀

DO EXERCISES 18 AND 19.

▶ **EXAMPLE 12**　Multiply: $(2x^2 + 3x - 4)(2x^2 - x + 3)$.

$$
\begin{array}{r}
2x^2 + 3x - 4 \\
2x^2 - x + 3 \\
\hline
6x^2 + 9x - 12 \\
-2x^3 - 3x^2 + 4x \\
4x^4 + 6x^3 - 8x^2 \\
\hline
4x^4 + 4x^3 - 5x^2 + 13x - 12
\end{array}
$$

Multiplying by 3
Multiplying by $-x$
Multiplying by $2x^2$
Collecting like terms　◀

DO EXERCISE 20.

❖　SIDELIGHTS

Factors and Sums

To *factor* a number is to express it as a product. Since $12 = 4 \cdot 3$, we say that 12 is *factored* and that 4 and 3 are *factors* of 12. In the table below, the top number has been factored in such a way that the sum of the factors is the bottom number. For example, in the first column 40 has been factored as $5 \cdot 8$, and $5 + 8 = 13$, the bottom number. Such thinking is important in algebra when we factor trinomials of the type $x^2 + bx + c$.

Product	40	63	36	72	−140	−96	48	168	110			
Factor	5									−9	−24	−3
Factor	8									−10	18	
Sum	13	16	−20	−38	−4	4	−14	−29	−21			18

EXERCISES

Find the missing numbers in the table.

NAME   SECTION   DATE

EXERCISE SET 9.5

a Multiply.

1. $(6x^2)(7)$

2. $(5x^2)(-2)$

3. $(-x^3)(-x)$

4. $(-x^4)(x^2)$

5. $(7x^5)(4x^3)$

6. $(10a^2)(3a^2)$

7. $(-0.1x^6)(0.2x^4)$

8. $(0.3x^3)(-0.4x^6)$

9. $(-\frac{1}{5}x^3)(-\frac{1}{3}x)$

10. $(-\frac{1}{4}x^4)(\frac{1}{5}x^8)$

11. $(-4x^2)(0)$

12. $(-4m^5)(-1)$

13. $(3x^2)(-4x^3)(2x^6)$

14. $(-2y^5)(10y^4)(-3y^3)$

b Multiply.

15. $3x(-x+5)$

16. $2x(4x-6)$

17. $-3x(x-1)$

18. $-5x(-x-1)$

19. $x^2(x^3+1)$

20. $-2x^3(x^2-1)$

21. $3x(2x^2-6x+1)$

22. $-4x(2x^3-6x^2-5x+1)$

23. $(-6x^2)(x^2+x)$

24. $(-4x^2)(x^2-x)$

25. $(3y^2)(6y^4+8y^3)$

26. $(4y^4)(y^3-6y^2)$

c Multiply.

27. $(x+6)(x+3)$

28. $(x+5)(x+2)$

29. $(x+5)(x-2)$

30. $(x+6)(x-2)$

31. $(x-4)(x-3)$

32. $(x-7)(x-3)$

33. $(x+3)(x-3)$

34. $(x+6)(x-6)$

35. $(5-x)(5-2x)$

36. $(3+x)(6+2x)$

37. $(2x+5)(2x+5)$

38. $(3x-4)(3x-4)$

39. $(x-\frac{5}{2})(x+\frac{2}{5})$

40. $(x+\frac{4}{3})(x+\frac{3}{2})$

ANSWERS

1. _____
2. _____
3. _____
4. _____
5. _____
6. _____
7. _____
8. _____
9. _____
10. _____
11. _____
12. _____
13. _____
14. _____
15. _____
16. _____
17. _____
18. _____
19. _____
20. _____
21. _____
22. _____
23. _____
24. _____
25. _____
26. _____
27. _____
28. _____
29. _____
30. _____
31. _____
32. _____
33. _____
34. _____
35. _____
36. _____
37. _____
38. _____
39. _____
40. _____

ANSWERS

41. _____

42. _____

43. _____

44. _____

45. _____

46. _____

47. _____

48. _____

49. _____

50. _____

51. _____

52. _____

53. _____

54. _____

55. _____

56. _____

57. _____

58. _____

59. _____

60. _____

61. _____

62. _____

63. _____

64. _____

65. _____

d Multiply.

41. $(x^2 + x + 1)(x - 1)$

42. $(x^2 - x + 2)(x + 2)$

43. $(2x + 1)(2x^2 + 6x + 1)$

44. $(3x - 1)(4x^2 - 2x - 1)$

45. $(y^2 - 3)(3y^2 - 6y + 2)$

46. $(3y^2 - 3)(y^2 + 6y + 1)$

47. $(x^3 + x^2)(x^3 + x^2 - x)$

48. $(x^3 - x^2)(x^3 - x^2 + x)$

49. $(-5x^3 - 7x^2 + 1)(2x^2 - x)$

50. $(-4x^3 + 5x^2 - 2)(5x^2 + 1)$

51. $(1 + x + x^2)(-1 - x + x^2)$

52. $(1 - x + x^2)(1 - x + x^2)$

53. $(2t^2 - t - 4)(3t^2 + 2t - 1)$

54. $(3a^2 - 5a + 2)(2a^2 - 3a + 4)$

55. $(x - x^3 + x^5)(x^2 - 1 + x^4)$

56. $(x - x^3 + x^5)(3x^2 + 3x^6 + 3x^4)$

57. $(x^3 + x^2 + x + 1)(x - 1)$

58. $(x + 2)(x^3 - x^2 + x - 2)$

SKILL MAINTENANCE

59. Subtract: $-\frac{1}{4} - \frac{1}{2}$.

60. Factor: $16x - 24y + 36$.

SYNTHESIS

61. Find a polynomial for the shaded area.

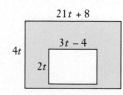

62. A box with a square bottom is to be made from a 12-in.-square piece of cardboard. Squares with side x are cut out of the corners and the sides are folded up. Find polynomials for the volume and the outside surface area of the box.

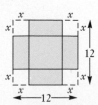

63. The height of a triangle is 4 ft longer than its base. Find a polynomial for the area.

Compute and simplify.

64. $(x + 3)(x + 6) + (x + 3)(x + 6)$

65. $(x - 2)(x - 7) - (x - 2)(x - 7)$

9.6 Special Products

We now consider a special way of multiplying any two binomials. Such a special technique is called a **special product**, meaning that we encounter certain products so often that it is helpful to have faster methods of computing.

a Products of Two Binomials

To multiply two binomials, we can select one binomial and multiply each term of that binomial by every term of the other. Then we collect like terms. Consider the product $(x + 5)(x + 4)$:

$$(x + 5)(x + 4) = x \cdot x + 5 \cdot x + x \cdot 4 + 5 \cdot 4$$
$$= x^2 + 5x + 4x + 20$$
$$= x^2 + 9x + 20.$$

We can rewrite the first line of this product to show a special technique for finding the product of two binomials:

First   Outside   Inside   Last
terms   terms   terms   terms

$$(x + 5)(x + 4) = x \cdot x \ + \ 4 \cdot x \ + \ 5 \cdot x \ + \ 5 \cdot 4.$$

To remember this method of multiplying, use the initials **FOIL**.

The FOIL Method

To multiply two binomials, $A + B$ and $C + D$, multiply the **F**irst terms AC, the **O**utside terms AD, the **I**nside terms BC, and then the **L**ast terms BD. Then collect like terms, if possible.

$$(A + B)(C + D) = AC + AD + BC + BD$$

1. Multiply **F**irst terms: AC.
2. Multiply **O**utside terms: AD.
3. Multiply **I**nside terms: BC.
4. Multiply **L**ast terms: BD.

↓

FOIL

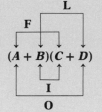

$$(A + B)(C + D)$$

▶ **EXAMPLE 1**   Multiply: $(x + 8)(x^2 + 5)$.

We have

$$\overset{\text{F}}{} \quad \overset{\text{O}}{} \quad \overset{\text{I}}{} \quad \overset{\text{L}}{}$$
$$(x + 8)(x^2 + 5) = x^3 + 5x + 8x^2 + 40$$
$$= x^3 + 8x^2 + 5x + 40.$$

Since each of the original binomials is in descending order, we write the product in descending order, as is customary, but this is not a "must." ◀

OBJECTIVES

After finishing Section 9.6, you should be able to:

a Multiply two binomials mentally using the FOIL method.

b Multiply the sum and difference of two terms mentally.

c Square a binomial mentally.

d Find special products when they are mixed together.

FOR EXTRA HELP

Tape 20D

Multiply mentally. Write just the answer.

1. $(x + 3)(x + 4)$

2. $(x + 3)(x - 5)$

3. $(2x + 1)(x + 4)$

4. $(2x^2 - 3)(x - 2)$

5. $(6x^2 + 5)(2x^3 + 1)$

6. $(y^3 + 7)(y^3 - 7)$

7. $(2x^4 + x^2)(-x^3 + x)$

Multiply.

8. $(t + 5)(t + 3)$

9. $\left(x + \dfrac{4}{5}\right)\left(x - \dfrac{4}{5}\right)$

10. $(x^3 - 0.5)(x^2 + 0.5)$

11. $(2 + 3x^2)(4 - 5x^2)$

12. $(6x^3 - 3x^2)(5x^2 + 2x)$

Often we can collect like terms after we multiply.

▶ **EXAMPLES** Multiply.

2. $(x + 6)(x - 6) = x^2 - 6x + 6x - 36$ Using FOIL
$$= x^2 - 36 \quad \text{Collecting like terms}$$

3. $(y + 3)(y - 2) = y^2 - 2y + 3y - 6$
$$= y^2 + y - 6$$

4. $(x^3 + 5)(x^3 - 5) = x^6 - 5x^3 + 5x^3 - 25$
$$= x^6 - 25$$

5. $(4t^3 + 5)(3t^2 - 2) = 12t^5 - 8t^3 + 15t^2 - 10$ ◀

DO EXERCISES 1–7.

▶ **EXAMPLES** Multiply.

6. $(x + 7)(x + 4) = x^2 + 4x + 7x + 28$
$$= x^2 + 11x + 28$$

7. $(x - \frac{2}{3})(x + \frac{2}{3}) = x^2 + \frac{2}{3}x - \frac{2}{3}x - \frac{4}{9}$
$$= x^2 - \frac{4}{9}$$

8. $(x^2 - 0.3)(x^2 - 0.3) = x^4 - 0.3x^2 - 0.3x^2 + 0.09$
$$= x^4 - 0.6x^2 + 0.09$$

9. $(3 - 4x)(7 - 5x^3) = 21 - 15x^3 - 28x + 20x^4$
$$= 21 - 28x - 15x^3 + 20x^4$$

(*Note:* If the original polynomials are in ascending order, it is natural to write the product in ascending order, but this is not a "must.")

10. $(5x^4 + 2x^3)(3x^2 - 7x) = 15x^6 - 35x^5 + 6x^5 - 14x^4$
$$= 15x^6 - 29x^5 - 14x^4$$ ◀

DO EXERCISES 8–12.

We can show the FOIL method geometrically as follows:

The area of the large rectangle is $(A + B)(C + D)$.

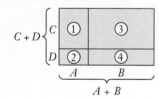

The area of rectangle ① is AC.

The area of rectangle ② is AD.

The area of rectangle ③ is BC.

The area of rectangle ④ is BD.

The area of the large rectangle is the sum of the areas of the smaller rectangles. Thus,

$$(A + B)(C + D) = AC + AD + BC + BD.$$

b Multiplying Sums and Differences of Two Terms

Consider the product of the sum and difference of the same two terms, such as

$$(x + 2)(x - 2).$$

Since this is the product of two binomials, we can use FOIL. This product occurs so often, however, that it will speed up our work to be able to use an even faster method. To find a faster way to compute such a product, look for a pattern in the following:

a) $(x + 2)(x - 2) = x^2 - 2x + 2x - 4 = x^2 - 4$;

b) $(3x - 5)(3x + 5) = 9x^2 + 15x - 15x - 25 = 9x^2 - 25$.

DO EXERCISES 13 AND 14.

Perhaps you discovered in each case that when you multiply the two binomials, two terms are opposites, or additive inverses, which add to 0 and "drop out."

> **The product of the sum and difference of the same two terms is the square of the first term minus the square of the second term:**
>
> $$(A + B)(A - B) = A^2 - B^2.$$

It is helpful to memorize this rule in both words and symbols. (If you do forget it, you can, of course, use FOIL.)

▶ **EXAMPLES** Multiply. (Carry out the rule and say the words as you go.)

$$(A + B)(A - B) = A^2 - B^2$$

11. $(x + 4)(x - 4) = x^2 - 4^2$ "The square of the first term, x^2, minus the square of the second, 4^2."

$$= x^2 - 16$$ Simplifying

12. $(5 + 2w)(5 - 2w) = 5^2 - (2w)^2$
$$= 25 - 4w^2$$

13. $(3x^2 - 7)(3x^2 + 7) = (3x^2)^2 - 7^2$
$$= 9x^4 - 49$$

14. $(-4x - 10)(-4x + 10) = (-4x)^2 - 10^2$
$$= 16x^2 - 100$$ ◀

DO EXERCISES 15–18.

c Squaring Binomials

Consider the square of a binomial, such as $(x + 3)^2$. This can be expressed as $(x + 3)(x + 3)$. Since this is the product of two binomials, we can again use FOIL. But again, this product occurs so often that it will speed up our work to be able to use an even faster method. Look for a pattern in the following:

a) $(x + 3)^2 = (x + 3)(x + 3)$
$$= x^2 + 3x + 3x + 9 = x^2 + 6x + 9;$$

b) $(5 + 3p)^2 = (5 + 3p)(5 + 3p)$
$$= 25 + 15p + 15p + 9p^2 = 25 + 30p + 9p^2;$$

Multiply.

13. $(x + 5)(x - 5)$

14. $(2x - 3)(2x + 3)$

Multiply.

15. $(x + 2)(x - 2)$

16. $(x - 7)(x + 7)$

17. $(6 - 4y)(6 + 4y)$

18. $(2x^3 - 1)(2x^3 + 1)$

ANSWERS ON PAGE A-7

Multiply.

19. $(x + 8)(x + 8)$

20. $(x - 5)(x - 5)$

Multiply.

21. $(x + 2)^2$

22. $(a - 4)^2$

23. $(2x + 5)^2$

24. $(4x^2 - 3x)^2$

25. $(7 + y)(7 + y)$

26. $(3x^2 - 5)(3x^2 - 5)$

c) $(x - 3)^2 = (x - 3)(x - 3)$
$$= x^2 - 3x - 3x + 9$$
$$= x^2 - 6x + 9;$$

d) $(3x - 5)^2 = (3x - 5)(3x - 5)$
$$= 9x^2 - 15x - 15x + 25$$
$$= 9x^2 - 30x + 25.$$

DO EXERCISES 19 AND 20.

When squaring a binomial, we multiply a binomial by itself. Perhaps you noticed that two terms are the same and when added give twice their product. The other two terms are squares.

> **The square of a sum or difference of two terms is the square of the first term, plus or minus twice the product of the two terms, plus the square of the last term:**
> $$(A + B)^2 = A^2 + 2AB + B^2;$$
> $$(A - B)^2 = A^2 - 2AB + B^2.$$

It is helpful to memorize this rule in both words and symbols.

▶ **EXAMPLES**   Multiply. (Carry out the rule and say the words as you go.)

$$(A + B)^2 = A^2 + 2 \cdot A \cdot B + B^2$$

15. $(x + 3)^2 = x^2 + 2 \cdot x \cdot 3 + 3^2$ "x^2 plus 2 times x times 3 plus 3^2."
$$= x^2 + 6x + 9$$

16. $(t - 5)^2 = t^2 - 2 \cdot t \cdot 5 + 5^2$ "t^2 minus 2 times t times 5 plus 5^2."
$$= t^2 - 10t + 25$$

17. $(2x + 7)^2 = (2x)^2 + 2 \cdot 2x \cdot 7 + 7^2$
$$= 4x^2 + 28x + 49$$

18. $(5x - 3x^2)^2 = (5x)^2 - 2 \cdot 5x \cdot 3x^2 + (3x^2)^2$
$$= 25x^2 - 30x^3 + 9x^4$$ ◀

DO EXERCISES 21–26.

> CAUTION!   Note carefully in these examples that the square of a sum is *not* the sum of the squares:
>
> The middle term $2AB$ is missing.
>
> $$(A + B)^2 \neq A^2 + B^2.$$
>
> To see this, note that
> $$(20 + 5)^2 = 25^2 = 625,$$
> but
> $$20^2 + 5^2 = 400 + 25 = 425 \neq 625.$$
> However, $20^2 + 2(20)(5) + 5^2 = 625$.

We can look at our rule for finding $(A + B)^2$ geometrically as follows. The area of the large square is

$$(A + B)(A + B) = (A + B)^2.$$

This is equal to the sum of the areas of the smaller rectangles:

$$A^2 + AB + AB + B^2 = A^2 + 2AB + B^2.$$

Thus,

$$(A + B)^2 = A^2 + 2AB + B^2.$$

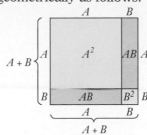

d Multiplications of Various Types

We have considered how to quickly multiply certain kinds of polynomials. Let us now try several kinds mixed together so that we can learn to sort them out. When you multiply, first see what kind of multiplication you have. Then use the best method. The formulas you should know and the questions you should ask yourself are as follows.

Multiplying Two Polynomials

1. **Is the product the square of a binomial? If so, use the following:**
   $$(A + B)(A + B) = (A + B)^2 = A^2 + 2AB + B^2,$$
   or $\quad (A - B)(A - B) = (A - B)^2 = A^2 - 2AB + B^2.$

   The square of a binomial is the square of the first term, plus or minus _twice_ the product of the two terms, plus the square of the last term.

   [The answer has 3 terms.]

2. **Is it the product of the sum and difference of the _same_ two terms? If so, use the following:**
   $$(A + B)(A - B) = A^2 - B^2.$$

   The product of the sum and difference of the same two terms is the difference of squares.

   [The answer has 2 terms.]

3. **Is it the product of two binomials other than those above? If so, use FOIL.**

   [The answer will have 3 or 4 terms.]

4. **The product of a monomial and any polynomial is found by multiplying each term of the polynomial by the monomial.**

5. **Is it the product of two polynomials other than those above? If so, multiply each term of one by every term of the other. Use columns if you wish.**

   [The answer will have 2 or more terms, usually more than 2 terms.]

Note that FOIL will actually work instead of either of the first two rules, but those rules will make your work go faster.

Multiply.

27. $(x + 5)(x + 6)$

▶ **EXAMPLE 19**　Multiply: $(x + 3)(x - 3)$.

$$(x + 3)(x - 3) = x^2 - 9 \qquad \text{Using method 2 (the product of the sum and difference of two terms)} \quad ◀$$

▶ **EXAMPLE 20**　Multiply: $(t + 7)(t - 5)$.

$$(t + 7)(t - 5) = t^2 + 2t - 35 \qquad \text{Using method 3 (the product of two binomials, but neither the square of a binomial nor the product of the sum and difference of two terms)} \quad ◀$$

28. $(t - 4)(t + 4)$

▶ **EXAMPLE 21**　Multiply: $(x + 7)(x + 7)$.

$$(x + 7)(x + 7) = x^2 + 14x + 49 \qquad \text{Using method 1 (the square of a binomial sum)} \quad ◀$$

29. $4x^2(-2x^3 + 5x^2 + 10)$

▶ **EXAMPLE 22**　Multiply: $2x^3(9x^2 + x - 7)$.

$$2x^3(9x^2 + x - 7) = 18x^5 + 2x^4 - 14x^3 \qquad \text{Using method 4 (the product of a monomial and a trinomial; multiplying each term of the trinomial by the monomial)} \quad ◀$$

30. $(9x^2 + 1)^2$

▶ **EXAMPLE 23**　Multiply: $(5x^3 - 7x)^2$.

$$(5x^3 - 7x)^2 = 25x^6 - 2(5x^3)(7x) + 49x^2 \qquad \text{Using method 1 (the square of a binomial difference)}$$
$$= 25x^6 - 70x^4 + 49x^2 \qquad ◀$$

31. $(2a - 5)(2a + 8)$

▶ **EXAMPLE 24**　Multiply: $(3x + \frac{1}{4})^2$.

$$(3x + \tfrac{1}{4})^2 = 9x^2 + 2(3x)(\tfrac{1}{4}) + \tfrac{1}{16} \qquad \text{Using method 1 (the square of a binomial sum. To get the middle term, we multiply } 3x \text{ by } \tfrac{1}{4} \text{ and double.)}$$
$$= 9x^2 + \tfrac{3}{2}x + \tfrac{1}{16} \qquad ◀$$

32. $\left(5x + \dfrac{1}{2}\right)^2$

▶ **EXAMPLE 25**　Multiply: $(4x - \frac{3}{4})^2$.

$$(4x - \tfrac{3}{4})^2 = 16x^2 - 2(4x)(\tfrac{3}{4}) + \tfrac{9}{16} \qquad \text{Using method 1}$$
$$= 16x^2 - 6x + \tfrac{9}{16} \qquad ◀$$

▶ **EXAMPLE 26**　Multiply: $(p + 3)(p^2 + 2p - 1)$.

$$
\begin{array}{ll}
\quad p^2 + 2p - 1 & \text{Using method 5} \\
\quad\quad\quad\ p + 3 & \\
\hline
\ 3p^2 + 6p - 3 & \text{Multiplying by 3} \\
p^3 + 2p^2 - \ \ p & \text{Multiplying by } p \\
\hline
p^3 + 5p^2 + 5p - 3 &
\end{array}
$$

　◀

33. $\left(2x - \dfrac{1}{2}\right)^2$

DO EXERCISES 27–34.

34. $(x^2 - x + 4)(x - 2)$

NAME   SECTION   DATE

EXERCISE SET 9.6

a Multiply. Try to write only the answer. If you need more steps, by all means use them.

1. $(x + 1)(x^2 + 3)$

2. $(x^2 - 3)(x - 1)$

3. $(x^3 + 2)(x + 1)$

4. $(x^4 + 2)(x + 12)$

5. $(y + 2)(y - 3)$

6. $(a + 2)(a + 2)$

7. $(3x + 2)(3x + 3)$

8. $(4x + 1)(2x + 2)$

9. $(5x - 6)(x + 2)$

10. $(x - 8)(x + 8)$

11. $(3t - 1)(3t + 1)$

12. $(2m + 3)(2m + 3)$

13. $(4x - 2)(x - 1)$

14. $(2x - 1)(3x + 1)$

15. $(p - \frac{1}{4})(p + \frac{1}{4})$

16. $(q + \frac{3}{4})(q + \frac{3}{4})$

17. $(x - 0.1)(x + 0.1)$

18. $(x + 0.3)(x - 0.4)$

19. $(2x^2 + 6)(x + 1)$

20. $(2x^2 + 3)(2x - 1)$

21. $(-2x + 1)(x + 6)$

22. $(3x + 4)(2x - 4)$

23. $(a + 7)(a + 7)$

24. $(2y + 5)(2y + 5)$

25. $(1 + 2x)(1 - 3x)$

26. $(-3x - 2)(x + 1)$

27. $(x^2 + 3)(x^3 - 1)$

28. $(x^4 - 3)(2x + 1)$

29. $(3x^2 - 2)(x^4 - 2)$

30. $(x^{10} + 3)(x^{10} - 3)$

1. _____

2. _____

3. _____

4. _____

5. _____

6. _____

7. _____

8. _____

9. _____

10. _____

11. _____

12. _____

13. _____

14. _____

15. _____

16. _____

17. _____

18. _____

19. _____

20. _____

21. _____

22. _____

23. _____

24. _____

25. _____

26. _____

27. _____

28. _____

29. _____

30. _____

31. $(3x^5 + 2)(2x^2 + 6)$ **32.** $(1 - 2x)(1 + 3x^2)$ **33.** $(8x^3 + 1)(x^3 + 8)$

31. _____

32. _____

33. _____   **34.** $(4 - 2x)(5 - 2x^2)$ **35.** $(4x^2 + 3)(x - 3)$ **36.** $(7x - 2)(2x - 7)$

34. _____

35. _____

36. _____   **37.** $(4y^4 + y^2)(y^2 + y)$ **38.** $(5y^6 + 3y^3)(2y^6 + 2y^3)$

37. _____

38. _____

39. _____

40. _____

41. _____

42. _____

43. _____

44. _____

45. _____

46. _____

47. _____

48. _____

49. _____

50. _____

51. _____

52. _____

53. _____

54. _____

55. _____

56. _____

57. _____

58. _____

59. _____

60. _____

61. _____

62. _____

63. _____

64. _____

b Multiply mentally, if possible. If you need extra steps, by all means use them.

39. $(x + 4)(x - 4)$ **40.** $(x + 1)(x - 1)$ **41.** $(2x + 1)(2x - 1)$

42. $(x^2 + 1)(x^2 - 1)$ **43.** $(5m - 2)(5m + 2)$ **44.** $(3x^4 + 2)(3x^4 - 2)$

45. $(2x^2 + 3)(2x^2 - 3)$ **46.** $(6x^5 - 5)(6x^5 + 5)$ **47.** $(3x^4 - 4)(3x^4 + 4)$

48. $(t^2 - 0.2)(t^2 + 0.2)$ **49.** $(x^6 - x^2)(x^6 + x^2)$ **50.** $(2x^3 - 0.3)(2x^3 + 0.3)$

51. $(x^4 + 3x)(x^4 - 3x)$ **52.** $(\frac{3}{4} + 2x^3)(\frac{3}{4} - 2x^3)$ **53.** $(x^{12} - 3)(x^{12} + 3)$

54. $(12 - 3x^2)(12 + 3x^2)$ **55.** $(2y^8 + 3)(2y^8 - 3)$ **56.** $(m - \frac{2}{3})(m + \frac{2}{3})$

c Multiply mentally, if possible.

57. $(x + 2)^2$ **58.** $(2x - 1)^2$ **59.** $(3x^2 + 1)^2$ **60.** $(3x + \frac{3}{4})^2$

61. $(a - \frac{1}{2})^2$ **62.** $(2a - \frac{1}{5})^2$ **63.** $(3 + x)^2$ **64.** $(x^3 - 1)^2$

65. $(x^2 + 1)^2$ **66.** $(8x - x^2)^2$ **67.** $(2 - 3x^4)^2$ **68.** $(6x^3 - 2)^2$

69. $(5 + 6t^2)^2$ **70.** $(3p^2 - p)^2$

d Multiply mentally, if possible.

71. $(3 - 2x^3)^2$ **72.** $(x - 4x^3)^2$ **73.** $4x(x^2 + 6x - 3)$

74. $8x(-x^5 + 6x^2 + 9)$ **75.** $(2x^2 - \frac{1}{2})(2x^2 - \frac{1}{2})$ **76.** $(-x^2 + 1)^2$

77. $(-1 + 3p)(1 + 3p)$ **78.** $(-3q + 2)(3q + 2)$ **79.** $3t^2(5t^3 - t^2 + t)$

80. $-6x^2(x^3 + 8x - 9)$ **81.** $(6x^4 + 4)^2$ **82.** $(8a + 5)^2$

83. $(3x + 2)(4x^2 + 5)$ **84.** $(2x^2 - 7)(3x^2 + 9)$ **85.** $(8 - 6x^4)^2$

86. $(\frac{1}{5}x^2 + 9)(\frac{3}{5}x^2 - 7)$ **87.** $(t - 1)(t^2 + t + 1)$ **88.** $(y + 5)(y^2 - 5y + 25)$

Compute each of the following and compare.

89. $3^2 + 4^2$;
    $(3 + 4)^2$

90. $6^2 + 7^2$;
    $(6 + 7)^2$

91. $9^2 - 5^2$;
    $(9 - 5)^2$

92. $11^2 - 4^2$;
    $(11 - 4)^2$

ANSWERS

93.

94.

95.

96.

97.

98.

99.

100.

101.

102.

103.

104.

105.

106.

107.

108.

109.

110.

111.

112.

113.

b)

c)

d)

114.

SKILL MAINTENANCE

93. In an apartment, lamps, an air conditioner, and a television set are all operating at the same time. The lamps use 10 times as many watts as the television set, and the air conditioner uses 40 times as many watts as the television set. The total wattage used in the apartment is 2550 watts. How many watts are used by each appliance?

94. Solve: $3x - 8x = 4(7 - 8x)$.

SYNTHESIS

Multiply.

95. $4y(y + 5)(2y + 8)$

96. $8x(2x - 3)(5x + 9)$

97. $[(x + 1) - x^2][(x - 2) + 2x^2]$

98. $[(2x - 1)(2x + 1)](4x^2 + 1)$

Solve.

99. $(x + 2)(x - 5) = (x + 1)(x - 3)$

100. $(2x + 5)(x - 4) = (x + 5)(2x - 4)$

The height of a box is one more than its length l, and the length is one more than its width w. Find a polynomial for the volume V in terms of the following.

101. The width w　　　　**102.** The length l　　　　**103.** The height h

Find two expressions for the shaded area.

104.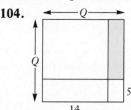

105.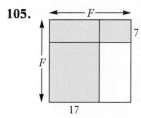

106.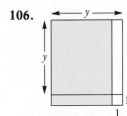

107. ▦ Multiply: $(67.58x + 3.225)^2$.

Calculate as the difference of squares.

108. 18×22　[*Hint:* $(20 - 2)(20 + 2)$.]　　　　**109.** 93×107

Multiply. (Do not collect like terms before multiplying.)

110. $[(3x - 2)(3x + 2)](9x^2 + 4)$　　　　**111.** $[3a - (2a - 3)][3a + (2a - 3)]$

112. $(5t^2 - 3)^2(5t^2 + 3)^2$

113. A polynomial for the shaded area in this rectangle is $(A + B)(A - B)$.

　　a) Find a polynomial for the area of the entire rectangle.

　　b) Find a polynomial for the sum of the areas of the two small unshaded rectangles.

　　c) Find a polynomial for the area in part (a) minus the area in part (b).

　　d) Find a polynomial for the area of the shaded region and compare this with the polynomial found in part (c).

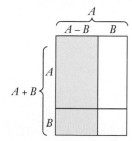

114. Find $(10x + 5)^2$. Use your result to show how to mentally square any two-digit number ending in 5.

9.7 Operations with Polynomials in Several Variables

The polynomials that we have been studying have only one variable. A **polynomial in several variables** is an expression like those you have already seen, but with more than one variable. Here are some examples:

$$3x + xy^2 + 5y + 4, \qquad 8xy^2z - 2x^3z - 13x^4y^2 + 15.$$

a Evaluating Polynomials

▶ **EXAMPLE 1** Evaluate the polynomial $4 + 3x + xy^2 + 8x^3y^3$ when $x = -2$ and $y = 5$.

We replace x by -2 and y by 5:

$$4 + 3x + xy^2 + 8x^3y^3 = 4 + 3(-2) + (-2) \cdot 5^2 + 8(-2)^3 \cdot 5^3$$
$$= 4 - 6 - 50 - 8000$$
$$= -8052. \qquad ◀$$

▶ **EXAMPLE 2** *Surface area of a right circular cylinder.* The surface area of a right circular cylinder is given by the polynomial

$$2\pi rh + 2\pi r^2,$$

where h is the height and r is the radius of the base. (This formula can be derived by cutting the cylinder apart, as shown on the right below, and adding the areas of the parts.) A 12-oz beverage can has a height of 4.7 in. and a radius of 1.2 in. To find the surface area, we can evaluate the polynomial when $h = 4.7$ and $r = 1.2$. Use 3.14 as an approximation for π.

 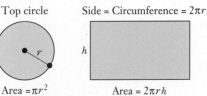 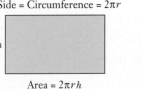

Top circle — Area $= \pi r^2$ Side = Circumference $= 2\pi r$ — Area $= 2\pi rh$ Bottom circle — Area $= \pi r^2$

We evaluate the polynomial when $h = 4.7$, $r = 1.2$, and $\pi \approx 3.14$:

$$2\pi rh + 2\pi r^2 \approx 2(3.14)(1.2)(4.7) + 2(3.14)(1.2)^2$$
$$= 2(3.14)(1.2)(4.7) + 2(3.14)(1.44)$$
$$= 35.4192 + 9.0432$$
$$= 44.4624.$$

The surface area is about 44.4624 in² (square inches.) ◀

DO EXERCISES 1–3.

1. Evaluate the polynomial
$$4 + 3x + xy^2 + 8x^3y^3$$
when $x = 2$ and $y = -5$.

2. Evaluate the polynomial
$$8xy^2 - 2x^3z - 13x^4y^2 + 5$$
when $x = -1$, $y = 3$, and $z = 4$.

3. For the situation of Example 2, find the surface area of a tank with $h = 20$ ft and $r = 3$ ft. Use 3.14 for π.

ANSWERS ON PAGE A-7

4. Identify the coefficient of each term:

$$-3xy^2 + 3x^2y - 2y^3 + xy + 2.$$

5. Identify the degree of each term and the degree of the polynomial
$$4xy^2 + 7x^2y^3z^2 - 5x + 2y + 4.$$

b Coefficients and Degrees

The **degree** of a term is the sum of the exponents of the variables. The **degree of a polynomial** is the degree of the term of highest degree.

▶ **EXAMPLE 3** Identify the coefficient and the degree of each term and the degree of the polynomial

$$9x^2y^3 - 14xy^2z^3 + xy + 4y + 5x^2 + 7.$$

Term	Coefficient	Degree	Degree of the polynomial
$9x^2y^3$	9	5	
$-14xy^2z^3$	-14	6	6
xy	1	2	
$4y$	4	1	Think: $4y = 4y^1$
$5x^2$	5	2	
7	7	0	Think: $7 = 7x^0$, or $7x^0y^0z^0$ ◀

DO EXERCISES 4 AND 5.

c Collecting Like Terms

Like terms (or **similar terms**) have exactly the same variables with exactly the same exponents. For example,

$3x^2y^3$ and $-7x^2y^3$ are like terms;

$9x^4z^7$ and $12x^4z^7$ are like terms.

But

$13xy^5$ and $-2x^2y^5$ are *not* like terms, because the x-factors have different exponents;

and

$3xyz^2$ and $4xy$ are *not* like terms, because there is no factor involving z in the second expression.

Collecting like terms is based on the distributive laws.

Collect like terms.
6. $4x^2y + 3xy - 2x^2y$

▶ **EXAMPLES** Collect like terms.

4. $5x^2y + 3xy^2 - 5x^2y - xy^2 = (5 - 5)x^2y + (3 - 1)xy^2 = 2xy^2$

5. $7xy - 5xy^2 + 3xy^2 + 6x^3 + 9xy - 11x^3 + y - 1$
$$= -2xy^2 + 16xy - 5x^3 + y - 1$$ ◀

DO EXERCISES 6 AND 7.

7. $-3pq - 5pqr^3 + 8pq + 5pqr^3 + 4$

d Addition

We can find the sum of two polynomials in several variables by writing a plus sign between them and then collecting like terms.

▶ **EXAMPLE 6**   Add: $(-5x^3 + 3y - 5y^2) + (8x^3 + 4x^2 + 7y^2)$.

$(-5x^3 + 3y - 5y^2) + (8x^3 + 4x^2 + 7y^2)$
$$= (-5 + 8)x^3 + 4x^2 + 3y + (-5 + 7)y^2$$
$$= 3x^3 + 4x^2 + 3y + 2y^2 \qquad ◀$$

▶ **EXAMPLE 7**   Add:

$$(5xy^2 - 4x^2y + 5x^3 + 2) + (3xy^2 - 2x^2y + 3x^3y - 5).$$

We first look for like terms. They are $5xy^2$ and $3xy^2$, $-4x^2y$ and $-2x^2y$, and 2 and -5. We collect these. Since there are no more like terms, the answer is

$$8xy^2 - 6x^2y + 5x^3 + 3x^3y - 3. \qquad ◀$$

DO EXERCISES 8–10.

e Subtraction

We subtract a polynomial by adding its opposite, or additive inverse. The opposite of the polynomial

$$4x^2y - 6x^3y^2 + x^2y^2 - 5y$$

can be represented by

$$-(4x^2y - 6x^3y^2 + x^2y^2 - 5y).$$

We find an equivalent expression for the opposite of a polynomial by replacing each coefficient by its opposite, or by changing the sign of each term. Thus,

$$-(4x^2y - 6x^3y^2 + x^2y^2 - 5y) = -4x^2y + 6x^3y^2 - x^2y^2 + 5y.$$

▶ **EXAMPLE 8**   Subtract:

$$(4x^2y + x^3y^2 + 3x^2y^3 + 6y) - (4x^2y - 6x^3y^2 + x^2y^2 - 5y).$$

We have

$(4x^2y + x^3y^2 + 3x^2y^3 + 6y) - (4x^2y - 6x^3y^2 + x^2y^2 - 5y)$
$$= 4x^2y + x^3y^2 + 3x^2y^3 + 6y - 4x^2y + 6x^3y^2 - x^2y^2 + 5y \qquad \text{Adding the opposite}$$
$$= 7x^3y^2 + 3x^2y^3 - x^2y^2 + 11y \qquad \begin{array}{l}\text{Collecting like terms.}\\\text{(Try to write just the answer!)}\end{array} \qquad ◀$$

DO EXERCISES 11 AND 12.

Add.

8. $4x^3 + 4x^2 - 8x - 3$ and $-8x^3 - 2x^2 + 4x + 5$

9. $(13x^3y + 3x^2y - 5y) + (x^3y + 4x^2y - 3xy + 3y)$

10. $(-5p^2q^4 + 2p^2q^2 + 3q) + (6pq^2 + 3p^2q + 5)$

Subtract.

11. $(-4s^4t + s^3t^2 + 2s^2t^3) - (4s^4t - 5s^3t^2 + s^2t^2)$

12. $(-5p^4q + 5p^3q^2 - 3p^2q^3 - 7q^4) - (4p^4q - 4p^3q^2 + p^2q^3 + 2q^4)$

ANSWERS ON PAGE A-7

Multiply.

13. $(x^2y^3 + 2x)(x^3y^2 + 3x)$

14. $(p^4q - 2p^3q^2 + 3q^3)(p + 2q)$

Multiply.

15. $(3xy + 2x)(x^2 + 2xy^2)$

16. $(x - 3y)(2x - 5y)$

17. $(4x + 5y)^2$

18. $(3x^2 - 2xy^2)^2$

19. $(2xy^2 + 3x)(2xy^2 - 3x)$

20. $(3xy^2 + 4y)(-3xy^2 + 4y)$

21. $(3y + 4 - 3x)(3y + 4 + 3x)$

22. $(2a + 5b + c)(2a - 5b - c)$

f Multiplication

To multiply polynomials in several variables, we can multiply each term of one by every term of the other. Where appropriate, we use the special products that we have learned.

▶ **EXAMPLE 9**   Multiply: $(3x^2y - 2xy + 3y)(xy + 2y)$.

$$3x^2y - 2xy + 3y$$
$$xy + 2y$$
$$\overline{6x^2y^2 - 4xy^2 + 6y^2}\quad \text{Multiplying by } 2y$$
$$3x^3y^2 - 2x^2y^2 + 3xy^2\quad \text{Multiplying by } xy$$
$$\overline{3x^3y^2 + 4x^2y^2 - xy^2 + 6y^2}\quad \text{Adding}$$ ◀

DO EXERCISES 13 AND 14.

▶ **EXAMPLES**   Multiply.

           F   O   I   L
10. $(x^2y + 2x)(xy^2 + y^2) = x^3y^3 + x^2y^3 + 2x^2y^2 + 2xy^2$

11. $(p + 5q)(2p - 3q) = 2p^2 - 3pq + 10pq - 15q^2$
$$= 2p^2 + 7pq - 15q^2$$

$(A + B)^2 = A^2 + 2 \cdot A \cdot B + B^2$

12. $(3x + 2y)^2 = (3x)^2 + 2(3x)(2y) + (2y)^2$
$$= 9x^2 + 12xy + 4y^2$$

$(A - B)^2 = A^2 - 2 \cdot A \cdot B + B^2$

13. $(2y^2 - 5x^2y)^2 = (2y^2)^2 - 2(2y^2)(5x^2y) + (5x^2y)^2$
$$= 4y^4 - 20x^2y^3 + 25x^4y^2$$

$(A + B)(A - B) = A^2 - B^2$

14. $(3x^2y + 2y)(3x^2y - 2y) = (3x^2y)^2 - (2y)^2$
$$= 9x^4y^2 - 4y^2$$

15. $(-2x^3y^2 + 5t)(2x^3y^2 + 5t) = (5t - 2x^3y^2)(5t + 2x^3y^2)$
$$= (5t)^2 - (2x^3y^2)^2$$
$$= 25t^2 - 4x^6y^4$$

$(A - B)(A + B) = A^2 - B^2$

16. $(2x + 3 - 2y)(2x + 3 + 2y) = (2x + 3)^2 - (2y)^2$
$$= 4x^2 + 12x + 9 - 4y^2$$ ◀

DO EXERCISES 15–22.

EXERCISE SET 9.7

ANSWERS

a Evaluate the polynomial when $x = 3$ and $y = -2$.

1. $x^2 - y^2 + xy$

2. $x^2 + y^2 - xy$

Evaluate the polynomial when $x = 2$, $y = -3$, and $z = -1$.

3. $xyz^2 + z$

4. $xy - xz + yz$

Interest compounded annually for two years. An amount of money P is invested at interest rate i. In 2 years, it will grow to an amount given by the polynomial

$$A = P(1 + i)^2.$$

5. Evaluate the polynomial when $P = 10,000$ and $i = 0.08$ to find the amount to which $10,000 will grow at 8% interest for 2 years.

6. Evaluate the polynomial when $P = 10,000$ and $i = 0.07$ to find the amount to which $10,000 will grow at 7% interest for 2 years.

Interest compounded annually for three years. An amount of money P is invested at interest rate i. In 3 years, it will grow to an amount given by the polynomial

$$A = P(1 + i)^3.$$

7. Evaluate the polynomial when $P = 10,000$ and $i = 0.08$ to find the amount to which $10,000 will grow at 8% interest for 3 years.

8. Evaluate the polynomial when $P = 10,000$ and $i = 0.07$ to find the amount to which $10,000 will grow at 7% interest for 3 years.

Surface area of a right circular cylinder. The area of a right circular cylinder is given by the polynomial

$$2\pi rh + 2\pi r^2,$$

where h is the height and r is the radius of the base.

9. A 26-oz coffee can has a height of 6.5 in. and a radius of 2.5 in. Evaluate the polynomial when $h = 6.5$ and $r = 2.5$ to find the area of the can. Use 3.14 for π.

10. A 16-oz beverage can has a height of 6.3 in. and a radius of 1.2 in. Evaluate the polynomial when $h = 6.3$ and $r = 1.2$ to find the area of the can. Use 3.14 for π.

b Identify the coefficient and the degree of each term of the polynomial. Then find the degree of the polynomial.

11. $x^3y - 2xy + 3x^2 - 5$

12. $5y^3 - y^2 + 15y + 1$

13. $17x^2y^3 - 3x^3yz - 7$

14. $6 - xy + 8x^2y^2 - y^5$

ANSWERS

1. _____

2. _____

3. _____

4. _____

5. _____

6. _____

7. _____

8. _____

9. _____

10. _____

11. _____

12. _____

13. _____

14. _____

Copyright © 1993 Addison-Wesley Publishing Co., Inc.

ANSWERS

15. _____

16. _____

17. _____

18. _____

19. _____

20. _____

21. _____

22. _____

23. _____

24. _____

25. _____

26. _____

27. _____

28. _____

29. _____

30. _____

31. _____

32. _____

33. _____

34. _____

35. _____

36. _____

37. _____

38. _____

c   Collect like terms.

15. $a + b - 2a - 3b$

16. $y^2 - 1 + y - 6 - y^2$

17. $3x^2y - 2xy^2 + x^2$

18. $m^3 + 2m^2n - 3m^2 + 3mn^2$

19. $2u^2v - 3uv^2 + 6u^2v - 2uv^2$

20. $3x^2 + 6xy + 3y^2 - 5x^2 - 10xy - 5y^2$

21. $6au + 3av + 14au + 7av$

22. $3x^2y - 2z^2y + 3xy^2 + 5z^2y$

d   Add.

23. $(2x^2 - xy + y^2) + (-x^2 - 3xy + 2y^2)$

24. $(2z - z^2 + 5) + (z^2 - 3z + 1)$

25. $(r - 2s + 3) + (2r + s) + (s + 4)$

26. $(b^3a^2 - 2b^2a^3 + 3ba + 4) + (b^2a^3 - 4b^3a^2 + 2ba - 1)$

27. $(2x^2 - 3xy + y^2) + (-4x^2 - 6xy - y^2) + (x^2 + xy - y^2)$

e   Subtract.

28. $(x^3 - y^3) - (-2x^3 + x^2y - xy^2 + 2y^3)$

29. $(xy - ab) - (xy - 3ab)$

30. $(3y^4x^2 + 2y^3x - 3y) - (2y^4x^2 + 2y^3x - 4y - 2x)$

31. $(-2a + 7b - c) - (-3b + 4c - 8d)$

32. Find the sum of $2a + b$ and $3a - b$. Then subtract $5a + 2b$.

f   Multiply.

33. $(3z - u)(2z + 3u)$

34. $(a - b)(a^2 + b^2 + 2ab)$

35. $(a^2b - 2)(a^2b - 5)$

36. $(xy + 7)(xy - 4)$

37. $(a + a^2 - 1)(a^2 + 1 - y)$

38. $(r + tx)(vx + s)$

39. $(a^3 + bc)(a^3 - bc)$

40. $(m^2 + n^2 - mn)(m^2 + mn + n^2)$

41. $(y^4x + y^2 + 1)(y^2 + 1)$

42. $(a - b)(a^2 + ab + b^2)$

43. $(3xy - 1)(4xy + 2)$

44. $(m^3n + 8)(m^3n - 6)$

45. $(3 - c^2d^2)(4 + c^2d^2)$

46. $(6x - 2y)(5x - 3y)$

47. $(m^2 - n^2)(m + n)$

48. $(pq + 0.2)(0.4pq - 0.1)$

49. $(xy + x^5y^5)(x^4y^4 - xy)$

50. $(x - y^3)(2y^3 + x)$

51. $(x + h)^2$

52. $(3a + 2b)^2$

53. $(r^3t^2 - 4)^2$

54. $(3a^2b - b^2)^2$

55. $(p^4 + m^2n^2)^2$

56. $(ab + cd)^2$

57. $(2a^3 - \frac{1}{2}b^3)^2$

58. $-5x(x + 3y)^2$

59. $3a(a - 2b)^2$

60. $(a^2 + b + 2)^2$

61. $(2a - b)(2a + b)$

62. $(x - y)(x + y)$

63. $(c^2 - d)(c^2 + d)$

64. $(p^3 - 5q)(p^3 + 5q)$

39. _____

40. _____

41. _____

42. _____

43. _____

44. _____

45. _____

46. _____

47. _____

48. _____

49. _____

50. _____

51. _____

52. _____

53. _____

54. _____

55. _____

56. _____

57. _____

58. _____

59. _____

60. _____

61. _____

62. _____

63. _____

64. _____

65. $(ab + cd^2)(ab - cd^2)$ **66.** $(xy + pq)(xy - pq)$

67. $(x + y - 3)(x + y + 3)$ **68.** $(p + q + 4)(p + q - 4)$

69. $[x + y + z][x - (y + z)]$ **70.** $[a + b + c][a - (b + c)]$

71. $(a + b + c)(a - b - c)$ **72.** $(3x + 2 - 5y)(3x + 2 + 5y)$

SYNTHESIS

Find a polynomial for the shaded area. (Leave results in terms of π where appropriate.)

73.

74.
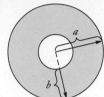

75.
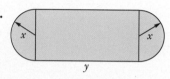

76.
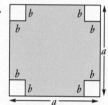

77. *Lung capacity.* The polynomial

$$0.041h - 0.018A - 2.69$$

can be used to estimate the lung capacity, in liters, of a female with height h, in centimeters, and age A, in years. Find the lung capacity of a 29-year-old woman who is 138.7 cm tall.

78. *The magic number.* The Boston Red Sox are leading the New York Yankees for the Eastern Division championship of the American League. The magic number is 8. This means that any combination of Red Sox wins and Yankee losses that totals 8 will ensure the championship for the Red Sox. The magic number is given by the polynomial

$$G - P - L + 1,$$

where G is the number of games in the season, P is the number of games that the leading team has played, and L is the number of games ahead in the loss column.

Given the situation shown in the table and assuming a 162-game season, what is the magic number for the Philadelphia Phillies?

EASTERN DIVISION			
	W	L	Pct.	GB
Philadelphia	77	40	.658	—
Pittsburgh	65	53	.551	$12\frac{1}{2}$
New York	61	60	.504	18
Chicago	55	67	.451	$24\frac{1}{2}$
St. Louis	51	65	.440	$25\frac{1}{2}$
Montreal	41	73	.360	$34\frac{1}{2}$

79. Find a formula for $(A + B)^3$.

9.8 Division of Polynomials

In this section, we consider division of polynomials. You will see that such division is similar to what is done in arithmetic.

a Divisor a Monomial

We first consider division by a monomial. When we are dividing a monomial by a monomial, we can use our rules of exponents and subtract exponents when bases are the same. We studied this in Section 9.1. For example,

$$\frac{15x^{10}}{3x^4} = 5x^{10-4} = 5x^6; \qquad \frac{42a^2b^5}{-3ab^2} = \frac{42}{-3}a^{2-1}b^{5-2} = -14ab^3.$$

When we are dividing a monomial into a polynomial, we break up the division into an addition of quotients of monomials. To do this, we use the rule for addition using fractional notation. That is, since

$$\frac{A}{C} + \frac{B}{C} = \frac{A+B}{C},$$

we know that

$$\frac{A+B}{C} = \frac{A}{C} + \frac{B}{C}.$$

▶ **EXAMPLE 1**   Divide and check: $x^3 + 10x^2 + 8x$ by $2x$.

We write the division as follows:

$$\frac{x^3 + 10x^2 + 8x}{2x}.$$

This is equivalent to

$$\frac{x^3}{2x} + \frac{10x^2}{2x} + \frac{8x}{2x}. \qquad \text{To see this, add and get the original expression.}$$

Next, we do the separate divisions:

$$\frac{x^3}{2x} + \frac{10x^2}{2x} + \frac{8x}{2x} = \frac{1}{2}x^{3-1} + \frac{10}{2}x^{2-1} + \frac{8}{2}x^{1-1} = \frac{1}{2}x^2 + 5x + 4.$$

We can check by multiplying the quotient by $2x$:

$$\begin{array}{r} \frac{1}{2}x^2 + 5x + 4 \\ \underline{2x} \\ x^3 + 10x^2 + 8x \end{array}$$

We multiply.

The answer checks.   ◀

DO EXERCISES 1 AND 2.

OBJECTIVES

After finishing Section 9.8, you should be able to:

a   Divide a polynomial by a monomial and check the result.

b   Divide a polynomial by a divisor that is not a monomial and, if there is a remainder, express the result in two ways.

FOR EXTRA HELP

Tape 21A

Divide.

1. $\dfrac{2x^3 + 6x^2 + 4x}{2x}$

2. $(6x^2 + 3x - 2) \div 3$

Divide and check.

3. $(8x^2 - 3x + 1) \div 2$

▶ **EXAMPLE 2**   Divide and check: $(10a^5b^4 - 2a^3b^2 + 6a^2b) \div 2a^2b$.

$$\frac{10a^5b^4 - 2a^3b^2 + 6a^2b}{2a^2b} = \frac{10a^5b^4}{2a^2b} - \frac{2a^3b^2}{2a^2b} + \frac{6a^2b}{2a^2b}$$

$$= \frac{10}{2}a^{5-2}b^{4-1} - \frac{2}{2}a^{3-2}b^{2-1} + \frac{6}{2}$$

$$= 5a^3b^3 - ab + 3$$

Check:
$$5a^3b^3 - ab + 3$$
$$\underline{\qquad\qquad 2a^2b} \qquad \text{We multiply.}$$
$$10a^5b^4 - 2a^3b^2 + 6a^2b \qquad \text{The answer checks.} \qquad ◀$$

> To divide a polynomial by a monomial, divide each term by the monomial.

DO EXERCISES 3 AND 4.

b   **Divisor not a Monomial**

When the divisor is not a monomial, we use long division very much as we do in arithmetic. We write polynomials in descending order and write in missing terms.

4. $\dfrac{2x^4y^6 - 3x^3y^4 + 5x^2y^3}{x^2y^2}$

▶ **EXAMPLE 3**   Divide $x^2 + 5x + 6$ by $x + 2$.

We have

$$
\begin{array}{r}
x \phantom{{}+2)\,x^2+5x+6} \\
x+2\,\overline{)\,x^2 + 5x + 6} \\
x^2 + 2x \phantom{{}+6} \\
\hline
3x \phantom{{}+6}
\end{array}
$$

— Divide the first term by the first term: $x^2/x = x$. Ignore the term 2.

— Multiply x above by the divisor, $x + 2$.

— Subtract: $(x^2 + 5x) - (x^2 + 2x) = x^2 + 5x - x^2 - 2x = 3x$.

We now "bring down" the next term of the dividend—in this case, 6.

$$
\begin{array}{r}
x \; + \; 3 \\
x+2\,\overline{)\,x^2 + 5x + 6} \\
x^2 + 2x \phantom{{}+6} \\
\hline
3x + 6 \\
3x + 6 \\
\hline
0
\end{array}
$$

— Divide the first term by the first term: $3x/x = 3$.

— The 6 has been "brought down."

— Multiply 3 by the divisor, $x + 2$.

— Subtract: $(3x + 6) - (3x + 6) = 3x + 6 - 3x - 6 = 0$.

The quotient is $x + 3$. The remainder is 0, usually expressed as R = 0. A remainder of 0 is generally not listed in an answer.

   To check, we multiply the quotient by the divisor and add the remainder, if any, to see if we get the dividend:

Divisor   Quotient   Remainder   Dividend

$\overbrace{(x + 2)} \quad \overbrace{(x + 3)} \; + \quad \overbrace{0} \quad = \overbrace{x^2 + 5x + 6}.$ The division checks.   ◀

▶ **EXAMPLE 4**   Divide and check: $(x^2 + 2x - 12) \div (x - 3)$.

We have

$$
\begin{array}{r}
x \longleftarrow \text{Divide the first term by the first term: } x^2/x = x. \\
x - 3 \overline{)\, x^2 + 2x - 12} \\
\underline{x^2 - 3x} \longleftarrow \text{Multiply } x \text{ above by the divisor, } x - 3. \\
5x \longleftarrow \text{Subtract: } (x^2 + 2x) - (x^2 - 3x) = x^2 + 2x - x^2 + 3x \\
= 5x.
\end{array}
$$

We now "bring down" the next term of the dividend—in this case, -12.

$$
\begin{array}{r}
x \; + \; 5 \longleftarrow \text{Divide the first term by the first term: } 5x/x = 5. \\
x - 3 \overline{)\, x^2 + 2x - 12} \\
\underline{x^2 - 3x} \\
5x - 12 \longleftarrow \text{Bring down the } -12. \\
\underline{5x - 15} \longleftarrow \text{Multiply 5 above by the divisor, } x - 3. \\
3 \longleftarrow \text{Subtract: } (5x - 12) - (5x - 15) = 5x - 12 - 5x + 15 \\
= 3.
\end{array}
$$

The answer is $x + 5$ with R $= 3$, or

$$
\underbrace{x + 5}_{\text{Quotient}} + \underbrace{\dfrac{3}{x - 3}}
$$

Quotient $x + 5 + \dfrac{3 \longrightarrow \text{Remainder}}{x - 3}$

$\longrightarrow$ Divisor

(This is the way answers will be given at the back of the book.)

Check: When the answer is given in the preceding form, we can check by multiplying the divisor by the quotient and adding, as follows:

$$
\begin{aligned}
(x - 3)(x + 5) + 3 &= x^2 + 2x - 15 + 3 \\
&= x^2 + 2x - 12.
\end{aligned}
$$ ◀

When dividing, an answer may "come out even" (that is, have a remainder of 0, as in Example 1), or it may not (as in Example 2). If a remainder is not 0, we continue dividing until the degree of the remainder is less than the degree of the divisor. Check this in each of Examples 1 and 2.

DO EXERCISES 5 AND 6.

▶ **EXAMPLE 5**   Divide: $(x^3 + 1) \div (x + 1)$.

$$
\begin{array}{r}
x^2 - \; x \; + \; 1 \\
x + 1 \overline{)\, x^3 + 0x^2 + 0x + 1} \longleftarrow \text{Fill in the missing terms.} \\
\underline{x^3 + \; x^2} \\
- \; x^2 + 0x \qquad \text{This subtraction is } x^3 - (x^3 + x^2). \\
\underline{- \; x^2 - \; x} \\
x + 1 \qquad \text{This subtraction is } -x^2 - (-x^2 - x). \\
\underline{x + 1} \\
0
\end{array}
$$

The answer is $x^2 - x + 1$.

Check: $(x + 1)(x^2 - x + 1) + 0 = x^2 - x + 1 + x^3 - x^2 + x + 0$
$$
= x^3 + 1.
$$ ◀

Divide and check.

5. $(x^2 + x - 6) \div (x + 3)$

6. $x - 2 \overline{)\, x^2 + 2x - 8}$

ANSWERS ON PAGE A-7

Divide and check.

7. $x + 3 \overline{)\, x^2 + 7x + 10}$

▶ **EXAMPLE 6**   Divide: $(x^4 - 3x^2 + 1) \div (x - 4)$.

$$
\begin{array}{r}
x^3 + 4x^2 + 13x\ + 52 \\
x - 4 \overline{)\, x^4 + 0x^3 - \ 3x^2 + \ 0x + \ \ \ 1} \quad \longleftarrow \text{Fill in the missing terms.} \\
\underline{x^4 - 4x^3} \\
4x^3 - \ 3x^2 \qquad\qquad x^4 - (x^4 - 4x^3) \\
\underline{4x^3 - 16x^2} \\
13x^2 + \ 0x \quad\longleftarrow\quad (4x^3 - 3x^2) - (4x^3 - 16x^2) \\
\underline{13x^2 - 52x} \\
52x + \ \ 1 \\
\underline{52x - 208} \\
209
\end{array}
$$

The answer is $x^3 + 4x^2 + 13x + 52$, with R = 209, or

$$ x^3 + 4x^2 + 13x + 52 + \frac{209}{x - 4}. $$

Check: $(x - 4)(x^3 + 4x^2 + 13x + 52) + 209$

$= -4x^3 - 16x^2 - 52x - 208 + x^4 + 4x^3 + 13x^2 + 52x + 209$

$= x^4 - 3x^2 + 1$ ◀

DO EXERCISES 7 AND 8.

8. $(x^3 - 1) \div (x - 1)$

EXERCISE SET 9.8

a Divide and check.

1. $\dfrac{24x^4 - 4x^3 + x^2 - 16}{8}$

2. $\dfrac{12a^4 - 3a^2 + a - 6}{6}$

3. $\dfrac{u - 2u^2 - u^5}{u}$

4. $\dfrac{50x^5 - 7x^4 + x^2}{x}$

5. $(15t^3 + 24t^2 - 6t) \div 3t$

6. $(25t^3 + 15t^2 - 30t) \div 5t$

7. $(20x^6 - 20x^4 - 5x^2) \div (-5x^2)$

8. $(24x^6 + 32x^5 - 8x^2) \div (-8x^2)$

9. $(24x^5 - 40x^4 + 6x^3) \div (4x^3)$

10. $(18x^6 - 27x^5 - 3x^3) \div (9x^3)$

11. $\dfrac{18x^2 - 5x + 2}{2}$

12. $\dfrac{15x^2 + 30x - 4}{3}$

13. $\dfrac{12x^3 + 26x^2 + 8x}{2x}$

14. $\dfrac{2x^4 - 3x^3 + 5x^2}{x^2}$

15. $\dfrac{9r^2s^2 + 3r^2s - 6rs^2}{3rs}$

16. $\dfrac{4x^4y - 8x^6y^2 + 12x^8y^6}{4x^4y}$

b Divide.

17. $(x^2 + 4x + 4) \div (x + 2)$

18. $(x^2 - 6x + 9) \div (x - 3)$

19. $(x^2 - 10x - 25) \div (x - 5)$

20. $(x^2 + 8x - 16) \div (x + 4)$

21. $(x^2 + 4x - 14) \div (x + 6)$

22. $(x^2 + 5x - 9) \div (x - 2)$

ANSWERS

1. _____

2. _____

3. _____

4. _____

5. _____

6. _____

7. _____

8. _____

9. _____

10. _____

11. _____

12. _____

13. _____

14. _____

15. _____

16. _____

17. _____

18. _____

19. _____

20. _____

21. _____

22. _____

23. $\dfrac{x^2 - 9}{x + 3}$

24. $\dfrac{x^2 - 25}{x + 5}$

25. $\dfrac{x^5 + 1}{x + 1}$

26. $\dfrac{x^5 - 1}{x - 1}$

27. $\dfrac{8x^3 - 22x^2 - 5x + 12}{4x + 3}$

28. $\dfrac{2x^3 - 9x^2 + 11x - 3}{2x - 3}$

29. $(x^6 - 13x^3 + 42) \div (x^3 - 7)$

30. $(x^6 + 5x^3 - 24) \div (x^3 - 3)$

31. $(x^4 - 16) \div (x - 2)$

32. $(x^4 - 81) \div (x - 3)$

33. $(t^3 - t^2 + t - 1) \div (t - 1)$

34. $(t^3 - t^2 + t - 1) \div (t + 1)$

SKILL MAINTENANCE

35. Subtract: $-2.3 - (-9.1)$.

36. Factor: $4x - 12 + 24y$.

37. The perimeter of a rectangle is 640 ft. The length is 15 ft more than the width. Find the area of the rectangle.

38. Solve: $-6(2 - x) + 10(5x - 7) = 10$.

SYNTHESIS

Divide.

39. $(x^4 + 9x^2 + 20) \div (x^2 + 4)$

40. $(y^4 + a^2) \div (y + a)$

41. $(5a^3 + 8a^2 - 23a - 1) \div (5a^2 - 7a - 2)$

42. $(15y^3 - 30y + 7 - 19y^2) \div (3y^2 - 2 - 5y)$

43. $(6x^5 - 13x^3 + 5x + 3 - 4x^2 + 3x^4) \div (3x^3 - 2x - 1)$

44. $(5x^7 - 3x^4 + 2x^2 - 10x + 2) \div (x^2 - x + 1)$

45. $(a^6 - b^6) \div (a - b)$

46. $(x^5 + y^5) \div (x + y)$

If the remainder is 0 when one polynomial is divided by another, the divisor is a *factor* of the dividend. Find the value(s) of c for which $x - 1$ is a factor of the polynomial.

47. $x^2 + 4x + c$

48. $2x^2 + 3cx - 8$

49. $c^2x^2 - 2cx + 1$

SUMMARY AND REVIEW: CHAPTER 9

IMPORTANT PROPERTIES AND FORMULAS

FOIL: $(A + B)(C + D) = AC + AD + BC + BD,$ $(A + B)(A + B) = (A + B)^2 = A^2 + 2AB + B^2$

$(A - B)(A - B) = (A - B)^2 = A^2 - 2AB + B^2,$ $(A + B)(A - B) = A^2 - B^2$

Definitions and Rules for Exponents
See p. 488.

REVIEW EXERCISES

The review sections and objectives to be tested in addition to the material in this chapter are [7.4a], [7.7d], [8.3b, c], and [8.4a].

Multiply.

1. $7^2 \cdot 7^{-4}$ **2.** $y^7 \cdot y^3 \cdot y$ **3.** $(3x)^5 \cdot (3x)^9$ **4.** $t^8 \cdot t^0$

Divide.

5. $\dfrac{4^5}{4^2}$ **6.** $\dfrac{a^5}{a^8}$ **7.** $\dfrac{(7x)^4}{(7x)^4}$

Simplify.

8. $(3t^4)^2$ **9.** $(2x^3)^2(-3x)^2$ **10.** $\left(\dfrac{2x}{y}\right)^{-3}$

11. Express using a negative exponent: $\dfrac{1}{t^5}$.

12. Express using a positive exponent: y^{-4}.

13. Convert to scientific notation: 0.0000328.

14. Convert to decimal notation: 8.3×10^6.

Multiply or divide and write scientific notation for the result.

15. $(3.8 \times 10^4)(5.5 \times 10^{-1})$ **16.** $\dfrac{1.28 \times 10^{-8}}{2.5 \times 10^{-4}}$

17. Each day Americans eat 170 million eggs. How many eggs are eaten in one year? Write scientific notation for the answer.

18. Evaluate the polynomial $x^2 - 3x + 6$ when $x = -1$.

19. Identify the terms of the polynomial $-4y^5 + 7y^2 - 3y - 2$.

20. Identify the missing terms in $x^3 + x$.

21. Identify the degree of each term and the degree of the polynomial $4x^3 + 6x^2 - 5x + \frac{5}{3}$.

Classify the polynomial as a monomial, binomial, trinomial, or none of these.

22. $4x^3 - 1$ **23.** $4 - 9t^3 - 7t^4 + 10t^2$ **24.** $7y^2$

Collect like terms and then arrange in descending order.

25. $3x^2 - 2x + 3 - 5x^2 - 1 - x$ **26.** $-x + \frac{1}{2} + 14x^4 - 7x^2 - 1 - 4x^4$

Add.

27. $(3x^4 - x^3 + x - 4) + (x^5 + 7x^3 - 3x^2 - 5) + (-5x^4 + 6x^2 - x)$

28. $(3x^5 - 4x^4 + x^3 - 3) + (3x^4 - 5x^3 + 3x^2) + (4x^5 + 4x^3) + (-5x^5 - 5x^2) + (-5x^4 + 2x^3 + 5)$

Subtract.

29. $(5x^2 - 4x + 1) - (3x^2 + 7)$

30. $(3x^5 - 4x^4 + 3x^2 + 3) - (2x^5 - 4x^4 + 3x^3 + 4x^2 - 5)$

31. The length of a rectangle is 4 m greater than its width. Find a polynomial for the perimeter and a polynomial for the area.

Multiply.

32. $(x + \frac{2}{3})(x + \frac{1}{2})$

33. $(7x + 1)^2$

34. $(4x^2 - 5x + 1)(3x - 2)$

35. $(3x^2 + 4)(3x^2 - 4)$

36. $5x^4(3x^3 - 8x^2 + 10x + 2)$

37. $(x + 4)(x - 7)$

38. $(3y^2 - 2y)^2$

39. $(2t^2 + 3)(t^2 - 7)$

40. Evaluate the polynomial $2 - 5xy + y^2 - 4xy^3 + x^6$ when $x = -1$ and $y = 2$.

41. Identify the coefficient and degree of each term of the polynomial $x^5y - 7xy + 9x^2 - 8$. Then find the degree of the polynomial.

Collect like terms.

42. $y + w - 2y + 8w - 5$

43. $m^6 - 2m^2n + m^2n^2 + n^2m - 6m^3 + m^2n^2 + 7n^2m$

44. Add:
$(5x^2 - 7xy + y^2) + (-6x^2 - 3xy - y^2) + (x^2 + xy - 2y^2)$.

45. Subtract:
$(6x^3y^2 - 4x^2y - 6x) - (-5x^3y^2 + 4x^2y + 6x^2 - 6)$.

Multiply.

46. $(p - q)(p^2 + pq + q^2)$

47. $(3a^4 - \frac{1}{3}b^3)^2$

Divide.

48. $(10x^3 - x^2 + 6x) \div 2x$

49. $(6x^3 - 5x^2 - 13x + 13) \div (2x + 3)$

SKILL MAINTENANCE

50. Factor: $25t - 50 + 100m$.

51. Solve: $7x + 6 - 8x = 11 - 5x + 4$.

52. Subtract: $-3.4 - 7.8$.

53. The perimeter of a rectangle is 540 m. The width is 19 m less than the length. Find the width and the length.

SYNTHESIS

54. Collect like terms:

$-3x^5 \cdot 3x^3 - x^6(2x)^2 + (3x^4)^2 + (2x^2)^4 - 40x^2(x^3)^2$.

55. Solve:

$$(x - 7)(x + 10) = (x - 4)(x - 6).$$

❖ THINKING IT THROUGH

Explain the error(s) in each of the following.

1. $(a + 2)^2 = a^2 + 4$

2. $(p + 7)(p - 7) = p^2 + 14p - 49$

3. $(t - 3)^2 = t^2 - 9$

4. $2^{-3} = -6$

5. $\frac{a^2}{a^5} = a^3$

6. $m^{-2}m^5 = m^{-10}$

7. Explain why 0.23×10^5 is not scientific notation.

NAME   SECTION   DATE

TEST: CHAPTER 9

Multiply.

1. $6^{-2} \cdot 6^{-3}$

2. $x^6 \cdot x^2 \cdot x$

3. $(4a)^3 \cdot (4a)^8$

Divide.

4. $\dfrac{3^5}{3^2}$

5. $\dfrac{x^3}{x^8}$

6. $\dfrac{(2x)^5}{(2x)^5}$

Simplify.

7. $(x^3)^2$

8. $(-3y^2)^3$

9. $(2a^3 b)^4$

10. $\left(\dfrac{ab}{c}\right)^3$

11. $(3x^2)^3(-2x^5)^3$

12. $3(x^2)^3(-2x^5)^3$

13. $2x^2(-3x^2)^4$

14. $(2x)^2(-3x^2)^4$

15. Express using a positive exponent: 5^{-3}.

16. Express using a negative exponent: $\dfrac{1}{y^8}$.

17. Convert to scientific notation: 3,900,000,000.

18. Convert to decimal notation: 5×10^{-8}.

Multiply or divide and write scientific notation for the answer.

19. $\dfrac{5.6 \times 10^6}{3.2 \times 10^{-11}}$

20. $(2.4 \times 10^5)(5.4 \times 10^{16})$

21. Each day Americans eat 170 million eggs. There are 243 million people in this country. How many eggs does each person eat in one year? Write scientific notation for the answer.

22. Evaluate the polynomial $x^5 + 5x - 1$ when $x = -2$.

23. Identify the coefficient of each term of the polynomial $\frac{1}{3}x^5 - x + 7$.

24. Identify the degree of each term and the degree of the polynomial $2x^3 - 4 + 5x + 3x^6$.

25. Classify the polynomial $7 - x$ as a monomial, binomial, trinomial, or none of these.

1. _____

2. _____

3. _____

4. _____

5. _____

6. _____

7. _____

8. _____

9. _____

10. _____

11. _____

12. _____

13. _____

14. _____

15. _____

16. _____

17. _____

18. _____

19. _____

20. _____

21. _____

22. _____

23. _____

24. _____

25. _____

26. _____

27. _____

28. _____

29. _____

30. _____

31. _____

32. _____

33. _____

34. _____

35. _____

36. _____

37. _____

38. _____

39. _____

40. _____

41. _____

42. _____

43. _____

44. _____

45. _____

46. _____

47. _____

48. _____

49. _____

50. _____

51. _____

Collect like terms.

26. $4a^2 - 6 + a^2$

27. $y^2 - 3y - y + \dfrac{3}{4}y^2$

28. Collect like terms and then arrange in descending order:
$$3 - x^2 + 2x^3 + 5x^2 - 6x - 2x + x^5.$$

Add.

29. $(3x^5 + 5x^3 - 5x^2 - 3) +$
$(x^5 + x^4 - 3x^3 - 3x^2 + 2x - 4)$

30. $\left(x^4 + \dfrac{2}{3}x + 5\right) + \left(4x^4 + 5x^2 + \dfrac{1}{3}x\right)$

Subtract.

31. $(2x^4 + x^3 - 8x^2 - 6x - 3) -$
$(6x^4 - 8x^2 + 2x)$

32. $(x^3 - 0.4x^2 - 12) -$
$(x^5 + 0.3x^3 + 0.4x^2 + 9)$

Multiply.

33. $-3x^2(4x^2 - 3x - 5)$

34. $\left(x - \dfrac{1}{3}\right)^2$

35. $(3x + 10)(3x - 10)$

36. $(3b + 5)(b - 3)$

37. $(x^6 - 4)(x^8 + 4)$

38. $(8 - y)(6 + 5y)$

39. $(2x + 1)(3x^2 - 5x - 3)$

40. $(5t + 2)^2$

41. Collect like terms: $x^3y - y^3 + xy^3 + 8 - 6x^3y - x^2y^2 + 11.$

42. Subtract: $(8a^2b^2 - ab + b^3) - (-6ab^2 - 7ab - ab^3 + 5b^3).$

43. Multiply: $(3x^5 - 4y^5)(3x^5 + 4y^5).$

Divide.

44. $(12x^4 + 9x^3 - 15x^2) \div 3x^2$

45. $(6x^3 - 8x^2 - 14x + 13) \div (3x + 2)$

SKILL MAINTENANCE

46. Solve: $7x - 4x - 2 = 37.$

47. Factor: $64t - 32m + 16.$

48. Subtract: $\frac{2}{5} - (-\frac{3}{4}).$

49. The first angle of a triangle is four times as large as the second. The measure of the third angle is 30° greater than that of the second. How large are the angles?

SYNTHESIS

50. The height of a box is one less than its length, and the length is two more than its width. Find the volume in terms of the length.

51. Solve: $(x - 5)(x + 5) = (x + 6)^2.$

INTRODUCTION   *Factoring* is the reverse of multiplying. To *factor* a polynomial, or other algebraic expression, is to find an equivalent expression that is a product. In this chapter we study factoring polynomials. To learn to factor quickly, we use the quick methods for multiplication learned in Chapter 9.

At the end of the chapter, we get the payoff for learning to factor. We have certain new equations containing second-degree polynomials that we can now solve. This then allows us to solve problems that we could not have solved before.

The review sections to be tested in addition to the material in this chapter are 7.6, 8.6, 8.7, and 9.6.   ❖

Polynomials: Factoring

10

AN APPLICATION

A beverage can has height h and radius r. Its surface area is given by the polynomial

$$2\pi rh + 2\pi r^2.$$

THE MATHEMATICS

The polynomial can be *factored* as follows:

$$2\pi rh + 2\pi r^2 = 2\pi r(h + r).$$

❖ POINTS TO REMEMBER: CHAPTER 10

Methods to find special products:	Chapter 9
Pythagorean Theorem:	If a and b are the lengths of the legs of a right triangle and c is the length of the hypotenuse, then $a^2 + b^2 = c^2$.
Equation-Solving Skills:	Sections 8.1–8.3

PRETEST: CHAPTER 10

1. Find three factorizations of $-20x^6$.

Factor.

2. $2x^2 + 4x + 2$

3. $x^2 + 6x + 8$

4. $8a^5 + 4a^3 - 20a$

5. $-6 + 5x^2 - 13x$

6. $81 - z^4$

7. $y^6 - 4y^3 + 4$

8. $3x^3 + 2x^2 + 12x + 8$

9. $p^2 - p - 30$

Solve.

10. $x^2 - 5x = 0$

11. $(x - 4)(5x - 3) = 0$

12. $3x^2 + 10x - 8 = 0$

Solve.

13. Six less than the square of a number is five times the number. Find all such numbers.

14. The height of a triangle is 3 cm longer than the base. The area of the triangle is 44 cm². Find the base and the height.

Factor.

15. $x^4y^2 - 64$

16. $2p^2 + 7pq - 4q^2$

10.1 Introduction to Factoring

To solve certain types of algebraic equations involving polynomials of second degree, we must learn to factor polynomials.

> To *factor* a polynomial is to find an equivalent expression that is a product.

When we factor, we do the reverse of multiplication.

a Factoring Monomials

To factor a monomial, we find two monomials whose product is equivalent to the original monomial. Compare.

Multiplying	*Factoring*
a) $(4x)(5x) = 20x^2$	$20x^2 = (4x)(5x)$
b) $(2x)(10x) = 20x^2$	$20x^2 = (2x)(10x)$
c) $(-4x)(-5x) = 20x^2$	$20x^2 = (-4x)(-5x)$
d) $(x)(20x) = 20x^2$	$20x^2 = (x)(20x)$

You can see that the monomial $20x^2$ has many factorizations. There are still other ways to factor $20x^2$.

DO EXERCISES 1 AND 2.

▶ **EXAMPLE 1** Find three factorizations of $15x^3$.

a) $15x^3 = (3 \cdot 5)(x \cdot x^2)$
$= (3x)(5x^2)$

b) $15x^3 = (3 \cdot 5)(x^2 \cdot x)$
$= (3x^2)(5x)$

c) $15x^3 = (-15)(-1)x^3$
$= (-15)(-x^3)$ ◀

DO EXERCISES 3–5.

OBJECTIVES

After finishing Section 10.1, you should be able to:

a Factor monomials.

b Factor polynomials when the terms have a common factor, factoring out the largest common factor.

c Factor certain expressions with four terms using factoring by grouping.

FOR EXTRA HELP

Tape 21B

1. a) Multiply: $(3x)(4x)$.

b) Factor: $12x^2$.

2. a) Multiply: $(2x)(8x^2)$.

b) Factor: $16x^3$.

Find three factorizations of the monomial.

3. $8x^4$

4. $21x^2$

5. $6x^5$

6. a) Multiply: $3(x + 2)$.

b) Factor: $3x + 6$.

7. a) Multiply: $2x(x^2 + 5x + 4)$.

b) Factor: $2x^3 + 10x^2 + 8x$.

b   **Factoring When Terms Have a Common Factor**

To factor polynomials quickly, we consider the special-product rules learned in Chapter 9, but we first factor out the largest common factor.

To multiply a monomial and a polynomial with more than one term, we multiply each term by the monomial using the distributive laws, $a(b + c) = ab + ac$ and $a(b - c) = ab - ac$. To factor, we do the reverse. We express a polynomial as a product using the distributive laws in reverse: $ab + ac = a(b + c)$ and $ab - ac = a(b - c)$. Compare.

Multiply	*Factor*
$3x(x^2 + 2x - 4)$	$3x^3 + 6x^2 - 12x$
$\quad = 3x \cdot x^2 + 3x \cdot 2x - 3x \cdot 4$	$\quad = 3x \cdot x^2 + 3x \cdot 2x - 3x \cdot 4$
$\quad = 3x^3 + 6x^2 - 12x$	$\quad = 3x(x^2 + 2x - 4)$

DO EXERCISES 6 AND 7.

CAUTION!   Consider the following:
$$3x^3 + 6x^2 - 12x = 3 \cdot x \cdot x \cdot x + 2 \cdot 3 \cdot x \cdot x - 2 \cdot 2 \cdot 3x.$$
The terms of the polynomial, $3x^3$, $6x^2$, and $-12x$, have been factored but the polynomial itself has not been factored. This is not a factorization. The *factorization* is
$$3x(x^2 + 2x - 4).$$
The expressions $3x$ and $x^2 + 2x - 4$ are *factors*.

To factor, we first try to find a factor common to all terms. There may not always be one other than 1. When there is, we generally use the factor with the largest possible coefficient and the largest possible exponent.

▶   **EXAMPLE 2**   Factor: $3x^2 + 6$.

We have

$$3x^2 + 6 = 3 \cdot x^2 + 3 \cdot 2 \qquad \text{Factoring each term}$$
$$= 3(x^2 + 2). \qquad \text{Factoring out the common factor, 3}$$

We can check by multiplying: $3(x^2 + 2) = 3 \cdot x^2 + 3 \cdot 2 = 3x^2 + 6$.   ◀

▶   **EXAMPLE 3**   Factor: $16x^3 + 20x^2$.

$$16x^3 + 20x^2 = (4x^2)(4x) + (4x^2)(5) \qquad \text{Factoring each term}$$
$$= 4x^2(4x + 5) \qquad \text{Factoring out } 4x^2 \qquad ◀$$

Suppose in Example 3 that you had not recognized the largest common factor and only removed part of it, as follows:

$$16x^3 + 20x^2 = (2x^2)(8x) + (2x^2)(10)$$
$$= 2x^2(8x + 10).$$

Note that $8x + 10$ still has a common factor of 2. You need not begin again. Just continue factoring out common factors, as follows, until finished:

$$= 2x^2[2(4x + 5)]$$
$$= 4x^2(4x + 5).$$

▶ **EXAMPLE 4**   Factor: $15x^5 - 12x^4 + 27x^3 - 3x^2$.

$$15x^5 - 12x^4 + 27x^3 - 3x^2 = (3x^2)(5x^3) - (3x^2)(4x^2) + (3x^2)(9x) - (3x^2)(1)$$
$$= 3x^2(5x^3 - 4x^2 + 9x - 1) \qquad \text{Factoring out } 3x^2 \qquad ◀$$

> CAUTION!   Don't forget the term -1.

If you can spot the largest common factor without factoring each term, you can write just the answer.

▶ **EXAMPLES**   Factor.

5. $8m^3 - 16m = 8m(m^2 - 2)$

6. $14p^2y^3 - 8py^2 + 2py = 2py(7py^2 - 4y + 1)$

7. $\dfrac{4}{5}x^2 + \dfrac{1}{5}x + \dfrac{2}{5} = \dfrac{1}{5}(4x^2 + x + 2)$ ◀

DO EXERCISES 8–12.

Below is one of the most important points to keep in mind as we study this chapter.

> Before doing any other kind of factoring, first try to factor out the largest common factor.

Another tip is the following.

> You can always check the result of factoring by multiplying.

Factor.

8. $x^2 + 3x$

9. $3y^6 - 5y^3 + 2y^2$

10. $9x^4 - 15x^3 + 3x^2$

11. $\dfrac{3}{4}t^3 + \dfrac{5}{4}t^2 + \dfrac{7}{4}t + \dfrac{1}{4}$

12. $35x^7 - 49x^6 + 14x^5 - 63x^3$

ANSWERS ON PAGE A-8

Factor.

13. $x^2(x + 7) + 3(x + 7)$

14. $x^2(a + b) + 2(a + b)$

Factor by grouping.

15. $x^3 + 7x^2 + 3x + 21$

16. $8t^3 + 2t^2 + 12t + 3$

17. $3m^5 - 15m^3 + 2m^2 - 10$

18. $4x^3 - 6x^2 - 6x + 9$

19. $y^4 - 2y^3 - 2y - 10$

---

c   **Factoring by Grouping**

Certain polynomials with four terms can be factored using a method called *factoring by grouping.*

▶ **EXAMPLE 8**   Factor: $x^2(x + 1) + 2(x + 1)$.

The binomial $x + 1$ is common to both terms:

$$x^2(x + 1) + 2(x + 1) = (x^2 + 2)(x + 1).$$

The factorization is $(x^2 + 2)(x + 1)$.   ◀

DO EXERCISES 13 AND 14.

Consider the four-term polynomial

$$x^3 + x^2 + 2x + 2.$$

There is no factor other than 1 that is common to all the terms. We can, however, factor $x^3 + x^2$ and $2x + 2$ separately:

$$x^3 + x^2 = x^2(x + 1); \quad \text{Factoring } x^3 + x^2$$
$$2x + 2 = 2(x + 1). \quad \text{Factoring } 2x + 2$$

We have grouped certain terms and factored each polynomial separately:

$$x^3 + x^2 + 2x + 2 = (x^3 + x^2) + (2x + 2)$$
$$= x^2(x + 1) + 2(x + 1)$$
$$= (x^2 + 2)(x + 1),$$

as in Example 8. This method is called **factoring by grouping.** We began with a polynomial with four terms. After grouping and removing common factors, we obtained a polynomial with two terms, each having a common factor $x + 1$. Not all polynomials with four terms can be factored by this method, but it does give us a method to try.

▶ **EXAMPLES**   Factor by grouping.

9. $6x^3 - 9x^2 + 4x - 6$
   $= (6x^3 - 9x^2) + (4x - 6)$
   $= 3x^2(2x - 3) + 2(2x - 3)$ **Factoring each binomial**
   $= (3x^2 + 2)(2x - 3)$ **Factoring out the common factor**

10. $x^3 + x^2 + x + 1 = (x^3 + x^2) + (x + 1)$
   $= x^2(x + 1) + 1(x + 1)$ **Factoring each binomial**
   $= (x^2 + 1)(x + 1)$ **Factoring out the common factor**

11. $12x^5 + 20x^2 - 21x^3 - 35 = 12x^5 + 20x^2 - 21x^3 - 35$
   $= 4x^2(3x^3 + 5) - 7(3x^3 + 5)$
   $= (4x^2 - 7)(3x^3 + 5)$

12. $x^3 + x^2 + 2x - 2 = x^2(x + 1) + 2(x - 1)$

This polynomial is not factorable using factoring by grouping. It may be factorable, but not by methods that we will consider in this text.   ◀

DO EXERCISES 15–19.

NAME   SECTION   DATE

EXERCISE SET 10.1

a Find three factorizations for the monomial.

1. $6x^3$ **2.** $9x^4$ **3.** $-9x^5$ **4.** $-12x^6$ **5.** $24x^4$ **6.** $15x^5$

b Factor. Check by multiplying.

7. $x^2 - 4x$ **8.** $x^2 + 8x$ **9.** $2x^2 + 6x$

10. $3x^2 - 3x$ **11.** $x^3 + 6x^2$ **12.** $4x^4 + x^2$

13. $8x^4 - 24x^2$ **14.** $5x^5 + 10x^3$ **15.** $2x^2 + 2x - 8$

16. $6x^2 + 3x - 15$ **17.** $17x^5y^3 + 34x^3y^2 + 51xy$

18. $16x^6y^4 - 32x^5y^3 - 48xy^2$ **19.** $6x^4 - 10x^3 + 3x^2$

20. $5x^5 + 10x^2 - 8x$ **21.** $x^5y^5 + x^4y^3 + x^3y^3 - x^2y^2$

22. $x^9y^6 - x^7y^5 + x^4y^4 + x^3y^3$ **23.** $2x^7 - 2x^6 - 64x^5 + 4x^3$

24. $10x^3 + 25x^2 + 15x - 20$ **25.** $1.6x^4 - 2.4x^3 + 3.2x^2 + 6.4x$

1. _____

2. _____

3. _____

4. _____

5. _____

6. _____

7. _____

8. _____

9. _____

10. _____

11. _____

12. _____

13. _____

14. _____

15. _____

16. _____

17. _____

18. _____

19. _____

20. _____

21. _____

22. _____

23. _____

24. _____

25. _____

26. $2.5x^6 - 0.5x^4 + 5x^3 + 10x^2$

27. $\dfrac{5}{3}x^6 + \dfrac{4}{3}x^5 + \dfrac{1}{3}x^4 + \dfrac{1}{3}x^3$

28. $\dfrac{5}{7}x^7 + \dfrac{3}{7}x^5 - \dfrac{6}{7}x^3 - \dfrac{1}{7}x$

c   Factor.

29. $x^2(x + 3) + 2(x + 3)$ **30.** $3z^2(2z + 1) + (2z + 1)$

Factor by grouping.

31. $x^3 + 3x^2 + 2x + 6$ **32.** $6z^3 + 3z^2 + 2z + 1$ **33.** $2x^3 + 6x^2 + x + 3$

34. $3x^3 + 2x^2 + 3x + 2$ **35.** $8x^3 - 12x^2 + 6x - 9$ **36.** $10x^3 - 25x^2 + 4x - 10$

37. $12x^3 - 16x^2 + 3x - 4$ **38.** $18x^3 - 21x^2 + 30x - 35$ **39.** $x^3 + 8x^2 - 3x - 24$

40. $2x^3 + 12x^2 - 5x - 30$ **41.** $2x^3 - 8x^2 - 9x + 36$ **42.** $20g^3 - 4g^2 - 25g + 5$

SKILL MAINTENANCE

Solve.

43. $-2x < 48$ **44.** $4x - 8x + 16 \geq 6(x - 2)$

45. Divide: $\dfrac{-108}{-4}$.   **46.** Solve $A = \dfrac{p + q}{2}$ for p.

Multiply.

47. $(y + 5)(y + 7)$ **48.** $(y + 7)^2$ **49.** $(y + 7)(y - 7)$ **50.** $(y - 7)^2$

SYNTHESIS

Factor.

51. $4x^5 + 6x^3 + 6x^2 + 9$ **52.** $x^6 + x^4 + x^2 + 1$ **53.** $x^{12} + x^7 + x^5 + 1$

54. $x^3 - x^2 - 2x + 5$ **55.** $p^3 + p^2 - 3p + 10$

56. Subtract $(x^2 + 1)^2$ from $x(x + 1)^2$ and factor the result.

10.2   Factoring Trinomials of the Type $x^2 + bx + c$

a   We now begin a study of the factoring of trinomials. We first try to factor trinomials like

$$x^2 + 5x + 6 \quad \text{and} \quad x^2 + 3x - 10$$

by *trial and error*. In this section, we restrict our attention to trinomials of the type $ax^2 + bx + c$, where $a = 1$. The coefficient a is often called the **leading coefficient.**

Constant Term Positive

Recall the FOIL method of multiplying two binomials:

$$\begin{array}{ccccc} & \text{F} & \text{O} & \text{I} & \text{L} \\ (x + 2)(x + 5) = & x^2 & + 5x & + 2x & + 10 \end{array}$$

$$= x^2 + \quad 7x \quad + 10.$$

The product above is a trinomial. The term of highest degree, x^2, called the leading term, has a coefficient of 1. The constant term, 10, is positive. To factor $x^2 + 7x + 10$, we think of FOIL in reverse. We multiplied x times x to get the first term of the trinomial, so we know that the first term of each binomial factor is x. Next we look for numbers p and q such that

$$x^2 + 7x + 10 = (x + p)(x + q).$$

To get the middle term and the last term of the trinomial, we look for two numbers p and q whose product is 10 and whose sum is 7. Those numbers are 2 and 5. Thus the factorization is

$$(x + 2)(x + 5).$$

▶   **EXAMPLE 1**   Factor: $x^2 + 5x + 6$.

Think of FOIL in reverse. The first term of each factor is x:

$$(x + p)(x + q).$$

We then look for two numbers p and q whose product is 6 and whose sum is 5. Since both 5 and 6 are positive, we need consider only positive factors.

Pairs of factors	Sums of factors
1, 6	7
2, 3	5 ←

The numbers we need are 2 and 3.

The factorization is $(x + 2)(x + 3)$. We can check by multiplying to see whether we get the original trinomial.

Check: $(x + 2)(x + 3) = x^2 + 3x + 2x + 6 = x^2 + 5x + 6.$ ◀

DO EXERCISES 1 AND 2.

OBJECTIVE

After finishing Section 10.2, you should be able to:

a   Factor trinomials of the type $x^2 + bx + c$ by examining the constant term c.

FOR EXTRA HELP

Tape 21C

Factor.

  1. $x^2 + 7x + 12$

  2. $x^2 + 13x + 36$

Factor.

3. $x^2 - 8x + 15$

Consider this multiplication:

$$(x - 2)(x - 5) = x^2 \overset{\text{F}}{} \overset{\text{O}}{- 5x} \overset{\text{I}}{- 2x} \overset{\text{L}}{+ 10}$$

$$= x^2 - 7x + 10.$$

> **When the constant term of a trinomial is positive, we look for two numbers with the same sign. The sign is that of the middle term:**
> $$(x^2 - 7x + 10) = (x - 2)(x - 5).$$

▶ **EXAMPLE 2**   Factor: $y^2 - 8y + 12$.

Since the constant term is positive and the coefficient of the middle term is negative, we look for a factorization of 12 in which both factors are negative. Their sum must be -8.

Pairs of factors	Sums of factors
$-1, -12$	-13
$-2, -6$	-8 ←
$-3, -4$	-7

The numbers we need are -2 and -6.

The factorization is $(y - 2)(y - 6)$.   ◀

DO EXERCISES 3 AND 4.

4. $t^2 - 9t + 20$

Constant Term Negative

Sometimes when we use FOIL, the product has a negative constant term. Consider these multiplications:

a) $(x - 5)(x + 2) = x^2 \overset{\text{F}}{} \overset{\text{O}}{+ 2x} \overset{\text{I}}{- 5x} \overset{\text{L}}{- 10}$

$$= x^2 - 3x - 10;$$

b) $(x + 5)(x - 2) = x^2 \overset{\text{F}}{} \overset{\text{O}}{- 2x} \overset{\text{I}}{+ 5x} \overset{\text{L}}{- 10}$

$$= x^2 + 3x - 10.$$

Reversing the signs of the factors changes the sign of the middle term.

> **When the constant term is negative, we look for two factors whose product is negative. One of them must be positive and the other negative. Their sum must be the coefficient of the middle term.**

▶ **EXAMPLE 3** Factor: $x^3 - 8x^2 - 20x$.

Always look first for a common factor. This time there is one, x. We first factor it out:

$$x^3 - 8x^2 - 20x = x(x^2 - 8x - 20).$$

Now consider $x^2 - 8x - 20$. Since the constant term is negative, we look for a factorization of -20 in which one factor is positive and one factor is negative. The sum must be -8, so the negative factor must have the larger absolute value. Thus we consider only pairs of factors in which the negative factor has the larger absolute value.

Pairs of factors	Sums of factors
1, −20	−19
2, −10	−8 ← The numbers we need are 2 and −10.
4, −5	−1

The numbers we need are 2 and -10. The factorization of $x^2 - 8x - 20$ is $(x + 2)(x - 10)$. But we must also remember to include the common factor. The factorization of the original polynomial is

$$x(x + 2)(x - 10). \qquad ◀$$

▶ **EXAMPLE 4** Factor: $t^2 - 24 + 5t$.

It helps to first write the trinomial in descending order: $t^2 + 5t - 24$. Since the constant term is negative, we look for a factorization of -24 in which one factor is positive and one factor is negative. Their sum must be 5, so the positive factor must have the larger absolute value. Thus we consider only pairs of factors in which the positive term has the larger absolute value.

Pairs of factors	Sums of factors
−1, 24	23
−2, 12	10
−3, 8	5 ← The numbers we need are −3 and 8.
−4, 6	2

The factorization is $(t - 3)(t + 8)$. ◀

▶ **EXAMPLE 5** Factor: $x^4 - x^2 - 110$.

Consider this trinomial as $(x^2)^2 - x^2 - 110$. We look for numbers p and q such that

$$x^4 - x^2 - 110 = (x^2 + p)(x^2 + q).$$

Since the constant term is negative, we look for a factorization of -110 in which one factor is positive and one factor is negative. Their sum must be -1. The middle-term coefficient, -1, is small compared to -110. This tells us that the desired factors are close to each other in absolute value. The numbers we want are 10 and -11. The factorization is

$$(x^2 + 10)(x^2 - 11). \qquad ◀$$

Factor.

5. $x^3 + 4x^2 - 12x$

6. $y^2 - 12 - 4y$

7. $t^4 + 5t^2 - 14$

8. $p^2 - pq - 3pq^2$

9. $x^2 + 2x + 7$

10. Factor: $x^2 + 8x + 16$.

▶ **EXAMPLE 6**   Factor: $a^2 + 4ab - 21b^2$.

We consider the trinomial in the equivalent form

$$a^2 + 4ba - 21b^2.$$

We think of $4b$ as a "coefficient" of a. Then we look for factors of $-21b^2$ whose sum is $4b$. Those factors are $-3b$ and $7b$. The factorization is

$$(a - 3b)(a + 7b). \qquad ◀$$

There are polynomials that are not factorable.

▶ **EXAMPLE 7**   Factor: $x^2 - x + 5$.

Since 5 has very few factors, we can easily check all possibilities.

Pairs of factors	Sums of factors
5, 1	6
-5, -1	-6

There are no factors whose sum is -1. Thus the polynomial is *not* factorable into binomials.   ◀

DO EXERCISES 5–9.

Can we factor a trinomial that is a perfect square using this method? The answer is "yes."

▶ **EXAMPLE 8**   Factor: $x^2 - 10x + 25$.

Since the constant term is positive and the coefficient of the middle term is negative, we look for a factorization of 25 in which both factors are negative. Their sum must be -10.

Pairs of factors	Sums of factors	
-25, -1	-26	
-5, -5	-10 ←	The numbers we need are -5 and -5.

The factorization is $(x - 5)(x - 5)$, or $(x - 5)^2$.   ◀

DO EXERCISE 10.

The following is a summary of our procedure for factoring $x^2 + bx + c$.

To factor $x^2 + bx + c$:

1. **First arrange in descending order. Use a trial-and-error process that looks for factors of c whose sum is b.**
2. **If c is positive, the signs of the factors are the same as the sign of b.**
3. **If c is negative, one factor is positive and the other is negative. If the sum of two factors is the opposite of b, changing the sign of each factor will give the desired factors whose sum is b.**
4. **Check by multiplying.**

NAME   SECTION   DATE

EXERCISE SET 10.2

a Factor. Remember that you can check by multiplying.

1. $x^2 + 8x + 15$

2. $x^2 + 5x + 6$

3. $x^2 + 7x + 12$

4. $x^2 + 9x + 8$

5. $x^2 - 6x + 9$

6. $y^2 + 11y + 28$

7. $x^2 + 9x + 14$

8. $a^2 + 11a + 30$

9. $b^2 + 5b + 4$

10. $x^2 - \dfrac{2}{5}x + \dfrac{1}{25}$

11. $x^2 + \dfrac{2}{3}x + \dfrac{1}{9}$

12. $z^2 - 8z + 7$

13. $d^2 - 7d + 10$

14. $x^2 - 8x + 15$

15. $y^2 - 11y + 10$

16. $x^2 - 2x - 15$

17. $x^2 + x - 42$

18. $x^2 + 2x - 15$

19. $x^2 - 7x - 18$

20. $y^2 - 3y - 28$

21. $x^3 - 6x^2 - 16x$

22. $x^3 - x^2 - 42x$

23. $y^2 - 4y - 45$

24. $x^2 - 7x - 60$

25. $-2x - 99 + x^2$

26. $x^2 - 72 + 6x$

27. $c^4 + c^2 - 56$

28. $b^4 + 5b^2 - 24$

29. $a^4 + 2a^2 - 35$

30. $2 - x^2 - x^4$

31. $x^2 + x + 1$

32. $x^2 + 2x + 3$

33. $7 - 2p + p^2$

34. $11 - 3w + w^2$

35. $x^2 + 20x + 100$

36. $x^2 + 20x + 99$

ANSWERS

1. _____
2. _____
3. _____
4. _____
5. _____
6. _____
7. _____
8. _____
9. _____
10. _____
11. _____
12. _____
13. _____
14. _____
15. _____
16. _____
17. _____
18. _____
19. _____
20. _____
21. _____
22. _____
23. _____
24. _____
25. _____
26. _____
27. _____
28. _____
29. _____
30. _____
31. _____
32. _____
33. _____
34. _____
35. _____
36. _____

ANSWERS

37. _____

38. _____

39. _____

40. _____

41. _____

42. _____

43. _____

44. _____

45. _____

46. _____

47. _____

48. _____

49. _____

50. _____

51. _____

52. _____

53. _____

54. _____

55. _____

56. _____

57. _____

58. _____

59. _____

60. _____

61. _____

62. _____

63. _____

64. _____

65. _____

66. _____

67. _____

68. _____

69. _____

70. _____

37. $x^2 - 21x - 100$ **38.** $x^2 - 20x + 96$ **39.** $x^2 - 21x - 72$

40. $4x^2 + 40x + 100$ **41.** $x^2 - 25x + 144$ **42.** $y^2 - 21y + 108$

43. $a^2 + a - 132$ **44.** $a^2 + 9a - 90$ **45.** $120 - 23x + x^2$

46. $96 + 22d + d^2$ **47.** $108 - 3x - x^2$ **48.** $112 + 9y - y^2$

49. $y^2 - 0.2y - 0.08$ **50.** $t^2 - 0.3t - 0.10$ **51.** $p^2 + 3pq - 10q^2$

52. $a^2 - 2ab - 3b^2$ **53.** $m^2 + 5mn + 4n^2$ **54.** $x^2 - 11xy + 24y^2$

55. $s^2 - 2st - 15t^2$ **56.** $b^2 + 8bc - 20c^2$

SKILL MAINTENANCE

Multiply.

57. $8x(2x^2 - 6x + 1)$ **58.** $(7w + 6)(4w - 11)$ **59.** $(7w + 6)^2$

60. Simplify: $(3x^4)^3$.

SYNTHESIS

61. Find all integers m for which $y^2 + my + 50$ can be factored.

62. Find all integers b for which $a^2 + ba - 50$ can be factored.

Factor completely.

63. $x^2 - \dfrac{1}{2}x - \dfrac{3}{16}$ **64.** $x^2 - \dfrac{1}{4}x - \dfrac{1}{8}$ **65.** $x^2 + \dfrac{30}{7}x - \dfrac{25}{7}$

66. $\dfrac{1}{3}x^3 + \dfrac{1}{3}x^2 - 2x$ **67.** $b^{2n} + 7b^n + 10$ **68.** $a^{2m} - 11a^m + 28$

Find a polynomial in factored form for the shaded area. (Leave answers in terms of π.)

69.

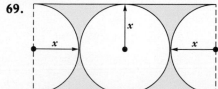

70.

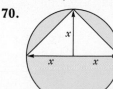

10.3 Factoring Trinomials of the Type $ax^2 + bx + c$, $a \neq 1$

In Section 10.2, we learned a trial-and-error method to factor trinomials of the type $x^2 + bx + c$. In this section, we factor trinomials in which the leading, or x^2, coefficient is not 1. The method we learn is the *standard* trial-and-error method. (In Section 10.4, we will consider an alternative method for the same kind of factoring. It involves *factoring by grouping*.)

OBJECTIVE

After finishing Section 10.3, you should be able to:

a Factor trinomials of the type $ax^2 + bx + c$, $a \neq 1$.

FOR EXTRA HELP

Tape 21D

a   We want to factor trinomials of the type $ax^2 + bx + c$. Consider the following multiplication:

$$
\begin{array}{ccccccc}
 & \text{F} & \text{O} & \text{I} & \text{L} \\
(2x + 5)(3x + 4) = 6x^2 & + & 8x & + & 15x & + & 20 \\
= 6x^2 & + & & 23x & & + & 20
\end{array}
$$

F	**O + I**	**L**
$2 \cdot 3$	$2 \cdot 4 + 5 \cdot 3$	$5 \cdot 4$

To factor $6x^2 + 23x + 20$, we reverse the above multiplication. We look for two binomials $rx + p$ and $sx + q$ whose product is this trinomial. The product of the First terms must be $6x^2$. The product of the Outside terms plus the product of the Inside terms must be $23x$. The product of the Last terms must be 20. We know from the preceding discussion that the answer is

$$(2x + 5)(3x + 4).$$

Generally, however, finding such an answer is a trial-and-error process. It turns out that $(-2x - 5)(-3x - 4)$ is also a correct answer, but we usually choose an answer in which the first coefficients are positive.

We will use the following trial-and-error method.

To factor $ax^2 + bx + c$, $a \neq 1$, using the FOIL method:

1. **Factor out a common factor, if any.**

2. **Factor the term ax^2. This gives these possibilities for r and s:**
$$(rx + p)(sx + q).$$
$$rx \cdot sx = ax^2$$

3. **Factor the last term c. This gives these possibilities for p and q:**
$$(rx + p)(sx + q).$$
$$p \cdot q = c$$

4. **Look for combinations of factors from steps (2) and (3) for which the sum of their products is the middle term bx:**
$$rx \cdot q$$
$$(rx + p)(sx + q). \qquad rx \cdot q + p \cdot sx \overset{?}{=} bx$$
$$p \cdot sx$$

Factor.

1. $2x^2 - x - 15$

▶ **EXAMPLE 1**   Factor: $3x^2 - 10x - 8$.

1) First, factor out a common factor, if any. There is none (other than 1 or -1).

2) Factor the first term, $3x^2$. The only possibility is $3x \cdot x$. The desired factorization is then of the form

$$(3x + \underline{\quad})(x + \underline{\quad}),$$

where we must determine the numbers in the blanks.

3) Factor the last term, -8, which is negative. The possibilities are

$$-8 = (-8)(1);$$
$$= 8(-1);$$
$$= (-2)(4);$$
$$= 2(-4).$$

4) From steps (2) and (3), we see that there are $1 \cdot (2 \cdot 4)$, or 8 possibilities for factorizations. We look for combinations of factors from steps (2) and (3) such that the sum of their products is the middle term, $-10x$:

$$\overbrace{(3x - 8)(x + 1)}^{3x} = 3x^2 - 5x - 8; \qquad \overbrace{(3x + 8)(x - 1)}^{-3x} = 3x^2 + 5x - 8;$$
$$\underbrace{}_{-8x} \quad \text{Wrong middle} \qquad \underbrace{}_{8x} \quad \text{Wrong middle}$$
$$\text{term} \qquad\qquad\qquad \text{term}$$

$$\overbrace{(3x - 2)(x + 4)}^{12x} = 3x^2 + 10x - 8; \qquad \overbrace{(3x + 2)(x - 4)}^{-12x} = 3x^2 - 10x - 8;$$
$$\underbrace{}_{-2x} \quad \text{Wrong middle} \qquad \underbrace{}_{2x} \quad \text{Correct middle}$$
$$\text{term} \qquad\qquad\qquad \text{term!}$$

2. $12x^2 - 17x - 5$

There are four other possibilities that we could try, but we need not since we have found a factorization. The factorization is $(3x + 2)(x - 4)$.

◀

DO EXERCISES 1 AND 2.

▶ **EXAMPLE 2**   Factor: $24x^2 - 76x + 40$.

1) Factor out a common factor, if any. This time there is one, 4. We factor it out:

$$4(6x^2 - 19x + 10).$$

Now we factor the trinomial $6x^2 - 19x + 10$.

2) Factor the first term, $6x^2$. These are $3x$, $2x$, or $6x$, x. Then we have these as possibilities for factorizations:

$$(3x + \underline{\quad})(2x + \underline{\quad}) \quad \text{or} \quad (6x + \underline{\quad})(x + \underline{\quad}).$$

3) Factor the last term, 10, which is positive. The possibilities are

$$10, 1 \quad \text{and} \quad -10, -1 \quad \text{and} \quad 5, 2 \quad \text{and} \quad -5, -2.$$

4) From steps (2) and (3), we see that there are $2 \cdot (2 \cdot 4)$, or 16 possibilities for factorizations. Look for combinations of factors from steps (2) and (3) such that the sum of their products is the middle term, $-19x$. The sign of the middle term is negative, but the sign of the last term, 10, is positive. Thus the signs of both factors of the last term, 10, must be negative. From our list of factors in step (3), we can only use $-10, -1$ and $-5, -2$ as possibilities. This reduces the possibilities for factorizations to 8. We start by using these factors with $(3x + \underline{})(2x + \underline{})$. Should we not find the correct factorization, we will consider $(6x + \underline{})(x + \underline{})$.

$$\overset{\overbrace{\hspace{3.5em}}^{-3x}}{(3x - 10)(2x - 1)} = 6x^2 \overset{\overbrace{\hspace{2.5em}}}{- 23x} + 10;$$
$$\underset{\underbrace{\hspace{3em}}_{-20x}}{} \qquad \text{Wrong middle term}$$

$$\overset{\overbrace{\hspace{3.5em}}^{-30x}}{(3x - 1)(2x - 10)} = 6x^2 \overset{\overbrace{\hspace{2.5em}}}{- 32x} + 10;$$
$$\underset{\underbrace{\hspace{3em}}_{-2x}}{} \qquad \text{Wrong middle term}$$

$$\overset{\overbrace{\hspace{3.5em}}^{-6x}}{(3x - 5)(2x - 2)} = 6x^2 \overset{\overbrace{\hspace{2.5em}}}{- 16x} + 10;$$
$$\underset{\underbrace{\hspace{3em}}_{-10x}}{} \qquad \text{Wrong middle term}$$

$$\overset{\overbrace{\hspace{3.5em}}^{-15x}}{(3x - 2)(2x - 5)} = 6x^2 \overset{\overbrace{\hspace{2.5em}}}{- 19x} + 10;$$
$$\underset{\underbrace{\hspace{3em}}_{-4x}}{} \qquad \text{Correct middle term!}$$

We have a correct answer. We need not consider $(6x + \underline{})(x + \underline{})$.

Look again at the possibility $(3x - 5)(2x - 2)$. Without multiplying, we can reject such a possibility. Look at the following:

$$(3x - 5)(2x - 2) = 2(3x - 5)(x - 1).$$

The expression $2x - 2$ has a common factor, 2. But we removed the largest common factor before we began. If this expression were a factorization, then 2 would have to be a common factor in addition to the original 4. Thus, as we saw when we multiplied, $(3x - 5)(2x - 2)$ cannot be part of the factorization of the original trinomial.

> Given that we factored out the largest common factor at the outset, we can eliminate factorizations that have a common factor.

The factorization of $6x^2 - 19x + 10$ is $(3x - 2)(2x - 5)$. But do not forget the common factor! We must include it in order to get a factorization of the original trinomial:

$$24x^2 - 76x + 40 = 4(3x - 2)(2x - 5). \qquad \blacktriangleleft$$

DO EXERCISES 3 AND 4.

▶ **EXAMPLE 3** Factor: $10x^2 + 37x + 7$.

1) First, factor out a common factor, if any. There is none (other than 1 or -1).

2) Factor the term $10x^2$: $10x, x$ or $5x, 2x$. We have these as possibilities for factorizations:

$$(10x + \underline{})(x + \underline{}) \quad \text{and} \quad (5x + \underline{})(2x + \underline{}).$$

Factor.

3. $3x^2 - 19x + 20$

4. $20x^2 - 46x + 24$

ANSWERS ON PAGE A-8

5. Factor: $6x^2 + 7x + 2$.

3) Factor the last term, 7. The possibilities are 1, 7 and -1, -7.

4) From steps (2) and (3), we see that there are 8 possibilities for factorizations. Look for factors from steps (2) and (3) such that the sum of their products is the middle term. In this case, all signs are positive, so we need consider only plus signs. The possibilities are

$$(10x + 1)(x + 7) = 10x^2 + 71x + 7,$$
$$(10x + 7)(x + 1) = 10x^2 + 17x + 7,$$
$$(5x + 7)(2x + 1) = 10x^2 + 19x + 7,$$
$$(5x + 1)(2x + 7) = 10x^2 + 37x + 7.$$

The factorization is $(5x + 1)(2x + 7)$.   ◀

Tips for factoring $ax^2 + bx + c$, $a \neq 1$:

1. **If the largest common factor has been factored out of the original trinomial, then no binomial factor can have a common factor (other than 1 or -1).**

2. **If all the signs of all the terms are positive, then the signs of all the terms of the binomial factors are positive.**

3. **Be systematic about your trials. Keep track of those you have tried and those you have not.**

Factor.

6. $6a^2 - 5ab + b^2$

DO EXERCISE 5.

Keep in mind that this method of factoring trinomials of the type $ax^2 + bx + c$ involves trial and error. As you practice, you will find that you can make better and better guesses. Don't forget: When factoring any polynomial, always look first for a common factor. Failure to do so is such a common error that this caution bears repeating.

7. $6x^2 + 15xy + 9y^2$

▶ **EXAMPLE 4**   Factor: $6p^2 - 13pq - 28q^2$.

1) Factor out a common factor, if any. There is none (other than 1 or -1).

2) Factor the first term, $6p^2$. Possibilities are $2p$, $3p$ and $6p$, p. We have these as possibilities for factorizations:

$$(2p + \underline{\quad})(3p + \underline{\quad}) \quad \text{and} \quad (6p + \underline{\quad})(p + \underline{\quad}).$$

3) Factor the last term, $-28q^2$, which has a negative coefficient. The possibilities are $-14q$, $2q$ and $14q$, $-2q$; $-28q$, q and $28q$, $-q$; and $-7q$, $4q$ and $7q$, $-4q$.

4) The coefficient of the middle term is negative, so we look for combinations of factors from steps (2) and (3) such that the sum of their products has a negative coefficient. We try some possibilities:

$$(2p - 14q)(3p + 2q) = 6p^2 - 38pq - 28q^2,$$
$$(2p - 28q)(3p + q) = 6p^2 - 82pq - 28q^2,$$
$$(2p - 7q)(3p + 4q) = 6p^2 - 13pq - 28q^2.$$

The factorization of $6p^2 - 13pq - 28q^2$ is $(2p - 7q)(3p + 4q)$.   ◀

DO EXERCISES 6 AND 7.

EXERCISE SET 10.3

a Factor.

1. $2x^2 - 7x - 4$

2. $3x^2 - x - 4$

3. $5x^2 + x - 18$

4. $3x^2 - 4x - 15$

5. $6x^2 + 23x + 7$

6. $6x^2 + 13x + 6$

7. $3x^2 + 4x + 1$

8. $7x^2 + 15x + 2$

9. $4x^2 + 4x - 15$

10. $9x^2 + 6x - 8$

11. $2x^2 - x - 1$

12. $15x^2 - 19x - 10$

13. $9x^2 + 18x - 16$

14. $2x^2 + 5x + 2$

15. $3x^2 - 5x - 2$

16. $18x^2 - 3x - 10$

17. $12x^2 + 31x + 20$

18. $15x^2 + 19x - 10$

19. $14x^2 + 19x - 3$

20. $35x^2 + 34x + 8$

21. $9x^2 + 18x + 8$

22. $6 - 13x + 6x^2$

23. $49 - 42x + 9x^2$

24. $25x^2 + 40x + 16$

25. $24x^2 + 47x - 2$

26. $16a^2 + 78a + 27$

27. $35x^2 - 57x - 44$

28. $9a^2 + 12a - 5$

29. $20 + 6x - 2x^2$

30. $15 + x - 2x^2$

31. $12x^2 + 28x - 24$

32. $6x^2 + 33x + 15$

33. $30x^2 - 24x - 54$

34. $20x^2 - 25x + 5$

35. $4x + 6x^2 - 10$

36. $-9 + 18x^2 - 21x$

ANSWERS

1.
2.
3.
4.
5.
6.
7.
8.
9.
10.
11.
12.
13.
14.
15.
16.
17.
18.
19.
20.
21.
22.
23.
24.
25.
26.
27.
28.
29.
30.
31.
32.
33.
34.
35.
36.

37. $3x^2 - 4x + 1$

38. $6x^2 - 13x + 6$

39. $12x^2 - 28x - 24$

40. $6x^2 - 33x + 15$

41. $-1 + 2x^2 - x$

42. $-19x + 15x^2 + 6$

43. $9x^2 - 18x - 16$

44. $14x^2 + 35x + 14$

45. $15x^2 - 25x - 10$

46. $18x^2 + 3x - 10$

47. $12x^3 + 31x^2 + 20x$

48. $15x^3 + 19x^2 - 10x$

49. $14x^4 + 19x^3 - 3x^2$

50. $70x^4 + 68x^3 + 16x^2$

51. $168x^3 - 45x^2 + 3x$

52. $144x^5 + 168x^4 + 48x^3$

53. $15x^4 - 19x^2 + 6$

54. $9x^4 + 18x^2 + 8$

55. $25t^2 + 80t + 64$

56. $9x^2 - 42x + 49$

57. $6x^3 + 4x^2 - 10x$

58. $18x^3 - 21x^2 - 9x$

59. $25x^2 + 79x + 64$

60. $9y^2 - 42y + 47$

61. $x^2 + 3x - 7$

62. $x^2 + 13x - 12$

63. $12m^2 + mn - 20n^2$

64. $12a^2 + 17ab + 6b^2$

65. $6a^2 - ab - 15b^2$

66. $3p^2 - 16pq - 12q^2$

67. $9a^2 + 18ab + 8b^2$

68. $10s^2 + 4st - 6t^2$

69. $35p^2 + 34pq + 8q^2$

70. $30a^2 + 87ab + 30b^2$

71. $18x^2 - 6xy - 24y^2$

72. $15a^2 - 5ab - 20b^2$

SKILL MAINTENANCE

73. Solve $A = pq - 7$ for q.

74. Solve: $2x - 4(x + 3x) \geq 6x - 8 - 9x$.

SYNTHESIS

Factor.

75. $20x^{2n} + 16x^n + 3$

76. $-15x^{2m} + 26x^m - 8$

77. $3x^{6a} - 2x^{3a} - 1$

78. $x^{2n+1} - 2x^{n+1} + x$

10.4 Factoring $ax^2 + bx + c$, $a \neq 1$, Using Grouping

OBJECTIVE

After finishing Section 10.4, you should be able to:

a Factor trinomials of the type $ax^2 + bx + c$, $a \neq 1$, by splitting the middle term and using grouping.

FOR EXTRA HELP

Tape 21E

a Another method of factoring trinomials of the type $ax^2 + bx + c$, $a \neq 1$, is known as the **grouping method.** It involves factoring by grouping. We know how to factor the trinomial $x^2 + 5x + 6$. We look for factors of the constant term, 6, whose sum is the coefficient of the middle term, 5:

$$x^2 + 5x + 6.$$
(1) Factor: $6 = 2 \cdot 3$
(2) Sum: $2 + 3 = 5$

What happens when the leading coefficient is not 1? Consider the trinomial $3x^2 - 10x - 8$. The method we use is similar to what we used for the preceding trinomial, but we need two more steps. The method is outlined as follows.

To factor $ax^2 + bx + c$, $a \neq 1$, using the grouping method:

1. **Factor out a common factor, if any.**

2. **Multiply the leading coefficient a and the constant c.**

3. **Try to factor the product ac so that the sum of the factors is b. That is, find integers p and q such that $pq = ac$ and $p + q = b$.**

4. **Split the middle term. That is, write it as a sum using the factors found in step (3).**

5. **Then factor by grouping.**

▶ **EXAMPLE 1** Factor: $3x^2 - 10x - 8$.

1) First, factor out a common factor, if any. There is none (other than 1 or -1).

2) Multiply the leading coefficient, 3, and the constant, -8:

$$3(-8) = -24.$$

3) Then look for a factorization of -24 in which the sum of the factors is the coefficient of the middle term, -10.

Pairs of factors	Sums of factors
-1, 24	23
-2, 12	10
-3, 8	5
-4, 6	2
-6, 4	-2
-8, 3	-5
-12, 2	-10 ← $\quad -12 + 2 = -10$
-24, 1	-23

4) Next, split the middle term as a sum or difference using the factors found in step (3):

$$-10x = -12x + 2x.$$

Factor.

1. $6x^2 + 7x + 2$

5) Factor by grouping as follows:

$$3x^2 - 10x - 8 = 3x^2 - 12x + 2x - 8$$
$$= 3x(x - 4) + 2(x - 4) \quad \text{Factoring by grouping;}$$
$$\text{see Section 10.1}$$
$$= (3x + 2)(x - 4).$$

It does not matter which way we split the middle term, so long as we split it correctly. We still get the same factorization, although the factors may be in a different order. Note the following:

$$3x^2 - 10x - 8 = 3x^2 + 2x - 12x - 8$$
$$= x(3x + 2) - 4(3x + 2)$$
$$= (x - 4)(3x + 2).$$

Check by multiplying: $(x - 4)(3x + 2) = 3x^2 - 10x - 8.$ ◄

2. $12x^2 - 17x - 5$

DO EXERCISES 1 AND 2.

► **EXAMPLE 2**　Factor: $8x^2 + 8x - 6$.

1) First, factor out a common factor, if any. The number 2 is common to all three terms, so we factor it out:

$$2(4x^2 + 4x - 3).$$

2) Next, factor the trinomial $4x^2 + 4x - 3$. Multiply the leading coefficient and the constant, 4 and -3:

$$4(-3) = -12.$$

Factor.

3. $6x^2 + 15x + 9$

3) Try to factor -12 so that the sum of the factors is 4.

Pairs of factors	Sums of factors
$-3,\quad 4$	1
$3, -4$	-1
$-12,\quad 1$	-11
$12, -1$	11
$-6,\quad 2$	-4
$6, -2$	4 ← ———— $6 + (-2) = 4$

4) Split the middle term, $4x$, as follows:

$$4x = 6x - 2x.$$

4. $20x^2 - 46x + 24$

5) Factor by grouping:

$$4x^2 + 4x - 3 = 4x^2 + 6x - 2x - 3 \quad \text{Substituting } 6x - 2x \text{ for } 4x$$
$$= 2x(2x + 3) - 1(2x + 3) \quad \text{Factoring by grouping}$$
$$= (2x - 1)(2x + 3).$$

The factorization of $4x^2 + 4x - 3$ is $(2x - 1)(2x + 3)$. But don't forget the common factor! We must include it to get a factorization of the original trinomial:

$$8x^2 + 8x - 6 = 2(2x - 1)(2x + 3). \quad ◄$$

DO EXERCISES 3 AND 4.

ANSWERS ON PAGE A-8

EXERCISE SET 10.4

a Factor. Note that the middle term has already been split.

1. $y^2 + 4y + y + 4$ **2.** $x^2 + 5x + 2x + 10$ **3.** $x^2 - 4x - x + 4$

4. $a^2 + 5a - 2a - 10$ **5.** $6x^2 + 4x + 9x + 6$ **6.** $3x^2 - 2x + 3x - 2$

7. $3x^2 - 4x - 12x + 16$ **8.** $24 - 18y - 20y + 15y^2$ **9.** $35x^2 - 40x + 21x - 24$

10. $8x^2 - 6x - 28x + 21$ **11.** $4x^2 + 6x - 6x - 9$ **12.** $2x^4 - 6x^2 - 5x^2 + 15$

13. $2x^4 + 6x^2 + 5x^2 + 15$ **14.** $4x^4 - 6x^2 - 6x^2 + 9$

Factor by grouping.

15. $2x^2 - 7x - 4$ **16.** $3x^2 - x - 4$ **17.** $5x^2 + x - 18$

18. $3x^2 - 4x - 15$ **19.** $6x^2 + 23x + 7$ **20.** $6x^2 + 13x + 6$

21. $3x^2 + 4x + 1$ **22.** $7x^2 + 15x + 2$ **23.** $4x^2 + 4x - 15$

1.
2.
3.
4.
5.
6.
7.
8.
9.
10.
11.
12.
13.
14.
15.
16.
17.
18.
19.
20.
21.
22.
23.

24. $9x^2 + 6x - 8$ **25.** $2x^2 - x - 1$ **26.** $15x^2 - 19x - 10$

27. $9x^2 + 18x - 16$ **28.** $2x^2 + 5x + 2$ **29.** $3x^2 - 5x - 2$

30. $18x^2 - 3x - 10$ **31.** $12x^2 + 31x + 20$ **32.** $15x^2 + 19x - 10$

33. $14x^2 + 19x - 3$ **34.** $35x^2 + 34x + 8$ **35.** $9x^2 + 18x + 8$

36. $6 - 13x + 6x^2$ **37.** $49 - 42x + 9x^2$ **38.** $25x^2 + 40x + 16$

39. $24x^2 + 47x - 2$ **40.** $16a^2 + 78a + 27$ **41.** $35x^5 - 57x^4 - 44x^3$

42. $18a^3 + 24a^2 - 10a$ **43.** $60x + 18x^2 - 6x^3$ **44.** $60x + 4x^2 - 8x^3$

SKILL MAINTENANCE

Solve.

45. $3x - 6x + 2(x - 4) > 2(9 - 4x)$ **46.** $-6(x - 4) + 8(4 - x) \le 3(x - 7)$

SYNTHESIS

Factor.

47. $9x^{10} - 12x^5 + 4$ **48.** $24x^{2n} + 22x^n + 3$

49. $16x^{10} + 8x^5 + 1$ **50.** $(a + 4)^2 - 2(a + 4) + 1$

10.5 Factoring Trinomial Squares and Differences of Squares

In this section, we first learn to factor trinomials that are squares of binomials. Then we factor binomials that are differences of squares.

a Recognizing Trinomial Squares

Some trinomials are squares of binomials. For example, the trinomial $x^2 + 10x + 25$ is the square of the binomial $x + 5$. To see this, we can calculate $(x + 5)^2$. It is $x^2 + 2 \cdot x \cdot 5 + 5^2$, or $x^2 + 10x + 25$. A trinomial that is the square of a binomial is called a **trinomial square.**

In Chapter 9, we considered squaring binomials as a special-product rule.

$$(A + B)^2 = A^2 + 2AB + B^2;$$
$$(A - B)^2 = A^2 - 2AB + B^2.$$

We can use these equations in reverse to factor trinomial squares.

$$A^2 + 2AB + B^2 = (A + B)^2;$$
$$A^2 - 2AB + B^2 = (A - B)^2$$

How can we recognize when an expression to be factored is a trinomial square? Look at $A^2 + 2AB + B^2$ and $A^2 - 2AB + B^2$. In order for an expression to be a trinomial square:

a) Two terms, A^2 and B^2, must be squares, such as

$$4, \quad x^2, \quad 25x^4, \quad 16t^2.$$

b) There must be no minus sign before A^2 or B^2.

c) If we multiply A and B (the square roots of A^2 and B^2) and double the result, we get the remaining term $2 \cdot A \cdot B$, or its opposite, $-2 \cdot A \cdot B$.

▶ **EXAMPLE 1** Determine whether $x^2 + 6x + 9$ is a trinomial square.

a) We know that x^2 and 9 are squares.

b) There is no minus sign before x^2 or 9.

c) If we multiply the square roots, x and 3, and double the product, we get the remaining term: $2 \cdot x \cdot 3 = 6x$.

Thus, $x^2 + 6x + 9$ is the square of a binomial. In fact, $x^2 + 6x + 9 = (x + 3)^2$.
◀

▶ **EXAMPLE 2** Determine whether $x^2 + 6x + 11$ is a trinomial square.
The answer is no, because only one term is a square. ◀

OBJECTIVES

After finishing Section 10.5, you should be able to:

a Recognize trinomial squares.

b Factor trinomial squares.

c Recognize differences of squares.

d Factor differences of squares, being careful to factor completely.

FOR EXTRA HELP

Tape 21F

Determine whether each is a trinomial square. Write "yes" or "no."

1. $x^2 + 8x + 16$

2. $25 - x^2 + 10x$

3. $t^2 - 12t + 4$

4. $25 + 20y + 4y^2$

5. $5x^2 + 16 - 14x$

6. $16x^2 + 40x + 25$

7. $p^2 + 6p - 9$

8. $25a^2 + 9 - 30a$

Factor.

9. $x^2 + 2x + 1$

10. $1 - 2x + x^2$

11. $4 + t^2 + 4t$

12. $25x^2 - 70x + 49$

13. $49 - 56y + 16y^2$

14. $48m^2 + 75 + 120m$

▶ **EXAMPLE 3**   Determine whether $16x^2 + 49 - 56x$ is a trinomial square.

It helps to first write the trinomial in descending order:
$$16x^2 - 56x + 49.$$

a) We know that $16x^2$ and 49 are squares.

b) There is no minus sign before $16x^2$ or 49.

c) If we multiply the square roots, $4x$ and 7, and double the product, we get the opposite of the remaining term: $2 \cdot 4x \cdot 7 = 56x$; $56x$ is the opposite of $-56x$.

Thus, $16x^2 + 49 - 56x$ is a trinomial square. In fact, $16x^2 - 56x + 49 = (4x - 7)^2$. ◀

DO EXERCISES 1–8.

b   **Factoring Trinomial Squares**

We can use the trial-and-error or grouping methods from Sections 10.2–10.4 to factor such trinomial squares, but there is a faster method using the following equations:

$$A^2 + 2AB + B^2 = (A + B)^2;$$
$$A^2 - 2AB + B^2 = (A - B)^2.$$

We use square roots of the squared terms and the sign of the remaining term.

▶ **EXAMPLE 4**   Factor: $x^2 + 6x + 9$.
$$x^2 + 6x + 9 = x^2 + 2 \cdot x \cdot 3 + 3^2 - (x + 3)^2$$
The sign of the middle term is positive. ◀

▶ **EXAMPLE 5**   Factor: $x^2 + 49 - 14x$.
$$x^2 + 49 - 14x = x^2 - 14x + 49 \quad \text{Changing order}$$
$$= x^2 - 2 \cdot x \cdot 7 + 7^2$$
$$= (x - 7)^2$$
The sign of the middle term is negative. ◀

▶ **EXAMPLE 6**   Factor: $16x^2 - 40x + 25$.
$$16x^2 - 40x + 25 = (4x)^2 - 2 \cdot 4x \cdot 5 + 5^2 = (4x - 5)^2$$
◀

DO EXERCISES 9–14.

▶ **EXAMPLE 7**   Factor: $t^4 + 20t^2 + 100$.
$$t^4 + 20t^2 + 100 = (t^2)^2 + 2(t^2)(10) + 10^2$$
$$= (t^2 + 10)^2$$
◀

▶ **EXAMPLE 8**   Factor: $75m^3 + 210m^2 + 147m$.

Always look first for a common factor. This time there is one, $3m$:

$$75m^3 + 210m^2 + 147m = 3m[25m^2 + 70m + 49]$$
$$= 3m[(5m)^2 + 2(5m)(7) + 7^2]$$
$$= 3m(5m + 7)^2. \qquad ◀$$

▶ **EXAMPLE 9**   Factor: $4p^2 - 12pq + 9q^2$.

$$4p^2 - 12pq + 9q^2 = (2p)^2 - 2(2p)(3q) + (3q)^2 = (2p - 3q)^2 \qquad ◀$$

DO EXERCISES 15–17.

C   Recognizing Differences of Squares

The following polynomials are *differences of squares:*

$$x^2 - 9, \qquad 4t^2 - 49, \qquad a^2 - 25b^2.$$

To factor a difference of squares such as $x^2 - 9$, think about the formula we used in Chapter 9:

$$(A + B)(A - B) = A^2 - B^2.$$

Equations are reversible, so we also know that

$$\boxed{A^2 - B^2 = (A + B)(A - B).}$$

Thus,

$$x^2 - 9 = (x + 3)(x - 3).$$

To use this formula, we must be able to recognize when it applies. A **difference of squares** is an expression like the following:

$$A^2 - B^2.$$

How can we recognize such expressions? Look at $A^2 - B^2$. In order for a binomial to be a difference of squares:

a) There must be two expressions, both squares, such as

$$4x^2, \quad 9, \quad 25t^4, \quad 1, \quad x^6, \quad 49y^8.$$

When the coefficient is a perfect square and the power(s) of the variable(s) is (are) even, then the expression is a perfect square.

b) The terms must have different signs.

▶ **EXAMPLE 10**   Is $9x^2 - 64$ a difference of squares?

a) The first expression is a square: $9x^2 = (3x)^2$.
   The second expression is a square: $64 = 8^2$.

b) The terms have different signs.

Thus we have a difference of squares, $(3x)^2 - 8^2$. ◀

Factor.

15. $p^4 + 18p^2 + 81$

16. $4z^5 - 20z^4 + 25z^3$

17. $9a^2 + 30ab + 25b^2$

Determine whether each is a difference of squares. Write "yes" or "no."

18. $x^2 - 25$

19. $t^2 - 24$

20. $y^2 + 36$

21. $4x^2 - 15$

22. $16x^4 - 49$

23. $9w^6 - 1$

24. $-49 + 25t^2$

▶ **EXAMPLE 11**   Is $25 - t^3$ a difference of squares?

a) The expression t^3 is not a square.

The expression is not a difference of squares.   ◀

▶ **EXAMPLE 12**   Is $-4x^2 + 16$ a difference of squares?

a) The expressions $4x^2$ and 16 are squares: $4x^2 = (2x)^2$ and $16 = 4^2$.

b) The terms have different signs.

Thus we have a difference of squares. We can also see this by rewriting in the equivalent form: $16 - 4x^2$.   ◀

DO EXERCISES 18–24.

d   **Factoring Differences of Squares**

To factor a difference of squares, we use the following equation:

$$A^2 - B^2 = (A + B)(A - B).$$

We consider 3 to be a square root of 9 because $3^2 = 9$. Similarly, A is a square root of A^2. To factor a difference of squares $A^2 - B^2$, we find A and B, which are square roots of the expressions A^2 and B^2. We then use A and B to form two factors. One is the sum $A + B$, and the other is the difference $A - B$.

▶ **EXAMPLE 13**   Factor: $x^2 - 4$.

$$x^2 - 4 = x^2 - 2^2 = (x + 2)(x - 2)$$
$$A^2 - B^2 = (A + B)(A - B)$$
    ◀

▶ **EXAMPLE 14**   Factor: $9 - 16t^4$.

$$9 - 16t^4 = 3^2 - (4t^2)^2 = (3 + 4t^2)(3 - 4t^2)$$
$$A^2 - B^2 = (A + B)(A - B)$$
    ◀

▶ **EXAMPLE 15**   Factor: $m^2 - 4p^2$.

$$m^2 - 4p^2 = m^2 - (2p)^2 = (m + 2p)(m - 2p)$$
    ◀

▶ **EXAMPLE 16** Factor: $18x^2 - 50x^6$.

Always look first for a factor common to all terms. This time there is one, $2x^2$.

$$18x^2 - 50x^6 = 2x^2(9 - 25x^4)$$
$$= 2x^2[3^2 - (5x^2)^2]$$
$$= 2x^2(3 - 5x^2)(3 + 5x^2) \qquad ◀$$

▶ **EXAMPLE 17** Factor: $49x^4 - 9x^6$.

$$49x^4 - 9x^6 = x^4(49 - 9x^2) = x^4(7 + 3x)(7 - 3x) \qquad ◀$$

DO EXERCISES 25–29.

> CAUTION! Note carefully in these examples that a difference of squares is *not* the square of the difference; that is,
> $$A^2 - B^2 \neq (A - B)^2 = A^2 - 2AB + B^2.$$
> For example,
> $$(45 - 5)^2 = 40^2 = 1600,$$
> but
> $$45^2 - 5^2 = 2025 - 25 = 2000.$$

Factoring Completely

If a factor with more than one term can still be factored, you should do so. When no factor can be factored further, you have **factored completely.** Always factor completely whenever told to factor.

▶ **EXAMPLE 18** Factor: $p^4 - 16$.

$$p^4 - 16 = (p^2)^2 - 4^2$$
$$= (p^2 + 4)(p^2 - 4) \qquad \text{Factoring a difference of squares}$$
$$= (p^2 + 4)(p + 2)(p - 2) \qquad \text{Factoring further. The factor } x^2 - 4 \text{ is a difference of squares.} \qquad ◀$$

The polynomial $p^2 + 4$ cannot be factored further into polynomials with real coefficients.

▶ **EXAMPLE 19** Factor: $y^4 - 16x^{12}$.

$$y^4 - 16x^{12} = (y^2 + 4x^6)(y^2 - 4x^6) \qquad \text{Factoring a difference of squares}$$
$$= (y^2 + 4x^6)(y + 2x^3)(y - 2x^3) \qquad \text{Factoring further. The factor } y^2 - 4x^6 \text{ is a difference of squares.} \qquad ◀$$

Factor.

25. $x^2 - 9$

26. $64 - 4t^2$

27. $a^2 - 25b^2$

28. $64x^4 - 25x^6$

29. $5 - 20t^6$
  [*Hint:* $1 = 1^2$, $t^6 = (t^3)^2$.]

ANSWERS ON PAGE A-8

Factor completely.

30. $81x^4 - 1$

Factoring Hints

1. **Always look first for a common factor. If there is one, factor it out!**

2. **Always factor completely.**

3. **Check by multiplying.**

CAUTION!   If the greatest common factor has been removed, then you cannot factor a sum of squares further. In particular,

$$(A + B)^2 \neq A^2 + B^2.$$

Consider $25x^2 + 100$. This is a case in which we have a sum of squares, but there is a common factor, 25. Factoring, we get $25(x^2 + 4)$. Now $x^2 + 4$ cannot be factored further.

DO EXERCISES 30 AND 31.

31. $49p^4 - 25q^6$

NAME   SECTION   DATE

EXERCISE SET 10.5

a Determine whether each of the following is a trinomial square.

1. $x^2 - 14x + 49$ **2.** $x^2 - 16x + 64$ **3.** $x^2 + 16x - 64$

4. $x^2 - 14x - 49$ **5.** $x^2 - 3x + 9$ **6.** $x^2 + 2x + 4$

7. $9x^2 - 36x + 24$ **8.** $36x^2 - 24x + 16$

b Factor completely. Remember to look first for a common factor and to check by multiplying.

9. $x^2 - 14x + 49$ **10.** $x^2 - 16x + 64$ **11.** $x^2 + 16x + 64$

12. $x^2 + 14x + 49$ **13.** $x^2 - 2x + 1$ **14.** $x^2 + 2x + 1$

15. $4 + 4x + x^2$ **16.** $4 + x^2 - 4x$ **17.** $y^4 + 6y^2 + 9$

18. $64 - 16p^2 + p^4$ **19.** $49 - 56y + 16y^2$ **20.** $120m + 75 + 48m^2$

21. $2x^2 - 4x + 2$ **22.** $2x^2 - 40x + 200$ **23.** $x^3 - 18x^2 + 81x$

24. $x^3 + 24x^2 + 144x$ **25.** $20x^2 + 100x + 125$ **26.** $12x^2 + 36x + 27$

ANSWERS

1. _____
2. _____
3. _____
4. _____
5. _____
6. _____
7. _____
8. _____
9. _____
10. _____
11. _____
12. _____
13. _____
14. _____
15. _____
16. _____
17. _____
18. _____
19. _____
20. _____
21. _____
22. _____
23. _____
24. _____
25. _____
26. _____

ANSWERS

27. _____

28. _____

29. _____

30. _____

31. _____

32. _____

33. _____

34. _____

35. _____

36. _____

37. _____

38. _____

39. _____

40. _____

41. _____

42. _____

43. _____

44. _____

45. _____

46. _____

47. _____

48. _____

27. $49 - 42x + 9x^2$ **28.** $64 - 112x + 49x^2$ **29.** $5y^4 + 10y^2 + 5$

30. $a^4 + 14a^2 + 49$ **31.** $1 + 4x^4 + 4x^2$ **32.** $1 - 2a^5 + a^{10}$

33. $4p^2 + 12pq + 9q^2$ **34.** $25m^2 + 20mn + 4n^2$ **35.** $a^2 - 14ab + 49b^2$

36. $x^2 - 6xy + 9y^2$ **37.** $64m^2 + 16mn + n^2$ **38.** $81p^2 - 18pq + q^2$

39. $16s^2 - 40st + 25t^2$ **40.** $36a^2 + 96ab + 64b^2$

c Determine whether each of the following is a difference of squares.

41. $x^2 - 4$ **42.** $x^2 - 36$ **43.** $x^2 + 36$ **44.** $x^2 + 4$

45. $x^2 - 35$ **46.** $x^2 - 50y^2$ **47.** $16x^2 - 25y^2$ **48.** $-1 + 36x^2$

d Factor completely. Remember to look first for a common factor.

49. $y^2 - 4$ **50.** $x^2 - 36$ **51.** $p^2 - 9$ **52.** $q^2 - 1$

53. $-49 + t^2$ **54.** $-64 + m^2$ **55.** $a^2 - b^2$ **56.** $p^2 - q^2$

57. $25t^2 - m^2$ **58.** $w^2 - 49z^2$ **59.** $100 - k^2$ **60.** $81 - w^2$

61. $16a^2 - 9$ **62.** $25x^2 - 4$ **63.** $4x^2 - 25y^2$ **64.** $9a^2 - 16b^2$

65. $8x^2 - 98$ **66.** $24x^2 - 54$ **67.** $36x - 49x^3$ **68.** $16x - 81x^3$

69. $49a^4 - 81$ **70.** $25a^4 - 9$ **71.** $x^4 - 1$ **72.** $x^4 - 16$

73. $4x^4 - 64$ **74.** $5x^4 - 80$ **75.** $1 - y^8$ **76.** $x^8 - 1$

49. 50. 51. 52. 53. 54. 55. 56. 57. 58. 59. 60. 61. 62. 63. 64. 65. 66. 67. 68. 69. 70. 71. 72. 73. 74. 75. 76.

77. $x^{12} - 16$ **78.** $x^8 - 81$ **79.** $y^2 - \dfrac{1}{16}$ **80.** $x^2 - \dfrac{1}{25}$

81. $25 - \dfrac{1}{49}x^2$ **82.** $4 - \dfrac{1}{9}y^2$ **83.** $16m^4 - t^4$ **84.** $1 - a^4 b^4$

SKILL MAINTENANCE

Divide.

85. $(-110) \div 10$ **86.** $-1000 \div (-2.5)$ **87.** $\left(-\dfrac{2}{3}\right) \div \dfrac{4}{5}$ **88.** $8.1 \div (-9)$

SYNTHESIS

Factor completely, if possible.

89. $49x^2 - 216$ **90.** $27x^3 - 13x$ **91.** $x^2 + 22x + 121$

92. $x^2 - 5x + 25$ **93.** $18x^3 + 12x^2 + 2x$ **94.** $162x^2 - 82$

95. $x^8 - 2^8$ **96.** $4x^4 - 4x^2$ **97.** $3x^5 - 12x^3$

98. $3x^2 - \dfrac{1}{3}$ **99.** $18x^3 - \dfrac{8}{25}x$ **100.** $x^2 - 2.25$

101. $0.49p - p^3$ **102.** $3.24x^2 - 0.81$ **103.** $0.64x^2 - 1.21$

104. $1.28x^2 - 2$ **105.** $(x + 3)^2 - 9$ **106.** $(y - 5)^2 - 36q^2$

107. $x^2 - \left(\dfrac{1}{x}\right)^2$ **108.** $a^{2n} - 49b^{2n}$ **109.** $81 - b^{4k}$

110. $9x^{18} + 48x^9 + 64$ **111.** $9b^{2n} + 12b^n + 4$ **112.** $(x + 7)^2 - 4x - 24$

113. $(y + 3)^2 + 2(y + 3) + 1$ **114.** $49(x + 1)^2 - 42(x + 1) + 9$

Find c so that the polynomial will be the square of a binomial.

115. $cy^2 + 6y + 1$ **116.** $cy^2 - 24y + 9$

10.6 Factoring: A General Strategy

a We now combine all of our factoring techniques and consider a general strategy for factoring polynomials. Here we will encounter polynomials of all the types we have considered, in random order, so you will have to determine which method to use.

> To factor a polynomial:
>
> a) **Always look first for a common factor. If there is one, factor out the largest common factor.**
>
> b) **Then look at the number of terms.**
>
> *Two terms:* Determine whether you have a difference of squares. Do not try to factor a sum of squares: $A^2 + B^2$.
>
> *Three terms:* Determine whether the trinomial is a square. If so, you know how to factor. If not, try trial and error, using the standard method or grouping.
>
> *Four terms:* Try factoring by grouping.
>
> c) **Always *factor completely*. If a factor with more than one term can still be factored, you should factor it. When no factor can be factored further, you have finished.**

▶ **EXAMPLE 1** Factor: $5t^4 - 80$.

a) We look for a common factor:

$$5t^4 - 80 = 5(t^4 - 16).$$

b) The factor $t^4 - 16$ has only two terms. It is a difference of squares: $(t^2)^2 - 4^2$. We factor it, being careful to include the common factor:

$$5(t^2 + 4)(t^2 - 4).$$

We see that one of the factors is again a difference of squares. We factor it:

$$5(t^2 + 4)(t - 2)(t + 2).$$

↑

This is a sum of squares. It cannot be factored!

c) We have factored completely because no factor with more than one term can be factored further. ◀

▶ **EXAMPLE 2** Factor: $2x^3 + 10x^2 + x + 5$.

a) We look for a common factor. There isn't one.

b) There are four terms. We try factoring by grouping:

$$2x^3 + 10x^2 + x + 5$$
$$= (2x^3 + 10x^2) + (x + 5) \qquad \text{Separating into two binomials}$$
$$= 2x^2(x + 5) + 1(x + 5) \qquad \text{Factoring each binomial}$$
$$= (2x^2 + 1)(x + 5). \qquad \text{Factoring out the common factor, } x + 5$$

c) No factor with more than one term can be factored further, so we have factored completely. ◀

OBJECTIVE

After finishing Section 10.6, you should be able to:

a Factor polynomials completely using any of the methods considered in this chapter.

FOR EXTRA HELP

Tape 22A

Factor.

1. $3m^4 - 3$

2. $x^6 + 8x^3 + 16$

3. $2x^4 + 8x^3 + 6x^2$

4. $3x^3 + 12x^2 - 2x - 8$

5. $8x^3 - 200x$

▶ **EXAMPLE 3**   Factor: $x^5 - 2x^4 - 35x^3$.

a) We look first for a common factor. This time there is one, x^3:

$$x^5 - 2x^4 - 35x^3 = x^3(x^2 - 2x - 35).$$

b) The factor $x^2 - 2x - 35$ has three terms, but it is not a trinomial square. We factor it using trial and error:

$$x^5 - 2x^4 - 35x^3 = x^3(x^2 - 2x - 35) = x^3(x - 7)(x + 5).$$

> Don't forget to include the common factor in the final answer!

We have studied two methods for such factoring: the standard trial-and-error method and grouping, which is also trial and error. Use the one that you prefer or follow the direction of your instructor.

c) No factor with more than one term can be factored further, so we have factored completely.   ◀

▶ **EXAMPLE 4**   Factor: $x^4 - 10x^2 + 25$.

a) We look first for a common factor. There isn't one.

b) There are three terms. We see that this polynomial is a trinomial square. We factor it:

$$x^4 - 10x^2 + 25 = (x^2)^2 - 2 \cdot x^2 \cdot 5 + 5^2 = (x^2 - 5)^2.$$

c) No factor with more than one term can be factored further, so we have factored completely.   ◀

DO EXERCISES 1–5.

▶ **EXAMPLE 5**   Factor: $6x^2y^4 - 21x^3y^5 + 3x^2y^6$.

a) We look first for a common factor:

$$6x^2y^4 - 21x^3y^5 + 3x^2y^6 = 3x^2y^4(2 - 7xy + y^2).$$

b) There are three terms in $2 - 7xy + y^2$. We determine whether the trinomial is a square. Since only y^2 is a square, we do not have a trinomial square. Can the trinomial be factored by trial and error? A key to the answer is that x is only in the term $-7xy$. The polynomial might be in a form like $(1 - y)(2 + y)$, but there would be no x in the middle term. Thus, $2 - 7xy + y^2$ cannot be factored.

c) Have we factored completely? Yes, because no factor with more than one term can be factored further.   ◀

▶ **EXAMPLE 6**   Factor: $(p + q)(x + 2) + (p + q)(x + y)$.

a) We look for a common factor:

$$(p + q)(x + 2) + (p + q)(x + y) = (p + q)[(x + 2) + (x + y)]$$
$$= (p + q)(2x + y + 2).$$

b) There are three terms in $2x + y + 2$, but this trinomial cannot be factored further.

c) No factor with more than one term can be factored further, so we have factored completely.   ◀

▶ **EXAMPLE 7**   Factor: $px + py + qx + qy$.

a) We look first for a common factor. There isn't one.

b) There are four terms. We try factoring by grouping:

$$px + py + qx + qy = p(x + y) + q(x + y)$$
$$= (p + q)(x + y).$$

c) Have we factored completely? Since no factor with more than one term can be factored further, we have factored completely.   ◀

▶ **EXAMPLE 8**   Factor: $25x^2 + 20xy + 4y^2$.

a) We look first for a common factor. There isn't one.

b) There are three terms. We determine whether the trinomial is a square. The first term and the last term are squares:

$$25x^2 = (5x)^2 \quad \text{and} \quad 4y^2 = (2y)^2.$$

Since twice the product of $5x$ and $2y$ is the other term,

$$2 \cdot 5x \cdot 2y = 20xy,$$

the trinomial is a perfect square.

　　We factor by writing the square roots of the square terms and the sign of the middle term:

$$25x^2 + 20xy + 4y^2 = (5x + 2y)^2.$$

We can check by squaring $5x + 2y$.

c) No factor with more than one term can be factored further, so we have factored completely.   ◀

Factor.

6. $x^4y^2 + 2x^3y + 3x^2y$

7. $10p^6q^2 + 4p^5q^3 + 2p^4q^4$

8. $(a - b)(x + 5) + (a - b)(x + y^2)$

9. $ax^2 + ay + bx^2 + by$

10. $x^4 + 2x^2y^2 + y^4$

11. $x^2y^2 + 5xy + 4$

12. $p^4 - 81q^4$

▶ **EXAMPLE 9**   Factor: $p^2q^2 + 7pq + 12$.

a) We look first for a common factor. There isn't one.

b) There are three terms. We determine whether the trinomial is a square. The first term is a square, but neither of the other terms is a square, so we do not have a trinomial square. We use the trial-and-error or grouping method, thinking of the product pq as a single variable. We consider this possibility for factorization:

$$(pq + \_\_)(pq + \_\_).$$

We factor the last term, 12. All the signs are positive, so we consider only positive factors. Possibilities are 1, 12 and 2, 6 and 3, 4. The pair 3, 4 gives a sum of 7 for the coefficient of the middle term. Thus,

$$p^2q^2 + 7pq + 12 = (pq + 3)(pq + 4).$$

c) No factor with more than one term can be factored further, so we have factored completely.   ◀

▶ **EXAMPLE 10**   Factor: $8x^4 - 20x^2y - 12y^2$.

a) We look first for a common factor:

$$8x^4 - 20x^2y - 12y^2 = 4(2x^4 - 5x^2y - 3y^2).$$

b) There are three terms in $2x^4 - 5x^2y - 3y^2$. We determine whether the trinomial is a square. Since none of the terms is a square, we do not have a trinomial square. We use trial and error to factor $2x^4$. Possibilities are $2x^2$, x^2 and $2x$, x^3 and others. We also factor the last term, $-3y^2$. Possibilities are $3y$, $-y$ and $-3y$, y and others. We look for factors such that the sum of their products is the middle term. We try some possibilities:

$$(2x - y)(x^3 + 3y) = 2x^4 + 6xy - x^3y - 3y^2,$$
$$(2x^2 - y)(x^2 + 3y) = 2x^4 + 5x^2y - 3y^2,$$
$$(2x^2 + y)(x^2 - 3y) = 2x^4 - 5x^2y - 3y^2.$$

c) No factor with more than one term can be factored further, so we have factored completely. The factorization, including the common factor, is

$$4(2x^2 + y)(x^2 - 3y).$$ ◀

▶ **EXAMPLE 11**   Factor: $a^4 - 16b^4$.

a) We look first for a common factor. There isn't one.

b) There are two terms. Since $a^4 = (a^2)^2$ and $16b^4 = (4b^2)^2$, we see that we do have a difference of squares. Thus,

$$a^4 - 16b^4 = (a^2 + 4b^2)(a^2 - 4b^2).$$

c) The last factor can be factored further. It is also a difference of squares. Thus,

$$a^4 - 16b^4 = (a^2 + 4b^2)(a + 2b)(a - 2b).$$ ◀

DO EXERCISES 6–12.

EXERCISE SET 10.6

a Factor completely.

1. $2x^2 - 128$

2. $3t^2 - 27$

3. $a^2 + 25 - 10a$

4. $y^2 + 49 + 14y$

5. $2x^2 - 11x + 12$

6. $8y^2 - 18y - 5$

7. $x^3 + 24x^2 + 144x$

8. $x^3 - 18x^2 + 81x$

9. $x^3 + 3x^2 - 4x - 12$

10. $x^3 - 5x^2 - 25x + 125$

11. $24x^2 - 54$

12. $8x^2 - 98$

13. $20x^3 - 4x^2 - 72x$

14. $9x^3 + 12x^2 - 45x$

15. $x^2 + 4$

16. $t^2 + 25$

17. $x^4 + 7x^2 - 3x^3 - 21x$

18. $m^4 + 8m^3 + 8m^2 + 64m$

19. $x^5 - 14x^4 + 49x^3$

20. $2x^6 + 8x^5 + 8x^4$

21. $20 - 6x - 2x^2$

22. $45 - 3x - 6x^2$

ANSWERS

1. _____

2. _____

3. _____

4. _____

5. _____

6. _____

7. _____

8. _____

9. _____

10. _____

11. _____

12. _____

13. _____

14. _____

15. _____

16. _____

17. _____

18. _____

19. _____

20. _____

21. _____

22. _____

ANSWERS

23. _____

24. _____

25. _____

26. _____

27. _____

28. _____

29. _____

30. _____

31. _____

32. _____

33. _____

34. _____

35. _____

36. _____

37. _____

38. _____

39. _____

40. _____

41. _____

42. _____

43. _____

44. _____

23. $x^2 + 3x + 1$

24. $x^2 + 5x + 2$

25. $4x^4 - 64$

26. $5x^5 - 80x$

27. $1 - y^8$

28. $t^8 - 1$

29. $x^5 - 4x^4 + 3x^3$

30. $x^6 - 2x^5 + 7x^4$

31. $36a^2 - 15a + \dfrac{25}{16}$

32. $\dfrac{1}{81}x^6 - \dfrac{8}{27}x^3 + \dfrac{16}{9}$

33. $12n^2 + 24n^3$

34. $ax^2 + ay^2$

35. $9x^2y^2 - 36xy$

36. $x^2y - xy^2$

37. $2\pi rh + 2\pi r^2$

38. $10p^4q^4 + 35p^3q^3 + 10p^2q^2$

39. $(a + b)(x - 3) + (a + b)(x + 4)$

40. $5c(a^3 + b) - (a^3 + b)$

41. $(x - 1)(x + 1) - y(x + 1)$

42. $x^2 + x + xy + y$

43. $n^2 + 2n + np + 2p$

44. $a^2 - 3a + ay - 3y$

45. $2x^2 - 4x + xz - 2z$

46. $6y^2 - 3y + 2py - p$

47. $x^2 + y^2 - 2xy$

48. $4b^2 + a^2 - 4ab$

49. $9c^2 + 6cd + d^2$

50. $16x^2 + 24xy + 9y^2$

51. $49m^4 - 112m^2n + 64n^2$

52. $4x^2y^2 + 12xyz + 9z^2$

53. $y^4 + 10y^2z^2 + 25z^4$

54. $0.01x^4 - 0.1x^2y^2 + 0.25y^4$

55. $\dfrac{1}{4}a^2 + \dfrac{1}{3}ab + \dfrac{1}{9}b^2$

56. $4p^2q + pq^2 + 4p^3$

57. $a^2 - ab - 2b^2$

58. $3b^2 - 17ab - 6a^2$

59. $2mn - 360n^2 + m^2$

60. $15 + x^2y^2 + 8xy$

61. $m^2n^2 - 4mn - 32$

62. $p^2q^2 + 7pq + 6$

63. $a^5b^2 + 3a^4b - 10a^3$

64. $m^2n^6 + 4mn^5 - 32n^4$

65. $a^5 + 4a^4b - 5a^3b^2$

66. $2s^6t^2 + 10s^3t^3 + 12t^4$

ANSWERS

45. _____

46. _____

47. _____

48. _____

49. _____

50. _____

51. _____

52. _____

53. _____

54. _____

55. _____

56. _____

57. _____

58. _____

59. _____

60. _____

61. _____

62. _____

63. _____

64. _____

65. _____

66. _____

67. $x^6 + x^3y - 2y^2$

68. $a^4 + a^2bc - 2b^2c^2$

69. $x^2 - y^2$

70. $p^2q^2 - r^2$

71. $7p^4 - 7q^4$

72. $a^4b^4 - 16$

73. $81a^4 - b^4$

74. $1 - 16x^{12}y^{12}$

75. $w^3 - 7w^2 - 4w + 28$

76. $y^3 + 8y^2 - y - 8$

SKILL MAINTENANCE

77. Divide: $\dfrac{7}{5} \div \left(-\dfrac{11}{10} \right)$.

78. Multiply: $(5x - t)^2$.

79. Solve $A = aX + bX - 7$ for X.

80. Solve: $4(x - 9) - 2(x + 7) < 14$.

SYNTHESIS

Factor completely.

81. $a^4 - 2a^2 + 1$ **82.** $x^4 + 9$ **83.** $12.25x^2 - 7x + 1$

84. $\dfrac{1}{5}x^2 - x + \dfrac{4}{5}$ **85.** $5x^2 + 13x + 7.2$ **86.** $x^3 - (x - 3x^2) - 3$

87. $18 + y^3 - 9y - 2y^2$ **88.** $-(x^4 - 7x^2 - 18)$ **89.** $a^3 + 4a^2 + a + 4$

90. $x^3 + x^2 - (4x + 4)$ **91.** $x^4 - 7x^2 - 18$ **92.** $3x^4 - 15x^2 + 12$

93. $x^3 - x^2 - 4x + 4$ **94.** $y^2(y + 1) - 4y(y + 1) - 21(y + 1)$

95. $y^2(y - 1) - 2y(y - 1) + (y - 1)$ **96.** $6(x - 1)^2 + 7y(x - 1) - 3y^2$

97. $(y + 4)^2 + 2x(y + 4) + x^2$ **98.** $2(a + 3)^2 - (a + 3)(b - 2) - (b - 2)^2$

99. Factor $x^{2k} - 2^{2k}$ when $k = 4$.   **100.** Factor: $a^4 - 81$.

19. The sum of the squares of two consecutive odd positive integers is 74. Find the integers.

20. The sum of the squares of two consecutive odd positive integers is 130. Find the integers.

Use $n^2 - n = N$ for Exercises 21–24.

21. A women's volleyball league has 23 teams. What is the total number of games to be played?

22. A chess league has 14 teams. What is the total number of games to be played?

23. A woman's slow-pitch softball league plays a total of 132 games. How many teams are in the league?

24. The basketball league plays a total of 90 games. How many teams are in the league?

The number of possible handshakes within a group of n people is given by $N = \frac{1}{2}(n^2 - n)$.

25. There are 40 people at a meeting. How many handshakes are possible?

26. There are 100 people at a party. How many handshakes are possible?

27. Everyone shook hands at a party. There were 190 handshakes in all. How many were at the party?

28. Everyone shook hands at a meeting. There were 300 handshakes in all. How many were at the meeting?

ANSWERS

19. _____

20. _____

21. _____

22. _____

23. _____

24. _____

25. _____

26. _____

27. _____

28. _____

ANSWERS

29. _____

30. _____

31. _____

32. a) _____

b) _____

33. _____

34. _____

35. _____

36. _____

37. _____

29. The length of one leg of a right triangle is 8 ft. The length of the hypotenuse is 2 ft longer than the other leg. Find the length of the hypotenuse and the other leg.

30. The length of one leg of a right triangle is 24 ft. The length of the other leg is 16 ft shorter than the hypotenuse. Find the length of the hypotenuse and the other leg.

SYNTHESIS

31. A cement walk of constant width is built around a 20-ft by 40-ft rectangular pool. The total area of the pool and walk is 1500 ft². Find the width of the walk.

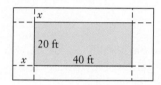

32. A model rocket is launched with an initial velocity of 180 ft/sec. Its height h, in feet, after t seconds is given by the formula $h = 180t - 16t^2$.

   a) After how many seconds will the rocket first reach a height of 464 ft?

   b) After how many seconds will it be at that height again?

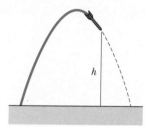

33. The one's digit of a number less than 100 is four greater than the ten's digit. The sum of the number and the product of the digits is 58. Find the number.

35. A rectangular piece of cardboard is twice as long as it is wide. A 4-cm square is cut out of each corner, and the sides are turned up to make a box with an open top. The volume of the box is 616 cm³. Find the original dimensions of the cardboard.

34. The total surface area of a closed box is 350 m². The box is 9 m high and has a square base and lid. Find the length of the side of the base.

36. An open rectangular gutter is made by turning up the sides of a piece of metal 20 in. wide. The area of the cross-section of the gutter is 50 in². Find the depth of the gutter.

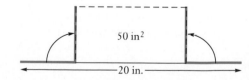

37. The length of each side of a square is increased by 5 cm to form a new square. The area of the new square is $2\frac{1}{4}$ times the area of the original square. Find the area of each square.

SUMMARY AND REVIEW: CHAPTER 10

IMPORTANT PROPERTIES AND FORMULAS

Factoring Formulas: $A^2 - B^2 = (A + B)(A - B),$
$A^2 + 2AB + B^2 = (A + B)^2,$
$A^2 - 2AB + B^2 = (A - B)^2$

REVIEW EXERCISES

The review sections and objectives to be tested in addition to the material in this chapter are [7.6a, c], [8.6a], [8.7e], and [9.6d].

Find three factorizations of the monomial.

1. $-10x^2$

2. $36x^5$

Factor completely.

3. $5 - 20x^6$

4. $x^2 - 3x$

5. $9x^2 - 4$

6. $x^2 + 4x - 12$

7. $x^2 + 14x + 49$

8. $6x^3 + 12x^2 + 3x$

9. $x^3 + x^2 + 3x + 3$

10. $6x^2 - 5x + 1$

11. $x^4 - 81$

12. $9x^3 + 12x^2 - 45x$

13. $2x^2 - 50$

14. $x^4 + 4x^3 - 2x - 8$

15. $16x^4 - 1$

16. $8x^6 - 32x^5 + 4x^4$

17. $75 + 12x^2 + 60x$

18. $x^2 + 9$

19. $x^3 - x^2 - 30x$

20. $4x^2 - 25$

21. $9x^2 + 25 - 30x$

22. $6x^2 - 28x - 48$

23. $x^2 - 6x + 9$

24. $2x^2 - 7x - 4$

25. $18x^2 - 12x + 2$

26. $3x^2 - 27$

27. $15 - 8x + x^2$

28. $25x^2 - 20x + 4$

Solve.

29. $(x - 1)(x + 3) = 0$

30. $x^2 + 2x - 35 = 0$

31. $x^2 + x - 12 = 0$

32. $3x^2 + 2 = 5x$

33. $2x^2 + 5x = 12$

34. $16 = x(x - 6)$

35. The square of a number is six more than the number. Find all such numbers.

36. The product of two consecutive even integers is 288. Find the integers.

37. The product of two consecutive odd integers is 323. Find the integers.

38. Twice the square of a number is ten more than the number. Find all such numbers.

Factor.

39. $49b^{10} + 4a^8 - 28a^4b^5$

40. $x^2y^2 + xy - 12$

41. $12a^2 + 84ab + 147b^2$

42. $m^2 + 5m + mt + 5t$

43. $32x^4 - 128y^4z^4$

SKILL MAINTENANCE

44. Divide: $-\dfrac{12}{25} \div \left(-\dfrac{21}{10}\right)$.

45. Solve: $20 - (3x + 2) \geq 2(x + 5) + x$.

46. Solve $A = a + 2b$ for b.

47. Multiply: $(2a + 3)^2$.

48. Multiply: $(2a - 3)(2a + 3)$.

49. Multiply: $(2a - 3)(5a + 7)$.

SYNTHESIS

Solve.

50. The pages of a book measure 15 cm by 20 cm. Margins of equal width surround the printing on each page and constitute one half of the area of the page. Find the width of the margins.

51. The cube of a number is the same as twice the square of the number. Find all such numbers.

52. The length of a rectangle is two times its width. When the length is increased by 20 and the width decreased by 1, the area is 160. Find the original length and width.

Solve.

53. $x^2 + 25 = 0$

54. $(x - 2)(x + 3)(2x - 5) = 0$

55. ▦ $(0.00005x + 0.1)(0.0097x + 0.5) = 0$

56. For each equation on the left, find an equivalent equation on the right.

a) $3x^2 - 4x + 8 = 0$

b) $(x - 6)(x + 3) = 0$

c) $x^2 + 2x + 9 = 0$

d) $(2x - 5)(x + 4) = 0$

e) $5x^2 - 5 = 0$

f) $x^2 + 10x - 2 = 0$

g) $4x^2 + 8x + 36 = 0$

h) $(2x + 8)(2x - 5) = 0$

i) $9x^2 - 12x + 24 = 0$

j) $(x + 1)(5x - 5) = 0$

k) $x^2 - 3x - 18 = 0$

l) $2x^2 + 20x - 4 = 0$

❖ THINKING IT THROUGH

1. Compare the type of equations we are able to solve after studying this chapter with those previously studied.

2. What is one procedure you can always use to check the result of factoring a polynomial?

3. Suppose we know that $(x - 5)(x + 2)$ would be a correct factorization of a trinomial $x^2 + bx + c$ except the sign of the middle term is incorrect. What would a correct factorization be?

Explain the error, if any, in each of the following when the direction is "Factor completely."

4. $x^2 + 9 = (x + 3)^2$

5. $x^2 - 6x + 8 = (x + 4)(x - 2)$

6. $p^2 - 9 = (p - 3)^2$

7. $a^2 + 6a - 9 = (a - 3)^2$

8. $16a^4 - 81 = (4a^2 - 9)(4a^2 + 9)$

9. $16m^2 - 80m + 100 = (4m - 10)^2$

NAME   SECTION   DATE

TEST: CHAPTER 10

1. Find three factorizations of $4x^3$.

1. _____

2. _____

Factor completely.

3. _____

2. $x^2 - 7x + 10$ **3.** $x^2 + 25 - 10x$ **4.** $6y^2 - 8y^3 + 4y^4$

4. _____

5. _____

5. $x^3 + x^2 + 2x + 2$ **6.** $x^2 - 5x$ **7.** $x^3 + 2x^2 - 3x$

6. _____

7. _____

8. $28x - 48 + 10x^2$ **9.** $4x^2 - 9$ **10.** $x^2 - x - 12$

8. _____

9. _____

10. _____

11. $6m^3 + 9m^2 + 3m$ **12.** $3w^2 - 75$ **13.** $60x + 45x^2 + 20$

11. _____

12. _____

13. _____

14. $3x^4 - 48$ **15.** $49x^2 - 84x + 36$ **16.** $5x^2 - 26x + 5$

14. _____

15. _____

16. _____

ANSWERS

17. _____

18. _____

19. _____

20. _____

21. _____

22. _____

23. _____

24. _____

25. _____

26. _____

27. _____

28. _____

29. _____

30. _____

31. _____

32. _____

33. _____

34. _____

17. $x^4 + 2x^3 - 3x - 6$

18. $80 - 5x^4$

19. $4x^2 - 4x - 15$

20. $6t^3 + 9t^2 - 15t$

Solve.

21. $x^2 - x - 20 = 0$

22. $2x^2 + 7x = 15$

23. $x(x - 3) = 28$

24. The square of a number is 24 more than five times the number. Find all such numbers.

25. The length of a rectangle is 6 m more than the width. The area of the rectangle is 40 m². Find the length and the width.

26. Factor: $3m^2 - 9mn - 30n^2$.

SKILL MAINTENANCE

27. Divide: $\dfrac{5}{8} \div \left(-\dfrac{11}{16}\right)$.

28. Solve: $10(x - 3) < 4(x + 2)$.

29. Solve $I = PRT$ for T.

30. Multiply: $(5x^2 - 7)^2$.

SYNTHESIS

31. The length of a rectangle is five times its width. When the length is decreased by 3 and the width is increased by 2, the area of the new rectangle is 60. Find the original length and width.

32. Factor: $(a + 3)^2 - 2(a + 3) - 35$.

33. If $x^2 - 4 = (14)(18)$, then one possibility for x is which of the following?

a) 12   b) 14
c) 16   d) 18

34. If $x + y = 4$ and $x - y = 6$, then $x^2 - y^2 = ?$

a) 2   b) 10
c) 34   d) 24

INTRODUCTION In this chapter, we learn to manipulate rational expressions. We learn how to simplify rational expressions as well as to add, subtract, multiply, and divide them. Then we use these skills to solve equations, formulas, and problems.

The review sections to be tested in addition to the material in this chapter are 9.2, 9.4, 10.6, and 10.8. ❖

Rational Expressions and Equations

11

AN APPLICATION

One car travels 20 km/h faster than another. While one of them goes 240 km, the other goes 160 km. How can we use rational equations to find their speeds?

THE MATHEMATICS

Let r = the speed of the slow car. The problem translates to the following equation:

These are rational expressions.

$$\underbrace{\frac{160}{r}} = \underbrace{\frac{240}{r + 20}}.$$

This is a rational equation.

We now have a new type of equation that we must solve in order to solve the problem. This equation has a variable in a denominator and thus differs from the kinds of equations we have solved up to this point.

Motion Formulas:	$d = rt, \quad t = \dfrac{d}{r}, \quad r = \dfrac{d}{t}$
Equation-Solving Skills:	Sections 8.1–8.3
Formula-Solving Skills:	Section 8.6

PRETEST: CHAPTER 11

1. Find the LCM of $x^2 + 5x + 6$ and $x^2 + 6x + 9$.

Perform the indicated operations and simplify.

2. $\dfrac{b-1}{2-b} + \dfrac{b^2 - 3}{b^2 - 4}$

3. $\dfrac{4y - 4}{y^2 - y - 2} - \dfrac{3y - 5}{y^2 - y - 2}$

4. $\dfrac{4}{a+2} + \dfrac{3}{a}$

5. $\dfrac{x}{x+1} - \dfrac{x}{x-1} + \dfrac{2x^2}{x^2 - 1}$

6. $\dfrac{4x+8}{x+1} \cdot \dfrac{x^2 - 2x - 3}{2x^2 - 8}$

7. Simplify: $\dfrac{\dfrac{1}{x} + \dfrac{1}{y}}{\dfrac{1}{x} - \dfrac{1}{y}}$.

Solve.

8. $\dfrac{1}{x+4} = \dfrac{5}{x}$

9. $\dfrac{3}{x-2} + \dfrac{x}{2} = \dfrac{6}{2x - 4}$

10. Solve $R = \dfrac{1}{3}M(a - b)$ for M.

11. It takes 6 hr for a typist to address 200 envelopes. At this rate, how long would it take to address 350 envelopes?

12. One typist can type a report in 6 hr. Another typist can type the same report in 5 hr. How long would it take them to type the same report working together?

13. One car travels 20 mph faster than another. While one car travels 300 mi, the other travels 400 mi. Find their speeds.

11.1 Multiplying and Simplifying Rational Expressions

a Rational Expressions and Replacements

Rational numbers are quotients of integers. Some examples are

$$\frac{2}{3}, \quad \frac{4}{-5}, \quad \frac{-8}{17}, \quad \frac{563}{1}.$$

The following are called **rational expressions** or **fractional expressions.** They are quotients of polynomials:

$$\frac{3}{4}, \quad \frac{5}{x+2}, \quad \frac{t^2 + 3t - 10}{7t^2 - 4}.$$

A rational expression is also a division. For example,

$$\frac{3}{4} \quad \text{means} \quad 3 \div 4 \quad \text{and} \quad \frac{x-8}{x+2} \quad \text{means} \quad (x-8) \div (x+2).$$

Because division is indicated by a rational expression, replacements of a variable by a number that makes the denominator 0 cannot be allowed. Such replacements are *not meaningful.* For example, in

$$\frac{x-8}{x+2},$$

-2 is not a meaningful replacement because it allows the denominator to be 0, and division by 0 is not defined. The number 3 is a meaningful replacement because, as we see below, the denominator is nonzero and the expression can be evaluated:

$$\frac{x-8}{x+2} = \frac{3-8}{3+2} = \frac{-5}{5} = -1.$$

The meaningful replacements are all real numbers except -2; that is, all x such that $x \neq -2$.

▶ **EXAMPLE 1** Find the meaningful replacements in

$$\frac{x+7}{x^2 - 3x - 10}.$$

The meaningful replacements are all those real numbers for which the denominator is not 0. To find them, we first find those that do make the denominator 0. We set the denominator equal to 0 and solve:

$$x^2 - 3x - 10 = 0$$
$$(x-5)(x+2) = 0 \quad \text{Factoring}$$
$$x - 5 = 0 \quad \text{or} \quad x + 2 = 0 \quad \text{Using the principle of zero products}$$
$$x = 5 \quad \text{or} \quad x = -2.$$

The meaningful replacements are all real numbers except 5 and -2; that is, all x such that $x \neq 5$ and $x \neq -2$. ◄

DO EXERCISES 1 AND 2.

OBJECTIVES

After finishing Section 11.1, you should be able to:

a Find the meaningful replacements in a rational expression.

b Multiply a rational expression by 1, using an expression such as A/A.

c Simplify rational expressions by factoring the numerator and the denominator and removing factors of 1.

d Multiply rational expressions and simplify.

FOR EXTRA HELP

Tape 22D

Find the meaningful replacements.

1. $\dfrac{16}{x-3}$

2. $\dfrac{2x-7}{x^2 + 5x - 24}$

ANSWERS ON PAGE A-8

Multiply.

3. $\dfrac{2x+1}{3x-2} \cdot \dfrac{x}{x}$

b　**Multiplying by 1**

For rational expressions, multiplication is done as in arithmetic.

> **To multiply rational expressions, we multiply numerators and multiply denominators.**

For example,

$$\frac{x-2}{3} \cdot \frac{x+2}{x+7} = \frac{(x-2)(x+2)}{3(x+7)}. \qquad \text{Multiplying the numerators and the denominators}$$

Note that we leave the numerator, $(x-2)(x+2)$, and the denominator, $3(x+7)$, in factored form because it is easier to simplify if we do not multiply. In order to learn to simplify, we first need to consider multiplying the rational expression by 1.

Any rational expression with the same numerator and denominator is a symbol for 1:

$$\frac{x+8}{x+8} = 1, \qquad \frac{3x^2-4}{3x^2-4} = 1, \qquad \frac{-1}{-1} = 1.$$

4. $\dfrac{x+1}{x-2} \cdot \dfrac{x+2}{x+2}$

> **Expressions that have the same value for all meaningful replacements are called *equivalent expressions*.**

We can multiply by 1 to obtain an equivalent expression.

▶ **EXAMPLES**　Multiply.

2. $\dfrac{3x+2}{x+1} \cdot \dfrac{2x}{2x} = \dfrac{(3x+2)2x}{(x+1)2x}$　　**3.** $\dfrac{x+2}{x-7} \cdot \dfrac{x+3}{x+3} = \dfrac{(x+2)(x+3)}{(x-7)(x+3)}$

4. $\dfrac{2+x}{2-x} \cdot \dfrac{-1}{-1} = \dfrac{(2+x)(-1)}{(2-x)(-1)}$　　　　◀

DO EXERCISES 3–5.

c　**Simplifying Rational Expressions**

We now consider simplifying rational expressions. What we do is similar to simplifying fractional expressions in arithmetic. But, instead of simplifying an expression like

$$\frac{16}{64},$$

we may simplify an expression like

$$\frac{x^2-16}{x+4}.$$

Just as factoring is important in simplifying in arithmetic, so too is it important in simplifying rational expressions. The factoring we use most is the factoring of polynomials, which we studied in Chapter 10.

To simplify, we can do the reverse of multiplying. We factor the numerator and the denominator and "remove" a factor of 1.

5. $\dfrac{x-8}{x-y} \cdot \dfrac{-1}{-1}$

▶ **EXAMPLE 5**   Simplify by removing a factor of 1: $\dfrac{8x^2}{24x}$.

$$\frac{8x^2}{24x} = \frac{8 \cdot x \cdot x}{3 \cdot 8 \cdot x} \qquad \text{Factoring the numerator and the denominator}$$

$$= \frac{8x}{8x} \cdot \frac{x}{3} \qquad \text{Factoring the rational expression}$$

$$= 1 \cdot \frac{x}{3} \qquad \frac{8x}{8x} = 1$$

$$= \frac{x}{3} \qquad \text{We removed a factor of 1.}$$

◀

DO EXERCISES 6 AND 7.

▶ **EXAMPLES**   Simplify by removing a factor of 1.

6. $\dfrac{5a + 15}{10} = \dfrac{5(a + 3)}{5 \cdot 2} \qquad \text{Factoring the numerator and the denominator}$

$$= \frac{5}{5} \cdot \frac{a + 3}{2} \qquad \text{Factoring the rational expression}$$

$$= 1 \cdot \frac{a + 3}{2}$$

$$= \frac{a + 3}{2} \qquad \text{Removing a factor of 1: } \frac{5}{5} = 1$$

7. $\dfrac{6a + 12}{7a + 14} = \dfrac{6(a + 2)}{7(a + 2)} \qquad \text{Factoring the numerator and the denominator}$

$$= \frac{6}{7} \cdot \frac{a + 2}{a + 2} \qquad \text{Factoring the rational expression}$$

$$= \frac{6}{7} \cdot 1$$

$$= \frac{6}{7} \qquad \text{Removing a factor of 1: } \frac{a + 2}{a + 2} = 1$$

8. $\dfrac{6x^2 + 4x}{2x^2 + 2x} = \dfrac{2x(3x + 2)}{2x(x + 1)} \qquad \text{Factoring the numerator and the denominator}$

$$= \frac{2x}{2x} \cdot \frac{3x + 2}{x + 1} \qquad \text{Factoring the rational expression}$$

$$= 1 \cdot \frac{3x + 2}{x + 1}$$

$$= \frac{3x + 2}{x + 1} \qquad \begin{array}{l}\text{Removing a factor of 1. Note in this step that you}\\ \textit{cannot}\text{ remove the }x\text{'s because they are not factors}\\ \text{of the entire numerator and the entire denominator.}\end{array}$$

9. $\dfrac{x^2 + 3x + 2}{x^2 - 1} = \dfrac{(x + 2)(x + 1)}{(x + 1)(x - 1)}$

$$= \frac{x + 1}{x + 1} \cdot \frac{x + 2}{x - 1}$$

$$= 1 \cdot \frac{x + 2}{x - 1} = \frac{x + 2}{x - 1}$$

◀

Simplify by removing a factor of 1.

6. $\dfrac{5y}{y}$

7. $\dfrac{9x^2}{36x}$

ANSWERS ON PAGE A-8

Simplify by removing a factor of 1.

8. $\dfrac{2x^2 + x}{3x^2 + 2x}$

9. $\dfrac{x^2 - 1}{2x^2 - x - 1}$

10. $\dfrac{7x + 14}{7}$

11. $\dfrac{12y + 24}{48}$

Simplify.

12. $\dfrac{x - 8}{8 - x}$

13. $\dfrac{a - b}{b - a}$

CANCELING. You may have encountered "canceling" when working with rational expressions. With great concern, we mention it as a possibility to speed up your work. Our concern is that canceling be done with care and understanding. Example 9 might have been done faster as follows:

$$\frac{x^2 + 3x + 2}{x^2 - 1} = \frac{(x + 2)(x + 1)}{(x + 1)(x - 1)} \qquad \text{Factoring the numerator and the denominator}$$

$$= \frac{(x + 2)\cancel{(x + 1)}}{\cancel{(x + 1)}(x - 1)} \qquad \begin{array}{l}\text{When a factor of 1 is noted, it is} \\ \text{"canceled" as shown: } \dfrac{x + 1}{x + 1} = 1.\end{array}$$

$$= \frac{x + 2}{x - 1} \qquad \text{Simplifying}$$

CAUTION! The difficulty with canceling is that it is applied incorrectly in situations such as the following:

$$\frac{\cancel{2} + 3}{\cancel{2}} = 3; \qquad \frac{\cancel{4} + 1}{\cancel{4} + 2} = \frac{1}{2}; \qquad \frac{1\cancel{5}}{\cancel{5}4} = \frac{1}{4}.$$

Wrong!   Wrong!   Wrong!

In each of these situations, the expressions canceled were *not* factors of 1. Factors are parts of products. For example, in $2 \cdot 3$, 2 and 3 are factors, but in $2 + 3$, 2 and 3 are *not* factors. If you can't factor, you can't cancel. If in doubt, don't cancel!

DO EXERCISES 8–11.

Consider

$$\frac{x - 4}{4 - x}.$$

At first glance the numerator and the denominator do not appear to have any common factors other than 1. But $x - 4$ and $4 - x$ are opposites, or additive inverses, of each other. Thus we can rewrite one as the inverse of the other.

▶ **EXAMPLE 10**   Simplify: $\dfrac{x - 4}{4 - x}$.

$$\frac{x - 4}{4 - x} = \frac{x - 4}{-1(-4 + x)}$$

$$= \frac{x - 4}{-1(x - 4)}$$

$$= -1 \cdot \frac{x - 4}{x - 4}$$

$$= -1 \cdot 1$$

$$= -1 \qquad ◀$$

DO EXERCISES 12 AND 13.

d ■ Multiplying and Simplifying

We try to simplify after we multiply. That is why we do not multiply out the numerator and the denominator too soon. We would need to factor them again anyway in order to simplify.

Multiply and simplify.

14. $\dfrac{a^2 - 4a + 4}{a^2 - 9} \cdot \dfrac{a + 3}{a - 2}$

▶ **EXAMPLE 11**   Multiply and simplify: $\dfrac{5a^3}{4} \cdot \dfrac{2}{5a}$.

$$\dfrac{5a^3}{4} \cdot \dfrac{2}{5a} = \dfrac{5a^3(2)}{4(5a)} \qquad \text{Multiplying the numerators and the denominators}$$

$$= \dfrac{2 \cdot 5 \cdot a \cdot a \cdot a}{2 \cdot 2 \cdot 5 \cdot a} \qquad \text{Factoring the numerator and the denominator}$$

$$= \dfrac{2 \cdot 5 \cdot a \cdot a \cdot a}{2 \cdot 2 \cdot 5 \cdot a} \qquad \text{Removing a factor of 1: } \dfrac{2 \cdot 5 \cdot a}{2 \cdot 5 \cdot a} = 1$$

$$= \dfrac{a^2}{2} \qquad \text{Simplifying} \qquad ◀$$

▶ **EXAMPLE 12**   Multiply and simplify: $\dfrac{x^2 + 6x + 9}{x^2 - 4} \cdot \dfrac{x - 2}{x + 3}$.

$$\dfrac{x^2 + 6x + 9}{x^2 - 4} \cdot \dfrac{x - 2}{x + 3} = \dfrac{(x^2 + 6x + 9)(x - 2)}{(x^2 - 4)(x + 3)} \qquad \text{Multiplying the numerators and the denominators}$$

$$= \dfrac{(x + 3)(x + 3)(x - 2)}{(x + 2)(x - 2)(x + 3)} \qquad \text{Factoring the numerator and the denominator}$$

$$= \dfrac{(x + 3)(x + 3)(x - 2)}{(x + 2)(x - 2)(x + 3)} \qquad \text{Removing a factor of 1: } \dfrac{(x + 3)(x - 2)}{(x + 3)(x - 2)} = 1$$

$$= \dfrac{x + 3}{x + 2} \qquad \text{Simplifying} \qquad ◀$$

15. $\dfrac{x^2 - 25}{6} \cdot \dfrac{3}{x + 5}$

▶ **EXAMPLE 13**   Multiply and simplify: $\dfrac{x^2 + x - 2}{15} \cdot \dfrac{5}{2x^2 - 3x + 1}$.

$$\dfrac{x^2 + x - 2}{15} \cdot \dfrac{5}{2x^2 - 3x + 1} = \dfrac{(x^2 + x - 2)5}{15(2x^2 - 3x + 1)} \qquad \text{Multiplying the numerators and the denominators}$$

$$= \dfrac{(x + 2)(x - 1)5}{5(3)(x - 1)(2x - 1)} \qquad \text{Factoring the numerator and the denominator}$$

$$= \dfrac{(x + 2)(x - 1)5}{5(3)(x - 1)(2x - 1)} \qquad \text{Removing a factor of 1: } \dfrac{(x - 1)5}{(x - 1)5} = 1$$

$$= \dfrac{x + 2}{\underbrace{3(2x - 1)}} \qquad \text{Simplifying}$$

| You need not carry out this multiplication. |

◀

DO EXERCISES 14 AND 15.

ANSWERS ON PAGE A-8

❖ SIDELIGHTS

Careers Involving Mathematics

If you have done well, you might be considering a career in mathematics or one that involves mathematics. If either is the case, the following information may be valuable to you.

CAREERS INVOLVING MATHEMATICS The following is the result of a survey conducted by *The Jobs Related Almanac,* published by the American References Inc., of Chicago. It used the criteria of salary, stress, work environment, outlook, security, and physical demands to rate the desirability of 250 jobs. The top 10 of the 250 jobs listed were:

1. Actuary
2. Computer programmer
3. Computer systems analyst } The top 5 involve mathematics.
4. Mathematician
5. Statistician
6. Hospital administrator
7. Industrial engineer
8. Physicist
9. Astrologer
10. Paralegal.

Two things are interesting to note. First, the top five rated professions involve a heavy use of mathematics. The top, actuary, involves the application of mathematics to insurance. The second point of interest is that choices like doctor, lawyer, and astronaut are *not* in the top ten.

Perhaps you might be interested in a career in teaching mathematics. This profession will be expanding increasingly in the next ten years. The field of mathematics will need well-qualified mathematics teachers in all areas from elementary to junior high to secondary to two-year college to college instruction. Some questions you might ask yourself in making a decision about a career in mathematics teaching are the following.

1. Do you find yourself carefully observing the strengths and weaknesses of your teachers?
2. Are you deeply interested in mathematics?
3. Are you interested in the ways of learning? If a student is struggling with a topic, would it be challenging to you to discover two or three other ways to present the material so that the student might understand?
4. Are you able to put yourself in the place of the students in order to help them be successful in learning mathematics?

If you are interested in a career involving mathematics, the next courses you would take are *intermediate algebra, precalculus algebra and trigonometry* and *calculus.* You might want to seek out a counselor in the mathematics department at your college for further assistance.

WHAT KIND OF SALARIES ARE THERE IN VARIOUS FIELDS? The College Placement Council published the following comparisons of the average salaries of graduating students with bachelors degrees who were taking the following jobs:

Subject area	Annual salary
All engineering	$27,800
Computer science	$26,400
Mathematics	$25,900
Sciences other than math and computer science	$22,200
Humanities and social science	$21,800
Accounting	$21,700
All business	$21,300

Many people choose to go on to earn a masters degree. Here are salaries in the same fields for students just graduating with a masters degree:

Subject area	Annual salary
All engineering	$34,000
Computer science	$33,800
Mathematics	$27,900
Sciences other than math and computer science	$27,400
Humanities and social science	$22,300
Accounting	$26,000
Business administration	$30,700

NAME   SECTION   DATE

EXERCISE SET 11.1

a Find the meaningful replacements in the expression.

1. $\dfrac{-5}{2x}$

2. $\dfrac{14}{-5y}$

3. $\dfrac{a+7}{a-8}$

4. $\dfrac{a-8}{a+7}$

5. $\dfrac{3}{2y+5}$

6. $\dfrac{x^2-9}{4x-12}$

7. $\dfrac{x^2+11}{x^2-3x-28}$

8. $\dfrac{p^2-9}{p^2-7p+10}$

9. $\dfrac{m^3-2m}{m^2-25}$

10. $\dfrac{7-3x+x^2}{49-x^2}$

b Multiply. Do not simplify. Note that in each case you are multiplying by 1.

11. $\dfrac{3a}{3a}\cdot\dfrac{5a^2}{2c}$

12. $\dfrac{5x^2}{5x^2}\cdot\dfrac{6y^3}{3z^4}$

13. $\dfrac{2x}{2x}\cdot\dfrac{x-1}{x+4}$

14. $\dfrac{3y-1}{2y+1}\cdot\dfrac{y}{y}$

15. $\dfrac{-1}{-1}\cdot\dfrac{3-x}{4-x}$

16. $\dfrac{-1}{-1}\cdot\dfrac{x-5}{5-x}$

17. $\dfrac{y+6}{y+6}\cdot\dfrac{y-7}{y+2}$

18. $\dfrac{x-3}{x-3}\cdot\dfrac{x^2-4}{x^3+1}$

ANSWERS

1. _____

2. _____

3. _____

4. _____

5. _____

6. _____

7. _____

8. _____

9. _____

10. _____

11. _____

12. _____

13. _____

14. _____

15. _____

16. _____

17. _____

18. _____

ANSWERS

19. _____

20. _____

21. _____

22. _____

23. _____

24. _____

25. _____

26. _____

27. _____

28. _____

29. _____

30. _____

31. _____

32. _____

33. _____

34. _____

35. _____

36. _____

37. _____

38. _____

c Simplify.

19. $\dfrac{8x^3}{32x}$

20. $\dfrac{6x^2}{18x}$

21. $\dfrac{48p^7q^5}{18p^5q^4}$

22. $\dfrac{-76x^8y^3}{-24x^4y^3}$

23. $\dfrac{4x - 12}{4x}$

24. $\dfrac{8y + 20}{8}$

25. $\dfrac{3m^2 + 3m}{6m^2 + 9m}$

26. $\dfrac{4y^2 - 2y}{5y^2 - 5y}$

27. $\dfrac{a^2 - 9}{a^2 + 5a + 6}$

28. $\dfrac{t^2 - 25}{t^2 + t - 20}$

29. $\dfrac{a^2 - 10a + 21}{a^2 - 11a + 28}$

30. $\dfrac{y^2 - 3y - 18}{y^2 - 2y - 15}$

31. $\dfrac{x^2 - 25}{x^2 - 10x + 25}$

32. $\dfrac{x^2 + 8x + 16}{x^2 - 16}$

33. $\dfrac{a^2 - 1}{a - 1}$

34. $\dfrac{t^2 - 1}{t + 1}$

35. $\dfrac{x^2 + 1}{x + 1}$

36. $\dfrac{y^2 + 4}{y + 2}$

37. $\dfrac{6x^2 - 54}{4x^2 - 36}$

38. $\dfrac{8x^2 - 32}{4x^2 - 16}$

39. $\dfrac{6t + 12}{t^2 - t - 6}$

40. $\dfrac{5y + 5}{y^2 + 7y + 6}$

41. $\dfrac{2t^2 + 6t + 4}{4t^2 - 12t - 16}$

42. $\dfrac{3a^2 - 9a - 12}{6a^2 + 30a + 24}$

43. $\dfrac{t^2 - 4}{(t + 2)^2}$

44. $\dfrac{(a - 3)^2}{a^2 - 9}$

45. $\dfrac{6 - x}{x - 6}$

46. $\dfrac{x - 8}{8 - x}$

47. $\dfrac{a - b}{b - a}$

48. $\dfrac{q - p}{-p + q}$

49. $\dfrac{6t - 12}{2 - t}$

50. $\dfrac{5a - 15}{3 - a}$

51. $\dfrac{a^2 - 1}{1 - a}$

52. $\dfrac{a^2 - b^2}{b^2 - a^2}$

d Multiply and simplify.

53. $\dfrac{4x^3}{3x} \cdot \dfrac{14}{x}$

54. $\dfrac{32}{b^4} \cdot \dfrac{3b^2}{8}$

55. $\dfrac{3c}{d^2} \cdot \dfrac{4d}{6c^3}$

56. $\dfrac{3x^2y}{2} \cdot \dfrac{4}{xy^3}$

57. $\dfrac{x^2 - 3x - 10}{x^2 - 4x + 4} \cdot \dfrac{x - 2}{x - 5}$

58. $\dfrac{t^2}{t^2 - 4} \cdot \dfrac{t^2 - 5t + 6}{t^2 - 3t}$

Copyright © 1993 Addison-Wesley Publishing Co., Inc.

ANSWERS

59. _____

60. _____

61. _____

62. _____

63. _____

64. _____

65. _____

66. _____

67. _____

68. _____

69. _____

70. _____

71. _____

72. _____

73. _____

74. _____

75. _____

76. _____

77. _____

78. _____

59. $\dfrac{a^2 - 9}{a^2} \cdot \dfrac{a^2 - 3a}{a^2 + a - 12}$

60. $\dfrac{x^2 + 10x - 11}{x^2 - 1} \cdot \dfrac{x + 1}{x + 11}$

61. $\dfrac{4a^2}{3a^2 - 12a + 12} \cdot \dfrac{3a - 6}{2a}$

62. $\dfrac{5v + 5}{v - 2} \cdot \dfrac{v^2 - 4v + 4}{v^2 - 1}$

63. $\dfrac{x^4 - 16}{x^4 - 1} \cdot \dfrac{x^2 + 1}{x^2 + 4}$

64. $\dfrac{t^4 - 1}{t^4 - 81} \cdot \dfrac{t^2 + 9}{t^2 + 1}$

65. $\dfrac{(t - 2)^3}{(t - 1)^3} \cdot \dfrac{t^2 - 2t + 1}{t^2 - 4t + 4}$

66. $\dfrac{(y + 4)^3}{(y + 2)^3} \cdot \dfrac{y^2 + 4y + 4}{y^2 + 8y + 16}$

67. $\dfrac{5a^2 - 180}{10a^2 - 10} \cdot \dfrac{20a + 20}{2a - 12}$

68. $\dfrac{2t^2 - 98}{4t^2 - 4} \cdot \dfrac{8t + 8}{16t - 112}$

SKILL MAINTENANCE

69. The product of two consecutive even integers is 360. Find the integers.

Factor.

70. $16 - t^4$ **71.** $2y^3 - 10y^2 + y - 5$ **72.** $x^5 - 2x^4 - 35x^3$

SYNTHESIS

Simplify.

73. $\dfrac{x^4 - 16y^4}{(x^2 + 4y^2)(x - 2y)}$

74. $\dfrac{(a - b)^2}{b^2 - a^2}$

75. $\dfrac{t^4 - 1}{t^4 - 81} \cdot \dfrac{t^2 - 9}{t^2 + 1} \cdot \dfrac{(t - 9)^2}{(t + 1)^2}$

76. $\dfrac{(t + 2)^3}{(t + 1)^3} \cdot \dfrac{t^2 + 2t + 1}{t^2 + 4t + 4} \cdot \dfrac{t + 1}{t + 2}$

77. $\dfrac{x^2 - y^2}{(x - y)^2} \cdot \dfrac{x^2 - 2xy + y^2}{x^2 - 4xy - 5y^2}$

78. $\dfrac{x - 1}{x^2 + 1} \cdot \dfrac{x^4 - 1}{(x - 1)^2} \cdot \dfrac{x^2 - 1}{x^4 - 2x^2 + 1}$

11.2 Division and Reciprocals

There is a similarity throughout this chapter between what we do with rational expressions and what we do with rational numbers. In fact, after replacements of variables by rational numbers, a rational expression represents a rational number.

a Finding Reciprocals

Two expressions are reciprocals of each other if their product is 1. The reciprocal of a rational expression is found by interchanging the numerator and the denominator.

▶ **EXAMPLES**

1. The reciprocal of $\frac{2}{5}$ is $\frac{5}{2}$. $\left(\text{This is because } \frac{2}{5} \cdot \frac{5}{2} = \frac{10}{10} = 1.\right)$

2. The reciprocal of $\frac{2x^2 - 3}{x + 4}$ is $\frac{x + 4}{2x^2 - 3}$.

3. The reciprocal of $x + 2$ is $\frac{1}{x + 2}$. $\left(\text{Think of } x + 2 \text{ as } \frac{x + 2}{1}.\right)$ ◀

DO EXERCISES 1–4.

b Division

> **To divide rational expressions, multiply by the reciprocal of the divisor. Then factor and simplify the result.**

▶ **EXAMPLES** Divide.

4. $\dfrac{3}{4} \div \dfrac{2}{5} = \dfrac{3}{4} \cdot \dfrac{5}{2}$ **Multiplying by the reciprocal of the divisor**

$= \dfrac{3 \cdot 5}{4 \cdot 2}$

$= \dfrac{15}{8}$

5. $\dfrac{x + 1}{x + 2} \div \dfrac{x - 1}{x + 3} = \dfrac{x + 1}{x + 2} \cdot \dfrac{x + 3}{x - 1}$ **Multiplying by the reciprocal of the divisor**

$= \dfrac{(x + 1)(x + 3)}{(x + 2)(x - 1)}$ You need not carry out the multiplications in the numerator and the denominator. ◀

DO EXERCISES 5 AND 6.

OBJECTIVES

After finishing Section 11.2, you should be able to:

a Find the reciprocal of a rational expression.

b Divide rational expressions and simplify.

FOR EXTRA HELP

Tape 22E

Find the reciprocal.

1. $\dfrac{7}{2}$

2. $\dfrac{x^2 + 5}{2x^3 - 1}$

3. $x - 5$

4. $\dfrac{1}{x^2 - 3}$

Divide.

5. $\dfrac{3}{5} \div \dfrac{7}{2}$

6. $\dfrac{x - 3}{x + 5} \div \dfrac{x + 5}{x - 2}$

ANSWERS ON PAGE A-8

Divide and simplify.

7. $\dfrac{x-3}{x+5} \div \dfrac{x+2}{x+5}$

▶ **EXAMPLE 6**   Divide and simplify: $\dfrac{x+1}{x^2-1} \div \dfrac{x+1}{x^2-2x+1}$.

$$\dfrac{x+1}{x^2-1} \div \dfrac{x+1}{x^2-2x+1}$$

$$= \dfrac{x+1}{x^2-1} \cdot \dfrac{x^2-2x+1}{x+1} \qquad \text{Multiplying by the reciprocal}$$

$$= \dfrac{(x+1)(x^2-2x+1)}{(x^2-1)(x+1)}$$

$$= \dfrac{(x+1)(x-1)(x-1)}{(x-1)(x+1)(x+1)} \qquad \begin{array}{l}\text{Factoring the numerator} \\ \text{and the denominator}\end{array}$$

$$= \dfrac{(x+1)(x-1)(x-1)}{(x-1)(x+1)(x+1)} \qquad \text{Removing a factor of 1: } \dfrac{(x+1)(x-1)}{(x+1)(x-1)} = 1$$

$$= \dfrac{x-1}{x+1} \qquad\qquad\qquad\qquad\qquad ◀$$

8. $\dfrac{x^2-5x+6}{x+5} \div \dfrac{x+2}{x+5}$

▶ **EXAMPLE 7**   Divide and simplify: $\dfrac{x^2-2x-3}{x^2-4} \div \dfrac{x+1}{x+5}$.

$$\dfrac{x^2-2x-3}{x^2-4} \div \dfrac{x+1}{x+5}$$

$$= \dfrac{x^2-2x-3}{x^2-4} \cdot \dfrac{x+5}{x+1} \qquad \text{Multiplying by the reciprocal}$$

$$= \dfrac{(x^2-2x-3)(x+5)}{(x^2-4)(x+1)}$$

$$= \dfrac{(x-3)(x+1)(x+5)}{(x-2)(x+2)(x+1)} \qquad \begin{array}{l}\text{Factoring the numerator} \\ \text{and the denominator}\end{array}$$

$$= \dfrac{(x-3)(x+1)(x+5)}{(x-2)(x+2)(x+1)} \qquad \text{Removing a factor of 1: } \dfrac{x+1}{x+1} = 1$$

$$= \dfrac{(x-3)(x+5)}{(x-2)(x+2)} \Bigg\} \leftarrow \boxed{\begin{array}{l}\text{You need not carry out the multiplications} \\ \text{in the numerator and the denominator.}\end{array}}$$

$$◀$$

9. $\dfrac{y^2-1}{y+1} \div \dfrac{y^2-2y+1}{y+1}$

DO EXERCISES 7–9.

NAME   SECTION   DATE

EXERCISE SET 11.2

a Find the reciprocal.

1. $\dfrac{4}{x}$

2. $\dfrac{a+3}{a-1}$

3. $x^2 - y^2$

4. $\dfrac{1}{a+b}$

5. $\dfrac{x^2 + 2x - 5}{x^2 - 4x + 7}$

6. $\dfrac{x^2 - 3xy + y^2}{x^2 + 7xy - y^2}$

b Divide and simplify.

7. $\dfrac{2}{5} \div \dfrac{4}{3}$

8. $\dfrac{5}{6} \div \dfrac{2}{3}$

9. $\dfrac{2}{x} \div \dfrac{8}{x}$

10. $\dfrac{x}{2} \div \dfrac{3}{x}$

11. $\dfrac{x^2}{y} \div \dfrac{x^3}{y^3}$

12. $\dfrac{a}{b^2} \div \dfrac{a^2}{b^3}$

13. $\dfrac{a+2}{a-3} \div \dfrac{a-1}{a+3}$

14. $\dfrac{y+2}{4} \div \dfrac{y}{2}$

15. $\dfrac{x^2-1}{x} \div \dfrac{x+1}{x-1}$

16. $\dfrac{4y-8}{y+2} \div \dfrac{y-2}{y^2-4}$

17. $\dfrac{x+1}{6} \div \dfrac{x+1}{3}$

18. $\dfrac{a}{a-b} \div \dfrac{b}{a-b}$

19. $\dfrac{5x-5}{16} \div \dfrac{x-1}{6}$

20. $\dfrac{-4+2x}{8} \div \dfrac{x-2}{2}$

21. $\dfrac{-6+3x}{5} \div \dfrac{4x-8}{25}$

1. _____

2. _____

3. _____

4. _____

5. _____

6. _____

7. _____

8. _____

9. _____

10. _____

11. _____

12. _____

13. _____

14. _____

15. _____

16. _____

17. _____

18. _____

19. _____

20. _____

21. _____

22. $\dfrac{-12 + 4x}{4} \div \dfrac{-6 + 2x}{6}$ **23.** $\dfrac{a + 2}{a - 1} \div \dfrac{3a + 6}{a - 5}$ **24.** $\dfrac{t - 3}{t + 2} \div \dfrac{4t - 12}{t + 1}$

25. $\dfrac{x^2 - 4}{x} \div \dfrac{x - 2}{x + 2}$ **26.** $\dfrac{x + y}{x - y} \div \dfrac{x^2 + y}{x^2 - y^2}$ **27.** $\dfrac{x^2 - 9}{4x + 12} \div \dfrac{x - 3}{6}$

28. $\dfrac{x - b}{2x} \div \dfrac{x^2 - b^2}{5x^2}$ **29.** $\dfrac{c^2 + 3c}{c^2 + 2c - 3} \div \dfrac{c}{c + 1}$ **30.** $\dfrac{x - 5}{2x} \div \dfrac{x^2 - 25}{4x^2}$

31. $\dfrac{2y^2 - 7y + 3}{2y^2 + 3y - 2} \div \dfrac{6y^2 - 5y + 1}{3y^2 + 5y - 2}$ **32.** $\dfrac{x^2 - x - 20}{x^2 + 7x + 12} \div \dfrac{x^2 - 10x + 25}{x^2 + 6x + 9}$

33. $\dfrac{x^2 - 1}{4x + 4} \div \dfrac{2x^2 - 4x + 2}{8x + 8}$ **34.** $\dfrac{5x^2 + 5x - 30}{10x + 30} \div \dfrac{2x^2 - 8}{6x^2 + 36x + 54}$

SKILL MAINTENANCE

35. Sixteen more than the square of a number is eight times the number. Find the number.

36. Subtract:
$$(8x^3 - 3x^2 + 7) - (8x^2 + 3x - 5).$$

SYNTHESIS

Simplify.

37. $\dfrac{3a^2 - 5ab - 12b^2}{3ab + 4b^2} \div (3b^2 - ab)$ **38.** $\dfrac{3x^2 - 2xy - y^2}{x^2 - y^2} \div 3x^2 + 4xy + y^2$

39. $\dfrac{3x + 3y + 3}{9x} \div \left(\dfrac{x^2 + 2xy + y^2 - 1}{x^4 + x^2} \right)$

40. $\left(\dfrac{y^2 + 5y + 6}{y^2} \cdot \dfrac{3y^3 + 6y^2}{y^2 - y - 12} \right) \div \dfrac{y^2 - y}{y^2 - 2y - 8}$

11.3 Least Common Multiples and Denominators

a Least Common Multiples

To add when denominators are different, we first find a common denominator. For example, to add $\frac{5}{12}$ and $\frac{7}{30}$, we first look for the **least common multiple, LCM,** of both 12 and 30. That number becomes the **least common denominator, LCD.** To find the LCM of 12 and 30, we factor:

$$12 = 2 \cdot 2 \cdot 3;$$
$$30 = 2 \cdot 3 \cdot 5.$$

The LCM is the number that has 2 as a factor twice, 3 as a factor once, and 5 as a factor once:

$$\text{LCM} = 2 \cdot 2 \cdot 3 \cdot 5, \text{ or } 60.$$

> **To find the LCM, use each factor the greatest number of times that it appears in any one factorization.**

▶ **EXAMPLE 1** Find the LCM of 24 and 36.

$$\left.\begin{array}{l} 24 = 2 \cdot 2 \cdot 2 \cdot 3 \\ 36 = 2 \cdot 2 \cdot 3 \cdot 3 \end{array}\right\} \quad \text{LCM} = 2 \cdot 2 \cdot 2 \cdot 3 \cdot 3, \text{ or } 72 \quad ◀$$

DO EXERCISES 1–4.

b Adding Using the LCD

Let us finish adding $\frac{5}{12}$ and $\frac{7}{30}$:

$$\frac{5}{12} + \frac{7}{30} = \frac{5}{2 \cdot 2 \cdot 3} + \frac{7}{2 \cdot 3 \cdot 5}.$$

The least common denominator, LCD, is $2 \cdot 2 \cdot 3 \cdot 5$. To get the LCD in the first denominator, we need a 5. To get the LCD in the second denominator, we need another 2. We get these numbers by multiplying by 1:

$$\frac{5}{12} + \frac{7}{30} = \frac{5}{2 \cdot 2 \cdot 3} \cdot \frac{5}{5} + \frac{7}{2 \cdot 3 \cdot 5} \cdot \frac{2}{2} \qquad \text{Multiplying by 1}$$

$$= \frac{25}{2 \cdot 2 \cdot 3 \cdot 5} + \frac{14}{2 \cdot 3 \cdot 5 \cdot 2} \qquad \begin{array}{l}\text{The denominators are}\\\text{now the LCD.}\end{array}$$

$$= \frac{39}{2 \cdot 2 \cdot 3 \cdot 5} \qquad \begin{array}{l}\text{Adding the numerators}\\\text{and keeping the LCD}\end{array}$$

$$= \frac{\cancel{3} \cdot 13}{2 \cdot 2 \cdot \cancel{3} \cdot 5}$$

$$= \frac{13}{20} \qquad \text{Simplifying}$$

ANSWERS ON PAGE A-8

Find the LCM by factoring.

1. 16, 18

2. 6, 12

3. 2, 5

4. 24, 30, 20

Add, first finding the LCM of the denominators. Simplify if possible.

5. $\dfrac{3}{16} + \dfrac{1}{18}$

6. $\dfrac{1}{6} + \dfrac{1}{12}$

7. $\dfrac{1}{2} + \dfrac{3}{5}$

8. $\dfrac{1}{24} + \dfrac{1}{30} + \dfrac{3}{20}$

Find the LCM.

9. $12xy^2,\ 15x^3y$

10. $y^2 + 5y + 4,\ y^2 + 2y + 1$

11. $t^2 + 16,\ t - 2,\ 7$

12. $x^2 + 2x + 1,\ 3x^2 - 3x,\ x^2 - 1$

▶ **EXAMPLE 2**   Add: $\dfrac{5}{12} + \dfrac{11}{18}$.

$$\left.\begin{array}{l} 12 = 2 \cdot 2 \cdot 3 \\ 18 = 2 \cdot 3 \cdot 3 \end{array}\right\} \quad \text{LCD} = 2 \cdot 2 \cdot 3 \cdot 3,\ \text{or } 36.$$

$$\frac{5}{12} + \frac{11}{18} = \frac{5}{2 \cdot 2 \cdot 3} \cdot \frac{3}{3} + \frac{11}{2 \cdot 3 \cdot 3} \cdot \frac{2}{2} = \frac{37}{2 \cdot 2 \cdot 3 \cdot 3} = \frac{37}{36} \quad ◀$$

DO EXERCISES 5–8.

c LCMs of Algebraic Expressions

To find the LCM of two or more algebraic expressions, we factor them. Then we use each factor the greatest number of times it occurs in any one expression.

▶ **EXAMPLE 3**   Find the LCM of $12x$, $16y$, and $8xyz$.

$$\left.\begin{array}{l} 12x = 2 \cdot 2 \cdot 3 \cdot x \\ 16y = 2 \cdot 2 \cdot 2 \cdot 2 \cdot y \\ 8xyz = 2 \cdot 2 \cdot 2 \cdot x \cdot y \cdot z \end{array}\right\} \quad \begin{array}{l} \text{LCM} = 2 \cdot 2 \cdot 2 \cdot 2 \cdot 3 \cdot x \cdot y \cdot z \\ \qquad\quad = 48xyz \end{array} \quad ◀$$

▶ **EXAMPLE 4**   Find the LCM of $x^2 + 5x - 6$ and $x^2 - 1$.

$$\left.\begin{array}{l} x^2 + 5x - 6 = (x + 6)(x - 1) \\ x^2 - 1 = (x + 1)(x - 1) \end{array}\right\} \quad \text{LCM} = (x + 6)(x - 1)(x + 1) \quad ◀$$

▶ **EXAMPLE 5**   Find the LCM of $x^2 + 4$, $x + 1$, and 5.

These expressions are not factorable, so the LCM is their product:

$$5(x^2 + 4)(x + 1). \quad ◀$$

▶ **EXAMPLE 6**   Find the LCM of $x^2 - 25$ and $2x - 10$.

$$\left.\begin{array}{l} x^2 - 25 = (x + 5)(x - 5) \\ 2x - 10 = 2(x - 5) \end{array}\right\} \quad \text{LCM} = 2(x + 5)(x - 5) \quad ◀$$

▶ **EXAMPLE 7**   Find the LCM of $x^2 - 4y^2$, $x^2 - 4xy + 4y^2$, and $x - 2y$.

$$\left.\begin{array}{l} x^2 - 4y^2 = (x - 2y)(x + 2y) \\ x^2 - 4xy + 4y^2 = (x - 2y)(x - 2y) \\ x - 2y = x - 2y \end{array}\right\} \quad \begin{array}{l} \text{LCM} = (x + 2y)(x - 2y)(x - 2y) \\ \qquad\quad = (x + 2y)(x - 2y)^2 \end{array} \quad ◀$$

DO EXERCISES 9–12.

EXERCISE SET 11.3

| a | Find the LCM.

1. 12, 27   **2.** 10, 15   **3.** 8, 9   **4.** 12, 15

5. 6, 9, 21   **6.** 8, 36, 40   **7.** 24, 36, 40   **8.** 3, 4, 5

9. 28, 42, 60   **10.** 10, 100, 500

| b | Add, first finding the LCD. Simplify if possible.

11. $\dfrac{7}{24} + \dfrac{11}{18}$ **12.** $\dfrac{7}{60} + \dfrac{6}{75}$ **13.** $\dfrac{1}{6} + \dfrac{3}{40}$

14. $\dfrac{5}{24} + \dfrac{3}{20}$ **15.** $\dfrac{2}{15} + \dfrac{5}{9} + \dfrac{3}{20}$ **16.** $\dfrac{1}{20} + \dfrac{1}{30} + \dfrac{2}{45}$

| c | Find the LCM.

17. $6x^2$, $12x^3$ **18.** $2a^2b$, $8ab^2$

19. $2x^2$, $6xy$, $18y^2$ **20.** c^2d, cd^2, c^3d

21. $2(y-3)$, $6(y-3)$ **22.** $4(x-1)$, $8(x-1)$

23. t, $t+2$, $t-2$ **24.** x, $x+3$, $x-3$

25. $x^2 - 4$, $x^2 + 5x + 6$ **26.** $x^2 + 3x + 2$, $x^2 - 4$

ANSWERS

1.

2.

3.

4.

5.

6.

7.

8.

9.

10.

11.

12.

13.

14.

15.

16.

17.

18.

19.

20.

21.

22.

23.

24.

25.

26.

ANSWERS

27. _____

28. _____

29. _____

30. _____

31. _____

32. _____

33. _____

34. _____

35. _____

36. _____

37. _____

38. _____

39. _____

40. _____

41. _____

42. _____

43. _____

44. _____

45. _____

46. _____

47. _____

48. _____

27. $t^3 + 4t^2 + 4t,\ t^2 - 4t$

28. $y^3 - y^2,\ y^4 - y^2$

29. $a + 1,\ (a - 1)^2,\ a^2 - 1$

30. $x^2 - y^2,\ 2x + 2y,\ x^2 + 2xy + y^2$

31. $m^2 - 5m + 6,\ m^2 - 4m + 4$

32. $2x^2 + 5x + 2,\ 2x^2 - x - 1$

33. $2 + 3x,\ 4 - 9x^2,\ 2 - 3x$

34. $3 - 2x,\ 9 - 4x^2,\ 3 + 2x$

35. $10v^2 + 30v,\ 5v^2 + 35v + 60$

36. $12a^2 + 24a,\ 4a^2 + 20a + 24$

37. $9x^3 - 9x^2 - 18x,\ 6x^5 - 24x^4 + 24x^3$

38. $x^5 - 4x^3,\ x^3 + 4x^2 + 4x$

39. $x^5 + 4x^4 + 4x^3,\ 3x^2 - 12,\ 2x + 4$

40. $x^5 + 2x^4 + x^3,\ 2x^3 - 2x,\ 5x - 5$

SKILL MAINTENANCE

Factor.

41. $x^2 - 6x + 9$

42. $6x^2 + 4x$

43. $x^2 - 9$

44. $x^2 + 4x - 21$

SYNTHESIS

Find the LCM.

45. 72, 90, 96

46. $8x^2 - 8,\ 6x^2 - 12x + 6,\ 10x - 10$

47. Two joggers leave the starting point of a circular course at the same time. One jogger completes one round in 6 min and the second jogger in 8 min. Assuming they continue to run at the same pace, after how many minutes will they meet again at the starting place?

48. If the LCM of two expressions is the same as one of the expressions, what is their relationship?

11.4 Adding Rational Expressions

a We add rational expressions as we do rational numbers.

> **To add when the denominators are the same, add the numerators and keep the same denominator.**

▶ **EXAMPLES** Add.

1. $\dfrac{x}{x+1} + \dfrac{2}{x+1} = \dfrac{x+2}{x+1}$

2. $\dfrac{2x^2 + 3x - 7}{2x + 1} + \dfrac{x^2 + x - 8}{2x + 1} = \dfrac{(2x^2 + 3x - 7) + (x^2 + x - 8)}{2x + 1}$

$$= \dfrac{3x^2 + 4x - 15}{2x + 1}$$

3. $\dfrac{x - 5}{x^2 - 9} + \dfrac{2}{x^2 - 9} = \dfrac{(x - 5) + 2}{x^2 - 9} = \dfrac{x - 3}{x^2 - 9}$

$$= \dfrac{x - 3}{(x - 3)(x + 3)} \quad \text{Factoring}$$

$$= \dfrac{\cancel{x - 3}}{\cancel{(x - 3)}(x + 3)} \quad \text{Removing a factor of 1: } \dfrac{x - 3}{x - 3} = 1$$

$$= \dfrac{1}{x + 3} \quad \text{Simplifying} \qquad ◀$$

As in Example 3, simplifying should be done if possible after adding.

DO EXERCISES 1–3.

When denominators are not the same, we multiply by 1 to obtain equivalent expressions with the same denominator. When one denominator is the opposite of the other, we can first multiply either expression by $-1/-1$.

▶ **EXAMPLES**

4. $\dfrac{x}{2} + \dfrac{3}{-2} = \dfrac{x}{2} + \dfrac{-1}{-1} \cdot \dfrac{3}{-2} \quad \text{Multiplying by } \dfrac{-1}{-1}$

$$= \dfrac{x}{2} + \dfrac{-3}{2} \quad \text{The denominators are now the same.}$$

$$= \dfrac{x + (-3)}{2} = \dfrac{x - 3}{2}$$

5. $\dfrac{3x + 4}{x - 2} + \dfrac{x - 7}{2 - x} = \dfrac{3x + 4}{x - 2} + \dfrac{-1}{-1} \cdot \dfrac{x - 7}{2 - x}$

We could have chosen to multiply this expression by $-1/-1$. We multiply only one expression, *not* both.

$$= \dfrac{3x + 4}{x - 2} + \dfrac{-x + 7}{x - 2} \quad \textit{Note: } -1(2 - x) = -2 + x = x - 2$$

$$= \dfrac{(3x + 4) + (-x + 7)}{x - 2} = \dfrac{2x + 11}{x - 2} \qquad ◀$$

DO EXERCISES 4 AND 5.

OBJECTIVE

After finishing Section 11.4, you should be able to:

a Add rational expressions.

FOR EXTRA HELP

Tape 23B

Add.

1. $\dfrac{5}{9} + \dfrac{2}{9}$

2. $\dfrac{3}{x - 2} + \dfrac{x}{x - 2}$

3. $\dfrac{4x + 5}{x - 1} + \dfrac{2x - 1}{x - 1}$

Add.

4. $\dfrac{x}{4} + \dfrac{5}{-4}$

5. $\dfrac{2x + 1}{x - 3} + \dfrac{x + 2}{3 - x}$

Add.

6. $\dfrac{3x}{16} + \dfrac{5x^2}{24}$

When denominators are different, we find the least common denominator, LCD. The procedure we will use is as follows.

> **To add rational expressions with different denominators:**
> 1. **Find the LCM of the denominators. This is the least common denominator (LCD).**
> 2. **For each rational expression, find an equivalent expression with the LCD. To do so, multiply by 1 using an expression for 1 made up of factors of the LCD missing from the original denominator.**
> 3. **Add the numerators. Write the sum over the LCD.**
> 4. **Simplify, if possible.**

▶ **EXAMPLE 6**   Add: $\dfrac{5x^2}{8} + \dfrac{7x}{12}$.

First, we find the LCD:

$$\left.\begin{array}{l} 8 = 2 \cdot 2 \cdot 2 \\ 12 = 2 \cdot 2 \cdot 3 \end{array}\right\} \quad \text{LCD} = 2 \cdot 2 \cdot 2 \cdot 3, \text{ or } 24.$$

The factor of the LCD missing from 8 is 3. The factor of the LCD missing from 12 is 2. We multiply by 1 to get the LCD in each expression, and then add and simplify, if possible.

$$\begin{aligned}
\frac{5x^2}{8} + \frac{7x}{12} &= \frac{5x^2}{2 \cdot 2 \cdot 2} + \frac{7x}{2 \cdot 2 \cdot 3} \\
&= \frac{5x^2}{2 \cdot 2 \cdot 2} \cdot \frac{3}{3} + \frac{7x}{2 \cdot 2 \cdot 3} \cdot \frac{2}{2} \qquad \text{\small Multiplying by 1 to get}\\
&\qquad\qquad\qquad\qquad\qquad\qquad\qquad\quad \text{\small the same denominators}\\
&= \frac{15x^2}{24} + \frac{14x}{24} = \frac{15x^2 + 14x}{24}. \qquad ◀
\end{aligned}$$

7. $\dfrac{3}{16x} + \dfrac{5}{24x^2}$

▶ **EXAMPLE 7**   Add: $\dfrac{3}{8x} + \dfrac{5}{12x^2}$.

First, we find the LCD:

$$\left.\begin{array}{l} 8x = 2 \cdot 2 \cdot 2 \cdot x \\ 12x^2 = 2 \cdot 2 \cdot 3 \cdot x \cdot x \end{array}\right\} \quad \text{LCD} = 2 \cdot 2 \cdot 2 \cdot 3 \cdot x \cdot x, \text{ or } 24x^2.$$

The factors of the LCD missing from $8x$ are 3 and x. The factor of the LCD missing from $12x^2$ is 2. We multiply by 1 to get the LCD in each expression, and then add and simplify, if possible:

$$\begin{aligned}
\frac{3}{8x} + \frac{5}{12x^2} &= \frac{3}{8x} \cdot \frac{3 \cdot x}{3 \cdot x} + \frac{5}{12x^2} \cdot \frac{2}{2} \\
&= \frac{9x}{24x^2} + \frac{10}{24x^2} = \frac{9x + 10}{24x^2}. \qquad ◀
\end{aligned}$$

DO EXERCISES 6 AND 7.

▶ **EXAMPLE 8** Add: $\dfrac{2a}{a^2 - 1} + \dfrac{1}{a^2 + a}$.

First, we find the LCD:

$$\left.\begin{array}{l} a^2 - 1 = (a - 1)(a + 1) \\ a^2 + a = a(a + 1) \end{array}\right\} \quad \text{LCD} = a(a - 1)(a + 1).$$

We multiply by 1 to get the LCD in each expression, and then add and simplify:

$$\frac{2a}{(a - 1)(a + 1)} \cdot \frac{a}{a} + \frac{1}{a(a + 1)} \cdot \frac{a - 1}{a - 1}$$

$$= \frac{2a^2}{a(a - 1)(a + 1)} + \frac{a - 1}{a(a - 1)(a + 1)}$$

$$= \frac{2a^2 + a - 1}{a(a - 1)(a + 1)}$$

$$= \frac{(a + 1)(2a - 1)}{a(a - 1)(a + 1)} \quad \text{Factoring the numerator in order to simplify}$$

$$= \frac{(a + 1)(2a - 1)}{a(a - 1)(a + 1)} \quad \text{Removing a factor of 1: } \frac{a + 1}{a + 1} = 1$$

$$= \frac{2a - 1}{a(a - 1)}. \qquad \blacktriangleleft$$

DO EXERCISE 8.

▶ **EXAMPLE 9** Add: $\dfrac{x + 4}{x - 2} + \dfrac{x - 7}{x + 5}$.

First, we find the LCD. It is just the product of the denominators:

$$\text{LCD} = (x - 2)(x + 5).$$

We multiply by 1 to get the LCD in each expression, and then add and simplify:

$$\frac{x + 4}{x - 2} \cdot \frac{x + 5}{x + 5} + \frac{x - 7}{x + 5} \cdot \frac{x - 2}{x - 2} = \frac{(x + 4)(x + 5)}{(x - 2)(x + 5)} + \frac{(x - 7)(x - 2)}{(x - 2)(x + 5)}$$

$$= \frac{x^2 + 9x + 20}{(x - 2)(x + 5)} + \frac{x^2 - 9x + 14}{(x - 2)(x + 5)}$$

$$= \frac{x^2 + 9x + 20 + x^2 - 9x + 14}{(x - 2)(x + 5)}$$

$$= \frac{2x^2 + 34}{(x - 2)(x + 5)}. \qquad \blacktriangleleft$$

DO EXERCISE 9.

8. Add:

$$\frac{3}{x^3 - x} + \frac{4}{x^2 + 2x + 1}.$$

9. Add:

$$\frac{x - 2}{x + 3} + \frac{x + 7}{x + 8}.$$

ANSWERS ON PAGE A-8

10. Add:

$$\frac{5}{x^2 + 17x + 16} + \frac{3}{x^2 + 9x + 8}.$$

▶ **EXAMPLE 10**   Add: $\dfrac{x}{x^2 + 11x + 30} + \dfrac{-5}{x^2 + 9x + 20}$.

$$\frac{x}{x^2 + 11x + 30} + \frac{-5}{x^2 + 9x + 20}$$

$$= \frac{x}{(x + 5)(x + 6)} + \frac{-5}{(x + 5)(x + 4)}$$

     Factoring the denominators in order to find the LCM. The LCD is $(x + 4)(x + 5)(x + 6)$.

$$= \frac{x}{(x + 5)(x + 6)} \cdot \frac{x + 4}{x + 4} + \frac{-5}{(x + 5)(x + 4)} \cdot \frac{x + 6}{x + 6}$$

     Multiplying by 1

$$= \frac{x(x + 4) + (-5)(x + 6)}{(x + 4)(x + 5)(x + 6)} = \frac{x^2 + 4x - 5x - 30}{(x + 4)(x + 5)(x + 6)}$$

$$= \frac{x^2 - x - 30}{(x + 4)(x + 5)(x + 6)}$$

$$= \frac{(x - 6)(x + 5)}{(x + 4)(x + 5)(x + 6)}$$

$$= \frac{(x - 6)}{(x + 4)(x + 6)}$$

⟶ Always simplify at the end if possible: $\dfrac{x + 5}{x + 5} = 1$. ◀

DO EXERCISE 10.

Suppose that after we factor to find the LCD, we find factors that are opposites. There are several ways to handle this, but the easiest is to first go back and multiply by $-1/-1$ appropriately to change factors so they are not opposites.

11. Add:

$$\frac{x + 3}{x^2 - 16} + \frac{5}{12 - 3x}.$$

▶ **EXAMPLE 11**   Add: $\dfrac{x}{x^2 - 25} + \dfrac{3}{10 - 2x}$.

First, we factor as though we are going to find the LCD:

$$x^2 - 25 = (x - 5)(x + 5);$$
$$10 - 2x = 2(5 - x).$$

We note that there is an $x - 5$ as one factor and a $5 - x$ as another factor. If the denominator of the second expression were $2x - 10$, this situation would not arise. To avoid this, we first multiply by $-1/-1$ and continue as before:

$$\frac{x}{x^2 - 25} + \frac{3}{10 - 2x} = \frac{x}{(x - 5)(x + 5)} + \frac{-1}{-1} \cdot \frac{3}{10 - 2x}$$

$$= \frac{x}{(x - 5)(x + 5)} + \frac{-3}{2x - 10}$$

$$= \frac{x}{(x - 5)(x + 5)} + \frac{-3}{2(x - 5)}$$

     LCD $= 2(x - 5)(x + 5)$

$$= \frac{x}{(x - 5)(x + 5)} \cdot \frac{2}{2} + \frac{-3}{2(x - 5)} \cdot \frac{x + 5}{x + 5}$$

$$= \frac{2x - 3(x + 5)}{2(x - 5)(x + 5)} = \frac{2x - 3x - 15}{2(x - 5)(x + 5)}$$

     Collecting like terms

$$= \frac{-x - 15}{2(x - 5)(x + 5)}$$ ◀

DO EXERCISE 11.

NAME   SECTION   DATE

EXERCISE SET 11.4

a Add. Simplify, if possible.

1. $\dfrac{5}{12} + \dfrac{7}{12}$

2. $\dfrac{3}{14} + \dfrac{5}{14}$

3. $\dfrac{1}{3+x} + \dfrac{5}{3+x}$

4. $\dfrac{4x+1}{6x+5} + \dfrac{3x-7}{5+6x}$

5. $\dfrac{x^2+7x}{x^2-5x} + \dfrac{x^2-4x}{x^2-5x}$

6. $\dfrac{a}{x+y} + \dfrac{b}{y+x}$

7. $\dfrac{7}{8} + \dfrac{5}{-8}$

8. $\dfrac{11}{6} + \dfrac{5}{-6}$

9. $\dfrac{3}{t} + \dfrac{4}{-t}$

10. $\dfrac{5}{-a} + \dfrac{8}{a}$

11. $\dfrac{2x+7}{x-6} + \dfrac{3x}{6-x}$

12. $\dfrac{3x-2}{4x-3} + \dfrac{2x-5}{3-4x}$

13. $\dfrac{y^2}{y-3} + \dfrac{9}{3-y}$

14. $\dfrac{t^2}{t-2} + \dfrac{4}{2-t}$

15. $\dfrac{b-7}{b^2-16} + \dfrac{7-b}{16-b^2}$

16. $\dfrac{a-3}{a^2-25} + \dfrac{a-3}{25-a^2}$

17. $\dfrac{z}{(y+z)(y-z)} + \dfrac{y}{(z+y)(z-y)}$
[*Hint:* Multiply by $-1/-1$. Note that $(z+y)(z-y)(-1) = (z+y)(y-z)$.]

18. $\dfrac{a^2}{a-b} + \dfrac{b^2}{b-a}$

1. _____

2. _____

3. _____

4. _____

5. _____

6. _____

7. _____

8. _____

9. _____

10. _____

11. _____

12. _____

13. _____

14. _____

15. _____

16. _____

17. _____

18. _____

19. _____

20. _____

21. _____

22. _____

23. _____

24. _____

25. _____

26. _____

27. _____

28. _____

29. _____

30. _____

31. _____

32. _____

33. _____

34. _____

35. _____

36. _____

19. $\dfrac{x+3}{x-5} + \dfrac{2x-1}{5-x} + \dfrac{2(3x-1)}{x-5}$

20. $\dfrac{3(x-2)}{2x-3} + \dfrac{5(2x+1)}{2x-3} + \dfrac{3(x+1)}{3-2x}$

21. $\dfrac{2(4x+1)}{5x-7} + \dfrac{3(x-2)}{7-5x} + \dfrac{-10x-1}{5x-7}$

22. $\dfrac{5(x-2)}{3x-4} + \dfrac{2(x-3)}{4-3x} + \dfrac{3(5x+1)}{4-3x}$

23. $\dfrac{x+1}{(x+3)(x-3)} + \dfrac{4(x-3)}{(x-3)(x+3)} + \dfrac{(x-1)(x-3)}{(3-x)(x+3)}$

24. $\dfrac{2(x+5)}{(2x-3)(x-1)} + \dfrac{3x+4}{(2x-3)(1-x)} + \dfrac{x-5}{(3-2x)(x-1)}$

25. $\dfrac{2}{x} + \dfrac{5}{x^2}$

26. $\dfrac{4}{x} + \dfrac{8}{x^2}$

27. $\dfrac{5}{6r} + \dfrac{7}{8r}$

28. $\dfrac{2}{9t} + \dfrac{11}{6t}$

29. $\dfrac{4}{xy^2} + \dfrac{6}{x^2y}$

30. $\dfrac{2}{c^2d} + \dfrac{7}{cd^3}$

31. $\dfrac{2}{9t^3} + \dfrac{1}{6t^2}$

32. $\dfrac{-2}{3xy^2} + \dfrac{6}{x^2y^3}$

33. $\dfrac{x+y}{xy^2} + \dfrac{3x+y}{x^2y}$

34. $\dfrac{2c-d}{c^2d} + \dfrac{c+d}{cd^2}$

35. $\dfrac{3}{x-2} + \dfrac{3}{x+2}$

36. $\dfrac{2}{x-1} + \dfrac{2}{x+1}$

37. $\dfrac{3}{x+1} + \dfrac{2}{3x}$

38. $\dfrac{2}{x+5} + \dfrac{3}{4x}$

39. $\dfrac{2x}{x^2-16} + \dfrac{x}{x-4}$

40. $\dfrac{4x}{x^2-25} + \dfrac{x}{x+5}$

41. $\dfrac{5}{z+4} + \dfrac{3}{3z+12}$

42. $\dfrac{t}{t-3} + \dfrac{5}{4t-12}$

43. $\dfrac{3}{x-1} + \dfrac{2}{(x-1)^2}$

44. $\dfrac{2}{x+3} + \dfrac{4}{(x+3)^2}$

45. $\dfrac{4a}{5a-10} + \dfrac{3a}{10a-20}$

46. $\dfrac{3a}{4a-20} + \dfrac{9a}{6a-30}$

47. $\dfrac{x+4}{x} + \dfrac{x}{x+4}$

48. $\dfrac{x}{x-5} + \dfrac{x-5}{x}$

49. $\dfrac{x}{x^2+2x+1} + \dfrac{1}{x^2+5x+4}$

50. $\dfrac{7}{a^2+a-2} + \dfrac{5}{a^2-4a+3}$

51. $\dfrac{x+3}{x-5} + \dfrac{x-5}{x+3}$

52. $\dfrac{3x}{2y-3} + \dfrac{2x}{3y-2}$

53. $\dfrac{a}{a^2-1} + \dfrac{2a}{a^2-a}$

54. $\dfrac{3x+2}{3x+6} + \dfrac{x-2}{x^2-4}$

ANSWERS

37. _____

38. _____

39. _____

40. _____

41. _____

42. _____

43. _____

44. _____

45. _____

46. _____

47. _____

48. _____

49. _____

50. _____

51. _____

52. _____

53. _____

54. _____

55. _____

56. _____

57. _____

58. _____

59. _____

60. _____

61. _____

62. _____

63. _____

64. _____

65. _____

66. _____

67. _____

68. _____

69. _____

70. _____

55. $\dfrac{6}{x-y} + \dfrac{4x}{y^2 - x^2}$

56. $\dfrac{a-2}{3-a} + \dfrac{4-a^2}{a^2-9}$

57. $\dfrac{y+2}{y-7} + \dfrac{3-y}{49-y^2}$

58. $\dfrac{4-p}{25-p^2} + \dfrac{p+1}{p-5}$

59. $\dfrac{10}{x^2+x-6} + \dfrac{3x}{x^2-4x+4}$

60. $\dfrac{2}{z^2-z-6} + \dfrac{3}{z^2-9}$

SKILL MAINTENANCE

Subtract.

61. $(x^2 + x) - (x + 1)$

62. $(4y^3 - 5y^2 + 7y - 24) -$
$(-9y^3 + 9y^2 - 5y + 49)$

Simplify.

63. $(2x^4 y^3)^{-3}$

64. $\left(\dfrac{x^3}{5y}\right)^2$

SYNTHESIS

Find the perimeter and the area of the figure.

65.

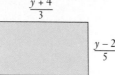

$\dfrac{y+4}{3}$

$\dfrac{y-2}{5}$

66.

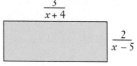

$\dfrac{3}{x+4}$

$\dfrac{2}{x-5}$

Add. Simplify, if possible.

67. $\dfrac{5}{z+2} + \dfrac{4z}{z^2-4} + 2$

68. $\dfrac{-2}{y^2-9} + \dfrac{4y}{(y-3)^2} + \dfrac{6}{3-y}$

69. $\dfrac{3z^2}{z^4-4} + \dfrac{5z^2-3}{2z^4+z^2-6}$

70. Find an expression equivalent to

$$\dfrac{a-3b}{a-b}$$

that is a sum of two fractional expressions. Answers can vary.

11.5 Subtracting Rational Expressions

a We subtract rational expressions as we do rational numbers.

> **To subtract when the denominators are the same, subtract the numerators and keep the same denominator.**

▶ **EXAMPLE 1** Subtract: $\dfrac{3x}{x+2} - \dfrac{x-2}{x+2}$.

$$\frac{3x}{x+2} - \frac{x-2}{x+2} = \frac{3x - (x-2)}{x+2}$$

> The parentheses are important to make sure that you subtract the entire numerator.

$$= \frac{3x - x + 2}{x+2} = \frac{2x+2}{x+2} \quad ◀$$

DO EXERCISES 1 AND 2.

When one denominator is the additive inverse of the other, we can first multiply one expression by $-1/-1$ to obtain a common denominator.

▶ **EXAMPLE 2** Subtract: $\dfrac{x}{5} - \dfrac{3x-4}{-5}$.

$$\frac{x}{5} - \frac{3x-4}{-5} = \frac{x}{5} - \frac{-1}{-1} \cdot \frac{3x-4}{-5}$$

Multiplying by $\dfrac{-1}{-1}$

$$= \frac{x}{5} - \frac{(-1)(3x-4)}{(-1)(-5)}$$

> This is equal to 1 (not -1).

$$= \frac{x}{5} - \frac{4-3x}{5}$$

Remember the parentheses!

$$= \frac{x - (4-3x)}{5}$$

$$= \frac{x - 4 + 3x}{5} = \frac{4x-4}{5} \quad ◀$$

▶ **EXAMPLE 3** Subtract: $\dfrac{5y}{y-5} - \dfrac{2y-3}{5-y}$.

$$\frac{5y}{y-5} - \frac{2y-3}{5-y} = \frac{5y}{y-5} - \frac{-1}{-1} \cdot \frac{2y-3}{5-y}$$

$$= \frac{5y}{y-5} - \frac{(-1)(2y-3)}{(-1)(5-y)} = \frac{5y}{y-5} - \frac{3-2y}{y-5}$$

Remember the parentheses!

$$= \frac{5y - (3-2y)}{y-5}$$

$$= \frac{5y - 3 + 2y}{y-5}$$

$$= \frac{7y-3}{y-5} \quad ◀$$

OBJECTIVES

After finishing Section 11.5, you should be able to:

a Subtract rational expressions.

b Simplify combined additions and subtractions of rational expressions.

FOR EXTRA HELP

Tape 23C

Subtract.

1. $\dfrac{7}{11} - \dfrac{3}{11}$

2. $\dfrac{2x^2 + 3x - 7}{2x+1} - \dfrac{x^2 + x - 8}{2x+1}$

Subtract.

3. $\dfrac{x}{3} - \dfrac{2x-1}{-3}$

4. $\dfrac{3x}{x-2} - \dfrac{x-3}{2-x}$

5. Subtract:

$$\dfrac{x-2}{3x} - \dfrac{2x-1}{5x}.$$

DO EXERCISES 3 AND 4.

To subtract rational expressions with different denominators, we use a procedure similar to what we used for addition, except that we subtract numerators and write the difference over the LCD.

To subtract rational expressions with different denominators:

1. **Find the LCM of the denominators. This is the least common denominator (LCD).**
2. **For each rational expression, find an equivalent expression with the LCD. To do so, multiply by 1 using a symbol for 1 made up of factors of the LCD missing from the original denominator.**
3. **Subtract the numerators. Write the difference over the LCD.**
4. **Simplify, if possible.**

▶ **EXAMPLE 4**   Subtract: $\dfrac{x+2}{x-4} - \dfrac{x+1}{x+4}$.

The LCM $= (x-4)(x+4)$.

$$\dfrac{x+2}{x-4}\cdot\dfrac{x+4}{x+4} - \dfrac{x+1}{x+4}\cdot\dfrac{x-4}{x-4}$$

$$= \dfrac{(x+2)(x+4)}{(x-4)(x+4)} - \dfrac{(x+1)(x-4)}{(x-4)(x+4)}$$

$$= \dfrac{x^2+6x+8}{(x-4)(x+4)} - \dfrac{x^2-3x-4}{(x-4)(x+4)}$$

$$= \dfrac{x^2+6x+8-(x^2-3x-4)}{(x-4)(x+4)}$$

Subtracting this numerator. Don't forget the parentheses.

$$= \dfrac{x^2+6x+8-x^2+3x+4}{(x-4)(x+4)}$$

$$= \dfrac{9x+12}{(x-4)(x+4)}$$ ◀

DO EXERCISE 5.

▶ **EXAMPLE 5**   Subtract: $\dfrac{x}{x^2+5x+6} - \dfrac{2}{x^2+3x+2}$.

$$\dfrac{x}{x^2+5x+6} - \dfrac{2}{x^2+3x+2}$$

$$= \dfrac{x}{(x+2)(x+3)} - \dfrac{2}{(x+2)(x+1)}$$

$$= \dfrac{x}{(x+2)(x+3)}\cdot\dfrac{x+1}{x+1} - \dfrac{2}{(x+2)(x+1)}\cdot\dfrac{x+3}{x+3}$$ LCD $= (x+1)(x+2)(x+3)$

$$= \dfrac{x^2+x}{(x+1)(x+2)(x+3)} - \dfrac{2x+6}{(x+1)(x+2)(x+3)}$$

Then

$$= \frac{x^2 + x - (2x + 6)}{(x + 1)(x + 2)(x + 3)}$$

— Subtracting this numerator.
Don't forget the parentheses.

$$= \frac{x^2 + x - 2x - 6}{(x + 1)(x + 2)(x + 3)}$$

$$= \frac{x^2 - x - 6}{(x + 1)(x + 2)(x + 3)}$$

$$= \frac{(x + 2)(x - 3)}{(x + 1)(x + 2)(x + 3)}$$

$$= \frac{(x + 2)(x - 3)}{(x + 1)(x + 2)(x + 3)}$$

Simplifying by removing a factor of 1: $\frac{x + 2}{x + 2} = 1$

$$= \frac{x - 3}{(x + 1)(x + 3)} \quad ◄$$

DO EXERCISE 6.

Suppose that after we factor to find the LCD, we find factors that are opposites. Then we multiply by $-1/-1$ appropriately to change factors so they are not opposites.

► **EXAMPLE 6** Subtract: $\dfrac{p}{64 - p^2} - \dfrac{5}{p - 8}$.

Factoring $64 - p^2$, we get $(8 - p)(8 + p)$. Note that the factor $8 - p$ in the first denominator and $p - 8$ in the second denominator are opposites. We multiply the first expression by $-1/-1$ to avoid this situation. Then we proceed as before.

$$\frac{p}{64 - p^2} - \frac{5}{p - 8} = \frac{-1}{-1} \cdot \frac{p}{64 - p^2} - \frac{5}{p - 8}$$

$$= \frac{-p}{p^2 - 64} - \frac{5}{p - 8}$$

$$= \frac{-p}{(p - 8)(p + 8)} - \frac{5}{p - 8} \qquad \text{LCD} = (p - 8)(p + 8)$$

$$= \frac{-p}{(p - 8)(p + 8)} - \frac{5}{p - 8} \cdot \frac{p + 8}{p + 8}$$

$$= \frac{-p}{(p - 8)(p + 8)} - \frac{5p + 40}{(p - 8)(p + 8)}$$

— Subtracting this numerator.
Don't forget the parentheses.

$$= \frac{-p - (5p + 40)}{(p - 8)(p + 8)}$$

$$= \frac{-p - 5p - 40}{(p - 8)(p + 8)}$$

$$= \frac{-6p - 40}{(p - 8)(p + 8)} \quad ◄$$

DO EXERCISE 7.

6. Subtract:

$$\frac{x}{x^2 + 15x + 56} - \frac{6}{x^2 + 13x + 42}.$$

7. Subtract:

$$\frac{y}{16 - y^2} - \frac{7}{y - 4}.$$

8. Perform the indicated operations and simplify:

$$\frac{x+2}{x^2-9} - \frac{x-7}{9-x^2} + \frac{-8-x}{x^2-9}.$$

b   **Combined Additions and Subtractions**

▶ **EXAMPLE 7**   Perform the indicated operations and simplify:

$$\frac{x+9}{x^2-4} + \frac{5-x}{4-x^2} - \frac{2+x}{x^2-4}.$$

We have

$$\frac{x+9}{x^2-4} + \frac{5-x}{4-x^2} - \frac{2+x}{x^2-4} = \frac{x+9}{x^2-4} + \frac{-1}{-1} \cdot \frac{5-x}{4-x^2} - \frac{2+x}{x^2-4}$$

$$= \frac{x+9}{x^2-4} + \frac{(-1)(5-x)}{(-1)(4-x^2)} - \frac{2+x}{x^2-4}$$

$$= \frac{(x+9) + (-5+x) - (2+x)}{x^2-4}$$

$$= \frac{x+9-5+x-2-x}{x^2-4}$$

$$= \frac{x+2}{x^2-4}$$

$$= \frac{(x+2) \cdot 1}{(x+2)(x-2)}$$

$$= \frac{1}{x-2}. \qquad \frac{x+2}{x+2} = 1 \qquad ◀$$

DO EXERCISE 8.

9. Perform the indicated operations and simplify:

$$\frac{1}{x} - \frac{5}{3x} + \frac{2x}{x+1}.$$

▶ **EXAMPLE 8**   Perform the indicated operations and simplify:

$$\frac{1}{x} - \frac{1}{x^2} + \frac{2}{x+1}.$$

The LCD = $x \cdot x(x+1)$, or $x^2(x+1)$.

$$\frac{1}{x} \cdot \frac{x(x+1)}{x(x+1)} - \frac{1}{x^2} \cdot \frac{(x+1)}{(x+1)} + \frac{2}{x+1} \cdot \frac{x^2}{x^2}$$

$$= \frac{x(x+1)}{x^2(x+1)} - \frac{x+1}{x^2(x+1)} + \frac{2x^2}{x^2(x+1)}$$

Subtract this numerator.
Don't forget the parentheses.

$$= \frac{x(x+1) - (x+1) + 2x^2}{x^2(x+1)}$$

$$= \frac{x^2 + x - x - 1 + 2x^2}{x^2(x+1)}$$

$$= \frac{3x^2 - 1}{x^2(x+1)} \qquad ◀$$

DO EXERCISE 9.

ANSWERS ON PAGE A-8

NAME   SECTION   DATE

EXERCISE SET 11.5

a Subtract. Simplify, if possible.

1. $\dfrac{7}{8} - \dfrac{3}{8}$

2. $\dfrac{5}{y} - \dfrac{7}{y}$

3. $\dfrac{x}{x-1} - \dfrac{1}{x-1}$

4. $\dfrac{x^2}{x+4} - \dfrac{16}{x+4}$

5. $\dfrac{x+1}{x^2-2x+1} - \dfrac{5-3x}{x^2-2x+1}$

6. $\dfrac{2x-3}{x^2+3x-4} - \dfrac{x-7}{x^2+3x-4}$

7. $\dfrac{11}{6} - \dfrac{5}{-6}$

8. $\dfrac{7}{8} - \dfrac{5}{-8}$

9. $\dfrac{5}{a} - \dfrac{8}{-a}$

10. $\dfrac{3}{t} - \dfrac{4}{-t}$

11. $\dfrac{x}{4} - \dfrac{3x-5}{-4}$

12. $\dfrac{2}{x-1} - \dfrac{2}{1-x}$

13. $\dfrac{3-x}{x-7} - \dfrac{2x-5}{7-x}$

14. $\dfrac{t^2}{t-2} - \dfrac{4}{2-t}$

1. _____

2. _____

3. _____

4. _____

5. _____

6. _____

7. _____

8. _____

9. _____

10. _____

11. _____

12. _____

13. _____

14. _____

Copyright © 1993 Addison-Wesley Publishing Co., Inc.

ANSWERS

15. _____

16. _____

17. _____

18. _____

19. _____

20. _____

21. _____

22. _____

23. _____

24. _____

25. _____

26. _____

27. _____

28. _____

15. $\dfrac{x-8}{x^2-16} - \dfrac{x-8}{16-x^2}$

16. $\dfrac{x-2}{x^2-25} - \dfrac{6-x}{25-x^2}$

17. $\dfrac{4-x}{x-9} - \dfrac{3x-8}{9-x}$

18. $\dfrac{3-x}{x-7} - \dfrac{2x-5}{7-x}$

19. $\dfrac{2(x-1)}{2x-3} - \dfrac{3(x+2)}{2x-3} - \dfrac{x-1}{3-2x}$

20. $\dfrac{3(x-2)}{2x-3} - \dfrac{5(2x+1)}{2x-3} - \dfrac{3(x-1)}{3-2x}$

Subtract. Simplify, if possible.

21. $\dfrac{x-2}{6} - \dfrac{x+1}{3}$

22. $\dfrac{a+2}{2} - \dfrac{a-4}{4}$

23. $\dfrac{4z-9}{3z} - \dfrac{3z-8}{4z}$

24. $\dfrac{x-1}{4x} - \dfrac{2x+3}{x}$

25. $\dfrac{4x+2t}{3xt^2} - \dfrac{5x-3t}{x^2t}$

26. $\dfrac{5x+3y}{2x^2y} - \dfrac{3x+4y}{xy^2}$

27. $\dfrac{5}{x+5} - \dfrac{3}{x-5}$

28. $\dfrac{2z}{z-1} - \dfrac{3z}{z+1}$

29. $\dfrac{3}{2t^2 - 2t} - \dfrac{5}{2t - 2}$

30. $\dfrac{8}{x^2 - 4} - \dfrac{3}{x + 2}$

31. $\dfrac{2s}{t^2 - s^2} - \dfrac{s}{t - s}$

32. $\dfrac{3}{12 + x - x^2} - \dfrac{2}{x^2 - 9}$

33. $\dfrac{y - 5}{y} - \dfrac{3y - 1}{4y}$

34. $\dfrac{3x - 2}{4x} - \dfrac{3x + 1}{6x}$

35. $\dfrac{a}{x + a} - \dfrac{a}{x - a}$

36. $\dfrac{t}{y - t} - \dfrac{y}{y + t}$

37. $\dfrac{8x}{16 - x^2} - \dfrac{5}{x - 4}$

38. $\dfrac{5x}{x^2 - 9} - \dfrac{4}{3 - x}$

39. $\dfrac{t^2}{2t^2 - 2t} - \dfrac{1}{2t - 2}$

40. $\dfrac{4}{5b^2 - 5b} - \dfrac{3}{5b - 5}$

41. $\dfrac{x}{x^2 + 5x + 6} - \dfrac{2}{x^2 + 3x + 2}$

42. $\dfrac{x}{x^2 + 11x + 30} - \dfrac{5}{x^2 + 9x + 20}$

ANSWERS

29. _____

30. _____

31. _____

32. _____

33. _____

34. _____

35. _____

36. _____

37. _____

38. _____

39. _____

40. _____

41. _____

42. _____

b   Perform the indicated operations and simplify.

43. $\dfrac{3(2x+5)}{x-1} - \dfrac{3(2x-3)}{1-x} + \dfrac{6x-1}{x-1}$

44. $\dfrac{2x-y}{x-y} + \dfrac{x-2y}{y-x} - \dfrac{3x-3y}{x-y}$

45. $\dfrac{x-y}{x^2-y^2} + \dfrac{x+y}{x^2-y^2} - \dfrac{2x}{x^2-y^2}$

46. $\dfrac{x+y}{2(x-y)} - \dfrac{2x-2y}{2(x-y)} + \dfrac{x-3y}{2(y-x)}$

47. $\dfrac{10}{2y-1} - \dfrac{6}{1-2y} + \dfrac{y}{2y-1} + \dfrac{y-4}{1-2y}$

48. $\dfrac{(x+1)(2x-1)}{(2x-3)(x-3)} - \dfrac{(x-3)(x+1)}{(3-x)(3-2x)} + \dfrac{(2x+1)(x+3)}{(3-2x)(x-3)}$

49. $\dfrac{4y}{y^2-1} - \dfrac{2}{y} - \dfrac{2}{y+1}$

50. $\dfrac{x+6}{4-x^2} - \dfrac{x+3}{x+2} + \dfrac{x-3}{2-x}$

51. $\dfrac{2z}{1-2z} + \dfrac{3z}{2z+1} - \dfrac{3}{4z^2-1}$

52. $\dfrac{1}{x+y} + \dfrac{1}{x-y} - \dfrac{2x}{x^2-y^2}$

53. $\dfrac{1}{x+y} - \dfrac{1}{x-y} + \dfrac{2x}{x^2-y^2}$

54. $\dfrac{1}{a-b} - \dfrac{1}{a+b} + \dfrac{2b}{a^2-b^2}$

SKILL MAINTENANCE

Simplify.

55. $\dfrac{x^8}{x^3}$ 56. $3x^4 \cdot 10x^8$ 57. $(a^2b^{-5})^{-4}$ 58. $\dfrac{54x^{10}}{3x^7}$

SYNTHESIS

Subtract. Simplify, if possible.

59. $\dfrac{5}{3-2x} + \dfrac{3}{2x-3} - \dfrac{x-3}{2x^2-x-3}$

60. $\dfrac{2r}{r^2-s^2} + \dfrac{1}{r+s} - \dfrac{1}{r-s}$

11.6 Solving Rational Equations

a In Sections 11.1–11.5, we studied operations with rational **expressions**. These were expressions not having an equals sign. We cannot clear expressions of fractions other than occasionally when simplifying by removing a factor of 1. In this section, we are studying rational **equations**. Equations do have an equals sign, and we can clear of fractions as we did in Section 8.3.

A **rational,** or **fractional, equation** is an equation containing one or more rational expressions. Here are some examples:

$$\frac{2}{3} + \frac{5}{6} = \frac{x}{9}, \qquad x + \frac{6}{x} = -5, \qquad \frac{x^2}{x-1} = \frac{1}{x-1}.$$

> To solve a rational equation, the first step is to clear the equation of fractions. To do this, multiply both sides of the equation by the LCM of all the denominators. Then carry out the equation-solving process as we learned it in Chapter 8.

When clearing an equation of fractions, we use the terminology LCM instead of LCD because we are *not* adding or subtracting rational expressions.

▶ **EXAMPLE 1** Solve: $\dfrac{2}{3} + \dfrac{5}{6} = \dfrac{x}{9}$.

The LCM of all denominators is $2 \cdot 3 \cdot 3$, or 18. We multiply on both sides by 18:

$$\frac{2}{3} + \frac{5}{6} = \frac{x}{9}$$

$$18\left(\frac{2}{3} + \frac{5}{6}\right) = 18 \cdot \frac{x}{9} \qquad \text{Multiplying on both sides by the LCM}$$

$$18 \cdot \frac{2}{3} + 18 \cdot \frac{5}{6} = 18 \cdot \frac{x}{9} \qquad \text{Multiplying to remove parentheses}$$

> When clearing an equation of fractions, be sure to multiply *each* rational expression in the equation by the LCM.

$$12 + 15 = 2x \qquad \text{Simplifying. Note that we have now cleared of fractions.}$$

$$27 = 2x$$

$$\frac{27}{2} = x.$$

◀

DO EXERCISE 1.

OBJECTIVE

After finishing Section 11.6, you should be able to:

a Solve rational equations.

FOR EXTRA HELP

Tape 23D

1. Solve: $\dfrac{3}{4} + \dfrac{5}{8} = \dfrac{x}{12}$.

ANSWER ON PAGE A-8

2. Solve: $\dfrac{1}{x} = \dfrac{1}{6 - x}$.

▶ **EXAMPLE 2**   Solve: $\dfrac{1}{x} = \dfrac{1}{4 - x}$.

The LCM is $x(4 - x)$. We multiply on both sides by $x(4 - x)$:

$$\frac{1}{x} = \frac{1}{4 - x}$$

$$x(4 - x) \cdot \frac{1}{x} = x(4 - x) \cdot \frac{1}{4 - x} \qquad \text{Multiplying on both sides by the LCM}$$

$$4 - x = x \qquad \text{Simplifying}$$

$$4 = 2x$$

$$x = 2.$$

Check:

$$\frac{1}{x} = \frac{1}{4 - x}$$

$$\begin{array}{c|c} \dfrac{1}{2} & \dfrac{1}{4 - 2} \\[2mm] & \dfrac{1}{2} \quad \text{TRUE} \end{array}$$

This checks, so 2 is the solution.   ◀

DO EXERCISE 2.

3. Solve: $\dfrac{x}{4} - \dfrac{x}{6} = \dfrac{1}{8}$.

▶ **EXAMPLE 3**   Solve: $\dfrac{x}{6} - \dfrac{x}{8} = \dfrac{1}{12}$.

The LCM is 24. We multiply on both sides by 24:

$$\frac{x}{6} - \frac{x}{8} = \frac{1}{12}$$

$$24\left(\frac{x}{6} - \frac{x}{8}\right) = 24 \cdot \frac{1}{12} \qquad \text{Multiplying on both sides by the LCM}$$

$$24 \cdot \frac{x}{6} - 24 \cdot \frac{x}{8} = 24 \cdot \frac{1}{12} \qquad \text{Multiplying to remove parentheses}$$

> Be sure to multiply *each* term by the LCM.

$$4x - 3x = 2 \qquad \text{Simplifying}$$

$$x = 2.$$

Check:

$$\frac{x}{6} - \frac{x}{8} = \frac{1}{12}$$

$$\begin{array}{c|c} \dfrac{2}{6} - \dfrac{2}{8} & \dfrac{1}{12} \\[2mm] \dfrac{1}{3} - \dfrac{1}{4} & \\[2mm] \dfrac{4}{12} - \dfrac{3}{12} & \\[2mm] \dfrac{1}{12} & \text{TRUE} \end{array}$$

This checks, so the solution is 2.   ◀

ANSWERS ON PAGE A-8

DO EXERCISE 3.

► **EXAMPLE 4**   Solve: $\dfrac{2}{3x} + \dfrac{1}{x} = 10$.

The LCM is $3x$. We multiply on both sides by $3x$:

$$\frac{2}{3x} + \frac{1}{x} = 10$$

$$3x\left(\frac{2}{3x} + \frac{1}{x}\right) = 3x \cdot 10 \qquad \text{Multiplying on both sides by the LCM}$$

$$3x \cdot \frac{2}{3x} + 3x \cdot \frac{1}{x} = 3x \cdot 10 \qquad \text{Multiplying to remove parentheses}$$

$$2 + 3 = 30x \qquad \text{Simplifying}$$

$$5 = 30x$$

$$\frac{5}{30} = x$$

$$\frac{1}{6} = x.$$

We leave the check to the student. The solution is $\frac{1}{6}$.   ◄

DO EXERCISE 4.

► **EXAMPLE 5**   Solve: $x + \dfrac{6}{x} = -5$.

The LCM is x. We multiply on both sides by x:

$$x + \frac{6}{x} = -5$$

$$x\left(x + \frac{6}{x}\right) = -5x \qquad \text{Multiplying on both sides by } x$$

$$x \cdot x + x \cdot \frac{6}{x} = -5x \qquad \begin{array}{l}\text{Note that each rational expression}\\ \text{on the left is now multiplied by } x.\end{array}$$

$$x^2 + 6 = -5x \qquad \text{Simplifying}$$

$$x^2 + 5x + 6 = 0 \qquad \text{Subtracting } 5x \text{ to get a 0 on one side}$$

$$(x + 3)(x + 2) = 0 \qquad \text{Factoring}$$

$$x + 3 = 0 \quad \text{or} \quad x + 2 = 0 \qquad \text{Using the principle of zero products}$$

$$x = -3 \quad \text{or} \qquad x = -2.$$

Check: For -3:   For -2:

$$\begin{array}{c|c} x + \dfrac{6}{x} = -5 & \\ \hline -3 + \dfrac{6}{-3} & -5 \\ -3 - 2 & \\ -5 & \text{TRUE} \end{array} \qquad \begin{array}{c|c} x + \dfrac{6}{x} = -5 & \\ \hline -2 + \dfrac{6}{-2} & -5 \\ -2 - 3 & \\ -5 & \text{TRUE} \end{array}$$

Both of these check, so there are two solutions, -3 and -2.   ◄

DO EXERCISE 5.

4. Solve: $\dfrac{1}{2x} + \dfrac{1}{x} = -12$.

5. Solve: $x + \dfrac{1}{x} = 2$.

6. Solve: $\dfrac{x^2}{x+2} = \dfrac{4}{x+2}$.

7. Solve: $\dfrac{4}{x-2} + \dfrac{1}{x+2} = \dfrac{26}{x^2-4}$.

CAUTION! We have introduced a new use of the LCM in this section. You previously used the LCM in adding or subtracting rational expressions. *Now* we have equations with equals signs. We clear of fractions by multiplying on both sides of the equation by the LCM. This eliminates the denominators. Do *not* make the mistake of trying to "clear of fractions" when you do not have an equation.

When we multiply on both sides of an equation by the LCM, we might not get equivalent equations. Thus we must *always* check possible solutions in the original equation.

1. If you have carried out all algebraic procedures correctly, you need only check to see if a number is a meaningful replacement in all parts of the original equation.

2. To be sure that no computational errors have been made and that you indeed have a solution, a complete check is necessary, as we did in Chapter 8.

The next example will illustrate the importance of the preceding comments.

▶ **EXAMPLE 6**   Solve: $\dfrac{x^2}{x-1} = \dfrac{1}{x-1}$.

The LCM is $x - 1$. We multiply on both sides by $x - 1$:

$$\frac{x^2}{x-1} = \frac{1}{x-1}$$

$$(x-1)\cdot\frac{x^2}{x-1} = (x-1)\cdot\frac{1}{x-1} \qquad \text{Multiplying on both sides by } x-1$$

$$x^2 = 1 \qquad \text{Simplifying}$$

$$x^2 - 1 = 0 \qquad \text{Subtracting 1 to get a 0 on one side}$$

$$(x-1)(x+1) = 0 \qquad \text{Factoring}$$

$$x - 1 = 0 \quad \text{or} \quad x + 1 = 0 \qquad \text{Using the principle of zero products}$$

$$x = 1 \quad \text{or} \qquad x = -1.$$

The numbers 1 and -1 are possible solutions. We look at the original equation and see that 1 is not a meaningful replacement because it makes a denominator zero. The number -1 checks and is a solution. ◀

DO EXERCISE 6.

▶ **EXAMPLE 7**   Solve: $\dfrac{3}{x-5} + \dfrac{1}{x+5} = \dfrac{2}{x^2-25}$.

The LCM is $(x - 5)(x + 5)$. We multiply on both sides by $(x - 5)(x + 5)$:

$$(x-5)(x+5)\left(\frac{3}{x-5} + \frac{1}{x+5}\right) = (x-5)(x+5)\left(\frac{2}{x^2-25}\right)$$

                                      Multiplying on both sides by the LCM

$$(x-5)(x+5)\cdot\frac{3}{x-5} + (x-5)(x+5)\cdot\frac{1}{x+5} = (x-5)(x+5)\cdot\frac{2}{x^2-25}$$

$$3(x+5) + (x-5) = 2 \qquad \text{Simplifying}$$

$$3x + 15 + x - 5 = 2 \qquad \text{Removing parentheses}$$

$$4x + 10 = 2$$

$$4x = -8$$

$$x = -2.$$

The check is left to the student. The number -2 checks and is the solution.

DO EXERCISE 7.   ◀

EXERCISE SET 11.6

a Solve.

1. $\dfrac{3}{8} + \dfrac{4}{5} = \dfrac{x}{20}$

2. $\dfrac{3}{5} + \dfrac{2}{3} = \dfrac{x}{9}$

3. $\dfrac{2}{3} - \dfrac{5}{6} = \dfrac{1}{x}$

4. $\dfrac{1}{8} - \dfrac{3}{5} = \dfrac{1}{x}$

5. $\dfrac{1}{6} + \dfrac{1}{8} = \dfrac{1}{t}$

6. $\dfrac{1}{8} + \dfrac{1}{10} = \dfrac{1}{t}$

7. $x + \dfrac{4}{x} = -5$

8. $x + \dfrac{3}{x} = -4$

9. $\dfrac{x}{4} - \dfrac{4}{x} = 0$

10. $\dfrac{x}{5} - \dfrac{5}{x} = 0$

11. $\dfrac{5}{x} = \dfrac{6}{x} - \dfrac{1}{3}$

12. $\dfrac{4}{x} = \dfrac{5}{x} - \dfrac{1}{2}$

13. $\dfrac{5}{3x} + \dfrac{3}{x} = 1$

14. $\dfrac{3}{4x} + \dfrac{5}{x} = 1$

15. $\dfrac{x-7}{x+2} = \dfrac{1}{4}$

16. $\dfrac{a-2}{a+3} = \dfrac{3}{8}$

17. $\dfrac{2}{x+1} = \dfrac{1}{x-2}$

18. $\dfrac{5}{x-1} = \dfrac{3}{x+2}$

19. $\dfrac{x}{6} - \dfrac{x}{10} = \dfrac{1}{6}$

20. $\dfrac{x}{8} - \dfrac{x}{12} = \dfrac{1}{8}$

21. $\dfrac{x+1}{3} - \dfrac{x-1}{2} = 1$

22. $\dfrac{x+2}{5} - \dfrac{x-2}{4} = 1$

23. $\dfrac{a-3}{3a+2} = \dfrac{1}{5}$

24. $\dfrac{x-1}{2x+5} = \dfrac{1}{4}$

ANSWERS

1. _____

2. _____

3. _____

4. _____

5. _____

6. _____

7. _____

8. _____

9. _____

10. _____

11. _____

12. _____

13. _____

14. _____

15. _____

16. _____

17. _____

18. _____

19. _____

20. _____

21. _____

22. _____

23. _____

24. _____

ANSWERS

25. _____

26. _____

27. _____

28. _____

29. _____

30. _____

31. _____

32. _____

33. _____

34. _____

35. _____

36. _____

37. _____

38. _____

39. _____

40. _____

41. _____

42. _____

43. _____

44. _____

45. _____

46. _____

47. _____

48. _____

25. $\dfrac{x-1}{x-5} = \dfrac{4}{x-5}$

26. $\dfrac{x-7}{x-9} = \dfrac{2}{x-9}$

27. $\dfrac{2}{x+3} = \dfrac{5}{x}$

28. $\dfrac{3}{x+4} = \dfrac{4}{x}$

29. $\dfrac{x-2}{x-3} = \dfrac{x-1}{x+1}$

30. $\dfrac{2b-3}{3b+2} = \dfrac{2b+1}{3b-2}$

31. $\dfrac{1}{x+3} + \dfrac{1}{x-3} = \dfrac{1}{x^2-9}$

32. $\dfrac{4}{x-3} + \dfrac{2x}{x^2-9} = \dfrac{1}{x+3}$

33. $\dfrac{x}{x+4} - \dfrac{4}{x-4} = \dfrac{x^2+16}{x^2-16}$

34. $\dfrac{5}{y-3} - \dfrac{30}{y^2-9} = 1$

35. $\dfrac{-3}{y-7} = \dfrac{-10-y}{7-y}$

36. $\dfrac{4-m}{8-m} = \dfrac{4}{m-8}$

SKILL MAINTENANCE

Simplify.

37. $(a^2 b^5)^{-3}$

38. $(x^{-2} y^{-3})^{-4}$

39. $\left(\dfrac{2x}{t^2}\right)^4$

40. $\left(\dfrac{y^3}{w^2}\right)^{-2}$

SYNTHESIS

Solve.

41. $\dfrac{4}{y-2} - \dfrac{2y-3}{y^2-4} = \dfrac{5}{y+2}$

42. $\dfrac{x}{x^2+3x-4} + \dfrac{x+1}{x^2+6x+8} = \dfrac{2x}{x^2+x-2}$

43. $\dfrac{y}{y+0.2} - 1.2 = \dfrac{y-0.2}{y+0.2}$

44. $\dfrac{x^2}{x^2-4} = \dfrac{x}{x+2} - \dfrac{2x}{2-x}$

45. $4a - 3 = \dfrac{a+13}{a+1}$

46. $\dfrac{3x-9}{x-3} = \dfrac{5x-4}{2}$

47. $\dfrac{y^2-4}{y+3} = 2 - \dfrac{y-2}{y+3}$

48. $\dfrac{3a-5}{a^2+4a+3} + \dfrac{2a+2}{a+3} = \dfrac{a-3}{a+1}$

11.7 Solving Problems and Proportions

a Solving Problems

▶ **EXAMPLE 1** If 2 is subtracted from a number and then the reciprocal is found, the result is twice the reciprocal of the number itself. What is the number?

1. *Familiarize.* Let us try to guess such a number. Try 10: $10 - 2$ is 8, and the reciprocal of 8 is $\frac{1}{8}$. Two times the reciprocal of 10 is $2(\frac{1}{10})$, or $\frac{1}{5}$. Since $\frac{1}{8} \neq \frac{1}{5}$, the number 10 does not check, but the process helps us understand the translation. Let $x =$ the number.

2. *Translate.* From the familiarization step, we get the following translation. Subtracting 2 from the number gives us $x - 2$. Twice the reciprocal of the original number is $2(1/x)$.

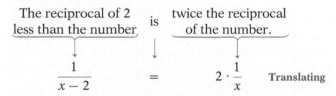

$$\frac{1}{x - 2} = 2 \cdot \frac{1}{x} \qquad \textbf{Translating}$$

3. *Solve.* We solve the equation. The LCM is $x(x - 2)$.

$$x(x - 2) \cdot \frac{1}{x - 2} = x(x - 2) \cdot \frac{2}{x} \qquad \textbf{Multiplying by the LCM}$$

$$x = 2(x - 2) \qquad \textbf{Simplifying}$$

$$x = 2x - 4$$

$$-x = -4$$

$$x = 4.$$

4. *Check.* We go back to the original problem. The number to be checked is 4. Two from 4 is 2. The reciprocal of 2 is $\frac{1}{2}$. The reciprocal of the number itself is $\frac{1}{4}$. Since $\frac{1}{2}$ is twice $\frac{1}{4}$, the conditions are satisfied.

5. *State.* The number is 4. ◀

DO EXERCISE 1.

▶ **EXAMPLE 2** One car travels 20 km/h faster than another. While one car goes 240 km, the other goes 160 km. Find their speeds.

1. *Familiarize.* First we make a drawing. We really do not know the directions in which the cars are traveling, but it does not matter. Let $r =$ the speed of the slow car. Then $r + 20 =$ the speed of the fast car.

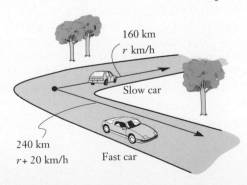

160 km
r km/h
Slow car

240 km
$r + 20$ km/h   Fast car

OBJECTIVES

After finishing Section 11.7, you should be able to:

a Solve applied problems using rational equations.

b Solve proportion problems.

FOR EXTRA HELP

Tape 24A

1. The reciprocal of two more than a number is three times the reciprocal of the number. Find the number.

ANSWER ON PAGE A-9

2. One car goes 10 km/h faster than another. While one car goes 120 km, the other goes 150 km. How fast does each car travel?

The cars travel for the same length of time, so we can just use t for time. We have the notions of distance, speed, and time in this problem. Are they related? Recall that we may need to find a formula that relates the parts of a problem. Indeed, you may need to look up such a formula. Actually we have considered this formula before; it is $d = rt$, *Distance = Speed · Time*. We can organize the information in a chart, as follows.

$$d \quad = \quad r \quad \cdot \quad t$$

	Distance	Speed	Time	
Slow car	160	r	t	$\longrightarrow 160 = rt$
Fast car	240	$r + 20$	t	$\longrightarrow 240 = (r + 20)t$

2. *Translate.* We can apply the formula $d = rt$ along the rows of the table to obtain two equations:

$$160 = rt, \qquad \textbf{(1)}$$
$$240 = (r + 20)t. \qquad \textbf{(2)}$$

The cars travel for the same length of time. Thus if we solve each equation for t and set the results equal, we get an equation in terms of r.

Solving $160 = rt$ for t: $t = \dfrac{160}{r}$

Solving $240 = (r + 20)t$: $t = \dfrac{240}{r + 20}$

Since the times are the same, we get the following equation:

$$\frac{160}{r} = \frac{240}{r + 20}.$$

3. *Solve.* To solve the equation, we first multiply on both sides by the LCM, which is $r(r + 20)$:

$$r(r + 20) \cdot \frac{160}{r} = r(r + 20) \cdot \frac{240}{r + 20} \qquad \text{\textbf{Multiplying on both sides}}$$
$$\text{\textbf{by the LCM, } } \boldsymbol{r(r + 20)}$$

$$160(r + 20) = 240r \qquad \text{\textbf{Simplifying}}$$
$$160r + 3200 = 240r \qquad \text{\textbf{Removing parentheses}}$$
$$3200 = 80r \qquad \text{\textbf{Subtracting } } \boldsymbol{160r}$$
$$\frac{3200}{80} = r \qquad \text{\textbf{Dividing by 80}}$$
$$40 = r.$$

We now have a possible solution. The speed of the slow car is 40 km/h, and the speed of the fast car is $r = 40 + 20$, or 60 km/h.

4. *Check.* We first reread the problem to see what we are to find. We check the speeds of 40 km/h for the slow car and 60 km/h for the fast car. The fast car does travel 20 km/h faster than the slow car. The fast car will travel farther than the slow car. If the fast car goes 240 km at 60 km/h, the time it has traveled is $\frac{240}{60}$, or 4 hr. If the slow car goes 160 km at 40 km/h, the time it travels is $\frac{160}{40}$, or 4 hr. Since the times are the same, the speeds check.

5. *State.* The slow car has a speed of 40 km/h, and the fast car has a speed of 60 km/h.   ◀

DO EXERCISE 2.

▶ **EXAMPLE 3**   The head of a secretarial pool examines work records and finds that it takes Helen 4 hr to type a certain report. It takes Willie 6 hr to type the same report. How long would it take them, working together, to type the report?

1. *Familiarize.*   We familiarize ourselves with the problem by considering two *incorrect* ways of translating the problem to mathematical language.

   a) A common incorrect way to translate the problem is just to add the two times:

$$4 \text{ hr} + 6 \text{ hr} = 10 \text{ hr}.$$

   Now think about this. Helen can do the job alone in 4 hr. If Helen and Willie work together, whatever time it takes them should be *less* than 4 hr. Thus we reject 10 hr as a solution, but we do have a partial check on any answer we get. The answer should be less than 4 hr.

   b) Another incorrect way to translate the problem is as follows. Suppose the two people split up the typing job in such a way that Helen does half the typing and Willie does the other half. Then

$$\text{Helen types } \frac{1}{2} \text{ the report in } \frac{1}{2}(4 \text{ hr}), \text{ or 2 hr,}$$

and $$\text{Willie types } \frac{1}{2} \text{ the report in } \frac{1}{2}(6 \text{ hr}), \text{ or 3 hr.}$$

   But time is wasted since Helen would get done 1 hr earlier than Willie. In effect, they have not worked together to get the job done as fast as possible. If Helen helps Willie after completing her half, the entire job could be done in a time somewhere between 2 hr and 3 hr.

We proceed to a translation by considering how much of the job is finished in 1 hr, 2 hr, 3 hr, and so on. It takes Helen 4 hr to do the typing job alone. Then, in 1 hr, she can do $\frac{1}{4}$ of the job. It takes Willie 6 hr to do the job alone. Then, in 1 hr, he can do $\frac{1}{6}$ of the job. Working together, they can do

$$\frac{1}{4} + \frac{1}{6}, \quad \text{or } \frac{5}{12} \text{ of the job in 1 hr.}$$

In 2 hr, Helen can do $2(\frac{1}{4})$ of the job and Willie can do $2(\frac{1}{6})$ of the job. Working together in two hours, they can do

$$2\left(\frac{1}{4}\right) + 2\left(\frac{1}{6}\right), \quad \text{or } \frac{5}{6} \text{ of the job in 2 hr.}$$

Continuing this reasoning, we can form a table like the following one.

Time	Fraction of the job completed		
	Helen	**Willie**	**Together**
1 hr	$\frac{1}{4}$	$\frac{1}{6}$	$\frac{1}{4} + \frac{1}{6}$, or $\frac{5}{12}$
2 hr	$2\left(\frac{1}{4}\right)$	$2\left(\frac{1}{6}\right)$	$2\left(\frac{1}{4}\right) + 2\left(\frac{1}{6}\right)$, or $\frac{5}{6}$
3 hr	$3\left(\frac{1}{4}\right)$	$3\left(\frac{1}{6}\right)$	$3\left(\frac{1}{4}\right) + 3\left(\frac{1}{6}\right)$, or $1\frac{1}{4}$
t hr	$t\left(\frac{1}{4}\right)$	$t\left(\frac{1}{6}\right)$	$t\left(\frac{1}{4}\right) + t\left(\frac{1}{6}\right)$

3. By checking work records, a contractor finds that it takes Red Bryck 6 hr to construct a wall of a certain size. It takes Lotta Mudd 8 hr to construct the same wall. How long would it take if they worked together?

4. Find the ratio of 145 km to 2.5 liters (L).

5. Recently, a baseball player got 7 hits in 25 times at bat. What was the rate, or batting average, in hits per times at bat?

6. Impulses in nerve fibers travel 310 km in 2.5 hr. What is the rate, or speed, in kilometers per hour?

7. A lake of area 550 yd² contains 1320 fish. What is the population density of the lake in fish per square yard?

From the table, we see that if they worked 3 hr, the fraction of the job that they get done is $1\frac{1}{4}$, which is more of the job than needs to be done. We also see that the answer is somewhere between 2 hr and 3 hr. What we want is a number t such that the fraction of the job that gets completed is 1; that is, the job is just completed—not more than $1\frac{1}{4}$ and not less than $\frac{5}{6}$.

2. *Translate.* From the table, we see that the time we want is some number t for which

$$t\left(\frac{1}{4}\right) + t\left(\frac{1}{6}\right) = 1, \quad \text{or} \quad \frac{t}{4} + \frac{t}{6} = 1,$$

where 1 represents the idea that the entire job is completed in time t.

3. *Solve.* We solve the equation:

$$\frac{t}{4} + \frac{t}{6} = 1$$

$$12\left(\frac{t}{4} + \frac{t}{6}\right) = 12 \cdot 1 \qquad \text{The LCM is } 2 \cdot 2 \cdot 3, \text{ or } 12.$$

$$12 \cdot \frac{t}{4} + 12 \cdot \frac{t}{6} = 12$$

$$3t + 2t = 12$$

$$5t = 12$$

$$t = \frac{12}{5}, \quad \text{or } 2\frac{2}{5} \text{ hr.}$$

4. *Check.* The check can be done by repeating the computations:

$$\frac{12}{5}\left(\frac{1}{4}\right) + \frac{12}{5}\left(\frac{1}{6}\right) = \frac{3}{5} + \frac{2}{5} = \frac{5}{5} = 1.$$

We also have another check in what we learned from our familiarization. The answer, $2\frac{2}{5}$ hr, is between 2 hr and 3 hr (see the table), and it is less than 4 hr, the time it takes Helen working alone.

5. *State.* It takes $2\frac{2}{5}$ hr for them to do the job working together.   ◄

The Work Principle

Suppose $a =$ the time it takes person A to do a job, $b =$ the time it takes person B to do the same job, and $t =$ the time it takes them to do the same job working together. Then

$$\frac{t}{a} + \frac{t}{b} = 1.$$

DO EXERCISE 3.

b   **Solving Proportion Problems**

We now consider problems concerning proportions. A **proportion** involves ratios. A **ratio** of two quantities is their quotient. For example, 37% is the ratio of 37 to 100, $\frac{37}{100}$. The ratio of two different kinds of measure is called a **rate**. If you travel 400 mi in 7 hr, your rate, or **speed**, is

$$\frac{400 \text{ mi}}{7 \text{ hr}} \approx 57.1 \frac{\text{mi}}{\text{hr}}, \quad \text{or } 57.1 \text{ mph.}$$

DO EXERCISES 4–7.

An equality of ratios, $A/B = C/D$, is called a *proportion*. The numbers named in a true proportion are said to be *proportional*.

Proportions can be used to solve applied problems by expressing a single ratio in two ways. For example, suppose it takes 9 gal of gas to drive 120 mi, and we wish to find how much will be required to go 550 mi. If we assume that the car uses gas at the same rate throughout the trip, the ratios are the same, and we can write a proportion.

$$\text{Gas} \longrightarrow \frac{9}{120} = \frac{x}{550} \longleftarrow \text{Gas} \atop \longleftarrow \text{Miles}$$

To solve this proportion, we multiply by 550 to get x alone on one side:

$$550 \cdot \frac{9}{120} = 550 \cdot \frac{x}{550}$$

$$\frac{550 \cdot 9}{120} = x$$

$$41.25 = x.$$

Thus, 41.25 gal will be required to go 550 mi. (Note that we could have multiplied by the LCM of 120 and 550, which is 66,000, but in this case, that would have been more complicated.) We can also use **cross products** to solve proportions:

$$\frac{9}{120} \diagdown\diagup \frac{x}{550}$$

$9 \cdot 550 = 120 \cdot x$ **9 · 550 and 120 · x are called *cross products*.**

$$\frac{9 \cdot 550}{120} = x$$

$$41.25 = x.$$

This method can be verified using the multiplication principle, multiplying on both sides by 550 and then by 120, but we will not do so here.

▶ **EXAMPLE 4**   A student is to read 32 essays. It takes the student 40 min to read 5 essays. At this rate, how long will it take to read all 32 essays?

1. *Familiarize.*   The student reads 5 essays in 40 min, and we wish to find how long it will take to read all 32 essays. We can set up ratios. We let t = the total time to read 32 essays.

2. *Translate.*   If we assume that the student continues to read at the same rate, the ratios are the same, and we have an equation:

$$\text{Number of essays} \longrightarrow \frac{5}{40} = \frac{32}{t} \longleftarrow \text{Number of essays} \atop \longleftarrow \text{Amount of time}$$

3. *Solve.*   We solve the equation:

$$40t \cdot \frac{5}{40} = 40t \cdot \frac{32}{t} \qquad \textbf{Multiplying by the LCM, 40\textit{t}}$$

$$5t = 40 \cdot 32$$

$$t = \frac{40 \cdot 32}{5} = 256 \text{ min}, \quad \text{or } 4\frac{4}{15} \text{ hr.}$$

8. It takes 60 oz of grass seed to seed 3000 ft² of lawn. At this rate, how much would be needed for 5000 ft² of lawn?

9. A sample of 184 light bulbs contained 6 defective bulbs. How many would you expect to find in 1288 bulbs?

10. To determine the number of deer in a forest, a conservationist catches 612 deer, tags them, and lets them loose. Later, 244 deer are caught. Seventy-two of them are tagged. Estimate how many deer are in the forest.

4. *Check.*   We leave the check to the student.

5. *State.*   It will take the student 256 min, or $4\frac{4}{15}$ hr, to read 32 essays.   ◄

DO EXERCISES 8 AND 9.

► **EXAMPLE 5**   *Estimating wildlife populations.* To determine the number of fish in a lake, a conservationist catches 225 fish, tags them, and throws them back into the lake. Later, 108 fish are caught. Fifteen of them are found to be tagged. Estimate how many fish are in the lake.

1. *Familiarize.*   The ratio of fish tagged to the total number of fish in the lake, F, is $\frac{225}{F}$. Of the 108 fish caught later, 15 fish were tagged. The ratio of fish tagged to fish caught is $\frac{15}{108}$.

2. *Translate.*   Assuming the two ratios are the same, we can translate to a proportion.

$$\text{Fish tagged originally} \longrightarrow \frac{225}{F} = \frac{15}{108} \longleftarrow \text{Tagged fish caught later}$$
$$\text{Fish in lake} \longrightarrow \qquad\qquad \longleftarrow \text{Fish caught later}$$

3. *Solve.*   We solve the proportion. We multiply by the LCM, which is $108F$:

$$108F \cdot \frac{225}{F} = 108F \cdot \frac{15}{108} \qquad \text{Multiplying by } \mathbf{108}\boldsymbol{F}$$

$$108 \cdot 225 = F \cdot 15$$

$$\frac{108 \cdot 225}{15} = F \qquad \text{Dividing by 15}$$

$$1620 = F.$$

4. *Check.*   We leave the check to the student.

5. *State.*   We estimate that there are about 1620 fish in the lake.   ◄

DO EXERCISE 10.

NAME   SECTION   DATE

EXERCISE SET 11.7

a Solve.

1. The reciprocal of 4 plus the reciprocal of 5 is the reciprocal of what number?

2. The reciprocal of 3 plus the reciprocal of 8 is the reciprocal of what number?

3. One number is 5 more than another. The quotient of the larger divided by the smaller is $\frac{4}{3}$. Find the numbers.

4. One number is 4 more than another. The quotient of the larger divided by the smaller is $\frac{5}{2}$. Find the numbers.

5. One car travels 40 km/h faster than another. While one travels 150 km, the other goes 350 km. Find their speeds.

Complete this table and the equations as part of the familiarization.

$$d = r \cdot t$$

	Distance	Speed	Time
Slow car	150	r		$\rightarrow 150 = r(\quad)$
Fast car	350		t	$\rightarrow 350 = (\quad)t$

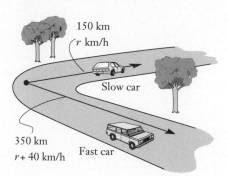

150 km
r km/h

Slow car

350 km
$r + 40$ km/h   Fast car

6. One car travels 30 km/h faster than another. While one goes 250 km, the other goes 400 km. Find their speeds.

7. The speed of a freight train is 14 km/h slower than the speed of a passenger train. The freight train travels 330 km in the same time that it takes the passenger train to travel 400 km. Find the speed of each train.

Complete this table and the equations as part of the familiarization.

$$d = r \cdot t$$

	Distance	Speed	Time
Freight	330		t	$\rightarrow 330 = (\quad)t$
Passenger	400	r		$\rightarrow 400 = r(\quad)$

8. The speed of a freight train is 15 km/h slower than the speed of a passenger train. The freight train travels 390 km in the same time that it takes the passenger train to travel 480 km. Find the speed of each train.

ANSWERS

1. _____

2. _____

3. _____

4. _____

5. _____

6. _____

7. _____

8. _____

9. A person traveled 120 mi in one direction. The return trip was accomplished at double the speed and took 3 hr less time. Find the speed going.

10. After making a trip of 126 mi, a person found that the trip would have taken 1 hr less time by increasing the speed by 8 mph. What was the actual speed?

9. _____

11. It takes David 4 hr to paint a certain area of a house. It takes Sierra 5 hr to do the same job. How long would it take them, working together, to do the painting job?

12. By checking work records, a carpenter finds that Juanita can build a certain type of garage in 12 hr. Antoine can do the same job in 16 hr. How long would it take if they worked together?

10. _____

11. _____

13. By checking work records, a plumber finds that Rory can do a certain job in 12 hr. Mira can do the same job in 9 hr. How long would it take if they worked together?

14. A tank can be filled in 18 hr by pipe A alone and in 24 hr by pipe B alone. How long would it take to fill the tank if both pipes were working?

12. _____

13. _____

14. _____

b Find the ratio of the following. Simplify, if possible.

15. 54 days, 6 days

16. 800 mi, 50 gal

15. _____

16. _____

17. A black racer snake travels 4.6 km in 2 hr. What is the speed in km/h?

18. Light travels 558,000 mi in 3 sec. What is the speed in mi/sec?

17. _____

18. _____

Solve.

19. The coffee beans from 14 trees are required to produce 7.7 kg of coffee (this is the average that each person in the United States drinks each year). How many trees are required to produce 320 kg of coffee?

20. Last season a minor-league baseball player got 240 hits in 600 times at bat. This season, his ratio of hits to number of times at bat is the same. He batted 500 times. How many hits has he had?

19. _____

20. _____

21. A student traveled 234 km in 14 days. At this same rate, how far would the student travel in 42 days?

22. In a potato bread recipe, the ratio of milk to flour is $\frac{3}{13}$. If 5 cups of milk are used, how many cups of flour are used?

21. _____

22. _____

23. 10 cm^3 of a normal specimen of human blood contains 1.2 g of hemoglobin. How many grams would 16 cm^3 of the same blood contain?

24. The winner of an election for class president won by a vote of 3 to 2, with 324 votes. How many votes did the loser get?

23. _____

25. To determine the number of trout in a lake, a conservationist catches 112 trout, tags them, and throws them back into the lake. Later, 82 trout are caught; 32 of them are tagged. How many trout are in the lake?

26. To determine the number of deer in a game preserve, a conservationist catches 318 deer, tags them, and lets them loose. Later, 168 deer are caught; 56 of them are tagged. How many deer are in the preserve?

24. _____

25. _____

26. _____

27. The ratio of the weight of an object on the moon to the weight of an object on earth is 0.16 to 1.
   a) How much would a 12-ton rocket weigh on the moon?
   b) How much would a 180-lb astronaut weigh on the moon?

28. The ratio of the weight of an object on Mars to the weight of an object on earth is 0.4 to 1.
   a) How much would a 12-ton rocket weigh on Mars?
   b) How much would a 120-lb astronaut weigh on Mars?

29. Simplest fractional notation for a rational number is $\frac{9}{17}$. Find an equal ratio where the sum of the numerator and the denominator is 104.

30. A baseball team has 12 more games to play. They have won 25 out of the 36 games they have played. How many more games must they win in order to finish with a 0.750 record?

SYNTHESIS

31. The denominator of a fraction is 1 more than the numerator. If 2 is subtracted from both the numerator and the denominator, the resulting fraction is $\frac{1}{2}$. Find the original fraction.

32. Ann and Betty work together and complete a job in 4 hr. It would take Betty 6 hr longer, working alone, to do the job than it would Ann. How long would it take each of them to do the job working alone?

33. The speed of a boat in still water is 10 mph. It travels 24 mi upstream and 24 mi downstream in a total time of 5 hr. What is the speed of the current?

34. Express 100 as the sum of two numbers for which the ratio of one number, increased by 5, to the other number, decreased by 5, is 4.

35. In a proportion

$$\frac{A}{B} = \frac{C}{D},$$

the numbers A and D are often called extremes, whereas the numbers B and C are called the means. Write four true proportions.

36. Compare

$$\frac{A + B}{B} = \frac{C + D}{D}$$

with the proportion

$$\frac{A}{B} = \frac{C}{D}.$$

37. Rosina, Ng, and Oscar can complete a certain job in 3 days. Rosina can do the job in 8 days and Ng can do it in 10 days. How many days will it take Oscar to complete the job?

38. How soon after 5 o'clock will the hands on a clock first be together?

39. To reach an appointment 50 mi away, Dr. Wright allowed 1 hr. After driving 30 mi, she realized that her speed would have to be increased 15 mph for the remainder of the trip. What was her speed for the first 30 mi?

40. Together, Michelle, Sal, and Kristen can do a job in 1 hr and 20 min. To do the job alone, Michelle needs twice the time that Sal needs and 2 hr more than Kristen. How long would it take each to complete the job working alone?

11.8 Formulas

a The use of formulas is important in many applications of mathematics. For rational formulas, we use the following procedure to solve a formula for a letter.

> **To solve a formula for a given letter, identify the letter, and:**
> 1. **Multiply on both sides to clear of fractions or decimals, if that is needed.**
> 2. **Multiply if necessary to remove parentheses.**
> 3. **Get all terms with the letter to be solved for on one side of the equation and all other terms on the other side, using the addition principle.**
> 4. **Collect like terms again, if necessary.**
> 5. **Solve for the letter in question, using the multiplication principle.**

▶ **EXAMPLE 1** *Gravitational force.* The gravitational force f between planets of mass M and m, at a distance d from each other, is given by

$$f = \frac{kMm}{d^2},$$

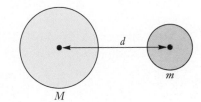

where k represents a fixed number constant. Solve for m.

We have

$$fd^2 = kMm \qquad \text{Multiplying by the LCM, } d^2$$

$$\frac{fd^2}{kM} = m. \qquad \text{Dividing by } kM \qquad ◀$$

DO EXERCISE 1.

▶ **EXAMPLE 2** *The area of a trapezoid.* The area A of a trapezoid is half the product of the height h and the sum of the lengths b_1 and b_2 of the parallel sides:

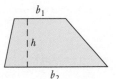

$$A = \frac{1}{2}(b_1 + b_2)h.$$

Solve for b_2.

We consider b_1 and b_2 to be different variables (or constants). The letter b_1 represents the length of the first parallel side and b_2 represents the length of the second parallel side. The small numbers 1 and 2 are called **subscripts.** Subscripts are used to identify different variables with related meanings.

$$2A = (b_1 + b_2)h \qquad \text{Multiplying by 2 to clear of fractions}$$

$$2A = b_1h + b_2h$$

$$2A - b_1h = b_2h \qquad \text{Subtracting } b_1h$$

$$\frac{2A - b_1h}{h} = b_2 \qquad \text{Dividing by } h \qquad ◀$$

DO EXERCISE 2.

1. Solve for M: $F = \dfrac{kMm}{d^2}$.

2. Solve for b_1: $A = \dfrac{1}{2}h(b_1 + b_2)$.

3. Solve for f: $\dfrac{1}{p} + \dfrac{1}{q} = \dfrac{1}{f}$.

This is an optics formula.

► **EXAMPLE 3**   *A work formula.* The following work formula was considered in Section 11.7. Solve it for t.

$$\frac{t}{a} + \frac{t}{b} = 1$$

We multiply by the LCM, which is ab:

$$ab \cdot \left(\frac{t}{a} + \frac{t}{b} \right) = ab \cdot 1 \qquad \text{Multiplying by } ab$$

$$ab \cdot \frac{t}{a} + ab \cdot \frac{t}{b} = ab$$

$$\frac{abt}{a} + \frac{abt}{b} = ab$$

$$bt + at = ab \qquad \text{Simplifying}$$

$$(b + a)t = ab \qquad \text{Factoring out } t$$

$$t = \frac{ab}{b + a}. \qquad \text{Dividing by } b + a \qquad ◄$$

The answer to Example 3 can be used to find solutions to problems such as Example 3 in Section 11.7:

$$t = \frac{4 \cdot 6}{6 + 4} = \frac{24}{10} = 2\frac{2}{5}.$$

DO EXERCISE 3.

4. Solve for a: $Q = \dfrac{a - b}{2b}$.

In Examples 1 and 2, the letter for which we solved was on the right side of the equation. In Example 3, the letter was on the left. The location of the letter is a matter of choice, since all equations are reversible.

Recall the following tip, which we also considered in Chapter 8.

Tip for Formula Solving

The variable to be solved for should be alone on one side of the equation, with *no* occurrence of that variable on the other side.

► **EXAMPLE 4**   Solve for b: $S = \dfrac{a + b}{3b}$.

We multiply by the LCM, which is $3b$:

$$3b \cdot S = 3b \cdot \frac{a + b}{3b} \qquad \text{Multiplying by } 3b$$

$$3bS = a + b \qquad \text{Simplifying}$$

> If we had divided by $3S$, we would have b alone on the left, but we would still have a term with b on the right.

$$3bS - b = a \qquad \text{Subtracting } b \text{ to get all terms involving } b \text{ on one side}$$

$$b(3S - 1) = a$$

$$b = \frac{a}{3S - 1}. \qquad ◄$$

DO EXERCISE 4.

NAME   SECTION   DATE

EXERCISE SET 11.8

a Solve.

1. $S = 2\pi rh$ for r

2. $A = P(1 + rt)$ for t
(An interest formula)

3. $A = \dfrac{1}{2}bh$ for b
(The area of a triangle)

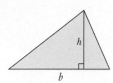

4. $s = \dfrac{1}{2}gt^2$ for g

5. $S = 180(n - 2)$ for n

6. $S = \dfrac{n}{2}(a + l)$ for a

7. $V = \dfrac{1}{3}k(B + b + 4M)$ for b

8. $A = P + Prt$ for P
(*Hint:* Factor the right-hand side.)

9. $S(r - 1) = rl - a$ for r

10. $T = mg - mf$ for m
(*Hint:* Factor the right-hand side.)

11. $A = \dfrac{1}{2}h(b_1 + b_2)$ for h

12. $S = 2\pi r(r + h)$ for h
(The area of a right circular cylinder)

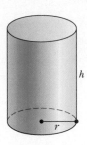

13. $\dfrac{A - B}{AB} = Q$ for B

14. $L = \dfrac{Mt + g}{t}$ for t

15. $\dfrac{1}{p} + \dfrac{1}{q} = \dfrac{1}{f}$ for p

16. $\dfrac{1}{a} + \dfrac{1}{b} = \dfrac{1}{t}$ for b

1. _____

2. _____

3. _____

4. _____

5. _____

6. _____

7. _____

8. _____

9. _____

10. _____

11. _____

12. _____

13. _____

14. _____

15. _____

16. _____

17. $\dfrac{A}{P} = 1 + r$ for A

18. $\dfrac{2A}{h} = a + b$ for h

19. $\dfrac{1}{R} = \dfrac{1}{r_1} + \dfrac{1}{r_2}$ for R
(An electricity formula)

20. $\dfrac{1}{R} = \dfrac{1}{r_1} + \dfrac{1}{r_2}$ for r_1

21. $\dfrac{A}{B} = \dfrac{C}{D}$ for D

22. $\dfrac{A}{B} = \dfrac{C}{D}$ for C

23. $h_1 = q\left(1 + \dfrac{h_2}{p}\right)$ for h_2

24. $S = \dfrac{a - ar^n}{1 - r}$ for a

25. $C = \dfrac{Ka - b}{a}$ for a

26. $Q = \dfrac{Pt + h}{t}$ for t

SKILL MAINTENANCE

27. Subtract: $(5x^4 - 6x^3 + 23x^2 - 79x + 24) - (-18x^4 - 56x^3 + 84x - 17)$.

Factor.

28. $x^2 - 4$

29. $30y^4 + 9y^2 - 12$

30. $49m^2 - 112mn + 64n^2$

SYNTHESIS

Solve.

31. $u = -F\left(E - \dfrac{P}{T}\right)$ for T

32. $l = a + (n - 1)d$ for d

33. The formula
$$C = \frac{5}{9}(F - 32)$$
is used to convert Fahrenheit temperatures to Celsius temperatures. At what temperature are the Fahrenheit and Celsius readings the same?

34. In
$$N = \frac{a}{c},$$
what is the effect on N when c increases? when c decreases? Assume that a, c, and N are positive.

11.9 Complex Rational Expressions

OBJECTIVE

After finishing Section 11.9, you should be able to:

a Simplify complex rational expressions.

FOR EXTRA HELP

Tape 24C

a A **complex rational expression**, or **complex fractional expression**, is a rational expression that has one or more rational expressions within its numerator or denominator. Here are some examples:

$$\frac{1 + \dfrac{2}{x}}{3}, \qquad \frac{\dfrac{x+y}{2}}{\dfrac{2x}{x+1}}, \qquad \frac{\dfrac{1}{3} + \dfrac{1}{5}}{\dfrac{2}{x} - \dfrac{x}{y}}.$$

These are rational expressions within the complex rational expression.

There are two methods to simplify complex rational expressions. We will consider them both. Use the one that works best for you or the one that your instructor directs you to use.

Multiplying by the LCM of All the Denominators: Method 1

Method 1

To simplify a complex rational expression:

1. First, find the LCM of all the denominators of all the rational expressions occurring *within* both the numerator and the denominator of the complex rational expression. Let *a* = the LCM.
2. Then multiply by 1 using *a/a*.
3. If possible, simplify by removing a factor of 1.

▶ **EXAMPLE 1** Simplify: $\dfrac{\dfrac{1}{2} + \dfrac{3}{4}}{\dfrac{5}{6} - \dfrac{3}{8}}.$

We have

$$\frac{\dfrac{1}{2} + \dfrac{3}{4}}{\dfrac{5}{6} - \dfrac{3}{8}}$$

⎰ The denominators *within* the complex rational expression
⎱ are 2, 4, 6, and 8. The LCM of these denominators is 24.
We multiply by 1 using $\dfrac{24}{24}$.

$$= \frac{\dfrac{1}{2} + \dfrac{3}{4}}{\dfrac{5}{6} - \dfrac{3}{8}} \cdot \frac{24}{24} \qquad \text{Multiplying by 1}$$

$$= \frac{\left(\dfrac{1}{2} + \dfrac{3}{4}\right)24}{\left(\dfrac{5}{6} - \dfrac{3}{8}\right)24} \begin{array}{l} \longleftarrow \text{ Multiplying the numerator by 24} \\[1.5em] \longleftarrow \text{ Multiplying the denominator by 24} \end{array}$$

1. Simplify. Use Method 1.

$$\dfrac{\dfrac{1}{3}+\dfrac{4}{5}}{\dfrac{7}{8}-\dfrac{5}{6}}$$

Using the distributive laws, we carry out the multiplications.

$$=\dfrac{\dfrac{1}{2}(24)+\dfrac{3}{4}(24)}{\dfrac{5}{6}(24)-\dfrac{3}{8}(24)}$$

$$=\dfrac{12+18}{20-9}\qquad \text{\small Simplifying}$$

$$=\dfrac{30}{11}. \qquad ◄$$

Multiplying in this manner has the effect of clearing of fractions in both the top and bottom of the complex rational expression.

DO EXERCISE 1.

2. Simplify. Use Method 1.

$$\dfrac{\dfrac{x}{2}+\dfrac{2x}{3}}{\dfrac{1}{x}-\dfrac{x}{2}}$$

► **EXAMPLE 2**   Simplify: $\dfrac{\dfrac{3}{x}+\dfrac{1}{2x}}{\dfrac{1}{3x}-\dfrac{3}{4x}}$.

The denominators within the complex expression are x, $2x$, $3x$, and $4x$. The LCM of these denominators is $12x$. We multiply by 1 using $12x/12x$.

$$\dfrac{\dfrac{3}{x}+\dfrac{1}{2x}}{\dfrac{1}{3x}-\dfrac{3}{4x}}\cdot\dfrac{12x}{12x}=\dfrac{\left(\dfrac{3}{x}+\dfrac{1}{2x}\right)12x}{\left(\dfrac{1}{3x}-\dfrac{3}{4x}\right)12x}=\dfrac{\dfrac{3}{x}(12x)+\dfrac{1}{2x}(12x)}{\dfrac{1}{3x}(12x)-\dfrac{3}{4x}(12x)}$$

$$=\dfrac{36+6}{4-9}=-\dfrac{42}{5}\qquad ◄$$

DO EXERCISE 2.

3. Simplify. Use Method 1.

$$\dfrac{1+\dfrac{1}{x}}{1-\dfrac{1}{x^2}}$$

► **EXAMPLE 3**   Simplify: $\dfrac{1-\dfrac{1}{x}}{1-\dfrac{1}{x^2}}$.

The denominators within the complex expression are x and x^2. The LCM of these denominators is x^2. We multiply by 1 using x^2/x^2. Then, after obtaining a single rational expression, we simplify:

$$\dfrac{1-\dfrac{1}{x}}{1-\dfrac{1}{x^2}}\cdot\dfrac{x^2}{x^2}=\dfrac{\left(1-\dfrac{1}{x}\right)x^2}{\left(1-\dfrac{1}{x^2}\right)x^2}=\dfrac{1(x^2)-\dfrac{1}{x}(x^2)}{1(x^2)-\dfrac{1}{x^2}(x^2)}=\dfrac{x^2-x}{x^2-1}$$

$$=\dfrac{x(x-1)}{(x+1)(x-1)}=\dfrac{x}{x+1}. \qquad ◄$$

DO EXERCISE 3.

Adding in the Numerator and the Denominator: Method 2

> Method 2
>
> To simplify a complex rational expression:
>
> 1. Add or subtract, as necessary, to get a single rational expression in the numerator.
> 2. Add or subtract, as necessary, to get a single rational expression in the denominator.
> 3. **Divide the numerator by the denominator.**
> 4. **If possible, simplify by removing a factor of 1.**

We will redo Examples 1–3 using this method.

▶ **EXAMPLE 4** Simplify: $\dfrac{\frac{1}{2}+\frac{3}{4}}{\frac{5}{6}-\frac{3}{8}}$.

We have

$$\frac{\frac{1}{2}+\frac{3}{4}}{\frac{5}{6}-\frac{3}{8}}=\frac{\frac{1}{2}\cdot\frac{2}{2}+\frac{3}{4}}{\frac{5}{6}\cdot\frac{4}{4}-\frac{3}{8}\cdot\frac{3}{3}}$$

Multiplying the $\frac{1}{2}$ by 1 to get a common denominator

Multiplying the $\frac{5}{6}$ and the $\frac{3}{8}$ by 1 to get a common denominator

$$=\frac{\frac{2}{4}+\frac{3}{4}}{\frac{20}{24}-\frac{9}{24}}$$

$$=\frac{\frac{5}{4}}{\frac{11}{24}}$$ Adding in the numerator; subtracting in the denominator

$$=\frac{5}{4}\cdot\frac{24}{11}$$ Multiplying by the reciprocal of the divisor

$$=\frac{5\cdot3\cdot2\cdot2\cdot2}{2\cdot2\cdot11}$$ Factoring

$$=\frac{5\cdot3\cdot2\cdot\cancel{2}\cdot\cancel{2}}{\cancel{2}\cdot\cancel{2}\cdot11}$$ Removing a factor of 1: $\frac{2\cdot2}{2\cdot2}=1$

$$=\frac{30}{11}.$$ ◀

DO EXERCISE 4.

4. Simplify. Use Method 2.

$$\frac{\frac{1}{3}+\frac{4}{5}}{\frac{7}{8}-\frac{5}{6}}$$

ANSWER ON PAGE A-9

5. Simplify. Use Method 2.

$$\dfrac{\dfrac{x}{2}+\dfrac{2x}{3}}{\dfrac{1}{x}-\dfrac{x}{2}}$$

▶ **EXAMPLE 5**   Simplify: $\dfrac{\dfrac{3}{x}+\dfrac{1}{2x}}{\dfrac{1}{3x}-\dfrac{3}{4x}}$.

We have

$$\dfrac{\dfrac{3}{x}+\dfrac{1}{2x}}{\dfrac{1}{3x}-\dfrac{3}{4x}}=\dfrac{\dfrac{3}{x}\cdot\dfrac{2}{2}+\dfrac{1}{2x}}{\dfrac{1}{3x}\cdot\dfrac{4}{4}-\dfrac{3}{4x}\cdot\dfrac{3}{3}}$$

   } Finding the LCM, $2x$, and multiplying by 1 in the numerator

   } Finding the LCM, $12x$, and multiplying by 1 in the denominator

$$=\dfrac{\dfrac{6}{2x}+\dfrac{1}{2x}}{\dfrac{4}{12x}-\dfrac{9}{12x}}=\dfrac{\dfrac{7}{2x}}{\dfrac{-5}{12x}}$$

Adding in the numerator and subtracting in the denominator

$$=\dfrac{7}{2x}\cdot\dfrac{12x}{-5}$$ Multiplying by the reciprocal of the divisor

$$=\dfrac{7}{2x}\cdot\dfrac{6(2x)}{-5}$$ Factoring

$$=\dfrac{7}{2x}\cdot\dfrac{6(2x)}{-5}$$ Removing a factor of 1: $\dfrac{2x}{2x}=1$

$$=\dfrac{42}{-5}=-\dfrac{42}{5}.$$

DO EXERCISE 5.

6. Simplify. Use Method 2.

$$\dfrac{1+\dfrac{1}{x}}{1-\dfrac{1}{x^2}}$$

▶ **EXAMPLE 6**   Simplify: $\dfrac{1-\dfrac{1}{x}}{1-\dfrac{1}{x^2}}$.

We have

$$\dfrac{1-\dfrac{1}{x}}{1-\dfrac{1}{x^2}}=\dfrac{\dfrac{x}{x}-\dfrac{1}{x}}{\dfrac{x^2}{x^2}-\dfrac{1}{x^2}}$$

   ← Finding the LCM, x, and multiplying by 1 in the numerator

   ← Finding the LCM, x^2, and multiplying by 1 in the denominator

$$=\dfrac{\dfrac{x-1}{x}}{\dfrac{x^2-1}{x^2}}$$

Subtracting in the numerator and subtracting in the denominator

$$=\dfrac{x-1}{x}\cdot\dfrac{x^2}{x^2-1}$$ Multiplying by the reciprocal of the divisor

$$=\dfrac{(x-1)x\cdot x}{x(x-1)(x+1)}$$ Factoring

$$=\dfrac{(x-1)x\cdot x}{x(x-1)(x+1)}$$ Removing a factor of 1: $\dfrac{x(x-1)}{x(x-1)}=1$

$$=\dfrac{x}{x+1}.$$

DO EXERCISE 6.

NAME   SECTION   DATE

EXERCISE SET 11.9

a Simplify.

1. $\dfrac{1 + \dfrac{9}{16}}{1 - \dfrac{3}{4}}$

2. $\dfrac{9 - \dfrac{1}{4}}{3 + \dfrac{1}{2}}$

3. $\dfrac{1 - \dfrac{3}{5}}{1 + \dfrac{1}{5}}$

4. $\dfrac{\dfrac{5}{27} - 5}{\dfrac{1}{3} + 1}$

5. $\dfrac{\dfrac{1}{2} + \dfrac{3}{4}}{\dfrac{5}{8} - \dfrac{5}{6}}$

6. $\dfrac{\dfrac{2}{3} - \dfrac{5}{6}}{\dfrac{3}{4} + \dfrac{7}{8}}$

7. $\dfrac{\dfrac{1}{x} + 3}{\dfrac{1}{x} - 5}$

8. $\dfrac{\dfrac{3}{s} + s}{\dfrac{s}{3} + s}$

9. $\dfrac{\dfrac{2}{y} + \dfrac{1}{2y}}{y + \dfrac{y}{2}}$

10. $\dfrac{4 - \dfrac{1}{x^2}}{2 - \dfrac{1}{x}}$

11. $\dfrac{8 + \dfrac{8}{d}}{1 + \dfrac{1}{d}}$

12. $\dfrac{2 - \dfrac{3}{b}}{2 - \dfrac{b}{3}}$

13. $\dfrac{\dfrac{x}{8} - \dfrac{8}{x}}{\dfrac{1}{8} + \dfrac{1}{x}}$

14. $\dfrac{\dfrac{2}{m} + \dfrac{m}{2}}{\dfrac{m}{3} - \dfrac{3}{m}}$

15. $\dfrac{1 + \dfrac{1}{y}}{1 - \dfrac{1}{y^2}}$

1. _____

2. _____

3. _____

4. _____

5. _____

6. _____

7. _____

8. _____

9. _____

10. _____

11. _____

12. _____

13. _____

14. _____

15. _____

16. _____

17. _____

18. _____

19. _____

20. _____

21. _____

22. _____

23. _____

24. _____

25. _____

26. _____

27. _____

28. _____

29. _____

30. _____

16. $\dfrac{\dfrac{1}{q^2} - 1}{\dfrac{1}{q} + 1}$

17. $\dfrac{\dfrac{1}{5} - \dfrac{1}{a}}{\dfrac{5 - a}{5}}$

18. $\dfrac{2 - \dfrac{1}{x}}{\dfrac{2}{x}}$

19. $\dfrac{\dfrac{x}{x - y}}{\dfrac{x^2}{x^2 - y^2}}$

20. $\dfrac{\dfrac{x}{y} - \dfrac{y}{x}}{\dfrac{1}{y} + \dfrac{1}{x}}$

21. $\dfrac{x - 3 + \dfrac{2}{x}}{x - 4 + \dfrac{3}{x}}$

22. $\dfrac{1 + \dfrac{a}{b - a}}{\dfrac{a}{a + b} - 1}$

SKILL MAINTENANCE

23. Add: $(2x^3 - 4x^2 + x - 7) + (4x^4 + x^3 + 4x^2 + x)$.

24. The length of a rectangle is 3 yd greater than the width. The area of the rectangle is 10 yd^2. Find the perimeter.

SYNTHESIS

25. Find the reciprocal of $\dfrac{2}{x - 1} - \dfrac{1}{3x - 2}$.

Simplify.

26. $\dfrac{\dfrac{a}{b} + \dfrac{c}{d}}{\dfrac{b}{a} + \dfrac{d}{c}}$

27. $\dfrac{\dfrac{a}{b} - \dfrac{c}{d}}{\dfrac{b}{a} - \dfrac{d}{c}}$

28. $\left[\dfrac{\dfrac{x + 1}{x - 1} + 1}{\dfrac{x + 1}{x - 1} - 1} \right]^5$

29. $1 + \dfrac{1}{1 + \dfrac{1}{1 + \dfrac{1}{1 + \dfrac{1}{x}}}}$

30. $\dfrac{\dfrac{z}{1 - \dfrac{z}{2 + 2z}} - 2z}{\dfrac{2z}{5z - 2} - 3}$

12.1 Graphs and Equations

We often see graphs of various kinds in newspapers and magazines and on television. In the past decade, graphs have been more common because they are easy to prepare using a computer. We first solve some problems with commonly used graphs.

a Problem Solving with Graphs

Bar Graphs

Graphs are used to illustrate information. A *bar graph* is convenient for showing comparisons. The bars may be vertical or horizontal. Typically, certain units, such as percent in the case of Example 1, are shown horizontally. With each horizontal number, there is associated a vertical number, or unit. In the case of Example 1, the vertical units are not numbers, but various "reasons" for dropping out of high school.

Let us solve some problems with this graph.

▶ **EXAMPLE 1** These reasons for dropping out of high school were given in a recent National Assessment of Educational Progress survey.

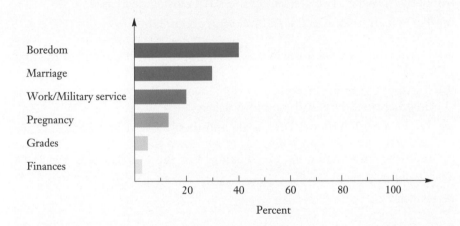

a) Approximately what percent in the survey dropped out because of pregnancy?

b) What reason was given least often for dropping out?

c) What reason was given by about 30% for dropping out?

a) We go to the right of the bar representing pregnancy and then go down to the percent scale. We find that approximately 12% dropped out because of pregnancy. Note that this is truly an estimate. We would need more detailed scaling to make a closer determination.

b) The shortest bar represents finances.

c) We go across to the 30% mark on the percent scale and then up until we reach a bar ending at approximately 30%. We then go across to the left and read the reason. The reason given by about 30% was marriage.

◀

OBJECTIVES

After finishing Section 12.1, you should be able to:

a Solve problems related to bar, line, and circle graphs.

b Plot points associated with ordered pairs of numbers.

c Determine the quadrant in which a point lies.

d Find the coordinates of a point on a graph.

FOR EXTRA HELP

Tape 24D

1. Consider the graph in Example 1.

   a) Approximately how many in the survey dropped out because of boredom?

   b) What reason was given by about 5% for dropping out?

2. Consider the graph in Example 2.

a) For which week was the DJIA closing about 2000?

Line Graphs

We often use *line graphs* to show change over time. Certain horizontal units are associated with vertical units. Each association determines a point. When the points are connected by line segments, we get a line graph.

▶ **EXAMPLE 2**   This line graph shows the closing Dow Jones Industrial Average (DJIA) for each of six weeks.

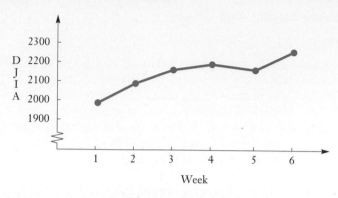

a) For which week was the DJIA closing the lowest?

b) Between which two weeks did the DJIA closing decrease?

c) For which week was the DJIA closing about 2200?

a) During the six weeks, the lowest closing was 2000 at the end of the first week.

b) For which week was the DJIA closing about 2150?

b) Reading the graph from left to right, we see that the line went down only between the fourth and fifth weeks.

c) We locate 2200 on the DJIA scale and then move to the right until we reach the line. At that point, we move down to the "Week" scale and read the information we are seeking. For the fourth week, the DJIA closing was about 2200.   ◀

DO EXERCISE 2.

Circle Graphs

Circle graphs are often used to show the percent of a quantity for each particular item in a group.

▶ **EXAMPLE 3**   This circle graph shows expenses as a percent of income by a family of four, according to the Bureau of Labor Statistics.

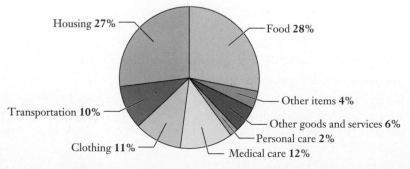

A family with $2000 monthly income would typically spend how much on housing per month?

1. *Familiarize.* The graph tells us that housing is 27% of income. We let y = the amount spent on housing.

2. *Translate.* We restate and translate the problem as follows:

Restate: What is 27% of income?

Translate: y = 27% · $2000

3. *Solve.* We solve by carrying out the computation:

$$y = 0.27 \cdot \$2000 = \$540.$$

4. *Check.* We leave the check to the student.

5. *State.* The family would spend $540 on housing.

DO EXERCISE 3.

b   Points and Ordered Pairs

We have graphed numbers on a line. To enable us to graph an equation that contains two variables, we now learn to graph number pairs on a plane.

On a number line each point is the graph of a number. On a plane, each point is the graph of a number pair. We use two perpendicular number lines called **axes.** They cross at a point called the **origin.** It has coordinates (0, 0) but is usually labeled with the number 0. The arrows show the positive directions. Consider the ordered pair (3, 4). The numbers in an ordered pair are called **coordinates.** In (3, 4), the **first coordinate** is 3 and the **second coordinate** is 4. To plot (3, 4), we start at the origin and move horizontally to the 3. Then we move up vertically 4 units and make a "dot." We can also plot this point by starting at the origin, going up 4 units vertically, and then moving to the right 3 units horizontally.

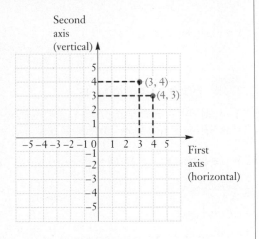

The point (4, 3) is also plotted. Note that (3, 4) and (4, 3) give different points. The order of the numbers in the pair is indeed important. They are called **ordered pairs** because it makes a difference which number comes first.

▶ **EXAMPLE 4**   Plot the point (−3, 4).

The first number, −3, is negative. Starting at the origin, we go −3 units in the horizontal direction (3 units to the left). The second number, 4, is positive. We go 4 units in the vertical direction (up). We could also go up 4 units and then 3 units to the left.

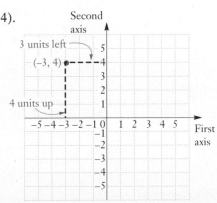

3. Consider the graph in Example 3.

   a) A family with a $2000 monthly income would typically spend how much on transportation per month?

   b) What percent of the income is spent on food?

Plot these points on the graph below.

4. (4, 5)   5. (5, 4)

6. (−2, 5)   7. (−3, −4)

8. (5, −3)   9. (−2, −1)

10. (0, −3)   11. (2, 0)

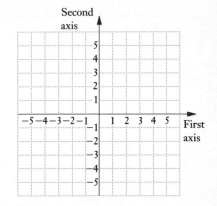

ANSWERS ON PAGE A-9

12. What can you say about the coordinates of a point in the third quadrant?

13. What can you say about the coordinates of a point in the fourth quadrant?

In which quadrant is the point located?

14. (5, 3)

15. (−6, −4)

16. (10, −14)

17. (−13, 9)

18. Find the coordinates of points *A*, *B*, *C*, *D*, *E*, *F*, and *G* on the graph below.

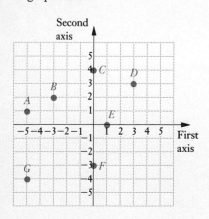

DO EXERCISES 4–11 ON THE PRECEDING PAGE.

c **Quadrants**

This figure shows some points and their coordinates. In region I (the *first quadrant*), both coordinates of any point are positive. In region II (the *second quadrant*), the first coordinate is negative and the second positive. In region III (the *third quadrant*), both coordinates are negative. In region IV (the *fourth quadrant*), the first coordinate is positive and the second is negative.

The point (−4, 5) is in the second quadrant. The point (5, −5) is in the fourth quadrant.

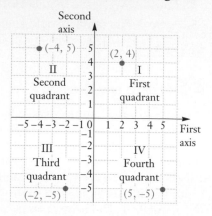

DO EXERCISES 12–17.

d **Finding Coordinates**

To find the coordinates of a point, we see how far to the right or left of zero it is located and how far up or down.

▶ **EXAMPLE 5** Find the coordinates of points *A*, *B*, *C*, *D*, *E*, *F*, and *G*.

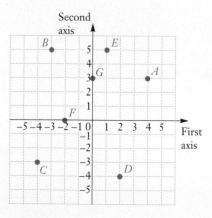

Point *A* is 4 units to the right (horizontal direction) and 3 units up (vertical direction). Its coordinates are (4, 3). The coordinates of the other points are as follows:

B: (−3, 5);	*C*: (−4, −3);	*D*: (2, −4);
E: (1, 5);	*F*: (−2, 0);	*G*: (0, 3).

DO EXERCISE 18.

EXERCISE SET 12.1

ANSWERS

a Use the bar graph in Example 1 to answer Exercises 1–3.

1. What reason was given most for dropping out?

2. What reason was given by about 20% for dropping out?

3. What percent in the survey dropped out because of grades?

Use the line graph in Example 2 to answer Exercises 4–6.

4. For which week was the DJIA closing the highest?

5. For which week was the DJIA closing about 2100?

6. About how many points was the increase in the DJIA between weeks 1 and 6?

Use the circle graph in Example 3 to answer Exercises 7 and 8.

7. What percent of the income is spent on medical expenses?

8. A family with $2000 monthly income would typically spend how much on clothing per month?

Use the following bar graph for Exercises 9–14. The graph shows the average daily expenses for lodging, food, and car rental for traveling executives in various cities.

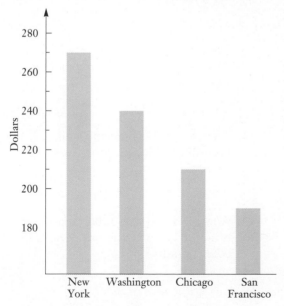

9. What are the average daily expenses in New York?

10. What are the average daily expenses in Chicago?

11. Which city is least expensive?

12. Which city is most expensive?

13. How much more are the average daily expenses in Washington than in San Francisco?

14. How much less are the average daily expenses in Chicago than in Washington?

1. _____

2. _____

3. _____

4. _____

5. _____

6. _____

7. _____

8. _____

9. _____

10. _____

11. _____

12. _____

13. _____

14. _____

Use the following line graph for Exercises 15–20. The graph shows the estimated sales (in millions) for a company for several years.

15. In what year are estimated sales the greatest?

16. In what year are estimated sales the least?

17. What are estimated sales in 1991?

19. How much greater are estimated sales in 1993 than in 1995?

18. What are estimated sales in 1997?

20. How much greater are estimated sales in 1997 than in 1991?

Use the following circle graph for Exercises 21–26. The graph shows music preferences.

Music Preferences

21. What percent of all recordings sold are jazz?

22. What percent of all recordings sold are country?

23. Together, what percent of all recordings sold are either soul or pop/rock?

24. Together, what percent of all recordings sold are either classical or jazz?

Source: National Association of Recording Merchandisers

25. A music store sells 3000 recordings a month. How many are pop/rock? soul? country?

26. A music store sells 2500 recordings a month. How many are pop/rock? classical? gospel?

b

27. Plot these points.

(2, 5) (−1, 3) (3, −2) (−2, −4)

(0, 4) (0, −5) (5, 0) (−5, 0)

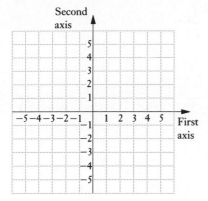

28. Plot these points.

(4, 4) (−2, 4) (5, −3) (−5, −5)

(0, 4) (0, −4) (3, 0) (−4, 0)

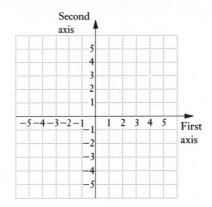

c In which quadrant is each point located?

29. (−5, 3)

30. (−12, 1)

31. (100, −1)

32. (35.6, −2.5)

33. (−6, −29)

34. (−3.6, −105.9)

35. (3.8, 9.2)

36. (1895, 1492)

37. In quadrant III, first coordinates are always _____ and second coordinates are always _____.

38. In quadrant II, _____ coordinates are always positive and _____ coordinates are always negative.

ANSWERS

27. See graph.

28. See graph.

29. _____

30. _____

31. _____

32. _____

33. _____

34. _____

35. _____

36. _____

37. _____

38. _____

ANSWERS

39. _____

40. _____

41. _____

42. _____

43. _____

44. _____

45. _____

46. _____

47. _____

48. _____

49. _____

50. _____

51. _____

52. _____

d

39. Find the coordinates of points *A, B, C, D,* and *E.*

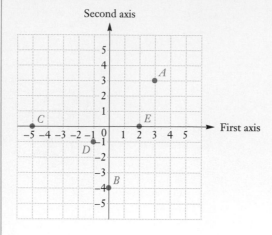

40. Find the coordinates of points *A, B, C, D,* and *E.*

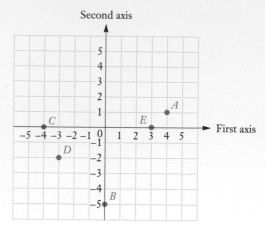

SKILL MAINTENANCE

41. A family making $19,600 a year will spend $5096 on food. At this rate, how much would a family making $20,500 spend on food?

42. Two cars leave town at the same time and drive in opposite directions. One travels at 54 mph and the other travels at 43 mph. In how many hours will they be 291 mi apart?

SYNTHESIS

In Exercises 43–46, tell in which quadrant(s) the point can be located.

43. The first coordinate is positive.

44. The second coordinate is negative.

45. The first and second coordinates are equal.

46. The first coordinate is the additive inverse of the second coordinate.

47. The points $(-1, 1)$, $(4, 1)$, and $(4, -5)$ are three vertices of a rectangle. Find the coordinates of the fourth vertex.

48. Three parallelograms share the vertices $(-2, -3)$, $(-1, 2)$, and $(4, -3)$. Find the fourth vertex of each parallelogram.

49. Graph eight points such that the sum of the coordinates in each pair is 6.

50. Graph eight points such that the first coordinate minus the second coordinate is 1.

51. Find the perimeter of a rectangle whose vertices have coordinates $(5, 3)$, $(5, -2)$, $(-3, -2)$, and $(-3, 3)$.

52. Find the area of a triangle whose vertices have coordinates $(0, 9)$, $(0, -4)$, and $(5, -4)$.

12.2 Graphing Linear Equations

A **linear equation** is equivalent to an equation of the type $Ax + By = C$. We now learn how to graph certain kinds of linear equations. We will see that the graphs of linear equations are straight lines.

a Solutions of Equations

An equation with two variables has *ordered pairs* of numbers for solutions. If not directed otherwise, we usually take the variables in alphabetical *order*. Then we get *ordered* pairs for solutions.

▶ **EXAMPLE 1** Determine whether $(-3, -5)$ is a solution of $y = 2x + 1$.

We substitute:

$$\begin{array}{c|c} & y = 2x + 1 \\ \hline -5 & 2(-3) + 1 \\ & -6 + 1 \\ & -5 \end{array}$$

We substitute -3 for x and -5 for y (alphabetical order of variables).

Since the equation becomes true, $(-3, -5)$ is a solution. ◀

Similarly, in Example 1 we can show that $(3, 7)$ and $(0, 1)$ are solutions. In fact, there are more solutions than we can list: There is an infinite number of solutions.

▶ **EXAMPLE 2** Determine whether $(-2, 3)$ is a solution of $2t = 4s - 8$.

We substitute:

$$\begin{array}{c|c} & 2t = 4s - 8 \\ \hline 2 \cdot 3 & 4(-2) - 8 \\ 6 & -8 - 8 \\ & -16 \end{array}$$

We substitute -2 for s and 3 for t.

Since the equation becomes false, $(-2, 3)$ is not a solution. ◀

DO EXERCISES 1 AND 2.

b Graphing Equations of the Type $y = mx$ and $y = mx + b$

The equations considered in Examples 1 and 2 have an infinite number of solutions, meaning that we cannot list them all. Because of this, it is convenient to make a drawing that represents the solutions. Such a drawing is called a **graph**.

> To *graph* an equation means to make a drawing that represents its solutions.

The graphs of linear equations of the type $y = mx$ and $y = mx + b$ are straight lines. If an equation has a graph that is a straight line, we can graph it by plotting two or more points and then drawing a line through them.

OBJECTIVES

After finishing Section 12.2, you should be able to:

a Determine whether an ordered pair of numbers is a solution of an equation with two variables.

b Graph equations of the type $y = mx$ and $y = mx + b$.

FOR EXTRA HELP

Tape 24E

1. Determine whether $(2, 3)$ is a solution of $y = 2x + 3$.

2. Determine whether $(-2, 4)$ is a solution of $4q - 3p = 22$.

ANSWERS ON PAGE A-9

Graph.

3. $y = 3x$

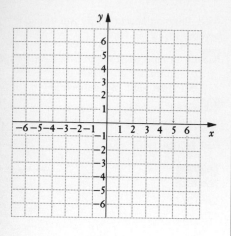

4. $y = \dfrac{1}{2}x$

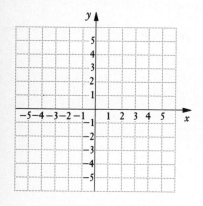

▶ **EXAMPLE 3**   Graph: $y = x$.

We will use alphabetical order. Thus the first (horizontal) axis will be the x-axis and the second (vertical) axis will be the y-axis. Next, we find some ordered pairs that are solutions of the equation, keeping the results in a table. We choose *any* number for x and then find y by substitution. In this case, it is easy. Here are a few:

Let $x = 0$.   Then $y = x = 0$.   We get a solution: the ordered pair (0, 0).

Let $x = 1$.   Then $y = x = 1$.   We get a solution: the ordered pair (1, 1).

Let $x = 5$.   Then $y = x = 5$.   We get a solution: the ordered pair (5, 5).

Let $x = -2$.   Then $y = x = -2$.   We get a solution: the ordered pair $(-2, -2)$.

Let $x = -4$.   Then $y = x = -4$.   We get a solution: the ordered pair $(-4, -4)$.

We gather our results in a table like the one shown below. Then we plot the points. We look for a pattern in the points plotted. It looks as if the points resemble a straight line. We draw the line with a ruler. Since the line is the graph of the equation $y = x$, we label the line $y = x$ on the graph paper.

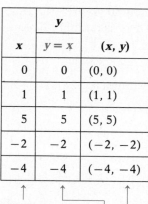

x	y $y = x$	(x, y)
0	0	(0, 0)
1	1	(1, 1)
5	5	(5, 5)
-2	-2	$(-2, -2)$
-4	-4	$(-4, -4)$

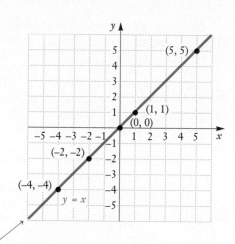

(1) Choose x.
(2) Compute y.
(3) Form the pair (x, y).
(4) Plot the points.

◀

▶ **EXAMPLE 4**   Graph: $y = 2x$.

We find some ordered pairs that are solutions. Since the graph is a line, we really need to find only two, but we will usually plot a third point as a check. We keep the results in a table. We choose *any* number for x and then determine y by substitution. Suppose we choose 3 for x. Then

$$y = 2x = 2 \cdot 3 = 6.$$

We get a solution: the ordered pair (3, 6). Suppose we choose 0 for x. Then

$$y = 2x = 2 \cdot 0 = 0.$$

We get a solution: the ordered pair (0, 0). For a third point, we make a negative choice for x. We now have enough points to plot the line, but if we wish we can compute more. If a number takes us off the graph paper, we

▶ **EXAMPLE 8**   Graph $y = 2x$ and $y = 2x - 3$ using the same set of axes. Compare.

We first make a table containing values for both equations.

x	y $y = 2x$	y $y = 2x - 3$
0	0	-3
1	2	-1
2	4	1
-1	-2	-5

The graph of $y = 2x - 3$ looks just like the graph of $y = 2x$, but $y = 2x$ is moved, or translated, down 3 units.

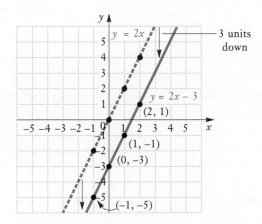

DO EXERCISE 11.

▶ **EXAMPLE 9**   Graph: $y = \frac{2}{5}x + 4$.

We make a table of values. Using multiples of 5 avoids fractions.

When $x = 0$, $y = \frac{2}{5} \cdot 0 + 4 = 0 + 4 = 4$.

When $x = 5$, $y = \frac{2}{5} \cdot 5 + 4 = 2 + 4 = 6$.

When $x = -5$, $y = \frac{2}{5} \cdot (-5) + 4 = -2 + 4 = 2$.

Since two points determine a line, that is all we really need to graph a line, but we will usually plot a third point as a check.

x	y
0	4
5	6
-5	2

10. Graph $y = x - 1$ and compare it with the graph of $y = x$.

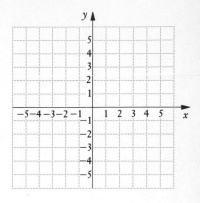

11. Graph $y = 2x + 3$ and compare it with the graph of $y = 2x$.

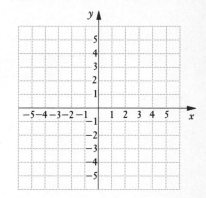

12. Graph: $y = \dfrac{3}{5}x + 2$.

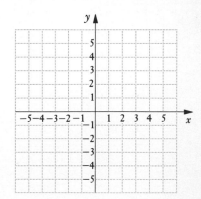

ANSWERS ON PAGE A-9

Graph.

13. $y = \dfrac{3}{5}x - 2$

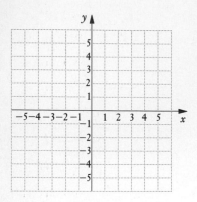

14. $y = -\dfrac{3}{5}x - 1$

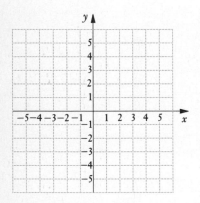

15. $y = -\dfrac{3}{5}x + 4$

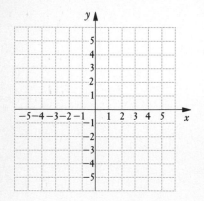

We draw the graph of $y = \frac{2}{5}x + 4$.

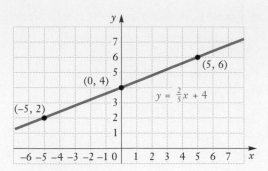

▶ **EXAMPLE 10**   Graph: $y = -\frac{3}{4}x - 2$.

We first make a table of values.

When $x = 0$, $y = -\frac{3}{4} \cdot 0 - 2 = 0 - 2 = -2$.

When $x = 4$, $y = -\frac{3}{4} \cdot 4 - 2 = -3 - 2 = -5$.

When $x = -4$, $y = -\frac{3}{4}(-4) - 2 = 3 - 2 = 1$.

x	y
0	−2
4	−5
−4	1

⎰ We plot these points and draw a line through them.
⎱ This line is a graph of the equation. We label the graph $y = -\frac{3}{4}x - 2$.

⎰ We plot this point for a check to see whether
⎱ it is on the line.

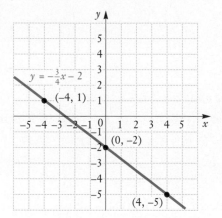

DO EXERCISES 12–15. (EXERCISE 12 IS ON THE PRECEDING PAGE.)

NAME   SECTION   DATE

EXERCISE SET 12.2

a Determine whether the given point is a solution of the equation.

1. $(2, 5)$; $y = 3x - 1$

2. $(1, 7)$; $y = 2x + 5$

3. $(2, -3)$; $3x - y = 4$

4. $(-1, 4)$; $2x + y = 6$

5. $(-2, -1)$; $2c + 2d = -7$

6. $(0, -4)$; $4p + 2q = -9$

b Graph.

7. $y = 4x$

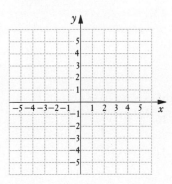

8. $y = 2x$

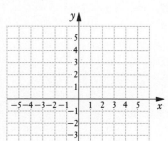

9. $y = -2x$

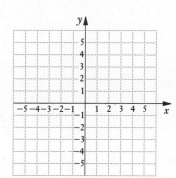

10. $y = -4x$

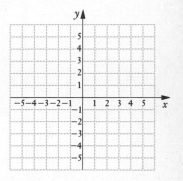

11. $y = \dfrac{1}{3}x$

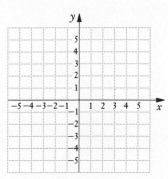

12. $y = \dfrac{1}{4}x$

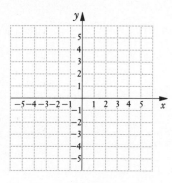

13. $y = -\dfrac{3}{2}x$

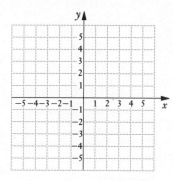

14. $y = -\dfrac{5}{4}x$

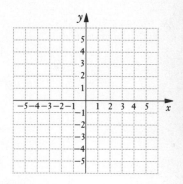

15. $y = x + 1$

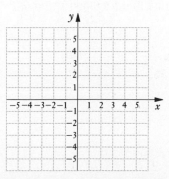

16. $y = -x + 1$

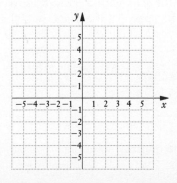

17. $y = 2x + 2$

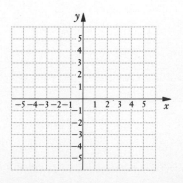

18. $y = 3x - 2$

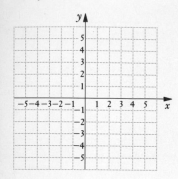

19. $y = \frac{1}{3}x - 1$

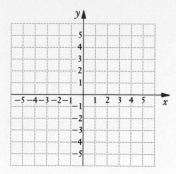

20. $y = \frac{1}{2}x + 1$

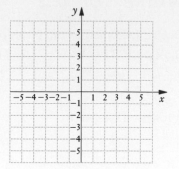

ANSWERS

21. See graph.

22. See graph.

23. See graph.

24. See graph.

25. See graph.

26. See graph.

27. See graph.

28. See graph.

29. See graph.

30. See graph.

31. See graph.

32. See graph.

33. _____

34. _____

35. _____

36. _____

37. _____

38. _____

Use your own graph paper. Draw and label x- and y-axes. Then graph the equation.

21. $y = -x - 3$

22. $y = -x - 2$

23. $y = \frac{5}{2}x + 3$

24. $y = \frac{5}{3}x - 2$

25. $y = -\frac{5}{3}x - 2$

26. $y = -\frac{2}{3}x + 1$

27. $y = x$

28. $y = -x$

29. $y = 3 - 2x$

30. $y = 7 - 5x$

31. $y = \frac{4}{3} - \frac{1}{3}x$

32. $y = -\frac{1}{4}x - \frac{1}{2}$

SKILL MAINTENANCE

33. An airplane flew for 7 hr with a 5 km/h tailwind. The return flight against the wind took 8 hr. Find the speed of the plane in still air.

Solve.

34. $\dfrac{3}{x - 5} + \dfrac{1}{x + 5} = \dfrac{2}{x^2 - 25}$ **35.** $25t^2 - 49 = 0$ **36.** $x^2 - 4x = 0$

SYNTHESIS

37. Find all the whole-number solutions of $x + y = 6$.

38. Find three solutions of $y = |x|$.

12.3 More on Graphing Linear Equations

a Graphing Using Intercepts

We graphed equations of the type $y = mx$ and $y = mx + b$ in Section 12.2. We now consider equations of the type $Ax + By = C$, where $A \neq 0$ and $B \neq 0$. These equations can be graphed conveniently using intercepts. Look at the graph of $y = 2x = 4$ shown below. We could graph this equation by solving for y to get $y = 2x + 4$ and proceed as before, but we want to develop a faster method.

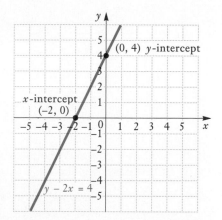

The y-intercept is $(0, 4)$. It occurs where the line crosses the y-axis and thus will always have 0 as the first coordinate. The x-intercept is $(-2, 0)$. It occurs where the line crosses the x-axis and thus will always have 0 as the second coordinate.

DO EXERCISE 1.

We find intercepts as follows.

> The y-intercept is $(0, b)$. To find b, let $x = 0$ and solve the original equation for y.
>
> The x-intercept is $(a, 0)$. To find a, let $y = 0$ and solve the original equation for x.

Now let's draw a graph using intercepts.

▶ **EXAMPLE 1** Graph: $4x + 3y = 12$.

To find the y-intercept, let $x = 0$. Then solve for y:

$$4 \cdot 0 + 3y = 12$$
$$3y = 12$$
$$y = 4.$$

Thus, $(0, 4)$ is the y-intercept. Note that this amounts to covering up the x-term and looking at the rest of the equation.

To find the x-intercept, let $y = 0$. Then solve for x:

$$4x + 3 \cdot 0 = 12$$
$$4x = 12$$
$$x = 3.$$

OBJECTIVES

After finishing Section 12.3, you should be able to:

a Find the intercepts of a linear equation, and graph using intercepts.

b Graph equations of the type $x = a$ or $y = b$.

FOR EXTRA HELP

Tape 24F

1. Look at the graph shown below.

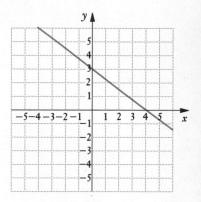

a) Find the coordinates of the x-intercept.

b) Find the coordinates of the y-intercept.

Graph using intercepts.

2. $2x + 3y = 6$

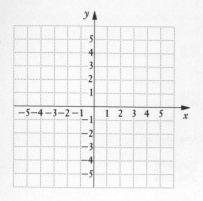

3. $3y - 4x = 12$

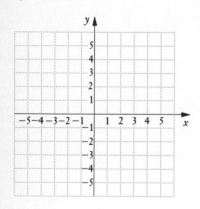

Thus, $(3, 0)$ is the x-intercept. Note that this amounts to covering up the y-term and looking at the rest of the equation.

We plot these points and draw the line, or graph.

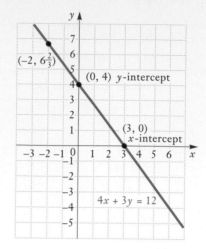

A third point should be used as a check. We substitute any convenient value for x and solve for y. In this case, we choose $x = -2$. Then

$$4(-2) + 3y = 12 \qquad \text{Substituting } -2 \text{ for } x$$
$$-8 + 3y = 12$$
$$3y = 12 + 8 = 20$$
$$y = \tfrac{20}{3}, \text{ or } 6\tfrac{2}{3}. \qquad \text{Solving for } y$$

It appears that the point $(-2, 6\tfrac{2}{3})$ is on the graph, though graphing fractional values can be inexact. The graph is probably correct.   ◄

Graphs of equations of the type $y = mx$ pass through the origin. Thus the x-intercept and the y-intercept are the same, $(0, 0)$. In such cases, we must calculate another point in order to complete the graph. Another point would also have to be calculated if a check is desired.

DO EXERCISES 2 AND 3.

b   **Equations Whose Graphs are Horizontal or Vertical Lines**

► **EXAMPLE 2**   Graph: $y = 3$.

Consider $y = 3$. We can also think of this equation as $0 \cdot x + y = 3$. No matter what number we choose for x, we find that y is 3. We make up a table with all 3's in the y-column.

x	y
	3
	3
	3

y must be 3.

Choose any number for x. ⟶

x	y	
-2	3	
0	3	⟵ y-intercept
4	3	

Now when we plot the ordered pairs $(-2, 3)$, $(0, 3)$, and $(4, 3)$ and connect the points, we will obtain a horizontal line. Any ordered pair $(x, 3)$ is a solution. So the line is parallel to the x-axis with y-intercept $(0, 3)$.

Graph.

4. $x = 5$

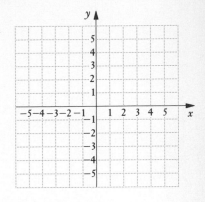

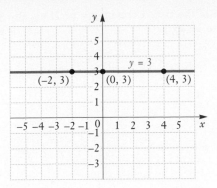

▶ **EXAMPLE 3** Graph: $x = -4$.

Consider $x = -4$. We can also think of this equation as $x + 0 \cdot y = -4$. We make up a table with all -4's in the x-column.

x	y
-4	
-4	
-4	

Choose any number for y. ⟶

x must be -4.

x	y
-4	-5
-4	1
-4	3

5. $y = -2$

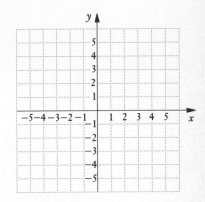

When we plot the ordered pairs $(-4, -5)$, $(-4, 1)$, and $(-4, 3)$ and connect them, we will obtain a vertical line. Any ordered pair $(-4, y)$ is a solution. So the line is parallel to the y-axis with x-intercept $(-4, 0)$.

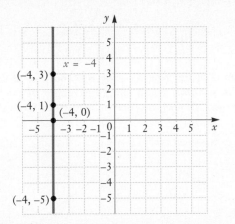

6. $x = 0$

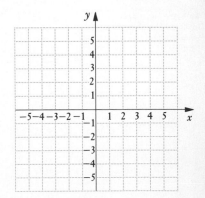

The graph of $y = b$ is a horizontal line. The graph of $x = a$ is a vertical line.

DO EXERCISES 4–7. (EXERCISE 7 IS ON THE FOLLOWING PAGE.)

ANSWERS ON PAGE A-10

7. Graph: $x = -3$.

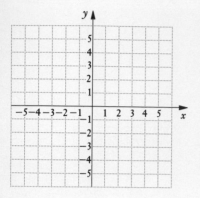

The following is a general procedure for graphing linear equations.

To Graph Linear Equations

1. **Is the equation of the type $x = a$ or $y = b$? If so, the graph will be a line parallel to an axis.**

   Examples.

   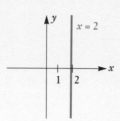

   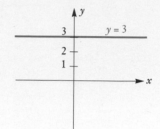

2. **If the line is of the type $y = mx$, both intercepts are the origin, $(0, 0)$. Plot $(0, 0)$ and one other point. A third point can be calculated as a check.**

   Example.

   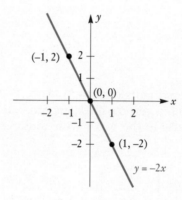

3. **If the equation is of the type $Ax + By = C$, but not of the type $x = a$, $y = b$, or $y = mx$, graph using intercepts. If the intercepts are too close together, choose another point farther from the origin.**

   Examples.

   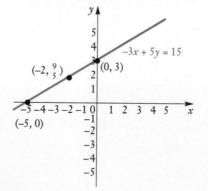

   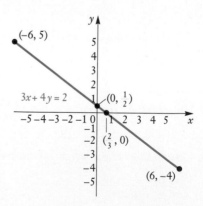

4. **In any case, use a third point as a check. Calculate more points if needed.**

ANSWER ON PAGE A-10

12.4 Slope and Equations of Lines

a Slope

The graphs of some linear equations slant upward from left to right. Others slant downward. Some are vertical and some are horizontal. Some slant more steeply than others. We now look for a way to describe such possibilities with numbers.

Consider a line with two points marked P and Q. As we move from P to Q, the y-coordinate changes from 1 to 3 and the x-coordinate changes from 2 to 6. The change in y is $3 - 1$, or 2. The change in x is $6 - 2$, or 4.

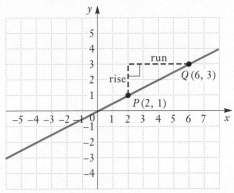

OBJECTIVES

After finishing Section 12.4, you should be able to:

a Given two points of a line, find the slope.

b Find the slope of a line from an equation.

c Given any equation, derive the equivalent slope–intercept equation and determine the slope and the y-intercept.

d Find an equation of a line given a point on the line and the slope, or given two points on the line.

FOR EXTRA HELP

Tape 25A

We call the change in y the **rise** and the change in x the **run**. The ratio rise/run is the same for any two points on a line. We call this ratio the **slope**. Slope describes the slant of a line. The slope of the line in the graph above is given by

$$\frac{\text{rise}}{\text{run}} = \frac{\text{the change in } y}{\text{the change in } x}, \text{ or } \frac{2}{4}, \text{ or } \frac{1}{2}.$$

> The *slope* of a line containing points (x_1, y_1) and (x_2, y_2) is given by
>
> $$m = \frac{\text{rise}}{\text{run}} = \frac{\text{the change in } y}{\text{the change in } x} = \frac{y_2 - y_1}{x_2 - x_1}.$$

▶ **EXAMPLE 1** Graph the line containing the points $(-4, 3)$ and $(2, -6)$ and find the slope.

The graph is shown below. From $(-4, 3)$ and $(2, -6)$, we see that the change in y, or the rise, is $-6 - 3$, or -9. The change in x, or the run, is $2 - (-4)$, or 6.

$$\text{Slope} = \frac{\text{rise}}{\text{run}} = \frac{\text{change in } y}{\text{change in } x}$$

$$= \frac{-6 - 3}{2 - (-4)}$$

$$= \frac{-9}{6} = -\frac{9}{6}, \text{ or } -\frac{3}{2}.$$

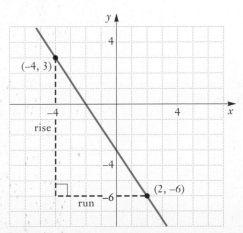

Graph the line containing the points and find the slope two different ways.

1. $(-2, 3)$ and $(3, 5)$

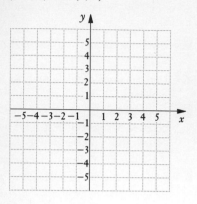

2. $(0, -3)$ and $(-3, 2)$

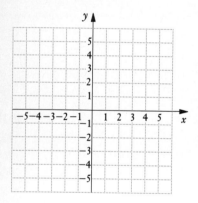

When we use the formula

$$m = \frac{y_2 - y_1}{x_2 - x_1},$$

we can subtract in two ways. We must remember, however, to subtract the y-coordinates in the same order that we subtract the x-coordinates. Let's do Example 1 again:

$$\text{Slope} = \frac{\text{change in } y}{\text{change in } x} = \frac{3 - (-6)}{-4 - 2} = \frac{9}{-6} = -\frac{3}{2}.$$

The slope of a line tells how it slants. A line with positive slope slants up from left to right. The larger the slope, the steeper the slant. A line with negative slope slants downward from left to right.

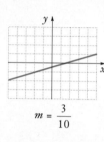

$m = \dfrac{3}{10}$

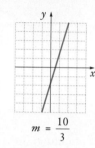

$m = \dfrac{10}{3}$

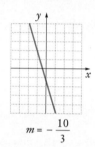

$m = -\dfrac{10}{3}$

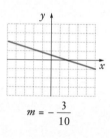

$m = -\dfrac{3}{10}$

DO EXERCISES 1 AND 2.

b   **Finding the Slope from an Equation**

What about the slope of a horizontal or a vertical line?

▶ **EXAMPLE 2**   Find the slope of the line $y = 5$.

Consider the points $(-3, 5)$ and $(4, 5)$, which are on the line. The change in $y = 5 - 5$, or 0. The change in $x = -3 - 4$, or -7. We have

$$m = \frac{5 - 5}{-3 - 4}$$

$$= \frac{0}{-7}$$

$$= 0.$$

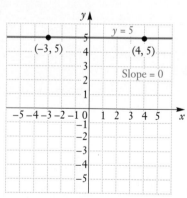

Any two points on a horizontal line have the same y-coordinate. Thus the change in y is 0.   ◀

▶ **EXAMPLE 3** Find the slope of the line $x = -4$.

Consider the points $(-4, 3)$ and $(-4, -2)$, which are on the line. The change in $y = 3 - (-2)$, or 5. The change in $x = -4 - (-4)$, or 0. We have

$$m = \frac{3 - (-2)}{-4 - (-4)}$$

$$= \frac{5}{0}. \quad \text{Not defined}$$

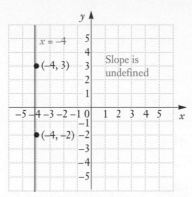

Find the slope, if it exists, of the line.

3. $x = 7$

Since division by 0 is not defined, the slope of this line is not defined. The answer in this example is "The slope of this line is not defined." ◀

> A horizontal line has slope 0. The slope of a vertical line is not defined.

DO EXERCISES 3 AND 4.

It is possible to find the slope of a line from its equation. Let us consider the equation

$$y = 2x + 3.$$

4. $y = -5$

We can find two points by choosing convenient values for x, say 0 and 1, and substituting to find the corresponding y-values. We find the two points on the line to be $(0, 3)$ and $(1, 5)$. The slope of the line is found using the definition of slope:

$$m = \frac{\text{change in } y}{\text{change in } x} = \frac{5 - 3}{1 - 0} = \frac{2}{1} = 2.$$

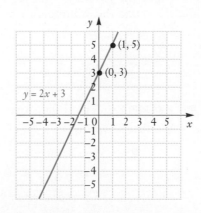

The slope is 2. Note that this is also the coefficient of the x-term in the equation $y = 2x + 3$.

> The slope of the line $y = mx + b$ is m. To find the slope of a nonvertical line, solve the linear equation in x and y for y and get the resulting equation in the form $y = mx + b$. The coefficient of the x-term, m, is the slope of the line. The slope of $x = a$ is not defined.

ANSWERS ON PAGE A-10

Find the slope of the line.

5. $4x + 4y = 7$

▶ **EXAMPLE 4**   Find the slope of the line $2x + 3y = 7$.

We solve for y in two ways, first multiplying by $\frac{1}{3}$ or first dividing by 3:

$$2x + 3y = 7 \qquad\qquad\qquad 2x + 3y = 7$$
$$3y = -2x + 7 \qquad\qquad\qquad 3y = -2x + 7$$
$$y = \frac{1}{3}(-2x + 7) \qquad\qquad\qquad y = \frac{-2x + 7}{3}$$
$$y = -\frac{2}{3}x + \frac{7}{3}; \qquad\qquad\qquad y = -\frac{2}{3}x + \frac{7}{3}.$$

The slope is $-\frac{2}{3}$.   ◀

DO EXERCISES 5 AND 6.

---

c   **The Slope–Intercept Equation of a Line**

In the equation $y = mx + b$, we know that m is the slope. What is the y-intercept? To find out, we let $x = 0$ and solve for y:

$$y = mx + b$$
$$y = m(0) + b$$
$$y = b.$$

Thus the y-intercept is $(0, b)$.

6. $5x - 4y = 8$

> ### The Slope–Intercept Equation
>
> **The equation $y = mx + b$ is called the *slope–intercept equation*. The slope is m and the y-intercept is $(0, b)$.**

▶ **EXAMPLE 5**   Find the slope and the y-intercept of $y = 3x - 4$.

Since the equation is already in the form $y = mx + b$, we simply read the slope and the y-intercept from the equation.

$$y = 3\,x - 4$$

The slope is 3.   The y-intercept is $(0, -4)$.   ◀

▶ **EXAMPLE 6**   Find the slope and the y-intercept of $2x - 3y = 8$.

We first solve for y:

$$2x - 3y = 8$$
$$-3y = -2x + 8 \qquad \text{This equation is not yet solved for } y.$$
$$y = -\tfrac{1}{3}(-2x + 8) \qquad \text{Multiplying by } -\tfrac{1}{3}$$
$$y = \tfrac{2}{3}x - \tfrac{8}{3}.$$

| CAUTION!   Only the coefficient of x is the slope. |

The slope is $\frac{2}{3}$ and the y-intercept is $(0, -\frac{8}{3})$.   ◀

▶ **EXAMPLE 7**   A line has slope -2.4 and y-intercept 11. Find an equation of the line.

12.5 Parallel and Perpendicular Lines

When we graph a pair of linear equations, there are three possibilities:

1. The graphs are the same.
2. The graphs intersect at exactly one point.
3. The graphs are parallel (they do not intersect).

a Parallel Lines

The graphs shown at the right
are of the linear equations

$$y = 2x + 5$$

and $$y = 2x - 3.$$

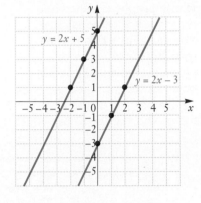

The slope of each line is 2. The y-intercepts are $(0, 5)$ and $(0, -3)$ and are different. The lines do not intersect and are parallel.

> **Parallel Lines**
>
> **Parallel nonvertical lines have the same slope and different y-intercepts.**
> **Parallel vertical lines have equations $x = p$ and $x = q$, where $p \neq q$.**
> **Parallel horizontal lines have equations $y = p$ and $y = q$, where $p \neq q$.**

▶ **EXAMPLE 1** Determine whether the graphs of $y = -3x + 4$ and $6x + 2y = -10$ are parallel.

The graphs of these equations are shown below. By simply graphing, we may find it difficult to determine whether lines are parallel. Sometimes they may intersect only very far from the origin. We can use the preceding result about slopes, y-intercepts, and parallel lines to determine for certain whether lines are parallel.

We first solve each equation for y. The first equation is already solved for y.

a) $y = -3x + 4$

b) $6x + 2y = -10$

$$2y = -6x - 10$$

$$y = \frac{1}{2}(-6x - 10)$$

$$y = -3x - 5$$

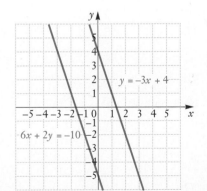

OBJECTIVES

After finishing Section 12.5, you should be able to:

a Determine whether the graphs of two linear equations are parallel.

b Determine whether the graphs of two linear equations are perpendicular.

Determine whether the graphs of the pair of equations are parallel.

1. $y - 3x = 1$,
    $-2y = 3x + 2$

2. $3x - y = -5$,
    $y - 3x = -2$

Determine whether the graphs of the pair of equations are perpendicular.

3. $y = -\dfrac{3}{4}x + 7$,

    $y = \dfrac{4}{3}x - 9$

4. $4x - 5y = 8$,
    $6x + 9y = -12$

The slope of each line is -3. The y-intercepts are $(0, 4)$ and $(0, -5)$ and are different. The lines are parallel.   ◀

DO EXERCISES 1 AND 2.

b   Perpendicular Lines

Perpendicular lines in a plane are lines that intersect at a right angle. The measure of a right angle is 90°. The lines whose graphs are shown at the right are perpendicular. You can check this partially by using a protractor or placing a rectangular piece of paper at the intersection.

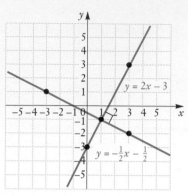

The slopes of the lines are 2 and $-\frac{1}{2}$. Note that $2(-\frac{1}{2}) = -1$. That is, the product of the slopes is -1.

> Two nonvertical lines are perpendicular if the product of their slopes is -1. (If one line has slope m, the slope of the line perpendicular to it is $-1/m$. If one equation in a pair of perpendicular lines is vertical, then the other is horizontal. These equations are of the form $x = a$ and $y = b$.)

▶ **EXAMPLE 2**   Determine whether the graphs of $3y = 9x + 3$ and $6y + 2x = 6$ are perpendicular.

The graphs are shown below, but they are not necessary in order to determine whether the lines are perpendicular.

We first solve each equation for y in order to determine the slopes:

a) $3y = 9x + 3$
    $y = \frac{1}{3}(9x + 3)$
    $y = 3x + 1$;

b) $6y + 2x = 6$
    $6y = -2x + 6$
    $y = \frac{1}{6}(-2x + 6)$
    $y = -\frac{1}{3}x + 1$.

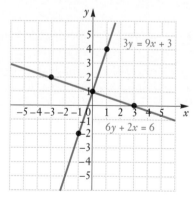

The slopes are 3 and $-\frac{1}{3}$. The product of the slopes is

$$3\left(-\tfrac{1}{3}\right) = -1.$$

The lines are perpendicular.   ◀

DO EXERCISES 3 AND 4.

NAME   SECTION   DATE

EXERCISE SET 12.5

a Determine whether the graphs of the equations are parallel lines.

1. $x + 4 = y,$
    $y - x = -3$

2. $3x - 4 = y,$
    $y - 3x = 8$

3. $y + 3 = 6x,$
    $-6x - y = 2$

4. $y = -4x + 2,$
    $-5 = -2y + 8x$

5. $y + 3.5 = 0.3125x,$
    $5y = -32x + 23.5$

6. $y = 6.4x + 8.9,$
    $5y - 32x = 5$

7. $y = 2x + 7,$
    $5y + 10x = 20$

8. $y = -7x - 5,$
    $2y = -7x - 10$

9. $3x - y = -9,$
    $2y - 6x = -2$

10. $y - 6 = -6x,$
     $-2x + y = 5$

11. $x = 3,$
     $x = 4$

12. $y = -4,$
     $y = 5$

b Determine whether the graphs of the equations are perpendicular lines.

13. $y = -4x + 3,$
     $4y + x = -1$

14. $y = -\dfrac{2}{3}x + 4,$
     $3x + 2y = 1$

15. $x + y = 6,$
     $4y - 4x = 12$

16. $2x - 5y = -3,$
     $5x + 2y = 6$

ANSWERS

1. _____

2. _____

3. _____

4. _____

5. _____

6. _____

7. _____

8. _____

9. _____

10. _____

11. _____

12. _____

13. _____

14. _____

15. _____

16. _____

17. _____

18. _____

19. _____

20. _____

21. _____

22. _____

23. _____

24. _____

25. _____

26. _____

27. _____

28. _____

29. _____

30. _____

31. _____

32. _____

33. _____

34. _____

35. _____

17. $y = -6.4x - 7,$
$64y - 5x = 32$

18. $y = -0.3125x + 11,$
$y - 3.2x = -14$

19. $y = -x + 8,$
$x - y = -1$

20. $2x + 6y = -3,$
$12y = 4x + 20$

21. $\dfrac{3}{8}x - \dfrac{y}{2} = 1,$
$\dfrac{4}{3}x - y + 1 = 0$

22. $\dfrac{1}{2}x + \dfrac{3}{4}y = 6,$
$-\dfrac{3}{2}x + y = 4$

SKILL MAINTENANCE

23. One car travels 10 km/h faster than another. While one car goes 130 km, the other goes 140 km. What is the speed of each car?

24. A train leaves a station and travels west at 70 km/h. Two hours later, a second train leaves on a parallel track and travels west at 90 km/h. When will it overtake the first train?

Solve.

25. $\dfrac{x^2}{x+4} = \dfrac{16}{x+4}$

26. $x^2 - 10x + 25 = 0$

SYNTHESIS

27. Find an equation of a line that contains the point $(0, 6)$ and is parallel to $y - 3x = 4$.

28. Find an equation of the line that contains $(-2, 4)$ and is parallel to $y = 2x - 3$.

29. Find an equation of the line that contains the point $(0, 2)$ and is perpendicular to the line $3y - x = 0$.

30. Find an equation of the line that contains the point $(1, 0)$ and is perpendicular to $2x + y = -4$.

31. Find an equation of the line that has x-intercept $(-2, 0)$ and is parallel to $4x - 8y = 12$.

32. Find the value of k so that $4y = kx - 6$ and $5x + 20y = 12$ are parallel.

33. Find the value of k so that $4y = kx - 6$ and $5x + 20y = 12$ are perpendicular.

The lines in each graph are perpendicular. Find an equation of each line.

34.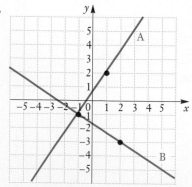

35.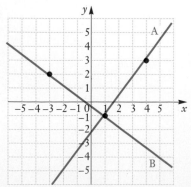

12.6 Direct and Inverse Variation

a Equations of Direct Variation

A bicycle is traveling at 10 km/h. In 1 hr, it goes 10 km. In 2 hr, it goes 20 km. In 3 hr, it goes 30 km, and so on. We will use the number of hours as the first coordinate and the number of kilometers traveled as the second coordinate: (1, 10), (2, 20), (3, 30), (4, 40), and so on. Note that as the first number gets larger, so does the second. Note also that the ratio of distance to time for each of these ordered pairs is $\frac{10}{1}$, or 10.

Whenever a situation produces pairs of numbers in which the *ratio is constant*, we say that there is **direct variation.** Here the distance varies directly as the time:

$$\frac{d}{t} = 10 \text{ (a constant)}, \quad \text{or} \quad d = 10t.$$

> **Direct Variation**
>
> **If a situation translates to an equation described by $y = kx$, where k is a positive constant, $y = kx$ is called an *equation of direct variation*, and k is called the *variation constant*. We say that y varies directly as x.**

The terminologies

"y varies as x,"

"y is directly proportional to x,"

and   "y is proportional to x"

also imply direct variation and are used in many situations. The constant k is often referred to as a **constant of proportionality.**

When there is direct variation $y = kx$, the variation constant can be found if one pair of values of x and y is known. Then other values can be found.

▶ **EXAMPLE 1** Find an equation of variation where y varies directly as x and $y = 7$ and $x = 25$.

We substitute to find k:

$$y = kx$$
$$7 = k \cdot 25$$
$$\frac{7}{25} = k, \quad \text{or} \quad k = 0.28.$$

Then the equation of variation is $y = 0.28x$. Note that the answer is an *equation*.   ◀

DO EXERCISES 1 AND 2.

OBJECTIVES

After finishing Section 12.6, you should be able to:

a Find an equation of direct variation given a pair of values of the variables.

b Solve problems involving direct variation.

c Find an equation of inverse variation given a pair of values of the variables.

d Solve problems involving inverse variation.

FOR EXTRA HELP

Tape 25B

Find an equation of variation where y varies directly as x and the following is true.

 1. $y = 84$ when $x = 12$

 2. $y = 50$ when $x = 80$

3. The cost C of operating a television varies directly as the number n of hours it is in operation. It costs $14.00 to operate a standard-size color TV continuously for 30 days. At this rate, how much would it cost to operate the TV for 1 day? for 1 hour?

4. The weight V of an object on Venus varies directly as its weight E on earth. A person weighing 165 lb on earth would weigh 145.2 lb on Venus. How much would a person weighing 198 lb on earth weigh on Venus?

b | **Solving Problems with Direct Variation**

▶ **EXAMPLE 2**   It is known that the karat rating K of a gold object varies directly as the actual percentage P of gold in the object. A 14-karat gold object is 58.25% gold. What is the percentage of gold in a 24-karat object?

1., 2. *Familiarize* and *Translate.*   The problem states that we have direct variation between the variables K and P. Thus an equation $K = kP$, $k > 0$, applies. As the percentage of gold increases, the karat rating increases. The letters K and k represent different quantities.

3. *Solve.*   The mathematical manipulation has two steps. First, we find the equation of variation by substituting known values for k. Second, we compute the percentage of gold in a 24-karat object.

  a) First, we find an equation of variation:

$$K = kP$$
$$14 = k(0.5825) \quad\quad \text{Substituting 14 for } K \text{ and 58.25\%, or 0.5825, for } P$$
$$\frac{14}{0.5825} = k$$
$$24.03 \approx k. \quad\quad \text{Dividing and rounding to the nearest hundredth}$$

  The equation of variation is $K = 24.03P$.

  b) We then use the equation to find the percentage of gold in a 24-karat object:

$$K = 24.03P$$
$$24 = 24.03P \quad\quad \text{Substituting 24 for } K$$
$$\frac{24}{24.03} = P$$
$$0.999 \approx P$$
$$99.9\% \approx P.$$

4. *Check.*   The check might be done by repeating the computations. You might also do some reasoning about the answer. The karat rating increased from 14 to 24. Similarly, the percentage increased from 58.25% to 99.9%.

5. *State.*   A 24-karat object is 99.9% gold.   ◀

DO EXERCISES 3 AND 4.

Let us consider direct variation from the standpoint of a graph. The graph of $y = kx$, $k > 0$, always goes through the origin and rises from left to right. Note that as x increases, y increases; and as x decreases, y decreases. This is why the terminology "direct" is used. What one variable does, so does the other.

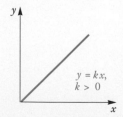

C **Equations of Inverse Variation**

A car is traveling a distance of 10 km. At a speed of 10 km/h, it will take 1 hr. At 20 km/h, it will take $\frac{1}{2}$ hr. At 30 km/h, it will take $\frac{1}{3}$ hr, and so on. This determines a set of pairs of numbers, all having the same product:

$$(10, 1), \quad (20, \tfrac{1}{2}), \quad (30, \tfrac{1}{3}), \quad (40, \tfrac{1}{4}), \quad \text{and so on.}$$

Note that as the first number gets larger, the second number gets smaller. Whenever a situation produces pairs of numbers whose *product is constant*, we say that there is **inverse variation.** Here the time varies inversely as the speed:

$$rt = 10 \ (\text{a constant}), \quad \text{or} \quad t = \frac{10}{r}.$$

> Inverse Variation
>
> **If a situation translates to an equation described by $y = k/x$, where k is a positive constant, $y = k/x$ is called an *equation of inverse variation*. We say that y varies inversely as x.**

The terminology

"y is inversely proportional to x"

also implies inverse variation and is used in some situations.

▶ **EXAMPLE 3**   Find an equation of variation where y varies inversely as x and $y = 145$ when $x = 0.8$.

We substitute to find k:

$$y = \frac{k}{x}$$

$$145 = \frac{k}{0.8}$$

$$(0.8)145 = k$$

$$116 = k.$$

The equation of variation is $y = \dfrac{116}{x}$.   ◀

DO EXERCISES 5 AND 6.

The graph of $y = k/x$, $k > 0$, is shaped like the following figure for positive values of x. (You do not need to know how to graph such equations at this time.) Note that as x increases, y decreases; and as x decreases, y increases. This is why the terminology "inverse" is used. One variable does the opposite of what the other does.

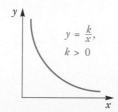

$$y = \frac{k}{x},$$
$$k > 0$$

Find an equation of variation where y varies inversely as x and the following is true.

5. $y = 105$ when $x = 0.6$

6. $y = 45$ when $x = 20$

7. In Example 4, how long would it take 10 people to do the job?

d ▪ Solving Problems with Inverse Variation

Often in an applied situation we must decide which kind of variation, if any, might apply to the problem.

▶ **EXAMPLE 4**   It takes 4 hr for 20 people to wash and wax the floors in a building. How long would it then take 25 people to do the job?

1. *Familiarize.*   Think about the problem situation. What kind of variation would be used? It seems reasonable that the more people there are working on the job, the less time it will take to finish. (One might argue that too many people in a crowded area would be counterproductive, but we will disregard that possibility.) Thus inverse variation might apply. We let $T =$ the time to do the job, in hours, and $N =$ the number of people. Assuming inverse variation, we know that an equation $T = k/N$, $k > 0$, applies. As the number of people increases, the time it takes to do the job decreases.

2. *Translate.*   We write an equation of variation:

$$T = \frac{k}{N}.$$

Time varies inversely as the number of people.

3. *Solve.*   The mathematical manipulation has two steps. First, we find the equation of variation by substituting known values to find k. Second, we compute the amount of time it would take 25 people to do the job.

   a) First, we find an equation of variation:

   $$T = \frac{k}{N}$$

   $$4 = \frac{k}{20} \qquad \text{Substituting 4 for } T \text{ and 20 for } N$$

   $$20 \cdot 4 = k$$

   $$80 = k.$$

   The equation of variation is $T = \dfrac{80}{N}$.

   b) We then use the equation to find the amount of time that it takes 25 people to do the job:

   $$T = \frac{80}{N}$$

   $$T = \frac{80}{25} \qquad \text{Substituting 25 for } N$$

   $$T = 3.2.$$

4. *Check.*   The check might be done by repeating the computations. We might also analyze the results. The number of people increased from 20 to 25. Did the time decrease? It did, and this confirms what we expect with inverse variation.

5. *State.*   It should take 3.2 hr for 25 people to do the job.   ◀

8. The time required to drive a fixed distance varies inversely as the speed r. It takes 5 hr at 60 km/h to drive a fixed distance. How long would it take at 40 km/h?

DO EXERCISES 7 AND 8.

NAME   SECTION   DATE

EXERCISE SET 12.6

ANSWERS

a Find an equation of variation where y varies directly as x and the following are true.

1. $y = 28$ when $x = 7$ **2.** $y = 30$ when $x = 8$ **3.** $y = 0.7$ when $x = 0.4$

1. _____

2. _____

4. $y = 0.8$ when $x = 0.5$ **5.** $y = 400$ when $x = 125$ **6.** $y = 630$ when $x = 175$

3. _____

4. _____

7. $y = 200$ when $x = 300$ **8.** $y = 500$ when $x = 60$

5. _____

b Solve.

6. _____

9. A person's paycheck P varies directly as the number H of hours worked. For working 15 hr, the pay is $78.75. Find the pay for 35 hr of work.

10. The number of bolts B that a machine can make varies directly as the time it operates. It can make 6578 bolts in 2 hr. How many can it make in 5 hr?

7. _____

8. _____

11. The number of servings S of meat that can be obtained from a turkey varies directly as its weight W. From a turkey weighing 14 kg, one can get 40 servings of meat. How many servings can be obtained from an 8-kg turkey?

12. The number of servings S of meat that can be obtained from round steak varies directly as the weight W. From 9 kg of round steak, one can get 70 servings of meat. How many servings can one get from 12 kg of round steak?

9. _____

10. _____

11. _____

12. _____

Copyright © 1993 Addison-Wesley Publishing Co., Inc.

ANSWERS

13. _____

14. _____

15. _____

16. _____

17. _____

18. _____

19. _____

20. _____

21. _____

22. _____

23. _____

24. _____

25. _____

26. _____

13. The weight M of an object on the moon varies directly as its weight E on earth. A person who weighs 171.6 lb on earth weighs 28.6 lb on the moon. How much would a 220-lb person weigh on the moon?

14. The weight M of an object on Mars varies directly as its weight E on earth. A person who weighs 209 lb on earth weighs 79.42 lb on Mars. How much would a 176-lb person weigh on Mars?

15. The number of kilograms W of water in a human body varies directly as the total body weight B. A person weighing 75 kg contains 54 kg of water. How many kilograms of water are in a person weighing 95 kg?

16. The amount C that a family spends on car expenses varies directly as its income I. A family making $21,760 a year will spend $3264 a year for car expenses. How much will a family making $30,000 a year spend for car expenses?

c Find an equation of variation where y varies inversely as x and the following are true.

17. $y = 25$ when $x = 3$

18. $y = 45$ when $x = 2$

19. $y = 8$ when $x = 10$

20. $y = 7$ when $x = 10$

21. $y = 0.125$ when $x = 8$

22. $y = 6.25$ when $x = 0.16$

23. $y = 42$ when $x = 25$

24. $y = 42$ when $x = 50$

25. $y = 0.2$ when $x = 0.3$

26. $y = 0.4$ when $x = 0.6$

d Solve.

27. It takes 16 hr for 2 people to resurface a gym floor. How long will it take 6 people to do the job?

  a) What kind of variation might apply to this situation?
  b) Solve the problem.

28. It takes 4 hr for 9 cooks to prepare a school lunch. How long will it take 8 cooks to prepare the lunch?

  a) What kind of variation might apply to the situation?
  b) Solve the problem.

29. A production line produces 15 compact disc players every 8 hr. How many players can it produce in 37 hr?

  a) What kind of variation might apply to the situation?
  b) Solve the problem.

30. A person works for 15 hr and makes $93.75. How much will the person make by working 35 hr?

  a) What kind of variation might apply to this situation?
  b) Solve the problem.

31. The volume V of a gas varies inversely as the pressure P on it. The volume of a gas is 200 cubic centimeters (cm^3) under a pressure of 32 kg/cm^2. What will be its volume under a pressure of 20 kg/cm^2?

32. The current I in an electrical conductor varies inversely as the resistance R of the conductor. The current is 2 amperes when the resistance is 960 ohms. What is the current when the resistance is 540 ohms?

33. The time t required to empty a tank varies inversely as the rate r of pumping. A pump can empty a tank in 90 min at the rate of 1200 L/min. How long will it take the pump to empty the tank at 2000 L/min?

34. The height H of triangles of fixed area varies inversely as the base B. Suppose the height is 50 cm when the base is 40 cm. Find the height when the base is 8 cm. What is the fixed area?

35. The pitch P of a musical tone varies inversely as its wavelength W. One tone has a pitch of 660 vibrations per second and a wavelength of 1.6 ft. Find the wavelength of another tone that has a pitch of 440 vibrations per second.

36. The time t required to drive a fixed distance varies inversely as the speed r. It takes 5 hr at 55 mph to drive a fixed distance. How long would it take at 40 mph?

27. a) _____

b) _____

28. a) _____

b) _____

29. a) _____

b) _____

30. a) _____

b) _____

31. _____

32. _____

33. _____

34. _____

35. _____

36. _____

Copyright © 1993 Addison-Wesley Publishing Co., Inc.

ANSWERS

37. _____

38. _____

39. _____

40. _____

41. _____

42. _____

43. _____

44. _____

45. _____

46. _____

47. _____

48. _____

49. _____

50. _____

51. _____

52. _____

53. _____

54. _____

55. _____

SYNTHESIS

Write an equation of direct variation for each situation in Exercises 37–40. If possible, give a value for k and graph the equation.

37. The perimeter P of an equilateral polygon varies directly as the length S of a side.

38. The circumference C of a circle varies directly as the radius r.

39. The number of bags B of peanuts sold at a baseball game varies directly as the number N of people in attendance.

40. The cost C of building a new house varies directly as the area A of the floor space of the house.

41. Show that if p varies directly as q, then q varies directly as p.

42. The area of a circle varies directly as the square of the length of the radius. What is the variation constant?

Write an equation of variation for each situation.

43. In a stream, the amount S of salt carried varies directly as the sixth power of the speed V of the stream.

44. The square of the pitch P of a vibrating string varies directly as the tension t on the string.

45. The volume V of a sphere varies directly as the cube of the radius r.

46. The power P in a windmill varies directly as the cube of the wind speed V.

Write an equation of inverse variation for each situation.

47. The cost C per person of chartering a fishing boat varies inversely as the number N of persons sharing the cost.

48. The number N of revolutions of a tire rolling over a given distance varies inversely as the circumference C of the tire.

49. The amount of current I flowing in an electrical circuit varies inversely with the resistance R of the circuit.

50. The density D of a given mass varies inversely as its volume V.

51. The intensity of illumination I from a light source varies inversely as the square of the distance d from the source.

Determine whether the given situation varies inversely.

52. The cost of mailing a letter in the United States and the distance it travels

53. A runner's speed in a race and the time it takes to run it

54. The number of plays to go 80 yd for a touchdown and the average gain per play

55. The weight of a turkey and the cooking time

12.7 Graphing Inequalities in Two Variables

A graph of an inequality is a drawing that represents its solutions. An inequality in one variable can be graphed on a number line. An inequality in two variables can be graphed on a coordinate plane.

a Solutions of Inequalities In Two Variables

The solutions of inequalities in two variables are ordered pairs.

▶ **EXAMPLE 1** Determine whether $(-3, 2)$ is a solution of $5x + 4y < 13$.

We use alphabetical order of the variables and replace x by -3 and y by 2.

$$\begin{array}{c|c} 5x + 4y < 13 \\ \hline 5(-3) + 4 \cdot 2 & 13 \\ -15 + 8 \\ -7 & \text{TRUE} \end{array}$$

Since $-7 < 13$ is true, $(-3, 2)$ is a solution. ◀

▶ **EXAMPLE 2** Determine whether $(6, 8)$ is a solution of $5x + 4y < 13$.

We use alphabetical order of the variables and replace x by 6 and y by 8.

$$\begin{array}{c|c} 5x + 4y < 13 \\ \hline 5(6) + 4(8) & 13 \\ 30 + 32 \\ 62 & \text{FALSE} \end{array}$$

Since $62 < 13$ is false, $(6, 8)$ is not a solution. ◀

DO EXERCISES 1 AND 2.

b Graphing Inequalities In Two Variables

▶ **EXAMPLE 3** Graph: $y > x$.

We first graph the line $y = x$ for comparison. Every solution of $y = x$ is an ordered pair like $(3, 3)$. The first and second coordinates are the same. The graph of $y = x$ is shown on the left below. We draw it dashed because these points are *not* solutions of $y > x$.

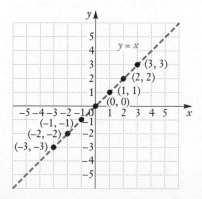   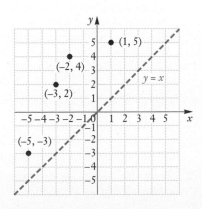

OBJECTIVES

After finishing Section 12.7, you should be able to:

a Determine whether an ordered pair of numbers is a solution of an inequality in two variables.

b Graph linear inequalities.

FOR EXTRA HELP

Tape 25C

1. Determine whether $(4, 3)$ is a solution of $3x - 2y < 1$.

2. Determine whether $(2, -5)$ is a solution of $4x + 7y \geq 12$.

ANSWERS ON PAGE A-10

3. Graph: $y < x$.

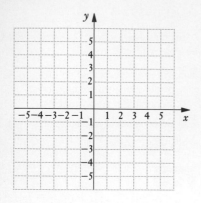

Now look at the graph on the right on the preceding page. Several pairs of numbers are plotted on the half-plane above the line $y = x$. Note that each of these ordered pairs is a solution of $y > x$. We can check a pair such as $(-2, 4)$ as follows:

$$\begin{array}{c|c} y & > & x \\ \hline 4 & | & -2 \end{array} \quad \text{TRUE}$$

It turns out that any point on the same side of $y = x$ as $(-2, 4)$ is also a solution. If we know that one point in a half-plane is a solution, then all points in that half-plane are solutions. The graph of $y > x$ is shown below. (Solutions will be indicated by color shading throughout.) We shade the half-plane above $y = x$.

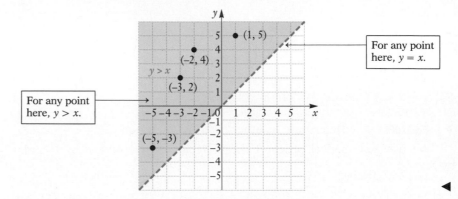

DO EXERCISE 3.

A **linear inequality** is one that we can get from a linear equation by changing the equals symbol to an inequality symbol. Every linear equation has a graph that is a straight line. The graph of a linear inequality is a half-plane, sometimes including the line along the edge.

> **To graph an inequality in two variables:**
>
> 1. **Replace the inequality symbol with an equals sign and graph this related equation.**
>
> 2. **If the inequality symbol is $<$ or $>$, draw the line dashed. If the inequality symbol is $\leq$ or $\geq$, draw the line solid.**
>
> 3. **The graph consists of a half-plane, either above or below or left or right of the line, and, if the line is solid, the line as well. To determine which half-plane to shade, choose a point not on the line as a test point. Substitute to find whether that point is a solution of the inequality. If so, shade the half-plane containing that point. If not, shade the opposite half-plane.**

▶ **EXAMPLE 4**   Graph: $6x - 2y < 10$.

1. We first graph the line $6x - 2y = 10$. The intercepts are $(0, -5)$ and $(\frac{5}{3}, 0)$. The point $(3, 4)$ is also on the graph. This line forms the boundary of the solutions of the inequality.

2. Since the inequality contains the $<$ symbol, points on the line are not solutions of the inequality, so we draw a dashed line.

3. To determine which half-plane to shade, we consider a test point *not* on the line. We try $(3, -2)$ and substitute:

$$\begin{array}{c|c} 6x - 2y < 10 \\ \hline 6(3) - 2(-2) & 10 \\ 18 + 4 & \\ 22 & \text{FALSE} \end{array}$$

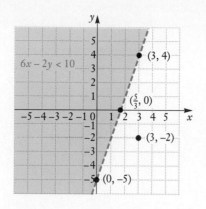

Since this inequality is false, the point $(3, -2)$ is *not* a solution; no point in the half-plane containing $(3, -2)$ is a solution. Thus the points in the opposite half-plane are solutions. The graph is shown above. ◀

DO EXERCISE 4.

▶ **EXAMPLE 5** Graph: $2x + 3y \leq 6$.

First we graph the line $2x + 3y = 6$. The intercepts are $(0, 2)$ and $(3, 0)$. Since the inequality contains the $\leq$ symbol, we draw the line solid to indicate that any pair on the line is a solution. Next, we pick a test point that does not belong to the line. We substitute to determine whether this point is a solution. The origin $(0, 0)$ is usually an easy one to use:

$$\begin{array}{c|c} 2x + 3y \leq 6 \\ \hline 2 \cdot 0 + 3 \cdot 0 & 6 \\ 0 & \text{TRUE} \end{array}$$

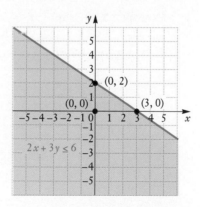

We see that $(0, 0)$ is a solution, so we shade the lower half-plane. Had the substitution given us a false inequality, we would have shaded the other half-plane. ◀

DO EXERCISES 5 AND 6.

▶ **EXAMPLE 6** Graph $x < 3$ on a plane.

There is a missing variable in this inequality. If we graph it on a line, its graph is as follows:

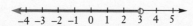

4. Graph: $2x + 4y < 8$.

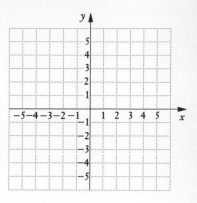

Graph.

5. $3x - 5y < 15$

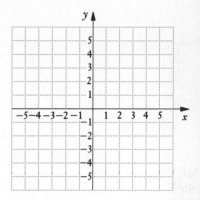

6. $2x + 3y \geq 12$

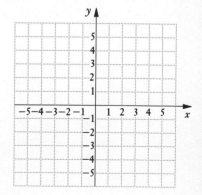

ANSWERS ON PAGE A-10

Graph.

7. $x > -3$

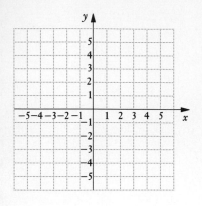

8. $y \leq 4$

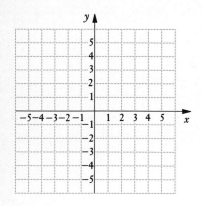

However, we can also write this inequality as $x + 0y < 3$ and consider graphing it on a plane. We use the same technique that we have used with the other examples. We first graph the related equation $x = 3$ on the plane and draw the graph with a dashed line.

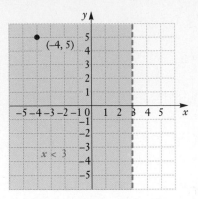

The rest of the graph is a half-plane either to the right or to the left of the line $x = 3$. To determine which, we consider a test point, $(-4, 5)$:

$$
\begin{array}{c|c}
\multicolumn{2}{c}{x + 0y < 3} \\
\hline
-4 + 0(5) & 3 \\
-4 & \text{TRUE}
\end{array}
$$

We see that $(-4, 5)$ is a solution, so all the pairs in the half-plane containing $(-4, 5)$ are solutions. We shade that half-plane.

We see from the graph that the solutions of $x < 3$ are all those ordered pairs whose first coordinates are less than 3. ◄

▶ **EXAMPLE 7** Graph $y \geq -4$ on a plane.

We first graph $y = -4$ using a solid line to indicate that all points on the line are solutions. We then use $(2, 3)$ as a test point and substitute:

$$
\begin{array}{c|c}
\multicolumn{2}{c}{0x + y \geq -4} \\
\hline
0(2) + 3 & -4 \\
3 & \text{TRUE}
\end{array}
$$

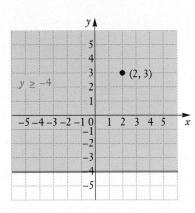

Since $(2, 3)$ is a solution, all points in the half-plane containing $(2, 3)$ are solutions. Note that this half-plane consists of all ordered pairs whose second coordinate is greater than or equal to -4. ◄

DO EXERCISES 7 AND 8.

NAME　　　　　　　　　　　SECTION　　　　DATE

EXERCISE SET 12.7

a

1. Determine whether $(-3, -5)$ is a solution of
$$-x - 3y < 18.$$

2. Determine whether $(5, -3)$ is a solution of
$$-2x + 4y \leq -2.$$

3. Determine whether $(\frac{1}{2}, -\frac{1}{4})$ is a solution of
$$7y - 9x > -3.$$

4. Determine whether $(-6, 5)$ is a solution of
$$x + 0 \cdot y < 3.$$

1. _____

2. _____

3. _____

4. _____

b Graph on a plane.

5. $x > 2y$

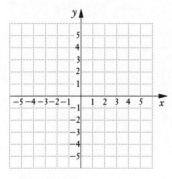

6. $x > 3y$

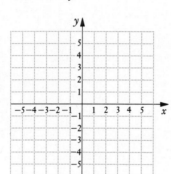

7. $y \leq x - 3$

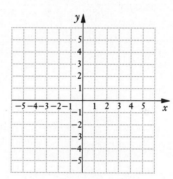

8. $y \leq x - 5$

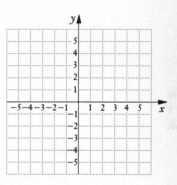

9. $y < x + 1$

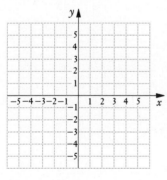

10. $y < x + 4$

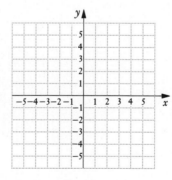

11. $y \geq x - 2$

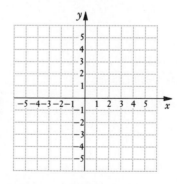

12. $y \geq x - 1$

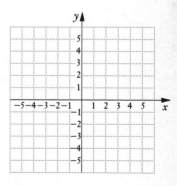

13. $y \leq 2x - 1$

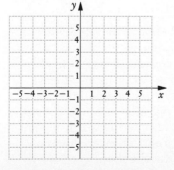

14. $y \leq 3x + 2$

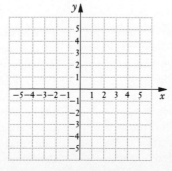

15. $x + y \leq 3$

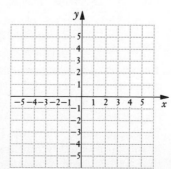

16. $x + y \leq 4$

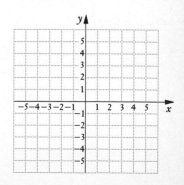

17. $x - y > 7$

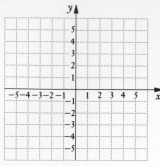

18. $x - y > -2$

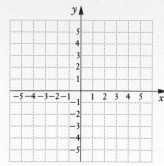

19. $2x + 3y \leq 12$

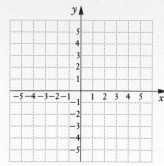

20. $5x + 4y \geq 20$

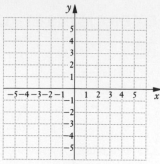

21. $y \geq 1 - 2x$

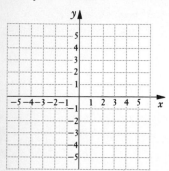

22. $y - 2x \leq -1$

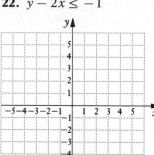

23. $y + 4x > 0$

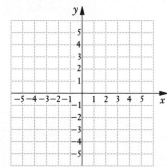

24. $y - x < 0$

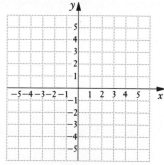

25. $y \leq 3$

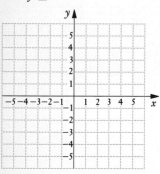

26. $y > -1$

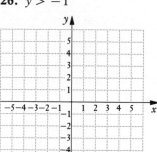

27. $y \geq -5$

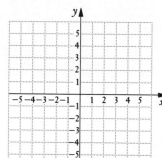

28. $y < 0$

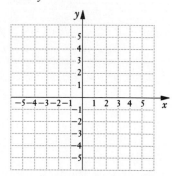

ANSWERS

29. _____

30. _____

31. _____

32. _____

33. _____

34. _____

Copyright © 1993 Addison-Wesley Publishing Co., Inc.

SKILL MAINTENANCE

Calculate.

29. $\dfrac{37 - 5(4 - 6)}{2 \cdot 6 + 8}$

30. $3^7 \div 3^4 \div 3^3 \div 3$

Solve.

31. $x + 5 = -\dfrac{6}{x}$

32. $\dfrac{12}{x} = \dfrac{48}{x + 9}$

SYNTHESIS

33. *Elevators.* Many elevators have a capacity of 1 metric ton (1000 kg). Suppose c children, each weighing 35 kg, and a adults, each weighing 75 kg, are on an elevator. Find and graph an inequality that asserts that the elevator is overloaded.

34. *Hockey wins and losses.* A hockey team figures that it needs at least 60 points for the season in order to make the playoffs. A win w is worth 2 points and a tie t is worth 1 point. Find and graph an inequality that describes the situation.

SUMMARY AND REVIEW: CHAPTER 12

IMPORTANT PROPERTIES AND FORMULAS

$$\text{Slope} = m = \frac{y_2 - y_1}{x_2 - x_1}$$

Slope–Intercept Equation: $y = mx + b$ *Parallel Lines:*   Slopes equal, y-intercepts different

Point–Slope Equation: $y - y_1 = m(x - x_1)$ *Perpendicular Lines:*   Product of slopes $= -1$

REVIEW EXERCISES

The review sections and objectives to be tested in addition to the material in this chapter are [7.8d], [10.7b], [11.6a], and [11.7a, b].

1. This line graph shows the prime rate (the interest rate charged by banks to their best customers) in June for several years.

    a) What was the highest prime rate?

    b) Between what two consecutive years did the prime rate decrease the most?

Find the coordinates of each point.

2. A **3.** B **4.** C

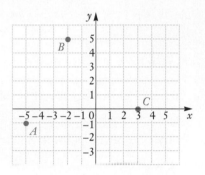

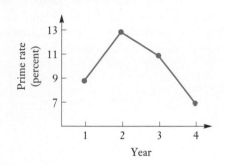

Plot these points using graph paper.

5. $(2, 5)$ **6.** $(0, -3)$ **7.** $(-4, -2)$

In which quadrant is the point located?

8. $(3, -8)$ **9.** $(-20, -14)$ **10.** $(4.9, 1.3)$

Determine whether the given point is a solution of the equation $2y - x = 10$.

11. $(2, -6)$ **12.** $(0, 5)$

Graph on a plane.

13. $y = 2x - 5$ **14.** $y = -\frac{3}{4}x$ **15.** $y = -x + 4$ **16.** $y = 3 - 4x$

17. $5x - 2y = 10$ **18.** $y = 3$ **19.** $4x + 3 = 0$ **20.** $x - 2y = 6$

Find the slope, if it exists, of the line containing the given pair of points.

21. $(6, 8)$ and $(-2, -4)$ **22.** $(5, 1)$ and $(-1, 1)$

23. $(-3, 0)$ and $(-3, 5)$ **24.** $(-8.3, 4.6)$ and $(-9.9, 1.4)$

Find the slope, if it exists, of the line.

25. $y = -6$

26. $x = 90$

27. $4x + 3y = -12$

Find the slope and the y-intercept of the line.

28. $y = -9x + 46$

29. $x + y = 9$

30. $3x - 5y = 4$

Find an equation of the line containing the given point and with the given slope.

31. $(1, 2), \quad m = 3$

32. $(-2, -5), \quad m = \frac{2}{3}$

33. $(0, -4), \quad m = -2$

Find an equation of the line that contains the given pair of points.

34. $(5, 7)$ and $(-1, 1)$

35. $(2, 0)$ and $(-4, -3)$

Determine whether the graphs of the equations are parallel, perpendicular, or neither.

36. $4x + y = 6,$
$\quad 4x + y = 8$

37. $2x + y = 10,$
$\quad y = \frac{1}{2}x - 4$

38. $x + 4y = 8,$
$\quad x = -4y - 10$

39. $3x - y = 6,$
$\quad 3x + y = 8$

Find an equation of variation where y varies directly as x and the following are true.

40. $y = 12$ when $x = 4$

41. $y = 4$ when $x = 8$

42. $y = 0.4$ when $x = 0.5$

Find an equation of variation where y varies inversely as x and the following are true.

43. $y = 5$ when $x = 6$

44. $y = 0.5$ when $x = 2$

45. $y = 1.3$ when $x = 0.5$

Solve.

46. A person's paycheck P varies directly as the number H of hours worked. The pay is $165.00 for working 20 hr. Find the pay for 30 hr of work.

47. It takes 5 hr for 2 washing machines to wash a fixed amount. How long would it take 10 washing machines? (The number of hours varies inversely as the number of washing machines.)

Determine whether the given point is a solution of the inequality $x - 2y > 1$.

48. $(0, 0)$

49. $(1, 3)$

50. $(4, -1)$

Graph on a plane.

51. $x < y$

52. $x + 2y \geq 4$

53. $x > -2$

SKILL MAINTENANCE

54. Judd can paint a shed alone in 5 hr. Mo can paint the same shed alone in 10 hr. How long would it take both of them working together to paint the shed?

55. Compute: $13 \cdot 6 \div 3 \cdot 26 \div 13$.

Solve.

56. $\dfrac{x^2}{x - 4} = \dfrac{16}{x - 4}$

57. $a^2 + 6a - 55 = 0$

❖ THINKING IT THROUGH

1. Briefly describe the concept of slope.

2. Graph $x < 1$ on a number line and on a plane, and explain the difference in the graphs.

NAME   SECTION   DATE

TEST: CHAPTER 12

ANSWERS

Consider the bar graph shown here for Exercises 1–4.

1. What kind of degree was awarded most?

2. How many more bachelor's degrees than associate degrees were awarded?

3. How many more master's degrees than doctoral degrees were awarded?

4. In all, how many graduate degrees were awarded; that is, how many master's, doctoral, and professional degrees were awarded?

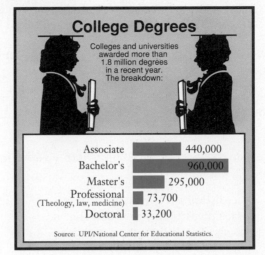

College Degrees

Colleges and universities awarded more than 1.8 million degrees in a recent year. The breakdown:

Associate	440,000
Bachelor's	960,000
Master's	295,000
Professional (Theology, law, medicine)	73,700
Doctoral	33,200

Source: UPI/National Center for Educational Statistics.

In which quadrant is the given point located?

5. $(-\frac{1}{2}, 7)$ **6.** $(-5, -6)$

Find the coordinates of the point.

7. A

8. B

9. Determine whether the ordered pair $(2, -4)$ is a solution of the equation $y - 3x = -10$.

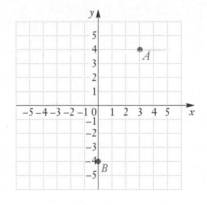

Graph.

10. $y = 2x - 1$ **11.** $2x - 4y = -8$ **12.** $y = 5$

13. $y = -\frac{3}{2}x$ **14.** $2x + 8 = 0$

Find the slope, if it exists, of the line containing the given pair of points.

15. $(4, 7)$ and $(4, -1)$ **16.** $(9, 2)$ and $(-3, -5)$

Find the slope, if it exists, of the given line.

17. $y = -7$ **18.** $x = 6$

1. _____

2. _____

3. _____

4. _____

5. _____

6. _____

7. _____

8. _____

9. _____

10. _____

11. _____

12. _____

13. _____

14. _____

15. _____

16. _____

17. _____

18. _____

Copyright © 1993 Addison-Wesley Publishing Co., Inc.

ANSWERS

19. _____

20. _____

21. _____

22. _____

23. _____

24. _____

25. _____

26. _____

27. _____

28. _____

29. _____

30. _____

31. _____

32. _____

33. _____

34. _____

35. _____

36. _____

37. _____

38. _____

39. _____

40. _____

41. _____

42. _____

43. _____

Find the slope and the y-intercept.

19. $y = 2x - \frac{1}{4}$ **20.** $-4x + 3y = -6$

Find an equation of the line that contains the given point and has the given slope.

21. $(3, 5),\quad m = 1$ **22.** $(-2, 0),\quad m = -3$

Find an equation of the line that contains the given pair of points.

23. $(1, 1)$ and $(2, -2)$ **24.** $(4, -1)$ and $(-4, -3)$

Determine whether the graphs of the equations are parallel, perpendicular, or neither.

25. $2x + y = 8,$
$\quad\; 2x + y = 4$ **26.** $2x + 5y = 2,$
$\qquad\quad y = 2x + 4$ **27.** $x + 2y = 8,$
$\qquad -2x + y = 8$

Find an equation of variation where y varies directly as x and the following are true.

28. $y = 6$ when $x = 3$ **29.** $y = 1.5$ when $x = 3$

Find an equation of variation where y varies inversely as x and the following are true.

30. $y = 6$ when $x = 2$ **31.** $y = \frac{1}{3}$ when $x = 3$

32. The distance d traveled by a train varies directly as the time t that it travels. The train travels 60 km in $\frac{1}{2}$ hr. How far will it travel in 2 hr?

33. It takes 3 hr for 2 cement mixers to mix a certain amount. The number of hours varies inversely as the number of cement mixers. How long would it take 5 cement mixers to do the job?

Determine whether the given point is a solution of the inequality $3y - 2x < -2$.

34. $(0, 0)$ **35.** $(-4, -10)$

Graph on a plane.

36. $y > x - 1$ **37.** $2x - y \le 4$

SKILL MAINTENANCE

38. The speed of a freight train is 15 mph slower than the speed of a passenger train. The freight train travels 360 mi in the same time that it takes the passenger train to travel 420 mi. Find the speed of each train.

39. Compute: $\dfrac{3^2 - 2^3}{2^2 + 3 - 12 \div 2}.$

Solve.

40. $3x^2 + 14x - 5 = 0$ **41.** $\dfrac{x + 1}{x + 3} = \dfrac{x + 2}{x + 4}$

SYNTHESIS

42. Find the area and the perimeter of a rectangle whose vertices are $(-3, 1)$, $(5, 1)$, $(5, 8)$, and $(-3, 8)$.

43. Find the slope–intercept equation of the line that contains the point $(-4, 1)$ and has the same slope as the line $2x - 3y = -6$.

INTRODUCTION We now consider how two graphs of linear equations might intersect. Such a point is a solution of what is called a *system of equations*. Many problems involve two facts about two quantities and are easier to solve by translating to a system of two equations in two variables. Systems of equations have extensive applications in many fields such as sociology, psychology, business, education, engineering, and science.

The review sections to be tested in addition to the material in this chapter are 9.1, 11.1, 11.5, and 12.3. ❖

Systems of Equations

13

AN APPLICATION

Denny's® is a national restaurant firm. The ad shown on p. 747 once appeared on the tables as a special. Determine the price of one item from the *A* side of the menu and the price of one item from the *B* side of the menu.

THE MATHEMATICS

The ad gives us the following pair of equations:

$$\left.\begin{array}{l} a + b = \$5.49, \\ a + 2b = \$6.99, \end{array}\right\} \xleftarrow{} \text{This is a } \textit{system} \\ \textit{of equations.}$$

where a = the price of one item from the *A* side of the menu and b = the price of one item from the *B* side of the menu.

❖ POINTS TO REMEMBER: CHAPTER 13

Supplementary Angles: Two angles are supplementary if the sum of their measures is 180°.
Complementary Angles: Two angles are complementary if the sum of their measures is 90°.
Perimeter of a Rectangle: $P = 2l + 2w$
Motion Formula: $d = rt$
Sum of the Angle Measures of a Triangle = 180°
Simple-Interest Formula: $I = Prt$

PRETEST: CHAPTER 13

1. Determine whether the ordered pair $(-1, 1)$ is a solution of the system of equations

$$2x + y = -1,$$
$$3x - 2y = -5.$$

2. Solve this system by graphing.

$$2x = y + 1,$$
$$2x - y = 5$$

Solve by the substitution method.

3. $x + y = 7,$
$x = 2y + 1$

4. $2x - 3y = 7,$
$x + y = 1$

Solve by the elimination method.

5. $2x - y = 1,$
$2x + y = 2$

6. $2x - 3y = -4,$
$3x - 4y = -7$

7. $\dfrac{3}{5}x - \dfrac{1}{4}y = 4,$

$\dfrac{1}{5}x + \dfrac{3}{4}y = 8$

8. Find two numbers whose sum is 74 and whose difference is 26.

9. Two angles are complementary. One angle is 15° more than twice the other. Find the angles. (Complementary angles are angles whose sum is 90°.)

10. A train leaves a station and travels north at 96 mph. Two hours later, a second train leaves on a parallel track and travels north at 120 mph. When will it overtake the first train?

13.1 Systems of Equations in Two Variables

a Systems of Equations and Solutions

Many problems can be solved more easily by translating to two equations in two variables. The following is a system of equations:

$$x + y = 8,$$
$$2x - y = 1.$$

> A *solution* of a system of two equations is an ordered pair that makes both equations true.

Consider the system shown above. Look at the graph below. **Recall that a graph of an equation is a drawing that represents its solution set. Each point on the graph corresponds to a solution of that equation.** Which points (ordered pairs) are solutions of *both* equations?

The point P with coordinates $(3, 5)$ is a drawing of the set of common solutions.

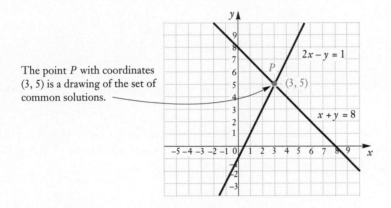

The graph shows that there is only one. It is the point P where the graphs cross. This point looks as if its coordinates are $(3, 5)$. We check to see if $(3, 5)$ is a solution of *both* equations. We substitute 3 for x and 5 for y:

$$
\begin{array}{c|c}
x + y = 8 \\
\hline
3 + 5 \ | \ 8 \\
8 \ | \quad \text{TRUE}
\end{array}
\qquad
\begin{array}{c|c}
2x - y = 1 \\
\hline
2 \cdot 3 - 5 \ | \ 1 \\
6 - 5 \\
1 \ | \quad \text{TRUE}
\end{array}
$$

There is just one solution of the system of equations. It is $(3, 5)$. In other words, $x = 3$ and $y = 5$.

OBJECTIVES

After finishing Section 13.1, you should be able to:

a Determine whether an ordered pair is a solution of a system of equations.

b Solve systems of two linear equations in two variables by graphing.

FOR EXTRA HELP

Tape 25D

Determine whether the given ordered pair is a solution of the system of equations.

1. $(2, -3)$;　$x = 2y + 8$,
　　　　　　　　$2x + y = 1$

▶ **EXAMPLE 1**　　Determine whether $(1, 2)$ is a solution of the system

$$y = x + 1,$$
$$2x + y = 4.$$

We check by substituting alphabetically 1 for x and 2 for y:

$$
\begin{array}{c|c}
\multicolumn{2}{l}{y = x + 1} \\
\hline
2 & 1 + 1 \\
 & 2 \qquad \text{TRUE}
\end{array}
\qquad
\begin{array}{c|c}
\multicolumn{2}{l}{2x + y = 4} \\
\hline
2 \cdot 1 + 2 & 4 \\
2 + 2 & \\
4 & \text{TRUE}
\end{array}
$$

This checks, so $(1, 2)$ is a solution of the system.　　　　◀

▶ **EXAMPLE 2**　　Determine whether $(-3, 2)$ is a solution of the system

$$p + q = -1,$$
$$q + 3p = 4.$$

We check by substituting alphabetically -3 for p and 2 for q:

$$
\begin{array}{c|c}
\multicolumn{2}{l}{p + q = -1} \\
\hline
-3 + 2 & -1 \\
-1 & \text{TRUE}
\end{array}
\qquad
\begin{array}{c|c}
\multicolumn{2}{l}{q + 3p = 4} \\
\hline
2 + 3(-3) & 4 \\
2 - 9 & \\
-7 & \text{FALSE}
\end{array}
$$

The point $(-3, 2)$ is not a solution of $q + 3p = 4$. Thus it is not a solution of the system.　　　　◀

Example 2 illustrates that an ordered pair may be a solution of one equation but not *both*. If that is the case, it is *not* a solution of the system.

DO EXERCISES 1 AND 2.

2. $(20, 40)$;　$a = \dfrac{1}{2}b$,
　　　　　　　　$b - a = 60$

b　Graphing Systems of Equations

Recall that the **graph** of an equation is a drawing that represents its solution set. If the graph of an equation is a line, then every point on the line corresponds to an ordered pair that is a solution of the equation. If we graph a **system** of two linear equations, we graph both equations and find the coordinates of the points of intersection, if any exist.

▶ **EXAMPLE 3**　　Solve this system of equations by graphing:

$$x + y = 6,$$
$$x = y + 2.$$

We graph the equations using any of the methods studied in Chapter 12. Point P with coordinates $(4, 2)$ looks as if it is the solution.

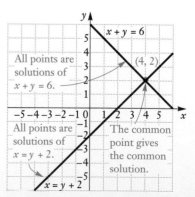

All points are solutions of $x + y = 6$.

All points are solutions of $x = y + 2$.

The common point gives the common solution.

Graphing is not perfectly accurate, so solving by graphing may give only approximate solutions. We check the pair as follows.

Check: $\dfrac{x + y = 6}{4 + 2 \mid 6}$ $\dfrac{x = y + 2}{4 \mid 2 + 2}$

$\qquad\qquad\quad 6 \mid$ TRUE $\qquad 4 \mid$ TRUE

The solution is (4, 2).   ◀

DO EXERCISE 3.

Sometimes the equations in a system have graphs that are parallel lines.

▶ **EXAMPLE 4**   Solve this system of equations by graphing:

$$y = 3x + 4,$$
$$y = 3x - 3.$$

We graph the equations, again using any of the methods studied in Chapter 12. The lines have the same slope, 3, and different intercepts, (0, 4) and (0, −3), so they are parallel.

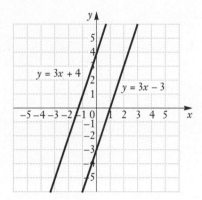

There is no point at which they cross, so the system has no solution. The solution set is the empty set, denoted ∅, or { }.   ◀

DO EXERCISE 4.

3. Solve this system by graphing:

$$2x + y = 1,$$
$$x = 2y + 8.$$

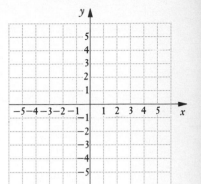

4. Solve this system by graphing:

$$y + 4 = x,$$
$$x - y = -2.$$

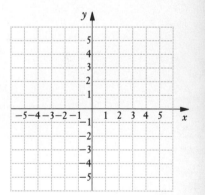

5. Solve this system by graphing:

$$2x + y = 4,$$
$$-6x - 3y = -12.$$

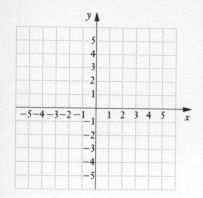

Sometimes the equations in a system have the same graph.

▶ **EXAMPLE 5**   Solve this system by graphing:

$$2x + 3y = 6,$$
$$-8x - 12y = -24.$$

We graph the equations and see that the graphs are the same. Thus any solution of one of the equations is a solution of the other. Each equation has an infinite number of solutions, some of which are indicated on the graph.

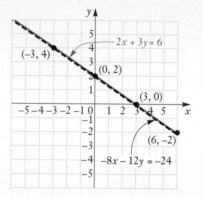

We check one such solution, (0, 2), which is the *y*-intercept of each equation.

$2x + 3y = 6$	
$2(0) + 3(2)$	6
$0 + 6$	
6	TRUE

$-8x - 12y = -24$	
$-4(0) - 12(2)$	-24
$0 - 24$	
-24	TRUE

On your own, check that $(-3, 4)$ is also a solution of the system. If (0, 2) and $(-3, 4)$ are solutions, then all points on the line containing them are solutions. The system has an infinite number of solutions.   ◀

DO EXERCISE 5.

When we graph a system of two equations in two variables, one of the following three things can happen.

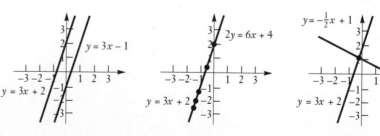

No solution.
Graphs are parallel.

Infinitely
many solutions.
Equations have
the same graph.

One solution.
Graphs intersect.

NAME   SECTION   DATE

EXERCISE SET 13.1

a Determine whether the given ordered pair is a solution of the system of equations. Use alphabetical order of the variables.

1. $(3, 2)$; $2x + 3y = 12$,
            $x - 4y = -5$

2. $(1, 5)$; $5x - 2y = -5$,
            $3x - 7y = -32$

3. $(3, 2)$; $3t - 2s = 0$,
            $t + 2s = 15$

4. $(2, -2)$; $b + 2a = 2$,
            $b - a = -4$

5. $(15, 20)$; $3x - 2y = 5$,
             $6x - 5y = -10$

6. $(-1, -3)$; $3r + s = -6$,
             $2r = 1 + s$

7. $(-1, 1)$; $x = -1$,
            $x - y = -2$

8. $(-3, 4)$; $2x = -y - 2$,
            $y = -4$

9. $(12, 3)$; $y = \dfrac{1}{4}x$,
            $3x - y = 33$

10. $(-3, 1)$; $y = -\dfrac{1}{3}x$,
             $3y = -5x - 12$

1.
2.
3.
4.
5.
6.
7.
8.
9.
10.

b Solve the system of equations by graphing.

11. $x + y = 3$,
       $x - y = 1$

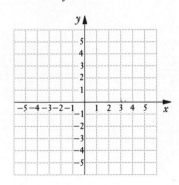

12. $x - y = 2$,
       $x + y = 6$

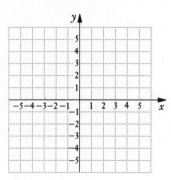

13. $8x - y = 29$,
       $2x + y = 11$

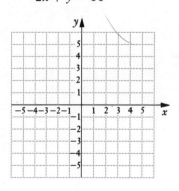

14. $4x - y = 10$,
       $3x + 5y = 19$

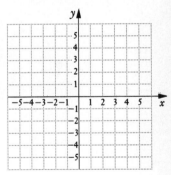

15. $u = v$,
       $4u = 2v - 6$

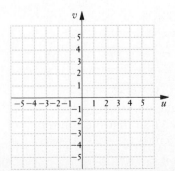

16. $x = 3y$,
       $3y - 6 = 2x$

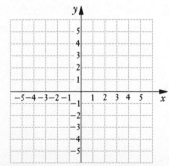

17. $x = -y$,
       $x + y = 4$

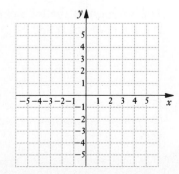

18. $-3x = 5 - y$,
       $2y = 6x + 10$

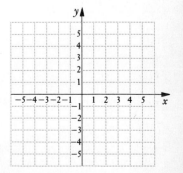

19. $a = \frac{1}{2}b + 1,$
$a - 2b = -2$

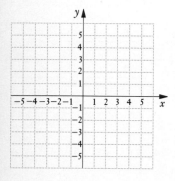

20. $x = \frac{1}{3}y + 2,$
$-2x - y = 1$

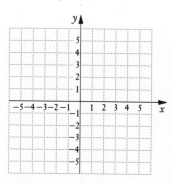

21. $y - 2x = 0,$
$y = 6x - 2$

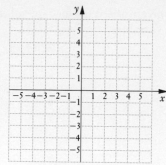

22. $y = 3x,$
$y = -3x + 2$

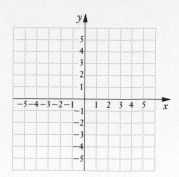

23. $x + y = 9,$
$3x + 3y = 27$

24. $x + y = 4,$
$x + y = -4$

25. $y = 2,$
$x = -4$

26. $x = 5,$
$y = -3$

ANSWERS

27. _____

28. _____

29. _____

30. _____

31. _____

32. _____

33. _____

34. _____

35. _____

36. _____

SKILL MAINTENANCE

27. Multiply: $(9x^{-5})(12x^{-8})$.

28. Divide: $\dfrac{9x^{-5}}{3x^{-8}}$.

Simplify.

29. $\dfrac{1}{x} - \dfrac{1}{x^2} + \dfrac{1}{x+1}$

30. $\dfrac{3-x}{x-2} - \dfrac{x-7}{2-x}$

31. $\dfrac{x+2}{x-4} - \dfrac{x+1}{x+4}$

32. $\dfrac{2x^2 - x - 15}{x^2 - 9}$

SYNTHESIS

33. The solution of the following system is $(2, -3)$. Find A and B.
$$Ax - 3y = 13,$$
$$x - By = 8$$

34. Graph this system. What happens when you check your possible solution?
$$x - 2y = 6,$$
$$3x + 2y = 4$$

35. Find a system of equations with $(2, -4)$ as a solution. Answers may vary.

36. Find an equation to go with $5x + 2y = 11$ so that the solution of the system is $(3, -2)$. Answers may vary.

13.2 The Substitution Method

Consider the following system of equations:

$$3x + 7y = 5,$$
$$6x - 7y = 1.$$

Suppose we try to solve this system graphically. We obtain the following graph.

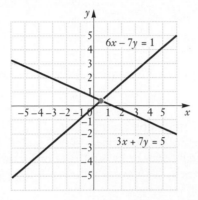

What is the solution? It is rather difficult to tell exactly. It would appear that fractions are involved. It turns out that the solution is $(\frac{2}{3}, \frac{3}{7})$. We need techniques involving algebra to determine the solution exactly. Graphing helps us picture the solution of a system of equations, but solving by graphing, though practical in many applied situations, is not always fast or accurate in cases where solutions are not integers. We now learn other methods using algebra. Because they use algebra, they are called **algebraic.**

a Solving by the Substitution Method

One nongraphical method for solving systems is known as the **substitution method.** In Example 1, we use the substitution method to solve a system we graphed in Example 3 of Section 13.1.

▶ **EXAMPLE 1**   Solve the system:

$$x + y = 6, \quad \textbf{(1)}$$
$$x = y + 2. \quad \textbf{(2)}$$

We graphed this system in Example 3 of Section 13.1. Equation (2) says that x and $y + 2$ name the same thing. Thus in Equation (1), we can substitute $y + 2$ for x:

$$x + y = 6 \qquad \text{Equation (1)}$$
$$(y + 2) + y = 6. \qquad \text{Substituting } y + 2 \text{ for } x$$

This last equation has only one variable. We solve it:

$$y + 2 + y = 6 \qquad \text{Removing parentheses}$$
$$2y + 2 = 6 \qquad \text{Collecting like terms}$$
$$2y = 4 \qquad \text{Subtracting 2 on both sides}$$
$$y = 2. \qquad \text{Dividing by 2}$$

OBJECTIVES

After finishing Section 13.2, you should be able to:

a Solve a system of two equations in two variables by the substitution method when one of the equations has a variable alone on one side.

b Solve a system of two equations in two variables by the substitution method when neither equation has a variable alone on one side.

c Solve problems by translating to a system of two equations and then solving using the substitution method.

FOR EXTRA HELP

Tape 25D

1. Solve by the substitution method. Do not graph.

$$x + y = 5,$$
$$x = y + 1$$

We have found the y-value of the solution. To find the x-value, we return to the original pair of equations. Substituting into either equation will give us the x-value. We choose Equation (1):

$$x + y = 6 \quad \text{Equation (1)}$$
$$x + 2 = 6 \quad \text{Substituting 2 for } y$$
$$x = 4. \quad \text{Subtracting 2}$$

The ordered pair (4, 2) may be a solution. We check.

Check:

$x + y = 6$		$x = y + 2$	
$4 + 2$	6	4	$2 + 2$
	6 TRUE		4 TRUE

Since (4, 2) checks, we have the solution. We could also express the answer as $x = 4$, $y = 2$. ◀

     Note in Example 1 that substituting 2 for y in the second equation will also give us the x-value of the solution: $x = y + 2 = 2 + 2 = 4$. Note also that we are using alphabetical order in listing the coordinates in an ordered pair. That is, since x precedes y, we have 4 before 2 in the pair (4, 2).

DO EXERCISE 1.

▶ **EXAMPLE 2**   Solve:

$$s = 13 - 3t, \quad \text{(1)}$$
$$s + t = 5. \quad \text{(2)}$$

We substitute $13 - 3t$ for s in Equation (2):

$$s + t = 5 \quad \text{Equation (2)}$$
$$(13 - 3t) + t = 5. \quad \text{Substituting } 13 - 3t \text{ for } s$$

2. Solve by the substitution method:

$$a - b = 4,$$
$$b = 2 - a.$$

> Remember to use parentheses when you substitute. Then remove them carefully.

Now we solve for t:

$$13 - 2t = 5 \quad \text{Collecting like terms}$$
$$-2t = -8 \quad \text{Subtracting 13}$$
$$t = \frac{-8}{-2}, \text{ or } 4. \quad \text{Dividing by } -2$$

Next we substitute 4 for t in Equation (2) of the original system:

$$s + t = 5 \quad \text{Equation (2)}$$
$$s + 4 = 5 \quad \text{Substituting 4 for } t$$
$$s = 1. \quad \text{Subtracting 4}$$

The pair (1, 4) checks and is the solution. ◀

DO EXERCISE 2.

b   Solving for the Variable First

Sometimes neither equation of a pair has a variable alone on one side. Then we solve one equation for one of the variables and proceed as before, substituting into the *other* equation. If possible, we solve in either equation for a variable that has a coefficient of 1.

▶ **EXAMPLE 3**   Solve:

$$x - 2y = 6, \qquad \textbf{(1)}$$
$$3x + 2y = 4. \qquad \textbf{(2)}$$

We solve one equation for one variable. Since the coefficient of x is 1 in Equation (1), it is easier to solve that equation for x:

$$x - 2y = 6 \qquad \text{Equation (1)}$$
$$x = 6 + 2y. \qquad \text{Adding } 2y \qquad \textbf{(3)}$$

We substitute $6 + 2y$ for x in Equation (2) of the original pair and solve for y:

$$3x + 2y = 4 \qquad \text{Equation (2)}$$
$$3(6 + 2y) + 2y = 4 \qquad \text{Substituting } 6 + 2y \text{ for } x$$
$$18 + 6y + 2y = 4 \qquad \text{Removing parentheses}$$
$$18 + 8y = 4 \qquad \text{Collecting like terms}$$
$$8y = -14 \qquad \text{Subtracting 18}$$
$$y = \frac{-14}{8}, \text{ or } -\frac{7}{4}. \qquad \text{Dividing by 8}$$

To find x, we go back to either of the original Equations (1) or (2) or to Equation (3), which we solved for x. It is generally easier to use an equation like Equation (3) where we have solved for a specific variable. We substitute $-\frac{7}{4}$ for y in Equation (3) and compute x:

$$x = 6 + 2y = 6 + 2\left(-\frac{7}{4}\right) = 6 - \frac{7}{2} = \frac{5}{2}.$$

We check the ordered pair $(\frac{5}{2}, -\frac{7}{4})$.

Check:

$$
\begin{array}{r|l}
x - 2y = 6 & \\
\hline
\dfrac{5}{2} - 2\left(-\dfrac{7}{4}\right) & 6 \\[2mm]
\dfrac{5}{2} + \dfrac{7}{2} & \\[2mm]
\dfrac{12}{2} & \\[2mm]
6 & \text{TRUE}
\end{array}
\qquad
\begin{array}{r|l}
3x + 2y = 4 & \\
\hline
3 \cdot \dfrac{5}{2} + 2\left(-\dfrac{7}{4}\right) & 4 \\[2mm]
\dfrac{15}{2} - \dfrac{7}{2} & \\[2mm]
\dfrac{8}{2} & \\[2mm]
4 & \text{TRUE}
\end{array}
$$

Since $(\frac{5}{2}, -\frac{7}{4})$ checks, it is the solution.   ◀

This solution would have been difficult to find graphically because it involves fractions.

DO EXERCISE 3.

---

3. Solve:

$$x - 2y = 8,$$
$$2x + y = 8.$$

ANSWER ON PAGE A-11

4. The perimeter of a rectangle is 76 cm. The length is 17 cm more than the width. Find the length and the width.

Solving Problems

Now let us use the substitution method to solve a problem.

▶ **EXAMPLE 4**   The state of Colorado is a rectangle whose perimeter is 1300 mi. The length is 110 mi more than the width. Find the length and the width.

1. *Familiarize.* We make a drawing and label it. We have called the length l and the width w.

2. *Translate.* The perimeter of the rectangle is $2l + 2w$. We translate the first statement.

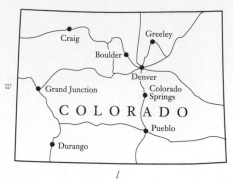

The perimeter is 1300 mi.

$$2l + 2w \ = \ 1300$$

We translate the second statement.

The length is 110 mi greater than the width.

$$l \ = \ 110 + w$$

We have translated to a system of equations:

$$2l + 2w = 1300, \quad \textbf{(1)}$$
$$l = 110 + w. \quad \textbf{(2)}$$

3. *Solve.* We solve the system. We substitute $110 + w$ for l in the first equation and solve:

$$2(110 + w) + 2w = 1300 \quad \text{Substituting } 110 + w \text{ for } l \text{ in Equation (1)}$$
$$220 + 2w + 2w = 1300 \quad \text{Removing parentheses}$$
$$220 + 4w = 1300 \quad \text{Collecting like terms}$$
$$4w = 1080 \quad \text{Subtracting 220}$$
$$w = \frac{1080}{4}, \text{ or } 270. \quad \text{Dividing by 4}$$

We go back to the original equations and substitute 270 for w. We use Equation (2):

$$l = 110 + w \quad \text{Equation (2)}$$
$$l = 110 + 270 \quad \text{Substituting 270 for } w$$
$$l = 380.$$

4. *Check.* A possible solution is a length of 380 mi and a width of 270 mi. The perimeter would be $2(380) + 2(270)$, or $760 + 540$, or 1300. Also, the length is 110 mi greater than the width. These check.

5. *State.* The length is 370 mi, and the width is 110 mi. ◀

This problem illustrates that many problems that can be solved by translating to *one* equation in *one* variable are actually easier to solve by translating to *two* equations in *two* variables.

DO EXERCISE 4.

EXERCISE SET 13.2

a Solve by the substitution method.

1. $x + y = 4,$
    $y = 2x + 1$

2. $x + y = 10,$
    $y = x + 8$

3. $y = x + 1,$
    $2x + y = 4$

4. $y = x - 6,$
    $x + y = -2$

5. $y = 2x - 5,$
    $3y - x = 5$

6. $y = 2x + 1,$
    $x + y = -2$

7. $x = -2y,$
    $x + 4y = 2$

8. $r = -3s,$
    $r + 4s = 10$

b Solve by the substitution method. First, solve one equation for one variable.

9. $s + t = -4,$
    $s - t = 2$

10. $x - y = 6,$
    $x + y = -2$

11. $y - 2x = -6,$
    $2y - x = 5$

12. $x - y = 5,$
    $x + 2y = 7$

13. $2x + 3y = -2,$
    $2x - y = 9$

14. $x + 2y = 10,$
    $3x + 4y = 8$

15. $x - y = -3,$
    $2x + 3y = -6$

16. $3b + 2a = 2,$
    $-2b + a = 8$

17. $r - 2s = 0,$
    $4r - 3s = 15$

18. $y - 2x = 0,$
    $3x + 7y = 17$

c Solve.

19. The sum of two numbers is 27. One number is three more than the other. Find the numbers.

20. The sum of two numbers is 36. One number is two more than the other. Find the numbers.

21. Find two numbers whose sum is 58 and whose difference is 16.

22. Find two numbers whose sum is 66 and whose difference is 8.

1. _____

2. _____

3. _____

4. _____

5. _____

6. _____

7. _____

8. _____

9. _____

10. _____

11. _____

12. _____

13. _____

14. _____

15. _____

16. _____

17. _____

18. _____

19. _____

20. _____

21. _____

22. _____

ANSWERS

23. _____

24. _____

25. _____

26. _____

27. _____

28. _____

29. See graph. _____

30. See graph. _____

31. See graph. _____

32. See graph. _____

33. _____

34. _____

35. _____

36. _____

37. _____

38. _____

39. _____

23. The difference between two numbers is 16. Three times the larger number is seven times the smaller. What are the numbers?

24. The difference between two numbers is 18. Twice the smaller number plus three times the larger is 74. What are the numbers?

25. The state of Wyoming is a rectangle whose perimeter is 1280 mi. The width is 90 mi less than the length. Find the length and the width.

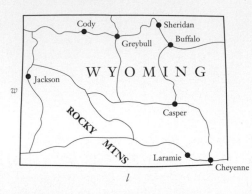

26. The perimeter of a standard-sized rectangular rug is 42 ft. The length is 3 ft more than the width. Find the length and the width.

27. The perimeter of a rectangle is 400 m. The length is 3 m more than twice the width. Find the length and the width.

28. The perimeter of a rectangle is 876 cm. The length is 1 cm less than three times the width. Find the length and the width.

SKILL MAINTENANCE

Graph.

29. $2x - 3y = 6$

30. $2x + 3y = 6$

31. $2x - 3 = 0$

32. $y = 2x - 5$

SYNTHESIS

Solve by the substitution method.

33. ▤ $y - 2.35x = -5.97,$
$2.14y - x = 4.88$

34. $\frac{1}{4}(a - b) = 2,$
$\frac{1}{6}(a + b) = 1$

35. $\frac{x}{2} + \frac{3y}{2} = 2,$
$\frac{x}{5} - \frac{y}{2} = 3$

36. A rectangle has a perimeter of P ft. The width is 5 ft less than the length. Find the length in terms of P.

37. The perimeter of a football field (excluding the end zones) is $306\frac{2}{3}$ yd. The length is $46\frac{2}{3}$ yd longer than the width. Find the length and the width.

38. Consider this system of equations:
$$3y + 3x = 14,$$
$$y = -x + 4.$$
Try to solve by the substitution method. Can you explain your results?

39. Consider this system of equations:
$$y = x + 5,$$
$$-3x + 3y = 15.$$
Try to solve by the substitution method. Can you explain your results?

13.3 The Elimination Method

a Solving by the Elimination Method

The **elimination method** for solving systems of equations makes use of the *addition principle*. Some systems are much easier to solve using this method. Trying to solve the system in Example 1 by substitution would necessitate the use of fractions and extra steps. Instead we use the elimination method.

▶ **EXAMPLE 1** Solve:

$$2x + 3y = 13, \quad (1)$$
$$4x - 3y = 17. \quad (2)$$

The key to the advantage of the elimination method for solving this system involves the $3y$ in one equation and the $-3y$ in the other. The terms are opposites. If we add the terms on the sides of the equations, these terms will add to 0, and in effect, the variable y will be eliminated.

We will use the addition principle for equations. According to Equation (2), $4x - 3y$ and 17 are the same number. Thus we can use a vertical form and add $4x - 3y$ to the left side of Equation (1) and 17 to the right side:

$$
\begin{array}{ll}
2x + 3y = 13 & (1) \\
\underline{4x - 3y = 17} & (2) \\
6x + 0y = 30. & \text{Adding}
\end{array}
$$

We have "eliminated" one variable. This is why we call this the **elimination method.** We now have an equation with just one variable that can be solved for x:

$$6x = 30$$
$$x = 5.$$

Next we substitute 5 for x in either of the original equations:

$$
\begin{array}{ll}
2x + 3y = 13 & \text{Equation (1)} \\
2(5) + 3y = 13 & \text{Substituting 5 for } x \\
10 + 3y = 13 & \\
3y = 3 & \\
y = 1. & \text{Solving for } y
\end{array}
$$

We check the ordered pair (5, 1).

Check:

$$
\begin{array}{c|c}
2x + 3y = 13 & \\
\hline
2(5) + 3(1) & 13 \\
10 + 3 & \\
13 & \text{TRUE}
\end{array}
\qquad
\begin{array}{c|c}
4x - 3y = 17 & \\
\hline
4(5) - 3(1) & 17 \\
20 - 3 & \\
17 & \text{TRUE}
\end{array}
$$

Since (5, 1) checks, it is the solution. ◀

DO EXERCISES 1 AND 2.

b Using the Multiplication Principle First

The elimination method allows us to eliminate a variable. We may need to multiply by certain numbers first, however, so that terms become opposites.

OBJECTIVES

After finishing Section 13.3, you should be able to:

a Solve a system of two equations in two variables using the elimination method when no multiplication is necessary.

b Solve a system of two equations in two variables using the elimination method when multiplication is necessary.

c Solve problems by translating to a system of two equations and then solving using the elimination method.

FOR EXTRA HELP

Tape 26A, 26B

Solve using the elimination method.

1. $x + y = 5,$
   $2x - y = 4$

2. $3x - 3y = 6,$
   $3x + 3y = 0$

ANSWERS ON PAGE A-11

3. Solve. Multiply one equation by
-1 first.

$$5x + 3y = 17,$$
$$5x - 2y = -3$$

▶ **EXAMPLE 2**   Solve:

$$2x + 3y = 8, \quad (1)$$
$$x + 3y = 7. \quad (2)$$

If we add, we will not eliminate a variable. However, if the $3y$ were $-3y$ in one equation, we could eliminate y. We multiply on both sides of Equation (2) by -1 and then add, using a vertical form.

$$
\begin{array}{ll}
2x + 3y = 8 & \text{Equation (1)} \\
\underline{-x - 3y = -7} & \text{Multiplying Equation (2) by } -1 \\
x = 1. & \text{Adding}
\end{array}
$$

Now we substitute 1 for x in one of the original equations:

$$
\begin{array}{ll}
x + 3y = 7 & \text{Equation (2)} \\
1 + 3y = 7 & \text{Substituting 1 for } x \\
3y = 6 & \\
y = 2. & \text{Solving for } y
\end{array}
$$

We can check the ordered pair $(1, 2)$.

Check:

$$
\begin{array}{c|c}
2x + 3y = 8 & \\
\hline
2 \cdot 1 + 3 \cdot 2 & 8 \\
2 + 6 & \\
8 & \text{TRUE}
\end{array}
\qquad
\begin{array}{c|c}
x + 3y = 7 & \\
\hline
1 + 3 \cdot 2 & 7 \\
1 + 6 & \\
7 & \text{TRUE}
\end{array}
$$

Since $(1, 2)$ checks, it is the solution.   ◀

DO EXERCISE 3.

In Example 2, we used the multiplication principle, multiplying by -1. We often need to multiply by something other than -1.

▶ **EXAMPLE 3**   Solve:

$$3x + 6y = -6, \quad (1)$$
$$5x - 2y = 14. \quad (2)$$

Looking at the terms with variables, we see that if $-2y$ were $-6y$, we would have terms that are opposites. We can achieve this by multiplying on both sides of Equation (2) by 3. Then we add:

$$
\begin{array}{ll}
3x + 6y = -6 & \text{Equation (1)} \\
\underline{15x - 6y = 42} & \text{Multiplying Equation (2) by 3} \\
18x = 36 & \text{Adding} \\
x = 2. & \text{Solving for } x
\end{array}
$$

We go back to Equation (1) and substitute 2 for x:

$$
\begin{array}{ll}
3 \cdot 2 + 6y = -6 & \text{Substituting} \\
6 + 6y = -6 & \\
6y = -12 & \\
y = -2. & \text{Solving for } y
\end{array}
$$

We check the ordered pair $(2, -2)$.

ANSWER ON PAGE A-11

Check:

$$\begin{array}{c|c} 3x + 6y = -6 \\ \hline 3 \cdot 2 + 6 \cdot (-2) & -6 \\ 6 + (-12) & \\ -6 & \text{TRUE} \end{array}$$

$$\begin{array}{c|c} 5x - 2y = 14 \\ \hline 5 \cdot 2 - 2 \cdot (-2) & 14 \\ 10 - (-4) & \\ 14 & \text{TRUE} \end{array}$$

Since $(2, -2)$ checks, it is the solution. ◄

> CAUTION! Solving a *system* of equations in two variables requires finding an ordered *pair* of numbers. Once you have solved for one variable, don't forget the other.

DO EXERCISE 4.

We have used the elimination method in Examples 1–3. Part of the strategy in doing so is making a decision about which variable to eliminate. So long as the algebra has been carried out correctly, the solution can be found by eliminating *either* variable. We multiply so that terms involving the variable to be eliminated are opposites. It is helpful to first get each equation in a form equivalent to $Ax + By = C$.

▶ **EXAMPLE 4** Solve:

$$3y + 1 + 2x = 0,$$
$$5x = 7 - 4y.$$

We first get each equation into a form equivalent to $Ax + By = C$:

$2x + 3y = -1,$ **Subtracting 1 on both sides and rearranging terms**

$5x + 4y = 7.$ **Adding 4y on both sides**

We then use the multiplication principle with both equations:

$$2x + 3y = -1, \quad \textbf{(1)}$$
$$5x + 4y = 7. \quad \textbf{(2)}$$

We decide to eliminate the *x*-term. We do this by multiplying on both sides of Equation (1) by 5 and on both sides of Equation (2) by -2:

$$\begin{array}{ll} 10x + 15y = -5 & \text{\textbf{Multiplying on both sides of Equation (1) by 5}} \\ \underline{-10x - 8y = -14} & \text{\textbf{Multiplying on both sides of Equation (2) by -2}} \\ 7y = -19 & \text{\textbf{Adding}} \\ y = \dfrac{-19}{7}, \text{ or } -\dfrac{19}{7}. & \text{\textbf{Dividing by 7}} \end{array}$$

We substitute $-\frac{19}{7}$ for y in one of the original equations:

$$\begin{array}{ll} 2x + 3y = -1 & \text{\textbf{Equation (1)}} \\ 2x + 3(-\frac{19}{7}) = -1 & \text{\textbf{Substituting } -\frac{19}{7} \text{ for } y} \\ 2x - \frac{57}{7} = -1 & \\ 2x = -1 + \frac{57}{7} & \\ 2x = -\frac{7}{7} + \frac{57}{7} & \\ 2x = \frac{50}{7} & \\ x = \frac{50}{7} \cdot \frac{1}{2}, \text{ or } \frac{25}{7}. & \text{\textbf{Solving for } x} \end{array}$$

We check the ordered pair $(\frac{25}{7}, -\frac{19}{7})$.

4. Solve:

$$4a + 7b = 11,$$
$$2a + 3b = 5.$$

ANSWER ON PAGE A-11

5. Solve:

$$3x = 5 + 2y,$$
$$2x + 3y - 1 = 0.$$

Check:

$$
\begin{array}{c|c}
2x + 3y = -1 & \\
\hline
2\left(\dfrac{25}{7}\right) + 3\left(-\dfrac{19}{7}\right) & -1 \\
\dfrac{50}{7} - \dfrac{57}{7} & \\
-\dfrac{7}{7} & \\
-1 & \text{TRUE}
\end{array}
\qquad
\begin{array}{c|c}
5x + 4y = 7 & \\
\hline
5\left(\dfrac{25}{7}\right) + 4\left(-\dfrac{19}{7}\right) & 7 \\
\dfrac{125}{7} - \dfrac{76}{7} & \\
\dfrac{49}{7} & \\
7 & \text{TRUE}
\end{array}
$$

The solution is $\left(\frac{25}{7}, -\frac{19}{7}\right)$.　◀

DO EXERCISE 5.

Let us consider a system with no solution and see what happens when we apply the elimination method.

▶ **EXAMPLE 5**　Solve:

$$y - 3x = 2, \qquad \textbf{(1)}$$
$$y - 3x = 1. \qquad \textbf{(2)}$$

We multiply by -1 on both sides of Equation (2) and then add:

$$
\begin{array}{ll}
y - 3x = 2 & \\
\underline{-y + 3x = -1} & \text{Multiplying by } -1 \\
\qquad\quad 0 = 1. & \text{Adding}
\end{array}
$$

We obtain a false equation, $0 = 1$, so there is *no solution*. The slope–intercept forms of these equations are

$$y = 3x + 2,$$
$$y = 3x + 1.$$

6. Solve:

$$2x + \;\; y = 15,$$
$$4x + 2y = 23.$$

The slopes are the same and the y-intercepts are different. Thus the lines are parallel. They do not intersect.　◀

DO EXERCISE 6.

Sometimes there is an infinite number of solutions. Let's look at a system that we graphed in Example 5 of Section 13.1.

▶ **EXAMPLE 6**　Solve:

$$2x + \;\; 3y = 6,$$
$$-8x - 12y = -24.$$

We multiply on both sides of Equation (1) by 4 and then add the two equations:

$$
\begin{array}{ll}
8x + 12y = \;\;\; 24 & \text{Multiplying by 4} \\
\underline{-8x - 12y = -24} & \\
\qquad\quad 0 = \;\;\;\; 0. & \text{Adding}
\end{array}
$$

7. Solve:

$$5x - 2y = 3,$$
$$-15x + 6y = -9$$

We have eliminated both variables, and what remains is an equation easily seen to be true. If this happens when we use the elimination method, we have an infinite number of solutions.　◀

DO EXERCISE 7.

When decimals or fractions appear, we first multiply to clear of them. Then we proceed as before.

▶ **EXAMPLE 7**   Solve:

$$\frac{1}{3}x + \frac{1}{2}y = -\frac{1}{6}, \quad \textbf{(1)}$$

$$\frac{1}{2}x + \frac{2}{5}y = \frac{7}{10}. \quad \textbf{(2)}$$

The number 6 is a multiple of all the denominators of Equation (1). The number 10 is a multiple of all the denominators of Equation (2). We multiply on both sides of Equation (1) by 6 and on both sides of Equation (2) by 10:

$$6\left(\frac{1}{3}x + \frac{1}{2}y\right) = 6\left(-\frac{1}{6}\right) \qquad 10\left(\frac{1}{2}x + \frac{2}{5}y\right) = 10\left(\frac{7}{10}\right)$$

$$6 \cdot \frac{1}{3}x + 6 \cdot \frac{1}{2}y = -1 \qquad 10 \cdot \frac{1}{2}x + 10 \cdot \frac{2}{5}y = 7$$

$$2x + 3y = -1; \qquad\qquad 5x + 4y = 7.$$

The resulting system is

$$2x + 3y = -1,$$
$$5x + 4y = 7.$$

As we saw in Example 4, the solution of this system is $(\frac{25}{9}, -\frac{19}{7})$. ◀

DO EXERCISE 8.

The following is a summary that compares the graphical, substitution, and elimination methods for solving systems of equations.

Method	Strengths	Weaknesses
Graphical	Can "see" solution.	Inexact when solution involves numbers that are not integers or are very large and off the graph.
Substitution	Works well when solutions are not integers. Easy to use when a variable is alone on one side.	Introduces extensive computations with fractions for more complicated systems where coefficients are not 1 or −1. Cannot "see" the solution.
Elimination	Works well when solutions are not integers, when coefficients are not 1 or −1, and when coefficients involve decimals or fractions	Cannot "see" the solution.

When deciding which method to use, consider the preceding chart and directions from your instructor. The situation is like having a piece of wood to cut and three saws with which to cut it. The saw you use depends on the type of wood, the type of cut you are making, and how you want the wood to turn out.

8. Solve:

$$\frac{1}{2}x + \frac{3}{10}y = \frac{1}{5},$$

$$\frac{3}{5}x + \quad y = -\frac{2}{5}.$$

ANSWER ON PAGE A-11

9. Acme Rent-A-Car rents a car at a daily rate of $41.95 plus 43 cents per mile. Speedo Rentzit rents a car for $44.95 plus 39 cents per mile. For what mileage is the cost the same?

c Solving Problems

We now use the elimination method to solve a problem.

▶ **EXAMPLE 8** At one time, Budget Rent-A-Car rented compact cars at a daily rate of $43.95 plus 40 cents per mile. Thrifty Rent-A-Car rented compact cars at a daily rate of $42.95 plus 42 cents per mile. For what mileage is the cost the same?

1. *Familiarize.* To become familiar with the problem, we make a guess. Suppose a person rents a compact car from each rental agency and drives it 100 miles. The total cost at Budget is $43.95 + $0.40(100) = $43.95 + $40.00, or $83.95. The total cost at Thrifty is $42.95 + $0.42(100) = $42.95 + $42.00, or $84.95. Note that we converted all of our money units to dollars. The resulting costs are very nearly the same, so our guess is close. We can, of course, refine our guess. Instead, we will use algebra to solve the problem. We let M = the number of miles driven and C = the total cost of the car rental.

2. *Translate.* We translate the first statement, using $0.40 for 40 cents. It helps to reword the problem before translating.

Rewording: $43.95 plus 40 cents times the number of miles driven is cost.

Translating: $43.95 + $0.40 · M = C

We translate the second statement, but again it helps to reword it first.

Rewording: $42.95 plus 42 cents times the number of miles driven is cost.

Translating: $42.95 + $0.42 · M = C

We have now translated to a system of equations:

$$43.95 + 0.40M = C,$$
$$42.95 + 0.42M = C.$$

3. *Solve.* We solve the system of equations. We clear the system of decimals by multiplying on both sides by 100. Then we multiply the second equation by -1 and add.

$$4395 + 40M = 100C$$
$$\underline{-4295 - 42M = -100C}$$
$$100 - 2M = 0$$
$$100 = 2M$$
$$50 = M$$

4. *Check.* For 50 mi, the cost of the Budget car is $43.95 + 0.40(50)$, or $43.95 + 20$, or $63.95, and the cost of the Thrifty car is $42.95 + 0.42(50)$, or $42.95 + 21$, or $63.95. Thus the costs are the same when the mileage is 50.

5. *State.* When the cars are driven 50 miles, the costs will be the same. ◀

DO EXERCISE 9.

ANSWER ON PAGE A-11

EXERCISE SET 13.3

a Solve using the elimination method.

1. $x + y = 10,$
$x - y = 8$

2. $x - y = 7,$
$x + y = 3$

3. $x + y = 8,$
$-x + 2y = 7$

4. $x + y = 6,$
$-x + 3y = -2$

5. $3x - y = 9,$
$2x + y = 6$

6. $4x - y = 1,$
$3x + y = 13$

7. $4a + 3b = 7,$
$-4a + b = 5$

8. $7c + 5d = 18,$
$c - 5d = -2$

9. $8x - 5y = -9,$
$3x + 5y = -2$

10. $3a - 3b = -15,$
$-3a - 3b = -3$

11. $4x - 5y = 7,$
$-4x + 5y = 7$

12. $2x + 3y = 4,$
$-2x - 3y = -4$

ANSWERS

1. _____

2. _____

3. _____

4. _____

5. _____

6. _____

7. _____

8. _____

9. _____

10. _____

11. _____

12. _____

13. _____

14. _____

15. _____

16. _____

17. _____

18. _____

19. _____

20. _____

21. _____

22. _____

23. _____

24. _____

25. _____

26. _____

27. _____

28. _____

29. _____

30. _____

b   Solve using the multiplication principle first. Then add.

13. $-x - y = 8,$
$\quad 2x - y = -1$

14. $x + y = -7,$
$\quad 3x + y = -9$

15. $x + 3y = 19,$
$\quad x - y = -1$

16. $3x - y = 8,$
$\quad x + 2y = 5$

17. $x + y = 5,$
$\quad 5x - 3y = 17$

18. $x - y = 7,$
$\quad 4x - 5y = 25$

19. $2w - 3z = -1,$
$\quad 3w + 4z = 24$

20. $7p + 5q = 2,$
$\quad 8p - 9q = 17$

21. $2a + 3b = -1,$
$\quad 3a + 5b = -2$

22. $3x - 4y = 16,$
$\quad 5x + 6y = 14$

23. $x = 3y,$
$\quad 5x + 14 = y$

24. $5a = 2b,$
$\quad 2a + 11 = 3b$

25. $3x - 2y = 10,$
$\quad 5x + 3y = 4$

26. $2p + 5q = 9,$
$\quad 3p - 2q = 4$

27. $3x = 8y + 11,$
$\quad x + 6y - 8 = 0$

28. $m = 32 + n,$
$\quad 3m = 8n + 6$

29. $3x - 2y = 10,$
$\quad -6x + 4y = -20$

30. $2x + y = 13,$
$\quad 4x + 2y = 23$

31. $0.06x + 0.05y = 0.07,$
$0.4x - 0.3y = 1.1$

32. $1.8x - 2y = 0.9,$
$0.04x + 0.18y = 0.15$

33. $\dfrac{1}{3}x + \dfrac{3}{2}y = \dfrac{5}{4},$
$\dfrac{3}{4}x - \dfrac{5}{6}y = \dfrac{3}{8}$

34. $x - \dfrac{3}{2}y = 13,$
$\dfrac{3}{2}x - y = 17$

c Solve.

35. At one time, Avis Rent-A-Car rented an intermediate-size car at a daily rate of $53.95 plus 30 cents per mile. Another company rents an intermediate-size car for $54.95 plus 20 cents per mile. For what mileage is the cost the same?

36. Budget Rent-A-Car rented a basic car at a daily rate of $45.95 plus 40 cents per mile. Another company rents a basic car for $46.95 plus 20 cents per mile. For what mileage is the cost the same?

37. Two angles are supplementary. One is 30° more than two times the other. Find the angles. (Supplementary angles are angles whose sum is 180°.)

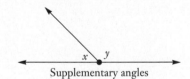

Supplementary angles

38. Two angles are supplementary. One is 8° less than three times the other. Find the angles.

39. Two angles are complementary. Their difference is 34°. Find the angles. (Complementary angles are angles whose sum is 90°.)

Complementary angles

40. Two angles are complementary. One angle is 42° more than one half the other. Find the angles.

ANSWERS

31. _____

32. _____

33. _____

34. _____

35. _____

36. _____

37. _____

38. _____

39. _____

40. _____

41. _____

42. _____

43. _____

44. _____

45. _____

46. _____

47. _____

48. _____

49. _____

50. _____

51. _____

52. _____

53. _____

54. _____

41. In a vineyard, a vintner uses 820 hectares to plant Chardonnay and Riesling grapes. The vintner knows that the profits will be greatest by planting 140 hectares more of Chardonnay than of Riesling. How many hectares of each grape should be planted?

42. The Hayburner Horse Farm allots 650 hectares to plant hay and oats. The owners know that their needs are best met if they plant 180 hectares more of hay than of oats. How many hectares of each should they plant?

SKILL MAINTENANCE

43. Simplify: $(a^2b^{-3})(a^5b^{-6})$.

44. Simplify: $\dfrac{a^2b^{-3}}{a^5b^{-6}}$.

45. Simplify: $\dfrac{x^2 - 5x + 6}{x^2 - 4}$.

46. Subtract: $\dfrac{x + 7}{x^2 - 1} - \dfrac{3}{x + 1}$.

SYNTHESIS

47. Several ancient Chinese books included problems that can be solved by translating to systems of equations. *Arithmetical Rules in Nine Sections* is a book of 246 problems compiled by a Chinese mathematician, Chang Tsang, who died in 152 B.C. One of the problems is: Suppose there are a number of rabbits and pheasants confined in a cage. In all, there are 35 heads and 94 feet. How many rabbits and how many pheasants are there? Solve the problem.

48. Patrick's age is 20% of his father's age. Twenty years from now, Patrick's age will be 52% of his father's age. How old are Patrick and his father now?

49. If 5 is added to a man's age and the total is divided by 5, the result will be his daughter's age. Five years ago, the man's age was eight times his daughter's age. Find their present ages.

50. When the base of a triangle is increased by 2 ft and the height is decreased by 1 ft, the height becomes one third of the base, and the area becomes 24 ft². Find the original dimensions of the triangle.

Solve.

51. $3(x - y) = 9,$
$\quad\quad x + y = 7$

52. $2(x - y) = 3 + x,$
$\quad\quad x = 3y + 4$

53. $\quad 2(5a - 5b) = 10,$
$\quad -5(6a + 2b) = 10$

54. $\dfrac{x}{3} + \dfrac{y}{2} = 1\dfrac{1}{3},$
$\quad x + 0.05y = 4$

13.4 More on Solving Problems

a   We continue solving problems using the five steps for problem solving and our methods for solving systems of equations.

▶ **EXAMPLE 1** *Denny's Restaurants.* Denny's® is a national restaurant firm. The ad shown here once appeared on the tables as a special.

Determine the price of one item from the *A* side of the menu and the price of one item from the *B* side of the menu.

1, 2. *Familiarize* and *Translate.*   The ad gives us the system of equations at the outset:

$$a + b = \$5.49, \quad \textbf{(1)}$$
$$a + 2b = \$6.99, \quad \textbf{(2)}$$

where $a =$ the price of one item from the *A* side of the menu and $b =$ the price of one item from the *B* side of the menu.

3. *Solve.*   We solve the system of equations. Which method should we use? As we discussed in Section 13.3, any method can be used. Each has its advantages and disadvantages. We decide to proceed with the elimination method, because we see that if we multiply Equation (1) by -1 and then add, the a-terms can be eliminated:

$$\begin{array}{ll} -a - b = -5.49 & \text{Multiplying by } -1 \\ \underline{a + 2b = 6.99} & \\ b = 1.50. & \text{Adding} \end{array}$$

We substitute 1.50 for b in Equation (1) and solve for a:

$$a + b = 5.49$$
$$a + 1.50 = 5.49$$
$$a = 3.99.$$

OBJECTIVE

After finishing Section 13.4, you should be able to:

a   Solve problems by translating them to systems of two equations in two variables.

FOR EXTRA HELP

Tape 26C

1. Suppose, in a later promotion, that Denny's changed the menu as follows:

$$A + B = \$6.59,$$
$$A + 2B = \$9.95.$$

Determine the price of one item from the *A* side of the menu and the price of one item from the *B* side.

4. *Check.* The sum of the two prices is $3.99 + $1.50, or $5.49. The *A* price plus twice the *B* price is $3.99 + 2($1.50) = $3.99 + $3.00, or $6.99. The prices check. Sometimes a "common sense" check is appropriate. If you look at the foods on the *B* side of the menu, it does not seem reasonable that such items would sell for $1.50 each. Note that the menu does not say that you can buy a *B* item alone for $1.50. That price is a bonus for buying an *A* item. Mathematically, the prices given do stand, though it is doubtful that you can buy a *B* item by itself.

5. *State.* The price of one *A* item is $3.99. The price of one *B* item is $1.50.   ◄

DO EXERCISE 1.

▶ **EXAMPLE 2**   Howie is 21 years older than Judy. In six years, Howie will be twice as old as Judy. How old are they now?

1. *Familiarize.* Let us consider some conditions of the problem. We let H = Howie's age now and J = Judy's age now. Everyone ages together. As one person gets 1 year older, so does the other. How do the ages relate in 6 years? In 6 years, Judy will be $J + 6$ and Howie will be $H + 6$. We make a table to organize our information.

	Howie	Judy	
Age now	H	J	$\longrightarrow H = 21 + J$
Age in 6 years	$H + 6$	$J + 6$	$\longrightarrow H + 6 = 2(J + 6)$

2. *Translate.* From the present ages, we get the following rewording and translation.

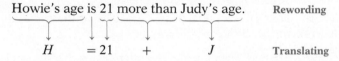

Howie's age is 21 more than Judy's age.   **Rewording**

$$H \qquad = 21 \quad + \qquad J \qquad\qquad \text{Translating}$$

From their ages in 6 years, we get the following rewording and translation.

Howie's age in six years will be twice Judy's age in six years.   **Rewording**

$$H + 6 \qquad\qquad = \quad 2 \cdot \qquad (J + 6) \qquad\qquad \text{Translating}$$

The problem has been translated to the following system of equations.

$$H = 21 + J, \qquad\qquad \textbf{(1)}$$
$$H + 6 = 2(J + 6). \qquad \textbf{(2)}$$

3. *Solve.* We solve the system of equations. This time we use the substitution method since there is a variable alone on one side. We substitute $21 + J$ for H in Equation (2):

$$H + 6 = 2(J + 6)$$
$$(21 + J) + 6 = 2(J + 6)$$
$$J + 27 = 2J + 12$$
$$15 = J.$$

We find *H* by substituting 15 for *J* in the first equation:

$$H = 21 + J$$
$$H = 21 + 15$$
$$H = 36.$$

4. *Check.*   Howie's age is 36, which is 21 more than 15, Judy's age. In 6 years, when Howie will be 42 and Judy 21, Howie's age will be twice Judy's age.

5. *State.*   Howie is now 36 and Judy is 15.   ◄

DO EXERCISE 2.

▶ **EXAMPLE 3**   There were 411 people at a movie. Admission was $7.00 for adults and $3.75 for children. The receipts were $2678.75. The box office manager loses the records of how many adults and how many children attended. Can you use algebra to help her? How many adults and how many children did attend?

1. *Familiarize.*   There are many ways to familiarize ourselves with a problem situation. This time, let us make a guess and do some calculations. The total number of people at the movie was 411, so we choose numbers that total 411. Let's try

240 adults and
171 children.

How much money was taken in? The problem says that adults paid $7.00 each, so the total amount of money collected from the adults was

240($7),   or $1680.

The children paid $3.75 each, so the total amount of money collected from the children was

171($3.75),   or $641.25.

This makes the total receipts $1680 + $641.25, or $2321.25.

Our guess is not the answer to the problem because the total taken in, according to the problem, was $2678.75. If we were to continue guessing, we would need to add more adults and fewer children, since our first guess was too low. The steps we have used to see if our guesses are correct help us to understand the actual steps involved in solving the problem.

Let us list the information in a table. That usually helps in the familiarization process. We let *a* = the number of adults and *c* = the number of children.

	Adults	Children	Total
Admission	$7.00	$3.75	
Number attending	*a*	*c*	411
Money taken in	7.00*a*	3.75*c*	$2678.75

$\longrightarrow a + c = 411$

$\longrightarrow 7.00a + 3.75c = 2678.75$

2. *Translate.*   The total number of people attending was 411, so

$$a + c = 411.$$

2. Jackie is 26 years older than Jack. In 5 years, Jackie will be twice as old as Jack. How old are they now?

Complete the following table to aid with the familiarization.

	Jackie	Jack
Age now	*J*	*K*
Age in 5 years		

ANSWER ON PAGE A-11

3. There were 166 paid admissions to a game. The price was $2.10 each for adults and $0.75 each for children. The amount taken in was $293.25. How many adults and how many children attended?

Complete the following table to aid with the familiarization.

Paid	Adults	Children $0.75	Total
Number attending	x	y	$\rightarrow x + y = (\quad)$
Money taken in			$\rightarrow 2.10x + (\quad) = 293.25$
		$293.25	

The amount taken in from the adults was $7.00a$, and the amount taken in from the children was $3.75c$. These amounts are in dollars. The total was $2678.75, so we have

$$7.00a + 3.75c = 2678.75.$$

We can multiply on both sides by 100 to clear of decimals. Thus we have a translation to a system of equations:

$$a + c = 411, \qquad \textbf{(1)}$$
$$700a + 375c = 267{,}875. \qquad \textbf{(2)}$$

3. *Solve.* We solve the system of equations. We use the elimination method since the equations are both in the form $Ax + By = C$. (A case can certainly be made for using the substitution method since we can solve for one of the variables quite easily in the first equation. Very often a decision is just a matter of choice.) We multiply on both sides of Equation (1) by -375 and then add:

$$
\begin{array}{llr}
-375a - 375c = -154{,}125 & \textbf{Multiplying by } -375 \\
\underline{700a + 375c = 267{,}875} & \\
325a = 113{,}750 & \textbf{Adding} \\
\end{array}
$$

$$a = \frac{113{,}750}{325} \qquad \textbf{Dividing by 325}$$

$$a = 350.$$

We go back to Equation (1) and substitute 350 for a:

$$a + c = 411$$
$$350 + c = 411$$
$$c = 61.$$

4. *Check.* We leave the check to the student. It is similar to what we did in the familiarization step.

5. *State.* 350 adults and 61 children attended.   ◄

DO EXERCISE 3.

► **EXAMPLE 4** A chemist has one solution that is 80% acid (the rest is water) and another solution that is 30% acid. What is needed is 200 liters (L) of a solution that is 62% acid. The chemist will prepare it by mixing the two solutions. How much of each should be used?

1. *Familiarize.* We can draw a picture of the situation. The chemist uses x liters of the first solution and y liters of the second solution.

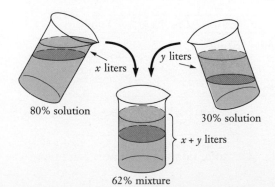

80% solution x liters y liters   30% solution

$x + y$ liters

62% mixture

We can also arrange the information in a table.

Type of solution	First	Second	Mixture	
Amount of solution	x	y	200 liters	→ $x + y = 200$
Percent of acid	80%	30%	62%	
Amount of acid in solution	$0.8x$	$0.3y$	0.62×200, or 124 liters	→ $0.8x + 0.3y = 124$

2. *Translate.* The chemist uses x liters of the first solution and y liters of the second. Since the total is to be 200 liters, we have

$$\text{Total amount of solution:}\quad x + y = 200.$$

The amount of acid in the new mixture is to be 62% of 200 liters, or 124 liters. The amounts of acid from the two solutions are 80%x and 30%y. Thus,

$$\text{Total amount of acid:}\quad 80\%x + 30\%y = 124$$

or

$$0.8x + 0.3y = 124.$$

We clear of decimals by multiplying on both sides by 10:

$$10(0.8x + 0.3y) = 10 \cdot 124$$
$$8x + 3y = 1240.$$

Thus we have a translation to a system of equations:

$$x + \ y = 200, \qquad \textbf{(1)}$$
$$8x + 3y = 1240. \qquad \textbf{(2)}$$

3. *Solve.* We solve the system. We use the elimination method, again because equations are in the form $Ax + By = C$ and a multiplication in one equation will allow us to eliminate a variable, but substitution would also work. We multiply on both sides of Equation (1) by -3 and then add:

$$
\begin{array}{rl}
-3x - 3y = -600 & \text{Multiplying by } -3 \\
\underline{\;8x + 3y = \ \ 1240\;} & \\
5x \quad\ \ = \ \ 640 & \text{Adding} \\
\end{array}
$$

$$x = \frac{640}{5} \qquad \text{Dividing by 5}$$
$$x = 128.$$

We go back to Equation (1) and substitute 128 for x:

$$x + y = 200$$
$$128 + y = 200$$
$$y = 72.$$

The solution is $x = 128$ and $y = 72$.

4. *Check.* The sum of 128 and 72 is 200. Also, 80% of 128 is 102.4 and 30% of 72 is 21.6. These add up to 124.

5. *State.* The chemist should use 128 liters of the 80%-acid solution and 72 liters of the 30%-acid solution.   ◀

4. One solution is 50% alcohol and a second is 70% alcohol. How much of each should be mixed to make 30 L of a solution that is 55% alcohol?

Complete the following table to aid in the familiarization.

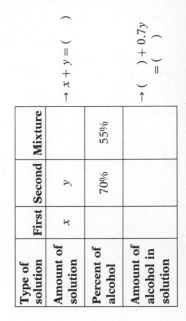

Type of solution	First	Second	Mixture	
Amount of solution	x	y		→ $x + y = (\quad)$
Percent of alcohol		70%	55%	
Amount of alcohol in solution				→ $(\quad) + 0.7y = (\quad)$

▶ **EXAMPLE 5**   A grocer wishes to mix some nuts worth 45 cents per pound and some worth 80 cents per pound to make 350 lb of a mixture worth 65 cents per pound. How much of each should be used?

1. *Familiarize.*   Arranging the information in a table will help. We let $x =$ the amount of 45-cents nuts and $y =$ the amount of 80-cents nuts.

Type of nuts	Inexpensive nuts	Expensive nuts	Mixture	
Cost of nuts	45 cents	80 cents	65 cents	
Amount (in pounds)	x	y	350	$\longrightarrow x + y = 350$
Mixture	$45x$	$80y$	65 cents · (350), or 22,750 cents	$\longrightarrow 45x + 80y = 22,750$

Note the similarity of this problem with Example 3. Here we consider nuts instead of tickets.

2. *Translate.*   We translate as follows. From the second row of the table, we find that

$$\textit{Total amount of nuts:} \quad x + y = 350.$$

Our second equation will come from the costs. The value of the inexpensive nuts, in cents, is $45x$ (x lb at 45 cents per pound). The value of the expensive nuts is $80y$, and the value of the mixture is 65×350, or 22,750 cents. Thus we have

$$\textit{Total cost of mixture:} \quad 45x + 80y = 22,750.$$

Remember the problem-solving tip about dimension symbols. In this last equation, all expressions stand for cents. We could have expressed them all in dollars, but we do not want some in cents and some in dollars. Thus we have a translation to a system of equations:

$$x + \quad y = 350,$$
$$45x + 80y = 22,750.$$

3. *Solve.*   We solve the system using the elimination method again. We multiply on both sides of Equation (1) by -45 and then add:

$$
\begin{aligned}
-45x - 45y &= -15,750 \qquad \textbf{Multiplying by } -45\\
\underline{45x + 80y} &= \underline{\;\;22,750}\\
35y &= \;\;\;\;7,000 \qquad \textbf{Adding}\\
y &= \frac{7,000}{35}\\
y &= 200.
\end{aligned}
$$

We go back to Equation (1) and substitute 200 for y:

$$
\begin{aligned}
x + y &= 350\\
x + 200 &= 350\\
x &= 150.
\end{aligned}
$$

4. *Check.* We consider $x = 150$ lb and $y = 200$ lb. The sum is 350 lb. The value of the nuts is $45(150) + 80(200)$, or 22,750 cents. These values check.

5. *State.* The grocer should mix 150 lb of the 45-cents nuts with 200 lb of the 80-cents nuts. ◄

DO EXERCISE 5.

▶ **EXAMPLE 6** A student has some nickels and dimes. The value of the coins is $1.65. There are 12 more nickels than dimes. How many of each kind of coin are there?

1. *Familiarize.* We let $d =$ the number of dimes and $n =$ the number of nickels.

2. *Translate.* We have one equation at once:

$$d + 12 = n.$$

The value of the nickels, in cents, is $5n$, since each is worth 5¢. The value of the dimes, in cents, is $10d$, since each is worth 10¢. The total value is given as $1.65. Since we have the values of the nickels and dimes in *cents*, we must use *cents* for the total value. This is 165. This gives us another equation:

$$10d + 5n = 165.$$

Thus we have a system of equations:

$$d + 12 = n, \qquad (1)$$
$$10d + 5n = 165. \qquad (2)$$

3. *Solve.* Since we have n alone on one side of one equation, we use the substitution method. We substitute $d + 12$ for n in Equation (2):

$$10d + 5n = 165$$
$$10d + 5(d + 12) = 165 \qquad \text{Substituting } d + 12 \text{ for } n$$
$$10d + 5d + 60 = 165 \qquad \text{Removing parentheses}$$
$$15d + 60 = 165 \qquad \text{Collecting like terms}$$
$$15d = 105 \qquad \text{Subtracting 60}$$
$$d = \frac{105}{15}, \text{ or } 7. \qquad \text{Dividing by 15}$$

We substitute 7 for d in either of the original equations to find n. We use Equation (1):

$$d + 12 = n$$
$$7 + 12 = n$$
$$19 = n.$$

4. *Check.* We have 7 dimes and 19 nickels. There are 12 more nickels than dimes. The value of the coins is $7(0.10) + 19(0.05)$, which is $1.65. This checks.

5. *State.* The student has 7 dimes and 19 nickels. ◄

DO EXERCISE 6.

5. Grass seed A is worth $1.00 per pound and seed B is worth $1.35 per pound. How much of each should be mixed to make 50 lb of a mixture worth $1.14 per pound?

Complete the following table to aid in the familiarization.

Type of seed	A	B	Mixture	
Cost of seed	$1.00	$1.35	$1.14	
Amount (in pounds)	x	y		$\rightarrow x + y = (\quad)$
Mixture		$1.35y$		$\rightarrow 1.00x + 1.35y = (\quad)$

6. On a table are 20 coins, quarters and dimes. Their value is $3.05. How many of each kind of coin are there?

You should look back over Examples 3–6. The problems are quite similar in their structure. Compare them and try to see the similarities. The problems in Examples 3–6 are often called *mixture problems*. In each case a situation is considered in two different ways. These problems provide a pattern, or model, for many related problems.

> **Problem-Solving Tip**
>
> **When solving problems, see if they are patterned or modeled after other problems that you have studied.**

❖ SIDELIGHTS

Study Tips: Extra Tips on Problem Solving

We will often present some tips and guidelines to enhance your learning abilities. The following tips are focused on problem solving. They summarize some points already considered and propose some new tips.

The following are the five steps for problem solving.

1. *Familiarize* **yourself with the problem situation.**
2. *Translate* **the problem to an equation.** As you study more mathematics, you will find that the translation may be to some other kind of mathematical language, such as an inequality.
3. *Solve* **the equation.** If the translation is to some other kind of mathematical language, you will carry out some other kind of mathematical manipulation.
4. *Check* **the answer in the original equation.** This does not mean to check in the translated equation. It means to go back to the original worded problem.
5. *State* **the answer to the problem clearly.**

For Step 4 on checking, some further comment is appropriate. *You may find that although you were able to translate to an equation and solve the equation, none of the solutions of the equation are solutions of the original problem.* To see how this can happen, consider the following problem.

EXAMPLE The sum of two even consecutive integers is 537. Find the integers.

1. *Familiarize.* Suppose we let x = the first number. Then $x + 2$ = the second number.
2. *Translate.* The problem can be translated to the following equation:

$$x + (x + 2) = 537.$$

3. *Solve.* We solve the equation as follows:

$$2x + 2 = 537$$
$$2x = 535$$
$$x = \frac{535}{2}, \quad \text{or } 267.5.$$

4. *Check.* Then $x + 2 = 269.5$. However, not only are the numbers 267.5 and 269.5 not even, they are also not integers.
5. *State.* The problem has no solution. ◀

The following are some additional tips for problem solving.

- *To be good at problem solving, do lots of problems.* The situation is similar to what happens when we learn to play tennis. At first, we are not successful. But the more we practice and work at the game, the more successful we become. For problem solving, do more than just two or three odd-numbered problems assigned—do them all, and if you have time, do the even-numbered problems. Then find another book on the same subject and do problems in that book.
- *Look for patterns when solving problems.* By using the preceding tip and doing lots of problems, you will eventually see patterns in similar kinds of problems. For example, there is a pattern in the way we solve problems involving consecutive integers.
- *When translating to an equation, or some other mathematical language, consider the dimensions of the variables and constants in the equation. The variables that represent length should be all in the same unit, those that represent money should be all in dollars, or all in cents, and so on.*

EXERCISE SET 13.4

ANSWERS

a Solve.

1. A firm sells cars and trucks. There is room on its lot for 510 vehicles. From experience they know that profits will be greatest if there are 190 more cars than trucks on the lot. How many of each vehicle should the firm have for the greatest profit?

2. A family went camping at a park 45 km from town. They drove 23 km more than they walked to get to the campsite. How far did they walk?

3. Sammy is twice as old as his daughter. In four years, Sammy's age will be three times what his daughter's age was six years ago. How old are they now?

4. Ann is eighteen years older than her son. She was three times as old one year ago. How old are they now?

5. Marge is twice as old as Consuelo. The sum of their ages seven years ago was 13. How old are they now?

6. Andy is four times as old as Wendy. In twelve years, Wendy's age will be half of Andy's. How old are they now?

7. A collection of dimes and quarters is worth $15.25. There are 103 coins in all. How many of each are there?

8. A collection of quarters and nickels is worth $1.25. There are 13 coins in all. How many of each are there?

9. A collection of nickels and dimes is worth $25. There are three times as many nickels as dimes. How many of each are there?

10. A collection of nickels and dimes is worth $2.90. There are nineteen more nickels than dimes. How many of each are there?

1. _____

2. _____

3. _____

4. _____

5. _____

6. _____

7. _____

8. _____

9. _____

10. _____

Copyright © 1993 Addison-Wesley Publishing Co., Inc.

ANSWERS

11. There were 429 people at a play. Admission was $1 each for adults and 75 cents each for children. The receipts were $372.50. How many adults and how many children attended?

12. The attendance at a school concert was 578. Admission was $2 each for adults and $1.50 each for children. The receipts were $985. How many adults and how many children attended?

13. There were 200 tickets sold for a women's basketball game. Tickets for students were $0.50 each and for adults were $0.75 each. The total amount of money collected was $132.50. How many of each type of ticket were sold?

14. There were 203 tickets sold for a volleyball game. For activity-card holders, the price was $1.25 each and for noncard holders the price was $2 each. The total amount of money collected was $310. How many of each type of ticket were sold?

15. Solution A is 50% acid and solution B is 80% acid. How many of each should be used to make 100 L of a solution that is 68% acid? (*Hint:* 68% of what is acid?) Complete the following to aid in the familiarization.

Type of solution	A	B	Mixture	
Amount of solution	x	y	liters	$\longrightarrow x + y = ($ $)$
Percent of acid	50%		68%	
Amount of acid in solution		$0.8y$	0.68×100, or liters	$\longrightarrow 0.5x + ($ $) = ($ $)$

16. Solution A is 30% alcohol and solution B is 75% alcohol. How much of each should be used to make 100 L of a solution that is 50% alcohol?

17. A solution containing 30% insecticide is to be mixed with a solution containing 50% insecticide to make 200 L of a solution containing 42% insecticide. How much of each solution should be used?

18. A solution containing 28% fungicide is to be mixed with a solution containing 40% fungicide to make 300 L of a solution containing 36% fungicide. How much of each solution should be used?

11. _____

12. _____

13. _____

14. _____

15. _____

16. _____

17. _____

18. _____

19. The Nuthouse has 10 kg of mixed cashews and pecans worth $8.40 per kilogram. Cashews alone sell for $8.00 per kilogram and pecans sell for $9.00 per kilogram. How many kilograms of each are in the mixture?

20. A coffee shop mixes Brazilian coffee worth $5 per kilogram with Turkish coffee worth $8 per kilogram. The mixture is to sell for $7 per kilogram. How much of each type of coffee should be used to make a 300-kg mixture? Complete the following table to aid in the familiarization.

Type of coffee	Brazilian	Turkish	Mixture	
Cost of coffee	$5		$7	
Amount (in kilograms)	x	y	300	$\rightarrow x + y = (\quad)$
Mixture		$8y$	$7(300)$, or $2100	$\rightarrow 5x + (\quad) = 2100$

21. Grass seed A is worth $2.50 per pound and seed B is worth $1.75 per pound. How much of each would you use to make 75 lb of a mixture worth $2.14 per pound?

22. A grocer wishes to mix some nuts worth 63 cents per pound and some worth 95 cents per pound to make 480 lb of a mixture worth 86 cents per pound. How much of each should be used?

23. You are taking a test in which items of type A are worth 10 points and items of type B are worth 15 points. It takes 3 min for each item of type A and 6 min for each item of type B. The total time allowed is 60 min and you can do exactly 16 questions. Your score is 180 points by using the entire 60 min. How many questions of each type did you answer correctly?

24. The goldsmith has two alloys that are different purities of gold. The first is three-fourths pure gold and the second is five-twelfths pure gold. How many ounces of each should be melted and mixed to obtain a 6-oz mixture that is two-thirds pure gold?

25. A merchant has two kinds of paint. If 9 gal of the inexpensive paint is mixed with 7 gal of the expensive paint, the mixture will be worth $19.70 per gallon. If 3 gal of the inexpensive paint is mixed with 5 gal of the expensive paint, the mixture will be worth $19.825 per gallon. What is the price per gallon of each type of paint?

26. A printer knows that a page of print contains 1300 words if large type is used and 1850 words if small type is used. A document containing 18,526 words fills exactly 12 pages. How many pages are in the large types? in the small type?

SYNTHESIS

27. A total of $27,000 is invested, part of it at 12% and part of it at 13%. The total yield after one year is $3385. How much was invested at each rate?

28. A student earned $288 on investments. If $1100 was invested at one yearly rate and $1800 at a rate that was 1.5% higher, find the two rates of interest.

29. A two-digit number is six times the sum of its digits. The tens digit is one more than the units digit. Find the number.

30. The sum of the digits of a two-digit number is 12. When the digits are reversed, the number is decreased by 18. Find the original number.

31. A farmer has 100 L of milk that is 4.6% butterfat. How much skim milk (no butterfat) should be mixed with it to make milk that is 3.2% butterfat?

32. A tank contains 8000 L of a solution that is 40% acid. How much water should be added to make a solution that is 30% acid?

33. An automobile radiator contains 16 L of antifreeze and water. This mixture is 30% antifreeze. How much of this mixture should be drained and replaced with pure antifreeze so that the mixture will be 50% antifreeze?

34. An employer has a daily payroll of $325 when employing some workers at $20 per day and others at $25 per day. When the number of $20 workers is increased by 50% and the number of $25 workers is decreased by $\frac{1}{5}$, the new daily payroll is $400. Find how many were originally employed at each rate.

35. In a two-digit number, the sum of the units digit and the number is 43 more than five times the tens digit. The sum of the digits is 11. Find the number.

36. The sum of the digits of a three-digit number is 9. If the digits are reversed, the number increases by 495. The sum of the tens and hundreds digits is half the units digit. Find the number.

37. Together, a bat, ball, and glove cost $99.00. The bat costs $9.95 more than the ball, and the glove costs $65.45 more than the bat. How much does each cost?

38. In Lewis Carroll's "Through the Looking Glass," Tweedledum says to Tweedledee, "The sum of your weight and twice mine is 361 pounds." Then Tweedledee says to Tweedledum, "Contrariwise, the sum of your weight and twice mine is 362 pounds." Find the weight of Tweedledum and Tweedledee.

13.5 Motion Problems

a We have studied problems involving motion in Chapter 11. Here we solve certain motion problems whose solutions can be found using systems of equations. Recall the motion formula.

The Motion Formula

$$\text{Distance} = \text{Rate (or speed)} \cdot \text{Time}$$

$$d = rt$$

We have five steps for problem solving. The following tips are also helpful when solving motion problems.

Tips for Solving Motion Problems

1. **Draw a diagram using an arrow or arrows to represent distance and the direction of each object in motion.**

2. **Organize the information in a chart.**

3. **Look for as many things as you can that are the same so that you can write equations.**

▶ **EXAMPLE 1** A train leaves Podunk traveling east at 35 kilometers per hour (km/h). An hour later, another train leaves Podunk on a parallel track at 40 km/h. How far from Podunk will the trains meet?

1. *Familiarize.* We first make a drawing.

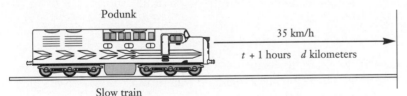

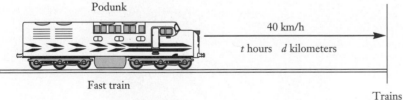

Trains
meet here

From the drawing, we see that the distances are the same. Let's call the distance d. We don't know the times. Let $t =$ the time for the faster train. Then the time for the slower train $= t + 1$, since it left 1 hr earlier. We can organize the information in a chart.

$$d \quad = \quad r \quad \cdot \quad t$$

	Distance	Speed	Time	
Slow train	d	35	$t + 1$	$\longrightarrow d = 35(t + 1)$
Fast train	d	40	t	$\longrightarrow d = 40t$

OBJECTIVE

After finishing Section 13.5, you should be able to:

a Solve motion problems using the formula $d = rt$.

FOR EXTRA HELP

Tape 26D

1. A car leaves Hereford traveling north at 56 km/h. Another car leaves Hereford one hour later traveling north at 84 km/h. How far from Hereford will the second car overtake the first? (*Hint:* The cars travel the same distance.)

2. *Translate.* In motion problems, we look for things that are the same so that we can write equations. From each row of the chart, we get an equation, $d = rt$. Thus we have two equations:

$$d = 35(t + 1), \quad \textbf{(1)}$$
$$d = 40t. \quad \textbf{(2)}$$

3. *Solve.* Since we have a variable alone on one side, we solve the system using the substitution method:

$$35(t + 1) = 40t \quad \text{Using the substitution method (substituting } 35(t+1) \text{ for } d \text{ in Equation 2)}$$

$$35t + 35 = 40t \quad \text{Removing parentheses}$$

$$35 = 5t \quad \text{Subtracting } 35t$$

$$\frac{35}{5} = t \quad \text{Dividing by 5}$$

$$7 = t.$$

The problem asks us to find how far from Podunk the trains meet. Thus we need to find d. We can do this by substituting 7 for t in the equation $d = 40t$:

$$d = 40(7)$$
$$= 280.$$

4. *Check.* If the time is 7 hr, then the distance that the slow train travels is $35(7 + 1)$, or 280 km. The fast train travels $40(7)$, or 280 km. Since the distances are the same, we know how far from Podunk the trains will meet.

5. *State.* The trains meet 280 km from Podunk. ◀

DO EXERCISE 1.

▶ **EXAMPLE 2** A motorboat took 3 hr to make a downstream trip with a 6-km/h current. The return trip against the same current took 5 hr. Find the speed of the boat in still water.

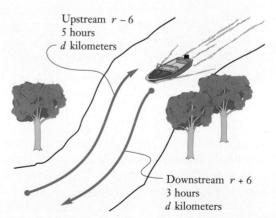

Upstream $r - 6$
5 hours
d kilometers

Downstream $r + 6$
3 hours
d kilometers

1. *Familiarize.* We first make a drawing. From the drawing, we see that the distances are the same. Let's call the distance d. Let $r =$ the speed of the boat in still water. Then, when the boat is traveling downstream, its speed is $r + 6$ (the current helps the boat along). When it is traveling upstream, its speed is $r - 6$ (the current holds the boat back). We can organize the information in a chart. In this case, the distances are the same, so we use the formula $d = rt$.

$$d \quad = \quad r \quad \cdot \quad t$$

	Distance	Speed	Time	
Downstream	d	$r + 6$	3	$\longrightarrow d = (r + 6)3$
Upstream	d	$r - 6$	5	$\longrightarrow d = (r - 6)5$

2. *Translate.*   From each row of the chart, we get an equation, $d = rt$:

$$d = (r + 6)3, \qquad \textbf{(1)}$$
$$d = (r - 6)5. \qquad \textbf{(2)}$$

3. *Solve.*   Since there is a variable alone on one side of an equation, we solve the system using substitution:

$$(r + 6)3 = (r - 6)5 \qquad \text{Substituting } (r + 6)3$$
$$ \qquad \text{for } d \text{ in the second equation}$$
$$3r + 18 = 5r - 30 \qquad \text{Removing parentheses}$$
$$-2r + 18 = -30 \qquad \text{Subtracting } 5r$$
$$-2r = -48 \qquad \text{Subtracting } 18$$
$$r = \frac{-48}{-2}, \text{ or } 24. \qquad \text{Dividing by } -2$$

4. *Check.*   When $r = 24$, $r + 6 = 30$, and $30 \cdot 3 = 90$, the distance downstream. When $r = 24$, $r - 6 = 18$, and $18 \cdot 5 = 90$, the distance upstream. In both cases we get the same distance. Now in this type of problem a problem-solving tip to keep in mind is "Have I found what the problem asked for?" We could solve for a certain variable but still have not answered the question of the original problem. For example, we might have found speed when the problem wanted distance. In this problem, we want the speed of the boat in still water, and that is r.

5. *State.*   The speed in still water is 24 km/h.   ◀

More Tips for Solving Motion Problems

1. Translating to a system of equations eases the solution of many motion problems.

2. When checking, be sure that you have solved for what the problem asked for.

DO EXERCISE 2.

2. An airplane flew for 5 hr with a 25-km/h tail wind. The return flight against the same wind took 6 hr. Find the speed of the airplane in still air. (*Hint:* The distance is the same both ways. The speeds are $r + 25$ and $r - 25$, where r is the speed in still air.)

ANSWER ON PAGE A-11

3. Two cars leave town at the same time traveling in opposite directions. One travels at 48 mph and the other at 60 mph. How far apart will they be 3 hr later? (*Hint:* The times are the same. Be *sure* to make a drawing.)

As we saw in Chapter 11, there are motion problems that can be solved with just one equation. The following is another such problem.

▶ **EXAMPLE 3**   Two cars leave town at the same time going in opposite directions. One of them travels at 60 mph and the other at 30 mph. In how many hours will they be 150 mi apart?

1. *Familiarize.*   We first make a drawing.

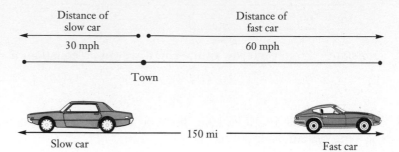

From the wording of the problem and the drawing, we see that the distances may *not* be the same. But the times the cars travel are the same, so we can just use t for time. We can organize the information in a chart.

$$d \quad = \quad r \quad \cdot \quad t$$

		Distance	**Speed**	**Time**
Fast car	Distance of fast car	60	t
Slow car	Distance of slow car	30	t

2. *Translate.*   From the drawing we see that

(Distance of fast car) + (Distance of slow car) = 150.

Then using $d = rt$ in each row of the table, we get

$$60t + 30t = 150.$$

3. *Solve.*   We solve the equation:

$$60t + 30t = 150$$
$$90t = 150 \qquad \text{Collecting like terms}$$
$$t = \frac{150}{90}, \text{ or } \frac{5}{3}, \text{ or } 1\frac{2}{3} \text{ hours.} \qquad \text{Dividing by 90}$$

4. Two cars leave town at the same time traveling in the same direction. One travels at 35 mph and the other at 40 mph. In how many hours will they be 15 mi apart? (*Hint:* The times are the same. Be *sure* to make a drawing.)

4. *Check.*   When $t = \frac{5}{3}$ hr,

$$\text{(Distance of fast car)} + \text{(Distance of slow car)} = 60\left(\frac{5}{3}\right) + 30\left(\frac{5}{3}\right)$$
$$= 100 + 50, \text{ or } 150 \text{ mi.}$$

Thus the time of $\frac{5}{3}$ hr, or $1\frac{2}{3}$ hr, checks.

5. *State.*   In $1\frac{2}{3}$ hr, the cars will be 150 mi apart.   ◀

DO EXERCISES 3 AND 4.

ANSWERS ON PAGE A-11

EXERCISE SET 13.5

a Solve.

1. A truck and a car leave a service station at the same time and travel in the same direction. The truck travels at 55 mph and the car at 40 mph. They can maintain CB radio contact within a range of 10 mi. When will they lose contact? Complete the following table to aid the translation.

$$d \quad = \quad r \quad \cdot \quad t$$

	Distance	Speed	Time
Truck	Distance of truck	55	
Car	Distance of car		t

2. Two cars leave town at the same time going in the same direction. One travels at 30 mph and the other travels at 46 mph. In how many hours will they be 72 mi apart?

1. _____

2. _____

3. A train leaves a station and travels east at 72 km/h. Three hours later, a second train leaves on a parallel track and travels east at 120 km/h. When will it overtake the first train? Complete the following table to aid the translation.

$$d \quad = \quad r \quad \cdot \quad t$$

	Distance	Speed	Time
Slow train	d		$t+3$	$\longrightarrow d = 72(\quad)$
Fast train	d	120		$\longrightarrow d = (\quad)t$

3. _____

4. A private airplane leaves an airport and flies due south at 192 km/h. Two hours later, a jet leaves the same airport and flies due south at 960 km/h. When will the jet overtake the plane?

4. _____

5. A canoeist paddled for 4 hr with a 6-km/h current to reach a campsite. The return trip against the same current took 10 hr. Find the speed of the canoe in still water. Complete the following table to aid the translation.

$$d \quad = \quad r \quad \cdot \quad t$$

	Distance	Speed	Time
Downstream	d	$r+6$		$\longrightarrow d = (\quad)4$
Upstream	d		10	$\longrightarrow \quad = (r-6)10$

5. _____

6. An airplane flew for 4 hr with a 20-km/h tailwind. The return flight against the same wind took 5 hr. Find the speed of the plane in still air.

6. _____

7. _____

8. _____

9. _____

10. _____

11. _____

12. _____

13. _____

14. _____

15. _____

16. _____

17. _____

18. _____

19. _____

20. _____

7. It takes a passenger train 2 hr less time than it takes a freight train to make the trip from Central City to Clear Creek. The passenger train averages 96 km/h, while the freight train averages 64 km/h. How far is it from Central City to Clear Creek?

8. It takes a small jet 4 hr less time than it takes a propeller-driven plane to travel from Glen Rock to Oakville. The jet averages 637 km/h, while the propeller plane averages 273 km/h. How far is it from Glen Rock to Oakville?

9. An airplane took 2 hr to fly 600 km against a headwind. The return trip with the wind took $1\frac{2}{3}$ hr. Find the speed of the plane in still air.

10. It took 3 hr to row a boat 18 km against the current. The return trip with the current took $1\frac{1}{2}$ hr. Find the speed of the rowboat in still water.

11. Two cars leave different towns at the same time traveling toward each other. The towns are 880 mi apart. One travels at 55 mph and the other travels at 48 mph. In how many hours will they meet?

12. Two airplanes start at the same time and fly toward each other from points 1000 km apart at rates of 420 km/h and 330 km/h. When will they meet?

13. A motorcycle breaks down and the rider has to walk the rest of the way to work. The motorcycle was being driven at 45 mph, and the rider walks at a speed of 6 mph. The distance from home to work is 25 mi, and the total time for the trip was 2 hr. How far did the motorcycle go before it broke down?

14. A student walks and jogs to college each day. The student averages 5 km/h walking and 9 km/h jogging. The distance from home to college is 8 km, and the student makes the trip in 1 hr. How far does the student jog?

SYNTHESIS

15. An airplane flew for 4.23 hr with a 25.5-km/h tailwind. The return flight against the same wind took 4.97 hr. Find the speed of the plane in still air.

16. An airplane took $2\frac{1}{2}$ hr to fly 625 mi with the wind. It took 4 hr and 10 min to make the return trip against the same wind. Find the wind speed and the speed of the plane in still air.

17. To deliver a package, a messenger must travel at a speed of 60 mph on land and then use a motorboat whose speed is 20 mph in still water. While delivering the package, the messenger goes by land to a dock and then travels on a river against a current of 4 mph. The messenger reaches the destination in 4.5 hr and then returns to the starting point in 3.5 hr. How far did the messenger travel by land and how far by water?

18. Against a headwind, Gary computes his flight time for a trip of 2900 mi at 5 hr. The flight would take 4 hr and 50 min if the headwind were half as much. Find the headwind and the plane's air speed.

19. A car travels from one town to another at a speed of 32 mph. If it had gone 4 mph faster, it could have made the trip in $\frac{1}{2}$ hr less time. How far apart are the towns?

20. Charles Lindbergh flew the Spirit of St. Louis in 1927 from New York to Paris at an average speed of 107.4 mph. Eleven years later, Howard Hughes flew the same route, averaged 217.1 mph, and took 16 hr and 57 min less time. Find the length of their route.

SUMMARY AND REVIEW: CHAPTER 13

IMPORTANT PROPERTIES AND FORMULAS

Motion Formula: $d = rt$

REVIEW EXERCISES

The review sections and objectives to be tested in addition to the material in this chapter are [9.1d, e], [11.1c], [11.5c], and [12.3a].

Determine whether the given ordered pair is a solution of the system of equations.

1. $(6, -1)$; $\quad x - y = 3$,
$\qquad 2x + 5y = 6$

2. $(2, -3)$; $\quad 2x + y = 1$,
$\qquad x - y = 5$

3. $(-2, 1)$; $\quad x + 3y = 1$,
$\qquad 2x - y = -5$

4. $(-4, -1)$; $\quad x - y = 3$,
$\qquad x + y = -5$

Solve the system of equations by graphing.

5. $x + y = 4$,
$\quad x - y = 8$

6. $x + 3y = 12$,
$\quad 2x - 4y = 4$

7. $y = 5 - x$,
$\quad 3x - 4y = -20$

8. $3x - 2y = -4$,
$\quad 2y - 3x = -2$

Solve using the substitution method.

9. $y = 5 - x$,
$\quad 3x - 4y = -20$

10. $x + 2y = 6$,
$\quad 2x + 3y = 8$

11. $3x + y = 1$,
$\quad x - 2y = 5$

12. $x + y = 6$,
$\quad y = 3 - 2x$

13. $s + t = 5$,
$\quad s = 13 - 3t$

14. $x - y = 4$,
$\quad y = 2 - x$

Solve using the elimination method.

15. $x + y = 4$,
$\quad 2x - y = 5$

16. $x + 2y = 9$,
$\quad 3x - 2y = -5$

17. $x - y = 8$,
$\quad 2x + y = 7$

18. $\frac{2}{3}x + y = -\frac{5}{3}$,
$\quad x - \frac{1}{3}y = -\frac{13}{3}$

19. $2x + 3y = 8$,
$\quad 5x + 2y = -2$

20. $5x - 2y = 2$,
$\quad 3x - 7y = 36$

21. $-x - y = -5$,
$\quad 2x - y = 4$

22. $6x + 2y = 4$,
$\quad 10x + 7y = -8$

23. $-6x - 2y = 5$,
$\quad 12x + 4y = -10$

Solve.

24. The sum of two numbers is 8. Their difference is 12. Find the numbers.

25. The sum of two numbers is 27. One half of the first number plus one third of the second number is 11. Find the numbers.

26. The perimeter of a rectangle is 96 cm. The length is 27 cm more than the width. Find the length and the width.

27. An airplane flew for 4 hr with a 15-km/h tailwind. The return flight against the wind took 5 hr. Find the speed of the airplane in still air.

28. There were 508 people at an organ recital. Orchestra seats cost $5.00 per person and balcony seats cost $3.00. The total receipts were $2118. Find the number of orchestra seats and the number of balcony seats sold.

29. Solution A is 30% alcohol, and solution B is 60% alcohol. How much of each is needed to make 80 L of a solution that is 45% alcohol?

30. Jeff is three times as old as his son. In nine years, Jeff will be twice as old as his son. How old is each now?

SKILL MAINTENANCE

Simplify.

31. $t^{-5} \cdot t^{13}$

32. $\dfrac{t^{-5}}{t^{13}}$

33. Subtract: $\dfrac{x}{x^2 - 9} - \dfrac{x - 1}{x^2 - 5x + 6}$.

34. Graph: $2y - x = 6$.

SYNTHESIS

35. The solution of the following system is (6, 2). Find C and D.

$$2x - Dy = 6,$$
$$Cx + 4y = 14$$

36. Solve:

$$3(x - y) = 4 + x,$$
$$x = 5y + 2.$$

37. For a two-digit number, the sum of the units digit and the tens digit is 6. When the digits are reversed, the new number is eighteen more than the original number. Find the original number.

38. A stablehand agreed to work for one year. At the end of that time, she was to receive $240 and one horse. After 7 months she quit the job, but still received the horse and $100. What was the value of the horse?

❖ **THINKING IT THROUGH**

1. Briefly compare the strengths and the weaknesses of the graphical, substitution, and elimination methods.

2. List a system of equations with no solution. Answers may vary.

3. List a system of equations with infinitely many solutions. Answers may vary.

4. Explain the advantages of using a system of equations to solve certain kinds of problems.

NAME   SECTION   DATE

TEST: CHAPTER 13

1. Determine whether the given ordered pair is a solution of the system of equations.

$$(-2, -1); \quad x = 4 + 2y,$$
$$2y - 3x = 4$$

2. Solve this system by graphing:

$$x - y = 3,$$
$$x - 2y = 4.$$

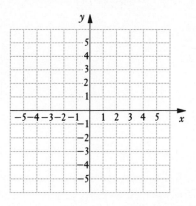

1. _____

2. _____

3. _____

4. _____

Solve using the substitution method.

3. $y = 6 - x,$
   $2x - 3y = 22$

4. $x + 2y = 5,$
   $x + y = 2$

5. $y = 5x - 2,$
   $y - 2 = 5x$

5. _____

6. _____

Solve using the elimination method.

6. $x - y = 6,$
   $3x + y = -2$

7. $\dfrac{1}{2}x - \dfrac{1}{3}y = 8,$

   $\dfrac{2}{3}x + \dfrac{1}{2}y = 5$

8. $4x + 5y = 5,$
   $6x + 7y = 7$

9. $2x + 3y = 13,$
   $3x - 5y = 10$

7. _____

8. _____

9. _____

ANSWERS

10. _____

11. _____

12. _____

13. _____

14. _____

15. _____

16. _____

17. _____

18. _____

10. The difference of two numbers is 12. One fourth of the larger number plus one half of the smaller is 9. Find the numbers.

11. A motorboat traveled for 2 hr with an 8-km/h current. The return trip against the same current took 3 hr. Find the speed of the motorboat in still water.

12. Solution A is 25% acid, and solution B is 40% acid. How much of each is needed to make 60 L of a solution that is 30% acid?

SKILL MAINTENANCE

13. Subtract: $\dfrac{1}{x^2 - 16} - \dfrac{x - 4}{x^2 - 3x - 4}$.

14. Graph: $3x - 4y = -12$.

Simplify.

15. $(2x^{-2}y^7)(5x^6y^{-9})$

16. $\dfrac{a^4 b^2}{a^{-6} b^8}$

SYNTHESIS

17. Find the numbers C and D such that $(-2, 3)$ is a solution of the system
$$Cx - 4y = 7,$$
$$3x + Dy = 8.$$

18. You are in line at a ticket window. There are two more people ahead of you than there are behind you. In the entire line there are three times as many people as there are behind you. How many are ahead of you in line?

INTRODUCTION The formula below illustrates the use of another kind of expression in problem solving. It is called a *radical expression* and involves a square root. We say that 3 is a square root of 9 because $3^2 = 9$. In this chapter, we study manipulations of radical expressions in addition, subtraction, multiplication, division, and simplifying. Finally, we consider another equation-solving principle and apply it to problem solving.

The review sections to be tested in addition to the material in this chapter are 11.2, 12.6, and 13.3. ❖

Radical Expressions and Equations

AN APPLICATION

How can we use the length of the skid marks of a car to estimate its speed before the brakes were applied?

THE MATHEMATICS

The formula

$r = 2\sqrt{5L}$ ← This is a *radical expression*.

can be used to approximate the speed r, in miles per hour, of a car that has left a skid mark of length L, in feet.

Pythagorean Theorem:	In a right triangle, the sum of the squares of the legs is equal to the square of the hypotenuse: $a^2 + b^2 = c^2$.
Product Rule of Exponents:	$a^m a^n = a^{m+n}$
Quotient Rule of Exponents:	$\dfrac{a^m}{a^n} = a^{m-n}$
Power Rule of Exponents:	$(a^m)^n = a^{mn}$
Raising a Product to a Power:	$(ab)^n = a^n b^n$
Raising a Quotient to a Power:	$\left(\dfrac{a}{b}\right)^n = \dfrac{a^n}{b^n}$

PRETEST: CHAPTER 14

1. Find the square roots of 49.

2. Identify the radicand in $\sqrt{3t}$.

3. Determine whether 8 is a meaningful replacement in $\sqrt{3x - 40}$.

4. Determine the meaningful replacements in $\sqrt{x - 2}$.

5. Approximate $\sqrt{47}$ to three decimal places.

6. Solve: $\sqrt{2x + 1} = 3$.

In the remaining questions on this Pretest, assume that *all* expressions under radicals represent positive numbers.
Simplify.

7. $\sqrt{4x^2}$

8. $4\sqrt{18} - 2\sqrt{8} + \sqrt{32}$

9. $(2 - \sqrt{3})^2$

10. $(2 - \sqrt{3})(2 + \sqrt{3})$

Multiply and simplify.

11. $\sqrt{6}\sqrt{10}$

12. $(2\sqrt{6} - 1)^2$

Divide and simplify.

13. $\dfrac{\sqrt{15}}{\sqrt{3}}$

14. $\sqrt{\dfrac{24a^7}{3a^3}}$

15. In a right triangle, $a = 5$ and $b = 8$. Find c. Give an exact answer and an approximation to three decimal places.

16. How long is a guy wire reaching from the top of a 12-m pole to a point 7 m from the base of the pole?

17. Rationalize the denominator:
$$\dfrac{\sqrt{5}}{\sqrt{x}}.$$

18. Rationalize the denominator:
$$\dfrac{8}{6 + \sqrt{5}}.$$

14.1 Introduction to Square Roots and Radical Expressions

a Square Roots

When we raise a number to the second power, we have squared the number. Sometimes we may need to find the number that was squared. We call this process finding a square root of a number.

> The number c is a *square root* of a if $c^2 = a$.

Every positive number has two square roots. For example, the square roots of 25 are 5 and -5 because $5^2 = 25$ and $(-5)^2 = 25$. The positive square root is also called the **principal square root.** The symbol $\sqrt{}$ is called a **radical** symbol. The radical symbol refers only to the principal root. Thus, $\sqrt{25} = 5$. To name the negative square root of a number, we use $-\sqrt{}$. The number 0 has only one square root, 0.

▶ **EXAMPLE 1** Find the square roots of 81.

The square roots are 9 and -9. ◀

▶ **EXAMPLE 2** Find $\sqrt{225}$.

The symbol $\sqrt{225}$ represents the principal square root. There are two square roots, 15 and -15. We want the positive square root since this is what $\sqrt{}$ represents. Thus, $\sqrt{225} = 15$. ◀

Table 2 at the back of the book contains a list of squares and square roots. It would be most helpful to memorize the squares of whole numbers from 0 to 25.

▶ **EXAMPLE 3** Find $-\sqrt{64}$.

The symbol $\sqrt{64}$ represents the positive square root. Then $-\sqrt{64}$ represents the negative square root. That is, $\sqrt{64} = 8$, so $-\sqrt{64} = -8$. ◀

DO EXERCISES 1–10.

b Approximating Square Roots

We often need to use rational numbers to approximate square roots that are irrational. Such approximations can be found using a calculator with a square root key $\boxed{\sqrt{}}$. They can also be found using Table 2 at the back of the book.

▶ **EXAMPLE 4** Use your calculator or Table 2 to approximate $\sqrt{10}$. Round to three decimal places.

Before finding square roots on a calculator, you will need to consult the instruction manual. Calculators vary in their methods of operation.

$$\sqrt{10} \approx 3.162277660 \quad \text{Using a calculator with a 10-digit readout}$$

Different calculators give different numbers of digits in their readouts. This may cause some variance in answers. We round to the third decimal place. Then $\sqrt{10} \approx 3.162$. This can also be found in Table 2. ◀

DO EXERCISES 11 AND 12.

OBJECTIVES

After finishing Section 14.1, you should be able to:

a Find the principal square roots and their opposites of the whole numbers from 0^2 to 25^2.

b Approximate square roots of real numbers using a calculator or a table.

c Solve problems involving applications of square roots.

d Identify radicands of radical expressions.

e Identify whether a radical expression represents a real number, determine whether a given number is a meaningful replacement in a radical expression, and determine the meaningful replacements in a radical expression.

f Simplify a radical expression with a perfect-square radicand.

FOR EXTRA HELP

Tape 27A

Find the square roots.

1. 36   2. 64

3. 225   4. 100

Find the following.

5. $\sqrt{16}$ 6. $\sqrt{49}$

7. $\sqrt{100}$ 8. $\sqrt{441}$

9. $-\sqrt{49}$ 10. $-\sqrt{169}$

Use a calculator or Table 2. Approximate to three decimal places.

11. $\sqrt{30}$ 12. $-\sqrt{98}$

13. In the situation of Example 5, find the number of spaces needed when the average number of arrivals in peak hours is **(a)** 64; **(b)** 83.

Identify the radicand.

14. $\sqrt{45 + x}$

15. $\sqrt{\dfrac{x}{x + 2}}$

---

c   Applications of Square Roots

We now consider an application involving a formula with a radical expression.

▶ **EXAMPLE 5**   *Parking lot arrival spaces.* A parking lot has attendants to park cars, and it uses spaces for cars to be left before they are taken to permanent parking stalls. The number N of such spaces needed is approximated by the formula

$$N = 2.5\sqrt{A},$$

where A is the average number of arrivals in peak hours. Find the number of spaces needed when the average number of arrivals in peak hours is 77.

We substitute 77 into the formula. We use a calculator or Table 2 to find an approximation:

$$N = 2.5\sqrt{77} \approx 2.5(8.775) = 21.938 \approx 22.$$

Note that we round up to 22 spaces because 21.938 spaces would give us part of a space, which we could not use. To ensure that we have enough, we need 22. ◀

Calculator note. In most situations when using a calculator for a calculation like that in Example 5, we find the approximation to some number of decimal places, say 10, and then multiply by 2.5 and round. Thus, on a calculator, we might find

$$N = 2.5\sqrt{77} \approx 2.5(8.774964387) = 21.93741097.$$

Note that this gives a variance in the third decimal place. If your instructor is allowing you to use a calculator for approximation, you should be aware of possible variance in answers. You may get answers different than those given at the back of the text. Answers to the exercises have been found by rounding at the end.

DO EXERCISE 13.

d   Radicands and Radical Expressions

When an expression is written under a radical, we have a **radical expression.** Here are some examples:

$$\sqrt{14}, \qquad \sqrt{x}, \qquad \sqrt{x^2 + 4}, \qquad \sqrt{\dfrac{x^2 - 5}{2}}.$$

The expression written under the radical is called the **radicand.**

▶ **EXAMPLES**   Identify the radicand in each expression.

6. $\sqrt{x}$ The radicand is x.

7. $\sqrt{y^2 - 5}$ The radicand is $y^2 - 5$.

8. $\sqrt{\dfrac{a - b}{a + b}}$ The radicand is $\dfrac{a - b}{a + b}$. ◀

DO EXERCISES 14 AND 15.

e   Expressions That Are Meaningful as Real Numbers

The square of any nonzero number is always positive. For example, $8^2 = 64$ and $(-11)^2 = 121$. There are no real numbers that can be squared to get negative numbers.

> **Radical expressions with negative radicands do not represent real numbers.**

Thus the following expressions do not represent real numbers (they are meaningless as real numbers):

$$\sqrt{-100}, \quad \sqrt{-49}, \quad -\sqrt{-3}.$$

Later in your study of mathematics, you may encounter a number system called the **complex numbers** in which negative numbers have square roots.

▶ **EXAMPLE 9**   Determine whether 6 is a meaningful replacement in $\sqrt{1-y}$.

If we replace y by 6, we get $\sqrt{1-6} = \sqrt{-5}$, which has no meaning as a real number because the radicand is negative.   ◄

▶ **EXAMPLE 10**   Determine whether 7 is a meaningful replacement in $\sqrt{3+2x}$.

If we replace x by 7, we get $\sqrt{3+2(7)} = \sqrt{17}$, which has meaning as a real number because the radicand is nonnegative.   ◄

DO EXERCISES 16–21.

▶ **EXAMPLES**   Determine the meaningful replacements in each expression.

11. $\sqrt{x}$ Any number greater than or equal to 0 is meaningful.
12. $\sqrt{x+2}$ We solve the inequality $x + 2 \geq 0$. Any number greater than or equal to -2 is meaningful.
13. $\sqrt{x^2}$ Squares of numbers are never negative. All replacements are meaningful.
14. $\sqrt{x^2+1}$ Since x^2 is never negative, $x^2 + 1$ is never negative. All real-number replacements are meaningful.   ◄

DO EXERCISES 22–25.

f   Perfect-Square Radicands

The expression $\sqrt{x^2}$, with a perfect-square radicand, can be troublesome. If x represents a nonnegative number, $\sqrt{x^2}$ simplifies to x. If x represents a negative number, $\sqrt{x^2}$ simplifies to $-x$ (the opposite of x). That is because $\sqrt{a}$ denotes the *principal* square root of a.

Suppose $x = 3$. Then $\sqrt{x^2} = \sqrt{3^2}$, which is $\sqrt{9}$, or 3. Suppose $x = -3$. Then $\sqrt{x^2} = \sqrt{(-3)^2}$, which is $\sqrt{9}$, or 3, the *absolute value* of -3. In either case, when replacements for x are considered to be any real number, it follows that $\sqrt{x^2} = |x|$.

Is the expression meaningless as a real number? Write "yes" or "no."

16. $-\sqrt{25}$ 17. $\sqrt{-25}$

18. $-\sqrt{-36}$ 19. $-\sqrt{36}$

20. Determine whether 8 is a meaningful replacement in $\sqrt{x}$.

21. Determine whether 10 is a meaningful replacement in $\sqrt{4-x}$.

Determine the meaningful replacements.

22. $\sqrt{a}$ 23. $\sqrt{x-3}$

24. $\sqrt{2x-5}$ 25. $\sqrt{x^2+3}$

ANSWERS ON PAGE A-11

Simplify. Assume that expressions under radicals represent any real number.

26. $\sqrt{(xy)^2}$

27. $\sqrt{x^2y^2}$

28. $\sqrt{(x-1)^2}$

29. $\sqrt{x^2+8x+16}$

Simplify. Assume that expressions under radicals represent nonnegative real numbers.

30. $\sqrt{(xy)^2}$

31. $\sqrt{x^2y^2}$

32. $\sqrt{(x-1)^2}$

33. $\sqrt{x^2+8x+16}$

34. $\sqrt{25y^2}$

35. $\sqrt{\frac{1}{4}t^2}$

For any real number A,
$$\sqrt{A^2} = |A|.$$
(That is, for any real number A, the principal square root of A squared is the absolute value of A.)

▶ **EXAMPLES**   Simplify. Assume that expressions under radicals represent any real number.

15. $\sqrt{(3x)^2} = |3x|$ Absolute-value notation is necessary.

16. $\sqrt{a^2b^2} = \sqrt{(ab)^2} = |ab|$

17. $\sqrt{x^2+2x+1} = \sqrt{(x+1)^2} = |x+1|$ ◀

DO EXERCISES 26–29.

Fortunately, in most uses of radicals, it can be assumed that expressions under radicals are nonnegative or positive. Indeed, many computers are programmed to consider only nonnegative radicands. Suppose that $x \geq 0$. Then
$$\sqrt{x^2} = |x| = x,$$
since x is nonnegative.

For any nonnegative real number A,
$$\sqrt{A^2} = A.$$
(That is, for any nonnegative real number A, the principal square root of A squared is A.)

▶ **EXAMPLES**   Simplify. Assume that expressions under radicals represent nonnegative real numbers.

18. $\sqrt{(3x)^2} = 3x$ Since $3x$ is assumed to be nonnegative

19. $\sqrt{a^2b^2} = \sqrt{(ab)^2} = ab$ Since ab is assumed to be nonnegative

20. $\sqrt{x^2+2x+1} = \sqrt{(x+1)^2} = x+1$ Since $x+1$ is assumed to be nonnegative   ◀

DO EXERCISES 30–35.

Henceforth, in this text we will assume that all expressions under radicals represent nonnegative real numbers.

We make this assumption in order to eliminate some confusion and because it is valid in many applications. As you study further in mathematics, however, you will frequently have to make a determination about expressions under radicals being nonnegative or positive. This will often be necessary in calculus.

ANSWERS ON PAGE A-11

EXERCISE SET 14.1

a Find the square roots.

1. 1   **2.** 4   **3.** 16   **4.** 9

5. 100   **6.** 121   **7.** 169   **8.** 144

Simplify.

9. $\sqrt{4}$ **10.** $\sqrt{1}$ **11.** $-\sqrt{9}$ **12.** $-\sqrt{25}$ **13.** $-\sqrt{64}$

14. $-\sqrt{81}$ **15.** $-\sqrt{225}$ **16.** $\sqrt{400}$ **17.** $\sqrt{361}$ **18.** $\sqrt{441}$

b Use the calculator or Table 2 to approximate these square roots. Round to three decimal places.

19. $\sqrt{5}$ **20.** $\sqrt{6}$ **21.** $\sqrt{17}$ **22.** $\sqrt{19}$ **23.** $\sqrt{93}$ **24.** $\sqrt{43}$

c Solve. Use the formula $N = 2.5\sqrt{A}$ of Example 5.

25. Find the number of spaces needed when the average number of arrivals is **(a)** 25; **(b)** 89.

26. Find the number of spaces needed when the average number of arrivals is **(a)** 62; **(b)** 100.

d Identify the radicand.

27. $\sqrt{a-4}$ **28.** $\sqrt{t+3}$ **29.** $5\sqrt{t^2+1}$

30. $8\sqrt{x^2+5}$ **31.** $x^2y\sqrt{\dfrac{3}{x+2}}$ **32.** $ab^2\sqrt{\dfrac{a}{a-b}}$

e Determine whether the expression is meaningful as a real number. Write "yes" or "no."

33. $\sqrt{-16}$ **34.** $\sqrt{-81}$ **35.** $-\sqrt{81}$ **36.** $-\sqrt{64}$

ANSWERS

1.
2.
3.
4.
5.
6.
7.
8.
9.
10.
11.
12.
13.
14.
15.
16.
17.
18.
19.
20.
21.
22.
23.
24.
25. a)
b)
26. a)
b)
27.
28.
29.
30.
31.
32.
33.
34.
35.
36.

Determine whether the given number is a meaningful replacement in the given radical expression.

37. $4; \sqrt{y}$ **38.** $-8; \sqrt{m}$ **39.** $-11; \sqrt{t-5}$ **40.** $-11; \sqrt{2-x}$

Determine the meaningful replacements.

41. $\sqrt{5x}$ **42.** $\sqrt{3y}$ **43.** $\sqrt{t-5}$ **44.** $\sqrt{y-8}$ **45.** $\sqrt{y+8}$

46. $\sqrt{m-18}$ **47.** $\sqrt{2y-7}$ **48.** $\sqrt{3x+8}$ **49.** $\sqrt{t^2+5}$ **50.** $\sqrt{y^2+1}$

f   Simplify. Remember that we have assumed that expressions under radicals represent nonnegative real numbers.

51. $\sqrt{t^2}$ **52.** $\sqrt{x^2}$ **53.** $\sqrt{9x^2}$ **54.** $\sqrt{4a^2}$

55. $\sqrt{(ab)^2}$ **56.** $\sqrt{(6y)^2}$ **57.** $\sqrt{(34d)^2}$ **58.** $\sqrt{(53b)^2}$

59. $\sqrt{(x+3)^2}$ **60.** $\sqrt{(x-7)^2}$ **61.** $\sqrt{a^2-10a+25}$ **62.** $\sqrt{x^2+2x+1}$

63. $\sqrt{4x^2-20x+25}$ **64.** $\sqrt{9p^2+12p+4}$

SKILL MAINTENANCE

65. The amount F that a family spends on food varies directly as its income I. A family making \$19,600 a year will spend \$5096 on food. At this rate, how much would a family making \$20,500 spend on food?

Divide and simplify.

66. $\dfrac{x-3}{x+4} \div \dfrac{x^2-9}{x+4}$ **67.** $\dfrac{x^2-x-2}{x-1} \div \dfrac{x-2}{x^2-1}$

SYNTHESIS

68. Simplify: $\sqrt{\sqrt{16}}$.   **69.** Simplify: $\sqrt{3^2+4^2}$.

70. Between what two consecutive integers is $-\sqrt{33}$?

▦ Use a calculator to approximate these square roots. Round to three decimal places.

71. $\sqrt{12.8}$ **72.** $\sqrt{930}$ **73.** $\sqrt{1043.89}$

Solve.

74. $\sqrt{x^2} = 6$ **75.** $\sqrt{y^2} = -7$ **76.** $t^2 = 49$

77. Suppose the area of a square is 3. Find the length of a side.

14.2 Multiplying and Simplifying with Radical Expressions

a Simplifying by Factoring

To see how to multiply with radical notation, consider the following.

a) $\sqrt{9} \cdot \sqrt{4} = 3 \cdot 2 = 6$ This is a product of square roots.

b) $\sqrt{9 \cdot 4} = \sqrt{36} = 6$ This is the square root of a product.

Note that

$$\sqrt{9} \cdot \sqrt{4} = \sqrt{9 \cdot 4}.$$

DO EXERCISE 1.

We can multiply radical expressions by multiplying the radicands.

> **The Product Rule for Radicals**
>
> **For any nonnegative radicands A and B,**
> $$\sqrt{A} \cdot \sqrt{B} = \sqrt{A \cdot B}.$$
> **(The product of square roots, provided they exist, is the square root of the product of the radicands.)**

▶ **EXAMPLES** Multiply.

1. $\sqrt{5}\sqrt{7} = \sqrt{5 \cdot 7} = \sqrt{35}$

2. $\sqrt{8}\sqrt{8} = \sqrt{8 \cdot 8} = \sqrt{64} = 8$

3. $\sqrt{\dfrac{2}{3}}\sqrt{\dfrac{4}{5}} = \sqrt{\dfrac{2}{3} \cdot \dfrac{4}{5}} = \sqrt{\dfrac{8}{15}}$

4. $\sqrt{2x}\sqrt{3x-1} = \sqrt{2x(3x-1)}$
$\qquad\qquad\quad = \sqrt{6x^2 - 2x}$

DO EXERCISES 2–5.

To factor radical expressions, we can use the product rule for radicals in reverse. That is,

> $$\sqrt{AB} = \sqrt{A}\sqrt{B}.$$

In some cases, we can simplify after factoring.

> **A radical expression is simplified when its radicand has no factors that are perfect squares.**

When simplifying a radical expression, we first determine whether a radicand is a perfect square. Then we determine whether it has perfect-square factors. The radicand is then factored and the radical expression simplified using the preceding rule.

Compare the following:

$$\sqrt{50} = \sqrt{10 \cdot 5} = \sqrt{10}\sqrt{5};$$
$$\sqrt{50} = \sqrt{25 \cdot 2} = \sqrt{25}\sqrt{2} = 5\sqrt{2}.$$

In the second case, the radicand has the perfect-square factor 25. If you do not recognize perfect-square factors, try factoring the radicand into its prime

1. Simplify.

   a) $\sqrt{4} \cdot \sqrt{16}$

   b) $\sqrt{4 \cdot 16}$

Multiply.

2. $\sqrt{3}\sqrt{7}$

3. $\sqrt{5}\sqrt{5}$

4. $\sqrt{x}\sqrt{x+1}$

5. $\sqrt{x+1}\sqrt{x-1}$

Simplify by factoring.

6. $\sqrt{32}$

7. $\sqrt{x^2 + 14x + 49}$

8. $\sqrt{25x^2}$

9. $\sqrt{36m^2}$

10. $\sqrt{76}$

11. $\sqrt{x^2 - 8x + 16}$

12. $\sqrt{64t^2}$

13. $\sqrt{100a^2}$

factors. For example,

$$\sqrt{50} = \sqrt{2 \cdot \underbrace{5 \cdot 5}} = 5\sqrt{2}.$$

Perfect square (a pair of the same numbers)

Radical expressions in which the radicand has no perfect-square factors, such as $5\sqrt{2}$, are considered to be in simplest form.

▶ **EXAMPLES**

5. $\sqrt{18} = \sqrt{9 \cdot 2}$ Identifying a perfect-square factor and factoring the radicand. The factor 9 is a perfect square.

     $= \sqrt{9} \cdot \sqrt{2}$ Factoring into a product of radicals

     $= 3\sqrt{2}$ $3\sqrt{2}$ means $3 \cdot \sqrt{2}$

     The radicand has no factors that are perfect squares.

6. $\sqrt{48t} = \sqrt{16 \cdot 3t}$ Identifying a perfect-square factor and factoring the radicand. The factor 16 is a perfect square.

     $= \sqrt{16}\sqrt{3t}$ Factoring into a product of radicals

     $= 4\sqrt{3t}$ Taking a square root

7. $\sqrt{20t^2} = \sqrt{4 \cdot t^2 \cdot 5}$ Identifying perfect-square factors and factoring the radicand. The factors 4 and t^2 are perfect squares.

     $= \sqrt{4}\sqrt{t^2}\sqrt{5}$ Factoring into a product of several radicals

     $= 2t\sqrt{5}$ Taking square roots. No absolute-value signs are necessary since we have assumed that expressions under radicals are nonnegative.

8. $\sqrt{x^2 - 6x + 9} = \sqrt{(x-3)^2} = x - 3$ No absolute-value signs are necessary since we have assumed that expressions under radicals are nonnegative.

9. $\sqrt{36x^2} = \sqrt{36}\sqrt{x^2} = 6x$, or $\sqrt{36x^2} = \sqrt{(6x)^2} = 6x$

10. $\sqrt{3x^2 + 6x + 3} = \sqrt{3(x^2 + 2x + 1)}$ Factoring the radicand

     $= \sqrt{3}\sqrt{x^2 + 2x + 1}$ Factoring into a product of radicals

     $= \sqrt{3}\sqrt{(x+1)^2}$

     $= \sqrt{3}(x+1)$ Taking the square root ◀

DO EXERCISES 6–13.

b   **Approximating Square Roots**

Some numbers might be too large to find in a table of square roots. For example, Table 2 goes only to 100. We may still be able to find approximate square roots for other numbers, however. We do this by first looking for the largest perfect-square factor, if there is one. If there is none, we use any factorization for which all factors appear in Table 2.

▶ **EXAMPLES**   Approximate the square roots. Use Table 2.

11. $\sqrt{160} = \sqrt{16 \cdot 10}$ Factoring the radicand. (Make one factor a perfect square, if you can.)

     $= \sqrt{16}\sqrt{10}$ Factoring the radical expression

     $= 4\sqrt{10} \approx 4(3.162) = 12.648$ From Table 2, $\sqrt{10} \approx 3.162$.

12. $\sqrt{341} = \sqrt{11 \cdot 31}$ Factoring into a product where each factor is in Table 2. (There is no perfect-square factor.)

$= \sqrt{11}\sqrt{31}$

$\approx 3.317 \times 5.568$ From Table 2

≈ 18.469 Rounded to three decimal places   ◀

If the approximations in Examples 11 and 12 were done on a calculator, the simplifying would not be necessary and the square roots would be found directly, but there is variance in the answers. For example, on a calculator with a 10-digit readout, we would get

$$\sqrt{160} \approx 12.64911064 \quad \text{and} \quad \sqrt{341} \approx 18.46618531.$$

DO EXERCISES 14 AND 15.

c Simplifying Square Roots of Powers

To take the square root of an even power such as x^{10}, we note that $x^{10} = (x^5)^2$. Then

$$\sqrt{x^{10}} = \sqrt{(x^5)^2} = x^5.$$

We can find the answer by taking half the exponent. That is,

$$\sqrt{x^{10}} = x^5. \longleftarrow \tfrac{1}{2}(10) = 5$$

▶ **EXAMPLES** Simplify.

13. $\sqrt{x^6} = \sqrt{(x^3)^2} = x^3 \longleftarrow \tfrac{1}{2}(6) = 3$

14. $\sqrt{x^8} = x^4$

15. $\sqrt{t^{22}} = t^{11}$ ◀

DO EXERCISES 16–18.

If an odd power occurs, we express the power in terms of the largest even power. Then we simplify the even power as in Examples 13–15.

▶ **EXAMPLE 16** Simplify by factoring: $\sqrt{x^9}$.

$$\sqrt{x^9} = \sqrt{x^8 \cdot x}$$
$$= \sqrt{x^8}\sqrt{x}$$
$$= x^4\sqrt{x} \qquad ◀$$

Note in Example 16 that $\sqrt{x^9} \neq x^3$.

▶ **EXAMPLE 17** Simplify by factoring: $\sqrt{32x^{15}}$.

$$\sqrt{32x^{15}} = \sqrt{16x^{14}(2x)} \qquad \text{The largest even power is 14.}$$
$$\text{Then we factor the radicand.}$$
$$= \sqrt{16}\sqrt{x^{14}}\sqrt{2x} \qquad \text{Factoring into a product of radicals}$$
$$= 4x^7\sqrt{2x} \qquad \text{Simplifying} \qquad ◀$$

DO EXERCISES 19 AND 20.

Approximate the square roots using Table 2. Round to three decimal places.

14. $\sqrt{275}$

15. $\sqrt{102}$

Simplify.

16. $\sqrt{t^4}$

17. $\sqrt{t^{20}}$

18. $\sqrt{q^{34}}$

Simplify by factoring.

19. $\sqrt{x^7}$

20. $\sqrt{24x^{11}}$

ANSWERS ON PAGE A-11

Multiply and simplify.

21. $\sqrt{3}\sqrt{6}$

22. $\sqrt{2}\sqrt{50}$

Multiply and simplify.

23. $\sqrt{2x^3}\sqrt{8x^3y^4}$

24. $\sqrt{10xy^2}\sqrt{5x^2y^3}$

d Multiplying and Simplifying

Sometimes we can simplify after multiplying. We leave the radicand in factored form and factor further to determine perfect-square factors. Then we simplify the perfect-square factors.

▶ **EXAMPLE 18**   Multiply and then simplify by factoring: $\sqrt{2}\sqrt{14}$.

$$\sqrt{2}\sqrt{14} = \sqrt{2 \cdot 14} \qquad \text{Multiplying}$$
$$= \sqrt{2 \cdot 2 \cdot 7} \qquad \text{Factoring}$$
$$= \sqrt{2 \cdot 2}\sqrt{7} \qquad \text{Looking for perfect-square factors; pairs of factors}$$
$$= 2\sqrt{7} \qquad\qquad\qquad\qquad\qquad ◀$$

DO EXERCISES 21 AND 22.

▶ **EXAMPLE 19**   Multiply and then simplify by factoring: $\sqrt{3x^2}\sqrt{9x^3}$.

$$\sqrt{3x^2}\sqrt{9x^3} = \sqrt{3x^2 \cdot 9x^3} \qquad \text{Multiplying}$$
$$= \sqrt{9 \cdot x^2 \cdot x^2 \cdot 3 \cdot x} \qquad \begin{array}{l}\text{Looking for perfect-square factors or}\\\text{largest even powers}\end{array}$$

Perfect squares are listed first.

$$= \sqrt{9}\sqrt{x^2}\sqrt{x^2}\sqrt{3x}$$
$$= 3 \cdot x \cdot x \cdot \sqrt{3x}$$
$$= 3x^2\sqrt{3x} \qquad\qquad\qquad\qquad ◀$$

DO EXERCISES 23 AND 24.

We know that $\sqrt{AB} = \sqrt{A}\sqrt{B}$. That is, the square root of a product is the product of the square roots. What about the square root of a sum? That is, is the square root of a sum equal to the sum of the square roots? To check, consider $\sqrt{A + B}$ and $\sqrt{A} + \sqrt{B}$ when $A = 16$ and $B = 9$:

$$\sqrt{A + B} = \sqrt{16 + 9} = \sqrt{25} = 5;$$

and

$$\sqrt{A} + \sqrt{B} = \sqrt{16} + \sqrt{9} = 4 + 3 = 7.$$

Thus we see the following.

> CAUTION!   The square root of a sum is not the sum of the square roots.
> $$\sqrt{A + B} \neq \sqrt{A} + \sqrt{B}$$

NAME   SECTION   DATE

EXERCISE SET 14.2

a Simplify by factoring.

1. $\sqrt{12}$ 2. $\sqrt{8}$ 3. $\sqrt{75}$ 4. $\sqrt{50}$ 5. $\sqrt{20}$

6. $\sqrt{45}$ 7. $\sqrt{200}$ 8. $\sqrt{300}$ 9. $\sqrt{9x}$ 10. $\sqrt{4y}$

11. $\sqrt{48x}$ 12. $\sqrt{40m}$ 13. $\sqrt{16a}$ 14. $\sqrt{49b}$ 15. $\sqrt{64y^2}$

16. $\sqrt{9x^2}$ 17. $\sqrt{13x^2}$ 18. $\sqrt{29t^2}$ 19. $\sqrt{8t^2}$ 20. $\sqrt{125a^2}$

21. $\sqrt{180}$ 22. $\sqrt{448}$ 23. $\sqrt{288y}$ 24. $\sqrt{363p}$ 25. $\sqrt{20x^2}$

26. $\sqrt{28x^2}$ 27. $\sqrt{8x^2 + 8x + 2}$ 28. $\sqrt{27x^2 - 36x + 12}$

29. $\sqrt{36y + 12y^2 + y^3}$ 30. $\sqrt{x - 2x^2 + x^3}$

1. _____
2. _____
3. _____
4. _____
5. _____
6. _____
7. _____
8. _____
9. _____
10. _____
11. _____
12. _____
13. _____
14. _____
15. _____
16. _____
17. _____
18. _____
19. _____
20. _____
21. _____
22. _____
23. _____
24. _____
25. _____
26. _____
27. _____
28. _____
29. _____
30. _____

Copyright © 1993 Addison-Wesley Publishing Co., Inc.

ANSWERS

31. _____

32. _____

33. _____

34. _____

35. _____

36. _____

37. _____

38. _____

39. _____

40. _____

41. _____

42. _____

43. _____

44. _____

45. _____

46. _____

47. _____

48. _____

49. _____

50. _____

51. _____

52. _____

b Approximate the square roots using Table 2. Round to three decimal places.

31. $\sqrt{125}$ **32.** $\sqrt{180}$ **33.** $\sqrt{360}$ **34.** $\sqrt{105}$

35. $\sqrt{300}$ **36.** $\sqrt{143}$ **37.** $\sqrt{122}$ **38.** $\sqrt{2000}$

Speed of a skidding car. How do police determine the speed of a car after an accident? The formula

$$r = 2\sqrt{5L}$$

can be used to approximate the speed r, in miles per hour, of a car that has left a skid mark of length L, in feet.

39. What was the speed of a car that left skid marks of 20 ft? of 150 ft?

40. What was the speed of a car that left skid marks of 30 ft? of 70 ft?

c Simplify by factoring.

41. $\sqrt{x^6}$ **42.** $\sqrt{x^{10}}$ **43.** $\sqrt{x^{12}}$ **44.** $\sqrt{x^{16}}$

45. $\sqrt{x^5}$ **46.** $\sqrt{x^3}$ **47.** $\sqrt{t^{19}}$ **48.** $\sqrt{p^{17}}$

49. $\sqrt{(y-2)^8}$ **50.** $\sqrt{(x+3)^6}$ **51.** $\sqrt{4(x+5)^{10}}$ **52.** $\sqrt{16(a-7)^4}$

53. $\sqrt{36m^3}$ **54.** $\sqrt{250y^3}$ **55.** $\sqrt{8a^5}$ **56.** $\sqrt{12b^7}$

57. $\sqrt{104p^{17}}$ **58.** $\sqrt{284m^{23}}$ **59.** $\sqrt{448x^6y^3}$ **60.** $\sqrt{243x^5y^4}$

d Multiply and then simplify by factoring, if possible.

61. $\sqrt{3}\sqrt{18}$ **62.** $\sqrt{5}\sqrt{10}$ **63.** $\sqrt{15}\sqrt{6}$

64. $\sqrt{3}\sqrt{27}$ **65.** $\sqrt{18}\sqrt{14x}$ **66.** $\sqrt{12}\sqrt{18x}$

67. $\sqrt{3x}\sqrt{12y}$ **68.** $\sqrt{7x}\sqrt{21y}$ **69.** $\sqrt{10}\sqrt{10}$

70. $\sqrt{11}\sqrt{11x}$ **71.** $\sqrt{5b}\sqrt{15b}$ **72.** $\sqrt{6a}\sqrt{18a}$

73. $\sqrt{2t}\sqrt{2t}$ **74.** $\sqrt{3a}\sqrt{3a}$ **75.** $\sqrt{ab}\sqrt{ac}$

76. $\sqrt{xy}\sqrt{xz}$ **77.** $\sqrt{2x^2y}\sqrt{4xy^2}$ **78.** $\sqrt{15mn^2}\sqrt{5m^2n}$

ANSWERS

53. _____

54. _____

55. _____

56. _____

57. _____

58. _____

59. _____

60. _____

61. _____

62. _____

63. _____

64. _____

65. _____

66. _____

67. _____

68. _____

69. _____

70. _____

71. _____

72. _____

73. _____

74. _____

75. _____

76. _____

77. _____

78. _____

79. $\sqrt{18}\sqrt{18}$ **80.** $\sqrt{16}\sqrt{16}$ **81.** $\sqrt{5}\sqrt{2x-1}$

82. $\sqrt{3}\sqrt{4x+2}$ **83.** $\sqrt{x+2}\sqrt{x+2}$ **84.** $\sqrt{x-3}\sqrt{x-3}$

85. $\sqrt{18x^2y^3}\sqrt{6xy^4}$ **86.** $\sqrt{12x^3y^2}\sqrt{8xy}$

87. $\sqrt{50ab}\sqrt{10a^2b^4}$ **88.** $\sqrt{10xy^2}\sqrt{5x^2y^3}$

SKILL MAINTENANCE

Solve.

89. $x - y = 7,$ **90.** $3x + 5y = 6,$
$\quad\ x + y = 9$ $\qquad\ 5x + 3y = 4$

91. The perimeter of a rectangle is 642 ft. The length is 15 ft greater than the width. Find the area of the rectangle.

SYNTHESIS

Factor.

92. $\sqrt{3x-3}$ **93.** $\sqrt{x^2-x-2}$ **94.** $\sqrt{x^2-4}$
95. $\sqrt{2x^2-5x-12}$ **96.** $\sqrt{x^3-2x^2}$ **97.** $\sqrt{a^2-b^2}$

Simplify.

98. $\sqrt{0.01}$ **99.** $\sqrt{0.25}$ **100.** $\sqrt{x^8}$ **101.** $\sqrt{9a^6}$

102. Find $\sqrt{49}$, $\sqrt{490}$, $\sqrt{4900}$, $\sqrt{49,000}$, $\sqrt{490,000}$. What pattern do you see?

Use the proper symbol ($>$, $<$, or $=$) between each pair of values to make a true sentence.

103. 15 $4\sqrt{14}$ **104.** $15\sqrt{2}$ $\sqrt{450}$ **105.** 16 $\sqrt{15}\sqrt{17}$
106. $3\sqrt{11}$ $7\sqrt{2}$ **107.** $5\sqrt{7}$ $4\sqrt{11}$ **108.** 8 $\sqrt{15}+\sqrt{17}$

Multiply and then simplify by factoring.

109. $(\sqrt{2y})(\sqrt{3})(\sqrt{8y})$ **110.** $\sqrt{a}(\sqrt{a^3}-5)$
111. $\sqrt{27(x+1)}\sqrt{12y(x+1)^2}$ **112.** $\sqrt{18(x-2)}\sqrt{20(x-2)^3}$
113. $\sqrt{x}\sqrt{2x}\sqrt{10x^5}$ **114.** $\sqrt{2^{109}}\sqrt{x^{306}}\sqrt{x^{11}}$

Simplify.

115. $\sqrt{x^{8n}}$ **116.** $\sqrt{0.04x^{4n}}$

117. Determine whether it is true that $\sqrt{A}-\sqrt{B}=\sqrt{A-B}$.

14.3 Quotients Involving Square Roots

a Dividing Radical Expressions

Consider the expressions

$$\frac{\sqrt{25}}{\sqrt{16}} \quad \text{and} \quad \sqrt{\frac{25}{16}}.$$

Let us evaluate them separately:

a) $\dfrac{\sqrt{25}}{\sqrt{16}} = \dfrac{5}{4}$ since $\sqrt{25} = 5$ and $\sqrt{16} = 4$;

b) $\sqrt{\dfrac{25}{16}} = \dfrac{5}{4}$ because $\dfrac{5}{4} \cdot \dfrac{5}{4} = \dfrac{25}{16}$.

We see that both expressions represent the same number. This suggests that the quotient of two square roots is the square root of the quotient of the radicands.

The Quotient Rules for Radicals

For any nonnegative number A and any positive number B,

$$\frac{\sqrt{A}}{\sqrt{B}} = \sqrt{\frac{A}{B}}.$$

(The quotient of two square roots, provided they exist, is the square root of the quotients of the radicands.)

▶ **EXAMPLES** Divide and simplify.

1. $\dfrac{\sqrt{27}}{\sqrt{3}} = \sqrt{\dfrac{27}{3}} = \sqrt{9} = 3$

2. $\dfrac{\sqrt{30a^5}}{\sqrt{6a^2}} = \sqrt{\dfrac{30a^5}{6a^2}} = \sqrt{5a^3} = \sqrt{a^2 \cdot 5a} = \sqrt{a^2} \cdot \sqrt{5a} = a\sqrt{5a}$ ◀

DO EXERCISES 1–3.

b Roots of Quotients

To find the square root of a quotient, we can reverse the quotient rule for radicals. We can take the square root of a quotient by taking the square roots of the numerator and the denominator separately.

For any nonnegative number A and any positive number B,

$$\sqrt{\frac{A}{B}} = \frac{\sqrt{A}}{\sqrt{B}}.$$

(We can take the square roots of the numerator and the denominator separately.)

OBJECTIVES

After finishing Section 14.3, you should be able to:

a Divide radical expressions with fractional radicands.

b Simplify square roots of quotients.

c Rationalize the denominator of a radical expression.

d Approximate radical expressions involving division.

FOR EXTRA HELP

Tape 27C

Divide and simplify.

1. $\dfrac{\sqrt{48}}{\sqrt{3}}$

2. $\dfrac{\sqrt{75}}{\sqrt{3}}$

3. $\dfrac{\sqrt{42x^5}}{\sqrt{7x^2}}$

ANSWERS ON PAGE A-11

Simplify.

4. $\sqrt{\dfrac{16}{9}}$

5. $\sqrt{\dfrac{1}{25}}$

6. $\sqrt{\dfrac{36}{x^2}}$

Simplify.

7. $\sqrt{\dfrac{18}{32}}$

8. $\sqrt{\dfrac{2250}{2560}}$

9. $\sqrt{\dfrac{75x}{3x^7}}$

▶ **EXAMPLES**　Simplify by taking the square roots of the numerator and the denominator separately.

3. $\sqrt{\dfrac{25}{9}} = \dfrac{\sqrt{25}}{\sqrt{9}} = \dfrac{5}{3}$　　Taking the square roots of the numerator and the denominator

4. $\sqrt{\dfrac{1}{16}} = \dfrac{\sqrt{1}}{\sqrt{16}} = \dfrac{1}{4}$　　Taking the square roots of the numerator and the denominator

5. $\sqrt{\dfrac{49}{t^2}} = \dfrac{\sqrt{49}}{\sqrt{t^2}} = \dfrac{7}{t}$　　◀

DO EXERCISES 4–6.

We are assuming that expressions for numerators are nonnegative and expressions for denominators are positive. Thus we need not be concerned about absolute-value signs or zero denominators.

Sometimes a rational expression can be simplified to one that has a perfect-square numerator and a perfect-square denominator.

▶ **EXAMPLES**　Simplify.

6. $\sqrt{\dfrac{18}{50}} = \sqrt{\dfrac{9 \cdot 2}{25 \cdot 2}} = \sqrt{\dfrac{9}{25} \cdot \dfrac{2}{2}} = \sqrt{\dfrac{9}{25} \cdot 1} = \sqrt{\dfrac{9}{25}} = \dfrac{\sqrt{9}}{\sqrt{25}} = \dfrac{3}{5}$

7. $\sqrt{\dfrac{2560}{2890}} = \sqrt{\dfrac{256 \cdot 10}{289 \cdot 10}} = \sqrt{\dfrac{256}{289} \cdot \dfrac{10}{10}} = \sqrt{\dfrac{256}{289} \cdot 1} = \sqrt{\dfrac{256}{289}} = \dfrac{\sqrt{256}}{\sqrt{289}} = \dfrac{16}{17}$

8. $\dfrac{\sqrt{48x^3}}{\sqrt{3x^7}} = \sqrt{\dfrac{48x^3}{3x^7}} = \sqrt{\dfrac{16}{x^4}} = \dfrac{\sqrt{16}}{\sqrt{x^4}} = \dfrac{4}{x^2}$　　◀

DO EXERCISES 7–9.

c　**Rationalizing Denominators**

Sometimes in mathematics it is useful to find an equivalent expression without a radical in the denominator. This provides a standard notation for expressing results. The procedure for finding such an expression is called **rationalizing the denominator.** We carry this out by multiplying by 1 in either of two ways. One way is to multiply by 1 under the radical to make the denominator a perfect square. Another way is to multiply by 1 outside the radical to make the denominator a perfect square.

ANSWERS ON PAGE A-11

▶ **EXAMPLE 9** Rationalize the denominator: $\sqrt{\dfrac{2}{3}}$.

Method 1. We multiply by 1, choosing $\frac{3}{3}$ for 1. This makes the denominator a perfect square:

$$\sqrt{\frac{2}{3}} = \sqrt{\frac{2}{3} \cdot \frac{3}{3}} \quad \text{Multiplying by 1}$$
$$= \sqrt{\frac{6}{9}}$$
$$= \frac{\sqrt{6}}{\sqrt{9}}$$
$$= \frac{\sqrt{6}}{3}.$$

Method 2. We can also rationalize by first taking the square roots of the numerator and the denominator. Then we multiply by 1, using $\sqrt{3}/\sqrt{3}$:

$$\sqrt{\frac{2}{3}} = \frac{\sqrt{2}}{\sqrt{3}} = \frac{\sqrt{2}}{\sqrt{3}} \cdot \frac{\sqrt{3}}{\sqrt{3}} = \frac{\sqrt{2} \cdot \sqrt{3}}{\sqrt{3} \cdot \sqrt{3}} = \frac{\sqrt{6}}{\sqrt{9}} = \frac{\sqrt{6}}{3}.$$ ◄

DO EXERCISE 10.

We can always multiply by 1 to make a denominator a perfect square. Then we can take the square root of the denominator.

▶ **EXAMPLE 10** Rationalize the denominator: $\sqrt{\dfrac{5}{18}}$.

The denominator 18 is not a perfect square. Factoring, we get $18 = 3 \cdot 3 \cdot 2$. If we had another factor of 2, however, we would have a perfect square, 36. Thus we multiply by 1, choosing $\frac{2}{2}$. This makes the denominator a perfect square.

$$\sqrt{\frac{5}{18}} = \sqrt{\frac{5}{18} \cdot \frac{2}{2}} = \sqrt{\frac{10}{36}} = \frac{\sqrt{10}}{\sqrt{36}} = \frac{\sqrt{10}}{6}$$ ◄

▶ **EXAMPLE 11** Rationalize the denominator: $\dfrac{8}{\sqrt{7}}$.

This time we obtain an expression without a radical in the denominator by multiplying by 1, choosing $\sqrt{7}/\sqrt{7}$:

$$\frac{8}{\sqrt{7}} = \frac{8}{\sqrt{7}} \cdot \frac{\sqrt{7}}{\sqrt{7}} = \frac{8\sqrt{7}}{\sqrt{49}} = \frac{8\sqrt{7}}{7}.$$ ◄

DO EXERCISES 11 AND 12.

10. Rationalize the denominator:
$$\sqrt{\frac{3}{5}}.$$

Rationalize the denominator.
11. $\sqrt{\dfrac{5}{8}}$
(*Hint:* Multiply the radicand by $\frac{2}{2}$.)

12. $\dfrac{2}{\sqrt{3}}$

ANSWERS ON PAGE A-11

Rationalize the denominator.

13. $\dfrac{\sqrt{5}}{\sqrt{7}}$

14. $\dfrac{\sqrt{3}}{\sqrt{t}}$

15. $\dfrac{\sqrt{64y^2}}{\sqrt{7}}$

Approximate to three decimal places.

16. $\sqrt{\dfrac{2}{3}}$

17. $\dfrac{\sqrt{14}}{\sqrt{11}}$

▶ **EXAMPLE 12**   Rationalize the denominator: $\dfrac{\sqrt{3}}{\sqrt{2}}$.

We look at the denominator. It is $\sqrt{2}$. We multiply by 1, choosing $\sqrt{2}/\sqrt{2}$:

$$\frac{\sqrt{3}}{\sqrt{2}} = \frac{\sqrt{3}}{\sqrt{2}} \cdot \frac{\sqrt{2}}{\sqrt{2}} = \frac{\sqrt{3} \cdot \sqrt{2}}{\sqrt{2} \cdot \sqrt{2}} = \frac{\sqrt{6}}{2}, \quad \text{or} \quad \frac{1}{2}\sqrt{6}. \qquad ◀$$

▶ **EXAMPLES**   Rationalize the denominator.

13. $\dfrac{\sqrt{5}}{\sqrt{x}} = \dfrac{\sqrt{5}}{\sqrt{x}} \cdot \dfrac{\sqrt{x}}{\sqrt{x}}$ **Multiplying by 1**

$\qquad = \dfrac{\sqrt{5}\,\sqrt{x}}{\sqrt{x}\,\sqrt{x}}$

$\qquad = \dfrac{\sqrt{5x}}{x}$

14. $\dfrac{\sqrt{49a^5}}{\sqrt{12}} = \dfrac{\sqrt{49a^5}}{\sqrt{12}} \cdot \dfrac{\sqrt{3}}{\sqrt{3}} = \dfrac{\sqrt{49a^5}\,\sqrt{3}}{\sqrt{12}\,\sqrt{3}}$

$\qquad = \dfrac{\sqrt{49a^4 \cdot 3a}}{\sqrt{36}} = \dfrac{7a^2\sqrt{3a}}{6}$ ◀

DO EXERCISES 13–15.

d   **Approximating Expressions with Square Roots**

We can use a calculator or Table 2 to approximate square roots of quotients. There are at least two ways to do it.

▶ **EXAMPLE 15**   Approximate $\sqrt{\frac{3}{5}}$ to three decimal places.

Method 1.   Suppose we are using a calculator. We divide and then approximate the square root:

$$\sqrt{\frac{3}{5}} = \sqrt{0.6} \approx 0.774596669 \approx 0.775.$$

Method 2.   Suppose we are using a table like Table 2. We first rationalize the denominator and then use Table 2 to approximate the square root in the numerator. Then we divide:

$$\sqrt{\frac{3}{5}} = \sqrt{\frac{3}{5} \cdot \frac{5}{5}} = \sqrt{\frac{15}{25}} = \frac{\sqrt{15}}{\sqrt{25}} = \frac{\sqrt{15}}{5} \approx \frac{3.873}{5} \approx 0.775. \qquad \begin{smallmatrix}\textbf{Rounding to}\\\textbf{three decimal}\\\textbf{places}\end{smallmatrix} \quad ◀$$

DO EXERCISES 16 AND 17.

EXERCISE SET 14.3

a Divide and simplify.

1. $\dfrac{\sqrt{18}}{\sqrt{2}}$

2. $\dfrac{\sqrt{20}}{\sqrt{5}}$

3. $\dfrac{\sqrt{60}}{\sqrt{15}}$

4. $\dfrac{\sqrt{108}}{\sqrt{3}}$

5. $\dfrac{\sqrt{75}}{\sqrt{15}}$

6. $\dfrac{\sqrt{18}}{\sqrt{3}}$

7. $\dfrac{\sqrt{3}}{\sqrt{75}}$

8. $\dfrac{\sqrt{3}}{\sqrt{48}}$

9. $\dfrac{\sqrt{12}}{\sqrt{75}}$

10. $\dfrac{\sqrt{18}}{\sqrt{32}}$

11. $\dfrac{\sqrt{8x}}{\sqrt{2x}}$

12. $\dfrac{\sqrt{18b}}{\sqrt{2b}}$

13. $\dfrac{\sqrt{63y^3}}{\sqrt{7y}}$

14. $\dfrac{\sqrt{48x^3}}{\sqrt{3x}}$

b Simplify.

15. $\sqrt{\dfrac{9}{49}}$

16. $\sqrt{\dfrac{16}{25}}$

17. $\sqrt{\dfrac{1}{36}}$

18. $\sqrt{\dfrac{1}{4}}$

19. $-\sqrt{\dfrac{16}{81}}$

1. _____

2. _____

3. _____

4. _____

5. _____

6. _____

7. _____

8. _____

9. _____

10. _____

11. _____

12. _____

13. _____

14. _____

15. _____

16. _____

17. _____

18. _____

19. _____

20. _____

21. _____

22. _____

23. _____

24. _____

25. _____

26. _____

27. _____

28. _____

29. _____

30. _____

31. _____

32. _____

33. _____

34. _____

35. _____

36. _____

37. _____

38. _____

39. _____

40. _____

41. _____

42. _____

43. _____

44. _____

45. _____

46. _____

47. _____

48. _____

20. $-\sqrt{\dfrac{25}{49}}$ **21.** $\sqrt{\dfrac{64}{289}}$ **22.** $\sqrt{\dfrac{81}{361}}$ **23.** $\sqrt{\dfrac{1690}{1960}}$ **24.** $\sqrt{\dfrac{1440}{6250}}$

25. $\sqrt{\dfrac{36}{a^2}}$ **26.** $\sqrt{\dfrac{25}{x^2}}$ **27.** $\sqrt{\dfrac{9a^2}{625}}$ **28.** $\sqrt{\dfrac{x^2y^2}{256}}$

C   Rationalize the denominator.

29. $\sqrt{\dfrac{2}{5}}$ **30.** $\sqrt{\dfrac{2}{7}}$ **31.** $\sqrt{\dfrac{3}{8}}$ **32.** $\sqrt{\dfrac{7}{8}}$ **33.** $\sqrt{\dfrac{7}{12}}$

34. $\sqrt{\dfrac{1}{12}}$ **35.** $\sqrt{\dfrac{1}{18}}$ **36.** $\sqrt{\dfrac{5}{18}}$ **37.** $\dfrac{3}{\sqrt{5}}$ **38.** $\dfrac{4}{\sqrt{3}}$

39. $\sqrt{\dfrac{8}{3}}$ **40.** $\sqrt{\dfrac{12}{5}}$ **41.** $\sqrt{\dfrac{3}{x}}$ **42.** $\sqrt{\dfrac{2}{x}}$ **43.** $\sqrt{\dfrac{x}{y}}$

44. $\sqrt{\dfrac{a}{b}}$ **45.** $\sqrt{\dfrac{x^2}{18}}$ **46.** $\sqrt{\dfrac{x^2}{20}}$ **47.** $\dfrac{\sqrt{7}}{\sqrt{3}}$ **48.** $\dfrac{\sqrt{2}}{\sqrt{5}}$

49. $\dfrac{\sqrt{9}}{\sqrt{8}}$

50. $\dfrac{\sqrt{4}}{\sqrt{27}}$

51. $\dfrac{\sqrt{2}}{\sqrt{5}}$

52. $\dfrac{\sqrt{3}}{\sqrt{2}}$

53. $\dfrac{2}{\sqrt{2}}$

54. $\dfrac{3}{\sqrt{3}}$

55. $\dfrac{\sqrt{5}}{\sqrt{11}}$

56. $\dfrac{\sqrt{7}}{\sqrt{27}}$

57. $\dfrac{\sqrt{7}}{\sqrt{12}}$

58. $\dfrac{\sqrt{5}}{\sqrt{18}}$

59. $\dfrac{\sqrt{48}}{\sqrt{32}}$

60. $\dfrac{\sqrt{56}}{\sqrt{40}}$

61. $\dfrac{\sqrt{450}}{\sqrt{18}}$

62. $\dfrac{\sqrt{224}}{\sqrt{14}}$

63. $\dfrac{\sqrt{3}}{\sqrt{x}}$

64. $\dfrac{\sqrt{2}}{\sqrt{y}}$

65. $\dfrac{4y}{\sqrt{3}}$

66. $\dfrac{8x}{\sqrt{5}}$

67. $\dfrac{\sqrt{a^3}}{\sqrt{8}}$

68. $\dfrac{\sqrt{x^3}}{\sqrt{27}}$

69. $\dfrac{\sqrt{56}}{\sqrt{12x}}$

70. $\dfrac{\sqrt{45}}{\sqrt{8a}}$

71. $\dfrac{\sqrt{27c}}{\sqrt{32c^3}}$

72. $\dfrac{\sqrt{7x^3}}{\sqrt{12x}}$

73. $\dfrac{\sqrt{y^5}}{\sqrt{xy^2}}$

74. $\dfrac{\sqrt{x^3}}{\sqrt{xy}}$

75. $\dfrac{\sqrt{16a^4b^6}}{\sqrt{128a^6b^6}}$

76. $\dfrac{\sqrt{45mn^2}}{\sqrt{32m}}$

ANSWERS

49. _____ 50. _____ 51. _____ 52. _____ 53. _____ 54. _____ 55. _____ 56. _____ 57. _____ 58. _____ 59. _____ 60. _____ 61. _____ 62. _____ 63. _____ 64. _____ 65. _____ 66. _____ 67. _____ 68. _____ 69. _____ 70. _____ 71. _____ 72. _____ 73. _____ 74. _____ 75. _____ 76. _____

d Approximate to three decimal places.

77. $\sqrt{\dfrac{1}{3}}$ **78.** $\sqrt{\dfrac{3}{2}}$ **79.** $\sqrt{\dfrac{7}{8}}$ **80.** $\sqrt{\dfrac{3}{8}}$ **81.** $\sqrt{\dfrac{1}{12}}$ **82.** $\sqrt{\dfrac{5}{12}}$

83. $\sqrt{\dfrac{1}{2}}$ **84.** $\sqrt{\dfrac{1}{7}}$ **85.** $\dfrac{17}{\sqrt{20}}$ **86.** $\dfrac{28}{\sqrt{13}}$ **87.** $\dfrac{\sqrt{13}}{\sqrt{18}}$ **88.** $\dfrac{\sqrt{11}}{\sqrt{18}}$

SKILL MAINTENANCE

Solve.

89. $x = y + 2,$
$\quad x + y = 6$

90. $2x - 3y = 7,$
$\quad 2x + 3y = 9$

91. $2x - 3y = 7,$
$\quad 2x - 3y = 9$

92. $2x - 3y = 7,$
$\quad -4x + 6y = -14$

SYNTHESIS

The period T of a pendulum is the time it takes to move from one side to the other and back. A formula for the period is

$$T = 2\pi\sqrt{\dfrac{L}{32}},$$

where T is in seconds and L is in feet. Use 3.14 for π.

93. Find the periods of pendulums of lengths 2 ft, 8 ft, 64 ft, and 100 ft.

94. Find the period of a pendulum of length $\frac{2}{3}$ in.

95. The pendulum of a grandfather clock is $(32/\pi^2)$ ft long. How long does it take to swing from one side to the other?

96. The pendulum of a grandfather clock is $(45/\pi^2)$ ft long. How long does it take to swing from one side to the other?

Rationalize the denominator.

97. $\sqrt{\dfrac{5}{1600}}$ **98.** $\sqrt{\dfrac{3}{1000}}$ **99.** $\sqrt{\dfrac{1}{5x^3}}$ **100.** $\sqrt{\dfrac{3x^2y}{a^2x^5}}$

101. $\sqrt{\dfrac{3a}{b}}$ **102.** $\sqrt{\dfrac{1}{5zw^2}}$ **103.** $\sqrt{0.007}$ **104.** $\sqrt{0.012}$

Simplify.

105. $\sqrt{\dfrac{1}{x^2} - \dfrac{2}{xy} + \dfrac{1}{y^2}}$

106. $\sqrt{2 - \dfrac{4}{z^2} + \dfrac{2}{z^4}}$

14.4 Addition, Subtraction, and More Multiplication

a Addition and Subtraction

We can add any two real numbers. The sum of 5 and $\sqrt{2}$ can be expressed as

$$5 + \sqrt{2}.$$

We cannot simplify this unless we use rational approximations. However, when we have *like radicals*, a sum can be simplified using the distributive laws and collecting like terms. **Like radicals** have the same radicands.

▶ **EXAMPLE 1** Add: $3\sqrt{5} + 4\sqrt{5}$.

Suppose we were considering $3x + 4x$. Recall that to add, we use the distributive laws as follows:

$$3x + 4x = (3 + 4)x = 7x.$$

The situation is similar in this example, but we let $x = \sqrt{5}$:

$$3\sqrt{5} + 4\sqrt{5} = (3 + 4)\sqrt{5} \qquad \text{Using the distributive law to factor out } \sqrt{5}$$
$$= 7\sqrt{5}. \qquad\qquad◀$$

To add or subtract as we did in Example 1, the radicands must be the same. Sometimes after simplifying the radical terms, we discover that we have like radicals.

▶ **EXAMPLES** Add or subtract. Simplify, if possible, by collecting like radical terms.

2. $5\sqrt{2} - \sqrt{18} = 5\sqrt{2} - \sqrt{9 \cdot 2} \qquad \text{Factoring 18}$
$$= 5\sqrt{2} - \sqrt{9}\sqrt{2}$$
$$= 5\sqrt{2} - 3\sqrt{2}$$
$$= (5 - 3)\sqrt{2} \qquad \text{Using the distributive law to factor out the common factor, } \sqrt{2}$$
$$= 2\sqrt{2}$$

3. $\sqrt{4x^3} + 7\sqrt{x} = \sqrt{4x^2 \cdot x} + 7\sqrt{x}$
$$= 2x\sqrt{x} + 7\sqrt{x}$$
$$= (2x + 7)\sqrt{x} \qquad \text{Using the distributive law to factor out } \sqrt{x}$$

Don't forget the parentheses!

4. $\sqrt{x^3 - x^2} + \sqrt{4x - 4} = \sqrt{x^2(x - 1)} + \sqrt{4(x - 1)} \qquad \text{Factoring radicands}$
$$= \sqrt{x^2}\sqrt{x - 1} + \sqrt{4}\sqrt{x - 1}$$
$$= x\sqrt{x - 1} + 2\sqrt{x - 1}$$
$$= (x + 2)\sqrt{x - 1} \qquad \text{Using the distributive law to factor out the common factor, } \sqrt{x - 1}$$

Don't forget the parentheses! ◀

DO EXERCISES 1–5.

OBJECTIVES

After finishing Section 14.4, you should be able to:

a Add or subtract with radical notation, using the distributive law to simplify.

b Multiply expressions involving radicals, where some of the expressions contain more than one term.

c Rationalize denominators having two terms.

FOR EXTRA HELP

Tape 27D

Add or subtract and simplify by collecting like radical terms, if possible.

1. $3\sqrt{2} + 9\sqrt{2}$

2. $8\sqrt{5} - 3\sqrt{5}$

3. $2\sqrt{10} - 7\sqrt{40}$

4. $\sqrt{24} + \sqrt{54}$

5. $\sqrt{9x + 9} - \sqrt{4x + 4}$

ANSWERS ON PAGE A-12

Add or subtract.

6. $\sqrt{2} + \sqrt{\dfrac{1}{2}}$

Sometimes rationalizing denominators enables us to combine like radicals.

▶ **EXAMPLE 5**   Add: $\sqrt{3} + \sqrt{\dfrac{1}{3}}$.

$$\sqrt{3} + \sqrt{\frac{1}{3}} = \sqrt{3} + \sqrt{\frac{1}{3} \cdot \frac{3}{3}} \qquad \text{Multiplying by 1 in order to rationalize denominators}$$

$$= \sqrt{3} + \sqrt{\frac{3}{9}}$$

$$= \sqrt{3} + \frac{\sqrt{3}}{\sqrt{9}}$$

$$= \sqrt{3} + \frac{\sqrt{3}}{3}$$

$$= 1 \cdot \sqrt{3} + \frac{1}{3}\sqrt{3}$$

$$= \left(1 + \frac{1}{3}\right)\sqrt{3} \qquad \text{Factoring out the common factor, } \sqrt{3}$$

$$= \frac{4}{3}\sqrt{3} \qquad\qquad\qquad\qquad ◀$$

DO EXERCISES 6 AND 7.

7. $\sqrt{\dfrac{5}{3}} + \sqrt{\dfrac{3}{5}}$

b   Multiplication

Now let us multiply where some of the expressions may contain more than one term. To do this, we use procedures already studied in this chapter as well as the distributive law and special products for multiplying with polynomials.

▶ **EXAMPLE 6**   Multiply: $\sqrt{2}(\sqrt{3} + \sqrt{7})$.

$$\sqrt{2}(\sqrt{3} + \sqrt{7}) = \sqrt{2}\sqrt{3} + \sqrt{2}\sqrt{7} \qquad \text{Multiplying using a distributive law}$$

$$= \sqrt{6} + \sqrt{14} \qquad \text{Using the rule for multiplying with radicals} ◀$$

▶ **EXAMPLE 7**   Multiply: $(2 + \sqrt{3})(5 - 4\sqrt{3})$.

$$(2 + \sqrt{3})(5 - 4\sqrt{3}) = 2 \cdot 5 - 2 \cdot 4\sqrt{3} + \sqrt{3} \cdot 5 - \sqrt{3} \cdot 4\sqrt{3} \qquad \text{Using FOIL}$$

$$= 10 - 8\sqrt{3} + 5\sqrt{3} - 4 \cdot 3$$

$$= 10 - 12 - 3\sqrt{3}$$

$$= -2 - 3\sqrt{3} \qquad\qquad ◀$$

▶ **EXAMPLE 8**   Multiply: $(\sqrt{3} - \sqrt{x})(\sqrt{3} + \sqrt{x})$.

$(\sqrt{3} - \sqrt{x})(\sqrt{3} + \sqrt{x}) = (\sqrt{3})^2 - (\sqrt{x})^2$ Using $(A - B)(A + B) = A^2 - B^2$

$= 3 - x$ ◀

▶ **EXAMPLE 9**   Multiply: $(3 - \sqrt{p})^2$.

$(3 - \sqrt{p})^2 = 3^2 - 2 \cdot 3 \cdot \sqrt{p} + (\sqrt{p})^2$ Using $(A - B)^2 = A^2 - 2AB + B^2$

$= 9 - 6\sqrt{6} + p$ ◀

▶ **EXAMPLE 10**   Multiply: $(2 - \sqrt{5})(2 + \sqrt{5})$.

$(2 - \sqrt{5})(2 + \sqrt{5}) = 2^2 - (\sqrt{5})^2$ Using $(A - B)(A + B) = A^2 - B^2$

$= 4 - 5$

$= -1$ ◀

DO EXERCISES 8–12.

c   More Rationalizing Denominators

Note in Example 10 that the result has no radicals. This will happen whenever we multiply expressions such as $\sqrt{a} - \sqrt{b}$ and $\sqrt{a} + \sqrt{b}$, where a and b are rational numbers. We see this in the following:

$$(\sqrt{a} + \sqrt{b})(\sqrt{a} - \sqrt{b}) = (\sqrt{a})^2 - (\sqrt{b})^2 = a - b.$$

Expressions such as $\sqrt{3} - \sqrt{5}$ and $\sqrt{3} + \sqrt{5}$ are known as **conjugates;** so too are $2 + \sqrt{5}$ and $2 - \sqrt{5}$. We can use conjugates to rationalize a denominator that involves a sum or difference of two terms, where one or both are radicals. To do so, we multiply by 1 using the conjugate in the numerator and the denominator.

▶ **EXAMPLE 11**   Rationalize the denominator: $\dfrac{3}{2 + \sqrt{5}}$.

We multiply by 1 using the conjugate of $2 + \sqrt{5}$, which is $2 - \sqrt{5}$, as the numerator and the denominator:

$\dfrac{3}{2 + \sqrt{5}} = \dfrac{3}{2 + \sqrt{5}} \cdot \dfrac{2 - \sqrt{5}}{2 - \sqrt{5}}$ **Multiplying by 1**

$= \dfrac{3(2 - \sqrt{5})}{(2 + \sqrt{5})(2 - \sqrt{5})}$ **Multiplying**

$= \dfrac{6 - 3\sqrt{5}}{2^2 - (\sqrt{5})^2}$

$= \dfrac{6 - 3\sqrt{5}}{4 - 5}$

$= \dfrac{6 - 3\sqrt{5}}{-1}$

$= -6 + 3\sqrt{5}$, or $3\sqrt{5} - 6$ ◀

Multiply.

8. $\sqrt{3}(\sqrt{5} + \sqrt{2})$

9. $(1 - \sqrt{2})(4 + 3\sqrt{5})$

10. $(\sqrt{2} + \sqrt{a})(\sqrt{2} - \sqrt{a})$

11. $(5 + \sqrt{x})^2$

12. $(3 - \sqrt{7})(3 + \sqrt{7})$

ANSWERS ON PAGE A-12

Rationalize the denominator.

13. $\dfrac{6}{7 + \sqrt{5}}$

14. $\dfrac{\sqrt{5} + \sqrt{2}}{\sqrt{5} - \sqrt{2}}$

▶ **EXAMPLE 12**   Rationalize the denominator: $\dfrac{\sqrt{3} + \sqrt{5}}{\sqrt{3} - \sqrt{5}}$.

We multiply by 1 using the conjugate of $\sqrt{3} - \sqrt{5}$, which is $\sqrt{3} + \sqrt{5}$, as the numerator and the denominator:

$$\dfrac{\sqrt{3} + \sqrt{5}}{\sqrt{3} - \sqrt{5}} = \dfrac{\sqrt{3} + \sqrt{5}}{\sqrt{3} - \sqrt{5}} \cdot \dfrac{\sqrt{3} + \sqrt{5}}{\sqrt{3} + \sqrt{5}} \qquad \text{Multiplying by 1}$$

$$= \dfrac{(\sqrt{3} + \sqrt{5})^2}{(\sqrt{3} - \sqrt{5})(\sqrt{3} + \sqrt{5})}$$

$$= \dfrac{(\sqrt{3})^2 + 2\sqrt{3}\sqrt{5} + (\sqrt{5})^2}{(\sqrt{3})^2 - (\sqrt{5})^2}$$

$$= \dfrac{3 + 2\sqrt{15} + 5}{3 - 5}$$

$$= \dfrac{8 + 2\sqrt{15}}{-2}$$

$$= \dfrac{2(4 + \sqrt{15})}{2(-1)} \qquad \text{Factoring in order to simplify}$$

$$= \dfrac{2}{2} \cdot \dfrac{4 + \sqrt{15}}{-1}$$

$$= \dfrac{4 + \sqrt{15}}{-1} = -4 - \sqrt{15}. \qquad ◀$$

ANSWERS ON PAGE A-12   **DO EXERCISES 13 AND 14.**

❖ **SIDELIGHTS**

▦ **Wind Chill Temperature**

Calculators are often used to approximate square roots. For example, using a calculator, we can approximate $\sqrt{73}$:

$$\sqrt{73} \approx 8.544003745.$$

Different calculators may give different numbers of digits in their readouts.

We can use approximations of square roots to consider an application involving the effect of wind on the feeling of cold in the winter. In cold weather, we feel colder when there is wind than when there is not. The **wind chill temperature** is what the temperature would have to be with no wind in order to give the same chilling effect. A formula for finding the wind chill temperature, T_w, is

$$T_w = 91.4 - \dfrac{(10.45 + 6.68\sqrt{v} - 0.447v)(457 - 5T)}{110},$$

where T is the actual temperature given by a thermometer, in degrees Fahrenheit, and v is the wind speed, in miles per hour.

EXERCISES

▦ Use a calculator to find the wind chill temperature in each case. You can find the square roots from Table 2. Round to the nearest degree.

1. $T = 30°\text{F}, \ v = 25$ mph
2. $T = 10°\text{F}, \ v = 25$ mph
3. $T = 20°\text{F}, \ v = 20$ mph
4. $T = 20°\text{F}, \ v = 40$ mph
5. $T = -10°\text{F}, \ v = 30$ mph
6. $T = -30°\text{F}, \ v = 30$ mph

EXERCISE SET 14.4

a Add or subtract. Simplify by collecting like radical terms, if possible.

1. $3\sqrt{2} + 4\sqrt{2}$

2. $8\sqrt{3} + 3\sqrt{3}$

3. $7\sqrt{5} - 3\sqrt{5}$

4. $8\sqrt{2} - 5\sqrt{2}$

5. $6\sqrt{x} + 7\sqrt{x}$

6. $9\sqrt{y} + 3\sqrt{y}$

7. $9\sqrt{x} - 11\sqrt{x}$

8. $6\sqrt{a} - 14\sqrt{a}$

9. $5\sqrt{8} + 15\sqrt{2}$

10. $3\sqrt{12} + 2\sqrt{3}$

11. $\sqrt{27} - 2\sqrt{3}$

12. $7\sqrt{50} - 3\sqrt{2}$

13. $\sqrt{45} - \sqrt{20}$

14. $\sqrt{27} - \sqrt{12}$

15. $\sqrt{72} + \sqrt{98}$

16. $\sqrt{45} + \sqrt{80}$

17. $2\sqrt{12} + \sqrt{27} - \sqrt{48}$

18. $9\sqrt{8} - \sqrt{72} + \sqrt{98}$

19. $3\sqrt{18} - 2\sqrt{32} - 5\sqrt{50}$

20. $\sqrt{18} - 3\sqrt{8} + \sqrt{50}$

21. $2\sqrt{27} - 3\sqrt{48} + 3\sqrt{12}$

22. $3\sqrt{48} - 2\sqrt{27} - 3\sqrt{12}$

23. $\sqrt{4x} + \sqrt{81x^3}$

24. $\sqrt{12x^2} + \sqrt{27}$

25. $\sqrt{27} - \sqrt{12x^2}$

26. $\sqrt{81x^3} - \sqrt{4x}$

27. $\sqrt{8x + 8} + \sqrt{2x + 2}$

28. $\sqrt{12x + 12} + \sqrt{3x + 3}$

29. $\sqrt{x^5 - x^2} + \sqrt{9x^3 - 9}$

30. $\sqrt{16x - 16} + \sqrt{25x^3 - 25x^2}$

31. $3x\sqrt{y^3x} - x\sqrt{yx^3} + y\sqrt{y^3x}$

32. $4a\sqrt{a^2b} + a\sqrt{a^2b^3} - 5\sqrt{b^3}$

33. $\sqrt{3} - \sqrt{\dfrac{1}{3}}$

34. $\sqrt{2} - \sqrt{\dfrac{1}{2}}$

35. $5\sqrt{2} + 3\sqrt{\dfrac{1}{2}}$

36. $4\sqrt{3} + 2\sqrt{\dfrac{1}{3}}$

ANSWERS

1. _____
2. _____
3. _____
4. _____
5. _____
6. _____
7. _____
8. _____
9. _____
10. _____
11. _____
12. _____
13. _____
14. _____
15. _____
16. _____
17. _____
18. _____
19. _____
20. _____
21. _____
22. _____
23. _____
24. _____
25. _____
26. _____
27. _____
28. _____
29. _____
30. _____
31. _____
32. _____
33. _____
34. _____
35. _____
36. _____

37. $\sqrt{\dfrac{2}{3}} - \sqrt{\dfrac{1}{6}}$ **38.** $\sqrt{\dfrac{1}{2}} - \sqrt{\dfrac{1}{8}}$ **39.** $\sqrt{\dfrac{1}{12}} - \sqrt{\dfrac{1}{27}}$ **40.** $\sqrt{\dfrac{5}{6}} - \sqrt{\dfrac{6}{5}}$

b   Multiply.

41. $(\sqrt{5} + 7)(\sqrt{5} - 7)$ **42.** $(1 + \sqrt{5})(1 - \sqrt{5})$

43. $(\sqrt{6} - \sqrt{3})(\sqrt{6} + \sqrt{3})$ **44.** $(\sqrt{2} + \sqrt{6})(\sqrt{2} - \sqrt{6})$

45. $(3\sqrt{5} - 2)(\sqrt{5} + 1)$ **46.** $(\sqrt{5} - 2\sqrt{2})(\sqrt{10} - 1)$

47. $(\sqrt{x} - \sqrt{y})^2$ **48.** $(\sqrt{w} + 11)^2$

c   Rationalize the denominator.

49. $\dfrac{2}{\sqrt{3} - \sqrt{5}}$ **50.** $\dfrac{5}{3 + \sqrt{7}}$ **51.** $\dfrac{\sqrt{3} - \sqrt{2}}{\sqrt{3} + \sqrt{2}}$ **52.** $\dfrac{2 - \sqrt{7}}{\sqrt{3} - \sqrt{2}}$

53. $\dfrac{4}{\sqrt{10} + 1}$ **54.** $\dfrac{6}{\sqrt{11} - 3}$ **55.** $\dfrac{1 - \sqrt{7}}{3 + \sqrt{7}}$ **56.** $\dfrac{2 + \sqrt{8}}{1 - \sqrt{5}}$

SKILL MAINTENANCE

57. The time t it takes a bus to travel a fixed distance varies inversely as its speed r. At a speed of 40 mph, it takes $\frac{1}{2}$ hr to travel a fixed distance. How long will it take to travel the same distance at 60 mph? Describe the variation constant.

58. Solution A is 3% alcohol, and solution B is 6% alcohol. A service station attendant wants to mix the two to get 80 gal of a solution that is 5.4% alcohol. How many gallons of each should the attendant use?

SYNTHESIS

59. Three students were asked to simplify $\sqrt{10} + \sqrt{50}$. Their answers were $\sqrt{10}(1 + \sqrt{5})$, $\sqrt{10} + 5\sqrt{2}$, and $\sqrt{2}(5 + \sqrt{5})$. Which, if any, are correct?

Add or subtract.

60. $\frac{3}{5}\sqrt{24} + \frac{2}{5}\sqrt{150} - \sqrt{96}$ **61.** $\frac{1}{3}\sqrt{27} + \sqrt{8} + \sqrt{300} - \sqrt{18} - \sqrt{162}$

62. Evaluate $\sqrt{a^2 + b^2}$ and $\sqrt{a^2} + \sqrt{b^2}$ for $a = 2$ and $b = 3$.

63. On the basis of Exercise 62, determine whether $\sqrt{a^2 + b^2}$ and $\sqrt{a^2} + \sqrt{b^2}$ are equivalent.

Determine whether each of the following is true. Show why or why not.

64. $(\sqrt{x + 2})^2 = x + 2$ **65.** $(3\sqrt{x + 2})^2 = 9(x + 2)$

14.5 Radical Equations

a Solving Radical Equations

The following are examples of *radical equations:*

$$\sqrt{2x - 4} = 7, \qquad \sqrt{x + 1} = \sqrt{2x - 5}.$$

A **radical equation** has variables in one or more radicands. To solve radical equations, we first convert them to equations without radicals. We do this by squaring both sides of the equation, using the following principle.

> The Principle of Squaring
>
> **If an equation $a = b$ is true, then the equation $a^2 = b^2$ is true.**

To solve radical equations, we first try to get a radical by itself. That is, we try to isolate the radical. Then we use the principle of squaring. This allows us to eliminate one radical.

▶ **EXAMPLE 1** Solve: $\sqrt{2x - 4} = 7$.

$$\sqrt{2x} - 4 = 7$$
$$\sqrt{2x} = 11 \qquad \text{Adding 4 to isolate the radical}$$
$$(\sqrt{2x})^2 = 11^2 \qquad \text{Squaring both sides}$$
$$2x = 121$$
$$x = \frac{121}{2}$$

Check:

$$\begin{array}{c|c} \sqrt{2x} - 4 = 7 & \\ \hline \sqrt{2 \cdot \dfrac{121}{2}} - 4 & 7 \\ \sqrt{121} - 4 & \\ 11 - 4 & \\ 7 & \text{TRUE} \end{array}$$

The solution is $\frac{121}{2}$. ◀

DO EXERCISE 1.

▶ **EXAMPLE 2** Solve: $2\sqrt{x + 2} = \sqrt{x + 10}$.

Each is already isolated. We proceed with the principle of squaring.

$$(2\sqrt{x + 2})^2 = (\sqrt{x + 10})^2 \qquad \text{Squaring both sides}$$
$$2^2(\sqrt{x + 2})^2 = x + 10 \qquad \begin{array}{l}\text{Raising the product to the power 2 on the left;}\\ \text{simplifying on the right}\end{array}$$
$$4(x + 2) = x + 10$$
$$4x + 8 = x + 10 \qquad \text{Removing parentheses}$$
$$3x = 2 \qquad \text{Subtracting } x \text{ and } 8$$
$$x = \frac{2}{3} \qquad \text{Dividing by 3}$$

OBJECTIVE

After finishing Section 14.5, you should be able to:

a Solve radical equations with one or more radical terms isolated, using the principle of squaring once.

b Solve radical expressions with two or more radical terms using the principle of squaring twice.

c Solve applied problems using radical equations.

FOR EXTRA HELP

Tape 27E

1. Solve: $\sqrt{3x} - 5 = 3$.

ANSWER ON PAGE A-12

Solve.

2. $\sqrt{3x + 1} = \sqrt{2x + 3}$

Check:

$$\dfrac{2\sqrt{x + 2} = \sqrt{x + 10}}{2\sqrt{\dfrac{2}{3} + 2} \;\Bigg|\; \sqrt{\dfrac{2}{3} + 10}}$$

$$2\sqrt{\dfrac{8}{3}} \;\Bigg|\; \sqrt{\dfrac{32}{3}}$$

$$4\sqrt{\dfrac{2}{3}} \;\Bigg|\; 4\sqrt{\dfrac{2}{3}} \qquad \text{TRUE}$$

The number $\frac{2}{3}$ checks. The solution is $\frac{2}{3}$.   ◀

DO EXERCISES 2 AND 3.

It is important to check when using the principle of squaring. This principle may not produce equivalent equations. When we square both sides of an equation, the new equation may have solutions that the first one does not. For example, the equation

$$x = 1 \qquad \textbf{(1)}$$

3. $3\sqrt{x + 1} = \sqrt{x + 12}$

has just one solution, the number 1. When we square both sides, we get

$$x^2 = 1, \qquad \textbf{(2)}$$

which has two solutions, 1 and -1. Thus the equations $x = 1$ and $x^2 = 1$ do not have the same solutions and thus are not equivalent. Whereas it is true that any solution of Equation (1) is a solution of Equation (2), it is not true that any solution of Equation (2) is a solution of Equation (1).

> **When the principle of squaring is used to solve an equation, solutions of an equation found by squaring *must* be checked in the original equation!**

Sometimes we may need to apply the principle of zero products after squaring. (See Section 4.7.)

4. Solve: $x - 1 = \sqrt{x + 5}$.

▶ **EXAMPLE 3**   Solve: $x - 5 = \sqrt{x + 7}$.

$$x - 5 = \sqrt{x + 7}$$
$$(x - 5)^2 = (\sqrt{x + 7})^2 \qquad \text{Using the principle of squaring}$$
$$x^2 - 10x + 25 = x + 7$$
$$x^2 - 11x + 18 = 0$$
$$(x - 9)(x - 2) = 0 \qquad \text{Factoring}$$
$$x - 9 = 0 \quad \text{or} \quad x - 2 = 0 \qquad \text{Using the principle of zero products}$$
$$x = 9 \quad \text{or} \qquad x = 2$$

Check:

$$\dfrac{x - 5 = \sqrt{x + 7}}{9 - 5 \;\Big|\; \sqrt{9 + 7}}$$
$$4 \;\Big|\; 4 \qquad \text{TRUE}$$

$$\dfrac{x - 5 = \sqrt{x + 7}}{2 - 5 \;\Big|\; \sqrt{2 + 7}}$$
$$-3 \;\Big|\; 3 \qquad \text{FALSE}$$

The number 9 checks, but 2 does not. Thus the solution is 9.   ◀

     DO EXERCISE 4.

▶ **EXAMPLE 4** Solve: $3 + \sqrt{27 - 3x} = x$.

In this case, we must first isolate the radical.

$$3 + \sqrt{27 - 3x} = x$$

$\sqrt{27 - 3x} = x - 3$ Subtracting 3 to isolate the radical

$(\sqrt{27 - 3x})^2 = (x - 3)^2$ Using the principle of squaring

$27 - 3x = x^2 - 6x + 9$

$0 = x^2 - 3x - 18$ We can have 0 on the left.

$0 = (x - 6)(x + 3)$ Factoring

$x - 6 = 0$ or $x + 3 = 0$ Using the principle of zero products

$x = 6$ or $x = -3$

Check:

$$\begin{array}{c|c} 3 + \sqrt{27 - 3x} = x & \\ \hline 3 + \sqrt{27 - 3 \cdot 6} & 6 \\ 3 + \sqrt{9} & \\ 3 + 3 & \\ 6 & \text{TRUE} \end{array}$$

$$\begin{array}{c|c} 3 + \sqrt{27 - 3x} = x & \\ \hline 3 + \sqrt{27 - 3 \cdot (-3)} & -3 \\ 3 + \sqrt{27 + 9} & \\ 3 + \sqrt{36} & \\ 3 + 6 & \\ 9 & \text{FALSE} \end{array}$$

The number 6 checks, but -3 does not. The solution is 6.   ◀

DO EXERCISE 5.

Suppose that in Example 4 we did not isolate the radical before squaring. Then we get an expression on the left side of the equation in which we have *not* eliminated the radical.

$$(3 + \sqrt{27 - 3x})^2 = (x)^2$$

$$3^2 + 2 \cdot 3 \cdot \sqrt{27 - 3x} + (\sqrt{27 - 3x})^2 = x^2$$

$$9 + 6\sqrt{27 - 3x} + (27 - 3x) = x^2$$

In fact, we have ended up with a more complicated expression than the one we squared.

b   Using the Principle of Squaring More Than Once

Sometimes when we have two radical terms, we may need to apply the principle of squaring a second time.

▶ **EXAMPLE 5** Solve: $\sqrt{x} - 1 = \sqrt{x - 5}$.

$$\sqrt{x} - 1 = \sqrt{x - 5}$$

$(\sqrt{x} - 1)^2 = (\sqrt{x - 5})^2$ Using the principle of squaring

$(\sqrt{x})^2 - 2 \cdot \sqrt{x} \cdot 1 + 1^2 = x - 5$ Using $(A + B)^2 = A^2 + 2AB = B^2$ on the left side

$x - 2\sqrt{x} + 1 = x - 5$ Simplifying

$-2\sqrt{x} = -6$ Isolating the radical

$\sqrt{x} = 3$

$(\sqrt{x})^2 = 3^2$ Using the principle of squaring

$x = 9$

The check is left to the student. The number 9 checks and is the solution.   ◀

5. Solve: $1 + \sqrt{1 - x} = x$.

ANSWER ON PAGE A-12

6. Solve: $\sqrt{x} - 1 = \sqrt{x - 3}$.

The following is a procedure for solving radical equations.

> **To solve radical equations:**
> 1. **Isolate one of the radical terms.**
> 2. **Use the principle of squaring.**
> 3. **If a radical term remains, perform steps (1) and (2) again.**
> 4. **Solve the equation and check possible solutions.**

DO EXERCISE 6.

c   Applications

How far can you see from a given height? There is a formula for this. At a height of h meters, you can see V kilometers to the horizon. These numbers are related as follows:

$$V = 3.5\sqrt{h}. \quad \textbf{(1)}$$

Earth

7. How far can you see to the horizon through an airplane window at a height of 8000 m?

▶ **EXAMPLE 6**   How far to the horizon can you see through an airplane window at a height, or altitude, of 9000 m?

We substitute 9000 for h in Equation (1) and find an approximation.

Method 1.   We use a calculator and approximate $\sqrt{9000}$ directly:

$$V = 3.5\sqrt{9000} \approx 3.5(94.868) = 332.038.$$

Method 2.   We simplify and then approximate:

$$V = 3.5\sqrt{9000} = 3.5\sqrt{900 \cdot 10} = 3.5 \times 30 \times \sqrt{10}$$
$$\approx 3.5 \times 30 \times 3.162 \approx 332.010 \text{ km.}$$

You can see about 332 km at a height of 9000 m.   ◀

8. How far can a sailor see to the horizon from the top of a 20-m mast?

DO EXERCISES 7 AND 8.

9. A sailor can see 91 km to the horizon from the top of a mast. How high is the mast?

▶ **EXAMPLE 7**   A person can see 50.4 km to the horizon from the top of a cliff. What is the altitude of the eyes of the person?

We substitute 50.4 for V in Equation (1) and solve:

$$50.4 = 3.5\sqrt{h}$$
$$\frac{50.4}{3.5} = \sqrt{h}$$
$$14.4 = \sqrt{h}$$
$$(14.4)^2 = (\sqrt{h})^2$$
$$207.36 = h.$$

50.4 km

The altitude of the eyes of the person is about 207 m.   ◀

DO EXERCISE 9.

EXERCISE SET 14.5

a Solve.

1. $\sqrt{x} = 5$

2. $\sqrt{x} = 7$

3. $\sqrt{x} = 6.2$

4. $\sqrt{x} = 4.3$

5. $\sqrt{x + 3} = 20$

6. $\sqrt{x + 4} = 11$

7. $\sqrt{2x + 4} = 25$

8. $\sqrt{2x + 1} = 13$

9. $3 + \sqrt{x - 1} = 5$

10. $4 + \sqrt{y - 3} = 11$

11. $6 - 2\sqrt{3n} = 0$

12. $8 - 4\sqrt{5n} = 0$

13. $\sqrt{5x - 7} = \sqrt{x + 10}$

14. $\sqrt{4x - 5} = \sqrt{x + 9}$

15. $\sqrt{x} = -7$

16. $\sqrt{x} = -5$

17. $\sqrt{2y + 6} = \sqrt{2y - 5}$

18. $2\sqrt{3x - 2} = \sqrt{2x - 3}$

19. $x - 7 = \sqrt{x - 5}$

20. $\sqrt{x + 7} = x - 5$

21. $\sqrt{x + 18} = x - 2$

22. $x - 9 = \sqrt{x - 3}$

23. $2\sqrt{x - 1} = x - 1$

24. $x + 4 = 4\sqrt{x + 1}$

25. $\sqrt{5x + 21} = x + 3$

26. $\sqrt{27 - 3x} = x - 3$

27. $x = 1 + 6\sqrt{x - 9}$

28. $\sqrt{2x - 1} + 2 = x$

29. $\sqrt{x^2 + 6} - x + 3 = 0$

ANSWERS

1. _____

2. _____

3. _____

4. _____

5. _____

6. _____

7. _____

8. _____

9. _____

10. _____

11. _____

12. _____

13. _____

14. _____

15. _____

16. _____

17. _____

18. _____

19. _____

20. _____

21. _____

22. _____

23. _____

24. _____

25. _____

26. _____

27. _____

28. _____

29. _____

30. $\sqrt{x^2 + 5} - x + 2 = 0$

31. $\sqrt{(p + 6)(p + 1)} - 2 = p + 1$

32. $\sqrt{(4x + 5)(x + 4)} = 2x + 5$

33. $\sqrt{2 - x} = \sqrt{3x - 7}$

34. $\sqrt{4x - 10} = \sqrt{2 - x}$

b Solve. Use the principle of squaring twice.

35. $\sqrt{x + 9} = 1 + \sqrt{x}$

36. $\sqrt{x - 5} = 5 - \sqrt{x}$

37. $\sqrt{3x + 1} = 1 - \sqrt{x + 4}$

38. $\sqrt{y + 8} - \sqrt{y} = 2$

c Solve.

Use $V = 3.5\sqrt{h}$ for Exercises 39–42.

39. How far can you see to the horizon through an airplane window at a height of 9800 m?

40. How far can a sailor see to the horizon from the top of a 24-m mast?

41. A person can see 371 km to the horizon from an airplane window. How high is the airplane?

42. A sailor can see 99.4 km to the horizon from the top of a mast. How high is the mast?

The formula $r = 2\sqrt{5L}$ can be used to approximate the speed r, in miles per hour, of a car that has left a skid mark of length L, in feet.

43. How far will a car skid at 50 mph? at 70 mph?

44. How far will a car skid at 60 mph? at 100 mph?

45. Find the number such that twice its square root is 14.

46. Find a number such that the square root of four more than five times the number is 8.

SKILL MAINTENANCE

Divide and simplify.

47. $\dfrac{x^2 - 49}{x + 8} \div \dfrac{x^2 - 14x + 49}{x^2 + 15x + 56}$

48. $\dfrac{x - 2}{x - 3} \div \dfrac{x - 4}{x - 5}$

49. Two angles are supplementary. One angle is 3° less than twice the other. Find the measures of the angles.

50. Two angles are complementary. The sum of the measure of the first angle and half the second is 64°. Find the measures of the angles.

SYNTHESIS

Solve.

51. $\sqrt{5x^2 + 5} = 5$

52. $\sqrt{x} = -x$

53. $4 + \sqrt{19 - x} = 6 + \sqrt{4 - x}$

54. $x = (x - 2)\sqrt{x}$

55. $\sqrt{x + 3} = \dfrac{8}{\sqrt{x - 9}}$

56. $\dfrac{12}{\sqrt{5x + 6}} = \sqrt{2x + 5}$

14.6 Right Triangles and Applications

a Right Triangles

A **right triangle** is a triangle with a 90° angle, as shown in the figure below. The small square in the corner indicates the 90° angle.

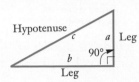

In a right triangle, the longest side is called the **hypotenuse.** It is also the side opposite the right angle. The other two sides are called **legs.** We generally use the letters a and b for the lengths of the legs and c for the length of the hypotenuse. They are related as follows.

> **The Pythagorean Theorem**
>
> **In any right triangle, if a and b are the lengths of the legs and c is the length of the hypotenuse, then**
> $$a^2 + b^2 = c^2.$$
> **The equation $a^2 + b^2 = c^2$ is called the *Pythagorean equation*.**

The Pythagorean theorem is named after the ancient Greek mathematician Pythagoras (569?–500? B.C.). It is uncertain who actually proved this result the first time. The proof can be found in most geometry books.

If we know the lengths of any two sides of a right triangle, we can find the length of the third side.

▶ **EXAMPLE 1** Find the length of the hypotenuse of this right triangle. Give an exact answer and an approximation to three decimal places.

$$4^2 + 5^2 = c^2 \qquad \text{Substituting in the Pythagorean equation}$$
$$16 + 25 = c^2$$
$$41 = c^2$$
$$c = \sqrt{41}$$
$$c \approx 6.403 \qquad \text{Using a calculator or Table 2}$$

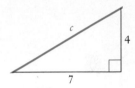

▶ **EXAMPLE 2** Find the length of the leg of this right triangle. Give an exact answer and an approximation to three decimal places.

$$10^2 + b^2 = 12^2 \qquad \text{Substituting in the Pythagorean equation}$$
$$100 + b^2 = 144$$
$$b^2 = 144 - 100$$
$$b^2 = 44$$
$$b^2 = \sqrt{44}$$
$$b \approx 6.633 \qquad \text{Using a calculator or Table 2}$$

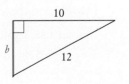

DO EXERCISES 1 AND 2.

OBJECTIVES

After finishing Section 14.6, you should be able to:

a Given the lengths of any two sides of a right triangle, find the length of the third side.

b Solve applied problems involving right triangles.

FOR EXTRA HELP

Tape 28A

1. Find the length of the hypotenuse of this right triangle. Give an exact answer and an approximation to three decimal places.

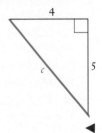

2. Find the length of the leg of this right triangle. Give an exact answer and an approximation to three decimal places.

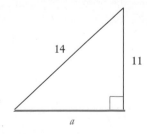

Find the length of the leg of the right triangle. Give an exact answer and an approximation to three decimal places.

3.

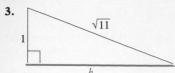

4.

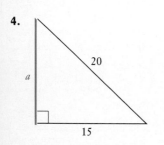

5. How long is a guy wire reaching from the top of a 15-ft pole to a point on the ground 10 ft from the pole? Give an exact answer and an approximation to three decimal places.

▶ **EXAMPLE 3** Find the length of the leg of this right triangle. Give an exact answer and an approximation to three decimal places.

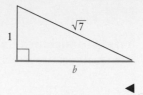

$$1^2 + b^2 = (\sqrt{7})^2 \qquad \text{Substituting in the Pythagorean equation}$$
$$1 + b^2 = 7$$
$$b^2 = 7 - 1 = 6$$
$$b = \sqrt{6} \approx 2.449 \qquad \text{Using a calculator or Table 2}$$ ◀

▶ **EXAMPLE 4** Find the length of the leg of this right triangle. Give an exact answer and an approximation to three decimal places.

$$a^2 + 10^2 = 15^2$$
$$a^2 + 100 = 225$$
$$a^2 = 225 - 100$$
$$a^2 = 125$$
$$a = \sqrt{125} \approx 11.180 \qquad \text{Using a calculator}$$ ◀

In Example 4, if you use Table 2 to find an approximation, you will need to simplify before finding an approximation:

$$\sqrt{125} = \sqrt{25 \cdot 5} = 5\sqrt{5} \approx 5(2.236) = 11.180.$$

A possible variance in answers can occur depending on the procedure used.

DO EXERCISES 3 AND 4.

b Applications

▶ **EXAMPLE 5** A slow-pitch softball diamond is actually a square 65 ft on a side. How far is it from home plate to second base? (This can be helpful information when lining up the bases.) Give an exact answer and an approximation to three decimal places.

a) We first make a drawing. We note that the first and second base lines, together with a line from home to second, form a right triangle. We label the unknown distance d.

b) We know that $65^2 + 65^2 = d^2$. We solve this equation:

$$4225 + 4225 = d^2$$
$$8450 = d^2.$$

Exact answer: $\sqrt{8450} = d$
Approximation: $91.924 \approx d$

If you use Table 2 to find an approximation, you will need to simplify before finding an approximation in the table:

$$d = \sqrt{8450} = \sqrt{25 \cdot 169 \cdot 2} = \sqrt{25}\sqrt{169}\sqrt{2}$$
$$\approx 5(13)(1.414) = 91.910.$$

Note that we get a variance in the last two decimal places.   ◀

DO EXERCISE 5.

NAME   SECTION   DATE

EXERCISE SET 14.6

a Find the length of the third side of the right triangle. Give an exact answer and an approximation to three decimal places.

1.

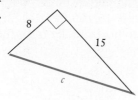

2.

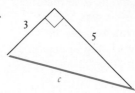

3.

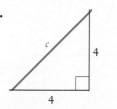

4.

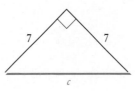

5.

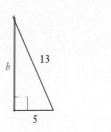

6.

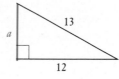

7.

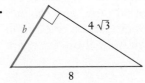

8.

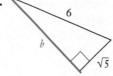

In a right triangle, find the length of the side not given. Give an exact answer and an approximation to three decimal places.

9. $a = 10$, $b = 24$

10. $a = 5$, $b = 12$

11. $a = 9$, $c = 15$

12. $a = 18$, $c = 30$

13. $b = 1$, $c = \sqrt{5}$

14. $b = 1$, $c = \sqrt{2}$

15. $a = 1$, $c = \sqrt{3}$

16. $a = \sqrt{3}$, $b = \sqrt{5}$

17. $c = 10$, $b = 5\sqrt{3}$

18. $a = 5$, $b = 5$

b Solve. Don't forget to make a drawing. Give an exact answer and an approximation to three decimal places.

19. A 10-m ladder is leaning against a building. The bottom of the ladder is 5 m from the building. How high is the top of the ladder?

20. Find the length of a diagonal of a square whose sides are 3 cm long.

1. _____

2. _____

3. _____

4. _____

5. _____

6. _____

7. _____

8. _____

9. _____

10. _____

11. _____

12. _____

13. _____

14. _____

15. _____

16. _____

17. _____

18. _____

19. _____

20. _____

21. How long is a guy wire reaching from the top of a 12-ft pole to a point 8 ft from the pole?

22. How long must a wire be to reach from the top of a 13-m telephone pole to a point on the ground 9 m from the foot of the pole?

23. A surveyor had poles located at points P, Q, and R. The distances that the surveyor was able to measure are marked on the drawing. What is the approximate distance from P to R?

24. An airplane is flying at an altitude of 4100 ft. The slanted distance directly to the airport is 15,100 ft. How far is the airplane horizontally from the airport?

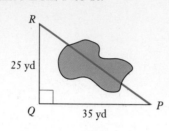

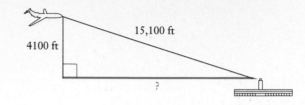

SKILL MAINTENANCE

Solve.

25. $5x + 7 = 8y$,
$3x = 8y - 4$

26. $5x + y = 17$,
$-5x + 2y = 10$

SYNTHESIS

27. The length and the width of a rectangle are given by consecutive integers. The area of the rectangle is 90 cm². Find the length of the diagonal of the rectangle.

28. Two cars leave a service station at the same time. One car travels east at a speed of 50 mph, and the other travels south at a speed of 60 mph. After one-half hour, how far apart are they?

Find x.

29.

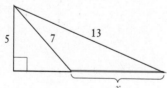

30.

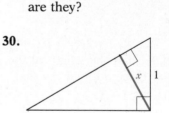

31.

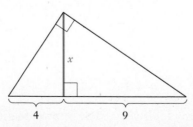

An **equilateral triangle** is shown at the right.

32. Find an expression for its height h in terms of a.

33. Find an expression for its area A in terms of a.

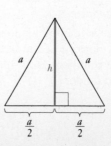

SUMMARY AND REVIEW: CHAPTER 14

IMPORTANT PROPERTIES AND FORMULAS

Products: $\qquad\qquad \sqrt{A}\sqrt{B} = \sqrt{AB}$

Quotients: $\qquad\quad \dfrac{\sqrt{A}}{\sqrt{B}} = \sqrt{\dfrac{A}{B}}$

Principle of Squaring: $\quad$ If an equation $a = b$ is true, then the equation $a^2 = b^2$ is true.

Pythagorean Equation: $\quad a^2 + b^2 = c^2$, where a and b are the lengths of the legs of a right triangle and c is the length of the hypotenuse.

REVIEW EXERCISES

The review sections and objectives to be tested in addition to the material in this chapter are [11.2b], [12.6b], and [13.3a, b, c].

Find the square roots. $\qquad\qquad\qquad\qquad\qquad$ Simplify.

1. 64 $\qquad\qquad\qquad$ **2.** 400 $\qquad\qquad\qquad$ **3.** $\sqrt{36}$ $\qquad\qquad\qquad$ **4.** $-\sqrt{169}$

Approximate the square roots to three decimal places.

5. $\sqrt{3}$ $\qquad$ **6.** $\sqrt{99}$ $\qquad$ **7.** $\sqrt{108}$ $\qquad$ **8.** $\sqrt{320}$ $\qquad$ **9.** $\sqrt{\dfrac{1}{8}}$ $\qquad$ **10.** $\sqrt{\dfrac{11}{20}}$

Identify the radicand.

11. $\sqrt{x^2 + 4}$ $\qquad\qquad\qquad\qquad\qquad$ **12.** $\sqrt{5ab^3}$

Determine whether the expression is meaningless. Write "yes" or "no."

13. $\sqrt{-22}$ $\qquad\qquad$ **14.** $-\sqrt{49}$ $\qquad\qquad$ **15.** $\sqrt{-36}$ $\qquad\qquad$ **16.** $\sqrt{-100}$

17. Determine whether the given number is a meaningful replacement in the given radical expression:

$$-3; \quad \sqrt{2x}.$$

18. Determine the meaningful replacements in

$$\sqrt{2y - 20}.$$

Simplify. $\qquad\qquad\qquad\qquad\qquad\qquad\qquad$ Multiply.

19. $\sqrt{m^2}$ $\qquad\qquad$ **20.** $\sqrt{(x-4)^2}$ $\qquad\qquad$ **21.** $\sqrt{3}\sqrt{7}$ $\qquad\qquad$ **22.** $\sqrt{x-3}\sqrt{x+3}$

Simplify by factoring.

23. $-\sqrt{48}$ $\qquad\qquad$ **24.** $\sqrt{32t^2}$ $\qquad\qquad\qquad$ **25.** $\sqrt{x^2 + 16x + 64}$

26. $\sqrt{t^2 - 49}$ $\qquad\qquad$ **27.** $\sqrt{x^8}$ $\qquad\qquad\qquad$ **28.** $\sqrt{m^{15}}$

Multiply and simplify.

29. $\sqrt{6}\sqrt{10}$ $\qquad$ **30.** $\sqrt{5x}\sqrt{8x}$ $\qquad$ **31.** $\sqrt{5x}\sqrt{10xy^2}$ $\qquad$ **32.** $\sqrt{20a^3b}\sqrt{5a^2b^2}$

Simplify.

33. $\sqrt{\dfrac{25}{64}}$ $\qquad\qquad$ **34.** $\sqrt{\dfrac{20}{45}}$ $\qquad\qquad\qquad$ **35.** $\sqrt{\dfrac{49}{t^2}}$

Rationalize the denominator.

36. $\sqrt{\dfrac{1}{2}}$ $\qquad$ **37.** $\sqrt{\dfrac{1}{8}}$ $\qquad$ **38.** $\sqrt{\dfrac{5}{y}}$ $\qquad$ **39.** $\dfrac{2}{\sqrt{3}}$

Divide and simplify.

40. $\dfrac{\sqrt{27}}{\sqrt{45}}$

41. $\dfrac{\sqrt{45x^2y}}{\sqrt{54y}}$

42. Rationalize the denominator: $\dfrac{4}{2 + \sqrt{3}}$.

Simplify.

43. $10\sqrt{5} + 3\sqrt{5}$

44. $\sqrt{80} - \sqrt{45}$

45. $3\sqrt{2} - 5\sqrt{\dfrac{1}{2}}$

46. $(2 + \sqrt{3})^2$

47. $(2 + \sqrt{3})(2 - \sqrt{3})$

In a right triangle, find the length of the side not given.

48. $a = 15, \quad c = 25$

49. $a = 1, \quad b = \sqrt{2}$

50. Find the length of the diagonal of a square whose sides are 7 m long.

Solve.

51. $\sqrt{x - 3} = 7$

52. $\sqrt{5x + 3} = \sqrt{2x - 1}$

53. $\sqrt{x} = \sqrt{x - 5} + 1$

54. $1 + x = \sqrt{1 + 5x}$

Solve.

55. The formula $r = 2\sqrt{5L}$ can be used to approximate the speed r, in miles per hour, of a car that has left a skid mark of length L, in feet. How far will a car skid at 90 mph?

SKILL MAINTENANCE

56. A person's paycheck P varies directly as the number H of hours worked. For working 15 hr, the pay is $168.75. Find the pay for 40 hr of work.

57. There were 12,000 people at a rock concert. Admission was $7.00 at the door and $6.50 if bought in advance. Total receipts were $81,165. How many people bought their tickets in advance?

58. Solve:

$$2x - 3y = 4,$$
$$3x + 4y = 2.$$

59. Divide and simplify:

$$\dfrac{x^2 - 10x + 25}{x^2 + 14x + 49} \div \dfrac{x^2 - 25}{x^2 - 49}.$$

SYNTHESIS

60. Simplify: $\sqrt{\sqrt{\sqrt{256}}}$.

61. Solve $A = \sqrt{a^2 + b^2}$ for b.

❖ THINKING IT THROUGH

1. Explain why the following is incorrect:

$$\sqrt{\dfrac{9 + 100}{25}} = \dfrac{3 + 10}{5}.$$

Determine whether each of the following is true or false. Explain your answer.

2. $\sqrt{5x^2} = x\sqrt{5}$

3. $\sqrt{b^2 - 4} = b - 2$

4. The solution of $\sqrt{11 - 2x} = -3$ is 1.

TEST: CHAPTER 14

1. Find the square roots of 81.

Simplify.

2. $\sqrt{64}$ **3.** $-\sqrt{25}$

Approximate the expression involving square roots to three decimal places.

4. $\sqrt{116}$ **5.** $\sqrt{87}$ **6.** $\dfrac{3}{\sqrt{3}}$

7. Identify the radicand in $\sqrt{4 - y^3}$.

Determine whether the expression is meaningless. Write "yes" or "no."

8. $\sqrt{24}$ **9.** $\sqrt{-23}$

10. Determine whether 6 is a meaningful replacement in $\sqrt{3 - 4x}$.   **11.** Determine the meaningful replacements in $\sqrt{8 - x}$.

Simplify.

12. $\sqrt{a^2}$ **13.** $\sqrt{36y^2}$

Multiply.

14. $\sqrt{5}\sqrt{6}$ **15.** $\sqrt{x - 8}\sqrt{x + 8}$

Simplify by factoring.

16. $\sqrt{27}$ **17.** $\sqrt{25x - 25}$ **18.** $\sqrt{t^5}$

Multiply and simplify.

19. $\sqrt{5}\sqrt{10}$ **20.** $\sqrt{3ab}\sqrt{6ab^3}$

1. _____

2. _____

3. _____

4. _____

5. _____

6. _____

7. _____

8. _____

9. _____

10. _____

11. _____

12. _____

13. _____

14. _____

15. _____

16. _____

17. _____

18. _____

19. _____

20. _____

Simplify.

21. $\sqrt{\dfrac{27}{12}}$

22. $\sqrt{\dfrac{144}{a^2}}$

Rationalize the denominator.

23. $\sqrt{\dfrac{2}{5}}$

24. $\sqrt{\dfrac{2x}{y}}$

Divide and simplify.

25. $\dfrac{\sqrt{27}}{\sqrt{32}}$

26. $\dfrac{\sqrt{35x}}{\sqrt{80xy^2}}$

Add or subtract.

27. $3\sqrt{18} - 5\sqrt{18}$

28. $\sqrt{5} + \sqrt{\dfrac{1}{5}}$

Simplify.

29. $(4 - \sqrt{5})^2$

30. $(4 - \sqrt{5})(4 + \sqrt{5})$

31. Rationalize the denominator: $\dfrac{10}{4 - \sqrt{5}}$.

32. In a right triangle, $a = 8$ and $b = 4$. Find c.

Solve.

33. $\sqrt{3x} + 2 = 14$

34. $\sqrt{6x + 13} = x + 3$

35. $\sqrt{1 - x} + 1 = \sqrt{6 - x}$

36. A person can see 247.49 km to the horizon from an airplane window. How high is the airplane? Use the formula $V = 3.5\sqrt{h}$.

SKILL MAINTENANCE

37. The perimeter of a rectangle is 118 yd. The width is 18 yd less than the length. Find the area of the rectangle.

38. The number of switches N that a production line can make varies directly as the time it operates. It can make 7240 switches in 6 hr. How many can it make in 13 hr?

39. Solve:
$$-6x + 5y = 10,$$
$$5x + 6y = 12.$$

40. Divide and simplify:
$$\frac{x^2 - 11x + 30}{x^2 - 12x + 35} \div \frac{x^2 - 36}{x^2 - 14x + 49}.$$

SYNTHESIS

Simplify.

41. $\sqrt{\sqrt{\sqrt{625}}}$

42. $\sqrt{y^{16n}}$

Copyright © 1993 Addison-Wesley Publishing Co., Inc.

INTRODUCTION A *quadratic equation* contains a polynomial of second degree. In this chapter we first learn to solve quadratic equations by factoring. Because certain quadratic equations are difficult to solve by factoring, we learn to use the *quadratic formula*, which is a "recipe" for finding solutions of quadratic equations.

We apply our skills for solving quadratic equations to problem solving. Then we graph quadratic equations.

The review sections to be tested in addition to the material in this chapter are 12.6, 14.2, 14.4, and 14.6. ❖

Quadratic Equations

AN APPLICATION

The Sears Tower in Chicago is 1451 ft tall. How long would it take an object to fall from the top to the ground?

THE MATHEMATICS

Let $t =$ the time required for the object to fall from the top to the ground. We determine t by solving the equation

$$1451 = 16t^2.$$

This is a *quadratic equation*.

Every positive real number has two square roots.
Factoring Skills: Chapter 10
Skills at Manipulating Square-Root Symbolism: Chapter 14
Pythagorean Theorem: $a^2 + b^2 = c^2$
Motion Formula: $d = rt$

PRETEST: CHAPTER 15

Solve.

1. $x^2 + 9 = 6x$

2. $x^2 - 7 = 0$

3. $3x^2 + 3x - 1 = 0$

4. $5y^2 - 3y = 0$

5. $\dfrac{3}{3x + 2} - \dfrac{2}{3x + 4} = 1$

6. $(x + 4)^2 = 5$

7. Solve $x^2 - 2x - 5 = 0$ by completing the square. Show your work.

8. Solve for n: $A = n^2 - pn$.

9. The length of a rectangle is three times the width. The area is 48 cm². Find the length and the width.

10. Find the x-intercepts: $y = 2x^2 + x - 4$.

11. The current in a stream moves at a speed of 2 km/h. A boat travels 24 km upstream and 24 km downstream in a total time of 5 hr. What is the speed of the boat in still water?

12. Graph: $y = 4 - x^2$.

15.1 Introduction to Quadratic Equations

a   Standard Form

The following are **quadratic equations.** They contain polynomials of second degree.

$$x^2 + 7x - 5 = 0, \qquad 3t^2 - \tfrac{1}{2}t = 9, \qquad 5y^2 = -6y, \qquad 5m^2 = 15.$$

The quadratic equation

$$4x^2 + 7x - 5 = 0$$

is said to be in **standard form.** The quadratic equation

$$4x^2 = 5 - 7x$$

is equivalent to the preceding equation, but it is *not* in standard form.

> A quadratic equation of the type $ax^2 + bx + c = 0$, where a, b, and c are real-number constants and $a > 0$, is called the *standard form of a quadratic equation.*

Often a quadratic equation is defined so that $a \neq 0$. We use $a > 0$ to ease the proof of the quadratic formula, which we consider later, and to ease solving by factoring, which we review in this section. Suppose we are studying an equation like $-3x^2 + 8x - 2 = 0$. It is not in standard form. We can find an equivalent equation that is in standard form by multiplying on both sides by -1:

$$-1(-3x^2 + 8x - 2) = -1(0)$$
$$3x^2 - 8x + 2 = 0.$$

▶ **EXAMPLES**   Write in standard form and determine a, b, and c.

1. $4x^2 + 7x - 5 = 0$ The equation is already in standard form.

   $a = 4; \quad b = 7; \quad c = -5$

2. $3x^2 - 0.5x = 9$

   $3x^2 - 0.5x - 9 = 0$ Subtracting 9. This is standard form.

   $a = 3; \quad b = -0.5; \quad c = -9$

3. $-4y^2 = 5y$

   $-4y^2 - 5y = 0$ Subtracting $5y$

   Not positive!

   $4y^2 + 5y = 0$ Multiplying by -1. This is standard form.

   $a = 4; \quad b = 5; \quad c = 0$ ◀

DO EXERCISES 1–3.

OBJECTIVES

After finishing Section 15.1, you should be able to:

a   Write a quadratic equation in standard form $ax^2 + bx + c = 0$, $a > 0$, and determine the coefficients a, b, and c.

b   Solve quadratic equations of the type $ax^2 + bx = 0$, where $a \neq 0$ and $b \neq 0$, by factoring.

c   Solve quadratic equations of the type $ax^2 + bx + c = 0$, where $a \neq 0$, $b \neq 0$, and $c \neq 0$, by factoring.

d   Solve problems involving quadratic equations.

FOR EXTRA HELP

Tape 28B

Write in standard form and determine a, b, and c.

1. $x^2 = 7x$

2. $3 - x^2 = 9x$

3. $3x + 5x^2 = x^2 - 4 + x$

ANSWERS ON PAGE A-12

Solve.

4. $3x^2 + 5x = 0$

5. $10x^2 - 6x = 0$

---

b   **Solving Quadratic Equations of the Type $ax^2 + bx = 0$**

Sometimes we can use factoring and the principle of zero products to solve quadratic equations. We are actually reviewing methods that we introduced in Section 10.7.

When c is 0 and $b \neq 0$, we can always factor and use the principle of zero products.

▶ **EXAMPLE 4**   Solve: $7x^2 + 2x = 0$.

$$7x^2 + 2x = 0$$
$$x(7x + 2) = 0 \quad \text{Factoring}$$
$$x = 0 \quad \text{or} \quad 7x + 2 = 0 \quad \text{Using the principle of zero products}$$
$$x = 0 \quad \text{or} \quad 7x = -2$$
$$x = 0 \quad \text{or} \quad x = -\tfrac{2}{7}$$

Check: For 0:

$$\begin{array}{c|c} 7x^2 + 2x = 0 \\ \hline 7 \cdot 0^2 + 2 \cdot 0 & 0 \\ 0 & \text{TRUE} \end{array}$$

For $-\tfrac{2}{7}$:

$$\begin{array}{c|c} 7x^2 + 2x = 0 \\ \hline 7(-\tfrac{2}{7})^2 + 2(-\tfrac{2}{7}) & 0 \\ 7(\tfrac{4}{49}) - \tfrac{4}{7} & \\ \tfrac{4}{7} - \tfrac{4}{7} & \\ 0 & \text{TRUE} \end{array}$$

The solutions are 0 and $-\tfrac{2}{7}$.   ◀

You may be tempted to divide each term in an equation like the one in Example 4 by x. This method would yield the equation

$$7x + 2 = 0,$$

whose only solution is $-\tfrac{2}{7}$. In effect, since 0 is also a solution of the original equation, we have divided by 0. The error of such division causes the loss of one of the solutions.

▶ **EXAMPLE 5**   Solve: $20x^2 - 15x = 0$.

$$20x^2 - 15x = 0$$
$$5x(4x - 3) = 0 \quad \text{Factoring}$$
$$5x = 0 \quad \text{or} \quad 4x - 3 = 0 \quad \text{Using the principle of zero products}$$
$$x = 0 \quad \text{or} \quad 4x = 3$$
$$x = 0 \quad \text{or} \quad x = \tfrac{3}{4}$$

The solutions are 0 and $\tfrac{3}{4}$.   ◀

A quadratic equation of the type $ax^2 + bx = 0$, where $a \neq 0$ and $b \neq 0$, will always have 0 as one solution and a nonzero number as the other solution.

DO EXERCISES 4 AND 5.

C Solving Quadratic Equations of the Type $ax^2 + bx + c = 0$

When neither b nor c is 0, we can sometimes solve by factoring.

▶ **EXAMPLE 6** Solve: $5x^2 - 8x + 3 = 0$.

$$5x^2 - 8x + 3 = 0$$
$$(5x - 3)(x - 1) = 0 \qquad \text{Factoring}$$
$$5x - 3 = 0 \quad \text{or} \quad x - 1 = 0 \qquad \text{Using the principle of zero products}$$
$$5x = 3 \quad \text{or} \qquad x = 1$$
$$x = \tfrac{3}{5} \quad \text{or} \qquad x = 1$$

The solutions are $\tfrac{3}{5}$ and 1. ◀

▶ **EXAMPLE 7** Solve: $(y - 3)(y - 2) = 6(y - 3)$.

We write the equation in standard form and then try to factor:

$$y^2 - 5y + 6 = 6y - 18 \qquad \text{Multiplying}$$
$$y^2 - 11y + 24 = 0 \qquad \text{Standard form}$$
$$(y - 8)(y - 3) = 0$$
$$y - 8 = 0 \quad \text{or} \quad y - 3 = 0$$
$$y = 8 \quad \text{or} \qquad y = 3.$$

The solutions are 8 and 3. ◀

DO EXERCISES 6 AND 7.

Recall that to solve a rational equation, we multiply on both sides by the LCM of all the denominators. We may obtain a quadratic equation after a few steps. When that happens, we know how to finish solving, but we must remember to check possible solutions because a replacement may result in division by 0.

▶ **EXAMPLE 8** Solve: $\dfrac{3}{x - 1} + \dfrac{5}{x + 1} = 2$.

We multiply by the LCM, which is $(x - 1)(x + 1)$:

$$(x - 1)(x + 1) \cdot \left(\frac{3}{x - 1} + \frac{5}{x + 1} \right) = 2 \cdot (x - 1)(x + 1).$$

We use the distributive law on the left:

$$(x - 1)(x + 1) \cdot \frac{3}{x - 1} + (x - 1)(x + 1) \cdot \frac{5}{x + 1} = 2(x - 1)(x + 1)$$
$$3(x + 1) + 5(x - 1) = 2(x - 1)(x + 1)$$
$$3x + 3 + 5x - 5 = 2(x^2 - 1)$$
$$8x - 2 = 2x^2 - 2$$
$$0 = 2x^2 - 8x$$
$$0 = 2x(x - 4) \qquad \text{Factoring}$$
$$2x = 0 \quad \text{or} \quad x - 4 = 0$$
$$x = 0 \quad \text{or} \qquad x = 4.$$

The check is left to the student. Since both numbers check, the solutions are 0 and 4. ◀

Solve.

6. $3x^2 + x - 2 = 0$

7. $(x - 1)(x + 1) = 5(x - 1)$

ANSWERS ON PAGE A-12

8. Solve:

$$\frac{20}{x+5} - \frac{1}{x-4} = 1.$$

DO EXERCISE 8.

d **Solving Problems**

▶ **EXAMPLE 9**   The number of diagonals d of a polygon of n sides is given by the formula

$$d = \frac{n^2 - 3n}{2}.$$

9. Use $d = \dfrac{n^2 - 3n}{2}$.

a) A heptagon has 7 sides. How many diagonals does it have?

If a polygon has 27 diagonals, how many sides does it have?

1. *Familiarize.*   We can make a drawing to familiarize ourselves with the problem. We draw an octagon (8 sides) and count the diagonals and see that there are 20. Let us check this in the formula. We evaluate the formula for $n = 8$:

$$d = \frac{8^2 - 3(8)}{2} = \frac{64 - 24}{2} = \frac{40}{2} = 20.$$

2. *Translate.*   We know that the number of diagonals is 27. We substitute 27 for d:

$$27 = \frac{n^2 - 3n}{2}.$$

This gives us a translation.

3. *Solve.*   We solve the equation for n, reversing the equation first for convenience:

$$\frac{n^2 - 3n}{2} = 27$$

$$n^2 - 3n = 54 \qquad \text{Multiplying by 2 to clear of fractions}$$

$$n^2 - 3n - 54 = 0$$

$$(n - 9)(n + 6) = 0$$

$$n - 9 = 0 \quad \text{or} \quad n + 6 = 0$$

$$n = 9 \quad \text{or} \qquad n = -6.$$

b) A polygon has 44 diagonals. How many sides does it have?

4. *Check.*   Since the number of sides cannot be negative, -6 cannot be a solution. We leave it to the student to show that 9 checks by substitution.

5. *State.*   The polygon has 9 sides (it is a nonagon).   ◀

DO EXERCISE 9.

NAME   SECTION   DATE

EXERCISE SET 15.1

a Write standard form and determine a, b, and c.

1. $x^2 - 3x + 2 = 0$ **2.** $x^2 - 8x - 5 = 0$ **3.** $7x^2 = 4x - 3$

4. $9x^2 = x + 5$ **5.** $5 = -2x^2 + 3x$ **6.** $2x - 1 = 3x^2 + 7$

b Solve.

7. $x^2 + 7x = 0$ **8.** $x^2 + 5x = 0$ **9.** $3x^2 + 6x = 0$

10. $4x^2 + 8x = 0$ **11.** $5x^2 = 2x$ **12.** $7x = 3x^2$

13. $4x^2 + 4x = 0$ **14.** $2x^2 - 2x = 0$ **15.** $0 = 10x^2 - 30x$

16. $0 = 10x^2 - 50x$ **17.** $11x = 55x^2$ **18.** $33x^2 = -11x$

19. $14t^2 = 3t$ **20.** $8m = 17m^2$

21. $5y^2 - 3y^2 = 72y + 9y$ **22.** $63p - 16p^2 = 17p + 58p^2$

c Solve.

23. $x^2 + 8x - 48 = 0$ **24.** $x^2 - 16x + 48 = 0$

25. $5 + 6x + x^2 = 0$ **26.** $x^2 + 6 + 7x = 0$

27. $18 = 7p + p^2$ **28.** $t^2 + 4t = 21$

29. $-15 = -8y + y^2$ **30.** $m^2 + 14 = 9m$

31. $x^2 + 6x + 9 = 0$ **32.** $x^2 + 10x + 25 = 0$

33. $r^2 = 8r - 16$ **34.** $x^2 + 1 = 2x$

35. $6x^2 + x - 2 = 0$ **36.** $2x^2 - 13x + 15 = 0$

37. $15b - 9b^2 = 4$ **38.** $3a^2 = 10a + 8$

1. _____
2. _____
3. _____
4. _____
5. _____
6. _____
7. _____
8. _____
9. _____
10. _____
11. _____
12. _____
13. _____
14. _____
15. _____
16. _____
17. _____
18. _____
19. _____
20. _____
21. _____
22. _____
23. _____
24. _____
25. _____
26. _____
27. _____
28. _____
29. _____
30. _____
31. _____
32. _____
33. _____
34. _____
35. _____
36. _____
37. _____
38. _____

39. $6x^2 - 4x = 10$

40. $3x^2 - 7x = 20$

41. $12w^2 - 5w = 2$

42. $2t^2 + 12t = -10$

43. $t(t - 5) = 14$

44. $6z^2 + z - 1 = 0$

45. $t(9 + t) = 4(2t + 5)$

46. $3y^2 + 8y = 12y + 15$

47. $16(p - 1) = p(p + 8)$

48. $(2x - 3)(x + 1) = 4(2x - 3)$

49. $(x - 2)(x + 2) = x + 2$

50. $(t - 1)(t + 3) = t - 1$

Solve.

51. $\dfrac{8}{x + 2} + \dfrac{8}{x - 2} = 3$

52. $\dfrac{24}{x - 2} + \dfrac{24}{x + 2} = 5$

53. $\dfrac{1}{x} + \dfrac{1}{x + 6} = \dfrac{1}{4}$

54. $\dfrac{1}{x} + \dfrac{1}{x + 9} = \dfrac{1}{20}$

55. $1 + \dfrac{12}{x^2 - 4} = \dfrac{3}{x - 2}$

56. $\dfrac{5}{t - 3} - \dfrac{30}{t^2 - 9} = 1$

57. $\dfrac{r}{r - 1} + \dfrac{2}{r^2 - 1} = \dfrac{8}{r + 1}$

58. $\dfrac{x + 2}{x^2 - 2} = \dfrac{2}{3 - x}$

59. $\dfrac{4 - x}{x - 4} + \dfrac{x + 3}{x - 3} = 0$

60. $\dfrac{x - 1}{1 - x} = -\dfrac{x + 8}{x - 8}$

d Solve.

61. A hexagon is a figure with 6 sides. How many diagonals does a hexagon have?

62. A decagon is a figure with 10 sides. How many diagonals does a decagon have?

63. A polygon has 14 diagonals. How many sides does it have?

64. A polygon has 9 diagonals. How many sides does it have?

SKILL MAINTENANCE

Simplify.

65. $\sqrt{20}$

66. $\sqrt{\dfrac{2890}{2560}}$

67. $\sqrt{\dfrac{3240}{2560}}$

68. $\sqrt{88}$

SYNTHESIS

Solve.

69. $4m^2 - (m + 1)^2 = 0$

70. $x^2 + \sqrt{3}\,x = 0$

71. $\sqrt{5}\,x^2 - x = 0$

72. $\sqrt{7}\,x^2 + \sqrt{3}\,x = 0$

73. $\dfrac{5}{y + 4} - \dfrac{3}{y - 2} = 4$

74. $\dfrac{2z + 11}{2z + 8} = \dfrac{3z - 1}{z - 1}$

75. Solve for x: $ax^2 + bx = 0$.

76. ▤ Solve: $0.0025x^2 + 70{,}400x = 0$.

Solve.

77. $z - 10\sqrt{z} + 9 = 0$ (Let $x = \sqrt{z}$.)

78. $(x - 2)^2 + 3(x - 2) = 4$

15.2 Solving Quadratic Equations by Completing the Square

a Solving Quadratic Equations of the Type $ax^2 = p$

For equations of the type $ax^2 = p$, we solve for x^2 and apply the *principle of square roots*, which states that a positive number has two square roots. The number 0 has one square root, 0.

The Principle of Square Roots

The equation $x^2 = k$ has two real solutions when $k > 0$. The solutions are $\sqrt{k}$ and $-\sqrt{k}$.

The equation $x^2 = 0$ has 0 as its only solution.

The equation $x^2 = k$ has no real-number solution when $k < 0$.

► **EXAMPLE 1**   Solve: $x^2 = 3$.

$$x^2 = 3$$
$$x = \sqrt{3} \quad \text{or} \quad x = -\sqrt{3}. \qquad \text{Using the principle of square roots}$$

Check: For $\sqrt{3}$:

$$\begin{array}{c|c} x^2 = 3 & \\ \hline (\sqrt{3})^2 & 3 \\ 3 & \text{TRUE} \end{array}$$

For $-\sqrt{3}$:

$$\begin{array}{c|c} x^2 = 3 & \\ \hline (-\sqrt{3})^2 & 3 \\ 3 & \text{TRUE} \end{array}$$

The solutions are $\sqrt{3}$ and $-\sqrt{3}$.   ◄

DO EXERCISE 1.

► **EXAMPLE 2**   Solve: $\frac{1}{3}x^2 = 0$.

$$\frac{1}{3}x^2 = 0$$
$$x^2 = 0 \qquad \text{Multiplying by 3}$$
$$x = 0 \qquad \text{Using the principle of square roots}$$

The solution is 0.   ◄

DO EXERCISE 2.

► **EXAMPLE 3**   Solve: $-3x^2 + 7 = 0$.

$$-3x^2 + 7 = 0$$
$$-3x^2 = -7 \qquad \text{Subtracting 7}$$
$$x^2 = \frac{-7}{-3} \qquad \text{Dividing by } -3$$
$$x^2 = \frac{7}{3}$$
$$x = \sqrt{\frac{7}{3}} \quad \text{or} \quad x = -\sqrt{\frac{7}{3}} \qquad \text{Using the principle of square roots}$$
$$x = \sqrt{\frac{7}{3} \cdot \frac{3}{3}} \quad \text{or} \quad x = -\sqrt{\frac{7}{3} \cdot \frac{3}{3}} \qquad \text{Rationalizing the denominators}$$
$$x = \frac{\sqrt{21}}{3} \quad \text{or} \quad x = -\frac{\sqrt{21}}{3}$$

OBJECTIVES

After finishing Section 15.2, you should be able to:

a Solve equations of the type $ax^2 = p$.

b Solve equations of the type $(x + k)^2 = p$.

c Solve quadratic equations by completing the square.

d Solve certain problems involving quadratic equations of the type $ax^2 = p$.

---

1. Solve: $x^2 = 5$.

2. Solve: $2x^2 = 0$.

ANSWERS ON PAGE A-12

3. Solve: $2x^2 - 3 = 0$.

Solve.

4. $(x - 3)^2 = 16$

5. $(x + 3)^2 = 10$

6. $(x - 1)^2 = 5$

7. Solve: $x^2 - 6x + 9 = 64$.

Check: For $\dfrac{\sqrt{21}}{3}$:   For $-\dfrac{\sqrt{21}}{3}$:

$$\begin{array}{c|c}
-3x^2 + 7 = 0 & \\
\hline
-3\left(\dfrac{\sqrt{21}}{3}\right)^2 + 7 & 0 \\
-3 \cdot \dfrac{21}{9} + 7 & \\
-7 + 7 & \\
0 & \text{TRUE}
\end{array}$$

$$\begin{array}{c|c}
-3x^2 + 7 = 0 & \\
\hline
-3\left(-\dfrac{\sqrt{21}}{3}\right)^2 + 7 & 0 \\
-3 \cdot \dfrac{21}{9} + 7 & \\
-7 + 7 & \\
0 & \text{TRUE}
\end{array}$$

The solutions are $\dfrac{\sqrt{21}}{3}$ and $-\dfrac{\sqrt{21}}{3}$.   ◄

DO EXERCISE 3.

b   **Solving Quadratic Equations of the Type $(x + k)^2 = p$**

The equation $(x - 5)^2 = 9$ can be solved by using the principle of square roots. We will see that other equations can be made to look like this one.

In an equation of the type $(x + k)^2 = p$, we have the square of a binomial equal to a constant. We can use the principle of square roots to solve such an equation.

▶ **EXAMPLE 4**   Solve: $(x - 5)^2 = 9$.

$$(x - 5)^2 = 9$$
$$x - 5 = 3 \quad \text{or} \quad x - 5 = -3 \qquad \text{Using the principle of square roots}$$
$$x = 8 \quad \text{or} \qquad x = 2$$

The solutions are 8 and 2.   ◄

▶ **EXAMPLE 5**   Solve: $(x + 2)^2 = 7$.

$$(x + 2)^2 = 7$$
$$x + 2 = \sqrt{7} \qquad \text{or} \quad x + 2 = -\sqrt{7} \qquad \text{Using the principle of square roots}$$
$$x = -2 + \sqrt{7} \quad \text{or} \qquad x = -2 - \sqrt{7}$$

The solutions are $-2 + \sqrt{7}$ and $-2 - \sqrt{7}$, or simply $-2 \pm \sqrt{7}$ (read "-2 plus or minus $\sqrt{7}$").   ◄

DO EXERCISES 4–6.

In Examples 4 and 5, the left sides of the equations are squares of binomials. If we can express an equation in such a form, we can proceed as we did in those examples.

▶ **EXAMPLE 6**   Solve: $x^2 + 8x + 16 = 49$.

$$x^2 + 8x + 16 = 49 \qquad \text{The left side is the square of a binomial.}$$
$$(x + 4)^2 = 49$$
$$x + 4 = 7 \quad \text{or} \quad x + 4 = -7 \qquad \text{Using the principle of square roots}$$
$$x = 3 \quad \text{or} \qquad x = -11$$

The solutions are 3 and -11.   ◄

DO EXERCISE 7.

C Completing the Square

We have seen that a quadratic equation like $(x - 5)^2 = 9$ can be solved by using the principle of square roots. We also noted that an equation like $x^2 + 8x + 16 = 49$ can be solved in the same manner because the expression on the left side is the square of a binomial, $(x + 4)^2$. This second procedure is the basis for a method of solving quadratic equations called **completing the square.** It can be used to solve any quadratic equation.

Suppose we have the following quadratic equation:

$$x^2 + 10x = 4.$$

If we could add to both sides of the equation a constant that would make the expression on the left the square of a binomial, we could then solve the equation using the principle of square roots.

How can we determine what to add to $x^2 + 10x$ in order to construct the square of a binomial? We want to find a number a such that the following equation is satisfied:

$$(x + a)(x + a) = x^2 + 10x + a^2$$
$$ax + ax = 2ax$$

Thus, a is such that $2ax = 10x$. Solving for a, we get

$$a = \frac{10x}{2x} = \frac{10}{2} = 5;$$

that is, a is half of the coefficient of x in $x^2 + 10x$. Since $a^2 = (\frac{10}{2})^2 = 5^2 = 25$, we add 25 to our original expression:

$$x^2 + 10x + 25 \text{ is the square of } x + 5;$$

that is, $\qquad x^2 + 10x + 25 = (x + 5)^2.$

> To *complete the square* of an expression like $x^2 + bx$, we take half the coefficient of x and square. Then we add that number, which is $(b/2)^2$.

Returning to solve our original equation, we first add 25 on both sides to complete the square. Then we solve as follows:

$$x^2 + 10x = 4$$
$$x^2 + 10x + 25 = 4 + 25 \qquad \text{Adding 25: } (\tfrac{10}{2})^2 = 5^2 = 25$$
$$(x + 5)^2 = 29$$
$$x + 5 = \sqrt{29} \qquad \text{or} \quad x + 5 = -\sqrt{29} \qquad \text{Using the principle of square roots}$$
$$x = -5 + \sqrt{29} \quad \text{or} \qquad x = -5 - \sqrt{29}.$$

The solutions are $-5 \pm \sqrt{29}$.

We have seen that a quadratic equation $(x + k)^2 = p$ can be solved by using the principle of square roots. Any equation can be put in this form by completing the square. Then we can solve as before.

Solve.

8. $x^2 - 6x + 8 = 0$

9. $x^2 + 8x - 20 = 0$

10. Solve: $x^2 + 6x - 1 = 0$.

11. Solve: $x^2 - 3x - 10 = 0$.

▶ **EXAMPLE 7**   Solve: $x^2 + 6x + 8 = 0$.

We have

$$x^2 + 6x + 8 = 0$$
$$x^2 + 6x \quad = -8. \qquad \text{Subtracting 8}$$

We take half of 6 and square it, to get 9. Then we add 9 on *both* sides of the equation. This makes the left side the square of a binomial. We have now completed the square.

$$x^2 + 6x + 9 = -8 + 9 \qquad \text{Adding 9}$$
$$(x + 3)^2 = 1$$
$$x + 3 = 1 \quad \text{or} \quad x + 3 = -1 \qquad \text{Using the principle of square roots}$$
$$x = -2 \quad \text{or} \qquad x = -4$$

The solutions are -2 and -4.   ◀

This method of solving is called *completing the square*.

DO EXERCISES 8 AND 9.

▶ **EXAMPLE 8**   Solve $x^2 - 4x - 7 = 0$ by completing the square.

$$x^2 - 4x - 7 = 0$$
$$x^2 - 4x \quad = 7 \qquad \text{Adding 7}$$
$$x^2 - 4x + 4 = 7 + 4 \qquad \text{Adding 4: } (\tfrac{-4}{2})^2 = (-2)^2 = 4$$
$$(x - 2)^2 = 11$$
$$x - 2 = \sqrt{11} \qquad \text{or} \quad x - 2 = -\sqrt{11} \qquad \text{Using the principle of square roots}$$
$$x = 2 + \sqrt{11} \quad \text{or} \qquad x = 2 - \sqrt{11}$$

The solutions are $2 \pm \sqrt{11}$.   ◀

DO EXERCISE 10.

Example 7, as well as the following example, can be solved more easily by factoring. We solved it by completing the square only to illustrate that completing the square can be used to solve any quadratic equation.

▶ **EXAMPLE 9**   Solve $x^2 + 3x - 10 = 0$ by completing the square.

We have

$$x^2 + 3x - 10 = 0$$
$$x^2 + 3x \quad = 10$$
$$x^2 + 3x + \tfrac{9}{4} = 10 + \tfrac{9}{4} \qquad \text{Adding } \tfrac{9}{4}: (\tfrac{3}{2})^2 = \tfrac{9}{4}$$
$$(x + \tfrac{3}{2})^2 = \tfrac{40}{4} + \tfrac{9}{4} = \tfrac{49}{4}$$
$$x + \tfrac{3}{2} = \tfrac{7}{2} \quad \text{or} \quad x + \tfrac{3}{2} = -\tfrac{7}{2} \qquad \text{Using the principle of square roots}$$
$$x = \tfrac{4}{2} \quad \text{or} \qquad x = -\tfrac{10}{2}$$
$$x = 2 \quad \text{or} \qquad x = -5.$$

The solutions are 2 and -5.   ◀

DO EXERCISE 11.

When the coefficient of x^2 is not 1, we can make it 1, as shown in the following example.

▶ **EXAMPLE 10** Solve $2x^2 = 3x + 1$ by completing the square.

We first obtain standard form. Then we multiply on both sides by $\frac{1}{2}$ to make the x^2-coefficient 1.

$$2x^2 = 3x + 1$$

$$2x^2 - 3x - 1 = 0 \qquad \text{Finding standard form}$$

$$\frac{1}{2}(2x^2 - 3x - 1) = \frac{1}{2} \cdot 0 \qquad \text{Multiplying by } \frac{1}{2} \text{ to make the } x^2\text{-coefficient 1}$$

$$x^2 - \frac{3}{2}x - \frac{1}{2} = 0$$

$$x^2 - \frac{3}{2}x = \frac{1}{2} \qquad \text{Adding } \frac{1}{2}$$

$$x^2 - \frac{3}{2}x + \frac{9}{16} = \frac{1}{2} + \frac{9}{16} \qquad \text{Adding } \frac{9}{16} : \left[\frac{1}{2}\left(-\frac{3}{2}\right)\right]^2 = \left[-\frac{3}{4}\right]^2 = \frac{9}{16}$$

$$\left(x - \frac{3}{4}\right)^2 = \frac{8}{16} + \frac{9}{16} \qquad \text{Finding a common denominator}$$

$$\left(x - \frac{3}{4}\right)^2 = \frac{17}{16}$$

$$x - \frac{3}{4} = \frac{\sqrt{17}}{4} \qquad \text{or} \qquad x - \frac{3}{4} = -\frac{\sqrt{17}}{4} \qquad \text{Using the principle of square roots}$$

$$x = \frac{3}{4} + \frac{\sqrt{17}}{4} \qquad \text{or} \qquad x = \frac{3}{4} - \frac{\sqrt{17}}{4}$$

The solutions are $\dfrac{3 \pm \sqrt{17}}{4}$. ◀

Solving by Completing the Square

To solve a quadratic equation $ax^2 + bx + c = 0$ by completing the square:

1. **If $a \neq 1$, multiply by $1/a$ so that the x^2-coefficient is 1.**

2. **If the x^2-coefficient is 1, add so that the equation is in the form**

$$x^2 + bx = -c, \quad \text{or} \quad x^2 + \frac{b}{a}x = -\frac{c}{a} \text{ if step (1) has been applied.}$$

3. **Take half of the x-coefficient and square it. Add the result on both sides of the equation.**

4. **Express the side with the variables as the square of a binomial.**

5. **Use the principle of square roots and complete the solution.**

DO EXERCISE 12.

12. Solve: $2x^2 + 3x - 3 = 0$.

ANSWER ON PAGE A-12

13. The Texas Building in Houston is 1002 ft tall. How long would it take an object to fall to the ground from the top?

d **Applications**

▶ **EXAMPLE 11**　The Sears Tower in Chicago is 1451 ft tall. How long would it take an object to fall to the ground from the top?

1. *Familiarize.*　If we did not know anything about this problem, we might consider looking up a formula in a mathematics or physics book. A formula that fits this situation is

$$s = 16t^2,$$

where s is the distance, in feet, traveled by a body falling freely from rest in t seconds. This formula is actually an approximation in that it does not account for air resistance. In this problem, we know the distance s to be 1451. We want to determine the time t for the object to reach the ground.

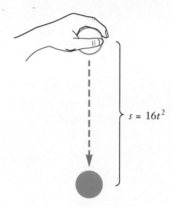

$s = 16t^2$

2. *Translate.*　We know that the distance is 1451 and that we need to solve for t. We substitute 1451 for s:

$$1451 = 16t^2.$$

This gives us a translation.

3. *Solve.*　We solve the equation:

$$1451 = 16t^2$$

$$\frac{1451}{16} = t^2 \qquad \text{Solving for } t^2$$

$$90.6875 = t^2 \qquad \text{Dividing}$$

$$\sqrt{90.6875} = t \quad \text{or} \quad -\sqrt{90.6875} = t \qquad \text{Using the principle of square roots}$$

$$9.5 \approx t \quad \text{or} \qquad\qquad -9.5 \approx t. \qquad \text{Using a calculator to find the square root and rounding to the nearest tenth}$$

4. *Check.*　The number -9.5 cannot be a solution because time cannot be negative in this situation. We substitute 9.5 in the original equation:

$$s = 16(9.5)^2 = 16(90.25) = 1444.$$

This is close. Remember that we approximated a solution. Thus we have a check.

5. *State.*　It takes about 9.5 sec for the object to fall to the ground from the top of the Sears Tower.　◀

DO EXERCISE 13.

NAME   SECTION   DATE

EXERCISE SET 15.2

a Solve.

1. $x^2 = 121$ **2.** $x^2 = 10$ **3.** $5x^2 = 35$ **4.** $3x^2 = 30$

5. $5x^2 = 3$ **6.** $2x^2 = 5$ **7.** $4x^2 - 25 = 0$ **8.** $9x^2 - 4 = 0$

9. $3x^2 - 49 = 0$ **10.** $5x^2 - 16 = 0$ **11.** $4y^2 - 3 = 9$ **12.** $49y^2 - 16 = 0$

13. $25y^2 - 36 = 0$ **14.** $5x^2 - 100 = 0$

b Solve.

15. $(x - 2)^2 = 49$ **16.** $(x + 1)^2 = 6$ **17.** $(x + 3)^2 = 21$

18. $(x - 3)^2 = 6$ **19.** $(x + 13)^2 = 8$ **20.** $(x - 13)^2 = 64$

21. $(x - 7)^2 = 12$ **22.** $(x + 1)^2 = 14$ **23.** $(x + 9)^2 = 34$

24. $(t + 2)^2 = 25$ **25.** $(x + \frac{3}{2})^2 = \frac{7}{2}$ **26.** $(y - \frac{3}{4})^2 = \frac{17}{16}$

27. $x^2 - 6x + 9 = 64$ **28.** $x^2 - 10x + 25 = 100$

29. $y^2 + 14y + 49 = 4$ **30.** $p^2 + 8p + 16 = 1$

c Solve by completing the square. Show your work.

31. $x^2 - 6x - 16 = 0$ **32.** $x^2 + 8x + 15 = 0$ **33.** $x^2 + 22x + 21 = 0$

34. $x^2 + 14x - 15 = 0$ **35.** $x^2 - 2x - 5 = 0$ **36.** $x^2 - 4x - 11 = 0$

1. _____
2. _____
3. _____
4. _____
5. _____
6. _____
7. _____
8. _____
9. _____
10. _____
11. _____
12. _____
13. _____
14. _____
15. _____
16. _____
17. _____
18. _____
19. _____
20. _____
21. _____
22. _____
23. _____
24. _____
25. _____
26. _____
27. _____
28. _____
29. _____
30. _____
31. _____
32. _____
33. _____
34. _____
35. _____
36. _____

37. $x^2 - 22x + 102 = 0$ **38.** $x^2 - 18x + 74 = 0$ **39.** $x^2 + 10x - 4 = 0$

40. $x^2 - 10x - 4 = 0$ **41.** $x^2 - 7x - 2 = 0$ **42.** $x^2 + 7x - 2 = 0$

43. $x^2 + 3x - 28 = 0$ **44.** $x^2 - 3x - 28 = 0$ **45.** $x^2 + \frac{3}{2}x - \frac{1}{2} = 0$

46. $x^2 - \frac{3}{2}x - 2 = 0$ **47.** $2x^2 + 3x - 17 = 0$ **48.** $2x^2 - 3x - 1 = 0$

49. $3x^2 + 4x - 1 = 0$ **50.** $3x^2 - 4x - 3 = 0$ **51.** $2x^2 = 9x + 5$

52. $2x^2 = 5x + 12$ **53.** $4x^2 + 12x = 7$ **54.** $6x^2 + 11x = 10$

d   Solve.

55. The height of the World Trade Center in New York is 1377 ft (excluding TV towers and antennas). How long would it take an object to fall to the ground from the top?

56. A body falls 2496 ft. How many seconds does this take?

57. The world record for free-fall by a woman to the ground, without a parachute, into a cushioned landing area is 175 ft and is held by Kitty O'Neill. Approximately how long did the fall take?

58. The world record for free-fall to the ground, without a parachute, by a man is 311 ft and is held by Dar Robinson. Approximately how long did the fall take?

SKILL MAINTENANCE

59. Find an equation of variation where y varies inversely as x, and $y = 235$ when $x = 0.6$.

60. The time T to do a certain job varies inversely as the number N of people working. It takes 5 hr for 24 people to wash and wax the floors in a building. How long would it take 36 people to do the job?

SYNTHESIS

Find b such that the trinomial is a square.

61. $x^2 + bx + 36$ **62.** $x^2 + bx + 55$ **63.** $x^2 + bx + 128$

64. $4x^2 + bx + 16$ **65.** $x^2 + bx + c$ **66.** $ax^2 + bx + c$

Solve.

67. ▤ $4.82x^2 = 12,000$ **68.** $\dfrac{x}{4} = \dfrac{9}{x}$ **69.** $1 = \dfrac{1}{3}x^2$

70. $\dfrac{x}{9} = \dfrac{36}{4x}$ **71.** $\dfrac{4}{m^2 - 7} = 1$

15.3 The Quadratic Formula

We learn to complete the square to enhance our ability to graph certain second-degree equations and to prove a general formula that can be used to solve quadratic equations.

a Solving Using the Quadratic Formula

Each time you solve by completing the square, you continually do nearly the same thing. When we repeat the same kind of computation many times, we look for a formula so we can speed up our work. Consider

$$ax^2 + bx + c = 0, \quad a > 0.$$

Let's solve by completing the square. As we carry out the steps, compare them with Example 10 in the preceding section.

$$x^2 + \frac{b}{a}x + \frac{c}{a} = 0 \qquad \textbf{Multiplying by } \frac{1}{a}$$

$$x^2 + \frac{b}{a}x \qquad = -\frac{c}{a} \qquad \textbf{Adding } -\frac{c}{a}$$

Half of $\frac{b}{a}$ is $\frac{b}{2a}$. The square is $\frac{b^2}{4a^2}$. Thus we add $\frac{b^2}{4a^2}$ on both sides.

$$x^2 + \frac{b}{a}x + \frac{b^2}{4a^2} = -\frac{c}{a} + \frac{b^2}{4a^2} \qquad \textbf{Adding } \frac{b^2}{4a^2}$$

$$\left(x + \frac{b}{2a}\right)^2 = -\frac{4ac}{4a^2} + \frac{b^2}{4a^2} \qquad \begin{array}{l}\textbf{Factoring the left side and finding a}\\\textbf{common denominator on the right}\end{array}$$

$$\left(x + \frac{b}{2a}\right)^2 = \frac{b^2 - 4ac}{4a^2}$$

$$x + \frac{b}{2a} = \sqrt{\frac{b^2 - 4ac}{4a^2}} \quad \text{or} \quad x + \frac{b}{2a} = -\sqrt{\frac{b^2 - 4ac}{4a^2}} \qquad \begin{array}{l}\textbf{Using the principle}\\\textbf{of square roots}\end{array}$$

Since $a > 0$, $\sqrt{4a^2} = 2a$, so we can simplify as follows:

$$x + \frac{b}{2a} = \frac{\sqrt{b^2 - 4ac}}{2a} \quad \text{or} \quad x + \frac{b}{2a} = -\frac{\sqrt{b^2 - 4ac}}{2a}.$$

Thus,

$$x = -\frac{b}{2a} + \frac{\sqrt{b^2 - 4ac}}{2a} \quad \text{or} \quad x = -\frac{b}{2a} + \frac{\sqrt{b^2 - 4ac}}{2a},$$

so

$$x = -\frac{b}{2a} \pm \frac{\sqrt{b^2 - 4ac}}{2a},$$

or

$$x = \frac{-b \pm \sqrt{b^2 - 4ac}}{2a}.$$

We now have the following.

The Quadratic Formula
The solutions of $ax^2 + bx + c = 0$ are given by $$x = \frac{-b \pm \sqrt{b^2 - 4ac}}{2a}.$$

OBJECTIVES

After finishing Section 15.3, you should be able to:

a Solve quadratic equations using the quadratic formula.

b Find approximate solutions of quadratic equations using a calculator or a square-root table.

FOR EXTRA HELP

Tape 28C

1. Solve using the quadratic formula:
$$2x^2 = 4 - 7x.$$

Note that the formula also holds when $a < 0$. A similar proof would show this, but we will not consider it here.

▶   **EXAMPLE 1**   Solve $5x^2 - 8x = -3$ using the quadratic formula.

We first find standard form and determine a, b, and c:
$$5x^2 - 8x + 3 = 0,$$
$$a = 5, \quad b = -8, \quad c = 3,$$

We then use the quadratic formula:
$$x = \frac{-b \pm \sqrt{b^2 - 4ac}}{2a}$$

$$x = \frac{-(-8) \pm \sqrt{(-8)^2 - 4 \cdot 5 \cdot 3}}{2 \cdot 5} \qquad \text{Substituting}$$

Be sure to write the fraction bar all the way across.

$$x = \frac{8 \pm \sqrt{64 - 60}}{10}$$

$$x = \frac{8 \pm \sqrt{4}}{10}$$

$$x = \frac{8 \pm 2}{10}$$

$$x = \frac{8 + 2}{10} \quad \text{or} \quad x = \frac{8 - 2}{10}$$

$$x = \frac{10}{10} \quad \text{or} \quad x = \frac{6}{10}$$

$$x = 1 \quad \text{or} \quad x = \frac{3}{5}.$$

The solutions are 1 and $\frac{3}{5}$.   ◀

DO EXERCISE 1.

It would have been easier to solve the equation in Example 1 by factoring. We used the quadratic formula only to illustrate that it can be used to solve any quadratic equation. The following is a general procedure for solving a quadratic equation.

To solve a quadratic equation:

1. **Check to see if it is in the form $ax^2 = p$ or $(x + k)^2 = p$. If it is, use the principle of square roots as in Section 15.2.**

2. **If it is not in the form of (1), write it in standard form, $ax^2 + bx + c = 0$ with a and b nonzero.**

3. **Then try factoring.**

4. **If it is not possible to factor or if factoring seems difficult, use the quadratic formula.**

The solutions of a quadratic equation can always be found using the quadratic formula. They cannot always be found by factoring. When $b^2 - 4ac \geq 0$, the equation has real-number solutions. When $b^2 - 4ac < 0$, the equation has no real-number solutions.

ANSWER ON PAGE A-12

The expression $b^2 - 4ac$ is called the **discriminant.** The square root of the discriminant is part of the quadratic formula.

When using the quadratic formula, it is wise to compute the discriminant first. If it is negative, there are no real-number solutions because we are taking the square root of a negative number. If it is a perfect square, you can solve by factoring if you wish.

▶ **EXAMPLE 2** Solve $x^2 + 3x - 10 = 0$ using the quadratic formula.

The equation is in standard form. So we determine a, b, and c:

$$x^2 + 3x - 10 = 0,$$
$$a = 1, \quad b = 3, \quad c = -10.$$

We compute the discriminant:

$$b^2 - 4ac = 3^2 - 4 \cdot 1 \cdot (-10) = 9 + 40 = 49.$$

The discriminant is positive and is also a perfect square, so we could use factoring to solve. But for purposes of illustration, we will use the quadratic formula (try factoring on your own):

$$x = \frac{-3 \pm \sqrt{49}}{2(1)} = \frac{-3 \pm 7}{2}.$$

Thus,

$$x = \frac{-3 + 7}{2} = \frac{4}{2} = 2 \quad \text{or} \quad x = \frac{-3 - 7}{2} = \frac{-10}{2} = -5.$$

The solutions are 2 and -5. ◀

DO EXERCISE 2.

▶ **EXAMPLE 3** Solve $x^2 = 4x + 7$ using the quadratic formula. Compare with Example 8 in Section 15.2.

We first find standard form and determine a, b, and c:

$$x^2 - 4x - 7 = 0,$$
$$a = 1, \quad b = -4, \quad c = -7.$$

We then compute the discriminant:

$$b^2 - 4ac = (-4)^2 - 4 \cdot (1) \cdot (-7) = 16 + 28 = 44.$$

The discriminant is positive, so there are real-number solutions. They are given by

$$x = \frac{-(-4) \pm \sqrt{44}}{2(1)} \qquad \text{Substituting into the quadratic formula}$$

$$= \frac{4 \pm \sqrt{44}}{2} = \frac{4 \pm \sqrt{4 \cdot 11}}{2} = \frac{4 \pm \sqrt{4}\sqrt{11}}{2}$$

$$= \frac{4 \pm 2\sqrt{11}}{2} = \frac{2 \cdot 2 \pm 2\sqrt{11}}{2 \cdot 1} \qquad \text{Factoring out 2 in the numerator and the denominator}$$

$$= \frac{2(2 \pm \sqrt{11})}{2 \cdot 1} = \frac{2}{2} \cdot \frac{2 \pm \sqrt{11}}{1} = 2 \pm \sqrt{11}.$$

The solutions are $2 + \sqrt{11}$ and $2 - \sqrt{11}$, or $2 \pm \sqrt{11}$. ◀

DO EXERCISE 3.

2. Solve using the quadratic formula:
$$x^2 - 3x - 10 = 0.$$

3. Solve using the quadratic formula:
$$x^2 + 4x = 7.$$

4. Solve using the quadratic formula:
$$x^2 = x - 1.$$

▶ **EXAMPLE 4**   Solve $x^2 + x = -1$ using the quadratic formula.

We first find standard form and determine a, b, and c:

$$x^2 + x + 1 = 0,$$
$$a = 1, \quad b = 1, \quad c = 1.$$

We then compute the discriminant:

$$b^2 - 4ac = 1^2 - 4 \cdot 1 \cdot 1 = 1 - 4 = -3.$$

Since the discriminant is negative, there are no real-number solutions because square roots of negative numbers do not exist as real numbers.   ◀

DO EXERCISE 4.

▶ **EXAMPLE 5**   Solve $3x^2 = 7 - 2x$ using the quadratic formula.

We first find standard form and determine a, b, and c:

$$3x^2 + 2x - 7 = 0,$$
$$a = 3, \quad b = 2, \quad c = -7.$$

5. Solve using the quadratic formula:
$$5x^2 - 8x = 3.$$

We then compute the discriminant:

$$b^2 - 4ac = 2^2 - 4 \cdot 3 \cdot (-7) = 4 + 84 = 88.$$

This is positive, so there are real-number solutions. They are given by

$$x = \frac{-2 \pm \sqrt{88}}{2(3)} \quad \text{Substituting into the quadratic formula}$$

$$= \frac{-2 \pm \sqrt{4 \cdot 22}}{6} = \frac{-2 \pm 2\sqrt{22}}{6}$$

$$= \frac{2(-1 \pm \sqrt{22})}{2 \cdot 3} \quad \text{Factoring out 2 in the numerator and the denominator}$$

$$= \frac{-1 \pm \sqrt{22}}{3}.$$

The solutions are $\dfrac{-1 + \sqrt{22}}{3}$ and $\dfrac{-1 - \sqrt{22}}{3}$, or $\dfrac{-1 \pm \sqrt{22}}{3}$.   ◀

DO EXERCISE 5.

6. Approximate the solutions to the equation in Margin Exercise 5. Round to the nearest tenth.

b   **Approximate Solutions**

A calculator or Table 2 can be used to approximate solutions.

▶ **EXAMPLE 6**   Use a calculator or Table 2 to approximate to the nearest tenth the solutions to the equation in Example 5.

Using a calculator or Table 2, we see that $\sqrt{22} \approx 4.690$. Thus we have

$$\frac{-1 + \sqrt{22}}{3} \approx \frac{-1 + 4.690}{3} \qquad \text{or} \qquad \frac{-1 - \sqrt{22}}{3} \approx \frac{-1 - 4.690}{3}$$

$$= \frac{3.69}{3} \qquad \text{or} \qquad = \frac{-5.69}{3}$$

$$\approx 1.2 \quad \text{to the} \qquad \text{or} \qquad \approx -1.9 \quad \text{to the}$$
$$\text{nearest tenth} \qquad\qquad\qquad\qquad \text{nearest tenth.}$$

The approximate solutions are 1.2 and -1.9.   ◀

DO EXERCISE 6.

EXERCISE SET 15.3

a Solve. Try factoring first. If factoring is not possible or is difficult, use the quadratic formula.

1. $x^2 - 4x = 21$

2. $x^2 + 7x = 18$

3. $x^2 = 6x - 9$

4. $x^2 = 8x - 16$

5. $3y^2 - 2y - 8 = 0$

6. $3y^2 - 7y + 4 = 0$

7. $4x^2 + 12x = 7$

8. $4x^2 + 4x = 15$

9. $x^2 - 9 = 0$

10. $x^2 - 4 = 0$

11. $x^2 - 2x - 2 = 0$

12. $x^2 - 4x - 7 = 0$

13. $y^2 - 10y + 22 = 0$

14. $y^2 + 6y - 1 = 0$

15. $x^2 + 4x + 4 = 7$

16. $x^2 - 2x + 1 = 5$

17. $3x^2 + 8x + 2 = 0$

18. $3x^2 - 4x - 2 = 0$

19. $2x^2 - 5x = 1$

20. $2x^2 + 2x = 3$

21. $4y^2 - 4y - 1 = 0$

22. $4y^2 + 4y - 1 = 0$

23. $2t^2 + 6t + 5 = 0$

24. $4y^2 + 3y + 2 = 0$

25. $3x^2 = 5x + 4$

26. $2x^2 + 3x = 1$

27. $2y^2 - 6y = 10$

ANSWERS

1. _____

2. _____

3. _____

4. _____

5. _____

6. _____

7. _____

8. _____

9. _____

10. _____

11. _____

12. _____

13. _____

14. _____

15. _____

16. _____

17. _____

18. _____

19. _____

20. _____

21. _____

22. _____

23. _____

24. _____

25. _____

26. _____

27. _____

28. $5m^2 = 3 + 11m$

29. $\dfrac{x^2}{x-4} - \dfrac{7}{x-4} = 0$

30. $\dfrac{x^2}{x+3} - \dfrac{5}{x+3} = 0$

31. $x + 2 = \dfrac{3}{x+2}$

32. $x - 3 = \dfrac{5}{x-3}$

33. $\dfrac{1}{x} + \dfrac{1}{x+6} = \dfrac{1}{5}$

34. $\dfrac{1}{x} + \dfrac{1}{x+1} = \dfrac{1}{3}$

b Solve using the quadratic formula. Use a calculator or Table 2 to approximate the solutions to the nearest tenth.

35. $x^2 - 4x - 7 = 0$

36. $x^2 + 2x - 2 = 0$

37. $y^2 - 6y - 1 = 0$

38. $y^2 + 10y + 22 = 0$

39. $4x^2 + 4x = 1$

40. $4x^2 = 4x + 1$

41. $3x^2 + 4x - 2 = 0$

42. $3x^2 - 8x + 2 = 0$

SKILL MAINTENANCE

43. Multiply and simplify: $\sqrt{3x^2}\sqrt{9x^3}$.

44. Subtract: $\sqrt{54} - \sqrt{24}$.

45. Simplify: $\sqrt{80}$.

46. Rationalize the denominator: $\sqrt{\tfrac{7}{3}}$.

SYNTHESIS

Solve.

47. $5x + x(x - 7) = 0$

48. $x(3x + 7) - 3x = 0$

49. $3 - x(x - 3) = 4$

50. $x(5x - 7) = 1$

51. $(y + 4)(y + 3) = 15$

52. $(y + 5)(y - 1) = 27$

53. $x^2 + (x + 2)^2 = 7$

54. $x^2 + (x + 1)^2 = 5$

°15.4   Formulas

a   To solve a formula for a given letter, we try to get the letter alone on one side.

▶ **EXAMPLE 1**   Solve for h: $V = 3.5\sqrt{h}$ (the distance to the horizon).

This is a radical equation. Recall that we first isolate the radical. Then we use the principle of squaring.

$$\frac{V}{3.5} = \sqrt{h}$$ **Isolating the radical**

$$\left(\frac{V}{3.5}\right)^2 = (\sqrt{h})^2$$ **Using the principle of squaring (Section 14.5)**

$$\frac{V^2}{12.25} = h$$ **Simplifying**   ◀

▶ **EXAMPLE 2**   Solve for g: $T = 2\pi\sqrt{\dfrac{L}{g}}$ (the period of a pendulum).

$$\frac{T}{2\pi} = \sqrt{\frac{L}{g}}$$ **Isolating the radical**

$$\left(\frac{T}{2\pi}\right)^2 = \left(\sqrt{\frac{L}{g}}\right)^2$$ **Using the principle of squaring**

$$\frac{T^2}{4\pi^2} = \frac{L}{g}$$

$$gT^2 = 4\pi^2 L$$ **Multiplying by $4\pi^2 g$ to clear of fractions**

$$g = \frac{4\pi^2 L}{T^2}$$ **Dividing by T^2 to get g alone**   ◀

DO EXERCISES 1–3.

In most formulas, the letters represent nonnegative numbers, so we need not use absolute values when taking square roots.

▶ **EXAMPLE 3**   *Torricelli's theorem.* The speed v of a liquid leaving a tank from an orifice is related to the height h of the top of the liquid above the orifice by the formula

$$h = \frac{v^2}{2g}.$$

Solve for v.

Since v^2 appears by itself and there is no expression involving v, we first solve for v^2. Then we use the principle of square roots, taking only the nonnegative square root because v is nonnegative.

$$2gh = v^2$$ **Multiplying by $2g$ to clear of fractions**
$$\sqrt{2gh} = v$$ **Using the principle of square roots. Assume that v is nonnegative.**   ◀

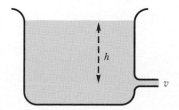

DO EXERCISE 4.

1. Solve for L: $r = 2\sqrt{5L}$ (the speed of a skidding car).

2. Solve for L: $T = 2\pi\sqrt{\dfrac{L}{g}}.$

3. Solve for m: $c = \sqrt{\dfrac{E}{m}}.$

4. Solve for r: $A = \pi r^2$ (the area of a circle).

5. Solve for d: $C = P(d - 1)^2$.

▶ **EXAMPLE 4**   Solve for r: $A = P(1 + r)^2$ (a compound-interest formula).

$$A = P(1 + r)^2$$

$$\frac{A}{P} = (1 + r)^2 \qquad \text{Dividing by } P$$

$$\sqrt{\frac{A}{P}} = 1 + r \qquad \begin{array}{l}\text{Using the principle of square roots.}\\ \text{Assume that } 1 + r \text{ is nonnegative.}\end{array}$$

$$-1 + \sqrt{\frac{A}{P}} = r \qquad \text{Subtracting 1 to get } r \text{ alone} \qquad ◀$$

DO EXERCISE 5.

Sometimes we must use the quadratic formula to solve a formula for a certain letter.

6. Solve for n: $N = n^2 - n$.

▶ **EXAMPLE 5**   Solve for n: $d = \dfrac{n^2 - 3n}{2}$, where d is the number of diagonals of a polygon.

This time there is a term involving n as well as an n^2-term. Thus we must use the quadratic formula.

$$d = \frac{n^2 - 3n}{2}$$

$$n^2 - 3n = 2d \qquad \text{Multiplying by 2 to clear of fractions}$$

$$n^2 - 3n - 2d = 0 \qquad \text{Finding standard form}$$

$$a = 1, \quad b = -3, \quad c = -2d \qquad \text{The letter } d \text{ represents a constant.}$$

$$n = \frac{-b \pm \sqrt{b^2 - 4ac}}{2a} \qquad \text{Quadratic formula}$$

$$n = \frac{-(-3) \pm \sqrt{(-3)^2 - 4 \cdot 1 \cdot (-2d)}}{2 \cdot 1} \qquad \begin{array}{l}\text{Substituting into the}\\ \text{quadratic formula}\end{array}$$

$$n = \frac{3 \pm \sqrt{9 + 8d}}{2} \qquad ◀$$

DO EXERCISE 6.

7. Solve for t: $h = vt + 8t^2$.

▶ **EXAMPLE 6**   Solve for t: $S = gt + 16t^2$.

$$S = gt + 16t^2$$

$$16t^2 + gt - S = 0 \qquad \text{Finding standard form}$$

$$a = 16, \quad b = g, \quad c = -S$$

$$t = \frac{-b \pm \sqrt{b^2 - 4ac}}{2a}$$

$$t = \frac{-g \pm \sqrt{g^2 - 4 \cdot 16 \cdot (-S)}}{2 \cdot 16} \qquad \begin{array}{l}\text{Substituting into the}\\ \text{quadratic formula}\end{array}$$

$$t = \frac{-g \pm \sqrt{g^2 + 64S}}{32} \qquad ◀$$

DO EXERCISE 7.

ANSWERS ON PAGE A-12

NAME   SECTION   DATE

EXERCISE SET 15.4

a Solve for the indicated letter.

1. $N = 2.5\sqrt{A}$, for A

2. $T = 2\pi\sqrt{\dfrac{L}{32}}$, for L

3. $Q = \sqrt{\dfrac{aT}{c}}$, for T

4. $v = \sqrt{\dfrac{2gE}{m}}$, for E

5. $E = mc^2$, for c

6. $S = 4\pi r^2$, for r

7. $Q = ad^2 - cd$, for d

8. $P = kA^2 + mA$, for A

9. $c^2 = a^2 + b^2$, for a

10. $c = \sqrt{a^2 + b^2}$, for b

11. $s = 16t^2$, for t

12. $V = \pi r^2 h$, for r

13. $A = \pi r^2 + 2\pi rh$, for r

14. $A = 2\pi r^2 + 2\pi rh$, for r

15. $A = \dfrac{\pi r^2 S}{360}$, for r

16. $H = \dfrac{D^2 N}{2.5}$, for D

17. $c = \sqrt{a^2 + b^2}$, for a

18. $c^2 = a^2 + b^2$, for b

19. $h = \dfrac{a}{2}\sqrt{3}$, for a

(The height of an equilateral triangle with sides of length a)

20. $d = s\sqrt{2}$, for s

(The hypotenuse of an isosceles right triangle with s the length of the legs)

1. _____

2. _____

3. _____

4. _____

5. _____

6. _____

7. _____

8. _____

9. _____

10. _____

11. _____

12. _____

13. _____

14. _____

15. _____

16. _____

17. _____

18. _____

19. _____

20. _____

21. _____

22. _____

23. _____

24. _____

25. _____

26. _____

27. _____

28. _____

29. _____

30. _____

31. _____

32. _____

33. a) _____

b) _____

34. _____

35. _____

36. _____

21. $n = aT^2 - 4T + m$, for T

22. $y = ax^2 + bx + c$, for x

23. $v = 2\sqrt{\dfrac{2kT}{\pi m}}$, for T

24. $E = \dfrac{1}{2}mv^2 + mgy$, for v

25. $c = \sqrt{\dfrac{E}{m}}$, for E

26. $3x^2 = d^2$, for x

27. $N = \dfrac{n^2 - n}{2}$, for n

28. $M = \dfrac{m}{\sqrt{1 - \left(\dfrac{v}{c}\right)^2}}$, for c

---

SKILL MAINTENANCE

In a right triangle, find the length of the side not given. Given an exact answer and an approximation to three decimal places.

29. $a = 4,\ b = 7$ **30.** $b = 11,\ c = 14$ **31.** $a = 4,\ b = 5$ **32.** $a = 10,\ c = 12$

SYNTHESIS

33. The circumference C of a circle is given by $C = 2\pi r$.

   a) Solve $C = 2\pi r$ for r.

   b) The area is given by $A = \pi r^2$. Express the area in terms of the circumference C.

34. In reference to Exercise 33, express the circumference C in terms of the area A.

35. Solve $3ax^2 - x - 3ax + 1 = 0$ for x.

36. Solve $h = 16t^2 + vt + s$ for t.

15.5 Solving Problems

a   Using Quadratic Equations to Solve Problems

▶ **EXAMPLE 1**   The area of a rectangle is 76 in². The length is 7 in. longer than three times the width. Find the dimensions of the rectangle.

1. *Familiarize.*   We first make a drawing and label it with both known and unknown information. We let w = the width of the rectangle. The length of the rectangle is 7 in. longer than three times the width. Thus the length is $3w + 7$.

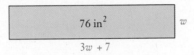

2. *Translate.*   Recall that area is length × width. Thus we have two expressions for the area of the rectangle: $(3w + 7)(w)$ and 76. This gives us a translation:

$$(3w + 7)(w) = 76.$$

3. *Solve.*   We solve the equation:

$$3w^2 + 7w = 76$$
$$3w^2 + 7w - 76 = 0$$
$(3w + 19)(w - 4) = 0$ Factoring (the quadratic formula could also be used)
$3w + 19 = 0$ or $w - 4 = 0$ Using the principle of zero products
$3w = -19$ or $w = 4$
$w = -\frac{19}{3}$ or $w = 4.$

4. *Check.*   We check in the original problem. We know that $-\frac{19}{3}$ is not a solution because width cannot be negative. When $w = 4$, $3w + 7 = 19$, and the area is 4(19), or 76. This checks.

5. *State.*   The width of the rectangle is 4 in., and the length is 19 in.   ◀

DO EXERCISE 1.

▶ **EXAMPLE 2**   The hypotenuse of a right triangle is 6 m long. One leg is 1 m longer than the other. Find the lengths of the legs. Round to the nearest tenth.

1. *Familiarize.*   We first make a drawing
~~and the area is 4(19), or 76. This checks.~~
one leg. Then $s + 1$ = the length of the
other leg.

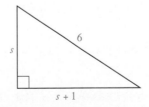

2. *Translate.*   To translate, we use the Pythagorean equation:

$$s^2 + (s + 1)^2 = 6^2.$$

1. The area of a rectangle is 68 in². The length is 1 in. longer than three times the width. Find the dimensions of the rectangle.

2. The hypotenuse of a right triangle is 4 cm long. One leg is 1 cm longer than the other. Find the lengths of the legs. Round to the nearest tenth.

3. *Solve.* We solve the equation:

$$s^2 + (s + 1)^2 = 6^2$$
$$s^2 + s^2 + 2s + 1 = 36$$
$$2s^2 + 2s - 35 = 0.$$

Since we cannot factor, we use the quadratic formula:

$$a = 2, \quad b = 2, \quad c = -35$$

$$s = \frac{-b \pm \sqrt{b^2 - 4ac}}{2a}$$

$$= \frac{-2 \pm \sqrt{2^2 - 4 \cdot 2(-35)}}{2 \cdot 2}$$

$$= \frac{-2 \pm \sqrt{4 + 280}}{4} = \frac{-2 \pm \sqrt{284}}{4}$$

$$= \frac{-2 \pm \sqrt{4 \cdot 71}}{4}$$

$$= \frac{-2 \pm 2 \cdot \sqrt{71}}{2 \cdot 2}$$

$$= \frac{2(-1 \pm \sqrt{71})}{2 \cdot 2}$$

$$= \frac{2}{2} \cdot \frac{-1 \pm \sqrt{71}}{2}$$

$$= \frac{-1 \pm \sqrt{71}}{2}.$$

Using a calculator or Table 2, we get an approximation: $\sqrt{71} \approx 8.426$. Thus,

$$\frac{-1 + 8.426}{2} \approx 3.7 \quad \text{or} \quad \frac{-1 - 8.426}{2} \approx -4.7.$$

4. *Check.* Since the length of a leg cannot be negative, -4.7 does not check. But 3.7 does check. If the smaller leg is 3.7, the other leg is 4.7. Then

$$(3.7)^2 + (4.7)^2 = 13.69 + 22.09 = 35.78.$$

Using a calculator, we get $\sqrt{35.78} \approx 5.96 \approx 6$. Note that our check is not exact because we are using an approximation.

5. *State.* One leg is about 3.7 m long, and the other is about 4.7 m long.

◀

DO EXERCISE 2.

▶ **EXAMPLE 3** The current in a stream moves at a speed of 2 km/h. A boat travels 24 km upstream and 24 km downstream in a total time of 5 hr. What is the speed of the boat in still water?

1. *Familiarize.* We first make a drawing. The distances are the same. Let r = the speed of the boat in still water. Then when the boat is traveling upstream, its speed is $r - 2$. When it is traveling downstream, its speed is $r + 2$. We let t_1 represent the time it takes the boat to go upstream and t_2 represent the time it takes to go downstream. We summarize in a table.

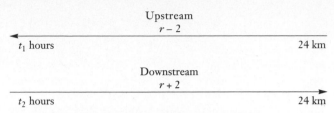

Upstream
$r - 2$

t_1 hours   24 km

Downstream
$r + 2$

t_2 hours   24 km

	d	r	t
Upstream	24	$r - 2$	t_1
Downstream	24	$r + 2$	t_2

2. *Translate.* Recall the basic formula for motion: $d = rt$. From it we can obtain an equation for time: $t = d/r$. Total time consists of the time to go upstream, t_1, plus the time to go downstream, t_2. Using $t = d/r$ and the rows of the table, we have

$$t_1 = \frac{24}{r - 2} \quad \text{and} \quad t_2 = \frac{24}{r + 2}.$$

Since the total time is 5 hr, $t_1 + t_2 = 5$, and we have

$$\frac{24}{r - 2} + \frac{24}{r + 2} = 5.$$

3. *Solve.* We solve the equation. We multiply on both sides by the LCM, which is $(r - 2)(r + 2)$:

$$(r - 2)(r + 2) \cdot \left[\frac{24}{r - 2} + \frac{24}{r + 2} \right] = (r - 2)(r + 2)5 \quad \text{Multiplying by the LCM}$$

$$(r - 2)(r + 2) \cdot \frac{24}{r - 2} + (r - 2)(r + 2) \cdot \frac{24}{r + 2} = (r^2 - 4)5$$

$$24(r + 2) + 24(r - 2) = 5r^2 - 20$$

$$24r + 48 + 24r - 48 = 5r^2 - 20$$

$$-5r^2 + 48r + 20 = 0$$

$$5r^2 - 48r - 20 = 0 \qquad \text{Multiplying by } -1$$

$$(5r + 2)(r - 10) = 0 \qquad \text{Factoring}$$

$$5r + 2 = 0 \quad \text{or} \quad r - 10 = 0 \qquad \text{Using the principle of zero products}$$

$$5r = -2 \quad \text{or} \quad r = 10$$

$$r = -\tfrac{2}{5} \quad \text{or} \quad r = 10.$$

4. *Check.* Since speed cannot be negative, $-\frac{2}{5}$ cannot be a solution. But suppose the speed of the boat in still water is 10 km/h. The speed upstream is then $10 - 2$, or 8 km/h. The speed downstream is $10 + 2$, or 12 km/h. The time upstream, using $t = d/r$, is 24/8, or 3 hr. The time downstream is 24/12, or 2 hr. The total time is 5 hr. This checks.

5. *State.* The speed of the boat in still water is 10 km/h. ◀

3. The speed of a boat in still water is 12 km/h. The boat travels 45 km upstream and 45 km downstream in a total time of 8 hr. What is the speed of the stream? (*Hint:* Let s = the speed of the stream. Then $12 - s$ is the speed upstream and $12 + s$ is the speed downstream. Note also that $12 - s$ cannot be negative, because the boat must be going faster than the current if it is moving forward.)

❖ SIDELIGHTS

Handling Dimension Symbols

In many applications, we add, subtract, multiply and divide quantities having units, or dimensions, such as ft, km, sec, hr, etc. For example, to find average speed, we divide total distance by total time. What results is notation very much like a rational expression.

EXAMPLE 1 A car travels 150 km in 2 hr. What is its average speed?

$$\text{Speed} = \frac{150 \text{ km}}{2 \text{ hr}}, \text{ or } 75 \frac{\text{km}}{\text{hr}}$$

(The standard abbreviation for km/hr is km/h, but it does not suit our present discussion well.)

The symbol km/hr makes it look as if we are dividing kilometers by hours. It may be argued that we can divide only numbers. Nevertheless, we treat dimension symbols, such as km, ft, and hr, as if they were numerals or variables, obtaining correct results mechanically.

EXAMPLE 2 Compare

$$\frac{150x}{2y} = \frac{150}{2} \cdot \frac{x}{y} = 75\frac{x}{y}$$

with

$$\frac{150 \text{ km}}{2 \text{ hr}} = \frac{150}{2} \frac{\text{km}}{\text{hr}} = 75\frac{\text{km}}{\text{hr}}.$$

EXAMPLE 3 Compare

$$3x + 2x = (3 + 2)x = 5x$$

with

$$3 \text{ ft} + 2 \text{ ft} = (3 + 2) \text{ ft} = 5 \text{ ft}.$$

EXAMPLE 4 Compare

$$5x \cdot 3x = 15x^2$$

with

$$5 \text{ ft} \cdot 3 \text{ ft} = 15 \text{ ft}^2 \text{ (square feet).}$$

EXAMPLE 5 Compare

$$5x \cdot 8y = 40xy$$

with

$$5 \text{ men} \cdot 8 \text{ hours} = 40 \text{ man-hours.}$$

If 5 men work 8 hours, the total amount of labor is 40 man-hours, which is the same as 4 men working 10 hours.

EXAMPLE 6 Compare

$$\frac{300x \cdot 240y}{15t} = 4800\frac{xy}{t}$$

with

$$\frac{300 \text{ kW} \cdot 240 \text{ hr}}{15 \text{ da}} = 4800\frac{\text{kW-hr}}{\text{da}}.$$

If an electrical device uses 300 kilowatts for 240 hours over a period of 15 days, its rate of usage of energy is 4800 kilowatt-hours per day. The standard abbreviation for kilowatt-hours is kWh.

These "multiplications" and "divisions" can have humorous interpretations. For example,

$$2 \text{ barns} \cdot 4 \text{ dances} = 8 \text{ barn-dances,}$$

$$2 \text{ dances} \cdot 4 \text{ dances} = 8 \text{ dances}^2 \text{ (8 square dances),}$$

and

$$\text{Ice} \cdot \text{Ice} \cdot \text{Ice} = \text{Ice}^3 \text{ (Ice cubed).}$$

However, the fact that such amusing examples exist causes us no trouble, since they do not come up in practice.

EXERCISES

Add these measures.

1. 45 ft + 23 ft   **2.** 55 km/hr + 27 km/hr

3. 17 g + 28 g   **4.** 3.4 lb + 5.2 lb

Find average speeds, given total distance and total time.

5. 90 mi, 6 hr   **6.** 640 km, 20 hr

7. 9.9 m, 3 sec   **8.** 76 ft, 4 min

Perform these calculations.

9. $\dfrac{3 \text{ in.} \cdot 8 \text{ lb}}{6 \text{ sec}}$ **10.** $\dfrac{60 \text{ men} \cdot 8 \text{ hr}}{20 \text{ da}}$

11. $36 \text{ ft} \cdot \dfrac{1 \text{ yd}}{3 \text{ ft}}$ **12.** $55\dfrac{\text{mi}}{\text{hr}} \cdot 4 \text{ hr}$

13. $5 \text{ ft}^3 + 11 \text{ ft}^3$ **14.** $\dfrac{3 \text{ lb}}{14 \text{ ft}} \cdot \dfrac{7 \text{ lb}}{6 \text{ ft}}$

15. Divide \$4850 by 5 days. **16.** Divide \$25.60 by 8 hr.

NAME   SECTION   DATE

EXERCISE SET 15.5

a Solve.

1. The hypotenuse of a right triangle is 25 ft long. One leg is 17 ft longer than the other. Find the lengths of the legs.

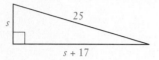

2. The hypotenuse of a right triangle is 26 yd long. One leg is 14 yd longer than the other. Find the lengths of the legs.

1. _____

2. _____

3. The length of a rectangle is 2 cm greater than the width. The area is 80 cm². Find the length and the width.

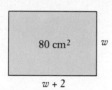

4. The length of a rectangle is 3 m greater than the width. The area is 70 m². Find the length and the width.

3. _____

4. _____

5. The width of a rectangle is 4 cm less than the length. The area is 320 cm². Find the length and the width.

6. The width of a rectangle is 3 cm less than the length. The area is 340 cm². Find the length and the width.

5. _____

6. _____

7. The length of a rectangle is twice the width. The area is 50 m². Find the length and the width.

8. The length of a rectangle is twice the width. The area is 32 cm². Find the length and the width.

7. _____

8. _____

Copyright © 1993 Addison-Wesley Publishing Co., Inc.

ANSWERS

Find the approximate answers for Exercises 9–14. Round to the nearest tenth.

9. The hypotenuse of a right triangle is 8 m long. One leg is 2 m longer than the other. Find the lengths of the legs.

10. The hypotenuse of a right triangle is 5 cm long. One leg is 2 cm longer than the other. Find the lengths of the legs.

9. _____

10. _____

11. The length of a rectangle is 2 in. greater than the width. The area is 20 in². Find the length and the width.

12. The length of a rectangle is 3 ft greater than the width. The area is 15 ft². Find the length and the width.

11. _____

13. The length of a rectangle is twice the width. The area is 10 m². Find the length and the width.

14. The length of a rectangle is twice the width. The area is 20 cm². Find the length and the width.

12. _____

15. A picture frame measures 20 cm by 12 cm. There is 84 cm² of picture showing. The frame is of uniform thickness. Find the thickness of the frame.

16. A picture frame measures 18 cm by 14 cm. There is 192 cm² of picture showing. The frame is of uniform thickness. Find the thickness of the frame.

13. _____

14. _____

15. _____

16. _____

17. The current in a stream moves at a speed of 3 km/h. A boat travels 40 km upstream and 40 km downstream in a total time of 14 hr. What is the speed of the boat in still water? Complete the following table to help with the familiarization.

	d	r	t
Upstream		$r-3$	t_1
Downstream	40		t_2

Upstream

$r - 3$

t_1 hours   40 km

Downstream

$r + 3$

t_2 hours   40 km

18. The current in a stream moves at a speed of 3 km/h. A boat travels 45 km upstream and 45 km downstream in a total time of 8 hr. What is the speed of the boat in still water?

19. The current in a stream moves at a speed of 4 mph. A boat travels 4 mi upstream and 12 mi downstream in a total time of 2 hr. What is the speed of the boat in still water?

20. The current in a stream moves at a speed of 4 mph. A boat travels 5 mi upstream and 13 mi downstream in a total time of 2 hr. What is the speed of the boat in still water?

21. The speed of a boat in still water is 10 km/h. The boat travels 12 km upstream and 28 km downstream in a total time of 4 hr. What is the speed of the stream?

22. The speed of a boat in still water is 8 km/h. The boat travels 60 km upstream and 60 km downstream in a total time of 16 hr. What is the speed of the stream?

ANSWERS

17. _____

18. _____

19. _____

20. _____

21. _____

22. _____

23. _____

24. _____

25. _____

26. _____

27. _____

28. _____

29. _____

30. _____

31. _____

32. _____

23. An airplane flies 738 mi against the wind and 1062 mi with the wind in a total time of 9 hr. The speed of the airplane in still air is 200 mph. What is the speed of the wind?

24. An airplane flies 520 km against the wind and 680 km with the wind in a total time of 4 hr. The speed of the airplane in still air is 300 km/h. What is the speed of the wind?

25. The speed of a boat in still water is 9 km/h. The boat travels 80 km upstream and 80 km downstream in a total time of 18 hr. What is the speed of the stream?

26. The speed of a boat in still water is 10 km/h. The boat travels 48 km upstream and 48 km downstream in a total time of 10 hr. What is the speed of the stream?

SYNTHESIS

27. Find the area of a square for which the diagonal is one unit longer than the length of the sides.

28. Two consecutive integers have squares that differ by 25. Find the integers.

29. Find r in this figure. Round to the nearest hundredth.

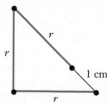

30. A 20-ft pole is struck by lightning and, while not completely broken, falls over and touches the ground 10 ft from the bottom of the pole. How high up did the pole break?

31. What should the diameter d of a pizza be so that it has the same area as two 10-in. pizzas? Do you get more to eat with a 13-in. pizza or with two 10-in. pizzas?

32. Find the side of a square whose diagonal is 3 cm longer than a side.

15.6 Graphs of Quadratic Equations

In this section, we will graph equations of the form

$$y = ax^2 + bx + c, \quad a \neq 0.$$

The polynomial on the right side of the equation is of second degree, or **quadratic.** Examples of the types of equations we are going to graph are

$$y = x^2, \qquad y = x^2 + 2x - 3, \qquad y = -2x^2 + 3.$$

a Graphing Quadratic Equations of the Type $y = ax^2 + bx + c$

Graphs of quadratic equations of the type $y = ax^2 + bx + c$ (where $a \neq 0$) are always cup-shaped. They have a **line of symmetry** like the dashed lines shown in the figures below. If we fold on this line, the two halves will match exactly. The curve goes on forever. The top or bottom point where the curve changes is called the **vertex.** The second coordinate is either the largest value of y or the smallest value of y. The vertex is also thought of as a turning point. Graphs of quadratic equations are called **parabolas.**

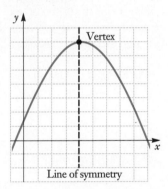

To graph a quadratic equation, we begin by choosing some numbers for x and computing the corresponding values of y.

▶ **EXAMPLE 1** Graph: $y = x^2$.

We choose numbers for x and find the corresponding values for y. Then we plot the ordered pairs (x, y) resulting from the computations and connect them with a smooth curve.

For $x = -3$, $y = x^2 = (-3)^2 = 9$.
For $x = -2$, $y = x^2 = (-2)^2 = 4$.
For $x = -1$, $y = x^2 = (-1)^2 = 1$.
For $x = 0$, $y = x^2 = (0)^2 = 0$.
For $x = 1$, $y = x^2 = (1)^2 = 1$.
For $x = 2$, $y = x^2 = (2)^2 = 4$.
For $x = 3$, $y = x^2 = (3)^2 = 9$.

x	y	(x, y)
-3	9	$(-3, 9)$
-2	4	$(-2, 4)$
-1	1	$(-1, 1)$
0	0	$(0, 0)$
1	1	$(1, 1)$
2	4	$(2, 4)$
3	9	$(3, 9)$

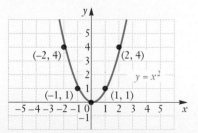

OBJECTIVES

After finishing Section 15.6, you should be able to:

a Graph quadratic equations.

b Find the x-intercepts of a quadratic equation.

FOR EXTRA HELP

Tape 29C

Graph. List the ordered pair for the vertex.

1. $y = x^2 - 3$

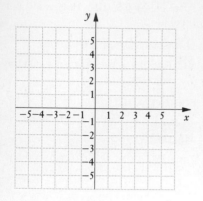

In Example 1, the vertex is the point (0, 0). The second coordinate of the vertex, 0, is the smallest y-value. The y-axis is the line of symmetry. Parabolas whose equations are $y = ax^2$ always have the origin (0, 0) as the vertex and the y-axis as the line of symmetry.

How do we graph a general equation? There are many methods, some of which you will study in your next mathematics course. Our goal here is to give you a basic graphing technique that is fairly easy to apply. A key in the graphing is knowing the vertex. By graphing it and then choosing x-values on both sides of the vertex, we can compute more points and complete the graph.

Finding the Vertex

For a parabola given by the quadratic equation $y = ax^2 + bx + c$:

1. The x-coordinate of the vertex is $-\dfrac{b}{2a}$.

2. The second coordinate of the vertex is found by substituting the x-coordinate into the equation and computing y.

---

2. $y = -3x^2 + 6x$

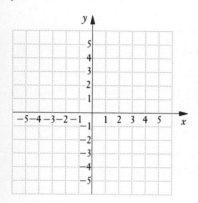

The proof that the vertex can be found in this way can be shown by completing the square in a manner similar to the proof of the quadratic formula, but it will not be considered here.

▶ **EXAMPLE 2**   Graph: $y = -2x^2 + 3$.

We first find the vertex. The x-coordinate of the vertex is

$$-\frac{b}{2a} = -\frac{0}{2(-2)} = 0.$$

We substitute 0 for x into the equation to find the second coordinate of the vertex:

$$y = -2x^2 + 3 = -2(0)^2 + 3 = 3.$$

The vertex is (0, 3). The line of symmetry is $x = 0$, which is the y-axis. We choose some x-values on both sides of the vertex and graph the parabola.

For $x = 1$, $y = -2x^2 + 3 = -2(1)^2 + 3 = -2 + 3 = 1$.
For $x = -1$, $y = -2x^2 + 3 = -2(-1)^2 + 3 = -2 + 3 = 1$.
For $x = 2$, $y = -2x^2 + 3 = -2(2)^2 + 3 = -8 + 3 = -5$.
For $x = -2$, $y = -2x^2 + 3 = -2(-2)^2 + 3 = -8 + 3 = -5$.

3. $y = x^2 - 4x + 4$

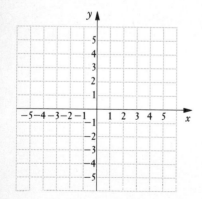

x	y
0	3
1	1
−1	1
2	−5
−2	−5

← This is the vertex.

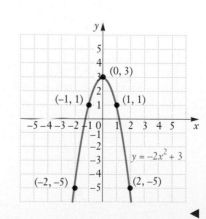

There are two other tips you might use when graphing quadratic equations. The first involves the coefficient of x^2. Note that a in $y = ax^2 + bx + c$ tells us whether the graph opens up or down. When a is positive, as in Example 1, the graph opens up; when a is negative, as in Example 2, the graph opens down. It is also helpful to plot the y-intercept. It occurs when $x = 0$.

Tips for Graphing Quadratic Equations

1. **Graphs of quadratic equations $y = ax^2 + bx + c$ are all parabolas. They are _smooth_ cup-shaped symmetric curves, with no sharp points or kinks in them.**
2. **The graph of $y = ax^2 + bx + c$ opens up if $a > 0$. It opens down if $a < 0$.**
3. **Find the y-intercept. It occurs when $x = 0$, and it is easy to compute.**

▶ **EXAMPLE 3** Graph: $y = x^2 + 2x - 3$.

We first find the vertex. The x-coordinate of the vertex is

$$-\frac{b}{2a} = -\frac{2}{2(1)} = -1.$$

We substitute -1 for x into the equation to find the second coordinate of the vertex:

$$y = x^2 + 2x - 3 = (-1)^2 + 2(-1) - 3 = 1 - 2 - 3 = -4.$$

The vertex is $(-1, -4)$. The line of symmetry is $x = -1$.

We choose some x-values on both sides of the vertex and graph the parabola. Since the coefficient of x^2 is 1, which is positive, we know that the graph opens up. Be sure to find y when $x = 0$. This gives the y-intercept.

x	y	
-1	-4	← Vertex
0	-3	← y-intercept
-2	-3	
1	0	
-3	0	
2	5	
-4	5	

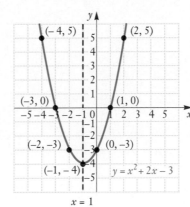

DO EXERCISES 1–3 ON THE PRECEDING PAGE.

Find the x-intercepts.

4. $y = x^2 - 3$

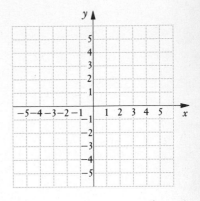

5. $y = x^2 + 6x + 8$

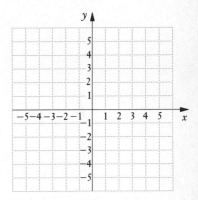

6. $y = -2x^2 - 4x + 1$

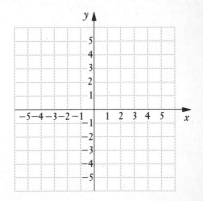

ANSWERS ON PAGE A-12

7. $y = x^2 + 3$

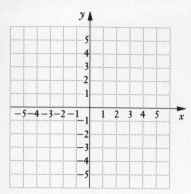

The x-intercepts of $y = ax^2 + bx + c$ occur at those values of x for which $y = 0$. Thus the first coordinates of the x-intercepts are solutions of the equation

$$0 = ax^2 + bx + c.$$

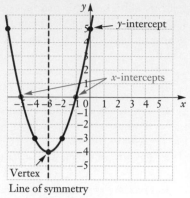

▶ **EXAMPLE 4**   Find the x-intercepts of $y = x^2 - 4x + 1$.

We solve the equation

$$x^2 - 4x + 1 = 0.$$

Factoring is not convenient, so we use the quadratic formula.

$$a = 1, \quad b = -4, \quad c = 1$$

$$x = \frac{-b \pm \sqrt{b^2 - 4ac}}{2a}$$

$$= \frac{-(-4) \pm \sqrt{(-4)^2 - 4(1)(1)}}{2(1)}$$

$$= \frac{4 \pm \sqrt{16 - 4}}{2}$$

$$= \frac{4 \pm \sqrt{12}}{2} = \frac{4 \pm \sqrt{4 \cdot 3}}{2}$$

$$= \frac{4 \pm 2\sqrt{3}}{2} = \frac{2 \cdot 2 \pm 2\sqrt{3}}{2 \cdot 1}$$

$$= \frac{2}{2} \cdot \frac{2 \pm \sqrt{3}}{1} = 2 \pm \sqrt{3}.$$

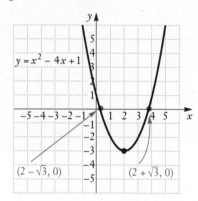

The x-intercepts are $(2 - \sqrt{3}, 0)$ and $(2 + \sqrt{3}, 0)$.   ◀

The discriminant, $b^2 - 4ac$, tells how many real-number solutions the equation $0 = ax^2 + bx + c$ has, so it also tells how many x-intercepts there are.

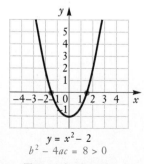

$$y = x^2 - 2$$
$$b^2 - 4ac = 8 > 0$$

Two real solutions
Two x-intercepts

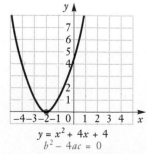

$$y = x^2 + 4x + 4$$
$$b^2 - 4ac = 0$$

One real solution
One x-intercept

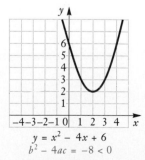

$$y = x^2 - 4x + 6$$
$$b^2 - 4ac = -8 < 0$$

No real solutions
No x-intercepts

DO EXERCISES 4–7. (EXERCISES 4–6 ARE ON THE PRECEDING PAGE.)

NAME   SECTION   DATE

EXERCISE SET 15.6

a Graph the quadratic equation. List the ordered pair for the vertex.

1. $y = x^2 + 1$

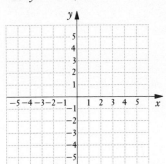

2. $y = 2x^2$

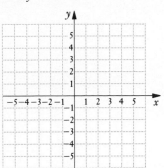

3. $y = -1 \cdot x^2$

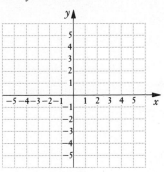

4. $y = x^2 - 1$

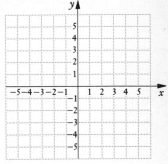

5. $y = -x^2 + 2x$

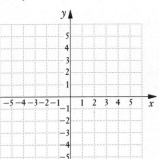

6. $y = x^2 + x - 6$

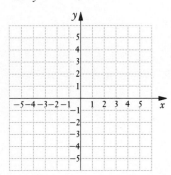

7. $y = 5 - x - x^2$

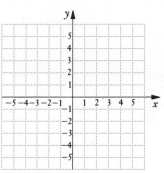

8. $y = x^2 + 2x + 1$

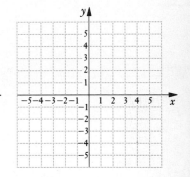

9. $y = x^2 - 2x + 1$

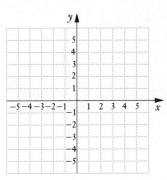

10. $y = -\frac{1}{2}x^2$

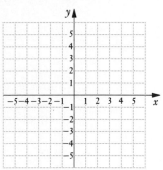

11. $y = -x^2 + 2x + 3$

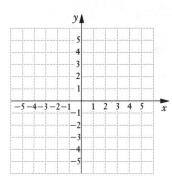

12. $y = -x^2 - 2x + 3$

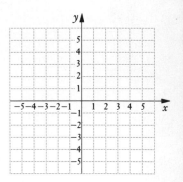

13. $y = -2x^2 - 4x + 1$

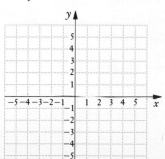

14. $y = 2x^2 + 4x - 1$

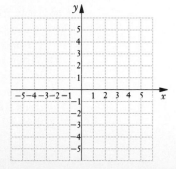

Graph the quadratic equation. Use your own graph paper.

15. $y = \dfrac{1}{4}x^2$ **16.** $y = -0.1x^2$ **17.** $y = 3 - x^2$ **18.** $y = x^2 + 3$

19. $y = -x^2 + x - 1$ **20.** $y = x^2 + 2x$ **21.** $y = -2x^2$ **22.** $y = -x^2 - 1$

23. $y = x^2 - x - 6$ **24.** $y = 8 + x - x^2$

ANSWERS

25. _____

26. _____

27. _____

28. _____

29. _____

30. _____

31. _____

32. _____

33. _____

34. _____

35. _____

36. _____

37. _____

38. _____

39. _____

40. _____

41. a) _____

b) _____

c) _____

b   Find the x-intercepts exactly.

25. $y = x^2 - 5$ **26.** $y = x^2 - 3$ **27.** $y = x^2 + 2x$

28. $y = x^2 - 2x$ **29.** $y = 8 - x - x^2$ **30.** $y = 8 + x - x^2$

31. $y = x^2 + 10x + 25$ **32.** $y = x^2 - 8x + 16$ **33.** $y = -x^2 - 4x + 1$

34. $y = x^2 + 4x - 1$ **35.** $y = x^2 + 5$ **36.** $y = x^2 + 3$

SKILL MAINTENANCE

Add.

37. $\sqrt{x^3 - x^2} + \sqrt{4x - 4}$ **38.** $\sqrt{8} + \sqrt{50} + \sqrt{98} + \sqrt{128}$

Multiply and simplify.

39. $\sqrt{2}\sqrt{14}$ **40.** $\sqrt{3x^2}\sqrt{9x^3}$

SYNTHESIS

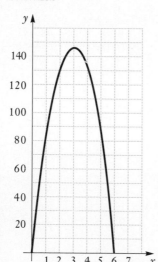

41. *Height of a projectile.* The height H, in feet, of a projectile with an initial velocity of 96 ft/sec is given by the equation

$$H = -16t^2 + 96t,$$

where $t =$ time, in seconds. Use the graph of this function, shown here, or any equation-solving technique to answer the following questions.

a) How many seconds after launch is the projectile 128 ft above ground?

b) When does the projectile reach its maximum height?

c) How many seconds after launch does the projectile return to the ground?

SUMMARY AND REVIEW: CHAPTER 15

IMPORTANT PROPERTIES AND FORMULAS

Standard Form: $\qquad\qquad\quad ax^2 + bx + c = 0,\ a > 0$

Principle of Square Roots: $\quad$ The equation $x^2 = k$, where $k > 0$, has two solutions, $\sqrt{k}$ and $-\sqrt{k}$. The solution of $x^2 = 0$ is 0.

Quadratic Formula: $\qquad\qquad x = \dfrac{-b \pm \sqrt{b^2 - 4ac}}{2a}$

Discriminant: $\qquad\qquad\qquad b^2 - 4ac$

The x-coordinate of the vertex of a parabola $= -\dfrac{b}{2a}$.

REVIEW EXERCISES

The review sections and objectives to be tested in addition to the material in this chapter are [12.6c, d], [14.2d], [14.6b], and [14.4a].

Solve.

1. $8x^2 = 24$

2. $5x^2 - 8x + 3 = 0$

3. $x^2 - 2x - 10 = 0$

4. $3y^2 + 5y = 2$

5. $(x + 8)^2 = 13$

6. $9x^2 = 0$

7. $5t^2 - 7t = 0$

8. $9x^2 - 6x - 9 = 0$

9. $x^2 + 6x = 9$

10. $1 + 4x^2 = 8x$

11. $6 + 3y = y^2$

12. $3m = 4 + 5m^2$

13. $3x^2 = 4x$

14. $40 = 5y^2$

15. $\dfrac{15}{x} - \dfrac{15}{x + 2} = 2$

16. $x + \dfrac{1}{x} = 2$

Solve by completing the square. Show your work.

17. $3x^2 - 2x - 5 = 0$

18. $x^2 - 5x + 2 = 0$

Approximate the solutions to the nearest tenth.

19. $x^2 - 5x + 2 = 0$

20. $4y^2 + 8y + 1 = 0$

21. Solve for T: $V = \dfrac{1}{2}\sqrt{1 + \dfrac{T}{L}}$.

Graph the quadratic equation.

22. $y = 2 - x^2$

23. $y = x^2 - 4x - 2$

Find the x-intercepts.

24. $y = 2 - x^2$

25. $y = x^2 - 4x - 2$

Solve.

26. The hypotenuse of a right triangle is 5 m long. One leg is 3 m longer than the other. Find the lengths of the legs. Round to the nearest tenth.

27. The length of a rectangle is 3 m greater than the width. The area is 70 m². Find the length and the width.

28. The current in a stream moves at a speed of 2 km/h. A boat travels 56 km upstream and 64 km downstream in a total time of 4 hr. What is the speed of the boat in still water?

SKILL MAINTENANCE

Multiply and simplify.

29. $\sqrt{18a}\sqrt{2}$

30. $\sqrt{12xy^2}\sqrt{5xy}$

31. Find an equation of variation where y varies inversely as x and $y = 16$ when $x = 0.0625$.

32. The sides of a rectangle are 1 and $\sqrt{2}$. Find the length of a diagonal.

Add or subtract.

33. $5\sqrt{11} + 7\sqrt{11}$

34. $2\sqrt{90} - \sqrt{40}$

SYNTHESIS

35. Two consecutive integers have squares that differ by 63. Find the integers.

36. Find b such that the trinomial $x^2 + bx + 49$ is a square.

37. Solve: $x - 4\sqrt{x} - 5 = 0$.

38. A square with sides of length s has the same area as a circle with radius of 5 in. Find s.

❖ THINKING IT THROUGH

1. Briefly explain the connection between the number of real-number solutions of a quadratic equation and its x-intercepts.

2. List a quadratic equation with exactly one real-number solution.

3. Solve the following system of equations graphically:

$$y = x^2 - 4x + 1,$$
$$y = 1 - x.$$

4. List the names and give an example of as many types of equations as you can that you have learned to solve in this text.

5. List a quadratic equation with no real-number solutions.

NAME   SECTION   DATE

TEST: CHAPTER 15

Solve.

1. $7x^2 = 35$

2. $7x^2 + 8x = 0$

3. $48 = t^2 + 2t$

4. $3y^2 - 5y = 2$

5. $(x - 8)^2 = 13$

6. $x^2 = x + 3$

7. $m^2 - 3m = 7$

8. $10 = 4x + x^2$

9. $3x^2 - 7x + 1 = 0$

10. $x - \dfrac{2}{x} = 1$

11. $\dfrac{4}{x} - \dfrac{4}{x + 2} = 1$

12. Solve $x^2 - 4x - 10 = 0$ by completing the square. Show your work.

13. Approximate the solutions to $x^2 - 4x - 10 = 0$ to the nearest tenth.

14. Solve for n: $d = an^2 + bn$.

ANSWERS

1. _____

2. _____

3. _____

4. _____

5. _____

6. _____

7. _____

8. _____

9. _____

10. _____

11. _____

12. _____

13. _____

14. _____

ANSWERS

15. _____

16. _____

17. _____

18. _____

19. _____

20. _____

21. _____

22. _____

23. _____

24. _____

25. _____

Graph.

15. $y = 4 - x^2$

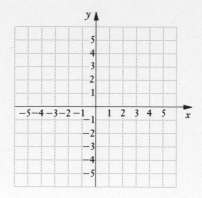

16. $y = -x^2 + x + 5$

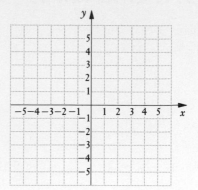

17. Find the x-intercepts: $y = -x^2 + x + 5$.

Solve.

18. The width of a rectangle is 4 m less than the length. The area is 16.25 m². Find the length and the width.

19. The current in a stream moves at a speed of 2 km/h. A boat travels 44 km upstream and 52 km downstream in a total of 4 hr. What is the speed of the boat in still water?

SKILL MAINTENANCE

20. Subtract: $\sqrt{240} - \sqrt{60}$.

21. Multiply and simplify: $\sqrt{7xy}\sqrt{14x^2y}$.

22. Find an equation of variation where y varies inversely as x and $y = 32$ when $x = 0.125$.

23. The sides of a rectangle are $\sqrt{2}$ and $\sqrt{3}$. Find the length of a diagonal.

SYNTHESIS

24. Find the side of a square whose diagonal is 5 ft longer than a side.

25. Solve this system for x. Use the substitution method.

$$x - y = 2,$$
$$xy = 4$$

NAME   SECTION   DATE

FINAL EXAMINATION

Add and simplify if possible.

1.   4 1.3 8
             2.0 1 3
        + 1 7 2.2 2 4 7

2. $3\frac{1}{4}$
       $+5\frac{1}{2}$

Subtract and simplify if possible.

3.   9 0 0 6
        − 3 0 6 9

4. $\frac{3}{4} - \frac{2}{3}$

Multiply and simplify if possible.

5.   2 5.4 3
        ×   8.9

6. $\frac{2}{5} \cdot 15$

7. $3\frac{1}{4} \cdot 7\frac{1}{2}$

Divide and simplify if possible.

8. $2\,1\,\overline{)4\,1\,3\,7}$

9. $\frac{3}{5} \div \frac{9}{10}$

10. $1.6\,\overline{)7\,6.8}$

11. Round 42,574 to the nearest thousand.

12. Round 3.004469 to the nearest thousandth.

13. Determine whether 3312 is divisible by 9.

14. Find the LCM of 23, 46, and 10.

15. Find the prime factorization of 96.

Simplify.

16. $\frac{63}{42}$

17. $\frac{100}{10}$

ANSWERS

1. _____

2. _____

3. _____

4. _____

5. _____

6. _____

7. _____

8. _____

9. _____

10. _____

11. _____

12. _____

13. _____

14. _____

15. _____

16. _____

17. _____

ANSWERS

18. _____

19. _____

20. _____

21. _____

22. _____

23. _____

24. _____

25. _____

26. _____

27. _____

28. _____

29. _____

30. _____

31. _____

32. _____

33. _____

34. _____

35. _____

36. _____

18. Use $<$ or $>$ for ▢ to write a true sentence:

$$\frac{6}{11} \ ▢ \ \frac{5}{9}.$$

19. Which is greater, 0.089 or 0.9?

20. Convert to a mixed numeral: $\frac{23}{3}$.

21. What part is shaded?

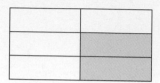

Convert to decimal notation.

22. 49.9%

23. $\frac{6}{25}$

24. $\frac{3}{11}$

25. $\frac{786}{100}$

Convert to fractional notation.

26. $5\frac{3}{4}$

27. 37%

28. 0.897

Convert to percent notation.

29. 0.77

30. $\frac{24}{25}$

Solve.

31. $\frac{25}{12} = \frac{8}{x}$

32. $3.9 + y = 249.6$

33. The enrollment in a college increased from 3000 to 3150. Find the percent of increase.

34. How many $\frac{1}{4}$-lb boxes of chocolate can be filled with 20 lb of chocolates?

35. A worker gets $58 a day for 6 days. How much was received?

36. A $5\frac{1}{2}$-m pole was set $1\frac{3}{4}$ m into the ground. How much was above the ground?

37. A student has $75 in a checking account. Checks of $17 and $19 are written. How much is left in the account?

38. A consumer paid $101.94 for 6 identical blouses. How much did each blouse cost?

39. A driver traveled 216 km in 6 hr. At this rate, how far would the driver travel in 15 hr?

40. A student got 78% of the questions correct on a test. There were 50 questions. How many of the questions were correct?

41. What is the simple interest on $2000 principal at 6% for ½ year?

42. Find the average, the median, and the mode of this set of numbers:
$11, $12, $12, $12, $19, $25.

43. The circle graph shows color preference for a new car.
   a) Which is the favorite color?
   b) The survey considered 5000 people. How many preferred red?

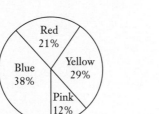

44. Find the perimeter and the area.

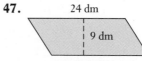
2.8 m
9.6 m

Find the area.

45.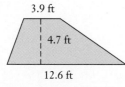
3.9 ft
4.7 ft
12.6 ft

46.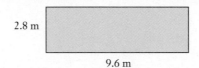
17 m
18 m

47. 24 dm
9 dm

ANSWERS

37. _____

38. _____

39. _____

40. _____

41. _____

42. _____

43. a) _____

b) _____

44. _____

45. _____

46. _____

47. _____

48. Find the radius, the circumference, and the area of this circle. Use 3.14 for π.

8.6 yd

49. Find the volume and the surface area.

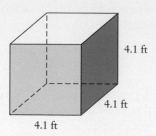

4.1 ft

4.1 ft

4.1 ft

48. _____

49. _____

50. Find the volume. Use 3.14 for π.

1000 m

7

10 m

51. Find the measure of a supplement of an angle of 62°.

50. _____

51. _____

52. Given that $m \parallel n$ and $m\angle 2 = 36°$, find $m\angle 5$.

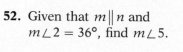

53. Find b.

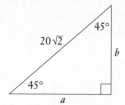

45°

$20\sqrt{2}$

b

45°

a

52. _____

53. _____

54. If $\triangle DEF \sim \triangle JGH$, find JH.

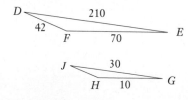

D   210

42

F   70   E

J   30

H   10   G

55. $\angle 1$ and $\angle 2$ are right angles, R is the midpoint of $\overline{QS}$, and $\overline{WQ} \cong \overline{TS}$. Explain why $\triangle WRQ \cong \triangle TRS$.

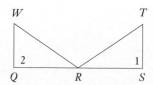

W   T

2   1

Q   R   S

54. _____

55. _____

56. Evaluate $x^3 + 5$ for $x = -10$.

57. Find the absolute value of $|-9|$.

Compute and simplify.

58. $-6.3 + (-8.4) + 5$

59. $-8 - (-3)$

60. $\dfrac{3}{11} \cdot \left(-\dfrac{22}{7}\right)$

61. Remove parentheses and simplify:

$$4y - 5(9 - 3y).$$

62. Simplify:

$$2^3 - 14 \cdot 10 + (3 + 4)^3.$$

Solve.

63. $x + 8 = 13.6$

64. $4x = -28$

65. $5x + 3 = 2x - 27$

66. $5(x - 3) - 2(x + 3) = 0$

67. $x^2 - 2x - 24 = 0$

68. $y = x - 7,$
$2x + y = 5$

69. $5x - 3y = -1,$
$4x + 2y = 30$

70. $\dfrac{1}{x} - 2 = 8x$

71. $\sqrt{x^2 - 11} = x - 1$

72. $x^2 = 7 - 3x$

73. $2 - 3x \le 12 - 7x$

56. _____

57. _____

58. _____

59. _____

60. _____

61. _____

62. _____

63. _____

64. _____

65. _____

66. _____

67. _____

68. _____

69. _____

70. _____

71. _____

72. _____

73. _____

ANSWERS

Solve each formula for the given letter.

74. $A = \dfrac{Bw + 1}{w}$, for w **75.** $K = MT + 2$, for M

74. _____

75. _____

Simplify.

76. $\dfrac{x^8}{x^{-2}}$ **77.** $(x^{-5})^2$ **78.** $x^{-5} \cdot x^{-7}$

76. _____

77. _____

79. Collect like terms and arrange in descending order:
$$2y^3 - 3 + 4y^3 - 3y^2 + 12 - y.$$

78. _____

79. _____

Compute and simplify.

80. $(2x^2 - 6x + 3) - (4x^2 + 2x - 4)$ **81.** $-3t^2(2t^4 + 4t^2 + 1)$

80. _____

81. _____

82. $(4x - 1)(x^2 - 5x + 2)$ **83.** $(x - 8)(x + 8)$

82. _____

83. _____

84. $(2m - 7)^2$ **85.** $(3ab^2 + 2c)^2$

84. _____

85. _____

86. $(3x^2 - 2y)(3x^2 + 4y)$ **87.** $\dfrac{x}{x^2 - 9} \cdot \dfrac{x - 3}{x^3}$

86. _____

87. _____

88. $\dfrac{3x^5}{4x - 4} \div \dfrac{x}{x^2 - 2x + 1}$ **89.** $\dfrac{2}{3x - 1} + \dfrac{1}{4x}$

88. _____

89. _____

90. $\dfrac{3}{x - 3} - \dfrac{x - 1}{x^2 - 2x - 3}$

90. _____

Factor.

91. $3x^3 - 15x$

92. $16x^2 - 25$

93. $6x^2 - 13x + 6$

94. $x^2 - 10x + 25$

95. $2ax + 6bx - ay - 3by$

96. $x^8 - 81y^4$

Simplify.

97. $\sqrt{72}$

98. $\dfrac{\sqrt{54}}{\sqrt{45}}$

99. $2\sqrt{8} + 3\sqrt{18}$

100. $\sqrt{24a^2b}\sqrt{a^3b^2}$

Graph on a plane.

101. $3x + 2y = -4$

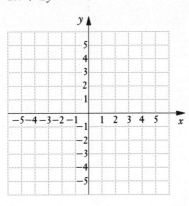

102. $x = -2$

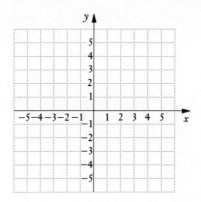

103. $3x - 2y < 6$

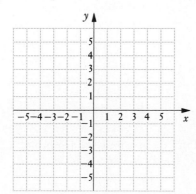

104. $y = x^2 - 2x + 1$

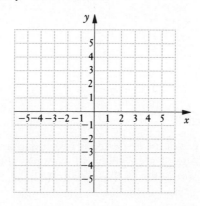

ANSWERS

91. _____

92. _____

93. _____

94. _____

95. _____

96. _____

97. _____

98. _____

99. _____

100. _____

101. _____

102. _____

103. _____

104. _____

ANSWERS

Solve.

105. The sum of the squares of two consecutive odd integers is 74. Find the integers.

106. Solution A is 75% alcohol and solution B is 50% alcohol. How much of each is needed to make 60 L of a solution that is $66\frac{2}{3}$% alcohol?

105. _____

106. _____

107. An airplane flew for 6 hr with a 10-km/h tailwind. The return flight against the same wind took 8 hr. Find the speed of the plane in still air.

108. The width of a rectangle is 3 m less than the length. The area is 88 m². Find the length and the width.

107. _____

108. _____

109. Find the slope of the line containing the points $(-2, 3)$ and $(4, -5)$.

110. Determine whether the graphs of the following equations are parallel, perpendicular, or neither.

$$y = 2x + 7,$$
$$2y + x = 6$$

109. _____

110. _____

Find an equation of variation where:

111. y varies directly as x and $y = 200$ when $x = 25$.

112. y varies inversely as x and $y = 200$ when $x = 25$.

111. _____

112. _____

SYNTHESIS

113. A side of a square is five less than a side of an equilateral triangle. The perimeter of the square is the same as the perimeter of the triangle. Find the length of a side of the square and the length of a side of the triangle.

114. Find c such that the trinomial $x^2 - 24x + c$ is a square.

113. _____

114. _____

Appendixes

OBJECTIVES

After finishing Appendix A, you should be able to:

a Convert from one American unit of length to another.

b Convert from one metric unit to another.

c Convert between American and metric units of length.

Use the unit below to measure the length of each segment or object.

1.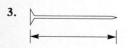

2.

3.

4.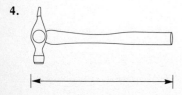

ANSWERS ON PAGE A-12

A   Linear Measures: American and Metric

Length, or distance, is one kind of measure. To find lengths, we *start* with some **unit segment** and assign to it a measure of 1. Suppose $\overline{AB}$ below is a unit segment.

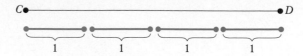

Let's measure segment $\overline{CD}$ below.

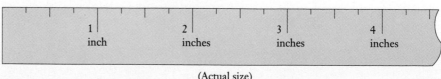

Since we can place 4 unit segments end to end along $\overline{CD}$, the measure of $\overline{CD}$ is 4.

Sometimes we have to use parts of units, called **subunits.** For example, the measure of the segment $\overline{MN}$ below is $1\frac{1}{2}$. We place one unit segment and one half-unit segment end to end.

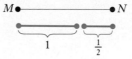

DO EXERCISES 1–4.

a   **American Units**

American units of length are related as follows:

American Units of Length
12 inches (in.) = 1 foot (ft);
3 feet = 1 yard (yd);
5280 feet = 1 mile (mi)

(Actual size)

These American units have also been called "English," or "British-American," because at one time they were used by both countries. Today, both Canada and England state that they have converted to the metric system. However, if you travel in England, you will still see units such as "miles" on road signs.

To change from certain American units to others, we make substitutions.

► **EXAMPLE 1** Complete: 1 yd = _____ in.

$$1 \text{ yd} = 3 \text{ ft}$$
$$= 3 \times 1 \text{ ft} \qquad \text{We think of 3 ft as 3 × ft, or 3 × 1 ft.}$$
$$= 3 \times 12 \text{ in.} \qquad \text{Substituting 12 in. for 1 ft}$$
$$= 36 \text{ in.} \qquad \text{Multiplying} \qquad \blacktriangleleft$$

► **EXAMPLE 2** Complete: 7 yd = _____ in.

$$7 \text{ yd} = 7 \times 1 \text{ yd}$$
$$= 7 \times 3 \text{ ft} \qquad \text{Substituting 3 ft for 1 yd}$$
$$= 7 \times 3 \times 1 \text{ ft}$$
$$= 7 \times 3 \times 12 \text{ in.} \qquad \text{Substituting 12 in. for 1 ft;}$$
$$\text{7 × 3 = 21; 21 × 12 = 252}$$
$$= 252 \text{ in.} \qquad \blacktriangleleft$$

DO EXERCISES 5 AND 6.

Sometimes it helps to use multiplying by 1 in making conversions. For example, 12 in. = 1 ft, so

$$\frac{12 \text{ in.}}{1 \text{ ft}} = 1 \quad \text{and} \quad \frac{1 \text{ ft}}{12 \text{ in.}} = 1.$$

These symbols represent division. If we divide 12 in. by 1 ft or 1 ft by 12 in., we would expect to get 1 because the lengths are the same.

► **EXAMPLE 3** Complete: 48 in. = _____ ft.

We want to convert from "in." to "ft." We multiply by 1 using a symbol for 1 with "in." on the bottom and "ft" on the top to eliminate inches and to convert to feet.

$$48 \text{ in.} = \frac{48 \text{ in.}}{1} \times \frac{1 \text{ ft}}{12 \text{ in.}} \qquad \text{Multiplying by 1 using } \frac{1 \text{ ft}}{12 \text{ in.}} \text{ to eliminate in.}$$
$$= \frac{48 \text{ in.}}{12 \text{ in.}} \times 1 \text{ ft}$$
$$= \frac{48}{12} \times \frac{\text{in.}}{\text{in.}} \times 1 \text{ ft}$$
$$= 4 \times 1 \text{ ft} \qquad \text{The } \frac{\text{in.}}{\text{in.}} \text{ acts like 1, so we can omit it.}$$
$$= 4 \text{ ft}$$

We can also look at this conversion as "canceling" units:

$$48 \text{ in.} = \frac{48 \text{ in.}}{1} \times \frac{1 \text{ ft}}{12 \text{ in.}} = \frac{48}{12} \times 1 \text{ ft} = 4 \text{ ft}. \qquad \blacktriangleleft$$

DO EXERCISES 7–9.

Complete.

5. 8 yd = _____ in.

6. 14.5 yd = _____ ft

Complete.

7. 72 in. = _____ ft

8. 17 in. = _____ ft

9. 24 ft = _____ yd

ANSWERS ON PAGE A-12

Complete.

10. 99 ft = _____ yd

▶ **EXAMPLE 4**   Complete: 25 ft = _____ yd.

Since we are converting from "ft" to "yd," we choose a symbol for 1 with "yd" on the top and "ft" on the bottom.

$$25 \text{ ft} = 25 \text{ ft} \times \frac{1 \text{ yd}}{3 \text{ ft}}$$ 3 ft = 1 yd, so $\frac{3 \text{ ft}}{1 \text{ yd}} = 1$, and $\frac{1 \text{ yd}}{3 \text{ ft}} = 1$. We use $\frac{1 \text{ yd}}{3 \text{ ft}}$ to eliminate ft.

$$= \frac{25}{3} \times \frac{\text{ft}}{\text{ft}} \times 1 \text{ yd}$$

$$= 8\frac{1}{3} \times 1 \text{ yd}$$ The $\frac{\text{ft}}{\text{ft}}$ acts like 1, so we can omit it.

$$= 8\frac{1}{3} \text{ yd, or } 8.3\overline{3} \text{ yd}$$

Again, in this example, we can consider conversion from the point of view of canceling:

$$25 \text{ ft} = 25 \text{ ft} \times \frac{1 \text{ yd}}{3 \text{ ft}} = \frac{25}{3} \times 1 \text{ yd} = 8\frac{1}{3} \text{ yd, or } 8.\overline{3} \text{ yd.} \quad ◀$$

11. 35 ft = _____ yd

DO EXERCISES 10 AND 11.

▶ **EXAMPLE 5**   Complete: 23,760 ft = _____ mi.

We choose a symbol for 1 with "mi" on the top and "ft" on the bottom.

$$23{,}760 \text{ ft} = 23{,}760 \text{ ft} \times \frac{1 \text{ mi}}{5280 \text{ ft}}$$ 5280 ft = 1 mi, so $\frac{1 \text{ mi}}{5280 \text{ ft}} = 1$.

$$= \frac{23{,}760}{5280} \times \frac{\text{ft}}{\text{ft}} \times 1 \text{ mi}$$

$$= 4.5 \times 1 \text{ mi}$$ Dividing

$$= 4.5 \text{ mi}$$

Complete.

12. 26,400 ft = _____ mi

Let us also consider this example using canceling:

$$23{,}760 \text{ ft} = 23{,}760 \text{ ft} \times \frac{1 \text{ mi}}{5280 \text{ ft}} = \frac{23{,}760}{5280} \times 1 \text{ mi} = 4.5 \times 1 \text{ mi} = 4.5 \text{ mi.}$$

◀

DO EXERCISES 12 AND 13.

13. 6 mi = _____ ft

Sometimes we multiply by 1 more than once.

▶ **EXAMPLE 10**   Complete: 8.42 mm = _____ cm.

$$8.42 \text{ mm} = 8.42 \text{ mm} \times \frac{1 \text{ m}}{1000 \text{ mm}} \times \frac{100 \text{ cm}}{1 \text{ m}}$$

Multiplying by 1 using $\frac{1 \text{ m}}{1000 \text{ mm}}$ and $\frac{100 \text{ cm}}{1 \text{ m}}$

$$= \frac{8.42 \times 100}{1000} \times \frac{\text{mm}}{\text{mm}} \times \frac{\text{m}}{\text{m}} \times 1 \text{ cm}$$

$$= \frac{842}{1000} \text{ cm}$$

$$= 0.842 \text{ cm}$$

Using canceling, we can work this example as follows:

$$8.42 \text{ mm} = 8.42 \cancel{\text{mm}} \times \frac{1 \cancel{\text{m}}}{1000 \cancel{\text{mm}}} \times \frac{100 \text{ cm}}{1 \cancel{\text{m}}}$$

$$= \frac{8.42 \times 100}{1000} \times 1 \text{ cm}$$

$$= 0.842 \text{ cm}. \qquad \blacktriangleleft$$

DO EXERCISES 26 AND 27.

Mental Conversion

Look back over the examples and exercises done thus far and you will see that changing from one unit to another in the metric system amounts to only the movement of a decimal point. That is because the metric system is based on 10. Let's find a faster way to convert. Look at the following table.

1000	100	10	1	0.1	0.01	0.001
km	hm	dam	m	dm	cm	mm

Each place in the table has a value $\frac{1}{10}$ that to the left or 10 times that to the right. Thus moving one place in the table corresponds to one decimal place. Let us convert mentally.

▶ **EXAMPLE 11**   Complete: 8.42 mm = _____ cm.

Think: To go from mm to cm in the table is a move of one place to the left. Thus we move the decimal point one place to the left.

8.42   0.8.42   8.42 mm = 0.842 cm   ◀

▶ **EXAMPLE 12**   Complete: 1.886 km = _____ cm.

Think: To go from km to cm is a move of five places to the right. Thus we move the decimal point five places to the right.

1.886   1.88600.   1.886 km = 188,600 cm   ◀

Complete.

26. 9.67 mm = _____ cm

27. 89 km = _____ cm

ANSWERS ON PAGE A-12

Complete. Try to do this mentally using the table.

28. 6780 m = _____ km

29. 9.74 cm = _____ mm

30. 1 mm = _____ cm

31. 845.1 mm = _____ dm

Complete.

32. 100 yd = _____ m
(The length of a football field)

33. 500 mi = _____ km
(The Indianapolis 500-mile race)

34. 3213 km = _____ mi
(The distance from Minneapolis to San Francisco)

▶ **EXAMPLE 13**   Complete: 1 m = _____ cm.

Think: To go from m to cm in the table is a move of two places to the right. Thus we move the decimal point two places to the right.

$$1 \qquad 1.00. \qquad 1 \text{ m} = 100 \text{ cm} \qquad ◀$$

| Make metric conversions mentally as much as possible. |

The fact that conversions can be done so easily is an important advantage of the metric system.

| The most commonly used metric units of length are km, m, cm, and mm. We have purposely used these more often than the others in the exercises. |

DO EXERCISES 28–31.

C   **Converting Between American and Metric Units**

We can make conversions between American and metric units by using the following table. Again, we either make a substitution or multiply by 1 appropriately.

Metric	American
1 m	39.37 in.
1 m	3.3 ft
2.54 cm	1 in.
1 km	0.621 mi
1.609 km	1 mi

▶ **EXAMPLE 14**   Complete: 26.2 mi = _____ km. (This is the length of the Olympic marathon.)

$$26.2 \text{ mi} = 26.2 \times 1 \text{ mi}$$
$$\approx 26.2 \times 1.609 \text{ km}$$
$$= 42.1558 \text{ km} \qquad ◀$$

▶ **EXAMPLE 15**   Complete: 100 m = _____ yd. (This is the length of a dash in track.)

$$100 \text{ m} = 100 \times 1 \text{ m}$$
$$\approx 100 \times 3.3 \text{ ft} = 330 \text{ ft}$$
$$= 330 \text{ ft} \times \frac{1 \text{ yd}}{3 \text{ ft}}$$
$$= \frac{330}{3} \text{ yd} = 110 \text{ yd} \qquad ◀$$

DO EXERCISES 32–34.

NAME   SECTION   DATE

EXERCISE SET A

a Complete.

1. 1 ft = _____ in.

2. 1 yd = _____ ft

3. 1 in. = _____ ft

4. 1 mi = _____ yd

5. 1 mi = _____ ft

6. 1 ft = _____ yd

7. 13 yd = _____ in.

8. 10 yd = _____ ft

9. 84 in. = _____ ft

10. 48 ft = _____ yd

11. 18 in. = _____ ft

12. 29 ft = _____ yd

13. 3 mi = _____ ft

14. 3 mi = _____ yd

15. 3 in. = _____ ft

16. 11,616 ft = _____ mi

17. 10 ft = _____ yd

18. 4.6 yd = _____ ft

19. 10 mi = _____ ft

20. 15,840 ft = _____ mi

21. $4\frac{1}{2}$ ft = _____ yd

1. _____

2. _____

3. _____

4. _____

5. _____

6. _____

7. _____

8. _____

9. _____

10. _____

11. _____

12. _____

13. _____

14. _____

15. _____

16. _____

17. _____

18. _____

19. _____

20. _____

21. _____

ANSWERS

22. _____

23. _____

24. _____

25. _____

26. _____

27. _____

28. _____

29. _____

30. _____

31. _____

32. _____

33. _____

34. _____

35. _____

36. _____

37. a) _____

b) _____

38. a) _____

b) _____

39. a) _____

b) _____

40. a) _____

b) _____

41. a) _____

b) _____

42. a) _____

b) _____

22. 36 in. = _____ ft   **23.** 36 in. = _____ yd   **24.** 10 yd = _____ in.

25. 330 ft = _____ yd   **26.** 1760 yd = _____ mi   **27.** 3520 yd = _____ mi

28. 25 mi = _____ ft   **29.** 100 yd = _____ ft   **30.** 240 in. = _____ ft

31. 360 in. = _____ ft   **32.** 360 in. = _____ yd   **33.** 1 in. = _____ yd

34. 13 in. = _____ ft   **35.** 2 mi = _____ in.   **36.** 63,360 in. = _____ mi

b   Complete. Do as much as possible mentally.

37. a) 1 km = _____ m   **38. a)** 1 hm = _____ m   **39. a)** 1 dam = _____ m

     b) 1 m = _____ km   **b)** 1 m = _____ hm   **b)** 1 m = _____ dam

40. a) 1 dm = _____ m   **41. a)** 1 cm = _____ m   **42. a)** 1 mm = _____ m

     b) 1 m = _____ dm   **b)** 1 m = _____ cm   **b)** 1 m = _____ mm

50. 45 cg = _____ g

51. 0.502 dg = _____ g

52. 0.0025 cg = _____ mg

53. 6780 g = _____ kg

54. 5677 g = _____ kg

55. 69 mg = _____ cg

56. 76.1 mg = _____ cg

57. 8 kg = _____ cg

58. 0.02 kg = _____ mg

59. 1 t = _____ kg

60. 2 t = _____ kg

61. 3.4 cg = _____ dag

62. 4.3 dg = _____ mg

e Complete.

63. 1 day = _____ hr

64. 1 hr = _____ min

65. 1 min = _____ sec

66. 1 wk = _____ days

67. 1 yr = _____ days

68. 2 yr = _____ days

69. 2 wk = _____ hr

70. 4 hr = _____ sec

71. 492 sec = _____ min
(the amount of time it takes for the
rays of the sun to reach the earth)

72. 5 hr = _____ sec

ANSWERS

50. _____

51. _____

52. _____

53. _____

54. _____

55. _____

56. _____

57. _____

58. _____

59. _____

60. _____

61. _____

62. _____

63. _____

64. _____

65. _____

66. _____

67. _____

68. _____

69. _____

70. _____

71. _____

72. _____

ANSWERS

Another metric unit used in medicine is the microgram (μg). It is defined as follows.

$$1 \text{ microgram} = 1\mu g = \frac{1}{1,000,000} \text{ g}; \qquad 1,000,000 \text{ } \mu g = 1 \text{ g}$$

Thus a microgram is one millionth of a gram, and one million micrograms is one gram.

Complete.

73. 1 mg = _____ μg

74. 1 μg = _____ mg

73. _____

74. _____

75. A physician orders 125 μg of digoxin. How many milligrams is the prescription?

76. A physician orders 0.25 mg of reserpine. How many micrograms is the prescription?

75. _____

77. A medicine called sulfisoxazole usually comes in tablets that are 500 mg each. A standard dosage is 2 g. How many tablets would have to be taken in order to achieve this dosage?

78. Quinidine is a liquid mixture, part medicine and part water. There is 80 mg of Quinidine for every milliliter of liquid. A standard dosage is 200 mg. How much of the liquid mixture would be required in order to achieve the dosage?

76. _____

77. _____

79. A medicine called cephalexin is obtainable in a liquid mixture, part medicine and part water. There is 250 mg of cephalexin in 5 mL of liquid. A standard dosage is 400 mg. How much of the liquid would be required in order to achieve the dosage?

80. A medicine called Albuterol is used for the treatment of asthma. It typically comes in an inhaler that contains 18 g. One actuation, or spray, is 90 mg.

   a) How many actuations are in one inhaler?

   b) A student is going away for 4 months of college and wants to take enough Albuterol to last for that time. Assuming that the student will need 4 actuations per day, estimate about how many inhalers the student will need for the 4-month period.

78. _____

79. _____

80. _____

C   The Distance Formula and Midpoints

a   The Distance Formula

We now develop a formula for finding the distance between any two points on a graph when we know their coordinates. First, we consider points on a vertical or a horizontal line.

If points are on a vertical line, they have the same first coordinate.

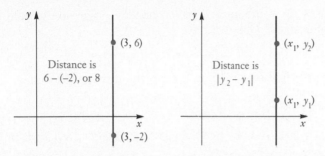

On the left above, we can find the distance between the points by taking the absolute value of the difference of their second coordinates:

$$|6 - (-2)| = |8| = 8. \qquad \text{The distance is 8.}$$

If we subtract the opposite way, we get

$$|-2 - 6| = |-8| = 8.$$

If points are on a horizontal line, we take the absolute value of the difference of their first coordinates.

▶ **EXAMPLES**   Find the distance between these points.

1. $(-5, 13)$ and $(-5, 2)$

We take the absolute value of the difference of the second coordinates, since the first coordinates are the same. The distance is

$$|13 - 2| = |11| = 11.$$

2. $(7, -3)$ and $(-5, -3)$

Since the second coordinates are the same, we take the absolute value of the difference of the first coordinates. The distance is

$$|-5 - 7| = |-12| = 12. \qquad ◀$$

DO EXERCISES 1 AND 2.

Next we consider two points that are not on either a vertical or a horizontal line, such as (x_1, y_1) and (x_2, y_2) in the figure on the following page. By drawing horizontal and vertical lines through these points, we form a right triangle. The vertex of the right angle of this triangle has coordinates (x_2, y_1). The legs have lengths $|x_2 - x_1|$ and $|y_2 - y_1|$. The distance we want is the length of the hypotenuse. By the Pythagorean theorem (Section 10.8),

$$d^2 = |x_2 - x_1|^2 + |y_2 - y_1|^2.$$

OBJECTIVES

After finishing Appendix C, you should be able to:

a Use the distance formula to find the distance between two points whose coordinates are known.

b Use the midpoint formula to find the midpoint of a segment when the coordinates of its endpoints are known.

Find the distance between the pair of points.

1. $(7, 12)$ and $(7, -2)$

2. $(6, 2)$ and $(-5, 2)$

ANSWERS ON PAGE A-13

Find the distance between the pair of points. Where appropriate, find an approximation to three decimal places.

3. $(2, 6)$ and $(-4, -2)$

4. $(-2, 1)$ and $(4, 2)$

Find the midpoint of the segment with the given endpoints.

5. $(-3, 1)$ and $(6, -7)$

6. $(10, -7)$ and $(8, -3)$

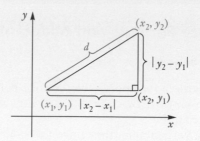

Since squares of numbers are never negative, we don't really need the absolute-value signs. Thus we have

$$d^2 = (x_2 - x_1)^2 + (y_2 - y_1)^2.$$

Taking the principal square root, we get the distance formula.

> **The Distance Formula**
>
> **The distance between any two points (x_1, y_1) and (x_2, y_2) is given by**
> $$d = \sqrt{(x_2 - x_1)^2 + (y_2 - y_1)^2}.$$

This formula holds even when the two points are on a vertical or a horizontal line.

▶   **EXAMPLE 3**   Find the distance between $(4, -3)$ and $(-5, 4)$. Find an exact answer and an approximation to three decimal places.

We substitute into the distance formula:

$$d = \sqrt{(-5 - 4)^2 + [4 - (-3)]^2}$$
$$d = \sqrt{(-9)^2 + 7^2} = \sqrt{130} \approx 11.402.$$

> Note that the distance formula has a radical sign in it. Do not make the mistake of writing $d = (x_2 - x_1)^2 + (y_2 - y_1)^2$.

◀

DO EXERCISES 3 AND 4.

b   Midpoints of Segments

The distance formula can be used to verify or derive a formula for finding the coordinates of the midpoint of a segment when the coordinates of the endpoints are known. We will not derive the formula but simply state it.

> **The Midpoint Formula**
>
> **If the endpoints of a segment are (x_1, y_1) and (x_2, y_2), then the coordinates of the midpoint are**
> $$\left(\frac{x_1 + x_2}{2}, \frac{y_1 + y_2}{2}\right).$$

▶   **EXAMPLE 4**   Find the midpoint of the segment with endpoints $(-2, 3)$ and $(4, -6)$.

Using the midpoint formula, we obtain

$$\left(\frac{-2 + 4}{2}, \frac{3 + (-6)}{2}\right), \quad \text{or} \quad \left(\frac{2}{2}, \frac{-3}{2}\right), \quad \text{or} \quad \left(1, -\frac{3}{2}\right). \qquad ◀$$

DO EXERCISES 5 AND 6.

EXERCISE SET C

ANSWERS

a Find the distance between the pair of points. Where appropriate, find an approximation to three decimal places.

1. (9, 5) and (6, 1)

2. (1, 10) and (7, 2)

3. (0, −7) and (3, −4)

4. (6, 2) and (6, −8)

5. (2, 2) and (−2, −2)

6. (5, 21) and (−3, 1)

7. (8.6, −3.4) and (−9.2, −3.4)

8. (5.9, 2) and (3.7, −7.7)

9. $\left(\dfrac{5}{7}, \dfrac{1}{14}\right)$ and $\left(\dfrac{1}{7}, \dfrac{11}{14}\right)$

10. (0, $\sqrt{7}$) and ($\sqrt{6}$, 0)

11. (−23, 10) and (56, −17)

12. (34, −18) and (−46, −38)

b Find the midpoint of the segment with the given endpoints.

13. (−3, 6) and (2, −8)

14. (6, 7) and (7, −9)

15. (8, 5) and (−1, 2)

16. (−1, 2) and (1, −3)

1. _____

2. _____

3. _____

4. _____

5. _____

6. _____

7. _____

8. _____

9. _____

10. _____

11. _____

12. _____

13. _____

14. _____

15. _____

16. _____

ANSWERS

17. _____

18. _____

19. _____

20. _____

21. _____

22. _____

23. _____

24. _____

25. _____

26. _____

27. _____

28. _____

29. _____

30. _____

31. _____

32. _____

33. _____

17. $(-8, -5)$ and $(6, -1)$ **18.** $(8, -2)$ and $(-3, 4)$

19. $(-3.4, 8.1)$ and $(2.9, -8.7)$ **20.** $(4.1, 6.9)$ and $(5.2, -6.9)$

21. $\left(\dfrac{1}{6}, -\dfrac{3}{4}\right)$ and $\left(-\dfrac{1}{3}, \dfrac{5}{6}\right)$ **22.** $\left(-\dfrac{4}{5}, -\dfrac{2}{3}\right)$ and $\left(\dfrac{1}{8}, \dfrac{3}{4}\right)$

23. $(\sqrt{2}, -1)$ and $(\sqrt{3}, 4)$ **24.** $(9, 2\sqrt{3})$ and $(-4, 5\sqrt{3})$

SYNTHESIS

Find the distance between the given points.

25. $(-1, 3k)$ and $(6, 2k)$ **26.** (a, b) and $(-a, -b)$

27. $(6m, -7n)$ and $(-2m, n)$ **28.** $(\sqrt{d}, -\sqrt{3c})$ and $(\sqrt{d}, \sqrt{3c})$

29. $(-3\sqrt{3}, 1 - \sqrt{6})$ and $(\sqrt{3}, 1 + \sqrt{6})$

If the sides of a triangle have lengths a, b, and c and $a^2 + b^2 = c^2$, then the triangle is a right triangle. Determine whether the given points are vertices of a right triangle.

30. $(9, 6)$, $(-1, 2)$, and $(1, -3)$ **31.** $(-8, -5)$, $(6, 1)$, and $(-4, 5)$

32. Find the point on the y-axis that is equidistant from $(2, 10)$ and $(6, 2)$.

33. Find the midpoint of the segments with the endpoints $(2 - \sqrt{3}, 5\sqrt{2})$ and $(2 + \sqrt{3}, 3\sqrt{2})$.

D ■ Equations Involving Absolute Value

a There are equations that have more than one solution. Examples are equations with absolute value. Remember, the absolute value of a number is its distance from 0 on a number line.

▶ **EXAMPLE 1**   Solve: $|x| = 4$. Then graph using a number line.

Note that $|x| = |x - 0|$, so that $|x - 0|$ is the distance from x to 0. The solutions of the equation are those numbers x whose distance from 0 is 4. Those numbers are -4 and 4. The solution set is $\{-4, 4\}$. The graph consists of just two points, as shown.

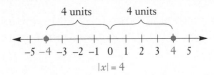

◀

▶ **EXAMPLE 2**   Solve: $|x| = 0$.

The only number whose absolute value is 0 is 0 itself. Thus the solution is 0. The solution set is $\{0\}$.   ◀

▶ **EXAMPLE 3**   Solve: $|x| = -7$.

The absolute value of a number is always nonnegative. There is no number whose absolute value is -7. Thus there is no solution. The solution set is $\varnothing$.   ◀

Examples 1–3 lead us to the following principle for solving linear equations with absolute value.

The Absolute-Value Principle

a) **For any positive number p, if $|X| = p$, then $X = -p$ or $X = p$. The solutions are $-p$ and p. The solution set is $\{-p, p\}$.**

b) **The solution of $|X| = 0$ is 0. The solution set is $\{0\}$.**

c) **If n is negative, $|X| = n$ has no solution. The solution set is $\varnothing$.**

DO EXERCISES 1–3.

We can use the absolute-value principle together with the addition and multiplication principles to solve many types of equations with absolute value.

▶ **EXAMPLE 4**   Solve: $2|x| + 5 = 9$.

We first use the addition and multiplication principles to get $|x|$ by itself. Then we use the absolute-value principle.

1. Solve: $|x| = 6$. Then graph using a number line.

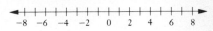

2. Solve: $|x| = -6$.

3. Solve: $|p| = 0$.

Solve.

4. $|3x| = 6$

5. $4|x| + 10 = 27$

6. $3|x| - 2 = 10$

7. Solve: $|x - 4| = 1$. Use two methods as in Example 5.

Solve.

8. $|3x - 4| = 17$

9. $|6 + 2x| = -3$

$$2|x| + 5 = 9$$
$$2|x| + 5 - 5 = 9 - 5 \qquad \text{Subtracting 5}$$
$$2|x| = 4$$
$$|x| = 2 \qquad \text{Dividing by 2}$$
$$x = -2 \quad or \quad x = 2 \qquad \text{Using the absolute-value principle}$$

The solutions are -2 and 2. The solution set is $\{-2, 2\}$.   ◀

DO EXERCISES 4–6.

▶ **EXAMPLE 5**   Solve: $|x - 2| = 3$.

We can consider solving this equation in two different ways.

Method 1. This method allows us to see the meaning of the solutions graphically. The solution set consists of those numbers that are 3 units from 2 on a number line.

3 units   3 units

The solutions of $|x - 2| = 3$ are -1 and 5.

Method 2. The method is more efficient. We use the absolute-value principle, replacing X by $x - 2$ and p by 3. Then we solve each equation separately.

$$|X| = a$$
$$|x - 2| = 3$$
$$x - 2 = -3 \quad or \quad x - 2 = 3 \qquad \text{Absolute-value principle}$$
$$x = -1 \quad or \qquad x = 5$$

The solutions are -1 and 5. The solution set is $\{-1, 5\}$.   ◀

DO EXERCISE 7.

▶ **EXAMPLE 6**   Solve: $|2x + 5| = 13$.

We use the absolute-value principle, replacing X by $2x + 5$ and p by 13:

$$|X| = p$$
$$|2x + 5| = 13$$
$$2x + 5 = -13 \quad or \quad 2x + 5 = 13 \qquad \text{Absolute-value principle}$$
$$2x = -18 \quad or \qquad 2x = 8$$
$$x = -9 \quad or \qquad x = 4.$$

The solutions are -9 and 4. The solution set is $\{-9, 4\}$.   ◀

▶ **EXAMPLE 7**   Solve: $|4 - 7x| = -8$.

Since absolute value is always nonnegative, this equation has no solution. The solution set is $\varnothing$.   ◀

DO EXERCISES 8 AND 9.

EXERCISE SET D

a Solve.

1. $|x| = 3$

2. $|x| = 5$

3. $|x| = -3$

4. $|x| = -5$

5. $|p| = 0$

6. $|y| = 8.6$

7. $|x - 3| = 12$

8. $|3x - 2| = 6$

9. $|2x - 3| = 4$

10. $|5x + 2| = 3$

11. $|4x - 9| = 14$

12. $|9y - 2| = 17$

13. $|x| + 7 = 18$

14. $|x| - 2 = 6.3$

15. $678 = 289 + |t|$

16. $-567 = -1000 + |x|$

17. $|5x| = 40$

18. $|2y| = 18$

19. $|3x| - 4 = 17$

20. $|6x| + 8 = 32$

1. _____

2. _____

3. _____

4. _____

5. _____

6. _____

7. _____

8. _____

9. _____

10. _____

11. _____

12. _____

13. _____

14. _____

15. _____

16. _____

17. _____

18. _____

19. _____

20. _____

ANSWERS

21. _____

22. _____

23. _____

24. _____

25. _____

26. _____

27. _____

28. _____

29. _____

30. _____

31. _____

32. _____

33. _____

34. _____

35. _____

36. _____

37. _____

21. $5|q| - 2 = 9$

22. $7|z| + 2 = 16$

23. $\left|\dfrac{2x - 1}{3}\right| = 5$

24. $\left|\dfrac{4 - 5x}{6}\right| = 7$

25. $|m + 5| + 9 = 16$

26. $|t - 7| - 5 = 4$

27. $10 - |2x - 1| = 4$

28. $2|2x - 7| + 11 = 25$

29. $|3x - 4| = -2$

30. $|x - 6| = -8$

31. $\left|\dfrac{5}{9} + 3x\right| = \dfrac{1}{6}$

32. $\left|\dfrac{2}{3} - 4x\right| = \dfrac{4}{5}$

SYNTHESIS

33. From the definition of absolute value, $|x| = x$ only when $x \geq 0$. Thus, $|x + 3| = x + 3$ only when $x + 3 \geq 0$ or $x \geq -3$. Solve $|2x - 5| = 2x - 5$ using this same argument.

Solve.

34. $1 - \left|\dfrac{1}{4}x + 8\right| = \dfrac{3}{4}$

35. $|x + 5| = x + 5$

36. $|x - 1| = x - 1$

37. $|7x - 2| = x + 4$

E   Probability

We say that when a coin is tossed, the chances that it will fall heads are 1 out of 2, or the **probability** that it will fall heads is $\frac{1}{2}$. Of course this does not mean that if a coin is tossed ten times, it will necessarily fall heads exactly five times. If the coin is tossed a great number of times, however, it will fall heads very nearly half of them.

Experimental and Theoretical Probability

If we toss a coin a great number of times, say 1000, and count the number of heads, we can determine the probability of getting a head. If there are 503 heads, we would calculate the probability of getting a head to be

$$\frac{503}{1000}, \quad \text{or} \quad 0.503.$$

This is an **experimental** determination of probability. Such a determination of probability is quite common.

    If we consider a coin and reason that it is just as likely to fall heads as tails, we would calculate the probability to be $\frac{1}{2}$. This is a **theoretical** determination of probability. Experimentally, we can determine probabilities within certain limits. These may or may not agree with what we obtain theoretically.

a   Computing Probabilities

Experimental Probabilities

We first consider experimental determination of probability. The basic principle we use in computing such probabilities is as follows.

Principle *P* (Experimental)

An experiment is performed in which *n* observations are made. If a situation *E*, or event, occurs *m* times out of the *n* observations, then we say that the *experimental probability* of that event is given by

$$P(E) = \frac{m}{n}.$$

▶ **EXAMPLE 1**   *Sociological survey.*
An actual experiment was conducted to determine the number of people who are left-handed, right-handed, or both. The results are shown in the graph.

a) Determine the probability that a person is left-handed.

b) Determine the probability that a person is ambidextrous (uses both hands equally well).

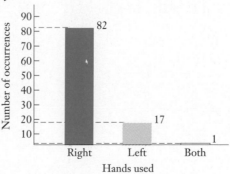

1. In reference to Example 1, what is the probability that a person is right-handed?

a) The number of people who are right-handed was 82, the number who are left-handed was 17, and there was 1 person who was ambidextrous. The total number of observations was $82 + 17 + 1$, or 100. Thus the probability that a person is left-handed is P, where

$$P = \frac{17}{100}.$$

b) The probability that a person is ambidextrous is P, where

$$P = \frac{1}{100}. \qquad \blacktriangleleft$$

DO EXERCISE 1.

▶ **EXAMPLE 2**   *TV ratings.* The major television networks and others such as cable TV are always concerned about the percentages of homes that have TVs and are watching their programs. It is too costly and unmanageable to contact every home in the country so a sample, or portion, of the homes are contacted. This is done by an electronic device attached to the TVs of about 1400 homes across the country. Viewing information is then fed into a computer. The following are the results of a recent survey.

Network	CBS	ABC	NBC	Other or not watching
Number of homes watching	258	231	206	705

What is the probability that a home was tuned to CBS during the time period considered? to ABC?

The probability that a home was tuned to CBS is P, where

$$P = \frac{258}{1400} \approx 0.184 = 18.4\%.$$

The probability that a home was tuned to ABC is P, where

$$P = \frac{231}{1400} \approx 0.165 = 16.5\%. \qquad \blacktriangleleft$$

DO EXERCISE 2.

2. In Example 2, what is the probability that a home was tuned to NBC? What is the probability that a home was tuned to a network other than CBS, ABC, or NBC, or was not tuned in at all?

The numbers that we found in Example 2 and in Margin Exercise 2 (18.4 for CBS, 16.5 for ABC, and 14.7 for NBC) are called the *ratings*.

Theoretical Probabilities

3. What is the probability of rolling a prime number on a die?

We need some terminology before we can continue. Suppose we perform an experiment such as flipping a coin, throwing a dart, drawing a card from a deck, or checking an item off an assembly line for quality. The results of an experiment are called **outcomes.** The set of all possible outcomes is called the **sample space.** An **event** is a set of outcomes, that is, a subset of the sample space. For example, for the experiment "throwing a dart," suppose the dartboard is as follows.

Then one event is

{black},   (the outcome is "hitting black")

which is a subset of the sample space

{black, white, gray},   (sample space)

assuming that the dart must hit the target somewhere.

We denote the probability that an event E occurs as $P(E)$. For example, "getting a head" may be denoted by H. Then $P(H)$ represents the probability of getting a head. When all the outcomes of an experiment have the same probability of occurring, we say that they are **equally likely.** A sample space that can be expressed as a union of equally likely events can allow us to calculate probabilities of other events.

Principle P (Theoretical)

If an event E can occur m ways out of n possible equally likely outcomes of a sample space S, then the *theoretical probability* of that event is given by

$$P(E) = \frac{m}{n}.$$

A die (pl., dice) is a cube, with six faces, each containing a number of dots from 1 to 6.

▶ **EXAMPLE 3** What is the probability of rolling a 3 on a die?

On a fair die, there are 6 equally likely outcomes and there is 1 way to get a 3. By Principle P, $P(3) = \frac{1}{6}$. ◀

▶ **EXAMPLE 4** What is the probability of rolling an even number on a die?

The event is getting an *even* number. It can occur in 3 ways (getting 2, 4, or 6). The number of equally likely outcomes is 6. By Principle P, $P(\text{even}) = \frac{3}{6}$, or $\frac{1}{2}$. ◀

ANSWER ON PAGE A-13

4. Suppose we draw a card from a well-shuffled deck of 52 cards.

  a) What is the probability of drawing a king?

  b) What is the probability of drawing a spade?

  c) What is the probability of drawing a black card?

  d) What is the probability of drawing a jack or a queen?

5. Suppose we select, without looking, one marble from a bag containing 5 red marbles and 6 green marbles. What is the probability of selecting a green marble?

6. On a single roll of a die, what is the probability of getting a 7?

7. On a single roll of a die, what is the probability of getting a 1, 2, 3, 4, 5, or 6?

We now use a number of examples related to a standard bridge deck of 52 cards. Such a deck is made up as shown in the following figure.

A DECK OF 52 CARDS:

▶ **EXAMPLE 5**   What is the probability of drawing an ace from a well-shuffled deck of 52 cards?

Since there are 52 outcomes (cards in the deck) and they are equally likely (from a well-shuffled deck) and there are 4 ways to obtain an ace, by Principle P we have

$$P(\text{drawing an ace}) = \frac{4}{52}, \quad \text{or} \quad \frac{1}{13}. \qquad ◀$$

▶ **EXAMPLE 6**   Suppose we select, without looking, one marble from a bag containing 3 red marbles and 4 green marbles. What is the probability of selecting a red marble?

There are 7 equally likely ways of selecting any marble, and since the number of ways of getting a red marble is 3,

$$P(\text{selecting a red marble}) = \frac{3}{7}. \qquad ◀$$

DO EXERCISES 4 AND 5.

If an event E cannot occur, then $P(E) = 0$. For example, in coin tossing, the event that a coin will land on its edge has probability 0. If an event E is certain to occur (that is, every trial is a success), then $P(E) = 1$. For example, in coin tossing, the event that a coin will fall either heads or tails has probability 1. In general, the probability that an event E will occur is a number from 0 to 1: $0 \leq P(E) \leq 1$.

DO EXERCISES 6 AND 7.

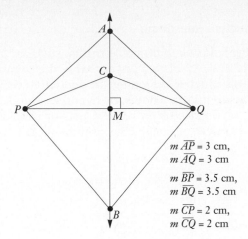

$m\ \overline{AP} = 3$ cm,
$m\ \overline{AQ} = 3$ cm

$m\ \overline{BP} = 3.5$ cm,
$m\ \overline{BQ} = 3.5$ cm

$m\ \overline{CP} = 2$ cm,
$m\ \overline{CQ} = 2$ cm

We see that $\overline{AP} \cong \overline{AQ}$, $\overline{CP} \cong \overline{CQ}$, and $\overline{BP} \cong \overline{BQ}$.

Conclusion: All points on the perpendicular bisector of a segment are equidistant from the endpoints of the segment.   ◀

DO EXERCISE 7.

There are certain lines that determine special points associated with a triangle.

▶ **EXAMPLE 5**   When three or more lines pass through a single point, we say that they are **concurrent.** Draw the bisectors of each of the three angles of each triangle, and draw a conclusion inductively. Use a protractor, a compass, or some other measuring device, or simply estimate where the angle bisectors are.

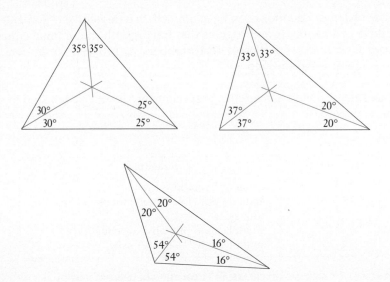

Conclusion: The bisectors of the three angles of a triangle are concurrent.   ◀

DO EXERCISE 8.

7. From each vertex of the following three triangles, draw segments to the midpoints of the opposite sides (such lines are called **medians**). Compare results and draw a conclusion about the intersection of the medians.

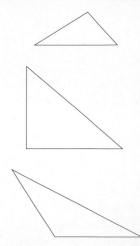

8. Use a ruler to locate the midpoint of each side of the three triangles, and draw perpendiculars to the sides at these midpoints (they are called **perpendicular bisectors**). In each case, measure from their common intersection to the three vertices, and draw a conclusion inductively.

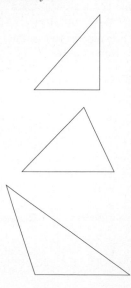

ANSWERS ON PAGE A-13

Draw a conclusion from the following.

9. *Given:*

   a) When it sleets, the highways become slick.

   b) On Tuesday, we had sleet.

   Conclusion:

10. *Given:*

   a) All Texans are Americans.

   b) All citizens of Dallas are Texans.

   Conclusion:

11. *Given:*

   a) Those who shop at Crazy Harry's will save money.

   b) Melanie shopped at Crazy Harry's.

   Conclusion:

12. *Given:*

   a) If a number has more than two factors, then it is a composite number.

   b) The number 10 has four factors.

   Conclusion:

13. Give the reasons in the deductive argument that justify each step in solving the equation $3x + 2 = 14$.

Statements	Reasons
1. $3x + 2 = 14$	1.
2. $3x = 12$	2.
3. $x = 4$	3.

c   Using Deductive Reasoning

Inductive reasoning leads us to probable truths, such as "the next number in the sequence 1, 2, 4, 7, 11, . . . , is *probably* the number 16." Proving the results requires deductive reasoning. In **deductive reasoning,** we start with given facts, assumptions, axioms, or hypotheses and, through steps of logical reasoning, we deduce or prove new facts or conclusions.

By a *proof*, we mean a convincing argument. Let us consider some examples.

▶ **EXAMPLE 6**

Given:

   a) All bricks are red.

   b) This is a brick.

Conclusion: This brick is red.

Of course, we know in real life that all bricks are not red, but from the assumptions, hypotheses, or given facts, we can make a convincing argument that this brick is red.   ◀

▶ **EXAMPLE 7**

Given:

   a) If a number is prime, then it has exactly two factors.

   b) 23 is a prime number.

Conclusion: 23 has exactly two factors.   ◀

DO EXERCISES 9–12.

The solving of equations can be examined as a deductive argument. We use a table of statements and reasons that begins with the original equation and uses laws and properties of real numbers to proceed to an equation whose solution is easy to find.

▶ **EXAMPLE 8**   Find a deductive argument that justifies each step in solving the equation

$$2x - 1 = 5.$$

Statements	Reasons
1. $2x - 1 = 5$	1. Given or hypothesis.
2. $2x = 6$	2. Addition principle for equations: adding 1 on both sides.
3. $x = 3$	3. Multiplication principle for equations: multiplying by $\frac{1}{2}$ on both sides.

DO EXERCISES 13 AND 14. (EXERCISE 14 IS ON THE FOLLOWING PAGE.)

d **Using Deductive Reasoning in Geometry**

Many results in geometry can be justified or proven using deductive reasoning.

▶ **EXAMPLE 9**

Given: Two intersecting lines forming vertical angles 1 and 3 with $m\angle 1 = x$.

Prove: $m\angle 3 = x$.

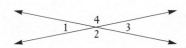

Statements	Reasons
1. Two intersecting lines with $m\angle 1 = x$.	1. Given.
2. $x + m\angle 2 = 180°$	2. $\angle 1$ and $\angle 2$ are supplementary angles.
3. $m\angle 2 + m\angle 3 = 180°$	3. $\angle 2$ and $\angle 3$ are supplementary angles.
4. $m\angle 2 + m\angle 3 = x + m\angle 2$	4. Substituting $x + m\angle 2$ for 180° in step (3).
5. $m\angle 3 = x$	5. Addition principle for equations: adding $-m\angle 2$ on both sides in step (4).

◀

DO EXERCISE 15.

In Section 6.1, it was deduced that the sum of the interior angles of a polygon is $(n - 2)180°$. With deductive reasoning, we can use this fact to prove a formula for the sum of the exterior angles.

▶ **EXAMPLE 10**

Given: A polygon of n sides.

Prove: The sum of the exterior angles is 360°.

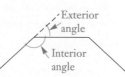

Statements	Reasons
1. The sum of the interior angle and the exterior angle at each vertex is 180°.	1. The angles are supplementary. (See the figure.)
2. $n(180°) =$ the sum of the interior and exterior angles.	2. Multiplying by n.
3. $(n - 2)180° =$ the sum of the interior angles.	3. Proved in Section 6.1.
4. The sum of the exterior angles $= 180°n - (n - 2)180°$ $= 180°n - 180°n + 360°$ $= 360°$.	4. Subtracting the interior-angle sum from the total and simplifying.

◀

DO EXERCISES 16–18.

14. Find a deductive argument that justifies each step in solving the equation $\frac{3}{4}x + 2 = 17$. Answers may vary.

Statements	Reasons
1.	1.
2.	2.
3.	3.
⋮	⋮

15. Using the result and the diagram of Example 9, prove that $m\angle 2 = m\angle 4$.

16. Find the sum of the interior angles of a quadrilateral and then find the sum of the exterior angles.

17. Find the sum of the interior angles of a pentagon (five-sided polygon) and then find the sum of the exterior angles.

18. Find the sum of the exterior angles of a hexagon.

ANSWERS ON PAGE A-13

19. Find the measure of each interior and each exterior angle of a regular decagon (10 sides).

Regular polygons have all sides congruent and all interior angles congruent. We can use our angle-sum formulas to calculate the measure of each interior and each exterior angle of a regular polygon. We use deductive reasoning, but this time we do not use a statement–reason table.

▶ **EXAMPLE 11**   Find the measure of each interior angle and each exterior angle of a regular hexagon (six-sided polygon).

$$\text{Each exterior angle} = \frac{360°}{n} = \frac{360°}{6} = 60°.$$

$$\text{Each interior angle} = 180° - 60° = 120°.$$

DO EXERCISES 19 AND 20.

◀

e   Proving Triangles Congruent

Using deductive reasoning and the congruence properties, we can prove pairs of triangles congruent.

▶ **EXAMPLE 12**

Given: In the figure at the right, $\overline{AB} \cong \overline{DE}$, $\overline{AC} \cong \overline{DF}$, and $\angle A \cong \angle D$.

Prove: $\triangle ABC \cong \triangle DEF$.

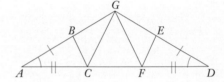

20. Find the measure of each interior and each exterior angle of a regular pentagon (5 sides).

Statements	Reasons
1. $\overline{AB} \cong \overline{DE}$	1. Given.
2. $\overline{AC} \cong \overline{DF}$	2. Given.
3. $\angle A \cong \angle D$	3. Given.
4. $\triangle ABC \cong \triangle DEF$	4. SAS property.

◀

In many cases, some of the corresponding congruent parts necessary to prove triangles congruent are given indirectly, but we can deduce their congruence.

▶ **EXAMPLE 13**

Given: In the figure at the right, $\overline{CP} \perp \overline{QP}$ and $\overline{EQ} \perp \overline{QP}$. Also, $\angle QDE \cong \angle PDC$ and D is the midpoint of $\overline{QP}$.

Prove: $\triangle CPD \cong \triangle EQD$.

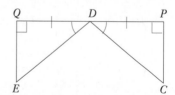

Statements	Reasons
1. $\overline{CP} \perp \overline{QP}$ and $\overline{EQ} \perp \overline{QP}$	1. Given.
2. $\angle P$ and $\angle Q$ are congruent right angles.	2. Perpendicular lines form right angles.
3. D is the midpoint of $\overline{QP}$.	3. Given.
4. $\overline{PD} \cong \overline{QD}$	4. Definition of midpoint.
5. $\angle PDC \cong \angle QDE$	5. Given.
6. $\triangle CPD \cong \triangle EQD$	6. ASA property.

◄

DO EXERCISE 21.

Sometimes we can conclude that angles and segments are congruent by first showing that triangles are congruent.

► **EXAMPLE 14**

Given: In the figure at the right, $\overline{AB} \cong \overline{CB}$ and $\overline{EB} \cong \overline{DB}$.

Prove: $\angle A \cong \angle C$.

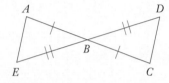

Statements	Reasons
1. $\overline{AB} \cong \overline{CB}$, $\overline{EB} \cong \overline{DB}$	1. Given.
2. $\angle ABE \cong \angle CBD$	2. Vertical angles are congruent.
3. $\triangle ABE \cong \triangle CBD$	3. SAS property.
4. $\angle A \cong \angle C$	4. Corresponding parts of congruent triangles are congruent (CPCTC).

◄

DO EXERCISE 22.

f Deductive Reasoning with Similar Triangles

As we saw in Section 6.8, there are properties we can use to justify that two triangles are congruent. There are also properties that justify that two triangles are similar.

> **THE AA SIMILARITY PROPERTY**
>
> **For any two triangles, if two pairs of corresponding angles are congruent, then the triangles are similar.**
>
> $\triangle PQR \sim \triangle ABC$
>
>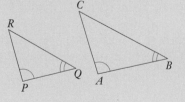

DO EXERCISES 23–25.

21. Given that $\overline{AB} \perp \overline{ED}$ and B is the midpoint of $\overline{ED}$, prove $\triangle ABD \cong \triangle ABE$. Use a table of statements and reasons.

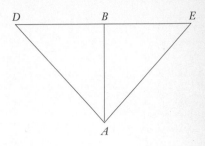

22. Given that $\angle R \cong \angle T$, $\angle W \cong \angle V$, and $\overline{RW} \cong \overline{TV}$, prove $\overline{RS} \cong \overline{TS}$. Use a table of statements and reasons.

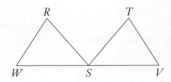

Determine whether the pair of triangles is similar by the AA property.

23.

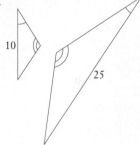

24.

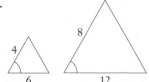

25.

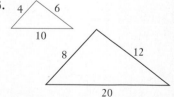

ANSWERS ON PAGE A-13

26. *Given:* $\angle B \cong \angle D$

Prove: $\triangle ABC \sim \triangle EDC$

Use a table of statements and reasons.

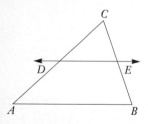

27. Write the proportions that result from the similarity in Margin Exercise 26.

28. *Given:* $\overline{DE} \parallel \overline{AB}$,

        $CD = 3$,

        $CA = 12$,

        $CB = 8$

Find: $CE = ?$

        $AD = ?$

        $EB = ?$

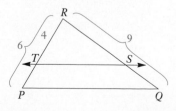

By showing that triangles are similar, we can conclude that the corresponding sides are proportional.

▶ **EXAMPLE 15**

Given: $\angle ABC \cong \angle DEC$

Prove: $\dfrac{AB}{DE} = \dfrac{BC}{EC} = \dfrac{AC}{DC}$

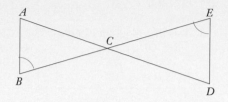

Statements	Reasons
1. $\angle ABC \cong \angle DEC$	1. Given.
2. $\angle ACB \cong \angle DCE$	2. Vertical angles are congruent.
3. $\triangle ABC \sim \triangle DEC$	3. AA property.
4. $\dfrac{AB}{DE} = \dfrac{BC}{EC} = \dfrac{AC}{DC}$	4. Definition of similarity; corresponding sides are proportional.

◀

DO EXERCISES 26 AND 27.

▶ **EXAMPLE 16**

Given: $\overline{DE} \parallel \overline{AB}$

Prove: $\dfrac{CD}{CA} = \dfrac{CE}{CB}$

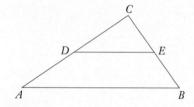

Statements	Reasons
1. $\overline{DE} \parallel \overline{AB}$	1. Given.
2. $\angle CDE \cong \angle CAB$, $\angle CED \cong \angle CBA$	2. Corresponding angles are congruent.
3. $\triangle CDE \sim \triangle CAB$	3. AA property.
4. $\dfrac{CD}{CA} = \dfrac{CE}{CB}$	4. Definition of similarity.

◀

> If a line is parallel to one side of a triangle and intersects the other sides at any points except a vertex, then a triangle similar to the given triangle is formed and the line divides the sides proportionally.

▶ **EXAMPLE 17**   In $\triangle RPQ$, $\overleftrightarrow{TS}$ intersects $\overline{RP}$ and $\overline{RQ}$ at T and S, respectively, and $\overleftrightarrow{TS} \parallel \overline{PQ}$. If $RP = 6$, $RT = 4$, and $RQ = 9$, find RS.

$$\frac{RP}{RT} = \frac{RQ}{RS}$$

$$\frac{6}{4} = \frac{9}{RS} \quad \text{Substituting}$$

$$6(RS) = 36$$

$$RS = 6 \qquad ◀$$

DO EXERCISE 28.

NAME   SECTION   DATE

EXERCISE SET F

a Use inductive reasoning to find the next number in the sequence.

1. 2, 1, 2, 1, 2, . . .

2. 1, 0, 0, 1, 0, 0, 1, . . .

3. 1, 1, 1, 2, 2, 2, 3, 3, 3, . . .

4. 1, 5, 8, 12, 15, . . .

5. 5, 10, 15, . . .

6. 6, 10, 14 . . .

7. 64, 32, 16, 8, 4, . . .

8. 625, −125, 25, −5, 1, . . .

9. 27, 24, 21, . . .

10. −18, −15, −12, . . .

11. $3x, 5x, 7x, \ldots$

12. $24x, 12x, 6x, \ldots$

13. 10, 1, 10, 2, 10, 3, 10, 4, 10, . . .

14. 9, 8, 10, 9, 11, . . .

b

15. Measure the three sides of each triangle, and compare the sum of the two shorter sides with the longest side. Draw an inductive conclusion in the form of an inequality.

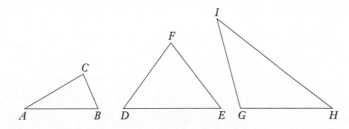

16. Measure the three angles of each triangle in Exercise 15. Then draw an inductive conclusion concerning the relation between the sizes of the angles and the sizes of the sides in a triangle.

17. Measure the length of the two diagonals of each rectangle, and draw an inductive conclusion regarding the lengths of the two diagonals of a rectangle.

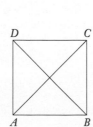

1. _____

2. _____

3. _____

4. _____

5. _____

6. _____

7. _____

8. _____

9. _____

10. _____

11. _____

12. _____

13. _____

14. _____

15. _____

16. _____

17. _____

18. In each rectangle of Exercise 17, measure the two segments into which each diagonal divides the other and draw a conclusion.

19. In each of the following three triangles, use a protractor to find the following angle measures and sums: $m\angle 1$, $m\angle 2$, $m\angle 1 + m\angle 2$, and $m\angle 3$. Draw a conclusion inductively.

18. _____

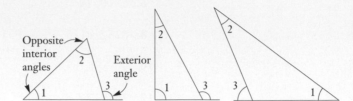

19. _____

20. The lines below are parallel and the distances between them are the same.

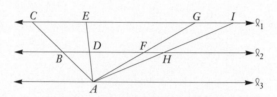

20. _____

Find and compare the measures of each of the following segments. Then draw a conclusion inductively.

$AB =$ _____ $AD =$ _____ $AF =$ _____ $AH =$ _____

$BC =$ _____ $ED =$ _____ $FG =$ _____ $HI =$ _____

C Draw a conclusion from each of the following.

21. *Given:*   **a)** All houses in the Woodland subdivision have two stories.
               b) Jose's house is in the Woodland subdivision.

21. _____

Conclusion:

22. *Given:*   **a)** When the wind blows from the southwest, it will rain.
               b) The wind is blowing from the southwest.

Conclusion:

22. _____

23. *Given:*   **a)** If a majority of voters in a state favor a lottery, then a lottery will be established.

          b) A majority of voters in Texas voted for a state lottery.

  Conclusion:

23. _____

24. _____

24. *Given:*   **a)** If a number is divisible by 3, then it is a multiple of 3.

          b) The number 5004 is divisible by 3.

  Conclusion:

25. Give the reasons in the deductive argument that justify each step in solving the equation $4x + 1 = 17$.

Statements	Reasons
1. $4x + 1 = 17$	1.
2. $4x = 16$	2.
3. $x = 4$	3.

26. Give the reasons in the deductive argument that justify each step in solving the equation $7x - 3 = 32$.

Statements	Reasons
1. $7x - 3 = 32$	1.
2. $7x = 35$	2.
3. $x = 5$	3.

Find a deductive argument that justifies each step in solving the equation. Answers may vary.

27. *Given:* $6x + 2 = 44$

Statements	Reasons
1.	1.
2.	2.
3.	3.
⋮	⋮

28. *Given:* $\frac{2}{3}x - 2 = 22$

Statements	Reasons
1.	1.
2.	2.
3.	3.
⋮	⋮

d   Complete each of the following proofs. The symbol *AB* represents the length or measure of segment *AB*.

29. *Given:* $AB = CD$
     Conclusion: $AC = DB$

Statements	Reasons
1. $AB = CD$	1.
2. $AB + BC = CD + BC$	2.
3. $AC = DB$	3.

30. *Given:* $AC = DB$
     Conclusion: $AB = DC$

Statements	Reasons
1. $AC = DB$	1.
2. $AC - BC = DB - BC$	2.
3. $AB = DC$	3.

31. *Given:* $m\angle 1 = m\angle 2$
    Conclusion: $m\angle 1 = m\angle 3$

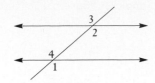

Statements	Reasons

32. *Given:* $m\angle 1 = m\angle 2$
    Conclusion: $m\angle 2 = m\angle 4$

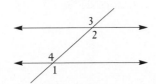

Statements	Reasons

33. *Given:* $m\angle ABC = m\angle BAC,$
           $m\angle ABD = m\angle BAD$
    Conclusion: $m\angle CAD = m\angle CBD$

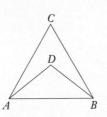

Statements	Reasons

34. *Given:* $m\angle ABD = m\angle CBE$
    Conclusion: $m\angle ABE = m\angle CBD$

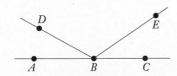

Statements	Reasons

35. Find the sum of the interior angles of a nonagon (nine-sided polygon) and then find the sum of the exterior angles.

36. Find the sum of the interior angles of a heptagon (seven-sided polygon) and then find the sum of the exterior angles.

37. Find the measure of each interior and each exterior angle of a regular octagon (eight sides).

38. Find the measure of each interior and each exterior angle of a regular dodecagon (twelve sides).

39. How many sides has a regular polygon whose exterior angles each measure 20°?

40. How many sides has a regular polygon whose exterior angles each measure 45°?

e

41. *Given:* *R* is the midpoint of both $\overline{PT}$ and $\overline{QS}$.

  Prove: $\triangle PRQ \cong \triangle TRS$

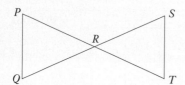

Statements	Reasons

42. *Given:* $\angle 1$ and $\angle 2$ are right angles.
  X is the midpoint of $\overline{AY}$.
  $\overline{XB} \cong \overline{YZ}$.

  Prove: $\triangle ABX \cong \triangle XZY$

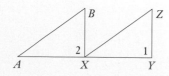

Statements	Reasons

43. *Given:* L is the midpoint of $\overline{KM}$.
$\overline{GL} \perp \overline{KM}$.

Prove: $\triangle KLG \cong \triangle MLG$

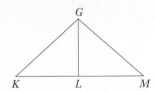

Statements	Reasons

44. *Given:* X is the midpoint of $\overline{QS}$ and $\overline{RP}$.
$\overline{RQ} \cong \overline{SP}$.

Prove: $\triangle RQX \cong \triangle PSX$

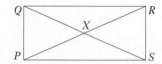

Statements	Reasons

45. *Given:* $\triangle AEB$ and $\triangle CDB$ are isosceles with
$\overline{AE} \cong \overline{AB} \cong \overline{CB} \cong \overline{CD}$.
B is the midpoint of $\overline{ED}$.

Prove: $\triangle AEB \cong \triangle CDB$

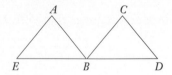

Statements	Reasons

46. *Given:* $\overline{AB} \perp \overline{BE}$ and $\overline{DE} \perp \overline{BE}$.
$\overline{AB} \cong \overline{DE}$.
$\angle BAC \cong \angle EDC$.

Prove: $\triangle ABC \cong \triangle DEC$

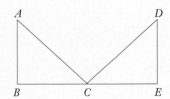

Statements	Reasons

47. *Given:* $\overline{AB} \cong \overline{DC}$.
       $\angle BAC \cong \angle DCA$.
  Prove: $\overline{AD} \cong \overline{CB}$

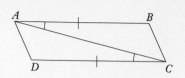

Statements	Reasons

48. *Given:* $\overline{GK} \perp \overline{LJ}$.
       $\overline{HK} \cong \overline{KJ}$.
       $\overline{GK} \cong \overline{LK}$.
  Prove: $\overline{HL} \cong \overline{JG}$

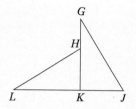

Statements	Reasons

ANSWERS

Multiple Choice

49. In the figure, $\overline{FT} \cong \overline{FR}$ and $\overline{ST} \cong \overline{SR}$. Which property justifies that $\triangle FST \cong \triangle FSR$?

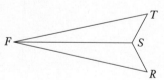

a) ASA   **b)** SSS   **c)** SAS   **d)** AAA   **e)** None of these

49. _____

50. In the figure, L is the midpoint of both $\overline{GN}$ and $\overline{KM}$ and $\overline{GK} \cong \overline{MN}$. Which property justifies that $\triangle GKL \cong \triangle NML$?

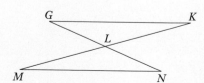

a) ASA   **b)** SSS   **c)** SAS   **d)** AAA   **e)** None of these

50. _____

51. In the figure, T is the midpoint of $\overline{RS}$ and $\angle AST$ is supplementary to $\angle 3$. Thus, $\angle RPT \cong \angle SAT$ because:

a) $\triangle AST \cong \triangle PRT$ by SAS.
b) $\triangle TSA \cong \triangle TRP$ by SSS.
c) $\triangle TRP \cong \triangle TSA$ by ASA.
d) $\triangle AST \cong \triangle PRT$ by AAA.
e) None of these

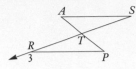

51. _____

52. In the figure, $\overline{TQ} \cong \overline{SQ}$, $\overline{TP} \cong \overline{SR}$, and Q is the midpoint of $\overline{PR}$. Thus, $\angle PTQ \cong \angle RSQ$ because:

a) $\triangle PTQ \cong \triangle RSQ$ by ASA.
b) $\triangle TQP \cong \triangle SQR$ by SSS.
c) $\triangle QPT \cong \triangle QRS$ by SAS.
d) $\triangle PQS \cong \triangle RQT$ by ASA.
e) None of these

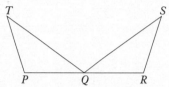

52. _____

53. _____

 Find the missing lengths from the given information, where $\overleftrightarrow{DE} \parallel \overline{AB}$.

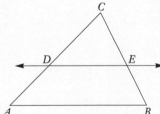

54. _____

53. $CE = 4$, $CB = 20$, $CA = 10$, $CD = ?$, $AD = ?$, $EB = ?$

54. $CA = 12$, $DA = 3$, $CE = 12$, $CB = ?$, $CD = ?$, $EB = ?$

55. _____

55. $DE = 9$, $AB = 15$, $DC = 6$, $DA = ?$

56. $CE = 10$, $EB = 4$, $AB = 18$, $DE = ?$

56. _____

57. *Given:* △*DEF* with parallelogram *DGHK*

    Prove: △*GEH* ~ △*KHF*

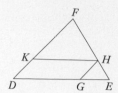

Statements	Reasons

58. *Given:* △*RSX* with parallelogram *RSTV*

    Prove: △*STY* ~ △*XVY*

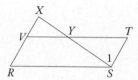

Statements	Reasons

ANSWERS

SYNTHESIS

59. Use inductive reasoning to find the next figure in this sequence.

60. Use inductive reasoning to determine the missing figure in this sequence.

     ?

59. _____

60. _____

Tables

TABLE 1

FRACTIONAL AND DECIMAL EQUIVALENTS

Fractional Notation	Decimal Notation	Percent Notation
$\dfrac{1}{10}$	0.1	10%
$\dfrac{1}{8}$	0.125	12.5%, or $12\dfrac{1}{2}$%
$\dfrac{1}{6}$	$0.16\overline{6}$	$16.6\overline{6}$%, or $16\dfrac{2}{3}$%
$\dfrac{1}{5}$	0.2	20%
$\dfrac{1}{4}$	0.25	25%
$\dfrac{3}{10}$	0.3	30%
$\dfrac{1}{3}$	$0.333\overline{3}$	$33.3\overline{3}$%, or $33\dfrac{1}{3}$%
$\dfrac{3}{8}$	0.375	37.5%, or $37\dfrac{1}{2}$%
$\dfrac{2}{5}$	0.4	40%
$\dfrac{1}{2}$	0.5	50%
$\dfrac{3}{5}$	0.6	60%
$\dfrac{5}{8}$	0.625	62.5%, or $62\dfrac{1}{2}$%
$\dfrac{2}{3}$	$0.6666\overline{6}$	$66.6\overline{6}$%, or $66\dfrac{2}{3}$%
$\dfrac{7}{10}$	0.7	70%
$\dfrac{3}{4}$	0.75	75%
$\dfrac{4}{5}$	0.8	80%
$\dfrac{5}{6}$	$0.83\overline{3}$	$83.3\overline{3}$%, or $83\dfrac{1}{3}$%
$\dfrac{7}{8}$	0.875	87.5%, or $87\dfrac{1}{2}$%
$\dfrac{9}{10}$	0.9	90%
$\dfrac{1}{1}$	1	100%

TABLE 2

SQUARES AND SQUARE ROOTS

N	$\sqrt{N}$	N^2	N	$\sqrt{N}$	N^2	N	$\sqrt{N}$	N^2	N	$\sqrt{N}$	N^2
2	1.414	4	27	5.196	729	52	7.211	2704	77	8.775	5929
3	1.732	9	28	5.292	784	53	7.280	2809	78	8.832	6084
4	2	16	29	5.385	841	54	7.348	2916	79	8.888	6241
5	2.236	25	30	5.477	900	55	7.416	3025	80	8.944	6400
6	2.449	36	31	5.568	961	56	7.483	3136	81	9	6561
7	2.646	49	32	5.657	1024	57	7.550	3249	82	9.055	6724
8	2.828	64	33	5.745	1089	58	7.616	3364	83	9.110	6889
9	3	81	34	5.831	1156	59	7.681	3481	84	9.165	7056
10	3.162	100	35	5.916	1225	60	7.746	3600	85	9.220	7225
11	3.317	121	36	6	1296	61	7.810	3721	86	9.274	7396
12	3.464	144	37	6.083	1369	62	7.874	3844	87	9.327	7569
13	3.606	169	38	6.164	1444	63	7.937	3969	88	9.381	7744
14	3.742	196	39	6.245	1521	64	8	4096	89	9.434	7921
15	3.873	225	40	6.325	1600	65	8.062	4225	90	9.487	8100
16	4	256	41	6.403	1681	66	8.124	4356	91	9.539	8281
17	4.123	289	42	6.481	1764	67	8.185	4489	92	9.592	8464
18	4.243	324	43	6.557	1849	68	8.246	4624	93	9.644	8649
19	4.359	361	44	6.633	1936	69	8.307	4761	94	9.695	8836
20	4.472	400	45	6.708	2025	70	8.367	4900	95	9.747	9025
21	4.583	441	46	6.782	2116	71	8.426	5041	96	9.798	9216
22	4.690	484	47	6.856	2209	72	8.485	5184	97	9.849	9409
23	4.796	529	48	6.928	2304	73	8.544	5329	98	9.899	9604
24	4.899	576	49	7	2401	74	8.602	5476	99	9.950	9801
25	5	625	50	7.071	2500	75	8.660	5625	100	10	10,000
26	5.099	676	51	7.141	2601	76	8.718	5776			

Margin Exercises, Section 6.4, pp. 286–288

1. 43.8 cm² **2.** 12.375 km² **3.** 96 m² **4.** 18.7 cm²
5. 100 m² **6.** 88 cm² **7.** 54 m²

Margin Exercises, Section 6.5, pp. 291–294

1. 12 km **2.** 5 ft **3.** 62.8 **4.** 88 m **5.** 20.096 cm
6. $78\frac{4}{7}$ km² **7.** 339.62 cm² **8.** The pizza pan by 13.04 in²

Margin Exercises, Section 6.6, pp. 299–302

1. 12 cm³ **2.** 38.4 m³ **3.** 128 ft³ **4.** 785 ft³
5. 67,914 m³ **6.** $91,989\frac{1}{3}$ ft³ **7.** 38.77272 cm³
8. 1695.6 m³ **9.** 528 in³

Margin Exercises, Section 6.7, pp. 307–314

1. $\angle 1$ and $\angle 2$, $\angle 1$ and $\angle 4$, $\angle 2$ and $\angle 3$, $\angle 3$ and $\angle 4$
2. 45° **3.** 72° **4.** 5°
5. $\angle 1$ and $\angle 2$, $\angle 1$ and $\angle 4$, $\angle 2$ and $\angle 3$, $\angle 3$ and $\angle 4$
6. 142° **7.** 23° **8.** 90° **9.** No **10.** Yes **11.** No **12.** Yes
13. $m\angle 1 = 10°$, $m\angle 3 = 129°$, $m\angle 5 = 41°$, $m\angle 6 = 129°$
14. $\angle 1$ and $\angle 3$, $\angle 2$ and $\angle 4$, $\angle 5$ and $\angle 7$, $\angle 6$ and $\angle 8$
15. $\angle 2$, $\angle 3$, $\angle 6$, and $\angle 7$ **16.** $\angle 2$ and $\angle 7$, $\angle 6$ and $\angle 3$
17. $m\angle 7 = m\angle 1 = m\angle 5 = 51°$,
$m\angle 8 = m\angle 2 = m\angle 6 = m\angle 4 = 129°$
18. $\angle CED \cong \angle BEA$, $\angle ECD \cong \angle EBA$, $\angle EDC \cong \angle EAB$,
$\angle CEA \cong \angle BED$
19. $\angle TPQ \cong \angle TRS$, $\angle TQP \cong \angle TSR$

Margin Exercises, Section 6.8, pp. 318–322

1. $\angle A \cong \angle D$, $\angle B \cong \angle E$, $\angle C \cong \angle F$; $\overline{AB} \cong \overline{DE}$, $\overline{AC} \cong \overline{DF}$,
$\overline{BC} \cong \overline{EF}$
2. $\angle N \cong \angle P$, $\angle M \cong \angle R$, $\angle O \cong \angle Q$; $\overline{NM} \cong \overline{PR}$, $\overline{NO} \cong \overline{PQ}$,
$\overline{MO} \cong \overline{RQ}$
3. (a), (c) **4.** a **5.** b **6.** None **7.** SAS **8.** ASA
9. SSS **10.** SAS
11. $\triangle SRW \cong \triangle STV$ by ASA; $\angle RSW \cong \angle TSV$, $\overline{RS} \cong \overline{TS}$,
$\overline{SW} \cong \overline{SV}$
12. $\triangle GKP \cong \triangle PTR$ by ASA. Thus, corresponding parts $\overline{GP}$
and $\overline{PR}$ are congruent, and P is the midpoint of $\overline{GR}$.
13. $m\angle C = 27°$, $m\angle B = m\angle D = 153°$
14. $m\angle S = m\angle Q = 114°$, $m\angle P = m\angle R = 66°$
15. $QR = 10$, $SR = 8$ **16.** $DG = EF = 13.6$, $DE = GF = 20.4$

Margin Exercises, Section 6.9, pp. 327–329

1. (a), (b), (d)
2. $\overline{PQ} \leftrightarrow \overline{GH}$, $\overline{QR} \leftrightarrow \overline{HK}$, $\overline{PR} \leftrightarrow \overline{GK}$, $\angle P \leftrightarrow \angle G$, $\angle Q \leftrightarrow \angle H$,
$\angle R \leftrightarrow \angle K$
3. $\angle J \cong \angle A$, $\angle K \cong \angle B$, $\angle L \cong \angle C$; $\dfrac{JK}{AB} = \dfrac{JL}{AC} = \dfrac{KL}{BC}$
4. $\dfrac{PN}{TS} = \dfrac{PM}{TR} = \dfrac{MN}{RS}$ **5.** $BT = 6\frac{3}{4}$, $CT = 9$ **6.** $QR = 10$

CHAPTER 7

Margin Exercises, Section 7.1, pp. 343–346

1. $2,866 - 2,128 = x$ **2.** 64 **3.** 28 **4.** 60 **5.** 192 ft²
6. 3.375 hr **7.** 25 **8.** 16 **9.** $x - 12$ **10.** $y + 12$, or $12 + y$
11. $m - 4$ **12.** $\frac{1}{2}p$ **13.** $6 + 8x$, or $8x + 6$ **14.** $a - b$
15. $59\%x$, or $0.59x$ **16.** $xy - 200$ **17.** $p + q$

Margin Exercises, Section 7.2, pp. 350–356

1. 8, -5 **2.** 134, -76 **3.** -10, 148 **4.** -137, 289
5.

6.

7.

8. -0.375 **9.** $-0.\overline{54}$ **10.** $1.\overline{3}$ **11.** $<$ **12.** $<$ **13.** $>$
14. $>$ **15.** $>$ **16.** $<$ **17.** $<$ **18.** $>$ **19.** $7 > -5$
20. $4 < x$ **21.** False **22.** True **23.** True **24.** 8 **25.** 0
26. 9 **27.** $\frac{2}{3}$ **28.** 5.6

Margin Exercises, Section 7.3, pp. 359–362

1. -8 **2.** -3 **3.** -8 **4.** 4 **5.** 0 **6.** -2 **7.** -11
8. -12 **9.** 2 **10.** -4 **11.** -2 **12.** 0 **13.** -22 **14.** 3
15. 0.53 **16.** 2.3 **17.** -7.7 **18.** -6.2 **19.** $-\frac{2}{9}$ **20.** $-\frac{19}{20}$
21. -58 **22.** -56 **23.** -14 **24.** -12 **25.** 4 **26.** -8.7
27. 7.74 **28.** $\frac{8}{9}$ **29.** 0 **30.** -12 **31.** $-14, 14$ **32.** $-1, 1$
33. 19, -19 **34.** 1.6, -1.6 **35.** $-\frac{2}{3}, \frac{2}{3}$ **36.** $\frac{9}{8}, -\frac{9}{8}$ **37.** 4
38. 13.4 **39.** 0 **40.** $-\frac{1}{4}$

Margin Exercises, Section 7.4, pp. 365–367

1. -10 **2.** 3 **3.** -5 **4.** -2 **5.** -11 **6.** 4 **7.** -2
8. -6 **9.** -16 **10.** 7.1 **11.** 3 **12.** 0 **13.** $\frac{3}{2}$ **14.** -8
15. 7 **16.** -3 **17.** -23.3 **18.** 0 **19.** -9 **20.** 17
21. 12.7 **22.** $17 profit **23.** 50°C

Margin Exercises, Section 7.5, pp. 373–375

1. $2 \cdot 10 = 20$; $1 \cdot 10 = 10$; $0 \cdot 10 = 0$; $-1 \cdot 10 = -10$;
$-2 \cdot 10 = -20$; $-3 \cdot 10 = -30$
2. -18 **3.** -100 **4.** -80 **5.** $-\frac{5}{9}$ **6.** -30.033 **7.** $-\frac{7}{10}$
8. $1 \cdot (-10) = -10$; $0 \cdot (-10) = 0$; $-1 \cdot (-10) = 10$;
$-2 \cdot (-10) = 20$; $-3 \cdot (-10) = 30$
9. 12 **10.** 32 **11.** 35 **12.** $\frac{20}{63}$ **13.** $\frac{2}{3}$ **14.** 13.455 **15.** -30
16. 30 **17.** 0 **18.** $-\frac{8}{3}$ **19.** -30 **20.** -30.75 **21.** $-\frac{5}{3}$
22. 120 **23.** -120 **24.** 6 **25.** 4, -4 **26.** 9, -9 **27.** 48, 48

Margin Exercises, Section 7.6, pp. 379–382

1. -2 **2.** 5 **3.** -3 **4.** 8 **5.** -6 **6.** $-\frac{30}{7}$ **7.** Undefined
8. 0 **9.** $\frac{3}{2}$ **10.** $-\frac{4}{5}$ **11.** $-\frac{1}{3}$ **12.** -5 **13.** $\frac{1}{5.78}$ **14.** $\frac{2}{3}$

15. *First row:* $\frac{2}{3}$, $-\frac{2}{3}$, $\frac{3}{2}$; *second row:* $-\frac{5}{4}$, $\frac{5}{4}$, $-\frac{4}{5}$; *third row:* 0, 0, undefined; *fourth row:* 1, -1, 1; *fifth row:* -4.5, 4.5, $-\frac{1}{4.5}$

16. $\frac{4}{7} \cdot \left(-\frac{5}{3}\right)$ **17.** $5 \cdot \left(-\frac{1}{8}\right)$ **18.** $(a-b) \cdot \left(\frac{1}{7}\right)$ **19.** $-23 \cdot a$

20. $-5 \cdot \left(\frac{1}{7}\right)$ **21.** $-\frac{20}{21}$ **22.** $-\frac{12}{5}$ **23.** $\frac{16}{7}$ **24.** -7

25. $\frac{5}{-6}$, $-\frac{5}{6}$ **26.** $\frac{-8}{7}$, $\frac{8}{-7}$ **27.** $\frac{-10}{3}$, $-\frac{10}{3}$

Margin Exercises, Section 7.7, pp. 385–392

1.

	$x + x$	$2x$
$x = 3$	6	6
$x = -6$	-12	-12
$x = 4.8$	9.6	9.6

2.

	$x + 3x$	$5x$
$x = 2$	8	10
$x = -6$	-24	-30
$x = 4.8$	19.2	24

3. $\frac{3y}{4y}$ **4.** $\frac{3}{4}$ **5.** $-\frac{4}{3}$ **6.** 1; 1   **7.** -10; -10 **8.** $9 + x$

9. qp **10.** $t + xy$, or $yx + t$ **11.** 19; 19   **12.** 150; 150

13. $(a + b) + 2$ **14.** $(3v)w$

15. $(4t)u$, $(tu)4$, $t(4u)$; answers may vary

16. $(2 + r) + s$, $(r + s) + 2$, $s + (r + 2)$; answers may vary

17. (a) 63; **(b)** 63   **18. (a)** 80; **(b)** 80   **19. (a)** 28; **(b)** 28

20. (a) 8; **(b)** 8   **21. (a)** -4; **(b)** -4 **22. (a)** -25; **(b)** -25

23. $5x$, $-4y$, 3   **24.** $-4y$, $-2x$, $3z$ **25.** $3x - 15$

26. $5x - 5y + 20$ **27.** $-2x + 6$ **28.** $-5x + 10y - 20z$

29. $6(x - 2)$ **30.** $3(x - 2y + 3)$ **31.** $b(x + y - z)$

32. $2(8a - 18b + 21)$ **33.** $\frac{1}{8}(3x - 5y + 7)$

34. $-4(3x - 8y + 4z)$ **35.** $3x$ **36.** $6x$ **37.** $-8x$

38. $0.59x$ **39.** $3x + 3y$ **40.** $-4x - 5y - 7$

Margin Exercises, Section 7.8, pp. 397–400

1. $-x - 2$ **2.** $-5x - 2y - 8$ **3.** $-6 + t$ **4.** $-x + y$

5. $4a - 3t + 10$ **6.** $-18 + m + 2n - 4z$ **7.** $2x - 9$

8. $3y + 2$ **9.** $2x - 7$ **10.** $3y + 3$ **11.** $-2a + 8b - 3c$

12. $-9x - 8y$ **13.** $-16a + 18$ **14.** $-26a + 41b - 48c$

15. 2   **16.** 18   **17.** 6   **18.** 17   **19.** $5x - y - 8$ **20.** -1237

21. 381

CHAPTER 8

Margin Exercises, Section 8.1, pp. 411–414

1. False   **2.** True   **3.** Neither true nor false   **4.** Yes   **5.** No

6. No   **7.** -5 **8.** 13.2   **9.** -6.5 **10.** -2 **11.** $\frac{31}{8}$

Margin Exercises, Section 8.2, pp. 417–420

1. $-\frac{4}{5}$ **2.** $-\frac{7}{4}$ **3.** 8   **4.** -18 **5.** 10   **6.** 28   **7.** 7800

8. -3

Margin Exercises, Section 8.3, pp. 423–428

1. 5   **2.** 4   **3.** 4   **4.** 39   **5.** $-\frac{3}{2}$ **6.** -4.3 **7.** -3 **8.** 800

9. 1   **10.** 2   **11.** 2   **12.** $\frac{17}{2}$ **13.** $\frac{8}{3}$ **14.** -4.3 **15.** 2   **16.** 3

17. -2 **18.** $-\frac{1}{2}$

Margin Exercises, Section 8.4, pp. 434–438

1. 28 in., 30 in.   **2.** 5   **3.** 228, 229   **4.** 240.9 mi

5. Width: 9 ft; length: 12 ft   **6.** 30°, 90°, 60°

Margin Exercises, Section 8.5, pp. 443–446

1. 32%   **2.** 25%   **3.** 225   **4.** 50   **5.** 11.04   **6.** 111,416 mi²

7. \$8400   **8.** \$658

Margin Exercises, Section 8.6, pp. 449–450

1. 2.8 mi   **2.** $I = \frac{E}{R}$ **3.** $D = \frac{C}{\pi}$ **4.** $c = 4A - a - b - d$

5. $I = \frac{9R}{E}$

Margin Exercises, Section 8.7, pp. 453–458

1. (a) No; **(b)** no; **(c)** no; **(d)** yes; **(e)** no

2. (a) Yes; **(b)** yes; **(c)** yes; **(d)** no; **(e)** yes

3. $x < 4$

4. $y \geq -2$

5. $-2 \leq x < 4$

6. $\{x \mid x > 2\}$;

7. $\{x \mid x \leq 3\}$;

8. $\{x \mid x < -3\}$;

9. $\{x \mid x \geq \frac{2}{15}\}$ **10.** $\{y \mid y \leq -3\}$

11. $\{x \mid x < 8\}$;

12. $\{y \mid y \geq 32\}$;

13. $\{x \mid x \geq -6\}$ **14.** $\{y \mid y < -\frac{13}{5}\}$ **15.** $\{x \mid x > -\frac{1}{4}\}$

16. $\{y \mid y \geq \frac{19}{9}\}$ **17.** $\{y \mid y \geq \frac{19}{9}\}$ **18.** $\{x \mid x \geq -2\}$

Margin Exercises, Section 8.8, pp. 463–464

1. $x \le 8$ 2. $y > -2$ 3. $s \le 180$ 4. $p \ge \$5800$
5. $2x - 32 > 5$ 6. $\{x \mid x \ge 84\}$ 7. $\{C \mid C < 1063°\}$

CHAPTER 9

Margin Exercises, Section 9.1, pp. 473–478

1. $5 \cdot 5 \cdot 5 \cdot 5$ 2. $x \cdot x \cdot x \cdot x \cdot x$ 3. $3t \cdot 3t$ 4. $3 \cdot t \cdot t$ 5. 6
6. 1 7. 8.4 8. 1 9. 125 10. 3215.36 cm² 11. 119
12. 3; -3 13. (a) 144; (b) 36 (c) No 14. 3^{10} 15. x^{10}
16. p^{24} 17. x^5 18. $a^9 b^8$ 19. 4^3 20. y^4 21. p^9 22. $a^4 b^2$
23. $\frac{1}{4^3} = \frac{1}{64}$ 24. $\frac{1}{5^2} = \frac{1}{25}$ 25. $\frac{1}{2^4} = \frac{1}{16}$ 26. $\frac{1}{(-2)^3} = -\frac{1}{8}$
27. $\frac{4}{p^3}$ 28. x^2 29. 5^2 30. $\frac{1}{x^7}$ 31. $\frac{1}{7^5}$ 32. b 33. t^6

Margin Exercises, Section 9.2, pp. 483–488

1. 3^{20} 2. $\frac{1}{x^{12}}$ 3. y^{15} 4. $\frac{1}{x^{32}}$ 5. $\frac{16x^{20}}{y^{12}}$ 6. $\frac{25x^{10}}{y^{12}z^6}$ 7. x^{74}
8. $\frac{27z^{24}}{y^6 x^{15}}$ 9. $\frac{x^{12}}{25}$ 10. $\frac{8t^{15}}{w^{12}}$ 11. $\frac{9}{x^8}$ 12. 5.17×10^{-4}
13. 5.23×10^8 14. 689,300,000,000 15. 0.0000567
16. 5.6×10^{-15} 17. 7.462×10^{-13} 18. 2.0×10^3
19. 5.5×10^2 20. $3.\overline{3} \times 10^{-2}$ 21. 2.3725×10^9 gal

Margin Exercises, Section 9.3, pp. 491–496

1. $4x^2 - 3x + \frac{5}{4}$; $15y^3$; $-7x^3 + 1.1$; answers may vary
2. -19 3. -104 4. -13 5. 8 6. 132 7. 360 ft
8. 7.55 parts per million 9. $-9x^3 + (-4x^5)$
10. $-2y^3 + 3y^7 + (-7y)$ 11. $3x^2, 6x, \frac{1}{2}$
12. $-4y^5, 7y^2, -3y, -2$ 13. $4x^3$ and $-x^3$
14. $4t^4$ and $-7t^4$; $-9t^3$ and $10t^3$ 15. $2, -7, -8.5, 10, -4$
16. $8x^2$ 17. $2x^3 + 7$ 18. $-\frac{1}{4}x^5 + 2x^2$ 19. $-4x^3$
20. $5x^3$ 21. $25 - 3x^5$ 22. $6x$ 23. $4x^3 + 4$
24. $-\frac{1}{4}x^3 + 4x^2 + 7$ 25. $3x^2 + x^3 + 9$
26. $6x^7 + 3x^5 - 2x^4 + 4x^3 + 5x^2 + x$
27. $7x^5 - 5x^4 + 2x^3 + 4x^2 - 3$ 28. $14t^7 - 10t^5 + 7t^2 - 14$
29. $-2x^2 - 3x + 2$ 30. $10x^4 - 8x - \frac{1}{2}$ 31. 4, 2, 1, 0; 4
32. x 33. x^3, x^2, x, x^0 34. x^2, x 35. x^3 36. Monomial
37. None of these 38. Binomial 39. Trinomial

Margin Exercises, Section 9.4, pp. 501–504

1. $x^2 + 7x + 3$ 2. $-4x^5 + 7x^4 + x^3 + 2x^2 + 4$
3. $24x^4 + 5x^3 + x^2 + 1$ 4. $2x^3 + \frac{10}{3}$ 5. $2x^2 - 3x - 1$
6. $8x^3 - 2x^2 - 8x + \frac{5}{2}$ 7. $-8x^4 + 4x^3 + 12x^2 + 5x - 8$
8. $-x^3 + x^2 + 3x + 3$
9. $-(12x^4 - 3x^2 + 4x)$; $-12x^4 + 3x^2 - 4x$
10. $-(-4x^4 + 3x^2 - 4x)$; $4x^4 - 3x^2 + 4x$
11. $-(-13x^6 + 2x^4 - 3x^2 + x - \frac{5}{13})$;
$13x^6 - 2x^4 + 3x^2 - x + \frac{5}{13}$
12. $-(-7y^3 + 2y^2 - y + 3)$; $7y^3 - 2y^2 + y - 3$

13. $-4x^3 + 6x - 3$ 14. $-5x^4 - 3x^2 - 7x + 5$
15. $-14x^{10} + \frac{1}{2}x^5 - 5x^3 + x^2 - 3x$ 16. $2x^3 + 2x + 8$
17. $x^2 - 6x - 2$ 18. $-8x^4 - 5x^3 + 8x^2 - 1$
19. $x^3 - x^2 - \frac{4}{3}x - 0.9$ 20. $2x^3 - 5x^2 - 2x - 5$
21. $-x^5 - 2x^3 + 3x^2 - 2x + 2$ 22. $\frac{7}{2}x^2$
23. $\pi x^2 - x^2$, or $(\pi - 1)x^2$

Margin Exercises, Section 9.5, pp. 509–512

1. $-15x$ 2. $-x^2$ 3. x^2 4. $-x^5$ 5. $12x^7$ 6. $-8y^{11}$
7. $7y^5$ 8. 0 9. $8x^2 + 16x$ 10. $-15t^3 + 6t^2$
11. $5x^6 + 25x^5 - 30x^4 + 40x^3$ 12. $x^3 + 13x + 40$
13. $x^2 + x - 20$ 14. $5x^2 - 17x - 12$ 15. $6x^2 - 19x + 15$
16. $x^4 + 3x^3 + x^2 + 15x - 20$
17. $6y^5 - 20y^3 + 15y^2 + 14y - 35$
18. $3x^3 + 13x^2 - 6x + 20$
19. $20x^4 - 16x^3 + 32x^2 - 32x - 16$
20. $6x^4 - x^3 - 18x^2 - x + 10$

Margin Exercises, Section 9.6, pp. 516–520

1. $x^2 + 7x + 12$ 2. $x^2 - 2x - 15$ 3. $2x^2 + 9x + 4$
4. $2x^3 - 4x^2 - 3x + 6$ 5. $12x^5 + 6x^2 + 10x^3 + 5$
6. $y^6 - 49$ 7. $-2x^7 + x^5 + x^3$ 8. $t^2 + 8t + 15$
9. $x^2 - \frac{16}{25}$ 10. $x^5 + 0.5x^3 - 0.5x^2 - 0.25$
11. $8 + 2x^2 - 15x^4$ 12. $30x^5 - 3x^4 - 6x^3$ 13. $x^2 - 25$
14. $4x^2 - 9$ 15. $x^2 - 4$ 16. $x^2 - 49$ 17. $36 - 16y^2$
18. $4x^6 - 1$ 19. $x^2 + 16x + 64$ 20. $x^2 - 10x + 25$
21. $x^2 + 4x + 4$ 22. $a^2 - 8a + 16$ 23. $4x^2 + 20x + 25$
24. $16x^4 - 24x^3 + 9x^2$ 25. $49 + 14y + y^2$
26. $9x^4 - 30x^2 + 25$ 27. $x^2 + 11x + 30$ 28. $t^2 - 16$
29. $-8x^5 + 20x^4 + 40x^2$ 30. $81x^4 + 18x^2 + 1$
31. $4a^2 + 6a - 40$ 32. $25x^2 + 5x + \frac{1}{4}$ 33. $4x^2 - 2x + \frac{1}{4}$
34. $x^3 - 3x^2 + 6x - 8$

Margin Exercises, Section 9.7, pp. 525–528

1. -7940 2. -176 3. 433.32 ft² 4. $-3, 3, -2, 1, 2$
5. $3, 7, 1, 1, 0; 7$ 6. $2x^2y + 3xy$ 7. $5pq + 4$
8. $-4x^3 + 2x^2 - 4x + 2$ 9. $14x^3y + 7x^2y - 3xy - 2y$
10. $-5p^2q^4 + 2p^2q^2 + 3p^2q + 6pq^2 + 3q + 5$
11. $-8s^4t + 6s^3t^2 + 2s^2t^3 - s^2t^2$
12. $-9p^4q + 9p^3q^2 - 4p^2q^3 - 9q^4$
13. $x^5y^5 + 2x^4y^2 + 3x^3y^3 + 6x^2$
14. $p^5q - 4p^3q^3 + 3pq^3 + 6q^4$
15. $3x^3y + 6x^2y^3 + 2x^3 + 4x^2y^2$
16. $2x^2 - 11xy + 15y^2$ 17. $16x^2 + 40xy + 25y^2$
18. $9x^4 - 12x^3y^2 + 4x^2y^4$ 19. $4x^2y^4 - 9x^2$
20. $16y^2 - 9x^2y^4$ 21. $9y^2 + 24y + 16 - 9x^2$
22. $4a^2 - 25b^2 - 10bc - c^2$

Margin Exercises, Section 9.8, pp. 533–536

1. $x^2 + 3x + 2$ 2. $2x^2 + x - \frac{2}{3}$ 3. $4x^2 - \frac{3}{2}x + \frac{1}{2}$
4. $2x^2y^4 - 3xy^2 + 5y$ 5. $x - 2$ 6. $x + 4$
7. $x + 4$, R -2, or $x + 4 + \dfrac{-2}{x + 3}$ 8. $x^2 + x + 1$

CHAPTER 10

Margin Exercises, Section 10.1, pp. 545–548

1. (a) $12x^2$; **(b)** $(3x)(4x)$, $(2x)(6x)$, answers may vary
2. (a) $16x^3$; **(b)** $(2x)(8x^2)$, $(4x)(4x^2)$, answers may vary
3. $(8x)(x^3)$; $(4x^2)(2x^2)$; $(2x^3)(4x)$; answers may vary
4. $(7x)(3x)$; $(-7x)(-3x)$; $(21x)(x)$; answers may vary
5. $(6x^4)(x)$; $(-2x^3)(-3x^2)$; $(3x^3)(2x^2)$; answers may vary
6. (a) $3x + 6$; **(b)** $3(x + 2)$
7. (a) $2x^3 + 10x^2 + 8x$; **(b)** $2x(x^2 + 5x + 4)$ **8.** $x(x + 3)$
9. $y^2(3y^4 - 5y + 2)$ **10.** $3x^2(3x^2 - 5x + 1)$
11. $\frac{1}{4}(3t^3 + 5t^2 + 7t + 1)$ **12.** $7x^3(5x^4 - 7x^3 + 2x^2 - 9)$
13. $(x^2 + 3)(x + 7)$ **14.** $(x^2 + 2)(a + b)$ **15.** $(x^2 + 3)(x + 7)$
16. $(2t^2 + 3)(4t + 1)$ **17.** $(3m^3 + 2)(m^2 - 5)$
18. $(2x^2 - 3)(2x - 3)$ **19.** Not factorable by grouping

Margin Exercises, Section 10.2, pp. 551–554

1. $(x + 4)(x + 3)$ **2.** $(x + 9)(x + 4)$ **3.** $(x - 5)(x - 3)$
4. $(t - 5)(t - 4)$ **5.** $x(x + 6)(x - 2)$ **6.** $(y - 6)(y + 2)$
7. $(t^2 + 7)(t^2 - 2)$ **8.** $p(p - q - 3q^2)$ **9.** Not factorable
10. $(x + 4)^2$

Margin Exercises, Section 10.3, pp. 558–560

1. $(2x + 5)(x - 3)$ **2.** $(4x + 1)(3x - 5)$ **3.** $(3x - 4)(x - 5)$
4. $2(5x - 4)(2x - 3)$ **5.** $(2x + 1)(3x + 2)$
6. $(2a - b)(3a - b)$ **7.** $3(2x + 3y)(x + y)$

Margin Exercises, Section 10.4, p. 564

1. $(2x + 1)(3x + 2)$ **2.** $(4x + 1)(3x - 5)$
3. $3(2x + 3)(x + 1)$ **4.** $2(5x - 4)(2x - 3)$

Margin Exercises, Section 10.5, pp. 568–572

1. Yes   **2.** No   **3.** No   **4.** Yes   **5.** No   **6.** Yes   **7.** No
8. Yes   **9.** $(x + 1)^2$ **10.** $(x - 1)^2$ **11.** $(t + 2)^2$ **12.** $(5x - 7)^2$
13. $(7 - 4y)^2$ **14.** $3(4m + 5)^2$ **15.** $(p^2 + 9)^2$ **16.** $z^3(2z - 5)^2$
17. $(3a + 5b)^2$ **18.** Yes   **19.** No   **20.** No   **21.** No   **22.** Yes
23. Yes   **24.** Yes   **25.** $(x + 3)(x - 3)$ **26.** $4(4 + t)(4 - t)$
27. $(a + 5b)(a - 5b)$ **28.** $x^4(8 + 5x)(8 - 5x)$
29. $5(1 + 2t^3)(1 - 2t^3)$ **30.** $(9x^2 + 1)(3x + 1)(3x - 1)$
31. $(7p^2 + 5q^3)(7p^2 - 5q^3)$

Margin Exercises, Section 10.6, pp. 578–580

1. $3(m^2 + 1)(m + 1)(m - 1)$ **2.** $(x^3 + 4)^2$
3. $2x^2(x + 1)(x + 3)$ **4.** $(3x^2 - 2)(x + 4)$
5. $8x(x - 5)(x + 5)$ **6.** $x^2y(x^2y + 2x + 3)$
7. $2p^4q^2(5p^2 + 2pq + q^2)$ **8.** $(a - b)(2x + 5 + y^2)$
9. $(a + b)(x^2 + y)$ **10.** $(x^2 + y^2)^2$ **11.** $(xy + 1)(xy + 4)$
12. $(p^2 + 9q^2)(p + 3q)(p - 3q)$

Margin Exercises, Section 10.7, pp. 586–588

1. $3, -4$ **2.** $7, 3$ **3.** $-\frac{1}{4}, \frac{2}{3}$ **4.** $0, \frac{17}{3}$ **5.** $-2, 3$ **6.** $7, -4$
7. 3 **8.** $0, 4$ **9.** $\frac{4}{3}, -\frac{4}{3}$ **10.** $3, -3$

Margin Exercises, Section 10.8, pp. 591–594

1. $5, -5$ **2.** $7, 8$ **3.** $-4, 5$ **4.** Length: 5 cm; width: 3 cm
5. (a) 342; **(b)** 9   **6.** 22 and 23   **7.** 3 m, 4 m

CHAPTER 11

Margin Exercises, Section 11.1, pp. 605–609

1. $\{x \,|\, x \neq 3\}$ **2.** $\{x \,|\, x \neq -8 \text{ and } x \neq 3\}$ **3.** $\frac{x(2x + 1)}{x(3x - 2)}$
4. $\frac{(x + 1)(x + 2)}{(x - 2)(x + 2)}$ **5.** $\frac{-1(x - 8)}{-1(x - y)}$ **6.** 5 **7.** $\frac{x}{4}$ **8.** $\frac{2x + 1}{3x + 2}$
9. $\frac{x + 1}{2x + 1}$ **10.** $x + 2$ **11.** $\frac{y + 2}{4}$ **12.** -1 **13.** -1
14. $\frac{a - 2}{a - 3}$ **15.** $\frac{x - 5}{2}$

Margin Exercises, Section 11.2, pp. 615–616

1. $\frac{2}{7}$ **2.** $\frac{2x^3 - 1}{x^2 + 5}$ **3.** $\frac{1}{x - 5}$ **4.** $x^2 - 3$ **5.** $\frac{6}{35}$
6. $\frac{(x - 3)(x - 2)}{(x + 5)(x + 5)}$ **7.** $\frac{x - 3}{x + 2}$ **8.** $\frac{(x - 3)(x - 2)}{x + 2}$ **9.** $\frac{y + 1}{y - 1}$

Margin Exercises, Section 11.3, pp. 619–620

1. 144   **2.** 12   **3.** 10   **4.** 120   **5.** $\frac{35}{144}$ **6.** $\frac{1}{4}$ **7.** $\frac{11}{10}$ **8.** $\frac{9}{40}$
9. $60x^3y^2$ **10.** $(y + 1)^2(y + 4)$ **11.** $7(t^2 + 16)(t - 2)$
12. $3x(x + 1)^2(x - 1)$

Margin Exercises, Section 11.4, pp. 623–626

1. $\frac{7}{9}$ **2.** $\frac{3 + x}{x - 2}$ **3.** $\frac{6x + 4}{x - 1}$ **4.** $\frac{x - 5}{4}$ **5.** $\frac{x - 1}{x - 3}$
6. $\frac{10x^2 + 9x}{48}$ **7.** $\frac{9x + 10}{48x^2}$ **8.** $\frac{4x^2 - x + 3}{x(x - 1)(x + 1)^2}$
9. $\frac{2x^2 + 16x + 5}{(x + 3)(x + 8)}$ **10.** $\frac{8x + 88}{(x + 16)(x + 1)(x + 8)}$
11. $\frac{-2x - 11}{3(x + 4)(x - 4)}$

Margin Exercises, Section 11.5, pp. 631–634

1. $\frac{4}{11}$ **2.** $\frac{x^2 + 2x + 1}{2x + 1}$ **3.** $\frac{3x - 1}{3}$ **4.** $\frac{4x - 3}{x - 2}$ **5.** $\frac{-x - 7}{15x}$
6. $\frac{x^2 - 48}{(x + 7)(x + 8)(x + 6)}$ **7.** $\frac{-8y - 28}{(y + 4)(y - 4)}$ **8.** $\frac{x - 13}{(x + 3)(x - 3)}$
9. $\frac{6x^2 - 2x - 2}{3x(x + 1)}$

Margin Exercises, Section 11.6, pp. 639–642

1. $\frac{33}{2}$ **2.** 3   **3.** $\frac{3}{2}$ **4.** $-\frac{1}{8}$ **5.** 1   **6.** 2   **7.** 4

Margin Exercises, Section 11.7, pp. 645–650

1. -3 **2.** 40 km/h, 50 km/h **3.** $\frac{24}{7}$, or $3\frac{3}{7}$ hr **4.** 58 km/L
5. 0.280 **6.** 124 km/h **7.** 2.4 fish/yd^2 **8.** 100 oz **9.** 42
10. 2074

Margin Exercises, Section 11.8, pp. 655–656

1. $M = \dfrac{Fd^2}{km}$ **2.** $b_1 = \dfrac{2A - hb_2}{h}$ **3.** $f = \dfrac{pq}{p + q}$
4. $a = 2Qb + b$

Margin Exercises, Section 11.9, pp. 660–662

1. $\dfrac{136}{5}$ **2.** $\dfrac{7x^2}{3(2 - x^2)}$ **3.** $\dfrac{x}{x - 1}$ **4.** $\dfrac{136}{5}$ **5.** $\dfrac{7x^2}{3(2 - x^2)}$
6. $\dfrac{x}{x - 1}$

CHAPTER 12

Margin Exercises, Section 12.1, pp. 671–674

1. (a) 40%; **(b)** Grades
2. (a) The first week; **(b)** The third and fifth weeks
3. (a) $200; **(b)** 28%
4.–11.

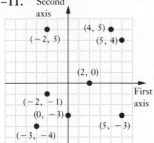

12. Both are negative numbers
13. First positive; second negative **14.** I **15.** III
16. IV **17.** II
18. A: $(-5, 1)$; B: $(-3, 2)$; C: $(0, 4)$; D: $(3, 3)$; E: $(1, 0)$;
F: $(0, -3)$; G: $(-5, -4)$

Margin Exercises, Section 12.2, pp. 679–684

1. No **2.** Yes
3.

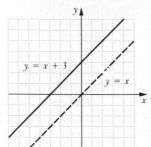

5.

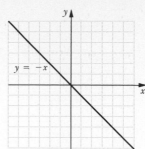

6.

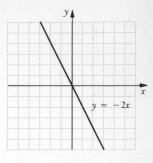

7.

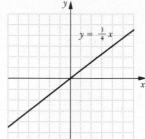

8.

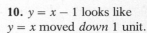
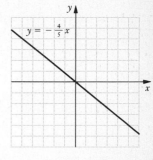

9. $y = x + 3$ looks like $y = x$ moved *up* 3 units.

10. $y = x - 1$ looks like $y = x$ moved *down* 1 unit.

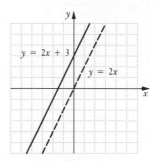

11. $y = 2x + 3$ looks like $y = 2x$ moved *up* 3 units.

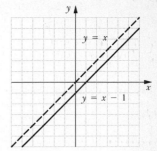

12.

13.

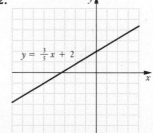
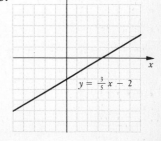

14.

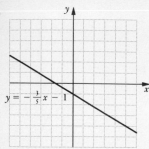

$y = -\frac{3}{5}x - 1$

15.

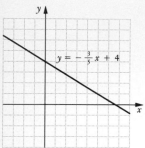

$y = -\frac{3}{5}x + 4$

Margin Exercises, Section 12.3, pp. 687–690

1. (a) (4, 0); **(b)** (0, 3)

2.

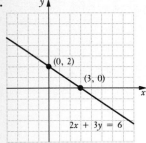

(0, 2) (3, 0) $2x + 3y = 6$

3.

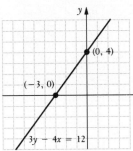

(0, 4) (−3, 0) $3y − 4x = 12$

4.

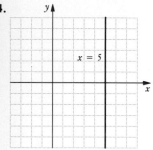

$x = 5$

5.

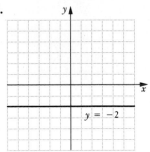

$y = -2$

6.

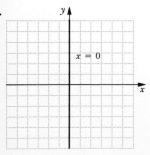

$x = 0$

7.

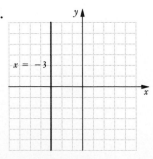

$x = -3$

Margin Exercises, Section 12.4, pp. 694–698

1. $\frac{2}{5}$

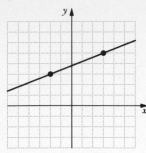

2. $-\frac{5}{3}$

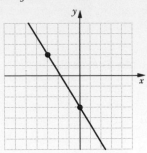

3. Not defined **4.** 0 **5.** −1 **6.** $\frac{5}{4}$ **7.** 5, (0, 0)
8. $-\frac{3}{2}$, (0, −6) **9.** $-\frac{3}{4}$, (0, $\frac{15}{4}$) **10.** 2, (0, $-\frac{17}{2}$)
11. $-\frac{7}{5}$, (0, $-\frac{22}{5}$) **12.** $y = 3.5x − 23$ **13.** $y = 5x − 18$
14. $y = −3x − 5$ **15.** $y = 6x − 13$ **16.** $y = -\frac{2}{3}x + \frac{14}{3}$
17. $y = x + 2$ **18.** $y = 2x + 4$

Margin Exercises, Section 12.5, p. 702

1. No **2.** Yes **3.** Yes **4.** No

Margin Exercises, Section 12.6, pp. 705–708

1. $y = 7x$ **2.** $y = \frac{5}{8}x$ **3.** $0.4667; $0.0194 **4.** 174.24 lb
5. $y = \dfrac{63}{x}$ **6.** $y = \dfrac{900}{x}$ **7.** 8 hr **8.** $7\frac{1}{2}$ hr

Margin Exercises, Section 12.7, pp. 713–716

1. No **2.** No

3.

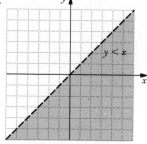

$y < x$

4.

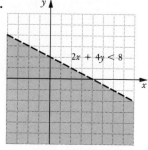

$2x + 4y < 8$

5.

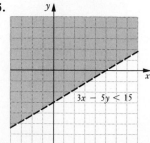

$3x − 5y < 15$

6.

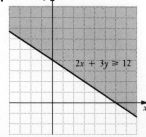

$2x + 3y \geqslant 12$

7.

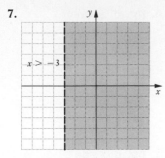

8.

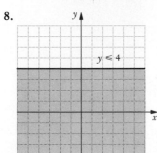

CHAPTER 13

Margin Exercises, Section 13.1, pp. 726–728

1. Yes **2.** No **3.** $(2, -3)$
4. No solution. The lines are parallel.
5. Infinite number of solutions. Same line.

Margin Exercises, Section 13.2, pp. 732–734

1. $(3, 2)$ **2.** $(3, -1)$ **3.** $(\frac{24}{5}, -\frac{8}{5})$
4. Length: 27.5 cm; width: 10.5 cm

Margin Exercises, Section 13.3, pp. 737–742

1. $(3, 2)$ **2.** $(1, -1)$ **3.** $(1, 4)$ **4.** $(1, 1)$ **5.** $(\frac{17}{13}, -\frac{7}{13})$
6. No solution **7.** Infinitely many solutions **8.** $(1, -1)$
9. 75 miles

Margin Exercises, Section 13.4, pp. 748–753

1. A: \$3.23; B: \$3.36
2. Jackie is 47; Jack is 21

	Jackie	Jack
Age now	J	K
Age in 5 yr	$J + 5$	$K + 5$

---

3. 125 adults and 41 children

Adults	Children	Totals
\$2.10	\$0.75	
x	y	166
\$2.10x	\$0.75y	\$293.25

$\longrightarrow x + y = 166$
$\longrightarrow 2.10x + 0.75y = 293.25$

4. 22.5 L of 50%, 7.5 L of 70%

First	Second	Mixture
x	y	30 L
50%	70%	55%
0.5x	0.7y	0.55 × 30, or 16.5 L

$\longrightarrow x + y = 30$
$\longrightarrow 0.5x + 0.7y = 16.5$

5. 30 lb of A, 20 lb of B

A	B	Mixture
\$1.00	\$1.35	\$1.14
x	y	50
1.00x	1.35y	\$1.14(50), or 57

$\longrightarrow x + y = 50$
$\longrightarrow 1.00x + 1.35y = 57$

6. 7 quarters; 13 dimes

Margin Exercises, Section 13.5, pp. 760–762

1. 168 km **2.** 275 km/h **3.** 324 mi **4.** 3 hr

CHAPTER 14

Margin Exercises, Section 14.1, pp. 771–774

1. 6, -6 **2.** 8, -8 **3.** 15, -15 **4.** 10, -10 **5.** 4 **6.** 7
7. 10 **8.** 21 **9.** -7 **10.** -13 **11.** 5.477 **12.** -9.899
13. (a) 20; **(b)** 23 **14.** $45 + x$ **15.** $\frac{x}{x+2}$ **16.** No **17.** Yes
18. Yes **19.** No **20.** Yes **21.** No **22.** $\{a \mid a \geq 0\}$
23. $\{x \mid x \geq 3\}$ **24.** $\{x \mid x \geq \frac{5}{2}\}$ **25.** All real numbers **26.** $|xy|$
27. $|xy|$ **28.** $|x - 1|$ **29.** $|x + 4|$ **30.** xy **31.** xy **32.** $x - 1$
33. $x + 4$ **34.** $5y$ **35.** $\frac{1}{2}t$

Margin Exercises, Section 14.2, pp. 777–780

1. (a) 8; **(b)** 8 **2.** $\sqrt{21}$ **3.** 5 **4.** $\sqrt{x^2 + x}$ **5.** $\sqrt{x^2 - 1}$
6. $4\sqrt{2}$ **7.** $x + 7$ **8.** $5x$ **9.** $6m$ **10.** $2\sqrt{19}$ **11.** $x - 4$
12. $8t$ **13.** $10a$ **14.** 16.585 **15.** 10.097 **16.** t^2 **17.** t^{10}
18. q^{17} **19.** $x^3\sqrt{x}$ **20.** $2x^5\sqrt{6x}$ **21.** $3\sqrt{2}$ **22.** 10
23. $4x^3y^2$ **24.** $5xy^2\sqrt{2xy}$

Margin Exercises, Section 14.3, pp. 785–788

1. 4 **2.** 5 **3.** $x\sqrt{6x}$ **4.** $\dfrac{4}{3}$ **5.** $\dfrac{1}{5}$ **6.** $\dfrac{6}{x}$ **7.** $\dfrac{3}{4}$ **8.** $\dfrac{15}{16}$
9. $\dfrac{5}{x^3}$ **10.** $\dfrac{\sqrt{15}}{5}$ **11.** $\dfrac{\sqrt{10}}{4}$ **12.** $\dfrac{2\sqrt{3}}{3}$ **13.** $\dfrac{\sqrt{35}}{7}$ **14.** $\dfrac{\sqrt{3t}}{t}$
15. $\dfrac{8y\sqrt{7}}{7}$ **16.** 0.816 **17.** 1.128

Margin Exercises, Section 14.4, pp. 793–796

1. $12\sqrt{2}$ **2.** $5\sqrt{5}$ **3.** $-12\sqrt{10}$ **4.** $5\sqrt{6}$ **5.** $\sqrt{x+1}$
6. $\dfrac{3}{2}\sqrt{2}$ **7.** $\dfrac{8\sqrt{15}}{15}$ **8.** $\sqrt{15}+\sqrt{6}$
9. $4+3\sqrt{5}-4\sqrt{2}-3\sqrt{10}$ **10.** $2-a$ **11.** $5+10\sqrt{x}+x$
12. 2 **13.** $\dfrac{21-3\sqrt{5}}{22}$ **14.** $\dfrac{7+2\sqrt{10}}{3}$

Margin Exercises, Section 14.5, pp. 799–802

1. $\frac{64}{3}$ **2.** 2 **3.** $\frac{3}{8}$ **4.** 4 **5.** 1 **6.** 4 **7.** Approx. 313 km
8. Approx. 16 km **9.** 676 m

Margin Exercises, Section 14.6, pp. 805–806

1. $c=\sqrt{65}\approx 8.062$ **2.** $a=\sqrt{75}\approx 8.660$
3. $b=\sqrt{10}\approx 3.162$ **4.** $a=\sqrt{175}\approx 13.229$
5. $\sqrt{325}\approx 18.028$ ft

CHAPTER 15

Margin Exercises, Section 15.1, pp. 815–818

1. $x^2-7x=0$; $a=1$, $b=-7$, $c=0$
2. $x^2+9x-3=0$; $a=1$, $b=9$, $c=-3$
3. $4x^2+2x+4=0$; $a=4$, $b=2$, $c=4$ **4.** $0,-\frac{5}{3}$ **5.** $0,\frac{3}{5}$
6. $\frac{2}{3},-1$ **7.** 4, 1 **8.** 13, 5 **9. (a)** 14; **(b)** 11

Margin Exercises, Section 15.2, pp. 821–826

1. $\sqrt{5},-\sqrt{5}$ **2.** 0 **3.** $\dfrac{\sqrt{6}}{2},-\dfrac{\sqrt{6}}{2}$ **4.** 7, -1 **5.** $-3\pm\sqrt{10}$
6. $1\pm\sqrt{5}$ **7.** $-5, 11$ **8.** 2, 4 **9.** 2, -10 **10.** $-3\pm\sqrt{10}$
11. 5, -2 **12.** $\dfrac{-3\pm\sqrt{33}}{4}$ **13.** About 7.9 sec

Margin Exercises, Section 15.3, pp. 830–832

1. $\frac{1}{2},-4$ **2.** 5, -2 **3.** $-2\pm\sqrt{11}$
4. No real-number solution **5.** $\dfrac{4\pm\sqrt{31}}{5}$ **6.** $-0.3, 1.9$

Margin Exercises, Section 15.4, pp. 835–836

1. $L=\dfrac{r^2}{20}$ **2.** $L=\dfrac{T^2g}{4\pi^2}$ **3.** $m=\dfrac{E}{c^2}$ **4.** $r=\sqrt{\dfrac{A}{\pi}}$
5. $d=\sqrt{\dfrac{C}{P}+1}$ **6.** $n=\dfrac{1\pm\sqrt{1+4N}}{2}$
7. $t=\dfrac{-v\pm\sqrt{v^2+32h}}{16}$

Margin Exercises, Section 15.5, pp. 839–841

1. Length: $\dfrac{1+\sqrt{817}}{2}\approx 14.8$ in.; width: $\dfrac{-1+\sqrt{817}}{6}\approx 4.6$ in.
2. 2.3 cm; 3.3 cm **3.** 3 km/h

Margin Exercises, Section 15.6, pp. 848–850

1. $(0, -3)$

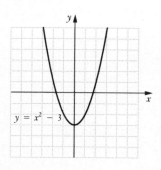

$y = x^2 - 3$

2. $(1, 3)$

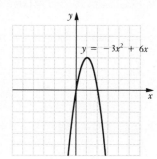

$y = -3x^2 + 6x$

3. $(2, 0)$

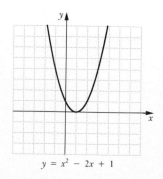

$y = x^2 - 2x + 1$

4. $(\sqrt{3}, 0)$; $(-\sqrt{3}, 0)$

5. $(-4, 0); (-2, 0)$ **6.** $\left(\dfrac{-2 - \sqrt{6}}{2}, 0\right); \left(\dfrac{-2 + \sqrt{6}}{2}, 0\right)$

7. None

APPENDIXES

Margin Exercises, Appendix A, pp. 866–874

1. 2 **2.** 3 **3.** $1\frac{1}{2}$ **4.** $2\frac{1}{2}$ **5.** 288 **6.** 43.5 **7.** 6 **8.** $1\frac{5}{12}$
9. 8 **10.** 33 **11.** $11\frac{2}{3}$, or $11.\overline{6}$ **12.** 5 **13.** 31,680 **14.** cm
15. km **16.** mm **17.** m **18.** cm **19.** m **20.** 23,000
21. 400 **22.** 178 **23.** 9040 **24.** 7.814 **25.** 781.4
26. 0.967 **27.** 8,900,000 **28.** 6.78 **29.** 97.4 **30.** 0.1
31. 8.451 **32.** 90.909 **33.** 804.5 **34.** 1995.273

Margin Exercises, Appendix B, pp. 879–884

1. 40 **2.** 20 **3.** mL **4.** mL **5.** L **6.** L **7.** 970 **8.** 8.99
9. 4.8 **10.** (a) 118.28 mL; (b) 0.11828 L **11.** $1.60 **12.** 80
13. 8640 **14.** 32,000 **15.** kg **16.** kg **17.** mg **18.** g
19. t **20.** 6200 **21.** 0.3048 **22.** 77 **23.** 234.4 **24.** 6700
25. 7200 **26.** 1461 **27.** 1440 **28.** 168

Margin Exercises, Appendix C, pp. 889–890

1. 14 **2.** 11 **3.** 10 **4.** $\sqrt{37} \approx 6.083$ **5.** $(\frac{3}{2}; -3)$
6. $(9, -5)$

Margin Exercises, Appendix D, pp. 893–894

1. $\{6, -6\}$;

2. $\varnothing$ **3.** $\{0\}$ **4.** $\{2, -2\}$ **5.** $\{\frac{17}{4}, -\frac{17}{4}\}$ **6.** $\{4, -4\}$
7. $\{3, 5\}$ **8.** $\{-\frac{13}{3}, 7\}$ **9.** $\varnothing$

Margin Exercises, Appendix E, pp. 898–900

1. $\frac{82}{100}$ **2.** 14.7%, 50.4% **3.** $\frac{1}{2}$ **4.** (a) $\frac{1}{13}$; (b) $\frac{1}{4}$; (c) $\frac{1}{2}$; (d) $\frac{2}{13}$
5. $\frac{6}{11}$ **6.** 0 **7.** 1

Margin Exercises, Appendix F, p. 903

1. 14 **2.** 16 **3.** Even **4.** Odd **5.** (a) Odd; (b) even; (c) even
6. The altitude from the vertex (formed by the congruent sides) to the base divides the base into two congruent segments.

7. The medians pass through a single point.
8. The intersection is equidistant from the vertices.
9. On Tuesday, the highway was slick.
10. All citizens of Dallas are Americans.
11. Melanie saved money.
12. The number 10 is a composite number.
13. (1) Given; (2) Addition principle for equations: adding -2 on both sides; (3) Multiplication principle for equations: multiplying by $\frac{1}{3}$ on both sides

14.

Statements	Reasons
1. $\frac{3}{4}x + 2 = 17$	1. Given.
2. $\frac{3}{4}x = 15$	2. Addition principle for equations: adding -2 on both sides.
3. $x = 20$	3. Multiplication principle for equations: multiplying by $\frac{4}{3}$ on both sides.

15. Answers may vary.

Statements	Reasons
1. Two intersecting lines with $m\angle 3 = x$	1. Given.
2. $x + m\angle 4 = 180°$	2. $\angle 3$ and $\angle 4$ are supplementary.
3. $x + m\angle 2 = 180°$	3. $\angle 3$ and $\angle 2$ are supplementary.
4. $x + m\angle 2 = x + m\angle 4$	4. Substituting $x + m\angle 4$ for $180°$ in step (3).
5. $m\angle 2 = m\angle 4$	5. Addition principle for equations: adding $-x$ on both sides in step (4).

16. 360°; 360° **17.** 540°; 360° **18.** 360° **19.** 144°; 36°
20. 108°; 72°

21.

Statements	Reasons
1. $\overline{AB} \perp \overline{ED}$	1. Given.
2. B is the midpoint of $\overline{ED}$.	2. Given.
3. $\angle ABD$ and $\angle ABE$ are congruent right angles.	3. Definition of perpendicular.
4. $\overline{BD} \cong \overline{BE}$	4. Definition of midpoint.
5. $\overline{AB} \cong \overline{AB}$	5. Same segment.
6. $\triangle ABD \cong \triangle ABE$	6. SAS.

22.

Statements	Reasons
1. $\angle R \cong \angle T$, $\angle W \cong \angle V$, $\overline{RW} \cong \overline{TV}$	1. Given.
2. $\triangle SWR \cong \triangle SVT$	2. ASA.
3. $\overline{RS} \cong \overline{TS}$	3. Corresponding parts of congruent triangles are congruent (CPCTC).

23. Yes **24.** No **25.** No

26.

Statements	Reasons
1. $\angle B \cong \angle D$	1. Given.
2. $\angle ACB \cong \angle ECD$	2. Vertical angles are congruent.
3. $\triangle ABC \sim \triangle EDC$	3. AA Property.

27. $\dfrac{AB}{ED} = \dfrac{AC}{EC} = \dfrac{CB}{CD}$ **28.** $CE = 2$, $AD = 9$, $EB = 6$

EXERCISE SET AND TEST ANSWERS

CHAPTER 1

Pretest: Chapter 1, p. 2

1. [1.1c] Three million, seventy-eight thousand, fifty-nine
2. [1.1a] 6 thousands + 9 hundreds + 8 tens + 7 ones
3. [1.1d] 2,047,398,589 **4.** [1.1e] 6 ten thousands
5. [1.1f] $<$ **6.** [1.1f] $>$ **7.** [1.2b] 10,216 **8.** [1.2f] 4108
9. [1.3b] 22,976 **10.** [1.3e] 503 R 11 **11.** [1.4b] 5542
12. [1.4b] 22 **13.** [1.4b] 34 **14.** [1.4b] 25 **15.** [1.5a] 12 lb
16. [1.5a] 126 **17.** [1.5a] 22,216,100 **18.** [1.5a] 2292 sq ft
19. [1.6b] 64 **20.** [1.9a] 120 **21.** [1.6c] 0 **22.** [1.6d] 0
23. [1.7c] Prime **24.** [1.7d] $2 \cdot 2 \cdot 5 \cdot 7$ **25.** [1.8a] No
26. [1.8a] Yes

Exercise Set 1.1, p. 7

1. 5 thousands + 7 hundreds + 4 tens + 2 ones
3. 2 ten thousands + 7 thousands + 3 hundreds + 4 tens + 2 ones
5. 9 thousands + 1 ten **7.** 2 thousands + 3 hundreds
9. 2475 **11.** 68,939 **13.** 7304 **15.** 1009 **17.** Seventy-seven
19. Eighty-eight thousand
21. One hundred twenty-three thousand, seven hundred sixty-five
23. Seven million, seven hundred fifty-four thousand, two hundred eleven
25. Two hundred forty-four million, eight hundred thirty-nine thousand, seven hundred seventy-two
27. One million, nine hundred fifty-four thousand, one hundred sixteen
29. 2,233,812 **31.** 8,000,000,000 **33.** 217,503
35. 2,173,638 **37.** 206,658,000 **39.** 5 thousands
41. 5 hundreds **43.** 3 **45.** 0 **47.** $<$ **49.** $>$ **51.** $<$ **53.** $>$

Exercise Set 1.2, p. 15

1. 3 yards + 6 yards = 9 yards **3.** $23 + $31 = $54 **5.** 387
7. 4998 **9.** 1110 **11.** 1010 **13.** 1201 **15.** 847 **17.** 10,139
19. 6608 **21.** 16,784 **23.** 101,310 **25.** 169 **27.** 22,654

29. $2400 - 800 = \square$ **31.** $10 = 3 + 7$ **33.** $13 = 5 + 8$
35. $6 = 15 - 9$; $9 = 15 - 6$ **37.** $8 = 15 - 7$; $7 = 15 - 8$
39. $190 + \square = 220$; $\square = 220 - 190$ **41.** 39 **43.** 298
45. 533 **47.** 1493 **49.** 7748 **51.** 84 **53.** 4206 **55.** 10,305
57. 7 ten thousands
59. $1 + 99 = 100$, $2 + 98 = 100$, and so on, . . . , $49 + 51 = 100$. Then $49 \cdot 100 = 4900$ and $4900 + 50 + 100 = 5050$.

Exercise Set 1.3, p. 27

1. $32 \cdot $10 = $320 **3.** $3 \cdot 6 = 18$ ft^2 **5.** 9600 **7.** 564
9. 1527 **11.** 64,603 **13.** 4770 **15.** 3120 **17.** 46,080
19. 14,652 **21.** 207,672 **23.** 503,076 **25.** 20,723,872
27. 362,128 **29.** 20,064,048 **31.** 25,236,000
33. $176 \div 4 = \square$ **35.** $24 = 3 \cdot 8$ **37.** $22 = 1 \cdot 22$
39. $9 = 45 \div 5$; $5 = 45 \div 9$ **41.** $37 = 37 \div 1$; $1 = 37 \div 37$
43. 55 R 2 **45.** 40 R 12 **47.** 307 **49.** 92 R 2 **51.** 1703
53. 29 R 5 **55.** 90 R 22 **57.** 29 **59.** 370 **61.** 609 R 15
63. 7 thousands + 8 hundreds + 8 tens + 2 ones

Exercise Set 1.4, p. 33

1. 14 **3.** 0 **5.** 29 **7.** 0 **9.** 8 **11.** 14 **13.** 1035 **15.** 25
17. 450 **19.** 90,900 **21.** 32 **23.** 143 **25.** 79 **27.** 45
29. 324 **31.** 743 **33.** 37 **35.** 66 **37.** 15 **39.** 48 **41.** 175
43. 335 **45.** 104 **47.** 45 **49.** 4056 **51.** 17,603 **53.** 18,252
55. 205 **57.** 55 **59.** $6 = 48 \div 8$; $8 = 48 \div 6$ **61.** $>$

Exercise Set 1.5, p. 43

1. 5693 **3.** 449 m **5.** 2995 cubic centimeters
7. 100 cubic centimeters **9.** 304,000 **11.** $91 **13.** 665 cal
15. 3600 sec **17.** 2808 sq ft **19.** 7815 mi **21.** $1638
23. 5130 sq yd **25.** 38 **27.** 15 **29.** $27
31. 38 bags; 11 kg left over **33.** 16 **35.** 11 in.; 770 mi
37. 480 **39.** 525 min, or 8 hr 45 min **41.** 186,000 mi

Sidelight: Palindrome Numbers, p. 50

1. 11,011 **2.** 5115

Exercise Set 1.6, p. 51

1. 3^4 **3.** 5^2 **5.** 7^5 **7.** 10^3 **9.** 49 **11.** 729 **13.** 20,736
15. 121 **17.** 22 **19.** 20 **21.** 100 **23.** 1 **25.** 49 **27.** 27
29. 434 **31.** 41 **33.** 88 **35.** 4 **37.** 303 **39.** 20 **41.** 70
43. 295 **45.** 32 **47.** 906 **49.** 62 **51.** 102 **53.** 110 **55.** 7
57. 544 **59.** 708 **61.** 24; $1 + 5 \cdot (4 + 3) = 36$
63. 7; $12 \div (4 + 2) \cdot 3 - 2 = 4$

Exercise Set 1.7, p. 57

1. 1, 2, 4, 8, 16 **3.** 1, 2, 3, 6, 9, 18, 27, 54 **5.** 1, 2, 4
7. 1, 7 **9.** 1 **11.** 1, 2, 7, 14, 49, 98
13. 4, 8, 12, 16, 20, 24, 28, 32, 36, 40
15. 20, 40, 60, 80, 100, 120, 140, 160, 180, 200
17. 3, 6, 9, 12, 15, 18, 21, 24, 27, 30
19. 12, 24, 36, 48, 60, 72, 84, 96, 108, 120
21. 10, 20, 30, 40, 50, 60, 70, 80, 90, 100
23. 9, 18, 27, 36, 45, 54, 63, 72, 81, 90 **25.** No
27. Yes **29.** Yes **31.** No **33.** No **35.** Neither
37. Composite **39.** Prime **41.** Prime **43.** $2 \cdot 2 \cdot 2$ **45.** $2 \cdot 7$
47. $2 \cdot 11$ **49.** $5 \cdot 5$ **51.** $2 \cdot 5 \cdot 5$ **53.** $13 \cdot 13$ **55.** $2 \cdot 2 \cdot 5 \cdot 5$
57. $5 \cdot 7$ **59.** $2 \cdot 2 \cdot 2 \cdot 3 \cdot 3$ **61.** $7 \cdot 11$ **63.** $2 \cdot 2 \cdot 2 \cdot 2 \cdot 7$
65. $2 \cdot 2 \cdot 3 \cdot 5 \cdot 5$ **67.** 26 **69.** 0
71. A rectangular array of 6 rows of 9 objects each, or 9 rows of 6 objects each

Exercise Set 1.8, p. 63

1. 46; 300; 224; 36; 45,270; 4444 **3.** 300; 224; 36; 4444
5. 300; 36; 45,270 **7.** 36; 711; 45,270
9. 75; 324; 42; 501; 3009; 2001 **11.** 200; 75; 2345; 55,555
13. 324 **15.** 200 **17.** 138 **19.** $680
21. $2 \cdot 2 \cdot 2 \cdot 3 \cdot 5 \cdot 5 \cdot 13$ **23.** $2 \cdot 2 \cdot 3 \cdot 3 \cdot 7 \cdot 11$

Exercise Set 1.9, p. 69

1. 4 **3.** 50 **5.** 40 **7.** 54 **9.** 150 **11.** 120 **13.** 72 **15.** 420
17. 144 **19.** 288 **21.** 30 **23.** 105 **25.** 72 **27.** 60 **29.** 36
31. 24 **33.** 48 **35.** 50 **37.** 143 **39.** 420 **41.** 378 **43.** 810
45. 250 **47.** 1964 **49.** 24 in. **51.** 70,200

Summary and Review: Chapter 1, p. 71

1. [1.1a] 2 thousands + 7 hundreds + 9 tens + 3 ones
2. [1.1c] Two million, seven hundred eighty-one thousand, four hundred twenty-seven
3. [1.1e] 7 ten thousands **4.** [1.1d] $2,626,100,000,000
5. [1.2b] 5979 **6.** [1.2b] 66,024 **7.** [1.2b] 22,098
8. [1.2b] 98,921 **9.** [1.2f] 1153 **10.** [1.2f] 1147
11. [1.2f] 2274 **12.** [1.2f] 17,757 **13.** [1.2f] 444
14. [1.2f] 4766 **15.** [1.3b] 420,000 **16.** [1.3b] 6,276,800
17. [1.3b] 684 **18.** [1.3b] 44,758 **19.** [1.3b] 3404
20. [1.3b] 506,748 **21.** [1.3b] 27,589 **22.** [1.3b] 3,456,000
23. [1.3d] 5 **24.** [1.3d] 12 R 3 **25.** [1.3d] 80
26. [1.3d] 207 R 2 **27.** [1.3d] 384 R 1 **28.** [1.3d] 4 R 46
29. [1.3d] 54 **30.** [1.3d] 452 **31.** [1.3d] 5008

32. [1.3d] 4389 **33.** [1.4b] 45 **34.** [1.4b] 546 **35.** [1.4b] 8
36. [1.6a] 1982 **37.** [1.6a] $19,748 **38.** [1.6a] 10
39. [1.6a] 2825 cal **40.** [1.6a] $501
41. [1.6a] 152 beakers, 17 L left over **42.** [1.1f] >
43. [1.1f] < **44.** [1.6a] 8^3 **45.** [1.6b] 16 **46.** [1.6c] 65
47. [1.6c] 56 **48.** [1.6c] 32 **49.** [1.6c] 233 **50.** [1.6d] 260
51. [1.7d] $2 \cdot 5 \cdot 7$ **52.** [1.7d] $2 \cdot 3 \cdot 5$ **53.** [1.7d] $5 \cdot 3 \cdot 3$
54. [1.7d] $2 \cdot 3 \cdot 5 \cdot 5$ **55.** [1.8a] No **56.** [1.8a] No
57. [1.8a] Yes **58.** [1.8a] No **59.** [1.7c] Prime
60. [1.9a] 36 **61.** [1.9a] 90 **62.** [1.9a] 30

Test: Chapter 1, p. 73

1. [1.1a] 8 thousands + 8 hundreds + 4 tens + 3 ones
2. [1.1c] Thirty-eight million, four hundred three thousand, two hundred seventy-seven
3. [1.1e] 5 **4.** [1.2b] 9989 **5.** [1.2b] 63,791 **6.** [1.2b] 34
7. [1.2b] 10,515 **8.** [1.2f] 3630 **9.** [1.2f] 1039
10. [1.2f] 6848 **11.** [1.2f] 5175 **12.** [1.3b] 41,112
13. [1.3b] 5,325,600 **14.** [1.3b] 2405 **15.** [1.3b] 534,264
16. [1.3e] 3 R 3 **17.** [1.3e] 70 **18.** [1.3e] 97
19. [1.3e] 805 R 8 **20.** [1.5a] 1955
21. [1.5a] 92 packages, 3 left over **22.** [1.5a] 18
23. [1.5a] 120,000 sq m **24.** [1.5a] 1808 lb **25.** [1.5a] 20
26. [1.5a] 305 sq mi **27.** [1.5a] 56 **28.** [1.5a] 66,444 sq mi
29. [1.5a] $271 **30.** [1.4b] 46 **31.** [1.4b] 13 **32.** [1.4b] 14
33. [1.1f] > **34.** [1.1f] < **35.** [1.6a] 12^4 **36.** [1.6b] 343
37. [1.6c] 64 **38.** [1.6c] 96 **39.** [1.6c] 2 **40.** [1.6d] 216
41. [1.9c] 18 **42.** [1.7d] $2 \cdot 3 \cdot 3$ **43.** [1.7d] $2 \cdot 2 \cdot 3 \cdot 5$
44. [1.8a] Yes **45.** [1.8a] No **46.** [1.9a] 48

CHAPTER 2

Pretest: Chapter 2, p. 76

1. [2.1b] 1 **2.** [2.1b] 68 **3.** [2.1b] 0 **4.** [2.1e] $\frac{1}{4}$
5. [2.3d] < **6.** [2.2b] $\frac{8}{7}$ **7.** [2.4a] $\frac{61}{8}$ **8.** [2.4a] $5\frac{1}{2}$
9. [2.4b] $11\frac{31}{60}$ **10.** [2.4c] $6\frac{1}{6}$ **11.** [2.4d] $21\frac{2}{3}$ **12.** [2.4e] 6
13. [2.3e] $\frac{2}{9}$ **14.** [2.2d] 30 **15.** [2.5a] $21\frac{1}{4}$ lb
16. [2.5a] $\frac{1}{24}$ m **17.** [2.5a] $351\frac{1}{5}$ km **18.** [2.5a] $22\frac{1}{2}$ cups

Exercise Set 2.1, p. 85

1. $\frac{2}{4}$ **3.** $\frac{1}{8}$ **5.** $\frac{2}{3}$ **7.** $\frac{3}{4}$ **9.** $\frac{4}{8}$ **11.** $\frac{6}{12}$ **13.** 0 **15.** 234 **17.** 1
19. 0 **21.** Not defined **23.** Not defined **25.** $\frac{1}{6}$ **27.** $\frac{5}{6}$
29. $\frac{2}{15}$ **31.** $\frac{4}{15}$ **33.** $\frac{9}{16}$ **35.** $\frac{14}{39}$ **37.** $\frac{21}{4}$ **39.** $\frac{49}{64}$ **41.** $\frac{5}{10}$ **43.** $\frac{36}{48}$
45. $\frac{75}{45}$ **47.** $\frac{42}{132}$ **49.** $\frac{3}{4}$ **51.** $\frac{1}{5}$ **53.** 3 **55.** $\frac{3}{4}$ **57.** $\frac{7}{8}$ **59.** $\frac{1}{4}$
61. $\frac{4}{9}$; $\frac{1}{5}$; $\frac{2}{15}$; $\frac{2}{9}$

Exercise Set 2.2, p. 91

1. $\frac{1}{3}$ **3.** $\frac{1}{6}$ **5.** $\frac{27}{10}$ **7.** $\frac{14}{9}$ **9.** 1 **11.** 1 **13.** 5 **15.** 9 **17.** $\frac{98}{35}$
19. 30 **21.** $\frac{1}{5}$ **23.** $\frac{9}{25}$ **25.** $\frac{11}{40}$ **27.** $\frac{5}{2}$ **29.** $\frac{6}{5}$ **31.** $\frac{1}{6}$ **33.** 6
35. $\frac{3}{10}$ **37.** $\frac{4}{5}$ **39.** $\frac{4}{15}$ **41.** 4 **43.** 2 **45.** $\frac{1}{8}$ **47.** $\frac{3}{7}$ **49.** 8
51. 35 **53.** 1 **55.** $\frac{2}{3}$ **57.** $\frac{9}{4}$ **59.** 144 **61.** 75 **63.** 2 **65.** $\frac{3}{5}$
67. 315 **69.** 35 **71.** 4673

Exercise Set 2.3, p. 99

1. $\frac{3}{2}$ **3.** $\frac{7}{24}$ **5.** $\frac{9}{10}$ **7.** $\frac{29}{18}$ **9.** $\frac{31}{100}$ **11.** $\frac{41}{60}$ **13.** $\frac{189}{100}$ **15.** $\frac{7}{8}$
17. $\frac{13}{24}$ **19.** $\frac{17}{24}$ **21.** $\frac{437}{500}$ **23.** $\frac{53}{40}$ **25.** $\frac{391}{144}$ **27.** $\frac{2}{3}$ **29.** $\frac{5}{9}$ **31.** $\frac{1}{2}$
33. $\frac{9}{14}$ **35.** $\frac{17}{60}$ **37.** $\frac{53}{100}$ **39.** $\frac{26}{75}$ **41.** $\frac{1}{100}$ **43.** <   **45.** >
47. <   **49.** <   **51.** >   **53.** >   **55.** $\frac{1}{15}$ **57.** $\frac{2}{15}$ **59.** $\frac{1}{15}$
61. 204   **63.** 4992 sq ft

Exercise Set 2.4, p. 107

1. $\frac{25}{4}$ **3.** $\frac{59}{6}$ **5.** $\frac{47}{3}$ **7.** $4\frac{2}{3}$ **9.** $5\frac{7}{10}$ **11.** $43\frac{1}{8}$ **13.** $6\frac{1}{2}$ **15.** $2\frac{11}{12}$
17. $14\frac{7}{12}$ **19.** $12\frac{1}{10}$ **21.** $27\frac{7}{8}$ **23.** $27\frac{13}{24}$ **25.** $1\frac{3}{5}$ **27.** $4\frac{1}{10}$
29. $21\frac{17}{24}$ **31.** $12\frac{1}{4}$ **33.** $13\frac{3}{8}$ **35.** $11\frac{5}{18}$ **37.** $22\frac{2}{3}$ **39.** $2\frac{5}{12}$
41. $8\frac{1}{6}$ **43.** $9\frac{31}{40}$ **45.** $24\frac{91}{100}$ **47.** $209\frac{1}{10}$ **49.** $6\frac{1}{4}$ **51.** $1\frac{1}{5}$
53. $3\frac{9}{16}$ **55.** $1\frac{1}{8}$ **57.** $1\frac{8}{43}$ **59.** $\frac{9}{40}$

Exercise Set 2.5, p. 115

1. 625   **3.** $\frac{1}{3}$ cup   **5.** 160 mi   **7.** 32   **9.** 288 km; 108 km
11. $\frac{23}{12}$ mi   **13.** $\frac{173}{100}$ cm   **15.** $\frac{1}{4}$ **17.** $17\frac{11}{20}$ cm   **19.** $18\frac{4}{5}$ cm
21. $\$103\frac{3}{8}$ **23.** $28\frac{3}{4}$ yd   **25.** $1\frac{1}{2}$ gal   **27.** $7\frac{3}{8}$ ft   **29.** $343\frac{3}{4}$ lb
31. 68°F   **33.** 15 mpg   **35.** 4 cu ft   **37.** $35\frac{115}{256}$ sq in.
39. $59{,}538\frac{1}{8}$ sq m   **41.** 58   **43.** 467   **45.** 33 ft

Summary and Review: Chapter 2, p. 119

1. [1.1a] $\frac{3}{5}$ **2.** [1.1a] $\frac{3}{8}$ **3.** [1.1b] 0   **4.** [1.1b] 1
5. [1.1b] 48   **6.** [1.1e] 6   **7.** [1.1e] $\frac{2}{3}$ **8.** [1.1e] $\frac{1}{4}$
9. [1.1e] $\frac{2}{5}$ **10.** [1.1e] $\frac{1}{3}$ **11.** [2.2a] $\frac{3}{2}$ **12.** [2.2a] 24
13. [2.2a] $\frac{2}{3}$ **14.** [2.2a] $\frac{1}{14}$ **15.** [2.2b] $\frac{5}{4}$ **16.** [2.2b] $\frac{1}{3}$
17. [2.2b] 9   **18.** [2.2b] $\frac{36}{47}$ **19.** [2.2c] 300   **20.** [2.2c] $\frac{1}{4}$
21. [2.2c] 1   **22.** [2.2c] $\frac{4}{9}$ **23.** [2.3b] $\frac{63}{40}$ **24.** [2.3b] $\frac{19}{48}$
25. [2.3b] $\frac{29}{27}$ **26.** [2.3b] $\frac{7}{16}$ **27.** [2.3c] $\frac{1}{3}$ **28.** [2.3c] $\frac{1}{8}$
29. [2.3c] $\frac{5}{27}$ **30.** [2.3c] $\frac{11}{18}$ **31.** [2.3d] >   **32.** [2.3d] >
33. [2.4a] $\frac{15}{2}$ **34.** [2.4a] $\frac{67}{8}$ **35.** [2.4a] $2\frac{1}{3}$ **36.** [2.4a] $6\frac{3}{4}$
37. [2.4b] $10\frac{2}{5}$ **38.** [2.4b] $11\frac{11}{15}$ **39.** [2.4c] $7\frac{7}{9}$ **40.** [2.4c] $4\frac{11}{15}$
41. [2.4c] 16   **42.** [2.4c] $3\frac{1}{2}$ **43.** [2.4d] $1\frac{7}{17}$ **44.** [2.4d] $\frac{1}{8}$
45. [2.2d] $\frac{3}{10}$ **46.** [2.2d] 240   **47.** [2.3e] $\frac{19}{40}$ **48.** [2.3e] $\frac{2}{5}$
49. [2.5a] 160 km   **50.** [2.5a] $\frac{2}{5}$ cup   **51.** [2.5a] $\$6$
52. [2.5a] 18   **53.** $\$70\frac{3}{8}$ **54.** [2.5a] $8\frac{3}{8}$ cups
55. [1.3e] 408 R 9   **56.** [1.4b] 469   **57.** [1.2f] 3607
58. [1.5a] $\$512$

Test: Chapter 2, p. 121

1. [1.1a] $\frac{3}{4}$ **2.** [2.3d] >   **3.** [1.1b] 26   **4.** [1.1b] 1
5. [1.1b] 0   **6.** [1.1e] $\frac{1}{14}$ **7.** [2.3a] 3   **8.** [2.3b] $\frac{37}{24}$
9. [2.3b] $\frac{79}{100}$ **10.** [2.3c] $\frac{1}{3}$ **11.** [2.3c] $\frac{1}{12}$ **12.** [2.3c] $\frac{1}{12}$
13. [2.2a] 32   **14.** [2.2a] $\frac{5}{2}$ **15.** [2.2a] $\frac{1}{10}$ **16.** [2.2b] $\frac{8}{5}$
17. [2.2b] $\frac{1}{18}$ **18.** [2.2c] $\frac{3}{10}$ **19.** [2.2c] $\frac{8}{5}$ **20.** [2.2c] 18
21. [2.2d] 64   **22.** [2.3e] $\frac{1}{4}$ **23.** [2.4a] $8\frac{2}{9}$ **24.** [2.4a] $\frac{7}{2}$
25. [2.4b] $14\frac{1}{5}$ **26.** [2.4c] $4\frac{7}{24}$ **27.** [2.4d] $4\frac{1}{2}$ **28.** [2.4e] 2
29. [2.5a] 28 lb   **30.** [2.5a] $\frac{3}{40}$ m   **31.** [2.5a] $17\frac{1}{2}$ cups
32. [2.5a] 80   **33.** [2.5a] $160\frac{5}{8}$ kg   **34.** [2.5a] $2\frac{1}{4}$ in.
35. [1.4b] 1805   **36.** [1.4b] 101   **37.** [1.5a] 3635 mi
38. [1.3e] 380 R 7   **39.** [1.2f] 4434

CHAPTER 3

Pretest: Chapter 3, p. 124

1. [3.1a] Three thousand, two hundred sixty-four and $\frac{78}{100}$ dollars
2. [3.2d] 3.2   **3.** [3.2d] 0.099   **4.** [3.1b] $\frac{5408}{1000}$
5. [3.1c] 0.0539   **6.** [3.2b] 39.0901   **7.** [3.3a] 38.54
8. [3.2a] 113.664   **9.** [3.3a] 0.32456   **10.** [3.3a] 0.6179
11. [3.3b] 1.32   **12.** [3.3b] 30.4   **13.** [3.3b] 0.00004653
14. [3.2c] 3.27   **15.** [3.3c] 84.26   **16.** [3.3d] 1.4
17. [3.3d] 1.4375   **18.** [3.3d] $0.\overline{7}$ **19.** [3.3d] $4.\overline{142857}$
20. [3.4a] 6156.0   **21.** [3.4a] 6200   **22.** [3.4a] 6156.045
23. [3.4b] 224   **24.** [3.4b] 3.5   **25.** [3.5a] $\$285.95$
26. [3.5a] 1081.6   **27.** [3.5a] $\$89.70$ **28.** [3.5a] 2.17 km

Exercise Set 3.1, p. 129

1. Twenty-three and two tenths
3. One hundred thirty-five and eighty-seven hundredths
5. Thirty-four and eight hundred ninety-one thousandths
7. Three hundred twenty-six and $\frac{48}{100}$ dollars
9. Zero and $\frac{67}{100}$ dollar   **11.** $\frac{68}{100}$ **13.** $\frac{17}{100}$ **15.** $\frac{146}{100}$ **17.** $\frac{2046}{10}$
19. $\frac{3142}{1000}$ **21.** $\frac{4603}{100}$ **23.** $\frac{13}{100{,}000}$ **25.** $\frac{20{,}003}{1000}$ **27.** $\frac{10{,}008}{10{,}000}$
29. $\frac{45{,}672}{10}$ **31.** 0.8   **33.** 0.92   **35.** 9.3   **37.** 8.89   **39.** 250.8
41. 3.798   **43.** 0.0078   **45.** 0.56788   **47.** 21.73   **49.** 0.66
51. 34.17   **53.** 0.376193   **55.** 54   **57.** 535, 10 ounces
59. 4.909

Exercise Set 3.2, p. 135

1. 334.37   **3.** 1576.215   **5.** 1.59535   **7.** 10.387   **9.** 20.8649
11. 227.4680   **13.** 1.3   **15.** 49.02   **17.** 45.61   **19.** 2.4975
21. 2546.973   **23.** 44.001   **25.** 0.36956   **27.** 199.897
29. 19.251   **31.** 0.58   **33.** 0.111   **35.** 0.001   **37.** 235.07
39. 0.4545   **41.** 0.4325   **43.** $11\frac{1}{5}$ **45.** 342   **47.** 345.8

Exercise Set 3.3, p. 145

1. 60.2   **3.** 0.252   **5.** 521.6   **7.** 322.07   **9.** 3487.5
11. 50.0004   **13.** 0.72523   **15.** 1.872115   **17.** 2.701644
19. 0.00836608   **21.** 780   **23.** 8.923   **25.** 0.09768
27. 287.93   **29.** 2.99   **31.** 7.48   **33.** 1.143   **35.** 42   **37.** 20
39. 225   **41.** 2.3   **43.** 0.2134567   **45.** 1023.7   **47.** 9.3
49. 0.0090678   **51.** 3.25   **53.** 0.6875   **55.** $0.\overline{4}$ **57.** $0.5\overline{3}$
59. $3\frac{2}{5}$ **61.** 325

Exercise Set 3.4, p. 151

1. 50   **3.** 70   **5.** 730   **7.** 900   **9.** 100   **11.** 1000   **13.** 3600
15. 2900   **17.** 6000   **19.** 8000   **21.** 45,000   **23.** 373,000
25. 0.1   **27.** 2.7   **29.** 0.6   **31.** 123.7   **33.** 0.89   **35.** 283.14
37. 0.42   **39.** 1.44   **41.** 0.325   **43.** 10.101   **45.** 17.002
47. 0.001   **49.** 300   **51.** 283.136   **53.** 283   **55.** 270
57. 15,200   **59.** $\$720$ **61.** $15\frac{1}{8}$ **63.** $\frac{6}{7}$

Exercise Set 3.5, p. 157

1. 118.5 gal **3.** $3.01 **5.** 1.4°F **7.** 22,691.5 **9.** $6.59
11. 18.09 min **13.** 2.31 cm **15.** $1171.74 **17.** $230.86
19. 62.5 mi **21.** $139.36 **23.** $57.35 **25.** $465.78
27. 20.2 mpg **29.** $10 **31.** 14.5 mpg **33.** 0.333
35. $394.03 **37.** 6020.48 sq m **39.** $196,987.20 **41.** $2^2 \cdot 3^3$
43. $\frac{5}{16}$ **45.** (a) $13.38; (b) $14.49; (c) (a); (d) $13.78; (e) (d)

Summary and Review: Chapter 3, p. 161

1. [3.1a] Three and forty-seven hundredths
2. [3.1a] Thirty-one thousandths
3. [3.1a] Five hundred ninety-seven and $\frac{25}{100}$ dollars
4. [3.1a] Zero and $\frac{98}{100}$ dollars
5. [3.1b] $\frac{9}{100}$ **6.** [3.1b] $\frac{4561}{1000}$ **7.** [3.1c] 0.034 **8.** [3.1c] 27.91
9. [3.2d] 0.034 **10.** [3.2d] 0.91 **11.** [3.2d] 0.741
12. [3.2d] 1.041 **13.** [3.2c] 496.2795 **14.** [3.3c] 6.95
15. [3.2c] 4.9911 **16.** [3.2a] 45.601 **17.** [3.2b] 29.2092
18. [3.3a] 0.2184 **19.** [3.3a] 0.2784 **20.** [3.3b] 1389.2
21. [3.3a] 24,680 **22.** [3.3b] 1.6 **23.** [3.3b] 3.2
24. [3.2b] 685.0519 **25.** [3.3d] 2.6 **26.** [3.3d] 1.28
27. [3.3d] 1.1$\overline{6}$ **28.** [3.3d] 3.25 **29.** [3.3d] 1.$\overline{54}$
30. [3.4a] 345,800 **31.** [3.4a] 345,760 **32.** [3.4a] 346,000
33. [3.4a] 345,759.4 **34.** [3.4a] 345,759.43
35. [3.4a] 345,759.429 **36.** [3.4b] 272 **37.** [3.4b] 4
38. [3.4b] 216 **39.** [3.4b] $125 **40.** [3.5a] 11.16
41. [3.5a] 3.5 yr **42.** [3.5a] 6365.1 bu **43.** [3.5a] $5888.74
44. [3.5a] $239.80 **45.** [3.5a] 82.67 km **46.** [3.5a] $32.59
47. [3.5a] 24.36 cups; 104.4 cups **48.** [3.5a] $8.98
49. [2.4b] 19$\frac{4}{5}$ **50.** [1.9a] 3300 **51.** [2.1e] $\frac{1}{2}$
52. [1.7d] $2^6 \cdot 3$

Test: Chapter 3, p. 163

1. [3.1a] Two and thirty-four hundredths
2. [3.1a] One thousand, two hundred thirty-four and $\frac{78}{100}$ dollars
3. [3.1b] $\frac{91}{100}$ **4.** [3.1b] $\frac{2769}{1000}$ **5.** [3.1c] 0.74
6. [3.1c] 3.7047 **7.** [3.2d] 0.162 **8.** [3.2d] 0.9
9. [3.2d] 0.078 **10.** [3.2c] 8.982 **11.** [3.3c] 84.26
12. [3.2a] 405.219 **13.** [3.2a] 186.5 **14.** [3.2b] 48.357
15. [3.2b] 1.9946 **16.** [3.3a] 8 **17.** [3.3a] 0.2079
18. [3.3a] 0.21345 **19.** [3.3b] 0.44 **20.** [3.3b] 0.0000123
21. [3.3b] 30.4 **22.** [3.3b] 0.19 **23.** [3.3d] 0.75
24. [3.3d] 1.$\overline{2}$ **25.** [3.3d] 0.88 **26.** [3.4a] 460
27. [3.4a] 457.68 **28.** [3.4a] 457.678 **29.** [3.4b] 198
30. [3.4b] 4 **31.** [3.5a] $3627.65 **32.** [3.5a] 10.57 sec
33. [3.5a] $119.70 **34.** [3.5a] 2.37 km **35.** [3.5a] $1675.50
36. [2.4c] 26$\frac{1}{2}$ **37.** [1.9a] 360 **38.** [2.1e] $\frac{11}{18}$
39. [1.7d] $2^3 \cdot 3^2 \cdot 5$

CHAPTER 4

Pretest: Chapter 4, p. 166

1. [4.1a] $\frac{35}{43}$ **2.** [4.1a] $\frac{0.079}{1.043}$ **3.** [4.1c] 22.5
4. [4.1d] 25.5 miles per gallon **5.** [4.2b] 0.87 **6.** [4.2c] 53.7%
7. [4.3a] 75% **8.** [4.3b] $\frac{37}{100}$ **9.** [4.4b] $x = 60\% \times 75$; 45

10. [4.5b] $\frac{n}{100} = \frac{35}{50}$; 70% **11.** [4.1e] 22
12. [4.1e] 393.75 miles **13.** [4.6a] 90 lb **14.** [4.6b] 20%
15. [4.7a] $14.30; $300.30
16. [4.7c] $112.50 discount; $337.50 sale price **17.** [4.7d] $20
18. [4.7e] $7128.60

Exercise Set 4.1, p. 173

1. $\frac{4}{5}$ **3.** $\frac{0.4}{12}$ **5.** $\frac{2}{12}$ **7.** No **9.** Yes **11.** 45 **13.** 10 **15.** 20
17. 18 **19.** 0.06 **21.** 5 **23.** 14 **25.** 1 **27.** 40 km/h
29. 25 km/hr; 0.04 hr/km **31.** 560 mi/hr **33.** 702 km
35. $84.60 **37.** 3.57 **39.** 1980
41. Approximately 11.54 m/sec; 0.08666 sec/m

Sidelight: Calculator Corner: Finding Whole-Number Remainders in Division, p. 178

1. 28 R 2 **2.** 116 R 3 **3.** 74 R 10 **4.** 415 R 3

Exercise Set 4.2, p. 179

1. $\frac{90}{100}$; 90 × $\frac{1}{100}$; 90 × 0.01 **3.** $\frac{12.5}{100}$; 12.5 × $\frac{1}{100}$; 12.5 × 0.01
5. 0.67 **7.** 0.456 **9.** 0.5901 **11.** 0.1 **13.** 0.01 **15.** 2
17. 0.001 **19.** 0.0009 **21.** 0.0018 **23.** 0.2319 **25.** 0.9
27. 0.108 **29.** 0.458 **31.** 47% **33.** 3% **35.** 100%
37. 33.4% **39.** 75% **41.** 40% **43.** 0.6% **45.** 1.7%
47. 27.18% **49.** 2.39% **51.** 2.5% **53.** 24% **55.** 33$\frac{1}{3}$
57. 0.$\overline{6}$ **59.** Multiply by 100.

Sidelight: Applications of Ratio and Percent: The Price-Earnings Ratio and Stock Yields, p. 184

1. 6.0, 8.1% **2.** 11.9, 1.8% **3.** 4.7, 3.2% **4.** 9.4, 6.8%

Exercise Set 4.3, p. 185

1. 41% **3.** 1% **5.** 20% **7.** 30% **9.** 50% **11.** 62.5%
13. 40% **15.** 66.$\overline{6}$%, or 66$\frac{2}{3}$% **17.** 16.$\overline{6}$%, or 16$\frac{2}{3}$% **19.** 16%
21. 5% **23.** 34% **25.** 36% **27.** $\frac{4}{5}$ **29.** $\frac{5}{8}$ **31.** $\frac{1}{3}$ **33.** $\frac{1}{6}$
35. $\frac{29}{400}$ **37.** $\frac{1}{125}$ **39.** $\frac{7}{20}$

41.

$\frac{1}{8}$	$\frac{1}{6}$	$\frac{1}{5}$	$\frac{1}{4}$	$\frac{1}{3}$	$\frac{3}{8}$	$\frac{2}{5}$
0.125	0.1$\overline{6}$	0.2	0.25	0.$\overline{3}$	0.375	0.4
12$\frac{1}{2}$%, or 12.5%	16$\frac{2}{3}$%, or 16.$\overline{6}$%	20%	25%	33$\frac{1}{3}$%, or 33.$\overline{3}$%	37$\frac{1}{2}$%, or 37.5%	40%

$\frac{1}{2}$	$\frac{3}{5}$	$\frac{5}{8}$	$\frac{2}{3}$	$\frac{3}{4}$	$\frac{4}{5}$	$\frac{5}{6}$
0.5	0.6	0.625	0.$\overline{6}$	0.75	0.8	0.8$\overline{3}$
50%	60%	62$\frac{1}{2}$%, or 62.5%	66$\frac{2}{3}$%, or 66.$\overline{6}$%	75%	80%	83$\frac{1}{3}$%, or 83.$\overline{3}$%

$\frac{7}{8}$	$\frac{1}{1}$
0.875	1
$87\frac{1}{2}\%$, or 87.5%	100%

43. 5 **45.** 18.75 **47.** $5.\overline{405}\%$

Exercise Set 4.4, p. 191

1. $y = 41\% \times 89$ **3.** $89 = a \times 99$ **5.** $13 = 25\% \times y$ **7.** 90
9. 45 **11.** $15 **13.** 1.05 **15.** 24% **17.** 200% **19.** 50%
21. 125% **23.** 40 **25.** $40 **27.** 88 **29.** 20 **31.** 6.25
33. $846.60 **35.** $\frac{9}{100}$ **37.** 0.89 **39.** $880 (can vary); $843.20

Exercise Set 4.5, p. 197

1. $\frac{82}{100} = \frac{a}{74}$ **3.** $\frac{n}{100} = \frac{4.3}{5.9}$ **5.** $\frac{25}{100} = \frac{14}{b}$ **7.** $42 **9.** 440
11. 80 **13.** 2.88 **15.** 25% **17.** 102% **19.** 25% **21.** 93.75%
23. $72 **25.** 90 **27.** 88 **29.** 20 **31.** 25 **33.** $780.20
35. $1134 (can vary); $1118.64

Exercise Set 4.6, p. 205

1. 27; 133 **3.** 536; 264 **5.** 32.5%; 67.5%
7. 20.4 mL; 659.6 mL **9.** 25% **11.** 45%; $37\frac{1}{2}\%$; $17\frac{1}{2}\%$
13. 8% **15.** 20% **17.** $9030 **19.** $8400
21. 5.2832 billion; about 5.3677 billion; about 5.4536 billion
23. $12,500 **25.** 166; 156; 146; 136; 122
27. Neither; they are the same **29.** About 5 ft, 6 in.

Exercise Set 4.7, p. 215

1. $20.46; $268.46 **3.** $11.40; $201.35 **5.** 5% **7.** 5.6%
9. $2800 **11.** $33.25 **13.** $3690 **15.** 5% **17.** $980
19. $6860 **21.** $519.80 **23.** $387; $30\frac{6}{17}\%$ **25.** $30; $270
27. $12.50; $112.50 **29.** 40%; $360 **31.** $26 **33.** $248
35. $7.70 **37.** $25 **39.** $484 **41.** $236.75 **43.** $466.56
45. $2184.05 **47.** $\frac{93}{100}$ **49.** $1.\overline{18}$ **51.** $5214.72 **53.** $1434.53

Summary and Review: Chapter 4, p. 219

1. [4.1a] $\frac{47}{84}$ **2.** [4.1a] $\frac{46}{1.27}$ **3.** [4.1a] $\frac{83}{100}$ **4.** [4.1a] $\frac{0.72}{197}$
5. [4.1c] 32 **6.** [4.1c] $\frac{1}{40}$ **7.** [4.1c] 7 **8.** [4.1c] 24
9. [4.1d] $25.36/kg **10.** [4.1d] 0.638 gal/sq ft
11. [4.2c] 48.3% **12.** [4.1c] 36% **13.** [4.3a] 37.5%
14. [4.3a] $33.\overline{3}\%$, or $33\frac{1}{3}\%$ **15.** [4.2b] 0.735 **16.** [4.2b] 0.065
17. [4.3b] $\frac{6}{25}$ **18.** [4.3b] $\frac{63}{1000}$
19. [4.4a, b] $30.6 = x\% \times 90$; 34%
20. [4.4a, b] $63 = 84\% \times n$; 75

21. [4.4a, b] $y = 38\frac{1}{2}\% \times 168$; 64.68
22. [4.5a, b] $\frac{24}{100} = \frac{16.8}{b}$; 70 **23.** [4.5a, b] $\frac{n}{100} = \frac{22.2}{30}$; 74%
24. [4.5a, b] $\frac{38\frac{1}{2}}{100} = \frac{a}{168}$; 64.68 **25.** [4.1e] $4.45
26. [4.1e] 27 acres **27.** [4.1e] 2622 **28.** [4.1e] 6 in.
29. [4.6a] 168 **30.** [4.6b] 12% **31.** [4.6b] 82,400
32. [4.6b] 20% **33.** [4.7a] 5% **34.** [4.7b] 11%
35. [4.7c] $42; $308 **36.** [4.7b] $29.40 **37.** [4.7d] $31.90
38. [4.7d] $15.25 **39.** [4.7e] $188.16 **40.** [4.7e] $224.72
41. [3.3c] 64 **42.** [3.3c] 7.6123 **43.** [3.1b] $\frac{1203}{100}$
44. [3.1b] $\frac{33}{1000}$ **45.** [3.3d] $3.\overline{6}$ **46.** [3.3d] 1.571428
47. [2.4a] $3\frac{2}{3}$ **48.** [2.4a] $17\frac{2}{7}$

Test: Chapter 4, p. 221

1. [4.1a] $\frac{85}{97}$ **2.** [4.1a] $\frac{0.34}{124}$ **3.** [4.1c] 12 **4.** [4.1c] 360
5. [4.1d] 0.625 m/sec **6.** [4.1d] $1\frac{1}{3}$ servings/lb **7.** [4.2b] 0.89
8. [4.2c] 67.4% **9.** [4.3a] 87.5% **10.** [4.3b] $\frac{13}{20}$
11. [4.4a, b] $m = 40\% \times 55$; 22
12. [4.5a, b] $\frac{n}{100} = \frac{65}{80}$; 81.25% **13.** [4.1e] 1512 km
14. [4.1e] 44 **15.** [4.1e] 4.8 min **16.** [4.6a] 50 lb
17. [4.6b] 20% **18.** [4.7a] $16.20; $340.20 **19.** [4.7b] $630
20. [4.7c] $40; $160 **21.** [4.7d] $4.30 **22.** [4.7e] $127.69
23. [3.3c] 222 **24.** [3.1b] $\frac{7}{1000}$ **25.** [3.3d] $1.41\overline{6}$
26. [2.4a] $3\frac{21}{44}$

CHAPTER 5

Pretest: Chapter 5, p. 224

1. [5.1a, b, c] **(a)** 51; **(b)** 51.5; **(c)** 46, 50, 53, 55
2. [5.1a, b, c] **(a)** 3; **(b)** 3; **(c)** 5, 4, 3, 2, 1
3. [5.1a, b, c] **(a)** 12.75; **(b)** 17; **(c)** 4
4. [5.1a] 55 km/h **5.** [5.1a] 76
6. [5.4b]

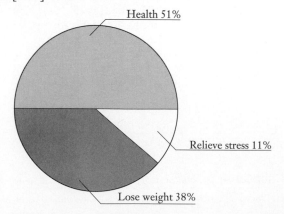

7. [5.2a] **(a)** $298; **(b)** $172; **(c)** $134

8. [5.3b]

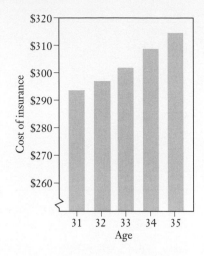

9. [5.3c] 1988   **10.** [5.3c] 19,000

Exercise Set 5.1, p. 229

1. Average: 12; median: 13.5; mode: 15
3. Average: 20; median: 20; mode: 5, 10, 15, 20, 25, 30, 35
5. Average: 5.2; median: 5.7; mode: 7.4
7. Average: 239.5; median: 234; mode: 234
9. Average: 256.25 lb; median: 257.5 lb; mode: 260 lb
11. Average: 40°; median: 40°; mode: 43°, 40°, 23°, 38°, 54°, 35°, 47°
13. 29 mpg   **15.** 2.75
17. Average: $9.75; median: $9.79; mode: $9.79   **19.** 90
21. $18,460   **23.** $\frac{4}{9}$ **25.** 1.999396   **27.** 171

Sidelight: A Problem-Solving Extra, p. 236

1. 520,000   **2.** 261,800   **3.** 401,900

Exercise Set 5.2, p. 237

1. 4 in.   **3.** 94   **5.** 21   **7.** Not given in table   **9.** 2740
11. 294   **13.** Calisthenics   **15.** Aerobic dance   **17.** 660
19. Moderate walking   **21.** 121   **23.** 1987   **25.** 1983 and 1984
27. 7000   **29.** 1986   **31.** 3   **33.** 16   **35.** 13   **37.** Out

39.

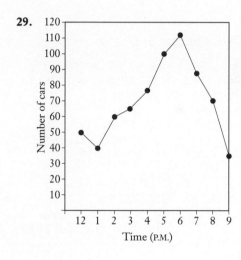

41. 27,859.5 sq mi

Exercise Set 5.3, p. 247

1. Los Angeles   **3.** 22   **5.** 2   **7.** Syracuse
9. Approximately $270   **11.** San Francisco
13. Approximately $50
15.

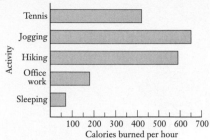

17. 3:00 P.M.   **19.** Approximately 15°
21. Between 5:00 P.M. and 6:00 P.M.   **23.** 1991
25. Approximately $17 million
27. Approximately $1.5 million

29.

31. Between 8 P.M. and 9 P.M.   **33.** 18%   **35.** 66.$\overline{6}$%, or 66$\frac{2}{3}$%

Exercise Set 5.4, p. 255

1. 3.7%   **3.** 270   **5.** 6.8%   **7.** Gas purchased   **9.** 4¢   **11.** 16¢

13.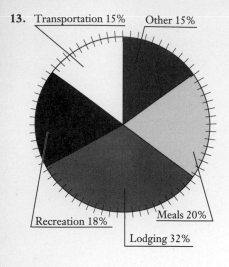

Transportation 15%   Other 15%
Recreation 18%   Meals 20%
Lodging 32%

15. 25% **17.** $\frac{3}{4}$

Summary and Review: Chapter 5, p. 257

1. [5.1a] 38.5 **2.** [5.1a] 13.4 **3.** [5.1a] 1.55 **4.** [5.1a] 1840
5. [5.1a] $16.\overline{6}$ **6.** [5.1a] $321.\overline{6}$ **7.** [5.1b] 38.5 **8.** [5.1b] 14
9. [5.1b] 1.8 **10.** [5.1b] 1900 **11.** [5.1b] $17
12. [5.1b] 375 **13.** [5.1c] 26 **14.** [5.1c] 11; 17
15. [5.1c] 0.2 **16.** [5.1c] 700; 800 **17.** [5.1c] $17
18. [5.1c] 20 **19.** [5.1a, b] $110.5; $107 **20.** [5.1a] $66.1\overline{6}°$
21. [5.1a] 96 **22.** [5.2a] Boston **23.** [5.2a] $0.50
24. [5.2a] $2.18 **25.** [5.2a] $70,716
26. [5.2a] Washington, D.C. **27.** [5.2a] Canton, Ohio
28. [5.2b] USSR **29.** [5.2b] 91 **30.** [5.2b] US
31. [5.2b] 103 **32.** [5.3a] $6.25 **33.** [5.3a] Hong Kong
34. [5.3a] New York City **35.** [5.3a] Dallas **36.** [5.3a] $4.50
37. [5.3a] Sydney **38.** [5.3c] Under 20
39. [5.3c] Approximately 12
40. [5.3c] Approximately 13 per 100 drivers
41. [5.3c] Between 45 and 74
42. [5.3c] Approximately 11 per 100 drivers
43. [5.3c] Under 20 **44.** [5.4a] 30%
45. [5.4a] Outlying suburbs **46.** [5.4a] 64% **47.** [5.4a] 7.5
48. [4.1e] 12,600 mi **49.** [4.6a] 215.28 million
50. [4.4a], [4.5a] $222.\overline{2}$%, or $222\frac{2}{9}$% **51.** [4.4a], [4.5a] 50%
52. [2.2c] $\frac{9}{10}$ **53.** [2.2c] $\frac{5}{12}$

Test: Chapter 5, p. 261

1. [5.1a] 50 **2.** [5.1a] 3 **3.** [5.1a] 15.5
4. [5.1b, c] Median: 50.5; mode: 45, 49, 52, 54
5. [5.1b, c] Median: 3; mode: 1, 2, 3, 4, 5
6. [5.1b, c] Median: 17.5; mode: 17, 18 **7.** [5.1a] 58 km/h
8. [5.1a] 76 **9.** [5.2a] Hiking with 20-lb load
10. [5.2a] Hiking with 10-lb load
11. [5.2a] Walking 3.5 mph **12.** [5.2a] Fitness walking

13. [5.3b]

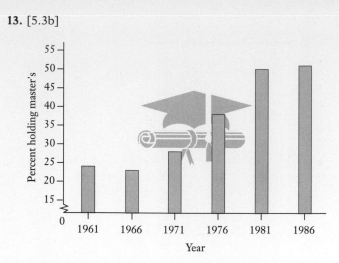

Percent holding master's
55
50
45
40
35
30
25
20
15
0
1961 1966 1971 1976 1981 1986
Year

14. [5.2b] 25 **15.** [5.2b] Carew **16.** [5.2b] 145
17. [5.2b] Garr **18.** [5.2b] 10 **19.** [5.3c] Increasing
20. [5.3c] 1970 to 1975 **21.** [5.3c] $1 billion
22. [5.3c] $2 billion
23. [5.4b]

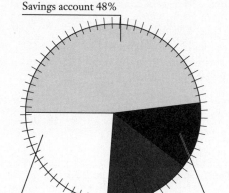

Savings account 48%
Retirement 24%
Mutual funds 16%
Stocks 12%

24. [2.2c] $\frac{25}{4}$ **25.** [4.4a], [4.5a] 68 **26.** [4.6a] 15,600
27. [4.1e] 340

CHAPTER 6

Pretest: Chapter 6, p. 266

1. [6.2a] 131 mm **2.** [6.3b] 92 in² **3.** [6.4a] 22 cm²
4. [6.4a] $32\frac{1}{2}$ ft² **5.** [6.4a] 4 m² **6.** [6.5a] 9.6 m
7. [6.5b], [6.5c] 30.144 m; 72.3456 m²
8. [6.6a] 160 cm³; 256 cm² **9.** [6.6b] 1256 ft³
10. [6.7c] $m\angle 1 = m\angle 7 = m\angle 3 = m\angle 5 = 151°$,
$m\angle 2 = m\angle 6 = m\angle 4 = 29°$
11. [6.8a] $\overline{PQ} \cong \overline{ST}$, $\overline{QR} \cong \overline{TV}$, $\overline{RP} \cong \overline{VS}$; $\angle P \cong \angle S$,
$\angle Q \cong \angle T$, $\angle R \cong \angle V$
12. [6.9a] $MA = 7$, $GT = 8$

Exercise Set 6.1, p. 273

1. •————————•
　 G　　　　　H , $\overline{GH}$, $\overline{HG}$

3. •————————→
　 Q　　　　　D , $\overrightarrow{QD}$　5. $\overline{DE}$, $\overline{ED}$, $\overline{DF}$, $\overline{FD}$, $\overline{EF}$, $\overline{FE}$, l

7. Angle GHI, angle IHG, $\angle GHI$, $\angle IHG$, or $\angle H$
9. 10°　11. 180°　13. 130°　15. Acute　17. Straight
19. Obtuse　21. No　23. Yes　25. Scalene, obtuse
27. Scalene, right　29. Equilateral, acute　31. Scalene, obtuse
33. Quadrilateral　35. Pentagon　37. Triangle　39. Pentagon
41. Hexagon　43. 1440°　45. 2160°　47. 46°　49. 1.75
51. 0.234　53. 13.85　55. 4

Exercise Set 6.2, p. 279

1. 17 mm　3. 15.25 cm　5. 13 m　7. 30 ft　9. 79.14 cm
11. 88 ft　13. 182 mm　15. 826 m; $1197.70　17. 99 cm
19. (a) 14; (b) $33.60; (c) 39 m; (d) $33.15; (e) $76.70
21. 0.561　23. 961

Exercise Set 6.3, p. 283

1. 15 km²　3. 1.4 cm²　5. 6.25 mm²　7. 8100 ft²　9. 50 ft²
11. 169.883 cm²　13. 484 ft²　15. 3237.61 km²　17. 1197 m²
19. 630.36 m²　21. (a) 24.75 m²; (b) $207.90　23. 107.5 mm²
25. 45.2%　27. 55%

Exercise Set 6.4, p. 289

1. 32 cm²　3. 36 m²　5. 51 ft²　7. 64 m²　9. 45.5 mm²
11. 8.05 cm²　13. 297 cm²　15. 7 m²　17. $55\frac{1}{8}$ ft²
19. 675 cm²　21. 10,816 in²　23. 852.04 m²　25. $\frac{37}{400}$
27. 137.5%

Exercise Set 6.5, p. 295

1. 14 cm　3. $1\frac{1}{2}$ in.　5. 16 ft　7. 0.7 cm　9. 44 cm　11. $4\frac{5}{7}$ in.
13. 100.48 ft　15. 4.396 cm　17. 154 cm²　19. $1\frac{43}{56}$ in²
21. 803.84 ft²　23. 1.5386 cm²
25. 3 cm; 18.84 cm; 28.26 cm²　27. 151,976 km²
29. 3.454 m　31. 2.5 cm; 1.25 cm; 4.90625 cm²
33. 65.94 m²　35. 45.68 ft　37. 26.84 yd　39. 45.7 yd
41. 100.48 m²　43. 6.9972 cm²　45. 48.8886 cm²　47. 87.5%
49. $66.\overline{6}$%　51. 3.142
53. $3d$; πd; circumference of one ball, since $\pi > 3$

Exercise Set 6.6, p. 303

1. 768 cm³　3. 45 cm³　5. 75 m³　7. $357\frac{1}{2}$ yd³　9. 803.84 in³
11. 353.25 cm³　13. 41,580,000 yd³　15. $2\frac{3}{4}$ ft³
17. $4,186,666\frac{2}{3}$ in³　19. 124.72 m³　21. $1437\frac{1}{3}$ km³
23. 113,982 ft³　25. 1617 in³　27. 24.64 cm³　29. 33,880 m³
31. 367.38 m³　33. 113.0 m³　35. 137,188,693,333.33 km³
37. $112\frac{1}{2}$　39. 1000　41. 57,480 in³; 33.3 ft³

Exercise Set 6.7, p. 315

1. 79°　3. 23°　5. 177°　7. 41°　9. No　11. Yes
13. $m\angle 2 = 67°$, $m\angle 3 = 33°$, $m\angle 4 = 80°$, $m\angle 6 = 33°$
15. (a) $\angle 1$ and $\angle 3$, $\angle 2$ and $\angle 4$, $\angle 8$ and $\angle 6$, $\angle 7$ and $\angle 5$;
(b) $\angle 2$, $\angle 3$, $\angle 6$, and $\angle 7$; (c) $\angle 2$ and $\angle 6$, $\angle 3$ and $\angle 7$
17. $m\angle 6 = m\angle 2 = m\angle 8 = 125°$,
$m\angle 5 = m\angle 3 = m\angle 7 = m\angle 1 = 55°$
19. $\angle ABE \cong \angle DCE$, 95°; $\angle BAE \cong \angle CDE$; $\angle AEB \cong \angle DEC$
21. $\angle AEC \cong \angle DCE$, 50°; $\angle BED \cong \angle EDC$, 41°

Exercise Set 6.8, p. 323

1. $\angle A \cong \angle R$, $\angle B \cong \angle S$, $\angle C \cong \angle T$;
$\overline{AB} \cong \overline{RS}$, $\overline{AC} \cong \overline{RT}$, $\overline{BC} \cong \overline{ST}$
3. $\angle D \cong \angle G$, $\angle E \cong \angle H$, $\angle F \cong \angle K$;
$\overline{DE} \cong \overline{GH}$, $\overline{DF} \cong \overline{GK}$, $\overline{EF} \cong \overline{HK}$
5. $\angle X \cong \angle U$, $\angle Y \cong \angle V$, $\angle Z \cong \angle W$;
$\overline{XY} \cong \overline{UV}$, $\overline{XZ} \cong \overline{UW}$, $\overline{YZ} \cong \overline{VW}$
7. $\angle A \cong \angle F$, $\angle C \cong \angle D$, $\angle B \cong \angle E$;
$\overline{AC} \cong \overline{FD}$, $\overline{AB} \cong \overline{FE}$, $\overline{CB} \cong \overline{DE}$
9. $\angle M \cong \angle Q$, $\angle N \cong \angle P$, $\angle O \cong \angle S$;
$\overline{MN} \cong \overline{QP}$, $\overline{MO} \cong \overline{QS}$, $\overline{NO} \cong \overline{PS}$
11. No　13. Yes　15. Yes　17. No　19. Yes　21. Yes
23. Yes　25. Yes　27. Yes　29. ASA　31. SAS
33. SSS or SAS
35. $\overline{PR} \cong \overline{TR}$, $\overline{SR} \cong \overline{QR}$, $\angle PRQ \cong \angle TRS$ (vertical angles);
$\triangle PRQ \cong \triangle TRS$ by SAS
37. $m\angle GLK = m\angle GLM = 90°$, $\angle GLK \cong \angle GLM$,
$\overline{GL} \cong \overline{GL}$, $\overline{KL} \cong \overline{ML}$, $\triangle KLG \cong \triangle MLG$ by SAS
39. $\overline{AE} \cong \overline{CD}$, $\overline{AB} \cong \overline{CB}$, $\overline{EB} \cong \overline{DB}$; $\triangle AEB \cong \triangle CDB$ by SSS
41. $\triangle LKH \cong \triangle GKJ$ by SAS; $\angle HLK \cong \angle JGK$,
$\angle LHK \cong \angle GJK$, $\overline{LH} \cong \overline{GJ}$
43. $\triangle PED \cong \triangle PFG$ by ASA. As corresponding parts,
$\overline{EP} \cong \overline{FP}$; thus, P is the midpoint of $\overline{EF}$.
45. $m\angle A = 70°$, $m\angle D = m\angle B = 110°$
47. $m\angle M = 71°$, $m\angle J = m\angle L = 109°$
49. $TU = 9$, $NU = 15$　51. $JM = KL = 3\frac{1}{2}$, $ML = JK = 7\frac{1}{2}$
53. $AC = 28$, $ED = 38$

Sidelight: An Application of Ratio: State Lottery Profits, p. 330

1. New York　2. Vermont　3. $618.3 million
4. $3.6042 billion　5. 0.1706　6. $461.3 million
7. $74.3 million　8. $13.67 per person　9. $34.81 per person
10. $45.08　11. Illinois

Exercise Set 6.9, p. 331

1. $\angle R \leftrightarrow \angle A$, $\angle S \leftrightarrow \angle B$, $\angle T \leftrightarrow \angle C$, $\overline{RS} \leftrightarrow \overline{AB}$, $\overline{RT} \leftrightarrow \overline{AC}$,
$\overline{ST} \leftrightarrow \overline{BC}$
3. $\angle C \leftrightarrow \angle W$, $\angle B \leftrightarrow \angle J$, $\angle S \leftrightarrow \angle Z$, $\overline{CB} \leftrightarrow \overline{WJ}$,
$\overline{CS} \leftrightarrow \overline{WZ}$, $\overline{BS} \leftrightarrow \overline{JZ}$
5. $\angle A \cong \angle R$, $\angle B \cong \angle S$, $\angle C \cong \angle T$; $\dfrac{AB}{RS} = \dfrac{AC}{RT} = \dfrac{BC}{ST}$
7. $\angle M \cong \angle C$, $\angle E \cong \angle L$, $\angle S \cong \angle F$; $\dfrac{ME}{CL} = \dfrac{MS}{CF} = \dfrac{ES}{LF}$

9. $\dfrac{PS}{ND} = \dfrac{SQ}{DM} = \dfrac{PQ}{NM}$ **11.** $\dfrac{TA}{GF} = \dfrac{TW}{GC} = \dfrac{AW}{FC}$
13. $QR = 10$, $PR = 8$ **15.** $EC = 24$ **17.** $97\frac{5}{8}$ **19.** 1296

Summary and Review: Chapter 6, p. 333

1. [6.2a] 4.4 m   **2.** [6.2b] 228 ft   **3.** [6.3a] 81 ft²
4. [6.3a] 12.6 cm²   **5.** [6.4a] 60 cm²   **6.** [6.4a] 35 mm²
7. [6.4a] 22.5 m²   **8.** [6.4a] 27.5 cm²   **9.** [6.3b] 840 ft²
10. [6.5a] 8 m   **11.** [6.5a] $\frac{14}{11}$ in., or $1\frac{3}{11}$ in.   **12.** [6.5a] 14 ft
13. [6.5a] 20 cm   **14.** [6.5b] 50.24 m   **15.** [6.5b] 8 in.
16. [6.5c] 200.96 m²   **17.** [6.5c] $5\frac{1}{11}$ in²
18. [6.6a] 93.6 m³, 150 m²   **19.** [6.6a] 193.2 cm³, 240.4 cm²
20. [6.6b] 31,400 ft³   **21.** [6.6c] $33.49\overline{3}$ cm³
22. [6.6d] 4.71 in³   **23.** [6.1f] 60°   **24.** [6.1e] Scalene
25. [6.1e] Right   **26.** [6.1e] 720°   **27.** [6.7a] 8°
28. [6.7a] 85°   **29.** [6.7a] 147°   **30.** [6.7a] 47°
31. [6.7c] $m\angle 2 = 105°$, $m\angle 3 = 37°$, $m\angle 4 = 38°$, $m\angle 6 = 37°$
32. [6.7d] **(a)** $\angle 1$ and $\angle 5$, $\angle 4$ and $\angle 8$, $\angle 3$ and $\angle 7$, $\angle 2$ and $\angle 6$; **(b)** $\angle 4$, $\angle 5$, $\angle 2$, and $\angle 7$;
(c) $\angle 4$ and $\angle 7$, $\angle 2$ and $\angle 5$
33. [6.7d] $m\angle 1 = m\angle 3 = m\angle 7 = m\angle 5 = 45°$, $m\angle 6 = m\angle 2 = m\angle 8 = 135°$
34. [6.8a] $\angle D \cong \angle R$, $\angle H \cong \angle Z$, $\angle J \cong \angle K$; $\overline{DH} \cong \overline{RZ}$, $\overline{DJ} \cong \overline{RK}$, $\overline{HJ} \cong \overline{ZK}$
35. [6.8a] $\angle A \cong \angle G$, $\angle B \cong \angle D$, $\angle C \cong \angle F$, $\overline{AB} \cong \overline{GD}$, $\overline{AC} \cong \overline{GF}$, $\overline{BC} \cong \overline{DF}$
36. [6.8a] ASA   **37.** [6.8a] SSS   **38.** [6.8a] None
39. [6.8a] $\overline{IJ} \cong \overline{KJ}$, $\angle HJI \cong \angle LJK$, $\angle HIJ \cong \angle LKJ$; $\triangle JIH \cong \triangle JKL$ by ASA
40. [6.8b] $m\angle C = 63°$, $m\angle B = m\angle D = 117°$; $BC = 23$, $CD = 13$
41. [6.9a] $\angle C \cong \angle F$, $\angle Q \cong \angle A$, $\angle W \cong \angle S$; $\dfrac{CQ}{FA} = \dfrac{CW}{FS} = \dfrac{QW}{AS}$
42. [6.9a] $MO = 14$ **43.** [4.7d] $54\frac{5}{8}$ **44.** [1.6b] 103.823
45. [1.6b] $\frac{1}{16}$ **46.** [4.3b] $\frac{73}{100}$ **47.** [4.2c] 47%   **48.** [4.3a] 92%

Test: Chapter 6, p. 337

1. [6.2a] 32.82 cm   **2.** [6.2b], [6.3b] $P = 14$ ft, $A = 11\frac{1}{4}$ ft²
3. [6.4a] 25 cm²   **4.** [6.4a] 12 m²   **5.** [6.4a] 18 ft²
6. [6.3a] 625 m²   **7.** [6.5d] 103.815 km²   **8.** [6.5a] $\frac{1}{4}$ in.
9. [6.5a] 9 cm   **10.** [6.5b] $\frac{11}{14}$ in.   **11.** [6.5c] 254.34 cm²
12. [6.6a] 84 cm³, 142 cm²   **13.** [6.6b] 1177.5 ft³
14. [6.6c] $4186.\overline{6}$ yd³   **15.** [6.6c] 113.04 cm³   **16.** [6.1f] 35°
17. [6.1e] Isosceles   **18.** [6.1e] Obtuse   **19.** [6.1e] 540°
20. [6.7a] 149°   **21.** [6.7a] 11°
22. [6.7c] $m\angle 2 = 110°$, $m\angle 3 = 8°$, $m\angle 4 = 62°$, $m\angle 6 = 8°$
23. [6.7d] $m\angle 6 = m\angle 2 = m\angle 8 = 120°$, $m\angle 5 = m\angle 3 = m\angle 7 = m\angle 1 = 60°$
24. [6.8a] $\angle C \cong \angle A$, $\angle W \cong \angle T$, $\angle S \cong \angle Z$, $\overline{CW} \cong \overline{AT}$, $\overline{WS} \cong \overline{TZ}$, $\overline{SC} \cong \overline{ZA}$
25. [6.8a] SAS   **26.** [6.8a] None   **27.** [6.8a] ASA
28. [6.8a] None
29. [6.8b] $m\angle G = 105°$, $m\angle D = m\angle F = 75°$
30. [6.8b] $LJ = 6.4$, $KM = 6$

31. [6.9a] $\angle E \cong \angle T$, $\angle R \cong \angle G$, $\angle S \cong \angle F$; $\dfrac{ER}{TG} = \dfrac{RS}{GF} = \dfrac{SE}{FT}$
32. [6.9a] $EK = 18$, $ZK = 27$ **33.** [4.7d] 10.6
34. [1.6b] 1000   **35.** [1.6b] $\frac{1}{16}$ **36.** [4.3a] 81.25%
37. [4.2b] 0.932   **38.** [4.3b] $\frac{1}{3}$

CHAPTER 7

Pretest: Chapter 7, p. 342

1. [7.1a] $\frac{5}{16}$ **2.** [7.1b] 78%x, or $0.78x$ **3.** [7.1a] 360 ft²
4. [7.3b] 12   **5.** [7.2d] >   **6.** [7.2d] >   **7.** [7.2d] >
8. [7.2d] <   **9.** [7.2e] 12   **10.** [7.2e] 2.3   **11.** [7.2e] 0
12. [7.3b] -5.4 **13.** [7.3b] $\frac{2}{3}$ **14.** [7.3a] -17
15. [7.4a] 38.6   **16.** [7.4a] $-\frac{17}{15}$ **17.** [7.3a] -5
18. [7.5a] 63   **19.** [7.5a] $-\frac{5}{12}$ **20.** [7.6c] -98 **21.** [7.6a] 8
22. [7.4a] 24   **23.** [7.8d] 26   **24.** [7.7c] $9z - 18$
25. [7.7c] $-4a - 2b + 10c$ **26.** [7.7d] $4(x - 3)$
27. [7.7d] $3(2y - 3z - 6)$ **28.** [7.8b] $-y - 13$
29. [7.8c] $y + 18$ **30.** [7.2d] $12 < x$

Exercise Set 7.1, p. 347

1. 23, 28, 41   **3.** 100.1 cm²   **5.** 220 mi   **7.** 42   **9.** 3   **11.** 1
13. 6   **15.** 2   **17.** $b + 6$, or $6 + b$ **19.** $c - 9$
21. $6 + q$, or $q + 6$ **23.** $b + a$, or $a + b$ **25.** $y - x$
27. $x + w$, or $w + x$ **29.** $n - m$ **31.** $r + s$, or $s + r$ **33.** $2x$
35. $5t$ **37.** 97%x, or $0.97x$ **39.** $d - \$29.95$ **41.** $2 \cdot 3 \cdot 3 \cdot 3$
43. 18   **45.** $x + 3y$ **47.** $2x - 3$

Exercise Set 7.2, p. 357

1. 18, -2 **3.** 750, -125 **5.** 20, -150, 300
7.
9.

11. $x < -6$ **13.** $y \geq -10$ **15.** -0.375 **17.** $1.\overline{6}$ **19.** $1.1\overline{6}$
21. $0.\overline{6}$ **23.** -0.5 **25.** 0.1   **27.** >   **29.** <   **31.** <   **33.** <
35. >   **37.** <   **39.** >   **41.** <   **43.** <   **45.** <   **47.** True
49. False   **51.** 3   **53.** 10   **55.** 0   **57.** 24   **59.** $\frac{2}{3}$ **61.** 0
63. $-\frac{5}{6}$, $-\frac{3}{4}$, $-\frac{2}{3}$, $\frac{1}{6}$, $\frac{3}{8}$, $\frac{1}{2}$

Exercise Set 7.3, p. 363

1. -7 **3.** -4 **5.** 0   **7.** -8 **9.** -7 **11.** -27 **13.** 0
15. -42 **17.** 0   **19.** 0   **21.** 3   **23.** -9 **25.** 7   **27.** 0   **29.** 45
31. -1.8 **33.** -8.1 **35.** $-\frac{1}{5}$ **37.** $-\frac{8}{7}$ **39.** $-\frac{3}{8}$ **41.** $-\frac{29}{35}$
43. $\frac{7}{16}$ **45.** 39   **47.** 50   **49.** -1409 **51.** -24 **53.** 26.9
55. -9 **57.** $\frac{14}{3}$ **59.** -65 **61.** $\frac{5}{3}$ **63.** 14   **65.** -10
67. All positive   **69.** Negative

Exercise Set 7.4, p. 369

1. -4 **3.** -7 **5.** -6 **7.** 0 **9.** -4 **11.** -7 **13.** -6 **15.** 0
17. 0 **19.** 14 **21.** 11 **23.** -14 **25.** 5 **27.** -7 **29.** -1
31. 18 **33.** -5 **35.** -3 **37.** -21 **39.** 5 **41.** -8 **43.** 12
45. -23 **47.** -68 **49.** -73 **51.** 116 **53.** 0 **55.** $-\frac{1}{4}$
57. $\frac{1}{12}$ **59.** $-\frac{17}{12}$ **61.** $\frac{1}{8}$ **63.** 19.9 **65.** -9 **67.** -0.01
69. -193 **71.** 500 **73.** -2.8 **75.** -3.53 **77.** $-\frac{1}{2}$ **79.** $\frac{6}{7}$
81. $-\frac{41}{30}$ **83.** $-\frac{1}{156}$ **85.** 37 **87.** -62 **89.** -139 **91.** 6
93. 107 **95.** 219 **97.** $-\$330.54$ **99.** $y + \$215.50$
101. 116 m **103.** 125 **105.** $-309,882$
107. False; $3 - 0 \neq 0 - 3$ **109.** True **111.** True

Exercise Set 7.5, p. 377

1. -16 **3.** -42 **5.** -24 **7.** -72 **9.** 16 **11.** 42
13. -120 **15.** -238 **17.** 1200 **19.** 98 **21.** -72
23. -12.4 **25.** 24 **27.** 21.7 **29.** $-\frac{2}{5}$ **31.** $\frac{1}{12}$ **33.** -17.01
35. $-\frac{5}{12}$ **37.** 420 **39.** $\frac{2}{7}$ **41.** -60 **43.** 150 **45.** $-\frac{2}{45}$
47. 1911 **49.** 50.4 **51.** $\frac{10}{189}$ **53.** -960 **55.** 17.64 **57.** $-\frac{5}{784}$
59. 0 **61.** -720 **63.** $-30, 240$ **65.** $441, -147$ **67.** 20, 20
69. 72 **71.** 1944 **73.** -17
75. **(a)** One must be negative and one must be positive;
(b) either or both must be zero; **(c)** both must be negative or
both must be positive.

Exercise Set 7.6, p. 383

1. -6 **3.** -13 **5.** -2 **7.** 4 **9.** -8 **11.** 2 **13.** -12
15. -8 **17.** Undefined **19.** $-\frac{88}{9}$ **21.** $\frac{7}{15}$ **23.** $-\frac{13}{47}$ **25.** $\frac{1}{13}$
27. $\frac{1}{4.3}$ **29.** -7.1 **31.** $\frac{q}{p}$ **33.** $4y$ **35.** $\frac{3b}{2a}$ **37.** $3 \cdot \left(\frac{1}{19}\right)$
39. $6 \cdot \left(-\frac{1}{13}\right)$ **41.** $13.9 \cdot \left(-\frac{1}{1.5}\right)$ **43.** $x \cdot y$ **45.** $(3x + 4) \cdot (\frac{1}{5})$
47. $(5a - b)\left(\frac{1}{5a + b}\right)$ **49.** $-\frac{9}{8}$ **51.** $\frac{5}{3}$ **53.** $\frac{9}{14}$ **55.** $\frac{9}{64}$
57. -2 **59.** $\frac{11}{13}$ **61.** -16.2 **63.** Undefined **65.** $\frac{22}{39}$ **67.** 33
69. $-\frac{1}{10.5}$, or $-0.\overline{095238}$ **71.** No real numbers **73.** Negative
75. Positive **77.** Negative

Exercise Set 7.7, p. 393

1. $\frac{2x}{5x}$ **3.** $\frac{10y}{15y}$ **5.** $-\frac{3}{2}$ **7.** $-\frac{7}{6}$ **9.** $8 + y$ **11.** nm
13. $xy + 9$, or $9 + yx$ **15.** $c + ab$, or $ba + c$ **17.** $(a + b) + 2$
19. $8(xy)$ **21.** $a + (b + 3)$ **23.** $(3a)b$
25. $2 + (b + a)$, $(2 + a) + b$, $(b + 2) + a$; answers may vary
27. $(5 + w) + v$, $(v + 5) + w$, $(w + v) + 5$; answers may vary
29. $(3x)y$, $y(x \cdot 3)$, $3(yx)$; answers may vary
31. $a(7b)$, $b(7a)$, $(7b)a$; answers may vary **33.** $2b + 10$
35. $7 + 7t$ **37.** $30x + 12$ **39.** $7x + 28 + 42y$ **41.** 7 **43.** 12
45. -12.71 **47.** $7x - 14$ **49.** $-7y + 14$ **51.** $45x + 54y - 72$
53. $-4x + 12y + 8z$ **55.** $-3.72x + 9.92y - 3.41$ **57.** $4x, 3x$
59. $7x, 8y, -9z$ **61.** $2(x + 2)$ **63.** $5(6 + y)$ **65.** $7(2x + 3y)$
67. $5(x + 2 + 3y)$ **69.** $8(x - 3)$ **71.** $4(8 - y)$
73. $2(4x + 5y - 11)$ **75.** $a(x - 1)$ **77.** $a(x - y - z)$
79. $6(3x - 2y + 1)$ **81.** $19a$ **83.** $9a$ **85.** $8x + 9z$
87. $7x + 15y^2$ **89.** $-19a + 88$ **91.** $4t + 6y - 4$ **93.** b

95. $\frac{13}{4}y$ **97.** $8x$ **99.** $5n$ **101.** $-16y$ **103.** $17a - 12b - 1$
105. $4x + 2y$ **107.** $7x + y$ **109.** $0.8x + 0.5y$ **111.** $\frac{3}{5}x + \frac{3}{5}y$
113. $\frac{89}{48}$ **115.** 144 **117.** Not equivalent
119. Equivalent; commutative law of addition
121. $q(1 + r + rs + rst)$

Exercise Set 7.8, p. 401

1. $-2x - 7$ **3.** $-5x + 8$ **5.** $-4a + 3b - 7c$
7. $-6x + 8y - 5$ **9.** $-3x + 5y + 6$ **11.** $8x + 6y + 43$
13. $5x - 3$ **15.** $-3a + 9$ **17.** $5x - 6$ **19.** $-19x + 2y$
21. $9y - 25z$ **23.** $-7x + 10y$ **25.** $37a - 23b + 35c$ **27.** 7
29. -40 **31.** 19 **33.** $12x + 30$ **35.** $3x + 30$ **37.** $9x - 18$
39. $-4x - 64$ **41.** -7 **43.** -7 **45.** -16 **47.** -334
49. 14 **51.** 1880 **53.** 12 **55.** 8 **57.** -86 **59.** 37 **61.** -1
63. -10 **65.** 25 **67.** -7988 **69.** -3000 **71.** 60 **73.** 1
75. 10 **77.** $-\frac{13}{45}$ **79.** $-\frac{23}{18}$ **81.** -118
83. $6y - (-2x + 3a - c)$ **85.** $6m - (-3n + 5m - 4b)$
87. $-2x - f$
89. True. $(-a)(-b) = (-1 \cdot a)(-1 \cdot b) = (-1)(-1)(a)(b) = 1 \cdot (a \cdot b) = ab$

Summary and Review: Chapter 7, p. 405

1. [7.1a] 4 **2.** [7.1b] 19%x, or $0.19x$ **3.** [7.2a] $-45, 72$
4. [7.2e] 38

5. [7.2b]

6. [7.2b]

7. [7.2d] $<$ **8.** [7.2d] $>$ **9.** [7.2d] $>$ **10.** [7.2d] $<$
11. [7.3b] -3.8 **12.** [7.3b] $\frac{3}{4}$ **13.** [7.6b] $\frac{8}{3}$ **14.** [7.6b] $-\frac{1}{7}$
15. [7.3b] 34 **16.** [7.3b] 5 **17.** [7.3a] -3 **18.** [7.3a] -4
19. [7.3a] -5 **20.** [7.4a] 4 **21.** [7.4a] $-\frac{7}{5}$ **22.** [7.4a] -7.9
23. [7.5a] 54 **24.** [7.5a] -9.18 **25.** [7.5a] $-\frac{2}{7}$
26. [7.5a] -210 **27.** [7.6a] -7 **28.** [7.6c] -3
29. [7.6c] $\frac{3}{4}$ **30.** [7.8d] 71.6 **31.** [7.8d] 62
32. [7.4b] 8-yd gain **33.** [7.4b] $-\$130$ **34.** [7.7c] $15x - 35$
35. [7.7c] $-8x + 10$ **36.** [7.7c] $4x + 15$
37. [7.7c] $-24 + 48x$ **38.** [7.7d] $2(x - 7)$
39. [7.7d] $6(x - 1)$ **40.** [7.7d] $5(x + 2)$ **41.** [7.7d] $3(4 - x)$
42. [7.7e] $7a - 3b$ **43.** [7.7e] $-2x + 5y$ **44.** [7.7e] $5x - y$
45. [7.7e] $-a + 8b$ **46.** [7.8b] $-3a + 9$
47. [7.8b] $-2b + 21$ **48.** [7.8c] 6 **49.** [7.8c] $12y - 34$
50. [7.8c] $5x + 24$ **51.** [7.8c] $-15x + 25$ **52.** [7.2d] True
53. [7.2d] False **54.** [7.2d] $x > -3$ **55.** [2.2c] $\frac{55}{42}$
56. [1.6b, c] $\frac{109}{18}$ **57.** [1.7d] $2 \cdot 2 \cdot 2 \cdot 3 \cdot 3 \cdot 3 \cdot 3$
58. [4.3a] 62.5% **59.** [4.2b] 0.0567 **60.** [1.9a] 270
61. [7.8d] $-\frac{5}{8}$ **62.** [7.8d] -2.1

Test: Chapter 7, p. 407

1. [7.1a] 6 **2.** [7.1b] $x - 9$ **3.** [7.1a] 240 ft^2 **4.** [7.2d] $<$
5. [7.2d] $>$ **6.** [7.2d] $>$ **7.** [7.2d] $<$ **8.** [7.2e] 7
9. [7.2e] $\frac{9}{4}$ **10.** [7.2e] 2.7 **11.** [7.3b] $-\frac{2}{3}$ **12.** [7.3b] 1.4
13. [7.3b] 8 **14.** [7.6b] $-\frac{1}{2}$ **15.** [7.6b] $\frac{7}{4}$ **16.** [7.4a] 7.8

17. [7.3a] -8 **18.** [7.3a] $\frac{7}{40}$ **19.** [7.4a] 10   **20.** [7.4a] -2.5
21. [7.4a] $\frac{7}{8}$ **22.** [7.5a] -48 **23.** [7.5a] $\frac{3}{16}$ **24.** [7.6a] -9
25. [7.6c] $\frac{3}{4}$ **26.** [7.6c] -9.728 **27.** [7.8d] -173
28. [7.4b] $148   **29.** [7.7c] $18 - 3x$ **30.** [7.7c] $-5y + 5$
31. [7.7d] $2(6 - 11x)$ **32.** [7.7d] $7(x + 3 + 2y)$
33. [7.4a] 12   **34.** [7.8b] $2x + 7$ **35.** [7.8b] $9a - 12b - 7$
36. [7.8c] $68y - 8$ **37.** [7.8d] -4 **38.** [7.8d] 448
39. [7.2d] $-2 \ge x$ **40.** [1.6b] 1.728   **41.** [4.3a] 12.5%
42. [1.7d] $2 \cdot 2 \cdot 2 \cdot 5 \cdot 7$ **43.** [1.9a] 240   **44.** [7.8d] 15
45. [7.8c] $4a$

CHAPTER 8

Pretest: Chapter 8, p. 410

1. [8.2a] -7 **2.** [8.3b] -1 **3.** [8.3a] 2   **4.** [8.1b] 8
5. [8.3c] -5 **6.** [8.3a] $\frac{135}{32}$ **7.** [8.3c] 1
8. [8.7d] $\{x | x \ge -6\}$ **9.** [8.7c] $\{y | y > -4\}$
10. [8.7e] $\{a | a > -1\}$ **11.** [8.7e] $\{x | x \ge 3\}$
12. [8.7d] $\left\{ y \middle| y < -\dfrac{9}{4} \right\}$ **13.** [8.6a] $G = \dfrac{P}{3K}$
14. [8.6a] $a = \dfrac{Ab + b}{3}$ **15.** [8.4a] Width: 34 m; length: 39 m
16. [8.5a] $650   **17.** [8.4a] 81, 82, 83
18. [8.8b] Numbers less than 17

19. [8.7b]
$$x > -3$$

20. [8.7b]
$$x \le 4$$

Exercise Set 8.1, p. 415

1. Yes   **3.** No   **5.** No   **7.** Yes   **9.** No   **11.** No   **13.** 4
15. -20 **17.** -14 **19.** -18 **21.** 15   **23.** -14 **25.** 2
27. 20   **29.** -6 **31.** $\frac{7}{3}$ **33.** $-\frac{7}{4}$ **35.** $\frac{41}{24}$ **37.** $-\frac{1}{20}$ **39.** 5.1
41. 12.4   **43.** -5 **45.** $1\frac{5}{6}$ **47.** $-\frac{10}{21}$ **49.** -11 **51.** $-\frac{5}{12}$
53. 342.246   **55.** $-\frac{26}{15}$ **57.** -10 **59.** All real numbers
61. $-\frac{5}{17}$ **63.** 13, -13

Exercise Set 8.2, p. 421

1. 6   **3.** 9   **5.** 12   **7.** -40 **9.** 1   **11.** -7 **13.** -6 **15.** 6
17. -63 **19.** 36   **21.** -21 **23.** $-\frac{3}{5}$ **25.** $-\frac{3}{2}$ **27.** $\frac{9}{2}$ **29.** 7
31. -7 **33.** 8   **35.** 15.9   **37.** $7x$ **39.** $x - 4$ **41.** -8655
43. No solution   **45.** No solution   **47.** $x = \dfrac{b}{3a}$ **49.** $x = \dfrac{4b}{a}$

Exercise Set 8.3, p. 429

1. 5   **3.** 8   **5.** 10   **7.** 14   **9.** -8 **11.** -8 **13.** -7 **15.** 15
17. 6   **19.** 4   **21.** 6   **23.** -3 **25.** 1   **27.** -20 **29.** 6   **31.** 7
33. 2   **35.** 5   **37.** 2   **39.** 10   **41.** 4   **43.** 0   **45.** -1 **47.** $-\frac{4}{3}$
49. $\frac{2}{5}$ **51.** -2 **53.** -4 **55.** $\frac{4}{5}$ **57.** $-\frac{28}{27}$ **59.** 6   **61.** 2   **63.** 6
65. 8   **67.** 1   **69.** 17   **71.** $-\frac{5}{3}$ **73.** -3 **75.** 2   **77.** 6   **79.** $\frac{4}{7}$

81. 8   **83.** $\frac{11}{18}$ **85.** $-\frac{51}{31}$ **87.** 2   **89.** -6.5 **91.** $<$
93. 4.4233464   **95.** $-\frac{7}{2}$ **97.** -2 **99.** 0   **101.** 10

Exercise Set 8.4, p. 439

1. 52   **3.** 56   **5.** 29   **7.** $1.99   **9.** 19   **11.** -10 **13.** 40
15. 20 m, 40 m, 120 m   **17.** 36, 37   **19.** 56, 58
21. 35, 36, 37   **23.** 61, 63, 65
25. Width: 100 ft; length: 160 ft; area: 16,000 ft^2
27. Length: 27.9 cm; width: 21.6 cm   **29.** 22.5°   **31.** 450.5 mi
33. 28°, 84°, 68°   **35.** 2020   **37.** 20   **39.** 19   **41.** 120
43. 5 half dollars, 10 quarters, 20 dimes, 60 nickels

Exercise Set 8.5, p. 447

1. 25%   **3.** 24%   **5.** 150   **7.** 2.5   **9.** 546   **11.** 125%   **13.** 0.8
15. 5%   **17.** 3.75%   **19.** 27   **21.** Approximately 86.36%
23. $480,000   **25.** $800   **27.** 36 cm^3; 436 cm^3 **29.** $6540
31. $16   **33.** 30   **35.** $9.17, not $9.10
37. Approximately 3.7%
39. Both are equal. In A, x is increased to $x + 0.25x = 1.25x$, then decreased to $1.25x - 0.25(1.25x) = 0.9375x$. In B, x is decreased to $x - 0.25x = 0.75x$, then increased to $0.75x + 0.25(0.75x) = 0.9375x$.

Exercise Set 8.6, p. 451

1. $b = \dfrac{A}{h}$ **3.** $r = \dfrac{d}{t}$ **5.** $P = \dfrac{I}{rt}$ **7.** $a = \dfrac{F}{m}$ **9.** $w = \dfrac{P - 2l}{2}$
11. $r^2 = \dfrac{A}{\pi}$ **13.** $b = \dfrac{2A}{h}$ **15.** $m = \dfrac{E}{c^2}$ **17.** $d = 2Q - c$
19. $b = 3A - a - c$ **21.** $t = \dfrac{3k}{v}$ **23.** $y = \dfrac{C - Ax}{B}$
25. $b = \dfrac{2A - ah}{h}$; $h = \dfrac{2A}{a + b}$ **27.** $a = \dfrac{Q}{3 + 5c}$ **29.** $D^2 = \dfrac{2.5H}{N}$
31. $S = \dfrac{360A}{\pi r^2}$ **33.** $t = \dfrac{R - 3.85}{-0.0075}$ **35.** 0.92   **37.** -13.2
39. A quadruples.   **41.** A increases by $2h$ units.

Exercise Set 8.7, p. 459

1. (a) Yes; (b) yes; (c) no; (d) yes; (e) yes
3. (a) No; (b) no; (c) yes; (d) yes; (e) no

5.
$$x > 4$$

7.
$$t < -3$$

9.
$$m \ge -1$$

11.
$$-3 < x \le 4$$

13.

$$0 < x < 3$$

15. $\{x \mid x > -5\}$;

17. $\{x \mid x \le -18\}$;

19. $\{y \mid y > -5\}$ **21.** $\{x \mid x > 2\}$ **23.** $\{x \mid x \le -3\}$

25. $\{x \mid x < 4\}$ **27.** $\{c \mid c > 14\}$ **29.** $\{y \mid y \le \frac{1}{4}\}$ **31.** $\{x \mid x > \frac{7}{12}\}$

33. $\{x \mid x < 7\}$;

35. $\{x \mid x < 3\}$;

37. $\{y \mid y \ge -\frac{2}{5}\}$ **39.** $\{x \mid x \ge -6\}$ **41.** $\{y \mid y \le 4\}$

43. $\{x \mid x > \frac{17}{3}\}$ **45.** $\{y \mid y < -\frac{1}{14}\}$ **47.** $\{x \mid x \le \frac{3}{10}\}$

49. $\{x \mid x < 8\}$ **51.** $\{x \mid x \le 6\}$ **53.** $\{x \mid x < -3\}$

55. $\{x \mid x > -3\}$ **57.** $\{x \mid x \le 7\}$ **59.** $\{x \mid x > -10\}$

61. $\{y \mid y < 2\}$ **63.** $\{y \mid y \ge 3\}$ **65.** $\{y \mid y > -2\}$

67. $\{x \mid x > -4\}$ **69.** $\{x \mid x \le 9\}$ **71.** $\{y \mid y \le -3\}$

73. $\{y \mid y < 6\}$ **75.** $\{m \mid m \ge 6\}$ **77.** $\{t \mid t < -\frac{5}{3}\}$

79. $\{r \mid r > -3\}$ **81.** $\{y \mid y > 5\}$ **83.** $\{x \mid x \ge 8\}$

85. $\{x \mid x \ge -\frac{57}{34}\}$ **87.** $\{a \mid a < 1\}$ **89.** -74 **91.** $-\frac{5}{8}$

93. True   **95.**

$$|x| < 3$$

97. All real numbers   **99.** $x \ge 6$

Exercise Set 8.8, p. 465

1. $x > 4$ **3.** $y \le -6$ **5.** $n \ge 1200$ **7.** $a \le 500$
9. $2 + 3x < 13$ **11.** $\{x \mid x \ge 97\}$ **13.** $\{Y \mid Y \ge 1935\}$
15. $\{x \mid x \le 341.4\}$ **17.** $\{x \mid x > 5\}$ **19.** $\{L \mid L < \frac{43}{2}\ \text{cm}\}$
21. $\{b \mid b > 6\ \text{cm}\}$ **23.** $\{x \mid x \ge 20\}$ **25.** \$49.02
27. $\{l \mid l \ge 64\ \text{km}\}$ **29.** $\{l \mid 0 < l \le 8\ \text{cm}\}$

Summary and Review: Chapter 8, p. 467

1. [8.1b] -22 **2.** [8.2a] 7 **3.** [8.2a] -192 **4.** [8.1b] 1
5. [8.2a] $-\frac{7}{3}$ **6.** [8.1b] 25 **7.** [8.1b] -8 **8.** [8.2a] $-\frac{15}{64}$
9. [8.1b] 9.99 **10.** [8.1b] $\frac{1}{2}$ **11.** [8.3b] -5 **12.** [8.3b] $-\frac{1}{3}$
13. [8.3a] 4 **14.** [8.3b] 3 **15.** [8.3b] 4 **16.** [8.3b] 16
17. [8.3c] 6 **18.** [8.3c] -3 **19.** [8.3c] 12 **20.** [8.3c] 4
21. [8.7a] Yes   **22.** [8.7a] No   **23.** [8.7a] Yes
24. [8.7c] $\{y \mid y \ge -\frac{1}{2}\}$ **25.** [8.7d] $\{x \mid x \ge 7\}$
26. [8.7e] $\{y \mid y > 2\}$ **27.** [8.7e] $\{y \mid y \le -4\}$
28. [8.7e] $\{x \mid x < -11\}$ **29.** [8.7d] $\{y \mid y > -7\}$
30. [8.7e] $\{x \mid x > -6\}$ **31.** [8.7e] $\{x \mid x > -\frac{9}{11}\}$
32. [8.7d] $\{y \mid y \le 7\}$ **33.** [8.7d] $\{x \mid x \ge -\frac{1}{12}\}$

34. [8.7b, e]

$$x < 3$$

35. [8.7b]

$$-2 < x \le 5$$

36. [8.7b]

$$y > 0$$

37. [8.6a] $d = \dfrac{C}{\pi}$ **38.** [8.6a] $B = \dfrac{3V}{h}$ **39.** [8.6a] $a = 2A - b$

40. [8.4a] \$591   **41.** [8.4a] 27   **42.** [8.4a] 3 m, 5 m
43. [8.4a] 9   **44.** [8.4a] 57, 59
45. [8.4a] Width: 11 cm; length: 17 cm   **46.** [8.5a] \$220
47. [8.5a] \$26,087   **48.** [8.4a] 35°, 85°, 60°   **49.** [8.8b] 86
50. [8.8b] $\{w \mid w > 17\ \text{cm}\}$ **51.** [3.1c] $1.41\overline{6}$ **52.** [3.3b] 2.3
53. [7.3a] -45 **54.** [7.8b] $-43x + 8y$
55. [8.4a] Amazon: 6437 km; Nile: 6671 km
56. [8.5a] \$14,150   **57.** [7.2e], [8.3a] 23, -23
58. [7.2e], [8.2a] 20, -20 **59.** [8.6a] $a = \dfrac{y - 3}{2 - b}$

Test: Chapter 8, p. 469

1. [8.1b] 8   **2.** [8.1b] 26   **3.** [8.2a] -6 **4.** [8.2a] 49
5. [8.3b] -12 **6.** [8.3a] 2   **7.** [8.1b] -8 **8.** [8.1b] $-\frac{7}{20}$
9. [8.3c] 7   **10.** [8.3c] -5 **11.** [8.3b] 2.5
12. [8.7c] $\{x \mid x \le -4\}$ **13.** [8.7e] $\{x \mid x > -13\}$
14. [8.7d] $\{x \mid x \le 5\}$ **15.** [8.7d] $\{y \mid y \le -13\}$
16. [8.7d] $\{y \mid y \ge 8\}$ **17.** [8.7d] $\{x \mid x \le -\frac{1}{20}\}$
18. [8.7e] $\{x \mid x < -6\}$ **19.** [8.7e] $\{x \mid x \le -1\}$

20. [8.7b]

$$y \le 9$$

21. [8.7b, e]

$$x < 1$$

22. [8.7b]

$$-2 \le x \le 2$$

23. [8.4a] Width: 7 cm; length: 11 cm   **24.** [8.4a] 6

25. [8.4a] 81, 83, 85   **26.** [8.5a] \$750   **27.** [8.6a] $r = \dfrac{A}{2\pi h}$

28. [8.6a] $l = \dfrac{2w - P}{-2}$ **29.** [8.8b] $\{x \mid x > 6\}$

30. [8.8b] $\{l \mid l \ge 174\ \text{yd}\}$ **31.** [7.3a] $-\frac{2}{9}$ **32.** [7.1a] $\frac{8}{3}$
33. [7.1b] $73\%p$, or $0.73p$ **34.** [7.8b] $-18x + 37y$

35. [8.6a] $d = \dfrac{ca - 1}{c}$ **36.** [7.2e], [8.3a] 15, -15

37. [8.4a] 60

CHAPTER 9

Pretest: Chapter 9, p. 472

1. [9.1d] x^2 **2.** [9.1e] $\dfrac{1}{x^7}$ **3.** [9.2b] $\dfrac{16x^4}{y^6}$ **4.** [9.1f] $\dfrac{1}{p^3}$

5. [9.2c] 3.47×10^{-4} **6.** [9.2c] 3,400,000
7. [9.3g] 3, 2, 1, 0; 3
8. [9.7c] $-3a^3b - 2a^2b^2 + ab^3 + 12b^3 + 9$
9. [9.4a] $11x^2 + 4x - 11$ **10.** [9.4c] $-x^2 - 18x + 27$

11. [9.5b] $15x^4 - 20x^3 + 5x^2$ **12.** [9.6c] $x^2 + 10x + 25$
13. [9.6b] $x^2 - 25$ **14.** [9.6a] $4x^6 + 19x^3 - 30$
15. [9.7f] $4x^2 - 12xy + 9y^2$

16. [9.8b] $x^2 + x + 3$, R 8; or $x^2 + x + 3 + \dfrac{8}{x-2}$

Exercise Set 9.1, p. 479

1. $2 \cdot 2 \cdot 2 \cdot 2$ **3.** $(1.4)(1.4)(1.4)(1.4)(1.4)$ **5.** $(7p)(7p)$
7. $(19k)(19k)(19k)(19k)$ **9.** 1 **11.** a **13.** 1 **15.** ab **17.** 27

19. 19 **21.** 256 **23.** 93 **25.** 3629.84 ft^2 **27.** $\dfrac{1}{3^2} = \dfrac{1}{9}$

29. $\dfrac{1}{10^4} = \dfrac{1}{10,000}$ **31.** $\dfrac{1}{7^3} = \dfrac{1}{343}$ **33.** $\dfrac{1}{a^3}$ **35.** y^4 **37.** z^n

39. 4^{-3} **41.** x^{-3} **43.** 2^7 **45.** 8^{14} **47.** x^7 **49.** 9^{38}

51. $(3y)^{12}$ **53.** $(7y)^{17}$ **55.** 3^3 **57.** $\dfrac{1}{x}$ **59.** x^7 **61.** $\dfrac{1}{x^{13}}$ **63.** 1

65. 7^3 **67.** 8^6 **69.** y^4 **71.** $\dfrac{1}{16^6}$ **73.** $\dfrac{1}{m^6}$ **75.** $\dfrac{1}{(8x)^4}$ **77.** 1

79. x^2 **81.** x^9 **83.** $\dfrac{1}{z^4}$ **85.** x^3 **87.** 1

89. 64, $\frac{1}{64}$, $\frac{1}{64}$, 64, -64, 64 **91.** $64\%t$, or $0.64t$ **93.** 64
95. No; $(5y)^0 = 1$ and $5y^0 = 5$ **97.** a^{2k} **99.** 2
101. No; for example, $(3 + 4)^2 = 49$, but $3^2 + 4^2 = 25$
103. < **105.** <
107. Let $a = 3$; then $(a + 3)^2 = 36$ and $a^2 + 3^2 = 18$

109. Let $y = 2$; then $\dfrac{y^6}{y^3} = 8$ and $y^2 = 4$

Exercise Set 9.2, p. 489

1. 2^6 **3.** $\dfrac{1}{5^6}$ **5.** x^{12} **7.** $16x^6$ **9.** $\dfrac{1}{x^{12}y^{15}}$ **11.** $x^{24}y^8$

13. $\dfrac{9x^6}{y^{16}z^6}$ **15.** $\dfrac{a^8}{b^{12}}$ **17.** $\dfrac{y^6}{4}$ **19.** $\dfrac{8}{y^6}$ **21.** $\dfrac{x^6y^3}{z^3}$ **23.** $\dfrac{c^2d^6}{a^4b^2}$

25. 7.8×10^{10} **27.** 9.07×10^{17} **29.** 3.74×10^{-6}
31. 1.8×10^{-8} **33.** 10^{11} **35.** 784,000,000
37. 0.0000000008764 **39.** 100,000,000 **41.** 0.0001
43. 6×10^9 **45.** 3.38×10^4 **47.** 8.1477×10^{-13}
49. 2.5×10^{13} **51.** 5.0×10^{-4} **53.** 3.0×10^{-21}
55. 9.125×10^7 **57.** $6.\overline{6} \times 10^{-2}$ **59.** 2.478125×10^{-1}
61. 2^{13} **63.** $\frac{1}{5}$ **65.** 3^{11} **67.** a^n **69.** False **71.** False

Exercise Set 9.3, p. 497

1. -18 **3.** 19 **5.** -12 **7.** 2 **9.** 4 **11.** 11
13. Approximately 449 **15.** 1024 ft **17.** \$18,750
19. \$155,000 **21.** 2, $-3x$, x^2 **23.** $6x^2$ and $-3x^2$
25. $2x^4$ and $-3x^4$; $5x$ and $-7x$ **27.** $-3, 6$ **29.** 5, 3, 3
31. $-7, 6, 3, 7$ **33.** $-5, 6, -3, 8, -2$ **35.** $-3x$ **37.** $-8x$
39. $11x^3 + 4$ **41.** $x^3 - x$ **43.** $4b^5$ **45.** $\frac{3}{4}x^5 - 2x - 42$
47. x^4 **49.** $\frac{15}{16}x^3 - \frac{7}{6}x^2$ **51.** $x^5 + 6x^3 + 2x^2 + x + 1$
53. $15y^9 + 7y^8 + 5y^3 - y^2 + y$ **55.** $x^6 + x^4$
57. $13x^3 - 9x + 8$ **59.** $-5x^2 + 9x$ **61.** $12x^4 - 2x + \frac{1}{4}$
63. 1, 0; 1 **65.** 2, 1, 0; 2 **67.** 3, 2, 1, 0; 3 **69.** 2, 1, 6, 4; 6

71.

Term	Coefficient	Degree of term	Degree of polynomial
$6x^3$	6	3	
$-3x^2$	-3	2	
$8x$	8	1	4
-2	-2	0	
$-7x^4$	-7	4	

73. x^2, x **75.** x^3, x^2, x^0 **77.** None missing **79.** Trinomial
81. None of these **83.** Binomial **85.** Monomial **87.** 27
89. $5x^9 + 4x^8 + x^2 + 5x$
91. $4x^5 - 3x^3 + x^2 - 7x$; answers may vary
93. $x^3 - 2x^2 - 6x + 3$

Exercise Set 9.4, p. 505

1. $-x + 5$ **3.** $x^2 - 5x - 1$ **5.** $2x^2$ **7.** $5x^2 + 3x - 30$
9. $-2.2x^3 - 0.2x^2 - 3.8x + 23$ **11.** $12x^2 + 6$
13. $9x^8 + 8x^7 - 3x^4 + 2x^2 - 2x + 5$ **15.** $-\frac{1}{2}x^4 + \frac{2}{3}x^3 + x^2$
17. $0.01x^5 + x^4 - 0.2x^3 + 0.2x + 0.06$
19. $-3x^4 + 3x^2 + 4x$
21. $1.05x^4 + 0.36x^3 + 14.22x^2 + x + 0.97$ **23.** $-(-5x), 5x$
25. $-(-x^2 + 10x - 2), x^2 - 10x + 2$
27. $-(12x^4 - 3x^3 + 3), -12x^4 + 3x^3 - 3$ **29.** $-3x + 7$
31. $-4x^2 + 3x - 2$ **33.** $4x^4 - 6x^2 - \frac{3}{4}x + 8$ **35.** $7x - 1$
37. $-x^2 - 7x + 5$ **39.** -18 **41.** $6x^4 + 3x^3 - 4x^2 + 3x - 4$
43. $4.6x^3 + 9.2x^2 - 3.8x - 23$ **45.** $\frac{3}{4}x^3 - \frac{1}{2}x$
47. $0.06x^3 - 0.05x^2 + 0.01x + 1$ **49.** $3x + 6$
51. $11x^4 + 12x^3 - 9x^2 - 8x - 9$ **53.** $x^4 - x^3 + x^2 - x$
55. $5x^2 + 4x$ **57.** $\frac{23}{2}a + 10$
59. $20 + 5(m - 4) + 4(m - 5) + (m - 5)(m - 4)$; m^2
61. $m^2 - 28$ **63.** $144 - 4x^2$ **65.** $12y^2 - 23y + 21$
67. $-3y^4 - y^3 + 5y - 2$

Sidelight: Factors and Sums, p. 512

First row: 90, -432, -63; second row:
7, -18, -36, -14, 12, -6, -21, -11; third row:
9, -2, -2, 10, -8, -8, -8, -10, 21; fourth row; -19, -6

Exercise Set 9.5, p. 513

1. $42x^2$ **3.** x^4 **5.** $28x^8$ **7.** $-0.02x^{10}$ **9.** $\frac{1}{15}x^4$ **11.** 0
13. $-24x^{11}$ **15.** $-3x^2 + 15x$ **17.** $-3x^2 + 3x$ **19.** $x^5 + x^2$
21. $6x^3 - 18x^2 + 3x$ **23.** $-6x^4 - 6x^3$ **25.** $18y^6 + 24y^5$
27. $x^2 + 9x + 18$ **29.** $x^2 + 3x - 10$ **31.** $x^2 - 7x + 12$
33. $x^2 - 9$ **35.** $25 - 15x + 2x^2$ **37.** $4x^2 + 20x + 25$
39. $x^2 - \frac{21}{10}x - 1$ **41.** $x^3 - 1$ **43.** $4x^3 + 14x^2 + 8x + 1$
45. $3y^4 - 6y^3 - 7y^2 + 18y - 6$ **47.** $x^6 + 2x^5 - x^3$
49. $-10x^5 - 9x^4 + 7x^3 + 2x^2 - x$ **51.** $x^4 - x^2 - 2x - 1$
53. $6t^4 + t^3 - 16t^2 - 7t + 4$ **55.** $x^9 - x^5 + 2x^3 - x$
57. $x^4 - 1$ **59.** $-\frac{3}{4}$ **61.** $78t^2 + 40t$ **63.** $A = \frac{1}{2}b^2 + 2b$ **65.** 0

Exercise Set 9.6, p. 521

1. $x^3 + x^2 + 3x + 3$ **3.** $x^4 + x^3 + 2x + 2$ **5.** $y^2 - y - 6$
7. $9x^2 + 15x + 6$ **9.** $5x^2 + 4x - 12$ **11.** $9t^2 - 1$
13. $4x^2 - 6x + 2$ **15.** $p^2 - \frac{1}{16}$ **17.** $x^2 - 0.01$
19. $2x^3 + 2x^2 + 6x + 6$ **21.** $-2x^2 - 11x + 6$
23. $a^2 + 14a + 49$ **25.** $1 - x - 6x^2$
27. $x^5 + 3x^3 - x^2 - 3$ **29.** $3x^6 - 2x^4 - 6x^2 + 4$
31. $6x^7 + 18x^5 + 4x^2 + 12$ **33.** $8x^6 + 65x^3 + 8$
35. $4x^3 - 12x^2 + 3x - 9$ **37.** $4y^6 + 4y^5 + y^4 + y^3$
39. $x^2 - 16$ **41.** $4x^2 - 1$ **43.** $25m^2 - 4$ **45.** $4x^4 - 9$
47. $9x^8 - 16$ **49.** $x^{12} - x^4$ **51.** $x^8 - 9x^2$ **53.** $x^{24} - 9$
55. $4y^{16} - 9$ **57.** $x^2 + 4x + 4$ **59.** $9x^4 + 6x^2 + 1$
61. $a^2 - a + \frac{1}{4}$ **63.** $9 + 6x + x^2$ **65.** $x^4 + 2x^2 + 1$
67. $4 - 12x^4 + 9x^8$ **69.** $25 + 60t^2 + 36t^4$
71. $9 - 12x^3 + 4x^6$ **73.** $4x^3 + 24x^2 - 12x$
75. $4x^4 - 2x^2 + \frac{1}{4}$ **77.** $9p^2 - 1$ **79.** $15t^5 - 3t^4 + 3t^3$
81. $36x^8 + 48x^4 + 16$ **83.** $12x^3 + 8x^2 + 15x + 10$
85. $64 - 96x^4 + 36x^8$ **87.** $t^3 - 1$ **89.** 25; 49 **91.** 56; 16
93. Lamps: 500 watts; air conditioner: 2000 watts;
television: 50 watts
95. $8y^3 + 72y^2 + 160y$ **97.** $-2x^4 + x^3 + 5x^2 - x - 2$
99. -7 **101.** $V = w^3 + 3w^2 + 2w$ **103.** $V = h^3 - 3h^2 + 2h$
105. $F^2 - (F - 17)(F - 7)$; $24F - 119$
107. $4567.0564x^2 + 435.891x + 10.400625$
109. $10{,}000 - 49 = 9951$ **111.** $5a^2 + 12a - 9$
113. (a) $A^2 + AB$; **(b)** $AB + B^2$; **(c)** $A^2 - B^2$;
(d) $(A + B)(A - B) = A^2 - B^2$

Exercise Set 9.7, p. 529

1. -1 **3.** -7 **5.** \$11,664 **7.** \$12,597.12 **9.** 141.3 in^2
11. Coefficients: 1, -2, 3, -5; degrees: 4, 2, 2, 0; 4
13. Coefficients: 17, -3, -7; degrees: 5, 5, 0; 5
15. $-a - 2b$ **17.** $3x^2y - 2xy^2 + x^2$ **19.** $8u^2v - 5uv^2$
21. $20au + 10av$ **23.** $x^2 - 4xy + 3y^2$ **25.** $3r + 7$
27. $-x^2 - 8xy - y^2$ **29.** $2ab$ **31.** $-2a + 10b - 5c + 8d$
33. $6z^2 + 7zu - 3u^2$ **35.** $a^4b^2 - 7a^2b + 10$
37. $a^4 + a^3 - a^2y - ay + a + y - 1$ **39.** $a^6 - b^2c^2$
41. $y^6x + y^4x + y^4 + 2y^2 + 1$ **43.** $12x^2y^2 + 2xy - 2$
45. $12 - c^2d^2 - c^4d^4$ **47.** $m^3 + m^2n - mn^2 - n^3$
49. $x^9y^9 - x^6y^6 + x^5y^5 - x^2y^2$ **51.** $x^2 + 2xh + h^2$
53. $r^6t^4 - 8r^3t^2 + 16$ **55.** $p^8 + 2m^2n^2p^4 + m^4n^4$
57. $4a^6 - 2a^3b^3 + \frac{1}{4}b^6$ **59.** $3a^3 - 12a^2b + 12ab^2$
61. $4a^2 - b^2$ **63.** $c^4 - d^2$ **65.** $a^2b^2 - c^2d^4$
67. $x^2 + 2xy + y^2 - 9$ **69.** $x^2 - y^2 - 2yz - z^2$
71. $a^2 - b^2 - 2bc - c^2$ **73.** $4xy - 4y^2$ **75.** $2xy + \pi x^2$
77. 2.4747 L **79.** $A^3 + 3A^2B + 3AB^2 + B^3$

Exercise Set 9.8, p. 537

1. $3x^4 - \frac{1}{2}x^3 + \frac{1}{8}x^2 - 2$ **3.** $1 - 2u - u^4$ **5.** $5t^2 + 8t - 2$
7. $-4x^4 + 4x^2 + 1$ **9.** $6x^2 - 10x + \frac{3}{2}$ **11.** $9x^2 - \frac{5}{2}x + 1$
13. $6x^2 + 13x + 4$ **15.** $3rs + r - 2s$ **17.** $x + 2$
19. $x - 5 + \dfrac{-50}{x - 5}$ **21.** $x - 2 + \dfrac{-2}{x + 6}$ **23.** $x - 3$
25. $x^4 - x^3 + x^2 - x + 1$ **27.** $2x^2 - 7x + 4$ **29.** $x^3 - 6$
31. $x^3 + 2x^2 + 4x + 8$ **33.** $t^2 + 1$ **35.** 6.8

37. 25,543.75 ft^2 **39.** $x^2 + 5$ **41.** $a + 3 + \dfrac{5}{5a^2 - 7a - 2}$
43. $2x^2 + x - 3$ **45.** $a^5 + a^4b + a^3b^2 + a^2b^3 + ab^4 + b^5$
47. -5 **49.** 1

Summary and Review: Chapter 9, p. 539

1. [9.1d] $\dfrac{1}{7^2}$ **2.** [9.1d] y^{11} **3.** [9.1d] $(3x)^{14}$ **4.** [9.1d] t^8

5. [9.1e] 4^3 **6.** [9.1e] $\dfrac{1}{a^3}$ **7.** [9.1e] 1 **8.** [9.2a, b] $9t^8$

9. [9.1d], [9.2a, b] $36x^8$ **10.** [9.2b] $\dfrac{y^3}{8x^3}$ **11.** [9.1f] t^{-5}

12. [9.1f] $\dfrac{1}{y^4}$ **13.** [9.2c] 3.28×10^{-5} **14.** [9.2c] 8,300,000

15. [9.2d] 2.09×10^4 **16.** [9.2d] 5.12×10^{-5}
17. [9.2e] 6.205×10^{10} **18.** [9.3a] 10
19. [9.3b] $-4y^5$, $7y^2$, $-3y$, -2 **20.** [9.3h] x^2, x^0
21. [9.3g] 3, 2, 1, 0; 3 **22.** [9.3i] Binomial
23. [9.3i] None of these **24.** [9.3i] Monomial
25. [9.3f] $-2x^2 - 3x + 2$ **26.** [9.3f] $10x^4 - 7x^2 - x - \frac{1}{2}$
27. [9.4a] $x^5 - 2x^4 + 6x^3 + 3x^2 - 9$
28. [9.4a] $2x^5 - 6x^4 + 2x^3 - 2x^2 + 2$
29. [9.4c] $2x^2 - 4x - 6$ **30.** [9.4c] $x^5 - 3x^3 - x^2 + 8$
31. [9.4d] $P = 4w + 8$; $A = w^2 + 4w$
32. [9.6a] $x^2 + \frac{7}{6}x + \frac{1}{3}$ **33.** [9.6c] $49x^2 + 14x + 1$
34. [9.5d] $12x^3 - 23x^2 + 13x - 2$ **35.** [9.6b] $9x^4 - 16$
36. [9.5b] $15x^7 - 40x^6 + 50x^5 + 10x^4$
37. [9.6a] $x^2 - 3x - 28$ **38.** [9.6c] $9y^4 - 12y^3 + 4y^2$
39. [9.6a] $2t^4 - 11t^2 - 21$ **40.** [9.7a] 49
41. [9.7b] Coefficients: 1, -7, 9, -8; degrees: 6, 2, 2, 0; 6
42. [9.7c] $-y + 9w - 5$
43. [9.7c] $m^6 - 2m^2n + 2m^2n^2 + 8n^2m - 6m^3$
44. [9.7d] $-9xy - 2y^2$
45. [9.7e] $11x^3y^2 - 8x^2y - 6x^2 - 6x + 6$ **46.** [9.7f] $p^3 - q^3$
47. [9.6c] $9a^8 - 2a^4b^3 + \frac{1}{9}b^6$ **48.** [9.8a] $5x^2 - \frac{1}{2}x + 3$

49. [9.8b] $3x^2 - 7x + 4 + \dfrac{1}{2x + 3}$ **50.** [7.7d] $25(t - 2 + 4m)$

51. [8.3b] $\frac{9}{4}$ **52.** [7.4a] -11.2
53. [8.4a] Width: 125.5 m; length: 144.5 m
54. [9.1d], [9.2a, b], [9.3e] $-28x^8$ **55.** [8.3b], [9.6a] $\frac{94}{13}$

Test: Chapter 9, p. 541

1. [9.1d] 6^{-5} **2.** [9.1d] x^9 **3.** [9.1d] $(4a)^{11}$ **4.** [9.1e] 3^3
5. [9.1e] $\dfrac{1}{x^5}$ **6.** [9.1b, e] 1 **7.** [9.2a] x^6

8. [9.2a, b] $-27y^6$ **9.** [9.2a, b] $16a^{12}b^4$ **10.** [9.2b] $\dfrac{a^3b^3}{c^3}$

11. [9.1d], [9.2a, b] $-216x^{21}$ **12.** [9.1d], [9.2a, b] $-24x^{21}$
13. [9.1d], [9.2a, b] $162x^{10}$ **14.** [9.1d], [9.2a, b] $324x^{10}$
15. [9.1f] $\dfrac{1}{5^3}$ **16.** [9.1f] y^{-8} **17.** [9.2c] 3.9×10^9
18. [9.2c] 0.00000005 **19.** [9.2d] 1.75×10^{17}
20. [9.2d] 1.296×10^{22}
21. [9.2e] Approximately 2.55×10^2 **22.** [9.3a] -43
23. [9.3d] $\frac{1}{3}$, -1, 7 **24.** [9.3g] 3, 0, 1, 6; 6

25. [9.3i] Binomial **26.** [9.3e] $5a^2 - 6$ **27.** [9.3e] $\frac{7}{4}y^2 - 4y$
28. [9.3e, f] $x^5 + 2x^3 + 4x^2 - 8x + 3$
29. [9.4a] $4x^5 + x^4 + 2x^3 - 8x^2 + 2x - 7$
30. [9.4a] $5x^4 + 5x^2 + x + 5$
31. [9.4c] $-4x^4 + x^3 - 8x - 3$
32. [9.4c] $-x^5 + 0.7x^3 - 0.8x^2 - 21$
33. [9.5b] $-12x^4 + 9x^3 + 15x^2$ **34.** [9.6c] $x^2 - \frac{2}{3}x + \frac{1}{9}$
35. [9.6b] $9x^2 - 100$ **36.** [9.6a] $3b^2 - 4b - 15$
37. [9.6a] $x^{14} - 4x^8 + 4x^6 - 16$ **38.** [9.6a] $48 + 34y - 5y^2$
39. [9.5d] $6x^3 - 7x^2 - 11x - 3$ **40.** [9.6c] $25t^2 + 20t + 4$
41. [9.7c] $-5x^3y - y^3 + xy^3 - x^2y^2 + 19$
42. [9.7e] $8a^2b^2 + 6ab - 4b^3 + 6ab^2 + ab^3$
43. [9.7f] $9x^{10} - 16y^{10}$ **44.** [9.8a] $4x^2 + 3x - 5$
45. [9.8b] $2x^2 - 4x - 2 + \dfrac{17}{3x + 2}$ **46.** [8.3b] 13
47. [7.7d] $16(4t - 2m + 1)$ **48.** [7.4a] $\frac{23}{20}$
49. [8.4a] $100°, 25°, 55°$ **50.** [9.6a] $V = l^3 - 3l^2 + 2l$
51. [8.3b], [9.6a] $-\frac{61}{12}$

CHAPTER 10

Pretest: Chapter 10, p. 544

1. [10.1a] $4(-5x^6)$, $(-2x^3)(10x^3)$, $x^2(-20x^4)$; answers may vary
2. [10.5b] $2(x + 1)^2$ **3.** [10.2a] $(x + 4)(x + 2)$
4. [10.6a] $4a(2a^4 + a^2 - 5)$
5. [10.3a], [10.4a] $(5x + 2)(x - 3)$
6. [10.5d] $(9 + z^2)(3 + z)(3 - z)$ **7.** [10.6a] $(y^3 - 2)^2$
8. [10.1c] $(x^2 + 4)(3x + 2)$ **9.** [10.2a] $(p - 6)(p + 5)$
10. [10.7b] 0, 5 **11.** [10.7a] 4, $\frac{3}{5}$ **12.** [10.7b] $\frac{2}{3}$, -4
13. [10.8a] 6, -1 **14.** [10.8a] Base: 8 cm; height: 11 cm
15. [10.6a] $(x^2y + 8)(x^2y - 8)$ **16.** [10.6a] $(2p - q)(p + 4q)$

Exercise Set 10.1, p. 549

1. $6x^2 \cdot x$; $3x^2 \cdot 2x$; $(-3x^2)(-2x)$; answers may vary
3. $(-9x^4) \cdot x$; $(-3x^2)(3x^3)$; $(-3x)(3x^4)$; answers may vary
5. $(8x^2)(3x^2)$; $(-8x^2)(-3x^2)$; $(4x^3)(6x)$; answers may vary
7. $x(x - 4)$ **9.** $2x(x + 3)$ **11.** $x^2(x + 6)$ **13.** $8x^2(x^2 - 3)$
15. $2(x^2 + x - 4)$ **17.** $17xy(x^4y^2 + 2x^2y + 3)$
19. $x^2(6x^2 - 10x + 3)$ **21.** $x^2y^2(x^3y^3 + x^2y + xy - 1)$
23. $2x^3(x^4 - x^3 - 32x^2 + 2)$ **25.** $0.8x(2x^3 - 3x^2 + 4x + 8)$
27. $\frac{1}{3}x^3(5x^3 + 4x^2 + x + 1)$ **29.** $(x^2 + 2)(x + 3)$
31. $(x^2 + 2)(x + 3)$ **33.** $(2x^2 + 1)(x + 3)$
35. $(4x^2 + 3)(2x - 3)$ **37.** $(4x^2 + 1)(3x - 4)$
39. $(x^2 - 3)(x + 8)$ **41.** $(2x^2 - 9)(x - 4)$ **43.** $\{x | x > -24\}$
45. 27 **47.** $y^2 + 12y + 35$ **49.** $y^2 - 49$
51. $(2x^3 + 3)(2x^2 + 3)$ **53.** $(x^7 + 1)(x^5 + 1)$
55. Not factorable by grouping

Exercise Set 10.2, p. 555

1. $(x + 3)(x + 5)$ **3.** $(x + 3)(x + 4)$ **5.** $(x - 3)^2$
7. $(x + 2)(x + 7)$ **9.** $(b + 1)(b + 4)$ **11.** $(x + \frac{1}{3})^2$
13. $(d - 2)(d - 5)$ **15.** $(y - 1)(y - 10)$ **17.** $(x - 6)(x + 7)$

19. $(x - 9)(x + 2)$ **21.** $x(x - 8)(x + 2)$ **23.** $(y - 9)(y + 5)$
25. $(x - 11)(x + 9)$ **27.** $(c^2 + 8)(c^2 - 7)$ **29.** $(a^2 + 7)(a^2 - 5)$
31. Not factorable **33.** Not factorable **35.** $(x + 10)^2$
37. $(x - 25)(x + 4)$ **39.** $(x - 24)(x + 3)$ **41.** $(x - 9)(x - 16)$
43. $(a + 12)(a - 11)$ **45.** $(x - 15)(x - 8)$
47. $(12 + x)(9 - x)$, or $-(x + 12)(x - 9)$
49. $(y - 0.4)(y + 0.2)$ **51.** $(p + 5q)(p - 2q)$
53. $(m + 4n)(m + n)$ **55.** $(s + 3t)(s - 5t)$
57. $16x^3 - 48x^2 + 8x$ **59.** $49w^2 + 84w + 36$
61. $15, -15, 27, -27, 51, -51$ **63.** $(x + \frac{1}{4})(x - \frac{3}{4})$
65. $(x + 5)(x - \frac{5}{7})$ **67.** $(b^n + 5)(b^n + 2)$ **69.** $2x^2(4 - \pi)$

Exercise Set 10.3, p. 561

1. $(2x + 1)(x - 4)$ **3.** $(5x - 9)(x + 2)$ **5.** $(3x + 1)(2x + 7)$
7. $(3x + 1)(x + 1)$ **9.** $(2x - 3)(2x + 5)$ **11.** $(2x + 1)(x - 1)$
13. $(3x - 2)(3x + 8)$ **15.** $(3x + 1)(x - 2)$
17. $(3x + 4)(4x + 5)$ **19.** $(7x - 1)(2x + 3)$
21. $(3x + 2)(3x + 4)$ **23.** $(3x - 7)(3x - 7)$
25. $(24x - 1)(x + 2)$ **27.** $(5x - 11)(7x + 4)$
29. $2(5 - x)(2 + x)$ **31.** $4(3x - 2)(x + 3)$
33. $6(5x - 9)(x + 1)$ **35.** $2(3x + 5)(x - 1)$
37. $(3x - 1)(x - 1)$ **39.** $4(3x + 2)(x - 3)$
41. $(2x + 1)(x - 1)$ **43.** $(3x + 2)(3x - 8)$
45. $5(3x + 1)(x - 2)$ **47.** $x(3x + 4)(4x + 5)$
49. $x^2(7x - 1)(2x + 3)$ **51.** $3x(8x - 1)(7x - 1)$
53. $(5x^2 - 3)(3x^2 - 2)$ **55.** $(5t + 8)^2$ **57.** $2x(3x + 5)(x - 1)$
59. Not factorable **61.** Not factorable
63. $(4m - 5n)(3m + 4n)$ **65.** $(2a + 3b)(3a - 5b)$
67. $(3a + 2b)(3a + 4b)$ **69.** $(5p + 2q)(7p + 4q)$
71. $6(3x - 4y)(x + y)$ **73.** $q = \dfrac{A + 7}{p}$ **75.** $(2x^n + 1)(10x^n + 3)$
77. $(x^{3a} - 1)(3x^{3a} + 1)$

Exercise Set 10.4, p. 565

1. $(y + 1)(y + 4)$ **3.** $(x - 1)(x - 4)$ **5.** $(2x + 3)(3x + 2)$
7. $(x - 4)(3x - 4)$ **9.** $(5x + 3)(7x - 8)$ **11.** $(2x - 3)(2x + 3)$
13. $(2x^2 + 5)(x^2 + 3)$ **15.** $(2x + 1)(x - 4)$
17. $(5x - 9)(x + 2)$ **19.** $(2x + 7)(3x + 1)$
21. $(3x + 1)(x + 1)$ **23.** $(2x - 3)(2x + 5)$
25. $(2x + 1)(x - 1)$ **27.** $(3x - 2)(3x + 8)$
29. $(3x + 1)(x - 2)$ **31.** $(3x + 4)(4x + 5)$
33. $(7x - 1)(2x + 3)$ **35.** $(3x + 2)(3x + 4)$ **37.** $(3x - 7)^2$
39. $(24x - 1)(x + 2)$ **41.** $x^3(5x - 11)(7x + 4)$
43. $6x(5 - x)(2 + x)$ **45.** $\{x | x > \frac{26}{7}\}$ **47.** $(3x^5 - 2)^2$
49. $(4x^5 + 1)^2$

Exercise Set 10.5, p. 573

1. Yes **3.** No **5.** No **7.** No **9.** $(x - 7)^2$ **11.** $(x + 8)^2$
13. $(x - 1)^2$ **15.** $(x + 2)^2$ **17.** $(y^2 + 3)^2$ **19.** $(4y - 7)^2$
21. $2(x - 1)^2$ **23.** $x(x - 9)^2$ **25.** $5(2x + 5)^2$ **27.** $(7 - 3x)^2$
29. $5(y^2 + 1)^2$ **31.** $(1 + 2x^2)^2$ **33.** $(2p + 3q)^2$ **35.** $(a - 7b)^2$
37. $(8m + n)^2$ **39.** $(4s - 5t)^2$ **41.** Yes **43.** No **45.** No

47. Yes **49.** $(y + 2)(y - 2)$ **51.** $(p + 3)(p - 3)$
53. $(t + 7)(t - 7)$ **55.** $(a + b)(a - b)$ **57.** $(5t + m)(5t - m)$
59. $(10 + k)(10 - k)$ **61.** $(4a + 3)(4a - 3)$
63. $(2x + 5y)(2x - 5y)$ **65.** $2(2x + 7)(2x - 7)$
67. $x(6 + 7x)(6 - 7x)$ **69.** $(7a^2 + 9)(7a^2 - 9)$
71. $(x^2 + 1)(x + 1)(x - 1)$ **73.** $4(x^2 + 4)(x + 2)(x - 2)$
75. $(y^4 + 1)(y^2 + 1)(1 + y)(1 - y)$
77. $(x^6 + 4)(x^3 + 2)(x^3 - 2)$ **79.** $(y + \frac{1}{4})(y - \frac{1}{4})$
81. $(5 + \frac{1}{7}x)(5 - \frac{1}{7}x)$ **83.** $(4m^2 + t^2)(2m + t)(2m - t)$
85. -11 **87.** $-\frac{5}{6}$ **89.** Not factorable **91.** $(x + 11)^2$
93. $2x(3x + 1)^2$ **95.** $(x^4 + 2^4)(x^2 + 2^2)(x + 2)(x - 2)$
97. $3x^3(x + 2)(x - 2)$ **99.** $2x(3x + \frac{2}{5})(3x - \frac{2}{5})$
101. $p(0.7 + p)(0.7 - p)$ **103.** $(0.8x + 1.1)(0.8x - 1.1)$
105. $x(x + 6)$ **107.** $\left(x + \dfrac{1}{x}\right)\left(x - \dfrac{1}{x}\right)$
109. $(9 + b^{2k})(3 + b^k)(3 - b^k)$ **111.** $(3b^n + 2)^2$
113. $(y + 4)^2$ **115.** 9

Exercise Set 10.6, p. 581

1. $2(x + 8)(x - 8)$ **3.** $(a - 5)^2$ **5.** $(2x - 3)(x - 4)$
7. $x(x + 12)^2$ **9.** $(x + 2)(x - 2)(x + 3)$
11. $6(2x + 3)(2x - 3)$ **13.** $4x(5x + 9)(x - 2)$
15. Not factorable **17.** $x(x^2 + 7)(x - 3)$ **19.** $x^3(x - 7)^2$
21. $2(2 - x)(5 + x)$, or $-2(x - 2)(x + 5)$
23. Not factorable **25.** $4(x^2 + 4)(x + 2)(x - 2)$
27. $(1 + y^4)(1 + y^2)(1 + y)(1 - y)$ **29.** $x^3(x - 3)(x - 1)$
31. $(6a - \frac{5}{4})^2$ **33.** $12n^2(1 + 2n)$ **35.** $9xy(xy - 4)$
37. $2\pi r(h + r)$ **39.** $(a + b)(2x + 1)$ **41.** $(x + 1)(x - 1 - y)$
43. $(n + p)(n + 2)$ **45.** $(2x + z)(x - 2)$ **47.** $(x - y)^2$
49. $(3c + d)^2$ **51.** $(7m^2 - 8n)^2$ **53.** $(y^2 + 5z^2)^2$
55. $(\frac{1}{2}a + \frac{1}{3}b)^2$ **57.** $(a + b)(a - 2b)$ **59.** $(m + 20n)(m - 18n)$
61. $(mn - 8)(mn + 4)$ **63.** $a^3(ab + 5)(ab - 2)$
65. $a^3(a - b)(a + 5b)$ **67.** $(x^3 - y)(x^3 + 2y)$
69. $(x - y)(x + y)$ **71.** $7(p^2 + q^2)(p + q)(p - q)$
73. $(9a^2 + b^2)(3a + b)(3a - b)$ **75.** $(w + 2)(w - 2)(w - 7)$
77. $-\dfrac{14}{11}$ **79.** $X = \dfrac{A + 7}{a + b}$ **81.** $(a + 1)^2(a - 1)^2$
83. $(3.5x - 1)^2$ **85.** $(5x + 4)(x + 1.8)$
87. $(y + 3)(y - 3)(y - 2)$ **89.** $(a^2 + 1)(a + 4)$
91. $(x + 3)(x - 3)(x^2 + 2)$ **93.** $(x + 2)(x - 2)(x - 1)$
95. $(y - 1)^3$ **97.** $(y + 4 + x)^2$
99. $(x^4 + 2^4)(x^2 + 2^2)(x + 2)(x - 2)$

Exercise Set 10.7, p. 589

1. $-8, -6$ **3.** $3, -5$ **5.** $-12, 11$ **7.** $0, -5$ **9.** $0, -10$
11. $-\frac{5}{2}, -4$ **13.** $-\frac{1}{5}, 3$ **15.** $4, \frac{1}{4}$ **17.** $0, \frac{2}{3}$ **19.** $0, 18$
21. $-\frac{1}{10}, \frac{1}{27}$ **23.** $\frac{1}{3}, 20$ **25.** $0, \frac{2}{3}, \frac{1}{2}$ **27.** $-1, -5$ **29.** $-9, 2$
31. $3, 5$ **33.** $0, 8$ **35.** $0, -19$ **37.** $4, -4$ **39.** $\frac{2}{3}, -\frac{2}{3}$
41. -3 **43.** 4 **45.** $0, \frac{6}{5}$ **47.** $\frac{5}{3}, -1$ **49.** $\frac{2}{3}, -\frac{1}{4}$ **51.** $7, -2$
53. $\frac{9}{8}, -\frac{9}{8}$ **55.** $-3, 1$ **57.** $\frac{4}{5}, \frac{3}{2}$ **59.** $(a + b)^2$ **61.** -16
63. $4, -5$ **65.** $9, -3$ **67.** $\frac{1}{8}, -\frac{1}{8}$ **69.** $4, -4$
71. **(a)** $x^2 - x - 12 = 0$; **(b)** $x^2 + 7x + 12 = 0$;
(c) $4x^2 - 4x + 1 = 0$; **(d)** $x^2 - 25 = 0$;
(e) $40x^3 - 14x^2 + x = 0$

Exercise Set 10.8, p. 595

1. $-\frac{3}{4}, 1$ **3.** $4, 2$ **5.** 14 and 15 **7.** 12 and 14; -12 and -14
9. 15 and 17; -15 and -17 **11.** Length: 12 m; width: 8 m
13. 5 **15.** Height: 4 cm; base: 14 cm **17.** 6 km **19.** 5 and 7
21. 506 **23.** 12 **25.** 780 **27.** 20
29. Hypotenuse: 17 ft; leg: 15 ft **31.** 5 ft **33.** 37
35. 30 cm by 15 cm **37.** 100 cm^2; 225 cm^2

Summary and Review: Chapter 10, p. 599

1. [10.1a] $-10x \cdot x$, $-5x \cdot 2x$, $(5x)(-2x)$; answers may vary
2. [10.1a] $6x \cdot 6x^4$, $4x^2 \cdot 9x^3$, $2x^4 \cdot 18x$; answers may vary
3. [10.5d] $5(1 + 2x^3)(1 - 2x^3)$ **4.** [10.1b] $x(x - 3)$
5. [10.5d] $(3x + 2)(3x - 2)$ **6.** [10.2a] $(x + 6)(x - 2)$
7. [10.5b] $(x + 7)^2$ **8.** [10.1b] $3x(2x^2 + 4x + 1)$
9. [10.1c] $(x^2 + 3)(x + 1)$
10. [10.3a], [10.4a] $(3x - 1)(2x - 1)$
11. [10.5d] $(x^2 + 9)(x + 3)(x - 3)$
12. [10.3a], [10.4a] $3x(3x - 5)(x + 3)$
13. [10.5d] $2(x + 5)(x - 5)$ **14.** [10.1c] $(x^3 - 2)(x + 4)$
15. [10.5d] $(4x^2 + 1)(2x + 1)(2x - 1)$
16. [10.1b] $4x^4(2x^2 - 8x + 1)$ **17.** [10.5b] $3(2x + 5)^2$
18. [10.5c] Not factorable **19.** [10.2a] $x(x - 6)(x + 5)$
20. [10.5d] $(2x + 5)(2x - 5)$ **21.** [10.5b] $(3x - 5)^2$
22. [10.3a], [10.4a] $2(3x + 4)(x - 6)$ **23.** [10.5b] $(x - 3)^2$
24. [10.3a], [10.4a] $(2x + 1)(x - 4)$ **25.** [10.5b] $2(3x - 1)^2$
26. [10.5d] $3(x + 3)(x - 3)$ **27.** [10.2a] $(x - 5)(x - 3)$
28. [10.5b] $(5x - 2)^2$ **29.** [10.7a] $1, -3$ **30.** [10.7b] $-7, 5$
31. [10.7b] $-4, 3$ **32.** [10.7b] $\frac{2}{3}, 1$ **33.** [10.7b] $\frac{3}{2}, -4$
34. [10.7b] $8, -2$ **35.** [10.8a] 3 and -2
36. [10.8a] -18 and -16; 16 and 18
37. [10.8a] -19 and -17; 17 and 19 **38.** [10.8a] $\frac{5}{2}$ and -2
39. [10.5b] $(7b^5 - 2a^4)^2$ **40.** [10.2a] $(xy + 4)(xy - 3)$
41. [10.5b] $3(2a + 7b)^2$ **42.** [10.1c] $(m + t)(m + 5)$
43. [10.5d] $32(x^2 - 2y^2z^2)(x^2 + 2y^2z^2)$ **44.** [7.6c] $\frac{8}{35}$
45. [8.7e] $\left\{x \middle| x \leq \dfrac{4}{3}\right\}$ **46.** [8.6a] $b = \dfrac{A - a}{2}$
47. [9.6d] $4a^2 + 12a + 9$ **48.** [9.6d] $4a^2 - 9$
49. [9.6d] $10a^2 - a - 21$ **50.** [10.8a] 2.5 cm
51. [10.8a] $0, 2$ **52.** [10.8a] Length: 12; width: 6
53. [10.7b] No solution **54.** [10.7a] $2, -3, \frac{5}{2}$
55. [10.7a] $-2000, -\frac{5000}{97}$
56. [10.6a] a, i; b, k; c, g; d, h; e, j; f, l

Test: Chapter 10, p. 601

1. [10.1a] $(4x)(x^2)$; $(2x^2)(2x)$; $(-2x)(-2x^2)$; answers
may vary
2. [10.2a] $(x - 5)(x - 2)$ **3.** [10.5b] $(x - 5)^2$
4. [10.1b] $2y^2(2y^2 - 4y + 3)$ **5.** [10.1c] $(x^2 + 2)(x + 1)$
6. [10.1b] $x(x - 5)$ **7.** [10.2a] $x(x + 3)(x - 1)$
8. [10.3a], [10.4a] $2(5x - 6)(x + 4)$
9. [10.5d] $(2x + 3)(2x - 3)$ **10.** [10.2a] $(x - 4)(x + 3)$
11. [10.3a], [10.4a] $3m(2m + 1)(m + 1)$
12. [10.5d] $3(w + 5)(w - 5)$ **13.** [10.5b] $5(3x + 2)^2$
14. [10.5d] $3(x^2 + 4)(x + 2)(x - 2)$ **15.** [10.5b] $(7x - 6)^2$
16. [10.3a], [10.4a] $(5x - 1)(x - 5)$

17. [10.1c] $(x^3 - 3)(x + 2)$

18. [10.5d] $5(4 + x^2)(2 + x)(2 - x)$

19. [10.3a], [10.4a] $(2x + 3)(2x - 5)$

20. [10.3a], [10.4a] $3t(2t + 5)(t - 1)$ **21.** [10.7b] $5, -4$

22. [10.7b] $\frac{3}{2}, -5$ **23.** [10.7b] $7, -4$ **24.** [10.8a] $8, -3$

25. [10.8a] Length: 10 m; width: 4 m

26. [10.2a] $3(m + 2n)(m - 5n)$ **27.** [7.6c] $-\frac{10}{11}$

28. [8.7e], [8.8a] $\left\{ x \,\middle|\, x < \dfrac{19}{3} \right\}$ **29.** [8.6a] $T = \dfrac{I}{PR}$

30. [9.6d] $25x^4 - 70x^2 + 49$

31. [10.8a] Length: 15; width: 3   **32.** [10.2a] $(a - 4)(a + 8)$

33. [10.7a] (c)   **34.** [9.6b], [10.5d] (d)

CHAPTER 11

Pretest: Chapter 11, p. 604

1. [11.3c] $(x + 2)(x + 3)^2$ **2.** [11.4a] $\dfrac{-b - 1}{b^2 - 4}$, or $\dfrac{b + 1}{4 - b^2}$

3. [11.5a] $\dfrac{1}{y - 2}$ **4.** [11.4a] $\dfrac{7a + 6}{a(a + 2)}$ **5.** [11.5b] $\dfrac{2x}{x + 1}$

6. [11.1d] $\dfrac{2(x - 3)}{x - 2}$ **7.** [11.9a] $\dfrac{y + x}{y - x}$ **8.** [11.6a] -5

9. [11.6a] 0   **10.** [11.8a] $M = \dfrac{3R}{a - b}$ **11.** [11.7b] 10.5 hr

12. [11.7a] $\frac{30}{11}$ hr   **13.** [11.7a] 60 mph, 80 mph

Exercise Set 11.1, p. 611

1. $\{x \,|\, x \neq 0\}$ **3.** $\{a \,|\, a \neq 8\}$ **5.** $\{y \,|\, y \neq -\frac{5}{2}\}$

7. $\{x \,|\, x \neq 7 \text{ and } x \neq -4\}$ **9.** $\{m \,|\, m \neq 5 \text{ and } m \neq -5\}$

11. $\dfrac{(3a)(5a^2)}{(3a)(2c)}$ **13.** $\dfrac{2x(x - 1)}{2x(x + 4)}$ **15.** $\dfrac{-1(3 - x)}{-1(4 - x)}$

17. $\dfrac{(y + 6)(y - 7)}{(y + 6)(y + 2)}$ **19.** $\dfrac{x^2}{4}$ **21.** $\dfrac{8p^2q}{3}$ **23.** $\dfrac{x - 3}{x}$ **25.** $\dfrac{m + 1}{2m + 3}$

27. $\dfrac{a - 3}{a + 2}$ **29.** $\dfrac{a - 3}{a - 4}$ **31.** $\dfrac{x + 5}{x - 5}$ **33.** $a + 1$ **35.** $\dfrac{x^2 + 1}{x + 1}$

37. $\dfrac{3}{2}$ **39.** $\dfrac{6}{t - 3}$ **41.** $\dfrac{t + 2}{2(t - 4)}$ **43.** $\dfrac{t - 2}{t + 2}$ **45.** -1 **47.** -1

49. -6 **51.** $-a - 1$ **53.** $\dfrac{56x}{3}$ **55.** $\dfrac{2}{dc^2}$ **57.** $\dfrac{x + 2}{x - 2}$

59. $\dfrac{(a + 3)(a - 3)}{a(a + 4)}$ **61.** $\dfrac{2a}{a - 2}$ **63.** $\dfrac{(x + 2)(x - 2)}{(x + 1)(x - 1)}$ **65.** $\dfrac{t - 2}{t - 1}$

67. $\dfrac{5(a + 6)}{a - 1}$ **69.** 18 and 20; -18 and -20

71. $(2y^2 + 1)(y - 5)$ **73.** $x + 2y$ **75.** $\dfrac{(t - 9)^2(t - 1)}{(t^2 + 9)(t + 1)}$

77. $\dfrac{x - y}{x - 5y}$

Exercise Set 11.2, p. 617

1. $\dfrac{x}{4}$ **3.** $\dfrac{1}{x^2 - y^2}$ **5.** $\dfrac{x^2 - 4x + 7}{x^2 + 2x - 5}$ **7.** $\dfrac{3}{10}$ **9.** $\dfrac{1}{4}$ **11.** $\dfrac{y^2}{x}$

13. $\dfrac{(a + 2)(a + 3)}{(a - 3)(a - 1)}$ **15.** $\dfrac{(x - 1)^2}{x}$ **17.** $\dfrac{1}{2}$ **19.** $\dfrac{15}{8}$ **21.** $\dfrac{15}{4}$

23. $\dfrac{a - 5}{3(a - 1)}$ **25.** $\dfrac{(x + 2)^2}{x}$ **27.** $\dfrac{3}{2}$ **29.** $\dfrac{c + 1}{c - 1}$ **31.** $\dfrac{y - 3}{2y - 1}$

33. $\dfrac{x + 1}{x - 1}$ **35.** 4   **37.** $-\dfrac{1}{b^2}$ **39.** $\dfrac{x(x^2 + 1)}{3(x + y - 1)}$

Exercise Set 11.3, p. 621

1. 108   **3.** 72   **5.** 126   **7.** 360   **9.** 420   **11.** $\frac{65}{72}$ **13.** $\frac{29}{120}$

15. $\frac{151}{180}$ **17.** $12x^3$ **19.** $18x^2y^2$ **21.** $6(y - 3)$

23. $t(t + 2)(t - 2)$ **25.** $(x + 2)(x - 2)(x + 3)$

27. $t(t + 2)^2(t - 4)$ **29.** $(a + 1)(a - 1)^2$ **31.** $(m - 3)(m - 2)^2$

33. $(2 + 3x)(2 - 3x)$ **35.** $10v(v + 4)(v + 3)$

37. $18x^3(x - 2)^2(x + 1)$ **39.** $6x^3(x + 2)^2(x - 2)$ **41.** $(x - 3)^2$

43. $(x + 3)(x - 3)$ **45.** 1440   **47.** 24 min

Exercise Set 11.4, p. 627

1. 1   **3.** $\dfrac{6}{3 + x}$ **5.** $\dfrac{2x + 3}{x - 5}$ **7.** $\dfrac{1}{4}$ **9.** $-\dfrac{1}{t}$ **11.** $\dfrac{-x + 7}{x - 6}$

13. $y + 3$ **15.** $\dfrac{2b - 14}{b^2 - 16}$ **17.** $-\dfrac{1}{y + z}$ **19.** $\dfrac{5x + 2}{x - 5}$ **21.** -1

23. $\dfrac{-x^2 + 9x - 14}{(x - 3)(x + 3)}$ **25.** $\dfrac{2x + 5}{x^2}$ **27.** $\dfrac{41}{24r}$ **29.** $\dfrac{4x + 6y}{x^2y^2}$

31. $\dfrac{4 + 3t}{18t^3}$ **33.** $\dfrac{x^2 + 4xy + y^2}{x^2y^2}$ **35.** $\dfrac{6x}{(x - 2)(x + 2)}$

37. $\dfrac{11x + 2}{3x(x + 1)}$ **39.** $\dfrac{x^2 + 6x}{(x + 4)(x - 4)}$ **41.** $\dfrac{6}{z + 4}$ **43.** $\dfrac{3x - 1}{(x - 1)^2}$

45. $\dfrac{11a}{10(a - 2)}$ **47.** $\dfrac{2x^2 + 8x + 16}{x(x + 4)}$ **49.** $\dfrac{x^2 + 5x + 1}{(x + 1)^2(x + 4)}$

51. $\dfrac{2x^2 - 4x + 34}{(x - 5)(x + 3)}$ **53.** $\dfrac{3a + 2}{(a + 1)(a - 1)}$ **55.** $\dfrac{2x + 6y}{(x + y)(x - y)}$

57. $\dfrac{y^2 + 10y + 11}{(y + 7)(y - 7)}$ **59.** $\dfrac{3x^2 + 19x - 20}{(x + 3)(x - 2)^2}$ **61.** $x^2 - 1$

63. $\dfrac{1}{8x^{12}y^9}$ **65.** Perimeter: $\dfrac{16y + 28}{15}$; area: $\dfrac{y^2 + 2y - 8}{15}$

67. $\dfrac{(z + 6)(2z - 3)}{(z - 2)(z + 2)}$ **69.** $\dfrac{11z^4 - 22z^2 + 6}{(z^2 + 2)(z^2 - 2)(2z^2 - 3)}$

Exercise Set 11.5, p. 635

1. $\dfrac{1}{2}$ **3.** 1   **5.** $\dfrac{4}{x - 1}$ **7.** $\dfrac{8}{3}$ **9.** $\dfrac{13}{a}$ **11.** $\dfrac{4x - 5}{4}$ **13.** $\dfrac{x - 2}{x - 7}$

15. $\dfrac{2x - 16}{x^2 - 16}$ **17.** $\dfrac{2x - 4}{x - 9}$ **19.** $\dfrac{-9}{2x - 3}$ **21.** $\dfrac{-x - 4}{6}$

23. $\dfrac{7z - 12}{12z}$ **25.** $\dfrac{4x^2 - 13xt + 9t^2}{3x^2t^2}$ **27.** $\dfrac{2x - 40}{(x + 5)(x - 5)}$

29. $\dfrac{3 - 5t}{2t(t - 1)}$ **31.** $\dfrac{2s - st - s^2}{(t + s)(t - s)}$ **33.** $\dfrac{y - 19}{4y}$ **35.** $\dfrac{-2a^2}{(x + a)(x - a)}$

37. $\dfrac{-13x - 20}{(x + 4)(x - 4)}$ **39.** $\dfrac{1}{2}$ **41.** $\dfrac{x - 3}{(x + 3)(x + 1)}$ **43.** $\dfrac{18x + 5}{x - 1}$

45. 0   **47.** $\dfrac{20}{2y - 1}$ **49.** $\dfrac{2}{y(y - 1)}$ **51.** $\dfrac{z - 3}{2z - 1}$ **53.** $\dfrac{2}{x + y}$

55. x^5 **57.** $\dfrac{b^{20}}{a^8}$ **59.** $\dfrac{1 - 3x}{(2x - 3)(x + 1)}$

Exercise Set 11.6, p. 643

1. $\frac{47}{2}$ 3. -6 5. $\frac{24}{7}$ 7. $-4, -1$ 9. $4, -4$ 11. 3 13. $\frac{14}{3}$
15. 10 17. 5 19. $\frac{5}{2}$ 21. -1 23. $\frac{17}{2}$ 25. No solution
27. -5 29. $\frac{5}{3}$ 31. $\frac{1}{2}$ 33. No solution 35. -13
37. $\frac{1}{a^6 b^{15}}$ 39. $\frac{16x^4}{t^8}$ 41. 7 43. $-\frac{1}{30}$ 45. $2, -2$ 47. 4

Exercise Set 11.7, p. 651

1. $\frac{20}{9}$ 3. 20 and 15
5. 30 km/h, 70 km/h

Speed	Time	
r	t	$150 = r(t)$
r + 40	t	$350 = (r + 40)t$

7. Passenger: 80 km/h; freight: 66 km/h

Speed	Time	
r − 14	t	$330 = (r - 14)t$
r	t	$400 = r(t)$

9. 20 mph 11. $2\frac{2}{9}$ hr 13. $5\frac{1}{7}$ hr 15. 9 17. 2.3 km/h
19. 582 21. 702 km 23. 1.92 g 25. 287
27. (a) 1.92 tons; (b) 28.8 lb 29. $\frac{36}{68}$ 31. $\frac{3}{4}$ 33. 2 mph
35. $\frac{A}{B}=\frac{C}{D}; \frac{A}{C}=\frac{B}{D}; \frac{D}{B}=\frac{C}{A}; \frac{D}{C}=\frac{B}{A}$ 37. $9\frac{3}{13}$ days 39. 45 mph

Exercise Set 11.8, p. 657

1. $r=\frac{S}{2\pi h}$ 3. $b=\frac{2A}{h}$ 5. $n=\frac{S+360}{180}$
7. $b=\frac{3V-kB-4kM}{k}$ 9. $r=\frac{S-a}{S-l}$ 11. $h=\frac{2A}{b_1+b_2}$
13. $B=\frac{A}{AQ+1}$ 15. $p=\frac{qf}{q-f}$ 17. $A=P(1+r)$
19. $R=\frac{r_1 r_2}{r_1+r_2}$ 21. $D=\frac{BC}{A}$ 23. $h_2=\frac{p(h_1-q)}{q}$
25. $a=\frac{b}{K-C}$ 27. $23x^4+50x^3+23x^2-163x+41$
29. $3(2y^2-1)(5y^2+4)$ 31. $T=\frac{FP}{u+EF}$ 33. $-40°$

Exercise Set 11.9, p. 663

1. $\frac{25}{4}$ 3. $\frac{1}{3}$ 5. -6 7. $\frac{1+3x}{1-5x}$ 9. $\frac{5}{3y^2}$ 11. 8 13. $x-8$
15. $\frac{y}{y-1}$ 17. $-\frac{1}{a}$ 19. $\frac{x+y}{x}$ 21. $\frac{x-2}{x-3}$
23. $4x^4+3x^3+2x-7$ 25. $\frac{(x-1)(3x-2)}{5x-3}$ 27. $-\frac{ac}{bd}$
29. $\frac{5x+3}{3x+2}$

Summary and Review: Chapter 11, p. 665

1. [11.1a] 0 2. [11.1a] 6 3. [11.1a] 6, -6
4. [11.1a] $-6, 5$ 5. [11.1a] -2 6. [11.1a] 0, 3, 5
7. [11.1c] $\frac{x-2}{x+1}$ 8. [11.1c] $\frac{7x+3}{x-3}$ 9. [11.1c] $\frac{y-5}{y+5}$
10. [11.1d] $\frac{a-6}{5}$ 11. [11.1d] $\frac{6}{2t-1}$ 12. [11.2b] $-20t$
13. [11.2b] $\frac{2x^2-2x}{x+1}$ 14. [11.3c] $30x^2y^2$
15. [11.3c] $4(a-2)$ 16. [11.3c] $(y-2)(y+2)(y+1)$
17. [11.4a] $\frac{-3x+18}{x+7}$ 18. [11.4a] -1 19. [11.5a] $\frac{4}{x-4}$
20. [11.5a] $\frac{x+5}{2x}$ 21. [11.5a] $\frac{2x+3}{x-2}$ 22. [11.4a] $\frac{2a}{a-1}$
23. [11.4a] $d+c$ 24. [11.5a] $\frac{-x^2+x+26}{(x-5)(x+5)(x+1)}$
25. [11.5b] $\frac{2(x-2)}{x+2}$ 26. [11.9a] $\frac{z}{1-z}$ 27. [11.9a] $c-d$
28. [11.6a] 8 29. [11.6a] 3, -5 30. [11.7a] $5\frac{1}{7}$ hr
31. [11.7a] 240 km/h, 280 km/h 32. [11.7a] -2
33. [11.7b] 160 34. [11.7a] 95 km/h, 175 km/h
35. [11.8a] $S=\frac{rt}{r-t}$
36. [11.8a] $C=\frac{5}{9}(F-32)$, or $C=\frac{5F-160}{9}$
37. [10.6a] $(5x^2-3)(x+4)$ 38. [9.2a, b] $\frac{1}{125x^9y^6}$
39. [9.4c] $-2x^3+3x^2+12x-18$
40. [10.8a] Length: 5 cm; width: 3 cm; perimeter: 16 cm
41. [11.1c], [11.2b] $\frac{5(a+3)^2}{a}$ 42. [11.5a] $\frac{10a}{(a-b)(b-c)}$
43. (a) [11.4a] $\frac{10x+6}{(x-3)(x+3)}$; (b) [11.6a] $\frac{1}{10}$; (c) In (a), the LCM is used to find an equivalent expression for each rational expression with the LCM as the least common denominator. In (b), the LCM is used to clear fractions.

Test: Chapter 11, p. 667

1. [11.1a] 0 2. [11.1a] -8 3. [11.1a] 7, -7
4. [11.1a] 1, 2 5. [11.1a] 1 6. [11.1a] 0, -3, -5
7. [11.1c] $\frac{3x+7}{x+3}$ 8. [11.1d] $\frac{a+5}{2}$
9. [11.2b] $\frac{(5x+1)(x+1)}{3x(x+2)}$ 10. [11.3c] $(y-3)(y+3)(y+7)$
11. [11.4a] $\frac{23-3x}{x^3}$ 12. [11.5a] $\frac{8-2t}{t^2+1}$ 13. [11.4a] $\frac{-3}{x-3}$
14. [11.5a] $\frac{2x-5}{x-3}$ 15. [11.4a] $\frac{8t-3}{t(t-1)}$
16. [11.5a] $\frac{-x^2-7x-15}{(x+4)(x-4)(x+1)}$ 17. [11.5b] $\frac{x^2+2x-7}{(x-1)^2(x+1)}$
18. [11.9a] $\frac{3y+1}{y}$ 19. [11.6a] 12 20. [11.6a] 5, -3
21. [11.7a] 4 22. [11.7b] 16 23. [11.7a] 45 km/h, 65 km/h

24. [11.8a] $t = \dfrac{g}{M - L}$ **25.** [10.6a] $(4a + 7)(4a - 7)$

26. [9.2a, b] $\dfrac{y^{12}}{81x^8}$ **27.** [9.4c] $13x^2 - 29x + 76$

28. [10.8a] 21 and 22, or -22 and -21

29. [11.7a] Team A: 4 hr; team B: 10 hr **30.** [11.9a] $\dfrac{3a + 2}{2a + 1}$

CHAPTER 12

Pretest: Chapter 12, p. 670

1. [12.2b]

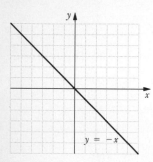

2. [12.3b]

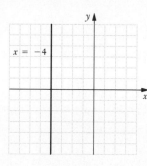

3. [12.3a]

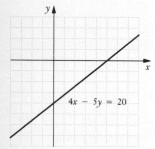

4. [12.2b]

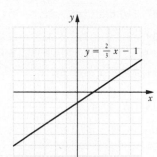

5. [12.1c] III **6.** [12.2a] No **7.** [12.4b] 4 **8.** [12.4b] 0
9. [12.4c] Slope: $\frac{1}{3}$; y-intercept: $(0, -\frac{7}{3})$
10. [12.4a] Not defined **11.** [12.4d] $y = x - 4$

12. [12.4d] $y = 4x + 7$ **13.** [12.6a] $y = \dfrac{5}{2}x$ **14.** [12.6c] $y = \dfrac{40}{x}$

15. [12.7b] **16.** [12.7b]

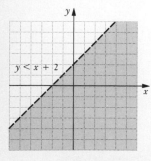

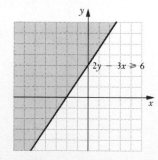

17. [12.5a] Parallel **18.** [12.5b] Perpendicular
19. [12.5b] Perpendicular **20.** [12.7a] Yes

Exercise Set 12.1, p. 675

1. Boredom **3.** Approximately 5% **5.** The second week
7. 12% **9.** $270 **11.** San Francisco **13.** $50 **15.** 1993
17. $17.0 million **19.** $1.5 million **21.** 3.7% **23.** 70.1%
25. 1743; 360; 270
27.

29. II **31.** IV **33.** III **35.** I **37.** Negative; negative
39. A: (3, 3); B: (0, -4); C: (-5, 0); D: (-1, -1); E: (2, 0)
41. $5330 **43.** I, IV **45.** I, III **47.** (-1, -5)
49.   **51.** 26

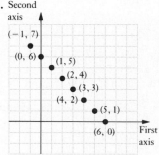

Exercise Set 12.2, p. 685

1. Yes **3.** No **5.** No
7.   **9.**

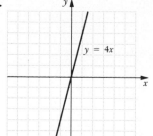   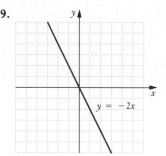

11.   **13.**

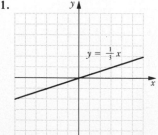   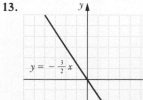

15.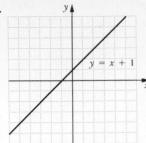

17.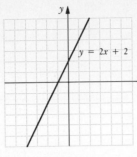

19.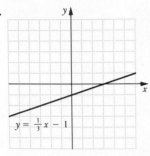

21.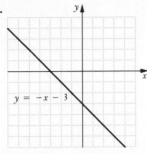

23.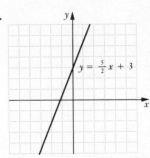

25.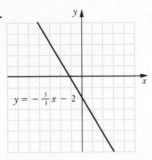

27.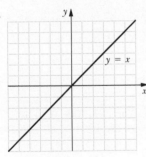

29.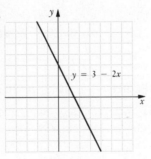

31.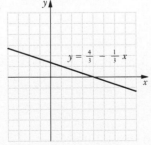

33. 75 km/h   **35.** $\frac{7}{5}$, $-\frac{7}{5}$

37. (0, 6), (1, 5), (2, 4), (3, 3), (4, 2), (5, 1), (6, 0)

Exercise Set 12.3, p. 691

1.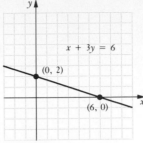

3.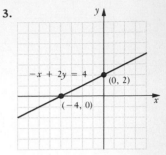

5.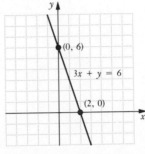

7.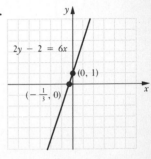

9.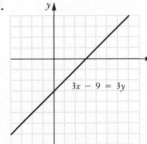

11.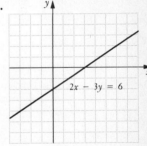

13.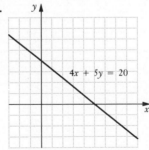

15.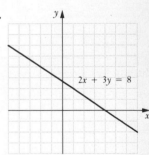

17.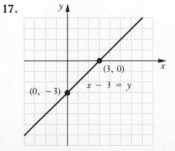

19.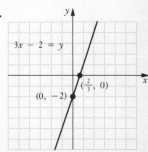

21.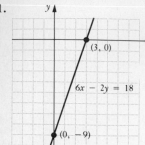

23.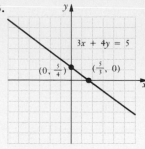

41.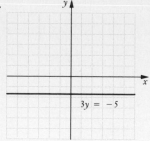

43.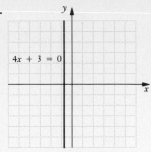

25.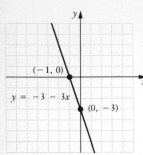

27.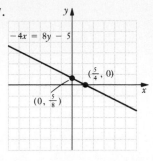

45.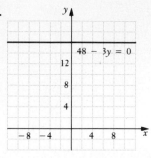

47. $5\frac{5}{11}$ hr   **49.** $-4, 3$ **51.** $x = 0$ **53.** $(-3, 6)$

29.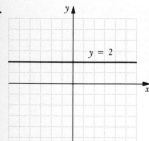

31.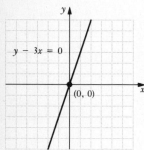

Exercise Set 12.4, p. 699

1. 0   **3.** $-\frac{4}{5}$ **5.** 7   **7.** 2   **9.** 0   **11.** Not defined
13. Not defined   **15.** 0   **17.** Not defined   **19.** 0   **21.** $-\frac{3}{2}$
23. $-\frac{1}{4}$ **25.** 2   **27.** $-4, (0, -9)$ **29.** 1.8, $(0, 0)$
31. $-\frac{8}{7}, (0, -3)$ **33.** 3, $(0, -\frac{5}{3})$ **35.** $-\frac{3}{2}, (0, -\frac{1}{2})$
37. 0, $(0, -17)$ **39.** $y = 5x - 5$ **41.** $y = \frac{3}{4}x + \frac{5}{2}$
43. $y = x - 8$ **45.** $y = -3x - 9$ **47.** $y = \frac{1}{4}x + \frac{5}{2}$
49. $y = -\frac{1}{2}x + 4$ **51.** $y = -\frac{3}{2}x + \frac{13}{2}$ **53.** $y = \frac{3}{4}x - \frac{5}{2}$ **55.** $\frac{44}{7}$
57. -5 **59.** $y = 3x - 9$ **61.** $y = \frac{3}{2}x - 2$

33.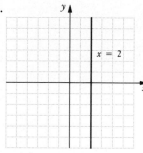

35.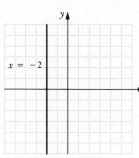

Exercise Set 12.5, p. 703

1. Yes   **3.** No   **5.** No   **7.** No   **9.** Yes   **11.** Yes   **13.** No
15. Yes   **17.** No   **19.** Yes   **21.** No   **23.** 130 km/h; 140 km/h
25. 4   **27.** $y = 3x + 6$ **29.** $y = -3x + 2$ **31.** $y = \frac{1}{2}x + 1$
33. $k = 16$ **35.** A: $y = \frac{4}{3}x - \frac{7}{3}$, B: $y = -\frac{3}{4}x - \frac{1}{4}$

37.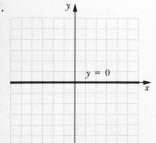

39.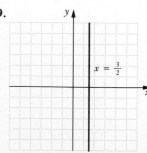

Exercise Set 12.6, p. 709

1. $y = 4x$ **3.** $y = 1.75x$ **5.** $y = 3.2x$ **7.** $y = \frac{2}{3}x$ **9.** $183.75
11. $22\frac{6}{7}$ **13.** 36.$\bar{6}$ lb   **15.** 68.4 kg   **17.** $y = \dfrac{75}{x}$ **19.** $y = \dfrac{80}{x}$
21. $y = \dfrac{1}{x}$ **23.** $y = \dfrac{1050}{x}$ **25.** $y = \dfrac{0.06}{x}$
27. (a) Inverse; **(b)** $5\frac{1}{3}$ hr   **29. (a)** Direct; **(b)** $69\frac{3}{8}$
31. 320 cm³   **33.** 54 min   **35.** 2.4 ft
37. $P = nS, k = n$, where n is the number of sides of the polygon
39. $B = kN$

41. If p varies directly as q, then $p = mq$. Then $q = \dfrac{1}{m}\, p$. Let $k = \dfrac{1}{m}$. Then $q = kp$, so q varies directly as p.

43. $S = kV^6$ **45.** $V = kr^3$ **47.** $C = \dfrac{k}{N}$ **49.** $I = \dfrac{k}{R}$ **51.** $I = \dfrac{k}{d^2}$

53. Yes   **55.** No

Exercise Set 12.7, p. 717

1. No   **3.** No

5.
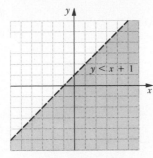

7.
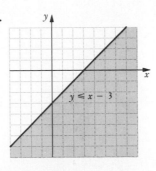

9.
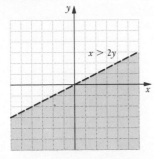

11.
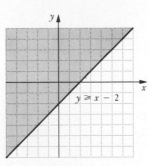

13.
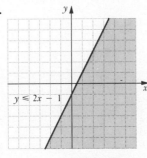

15.
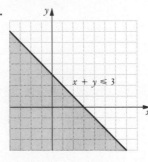

17.
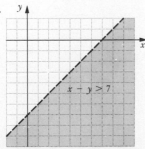

19.
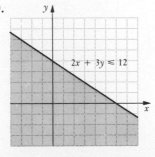

21.
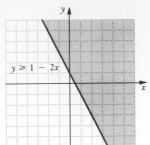

23.
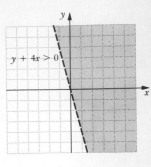

25.
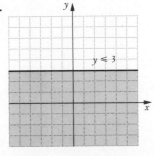

27.
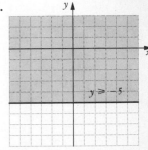

29. $\dfrac{47}{20}$ **31.** $-2, -3$
33. $35c + 75a > 1000$

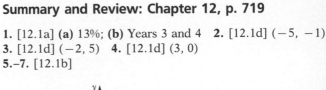

Summary and Review: Chapter 12, p. 719

1. [12.1a] **(a)** 13%; **(b)** Years 3 and 4   **2.** [12.1d] $(-5, -1)$
3. [12.1d] $(-2, 5)$ **4.** [12.1d] $(3, 0)$
5.–7. [12.1b]

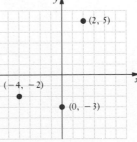

8. [12.1c] IV   **9.** [12.1c] III   **10.** [12.1c] I   **11.** [12.2a] No
12. [12.2a] Yes

13. [12.2b]

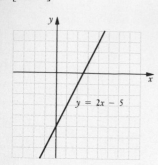

14. [12.2b]

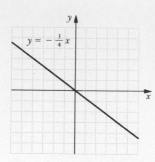

29. [12.4c] -1, $(0, 9)$ **30.** [12.4c] $\frac{3}{5}$, $(0, -\frac{4}{5})$
31. [12.4d] $y = 3x - 1$ **32.** [12.4d] $y = \frac{2}{3}x - \frac{11}{3}$
33. [12.4d] $y = -2x - 4$ **34.** [12.4d] $y = x + 2$
35. [12.4d] $y = \frac{1}{2}x - 1$ **36.** [12.5a] Parallel
37. [12.5b] Perpendicular   **38.** [12.5a] Parallel
39. [12.5a, b] Neither   **40.** [12.6a] $y = 3x$ **41.** [12.6a] $y = \frac{1}{2}x$
42. [12.6a] $y = \frac{4}{5}x$ **43.** [12.6c] $y = \frac{30}{x}$ **44.** [12.6c] $y = \frac{1}{x}$
45. [12.6c] $y = \frac{0.65}{x}$ **46.** [12.6b] $247.50   **47.** [12.6d] 1 hr
48. [12.7a] No   **49.** [12.7a] No   **50.** [12.7a] Yes
51. [12.7b]   **52.** [12.7b]

15. [12.2b]

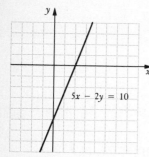

16. [12.2b]

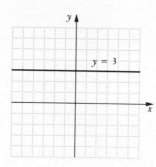

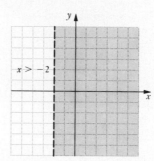

53. [12.7b]

17. [12.3a]

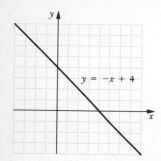

18. [12.3b]

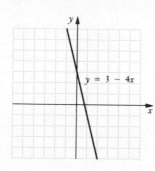

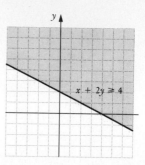

54. [11.7a] $3\frac{1}{3}$ hr   **55.** [7.8d] 52   **56.** [11.6a] -4
57. [10.7b] 5, -11

19. [12.3b]

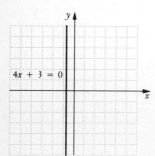

20. [12.3a]

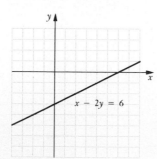

Test: Chapter 12, p. 721

1. [12.1a] Bachelor's   **2.** [12.1a] 520,000   **3.** [12.1a] 261,800
4. [12.1a] 401,900   **5.** [12.1c] II   **6.** [12.1c] III
7. [12.1d] (3, 4)   **8.** [12.1d] (0, -4)   **9.** [12.2a] Yes
10. [12.2b]   **11.** [12.3a]

21. [12.4a] $\frac{3}{2}$ **22.** [12.4a] 0   **23.** [12.4a] Not defined
24. [12.4a] 2   **25.** [12.4b] 0   **26.** [12.4b] Not defined
27. [12.4b] $-\frac{4}{3}$ **28.** [12.4c] -9, (0, 46)

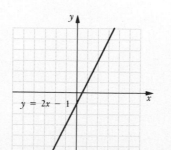

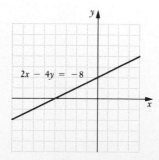

12. [12.3b]

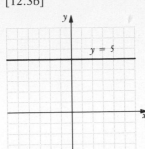

13. [12.2b]

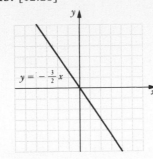

14. [12.3b]

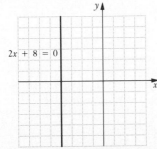

15. [12.4a] Not defined   **16.** [12.4a] $\frac{7}{12}$ **17.** [12.4b] 0
18. [12.4b] Not defined   **19.** [12.4c] 2, $(0, -\frac{1}{4})$
20. [12.4c] $\frac{4}{3}$, $(0, -2)$ **21.** [12.4d] $y = x + 2$
22. [12.4d] $y = -3x - 6$ **23.** [12.4d] $y = -3x + 4$
24. [12.4d] $y = \frac{1}{4}x - 2$ **25.** [12.5a] Parallel
26. [12.5a, b] Neither   **27.** [12.5b] Perpendicular
28. [12.6a] $y = 2x$ **29.** [12.6a] $y = 0.5x$
30. [12.6c] $y = \dfrac{12}{x}$ **31.** [12.6c] $y = \dfrac{1}{x}$ **32.** [12.6b] 240 km
33. [12.6d] $1\frac{1}{5}$ hr   **34.** [12.7a] No   **35.** [12.7a] Yes
36. [12.7b]   **37.** [12.7b]

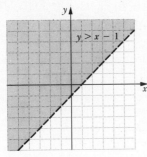
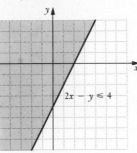

38. [11.7a] Freight: 90 mph; passenger: 105 mph
39. [7.8d] 1   **40.** [10.7b] $\frac{1}{3}$, -5 **41.** [11.6a] No solution
42. [12.1b] Area: 56; perimeter: 30   **43.** [12.4c, d] $y = \frac{2}{3}x + \frac{11}{3}$

CHAPTER 13

Pretest: Chapter 13, p. 724

1. [13.1a] Yes   **2.** [13.1b] No solution. The lines are parallel.
3. [13.2a] (5, 2)   **4.** [13.2b] (2, −1)   **5.** [13.3a] $(\frac{3}{4}, \frac{1}{2})$

6. [13.3b] (−5, −2)   **7.** [13.3b] (10, 8)   **8.** [13.2c] 50 and 24
9. [13.3c] 25° and 65°
10. [13.5a] 8 hr after the second train leaves

Exercise Set 13.1, p. 729

1. Yes   **3.** No   **5.** Yes   **7.** Yes   **9.** Yes   **11.** (2, 1)   **13.** (4, 3)
15. (−3, −3)   **17.** No solution. The lines are parallel.
19. (2, 2)   **21.** $(\frac{1}{2}, 1)$ **23.** Infinite number of solutions.
25. (−4, 2)   **27.** $\dfrac{108}{x^{13}}$ **29.** $\dfrac{2x^2 - 1}{x^2(x + 1)}$ **31.** $\dfrac{9x + 12}{(x - 4)(x + 4)}$
33. $A = 2$, $B = 2$ **35.** $2x + y = 0$, $y - x = -6$

Exercise Set 13.2, p. 735

1. (1, 3)   **3.** (1, 2)   **5.** (4, 3)   **7.** (−2, 1)   **9.** (−1, −3)
11. $(\frac{17}{3}, \frac{16}{3})$ **13.** $(\frac{25}{8}, -\frac{11}{4})$ **15.** (−3, 0)   **17.** (6, 3)
19. 12 and 15   **21.** 21 and 37   **23.** 28 and 12
25. Length: $365\frac{1}{2}$ mi; width: 275 mi
27. Length: $134\frac{1}{3}$ m; width: $65\frac{2}{3}$ m
29.   **31.**

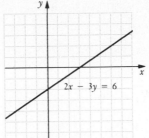

33. (4.3821792, 4.3281211)   **35.** (10, −2)
37. Length: 100 yd; width: $53\frac{1}{3}$ yd
39. You get $0 = 0$, a statement that is true for any values of x and y. There are infinitely many solutions; the lines coincide.

Exercise Set 13.3, p. 743

1. (9, 1)   **3.** (3, 5)   **5.** (3, 0)   **7.** $(-\frac{1}{2}, 3)$ **9.** $(-1, \frac{1}{5})$
11. No solution   **13.** (−3, −5)   **15.** (4, 5)   **17.** (4, 1)
19. (4, 3)   **21.** (1, −1)   **23.** (−3, −1)   **25.** (2, −2)   **27.** $(5, \frac{1}{2})$
29. Infinitely many solutions   **31.** (2, −1)   **33.** $(\frac{231}{202}, \frac{117}{202})$
35. 10 miles   **37.** 50° and 130°   **39.** 62° and 28°
41. 480 hectares Chardonnay; 340 hectares Riesling
43. $\dfrac{a^7}{b^9}$ **45.** $\dfrac{x - 3}{x + 2}$ **47.** 12 rabbits and 23 pheasants
49. The father is 45; the daughter 10   **51.** (5, 2)   **53.** (0, −1)

Exercise Set 13.4, p. 755

1. 350 cars; 160 trucks   **3.** Sammy is 44; his daughter is 22
5. Marge is 18; Consuelo is 9   **7.** 70 dimes; 33 quarters
9. 300 nickels; 100 dimes   **11.** 203 adults; 226 children
13. 130 adults; 70 students   **15.** 40 L of A; 60 L of B

A	B	Mixture	
x	y	100 liters	$\longrightarrow x + y = 100$
50%	80%	68%	
$0.5x$	$0.8y$	0.68×100, or 68 liters	$\longrightarrow 0.5x + 0.8y = 68$

17. 80 L of 30%; 120 L of 50%
19. 6 kg of cashews; 4 kg of pecans
21. 39 lb of A; 36 lb of B **23.** 12 of A; 4 of B
25. Inexpensive: $19.408; expensive: $20.075
27. $12,500 at 12%; $14,500 at 13% **29.** 54 **31.** 43.75 L
33. $4\frac{4}{7}$ L **35.** 74 **37.** Bat: $14.50; ball: $4.55; glove: $79.95

Exercise Set 13.5, p. 763

1. After $\frac{2}{3}$ hr, or 40 min

Speed	Time
55	t
40	t

3. $7\frac{1}{2}$ hr after the first train leaves, or $4\frac{1}{2}$ hr after the second train leaves

Speed	Time	
72	$t + 3$	$\longrightarrow d = 72(t + 3)$
120	t	$\longrightarrow d = 120t$

5. 14 km/h

Speed	Time	
$r + 6$	4	$\longrightarrow d = (r + 6)4$
$r - 6$	10	$\longrightarrow d = (r - 6)10$

7. 384 km **9.** 330 km/h **11.** 8.54 hr **13.** 15 mi
15. 317.02702 km/h **17.** 180 mi by land; 96 mi by water
19. 144 mi

Summary and Review: Chapter 13, p. 765

1. [13.1a] No **2.** [13.1a] Yes **3.** [13.1a] Yes **4.** [13.1a] No
5. [13.1b] (6, −2) **6.** [13.1b] (6, 2) **7.** [13.1b] (0, 5)
8. [13.1b] No solution. The lines are parallel.
9. [13.2a] (0, 5) **10.** [13.2b] (−2, 4) **11.** [13.2b] (1, −2)
12. [13.2a] (−3, 9) **13.** [13.2a] (1, 4) **14.** [13.2a] (3, −1)
15. [13.3a] (3, 1) **16.** [13.3a] (1, 4) **17.** [13.3a] (5, −3)
18. [13.3b] (−4, 1) **19.** [13.3b] (−2, 4)
20. [13.3b] (−2, −6) **21.** [13.3b] (3, 2)
22. [13.3b] (2, −4) **23.** [13.3b] Infinitely many solutions
24. [13.2c] 10 and −2 **25.** [13.2c] 12 and 15
26. [13.2c] Length: 37.5 cm; width: 10.5 cm
27. [13.5a] 135 km/h **28.** [13.4a] 297 orchestra, 211 balcony
29. [13.4a] 40 L of each **30.** [13.4a] Jeff: 27; son: 9

31. [9.1d] t^8 **32.** [9.1e] $\dfrac{1}{t^{18}}$

33. [11.5a] $\dfrac{-4x + 3}{(x - 2)(x - 3)(x + 3)}$

34. [12.3a]

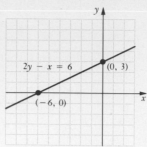

35. [13.1a] $C = 1$, $D = 3$ **36.** [7.7c], [13.2a] (2, 0)
37. [13.4a] 24 **38.** [13.4a] $96

Test: Chapter 13, p. 767

1. [13.1a] No **2.** [13.1b] (2, −1) **3.** [13.2a] (8, −2)
4. [13.2b] (−1, 3) **5.** [13.2a] No solution
6. [13.3a] (1, −5) **7.** [13.3a, b] (12, −6)
8. [13.3a, b] (0, 1) **9.** [13.3a, b] (5, 1) **10.** [13.2c] 20, 8
11. [13.5a] 40 km/h **12.** [13.4a] 40 L of A; 20 L of B

13. [11.5a] $\dfrac{-x^2 + x + 17}{(x - 4)(x + 4)(x + 1)}$

14. [12.3a]

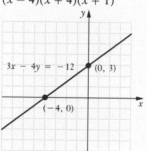

15. [9.1d] $\dfrac{10x^4}{y^2}$ **16.** [9.1e] $\dfrac{a^{10}}{b^6}$

17. [13.1a] $C = -\frac{19}{2}$; $D = \frac{14}{3}$ **18.** [13.4a] 5

CHAPTER 14

Pretest: Chapter 14, p. 770

1. [14.1a] 7, −7 **2.** [14.1d] $3t$ **3.** [14.1e] No
4. [14.1e] $\{x \mid x \geq 2\}$ **5.** [14.1b] 6.856 **6.** [14.5a] 4
7. [14.1f] $2x$ **8.** [14.4a] $12\sqrt{2}$ **9.** [14.4b] $7 - 4\sqrt{3}$
10. [14.4b] 1 **11.** [14.2d] $2\sqrt{15}$ **12.** [14.4b] $25 - 4\sqrt{6}$
13. [14.3a] $\sqrt{5}$ **14.** [14.3b] $2a^2\sqrt{2}$
15. [14.6a] $c = \sqrt{89} \approx 9.434$ **16.** [14.6b] $\sqrt{193} \approx 13.892$ m
17. [14.3c] $\dfrac{\sqrt{5x}}{x}$ **18.** [14.4c] $\dfrac{48 - 8\sqrt{5}}{31}$

Exercise Set 14.1, p. 775

1. 1, −1 **3.** 4, −4 **5.** 10, −10 **7.** 13, −13 **9.** 2 **11.** −3
13. −8 **15.** −15 **17.** 19 **19.** 2.236 **21.** 4.123 **23.** 9.644
25. (a) 13; (b) 24 **27.** $a - 4$ **29.** $t^2 + 1$ **31.** $\dfrac{3}{x + 2}$ **33.** No

35. Yes **37.** Yes **39.** No **41.** $\{x \mid x \geq 0\}$ **43.** $\{t \mid t \geq 5\}$
45. $\{y \mid y \geq -8\}$ **47.** $\{y \mid y \geq \frac{7}{2}\}$ **49.** All real numbers **51.** t
53. $3x$ **55.** ab **57.** $34d$ **59.** $x + 3$ **61.** $a - 5$ **63.** $2x - 5$
65. \$5330 **67.** $(x + 1)^2$ **69.** 5 **71.** 3.578 **73.** 32.309
75. No solution **77.** $\sqrt{3}$

Exercise Set 14.2, p. 781

1. $2\sqrt{3}$ **3.** $5\sqrt{3}$ **5.** $2\sqrt{5}$ **7.** $10\sqrt{2}$ **9.** $3\sqrt{x}$ **11.** $4\sqrt{3x}$
13. $4\sqrt{a}$ **15.** $8y$ **17.** $x\sqrt{13}$ **19.** $2t\sqrt{2}$ **21.** $6\sqrt{5}$ **23.** $12\sqrt{2y}$
25. $2x\sqrt{5}$ **27.** $\sqrt{2}(2x + 1)$ **29.** $\sqrt{y(6 + y)}$ **31.** 11.180
33. 18.972 **35.** 17.320 **37.** 11.043 **39.** 20 mph; 54.8 mph
41. x^3 **43.** x^6 **45.** $x^2\sqrt{x}$ **47.** $t^9\sqrt{t}$ **49.** $(y - 2)^4$
51. $2(x + 5)^5$ **53.** $6m\sqrt{m}$ **55.** $2a^2\sqrt{2a}$ **57.** $2p^8\sqrt{26p}$
59. $8x^3y\sqrt{7y}$ **61.** $3\sqrt{6}$ **63.** $3\sqrt{10}$ **65.** $6\sqrt{7x}$ **67.** $6\sqrt{xy}$
69. 10 **71.** $5b\sqrt{3}$ **73.** $2t$ **75.** $a\sqrt{bc}$ **77.** $2xy\sqrt{2xy}$ **79.** 18
81. $\sqrt{10x - 5}$ **83.** $x + 2$ **85.** $6xy^3\sqrt{3xy}$ **87.** $10ab^2\sqrt{5ab}$
89. $(8, 1)$ **91.** 25,704 ft² **93.** $\sqrt{x - 2}\sqrt{x + 1}$
95. $\sqrt{2x + 3}\sqrt{x - 4}$ **97.** $\sqrt{a + b}\sqrt{a - b}$ **99.** 0.5 **101.** $3a^3$
103. $>$ **105.** $>$ **107.** $<$ **109.** $4y\sqrt{3}$
111. $18(x + 1)\sqrt{y(x + 1)}$ **113.** $2x^3\sqrt{5x}$ **115.** x^{4n}
117. False. For example, $\sqrt{25} - \sqrt{9} = 5 - 3 = 2$; but $\sqrt{25 - 9} = \sqrt{16} = 4$

Exercise Set 14.3, p. 789

1. 3 **3.** 2 **5.** $\sqrt{5}$ **7.** $\frac{1}{5}$ **9.** $\frac{2}{5}$ **11.** 2 **13.** $3y$ **15.** $\frac{3}{7}$ **17.** $\frac{1}{6}$
19. $-\frac{4}{9}$ **21.** $\frac{8}{17}$ **23.** $\frac{13}{14}$ **25.** $\frac{6}{a}$ **27.** $\frac{3a}{25}$ **29.** $\frac{\sqrt{10}}{5}$ **31.** $\frac{\sqrt{6}}{4}$
33. $\frac{\sqrt{21}}{6}$ **35.** $\frac{\sqrt{2}}{6}$ **37.** $\frac{3\sqrt{5}}{5}$ **39.** $\frac{2\sqrt{6}}{3}$ **41.** $\frac{\sqrt{3x}}{x}$ **43.** $\frac{\sqrt{xy}}{y}$
45. $\frac{x\sqrt{2}}{6}$ **47.** $\frac{\sqrt{21}}{3}$ **49.** $\frac{3\sqrt{2}}{4}$ **51.** $\frac{\sqrt{10}}{5}$ **53.** $\sqrt{2}$ **55.** $\frac{\sqrt{55}}{11}$
57. $\frac{\sqrt{21}}{6}$ **59.** $\frac{\sqrt{6}}{2}$ **61.** 5 **63.** $\frac{\sqrt{3x}}{x}$ **65.** $\frac{4y\sqrt{3}}{3}$ **67.** $\frac{a\sqrt{2a}}{4}$
69. $\frac{\sqrt{42x}}{3x}$ **71.** $\frac{3\sqrt{6}}{8c}$ **73.** $\frac{y\sqrt{xy}}{x}$ **75.** $\frac{\sqrt{2}}{4a}$ **77.** 0.577
79. 0.935 **81.** 0.289 **83.** 0.707 **85.** 3.801 **87.** 0.850
89. $(4, 2)$ **91.** No solution
93. 1.57 sec; 3.14 sec; 8.88 sec; 11.10 sec **95.** 1 sec
97. $\frac{\sqrt{5}}{40}$ **99.** $\frac{\sqrt{5x}}{5x^2}$ **101.** $\frac{\sqrt{3ab}}{b}$ **103.** $\frac{\sqrt{70}}{100}$ **105.** $\frac{y - x}{xy}$

Sidelight: Wind Chill Temperature, p. 796

1. 0°F **2.** −29°F **3.** −10°F **4.** −22°F **5.** −64°F
6. −94°F

Exercise Set 14.4, p. 797

1. $7\sqrt{2}$ **3.** $4\sqrt{5}$ **5.** $13\sqrt{x}$ **7.** $-2\sqrt{x}$ **9.** $25\sqrt{2}$ **11.** $\sqrt{3}$
13. $\sqrt{5}$ **15.** $13\sqrt{2}$ **17.** $3\sqrt{3}$ **19.** $-24\sqrt{2}$ **21.** 0
23. $(2 + 9x)\sqrt{x}$ **25.** $(3 - 2x)\sqrt{3}$ **27.** $3\sqrt{2x + 2}$

29. $(x + 3)\sqrt{x^3 - 1}$ **31.** $(3xy - x^2 + y^2)\sqrt{xy}$ **33.** $\frac{2\sqrt{3}}{3}$
35. $\frac{13\sqrt{2}}{2}$ **37.** $\frac{\sqrt{6}}{6}$ **39.** $\frac{\sqrt{3}}{18}$ **41.** -44 **43.** 3 **45.** $13 + \sqrt{5}$
47. $x - 2\sqrt{xy} + y$ **49.** $-\sqrt{3} - \sqrt{5}$ **51.** $5 - 2\sqrt{6}$
53. $\frac{4\sqrt{10} - 4}{9}$ **55.** $5 - 2\sqrt{7}$
57. $\frac{1}{3}$ hr; the variation constant is the fixed distance
59. All **61.** $11\sqrt{3} - 10\sqrt{2}$ **63.** No
65. True; $(3\sqrt{x + 2})^2 = (3\sqrt{x + 2})(3\sqrt{x + 2}) =$
$(3 \cdot 3)(\sqrt{x + 2} \cdot \sqrt{x + 2}) = 9(x + 2)$.

Exercise Set 14.5, p. 803

1. 25 **3.** 38.44 **5.** 397 **7.** $\frac{621}{2}$ **9.** 5 **11.** 3 **13.** $\frac{17}{4}$
15. No solution **17.** No solution **19.** 9 **21.** 7 **23.** 1, 5
25. 3 **27.** 13, 25 **29.** No solution **31.** 3 **33.** No solution
35. 16 **37.** No solution **39.** Approximately 346 km
41. 11,236 m **43.** 125 ft, 245 ft **45.** 49 **47.** $\frac{(x + 7)^2}{x - 7}$
49. 61°, 119° **51.** 2, -2 **53.** $-\frac{57}{16}$ **55.** 13

Exercise Set 14.6, p. 807

1. $c = 17$ **3.** $c = \sqrt{32} \approx 5.657$ **5.** $b = 12$ **7.** $b = 4$
9. $c = 26$ **11.** $b = 12$ **13.** $a = 2$ **15.** $b = \sqrt{2} \approx 1.414$
17. $a = 5$ **19.** $\sqrt{75} \approx 8.660$ m **21.** $\sqrt{208} \approx 14.422$ ft
23. Approximately 43 yd **25.** $(-\frac{3}{2}, -\frac{1}{16})$
27. $\sqrt{181} \approx 13.454$ cm **29.** $12 - 2\sqrt{6} \approx 7.101$ **31.** 6
33. $A = \frac{a^2\sqrt{3}}{4}$

Summary and Review: Chapter 14, p. 809

1. [14.1a] 8, -8 **2.** [14.1a] 20, -20 **3.** [14.1a] 6
4. [14.1a] -13 **5.** [14.1b] 1.732 **6.** [14.1b] 9.950
7. [14.1b] 10.392 **8.** [14.1b] 17.889 **9.** [14.3d] 0.354
10. [14.3d] 0.742 **11.** [14.1d] $x^2 + 4$ **12.** [14.1d] $5ab^3$
13. [14.1e] Yes **14.** [14.1e] No **15.** [14.1e] Yes
16. [14.1e] Yes **17.** [14.1e] No **18.** [14.1e] $\{y \mid y \geq 10\}$
19. [14.1f] m **20.** [14.1f] $x - 4$ **21.** [14.2d] $\sqrt{21}$
22. [14.2d] $\sqrt{x^2 - 9}$ **23.** [14.2a] $-4\sqrt{3}$ **24.** [14.2a] $4t\sqrt{2}$
25. [14.2a] $x + 8$ **26.** [14.2a] $\sqrt{t - 7}\sqrt{t + 7}$ **27.** [14.2c] x^4
28. [14.2c] $m^7\sqrt{m}$ **29.** [14.2d] $2\sqrt{15}$ **30.** [14.2d] $2x\sqrt{10}$
31. [14.2d] $5xy\sqrt{2}$ **32.** [14.2d] $10a^2b\sqrt{ab}$ **33.** [14.3b] $\frac{5}{8}$
34. [14.3b] $\frac{2}{3}$ **35.** [14.3b] $\frac{7}{t}$ **36.** [14.3c] $\frac{\sqrt{2}}{2}$ **37.** [14.3c] $\frac{\sqrt{2}}{4}$
38. [14.3c] $\frac{\sqrt{5y}}{y}$ **39.** [14.3c] $\frac{2\sqrt{3}}{3}$ **40.** [14.3a] $\frac{\sqrt{15}}{5}$
41. [14.3a] $\frac{x\sqrt{30}}{6}$ **42.** [14.4c] $8 - 4\sqrt{3}$ **43.** [14.4a] $13\sqrt{5}$
44. [14.4a] $\sqrt{5}$ **45.** [14.4a] $\frac{\sqrt{2}}{2}$ **46.** [14.4b] $7 + 4\sqrt{3}$
47. [14.4b] 1 **48.** [14.6a] 20 **49.** [14.6a] $\sqrt{3} \approx 1.732$

50. [14.6b] $\sqrt{98} \approx 9.899$ **51.** [14.5a] 52
52. [14.5a] No solution **53.** [14.5b] 9 **54.** [14.5a] 0, 3
55. [14.5c] 405 ft **56.** [12.6b] \$450 **57.** [13.3c] 5670
58. [13.3b] $\left(\dfrac{22}{17}, -\dfrac{8}{17}\right)$ **59.** [11.2b] $\dfrac{(x-5)(x-7)}{(x+7)(x+5)}$
60. [14.1a] 2 **61.** [14.5a] $b = \sqrt{A^2 - a^2}$

Test: Chapter 14, p. 811

1. [14.1a] 9, -9 **2.** [14.1a] 8 **3.** [14.1a] -5
4. [14.1b] 10.770 **5.** [14.1b] 9.327 **6.** [14.3d] 1.732
7. [14.1d] $4 - y^3$ **8.** [14.1e] No **9.** [14.1e] Yes
10. [14.1e] No **11.** [14.1e] $\{x \mid x \le 8\}$ **12.** [14.1f] a
13. [14.1f] $6y$ **14.** [14.2d] $\sqrt{30}$ **15.** [14.2d] $\sqrt{x^2 - 64}$
16. [14.2a] $3\sqrt{3}$ **17.** [14.2a] $5\sqrt{x-1}$ **18.** [14.2c] $t^2\sqrt{t}$
19. [14.2d] $5\sqrt{2}$ **20.** [14.2d] $3ab^2\sqrt{2}$ **21.** [14.3b] $\frac{3}{2}$
22. [14.3b] $\dfrac{12}{a}$ **23.** [14.3c] $\dfrac{\sqrt{10}}{5}$ **24.** [14.3c] $\dfrac{\sqrt{2xy}}{y}$
25. [14.3a, c] $\dfrac{3\sqrt{6}}{8}$ **26.** [14.3a, c] $\dfrac{\sqrt{7}}{4y}$ **27.** [14.4a] $-6\sqrt{2}$
28. [14.4a] $\dfrac{6\sqrt{5}}{5}$ **29.** [14.4b] $21 - 8\sqrt{5}$ **30.** [14.4b] 11
31. [14.4c] $\dfrac{40 + 10\sqrt{5}}{11}$ **32.** [14.6a] $c = \sqrt{80} \approx 8.944$
33. [14.5a] 48 **34.** [14.5a] 2, -2 **35.** [14.5b] -3
36. [14.5c] About 5000 m **37.** [13.3c] 789.25 yd²
38. [12.6b] $15{,}686\frac{2}{3}$ **39.** [13.3b] (0, 2) **40.** [11.2b] $\dfrac{x-7}{x+6}$
41. [14.1a] $\sqrt{5}$ **42.** [14.2c] y^{8n}

CHAPTER 15

Pretest: Chapter 15, p. 814

1. [15.1c] 3 **2.** [15.2a] $\sqrt{7}, -\sqrt{7}$ **3.** [15.3a] $\dfrac{-3 \pm \sqrt{21}}{6}$
4. [15.1b] 0, $\frac{3}{5}$ **5.** [15.1b] 0, $-\frac{5}{3}$ **6.** [15.2b] $-4 \pm \sqrt{5}$
7. [15.2c] $1 \pm \sqrt{6}$ **8.** [15.4a] $n = \dfrac{p \pm \sqrt{p^2 + 4A}}{2}$
9. [15.5a] Width: 4 cm; length: 12 cm
10. [15.6b] $\left(\dfrac{-1 + \sqrt{33}}{4}, 0\right)\left(\dfrac{-1 - \sqrt{33}}{4}, 0\right)$
11. [15.5a] 10 km/h **12.** [15.6a]

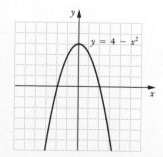

Exercise Set 15.1, p. 819

1. $a = 1, b = -3, c = 2$
3. $7x^2 - 4x + 3 = 0; a = 7, b = -4, c = 3$
5. $2x^2 - 3x + 5 = 0; a = 2, b = -3, c = 5$ **7.** 0, -7
9. 0, -2 **11.** 0, $\frac{2}{5}$ **13.** 0, -1 **15.** 0, 3 **17.** 0, $\frac{1}{5}$ **19.** 0, $\frac{3}{14}$
21. 0, $\frac{81}{2}$ **23.** -12, 4 **25.** -5, -1 **27.** -9, 2 **29.** 5, 3
31. -3 **33.** 4 **35.** $-\frac{2}{3}, \frac{1}{2}$ **37.** $\frac{1}{3}, \frac{4}{3}$ **39.** $\frac{5}{3}, -1$ **41.** $-\frac{1}{4}, \frac{2}{3}$
43. -2, 7 **45.** 4, -5 **47.** 4 **49.** 3, -2 **51.** 6, $-\frac{2}{3}$
53. 6, -4 **55.** 1 **57.** 5, 2 **59.** No solution **61.** 9 **63.** 7
65. $2\sqrt{5}$ **67.** $\dfrac{9}{8}$ **69.** $-\dfrac{1}{3}$, 1 **71.** 0, $\dfrac{\sqrt{5}}{5}$ **73.** $-\dfrac{5}{2}$, 1
75. 0, $-\dfrac{b}{a}$ **77.** 81, 1

Exercise Set 15.2, p. 827

1. 11, -11 **3.** $\sqrt{7}, -\sqrt{7}$ **5.** $\dfrac{\sqrt{15}}{5}, -\dfrac{\sqrt{15}}{5}$ **7.** $\dfrac{5}{2}, -\dfrac{5}{2}$
9. $\dfrac{7\sqrt{3}}{3}, -\dfrac{7\sqrt{3}}{3}$ **11.** $\sqrt{3}, -\sqrt{3}$ **13.** $\dfrac{6}{5}, -\dfrac{6}{5}$ **15.** -5, 9
17. $-3 \pm \sqrt{21}$ **19.** $-13 \pm 2\sqrt{2}$ **21.** $7 \pm 2\sqrt{3}$
23. $-9 \pm \sqrt{34}$ **25.** $\dfrac{-3 \pm \sqrt{14}}{2}$ **27.** 11, -5 **29.** -5, -9
31. -2, 8 **33.** -21, -1 **35.** $1 \pm \sqrt{6}$ **37.** $11 \pm \sqrt{19}$
39. $-5 \pm \sqrt{29}$ **41.** $\dfrac{7 \pm \sqrt{57}}{2}$ **43.** -7, 4 **45.** $\dfrac{-3 \pm \sqrt{17}}{4}$
47. $\dfrac{-3 \pm \sqrt{145}}{4}$ **49.** $\dfrac{-2 \pm \sqrt{7}}{3}$ **51.** $-\dfrac{1}{2}$, 5 **53.** $-\dfrac{7}{2}, \dfrac{1}{2}$
55. About 9.3 sec **57.** About 3.3 sec **59.** $y = \dfrac{141}{x}$
61. 12, -12 **63.** $16\sqrt{2}, -16\sqrt{2}$ **65.** $2\sqrt{c}, -2\sqrt{c}$
67. Approximately 50, -50 **69.** $\sqrt{3}, -\sqrt{3}$ **71.** $\sqrt{11}, -\sqrt{11}$

Exercise Set 15.3, p. 833

1. -3, 7 **3.** 3 **5.** $-\frac{4}{3}$, 2 **7.** $-\frac{7}{2}, \frac{1}{2}$ **9.** -3, 3 **11.** $1 \pm \sqrt{3}$
13. $5 \pm \sqrt{3}$ **15.** $-2 \pm \sqrt{7}$ **17.** $\dfrac{-4 \pm \sqrt{10}}{3}$ **19.** $\dfrac{5 \pm \sqrt{33}}{4}$
21. $\dfrac{1 \pm \sqrt{2}}{2}$ **23.** No real-number solutions **25.** $\dfrac{5 \pm \sqrt{73}}{6}$
27. $\dfrac{3 \pm \sqrt{29}}{2}$ **29.** $\sqrt{7}, -\sqrt{7}$ **31.** $-2 \pm \sqrt{3}$ **33.** $2 \pm \sqrt{34}$
35. -1.3, 5.3 **37.** -0.2, 6.2 **39.** -1.2, 0.2 **41.** -1.7, 0.4
43. $3x^2\sqrt{3x}$ **45.** $4\sqrt{5}$ **47.** 0, 2 **49.** $\dfrac{3 \pm \sqrt{5}}{2}$ **51.** $\dfrac{-7 \pm \sqrt{61}}{2}$
53. $\dfrac{-2 \pm \sqrt{10}}{2}$

Exercise Set 15.4, p. 837

1. $A = \dfrac{N^2}{6.25}$ **3.** $T = \dfrac{cQ^2}{a}$ **5.** $c = \sqrt{\dfrac{E}{m}}$ **7.** $d = \dfrac{c \pm \sqrt{c^2 + 4aQ}}{2a}$

9. $a = \sqrt{c^2 - b^2}$　**11.** $t = \dfrac{\sqrt{s}}{4}$　**13.** $r = \dfrac{-\pi h \pm \sqrt{\pi^2 h^2 + \pi A}}{\pi}$

15. $r = 6\sqrt{\dfrac{10A}{\pi S}}$　**17.** $a = \sqrt{c^2 - b^2}$　**19.** $a = \dfrac{2h\sqrt{3}}{3}$

21. $T = \dfrac{2 \pm \sqrt{4 - a(m - n)}}{a}$　**23.** $T = \dfrac{v^2 \pi m}{8k}$　**25.** $E = mc^2$

27. $n = \dfrac{1 \pm \sqrt{1 + 8N}}{2}$　**29.** $c = \sqrt{65} \approx 8.062$

31. $c = \sqrt{41} \approx 6.403$　**33. (a)** $r = \dfrac{C}{2\pi}$; **(b)** $A = \dfrac{C^2}{4\pi}$　**35.** $\dfrac{1}{3a}$, 1

Sidelight: Handling Dimension Symbols, p. 842

1. 68 ft　**2.** 82 km/h　**3.** 45 g　**4.** 8.6 lb　**5.** 15 mi/h
6. 32 km/h　**7.** 3.3 m/sec　**8.** 19 ft/min　**9.** $4\,\dfrac{\text{in.-lb}}{\text{sec}}$

10. $24\,\dfrac{\text{man-hr}}{\text{day}}$　**11.** 12 yd　**12.** 220 mi　**13.** 16 ft³　**14.** $\dfrac{1}{4}\,\dfrac{\text{lb}^2}{\text{ft}^2}$

15. $\dfrac{\$970}{\text{day}}$　**16.** $\dfrac{\$3.20}{\text{hr}}$

Exercise Set 15.5, p. 843

1. 7 ft; 24 ft　**3.** Width: 8 cm; length: 10 cm
5. Length: 20 cm; width: 16 cm　**7.** Length: 10 m; width: 5 m
9. 4.6 m; 6.6 m　**11.** Length: 5.6 in.; width: 3.6 in.
13. Length: 4.4 m; width: 2.2 m　**15.** 3 cm
17. 7 km/h

d	r	t
40	$r - 3$	t_1
40	$r + 3$	t_2

19. 8 mph　**21.** 4 km/h　**23.** 36 mph　**25.** 1 km/h
27. $3 + 2\sqrt{2} \approx 5.828$　**29.** $1 + \sqrt{2} \approx 2.41$
31. $d = 10\sqrt{2} \approx 14.14$ in.; two 10-in. pizzas

Exercise Set 15.6, p. 851

1. (0, 1)　　　　**3.** (0, 0)

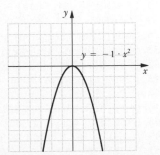

5. (1, 1)

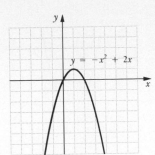

7. $\left(-\frac{1}{2}, \frac{21}{4}\right)$

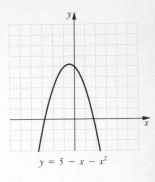

9. (1, 0)

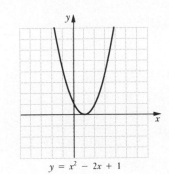

11. (1, 4)

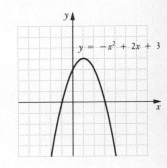

13. (−1, 3)

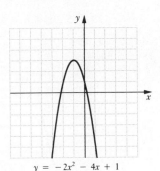

15.

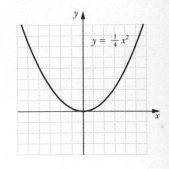

17.

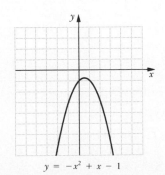

19.

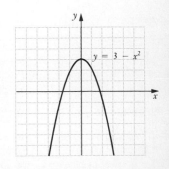

21.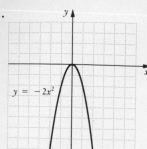

23.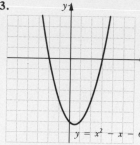

25. $(-\sqrt{5}, 0)$; $(\sqrt{5}, 0)$ **27.** $(-2, 0)$; $(0, 0)$
29. $\left(\dfrac{-1 - \sqrt{33}}{2}, 0\right)$; $\left(\dfrac{-1 + \sqrt{33}}{2}, 0\right)$ **31.** $(-5, 0)$
33. $(-2 - \sqrt{5}, 0)$; $(-2 + \sqrt{5}, 0)$ **35.** None
37. $(x + 2)\sqrt{x - 1}$ **39.** $2\sqrt{7}$
41. (a) After 2 sec, after 4 sec; **(b)** after 3 sec; **(c)** after 6 sec

Summary and Review: Chapter 15, p. 853

1. [15.2a] $\sqrt{3}, -\sqrt{3}$ **2.** [15.1c] $\frac{3}{5}, 1$ **3.** [15.3a] $1 \pm \sqrt{11}$
4. [15.1c] $\frac{1}{3}, -2$ **5.** [15.2b] $-8 \pm \sqrt{13}$ **6.** [15.2a] 0
7. [15.1b] $0, \frac{7}{5}$ **8.** [15.3a] $\dfrac{1 \pm \sqrt{10}}{3}$ **9.** [15.3a] $-3 \pm 3\sqrt{2}$
10. [15.3a] $\dfrac{2 \pm \sqrt{3}}{2}$ **11.** [15.3a] $\dfrac{3 \pm \sqrt{33}}{2}$
12. [15.3a] No real-number solution   **13.** [15.1b] $0, \frac{4}{3}$
14. [15.2a] $-2\sqrt{2}, 2\sqrt{2}$ **15.** [15.1c] $3, -5$ **16.** [15.1c] 1
17. [15.2c] $\frac{5}{3}, -1$ **18.** [15.2c] $\dfrac{5 \pm \sqrt{17}}{2}$ **19.** [15.3b] $4.6, 0.4$
20. [15.3b] $-1.9, -0.1$ **21.** [15.4a] $T = L(4V^2 - 1)$
22. [15.6a]   **23.** [15.6a]

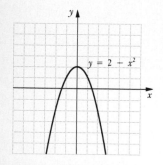 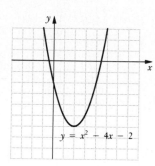

24. [15.6b] $(-\sqrt{2}, 0)$; $(\sqrt{2}, 0)$
25. [15.6b] $(2 - \sqrt{6}, 0)$; $(2 + \sqrt{6}, 0)$
26. [15.5a] 1.7 m, 4.7 m
27. [15.5a] Length: 10 m; width: 7 m   **28.** [15.5a] 30 km/h
29. [14.2d] $6\sqrt{a}$ **30.** [14.2d] $2xy\sqrt{15y}$ **31.** [12.6c] $y = \dfrac{1}{x}$
32. [14.6b] $\sqrt{3}$ **33.** [14.4a] $12\sqrt{11}$ **34.** [14.4a] $4\sqrt{10}$
35. [15.5a] 31 and 32; -32 and -31 **36.** [15.2c] $14, -14$
37. [15.1c], [14.5a] 25   **38.** [15.5a] $s = 5\sqrt{\pi}$

Test: Chapter 15, p. 855

1. [15.2a] $\sqrt{5}, -\sqrt{5}$ **2.** [15.1b] $0, -\frac{8}{7}$ **3.** [15.1c] $-8, 6$
4. [15.1c] $-\frac{1}{3}, 2$ **5.** [15.2b] $8 \pm \sqrt{13}$ **6.** [15.3a] $\dfrac{1 \pm \sqrt{13}}{2}$
7. [15.3a] $\dfrac{3 \pm \sqrt{37}}{2}$ **8.** [15.3a] $-2 \pm \sqrt{14}$
9. [15.3a] $\dfrac{7 \pm \sqrt{37}}{6}$ **10.** [15.1c] $2, -1$ **11.** [15.1c] $2, -4$
12. [15.2c] $2 \pm \sqrt{14}$ **13.** [15.3b] $5.7, -1.7$
14. [15.4a] $n = \dfrac{-b \pm \sqrt{b^2 + 4ad}}{2a}$
15. [15.6a]   **16.** [15.6a]

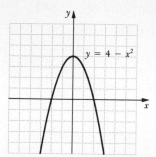 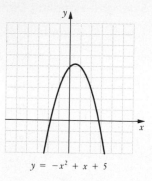

17. [15.6b] $\left(\dfrac{1 - \sqrt{21}}{2}, 0\right)\left(\dfrac{1 + \sqrt{21}}{2}, 0\right)$
18. [15.5a] Length: 6.5 m; width: 2.5 m   **19.** [15.5a] 24 km/h
20. [14.4a] $2\sqrt{15}$ **21.** [14.2d] $7xy\sqrt{2x}$ **22.** [12.6c] $y = \dfrac{4}{x}$
23. [14.6b] $\sqrt{5}$ **24.** [15.5a] $5 + 5\sqrt{2}$
25. [13.2b], [15.3a] $1 \pm \sqrt{5}$

FINAL EXAMINATION, p. 857

1. [3.2a] 215.6177   **2.** [2.4b] $8\frac{3}{4}$ **3.** [1.2f] 5937   **4.** [2.3c] $\frac{1}{12}$
5. [3.3a] 226.327   **6.** [2.2a] 6   **7.** [2.4d] $24\frac{3}{8}$ **8.** [1.3e] 197
9. [2.2c] $\frac{2}{3}$ **10.** [3.3b] 48   **11.** [3.4a] 43,000
12. [3.4a] 3.004   **13.** [1.8a] Yes   **14.** [1.9a] 230
15. [1.7d] $2^5 \cdot 3$ **16.** [2.1e] $\frac{3}{2}$ **17.** [2.1e] 10   **18.** [2.3d] $<$
19. [3.2d] 0.9   **20.** [2.4a] $7\frac{2}{3}$ **21.** [2.1a] $\frac{1}{3}$ **22.** [4.2b] 0.499
23. [3.3d] 0.24   **24.** [3.3d] $0.\overline{27}$ **25.** [3.1c] 7.86
26. [2.4a] $\frac{23}{4}$ **27.** [4.3b] $\frac{37}{100}$ **28.** [3.1b] $\frac{897}{1000}$ **29.** [4.2c] 77%
30. [4.3a] 96%   **31.** [4.1e] 3.84   **32.** [3.2c] 245.7
33. [4.6b] 5%   **34.** [2.5a] 80   **35.** [1.5a] $348
36. [2.5a] $3\frac{3}{4}$ m   **37.** [1.5a] $39   **38.** [3.5a] $16.99
39. [4.1e] 540 km   **40.** [4.6a] 39   **41.** [4.7d] $60
42. [5.1a, b, c] $15.1\overline{6}$; $12; $12
43. [5.4a] **(a)** Blue; **(b)** 1050
44. [6.2a], [6.3a] 24.8 m; 26.88 m^2 **45.** [6.4a] 38.775 ft^2
46. [6.4a] 153 m^2 **47.** [6.4a] 216 dm^2
48. [6.5a, b, c] 4.3 yd; 27.004 yd; 58.0586 yd^2
49. [6.6a] 68.921 ft^3; 100.86 ft^2 **50.** [6.6b] 314,000 m^3
51. [6.7a] 118°   **52.** [6.7d] 144°   **53.** [14.6a] 20   **54.** [6.9a] 6

55. [6.8a] $\angle 1 \cong \angle 2$, $\overline{QR} \cong \overline{SR}$; $\triangle WRQ \cong \triangle TRS$ by SAS
56. [9.1c] -995 **57.** [7.2e] 9 **58.** [1.3a] -9.7
59. [7.4a] -5 **60.** [7.5a] $-\frac{6}{7}$ **61.** [7.8b] $19y - 45$
62. [7.8d] 211 **63.** [8.1b] 5.6 **64.** [8.2a] -7
65. [8.3b] -10 **66.** [8.3c] 7 **67.** [10.7b] 6, -4
68. [13.2a] $(4, -3)$ **69.** [13.3b] $(4, 7)$ **70.** [15.1c] $\frac{1}{4}$, $-\frac{1}{2}$
71. [14.5a] 6 **72.** [15.3a] $\dfrac{-3 \pm \sqrt{37}}{2}$ **73.** [8.7e] $\left\{ x \middle| x \le \dfrac{5}{2} \right\}$
74. [11.8a] $w = \dfrac{1}{A - B}$ **75.** [8.6a] $M = \dfrac{K - 2}{T}$ **76.** [9.1e] x^{10}
77. [9.2a] $\dfrac{1}{x^{10}}$ **78.** [9.1d] $\dfrac{1}{x^{12}}$ **79.** [9.3f] $6y^3 - 3y^2 - y + 9$
80. [9.4c] $-2x^2 - 8x + 7$ **81.** [9.5b] $-6t^6 - 12t^4 - 3t^2$
82. [9.5d] $4x^3 - 21x^2 + 13x - 2$ **83.** [9.6b] $x^2 - 64$
84. [9.6c] $4m^2 - 28m + 49$ **85.** [9.7f] $9a^2b^4 + 12ab^2c + 4c^2$
86. [9.7f] $9x^4 + 6x^2y - 8y^2$ **87.** [11.1d] $\dfrac{1}{x^2(x + 3)}$
88. [11.2b] $\dfrac{3x^4(x - 1)}{4}$ **89.** [11.4a] $\dfrac{11x - 1}{4x(3x - 1)}$
90. [11.5a] $\dfrac{2x + 4}{(x - 3)(x + 1)}$ **91.** [10.1b] $3x(x^2 - 5)$
92. [10.5d] $(4x - 5)(4x + 5)$
93. [10.3a], [10.4a] $(3x - 2)(2x - 3)$ **94.** [10.5b] $(x - 5)^2$
95. [10.1c] $(2x - y)(a + 3b)$
96. [10.5d] $(x^4 + 9y^2)(x^2 - 3y)(x^2 + 3y)$ **97.** [14.2a] $6\sqrt{2}$
98. [14.3a, c] $\dfrac{\sqrt{30}}{5}$ **99.** [14.4a] $13\sqrt{2}$
100. [14.2d] $2a^2b\sqrt{6ab}$
101. [12.3a]   **102.** [12.3b]

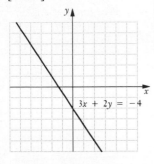

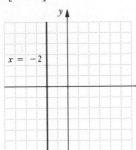

103. [12.7b]   **104.** [15.6a]

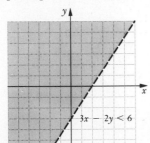

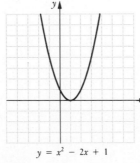

105. [10.8a] 5, 7; -7, -5 **106.** [13.4a] 40 L of A; 20 L of B
107. [13.5a] 70 km/h **108.** [15.5a] $l = 11$ m, $w = 8$ m
109. [12.4a] $-\frac{4}{3}$ **110.** [12.5a, b] Perpendicular

111. [12.6a] $y = 8x$ **112.** [6.6c] $y = \dfrac{5000}{x}$
113. [8.4a] Side of square is 15; side of triangle is 20
114. [15.2c] 144

APPENDIXES

Exercise Set A, p. 875

1. 12 **3.** $\frac{1}{12}$ **5.** 5280 **7.** 468 **9.** 7 **11.** $1\frac{1}{2}$ **13.** 15,840
15. $\frac{1}{4}$ **17.** $3\frac{1}{3}$ **19.** 52,800 **21.** $1\frac{1}{2}$ **23.** 1 **25.** 110 **27.** 2
29. 300 **31.** 30 **33.** $\frac{1}{36}$ **35.** 126,720 **37.** (a) 1000; (b) 0.001
39. (a) 10; (b) 0.1 **41.** (a) 0.01; (b) 100 **43.** 6700 **45.** 0.98
47. 8.921 **49.** 0.05666 **51.** 566,600 **53.** 4.77 **55.** 688
57. 0.1 **59.** 100,000 **61.** 142 **63.** 0.82 **65.** 450
67. 0.000024 **69.** 0.688 **71.** 230 **73.** 3.92 **75.** 100
77. 6.6 **79.** 88.495

Exercise Set B, p. 885

1. 1000; 1000 **3.** 87,000 **5.** 0.049 **7.** 0.000401 **9.** 78,100
11. 320 **13.** 128 **15.** 32 **17.** 500 mL **19.** 125 mL
21. 5832 yd³ **23.** 2000 **25.** 3 **27.** 64 **29.** 7000 **31.** 0.1
33. 6 **35.** 1000 **37.** 10 **39.** $\frac{1}{100}$, or 0.01 **41.** 1000 **43.** 10
45. 234,000 **47.** 5.2 **49.** 6.7 **51.** 0.0502 **53.** 6.78 **55.** 6.9
57. 800,000 **59.** 1000 **61.** 0.0034 **63.** 24 **65.** 60 **67.** $365\frac{1}{4}$
69. 336 **71.** 8.2 **73.** 1000 **75.** 0.125 mg **77.** 4 **79.** 8 mL

Exercise Set C, p. 891

1. 5 **3.** $\sqrt{18} \approx 4.243$ **5.** $\sqrt{32} \approx 5.657$ **7.** 17.8
9. $\dfrac{\sqrt{41}}{7} \approx 0.915$ **11.** $\sqrt{6970} \approx 83.487$ **13.** $\left(-\dfrac{1}{2}, -1 \right)$
15. $\left(\frac{7}{2}, \frac{7}{2} \right)$ **17.** $(-1, -3)$ **19.** $(-0.25, -0.3)$ **21.** $\left(-\frac{1}{12}, \frac{1}{24} \right)$
23. $\left(\dfrac{\sqrt{2} + \sqrt{3}}{2}, \dfrac{3}{2} \right)$ **25.** $\sqrt{49 + k^2}$ **27.** $8\sqrt{m^2 + n^2}$ **29.** $6\sqrt{2}$
31. Yes **33.** $(2, 4\sqrt{2})$

Exercise Set D, p. 895

1. $\{3, -3\}$ **3.** $\varnothing$ **5.** $\{0\}$ **7.** $\{15, -9\}$ **9.** $\{\frac{7}{2}, -\frac{1}{2}\}$
11. $\{\frac{23}{4}, -\frac{5}{4}\}$ **13.** $\{11, -11\}$ **15.** $\{389, -389\}$ **17.** $\{8, -8\}$
19. $\{7, -7\}$ **21.** $\{\frac{11}{5}, -\frac{11}{5}\}$ **23.** $\{8, -7\}$ **25.** $\{2, -12\}$
27. $\{\frac{7}{2}, -\frac{5}{2}\}$ **29.** $\varnothing$ **31.** $\{-\frac{13}{54}, -\frac{7}{54}\}$ **33.** $\{x | x \ge \frac{5}{2}\}$
35. $\{x | x \ge -5\}$ **37.** $\{1, -\frac{1}{4}\}$

Exercise Set E, p. 901

1. 0.57, 0.43 **3.** 0.075, 0.134, 0.057, 0.071, 0.030 **5.** 0.633
7. 52 **9.** $\frac{1}{4}$ **11.** $\frac{1}{2}$ **13.** $\frac{2}{13}$ **15.** $\frac{2}{7}$ **17.** 0 **19.** $\frac{5}{36}$ **21.** $\frac{5}{36}$
23. $\frac{1}{36}$

Exercise Set F, p. 911

1. 1 **3.** 4 **5.** 20 **7.** 2 **9.** 18 **11.** $9x$ **13.** 5
15. The sum of the lengths of the two shorter sides is greater than the length of the longest side.

17. The diagonals of a rectangle are congruent.
19. $m\angle 1 + m\angle 2 = m\angle 3$ **21.** Jose's house has two stories.
23. A lottery will be established in Texas.
25. (1) Given; (2) Addition principle for equations: adding -1 on both sides; (3) multiplication principle for equations: multiplying by $\frac{1}{4}$ on both sides.

27.

Statements	Reasons
1. $6x + 2 = 44$	1. Given.
2. $6x = 42$	2. Addition principle for equations: adding -2 on both sides.
3. $x = 7$	3. Multiplication principle for equations: multiplying by $\frac{1}{6}$ on both sides.

29. (1) Given; (2) Addition principle for equations: adding BC on both sides; (3) Simplifying

31.

Statements	Reasons
1. $m\angle 1 = m\angle 2$	1. Given.
2. $m\angle 2 = m\angle 3$	2. Vertical angles are congruent.
3. $m\angle 1 = m\angle 3$	3. Substituting $m\angle 1$ for $m\angle 2$ in step (2).

33.

Statements	Reasons
1. $m\angle ABC = m\angle BAC$, $m\angle ABD = m\angle BAD$	1. Given.
2. $m\angle ABC - m\angle ABD = m\angle BAC - m\angle BAD$	2. Addition principle for equations.
3. $m\angle CBD = m\angle CAD$	3. Simplifying.

35. $1260°$; $360°$ **37.** $135°$; $45°$ **39.** 18

41.

Statements	Reasons
1. R is the midpoint of both $\overline{PT}$ and $\overline{QS}$.	1. Given.
2. $\overline{PR} \cong \overline{RT}$, $\overline{QR} \cong \overline{RS}$	2. Definition of midpoint.
3. $\angle PRQ \cong \angle TRS$	3. Vertical angles are congruent.
4. $\triangle PRQ \cong \triangle TRS$	4. SAS.

43.

Statements	Reasons
1. L is the midpoint of $\overline{KM}$.	1. Given.
2. $\overline{GL} \perp \overline{KM}$	2. Given.
3. $\angle GLK$ and $\angle GLM$ are congruent right angles.	3. Definition of perpendicular.
4. $\overline{KL} \cong \overline{ML}$	4. Definition of midpoint.
5. $\overline{GL} \cong \overline{GL}$	5. Same line.
6. $\triangle KLG \cong \triangle MLG$	6. SAS.

45.

Statements	Reasons
1. $\triangle AEB$ and $\triangle CDB$ are isosceles with $\overline{AE} \cong \overline{AB} \cong \overline{CB} \cong \overline{CD}$.	1. Given.
2. B is the midpoint of $\overline{ED}$.	2. Given.
3. $\overline{EB} \cong \overline{BD}$	3. Definition of midpoint.
4. $\triangle AEB \cong \triangle CDB$	4. SSS.

47.

Statements	Reasons
1. $\overline{AB} \cong \overline{DC}$	1. Given.
2. $\angle BAC \cong \angle DCA$	2. Given.
3. $\overline{AC} \cong \overline{AC}$	3. Same line.
4. $\triangle ADC \cong \triangle CBA$	4. SAS.
5. $\overline{AD} \cong \overline{CB}$	5. CPCTC.

49. (b) **51.** (c) **53.** $CD = 2$, $AD = 8$, $EB = 16$ **55.** $DA = 4$

57.

Statements	Reasons
1. $\triangle DEF$ with parallelogram $DGHK$	1. Given.
2. $\overline{KH} \parallel \overline{DG}$, and thus $\overline{KH} \parallel \overline{DE}$. $\overline{GH} \parallel \overline{DK}$ and thus $\overline{GH} \parallel \overline{DF}$.	2. Definition of parallelogram.
3. $\angle FHK \cong \angle HEG$, $\angle EHG \cong \angle HFK$	3. If a transversal intersects two parallel lines, then the corresponding angles are congruent.
4. $\triangle GEH \sim \triangle KHF$	4. AA Property.

59.

Index

SKILL*	TEXT REFERENCE
FUNDAMENTAL MATHEMATICS	

Skill: **Use number concepts and computation skills.**

Includes: Adding, subtracting, multiplying, and dividing the following:

Fractions	Ch. 2
Decimals	Ch. 3
Integers	Ch. 7
Using the order of operations to solve problems	Sec. 7.8
Solving problems involving percents	Ch. 4
Performing calculations using exponents	Sec. 1.6
Performing calculations using scientific notation	Sec. 9.2
Estimating solutions to problems	Sec. 3.4
Using the concepts of "less than" and "greater than"	Sec. 2.3, 3.2

Skill: **Solve word problems involving integers, fractions, or decimals (including percents, ratios, and proportions).**

Includes: Determining the appropriate operations to solve word problems and solving word problems involving the following:

Integers	Sec. 1.5, 7.1, 7.2, 7.4
Fractions	Sec. 2.5
Decimals	Sec. 3.5
Percents, ratios, and proportions	Sec. 4.1, 4.4–4.7

Skill: **Interpret information from a graph, table, or chart.**

Includes:

Interpreting information in line graphs, bar graphs, pie graphs	Sec. 5.3, 5.4
Interpreting information in pictographs, tables, charts	Sec. 5.2
Interpreting information in graphs of functions	Sec. 5.3

* Many of these skills, particularly those in problem solving and interpreting information, are not confined to the sections or chapters specified here.

(continued)